Periodic Table of the Elements

Main-group elements

Metals · **Metalloids** · **Nonmetals** · **Noble gases**

Transition elements

Group	1 / 1A	2 / 2A	3 / 3B	4 / 4B	5 / 5B	6 / 6B	7 / 7B	8 / 8B	9 / 8B	10 / 8B	11 / 1B	12 / 2B	13 / 3A	14 / 4A	15 / 5A	16 / 6A	17 / 7A	18 / 8A
1	1 **H** 1.00794																	2 **He** 4.00260
2	3 **Li** 6.941	4 **Be** 9.01218											5 **B** 10.811	6 **C** 12.011	7 **N** 14.0067	8 **O** 15.9994	9 **F** 18.9984	10 **Ne** 20.1797
3	11 **Na** 22.9898	12 **Mg** 24.3050											13 **Al** 26.9815	14 **Si** 28.0855	15 **P** 30.9738	16 **S** 32.066	17 **Cl** 35.4527	18 **Ar** 39.948
4	19 **K** 39.0983	20 **Ca** 40.078	21 **Sc** 44.9559	22 **Ti** 47.88	23 **V** 50.9415	24 **Cr** 51.9961	25 **Mn** 54.9381	26 **Fe** 55.847	27 **Co** 58.9332	28 **Ni** 58.693	29 **Cu** 63.546	30 **Zn** 65.39	31 **Ga** 69.723	32 **Ge** 72.61	33 **As** 74.9216	34 **Se** 78.96	35 **Br** 79.904	36 **Kr** 83.80
5	37 **Rb** 85.4678	38 **Sr** 87.62	39 **Y** 88.9059	40 **Zr** 91.224	41 **Nb** 92.9064	42 **Mo** 95.94	43 **Tc** (98)	44 **Ru** 101.07	45 **Rh** 102.906	46 **Pd** 106.42	47 **Ag** 107.868	48 **Cd** 112.411	49 **In** 114.818	50 **Sn** 118.710	51 **Sb** 121.76	52 **Te** 127.60	53 **I** 126.904	54 **Xe** 131.29
6	55 **Cs** 132.905	56 **Ba** 137.327	57 **La* 138.906	72 **Hf** 178.49	73 **Ta** 180.948	74 **W** 183.84	75 **Re** 186.207	76 **Os** 190.23	77 **Ir** 192.22	78 **Pt** 195.08	79 **Au** 196.967	80 **Hg** 200.59	81 **Tl** 204.383	82 **Pb** 207.2	83 **Bi** 208.980	84 **Po** (209)	85 **At** (210)	86 **Rn** (222)
7	87 **Fr** (223)	88 **Ra** 226.025	89 †*Ac* 227.028	104 **Rf** (261)	105 **Db** (262)	106 **Sg** (266)	107 **Bh** (264)	108 **Hs** (269)	109 **Mt** (268)	110 **Ds** (271)	111 **Rg** (272)	112 **Cn** (285)	113 ** (284)	114 ** (284)	115 ** (288)	116 ** (292)	117 *** (293)	118 ** (294)

*Lanthanide series

58 **Ce** 140.115	59 **Pr** 140.908	60 **Nd** 144.24	61 **Pm** (145)	62 **Sm** 150.36	63 **Eu** 151.965	64 **Gd** 157.25	65 **Tb** 158.925	66 **Dy** 162.50	67 **Ho** 164.930	68 **Er** 167.26	69 **Tm** 168.934	70 **Yb** 173.04	71 **Lu** 174.967

†Actinide series

90 **Th** 232.038	91 **Pa** 231.036	92 **U** 238.029	93 **Np** 237.048	94 **Pu** (244)	95 **Am** (243)	96 **Cm** (247)	97 **Bk** (247)	98 **Cf** (251)	99 **Es** (252)	100 **Fm** (257)	101 **Md** (258)	102 **No** (259)	103 **Lr** (260)

** Not yet named

*** Discovered in 2010, element 117 is currently under review by IUPAC.

List of the Elements with Their Atomic Symbols and Atomic Weights

Name	Symbol	Atomic Number	Atomic Weight	Name	Symbol	Atomic Number	Atomic Weight
Actinium	Ac	89	227.028	Meitnerium	Mt	109	(268)
Aluminum	Al	13	26.9815	Mendelevium	Md	101	(258)
Americium	Am	95	(243)	Mercury	Hg	80	200.59
Antimony	Sb	51	121.76	Molybdenum	Mo	42	95.94
Argon	Ar	18	39.948	Neodymium	Nd	60	144.24
Arsenic	As	33	74.9216	Neon	Ne	10	20.1797
Astatine	At	85	(210)	Neptunium	Np	93	237.048
Barium	Ba	56	137.327	Nickel	Ni	28	58.693
Berkelium	Bk	97	(247)	Niobium	Nb	41	92.9064
Beryllium	Be	4	9.01218	Nitrogen	N	7	14.0067
Bismuth	Bi	83	208.980	Nobelium	No	102	(259)
Bohrium	Bh	107	(264)	Osmium	Os	76	190.23
Boron	B	5	10.811	Oxygen	O	8	15.9994
Bromine	Br	35	79.904	Palladium	Pd	46	106.42
Cadmium	Cd	48	112.411	Phosphorus	P	15	30.9738
Calcium	Ca	20	40.078	Platinum	Pt	78	195.08
Californium	Cf	98	(251)	Plutonium	Pu	94	(244)
Carbon	C	6	12.011	Polonium	Po	84	(209)
Cerium	Ce	58	140.115	Potassium	K	19	39.0983
Cesium	Cs	55	132.905	Praseodymium	Pr	59	140.908
Chlorine	Cl	17	35.4527	Promethium	Pm	61	(145)
Chromium	Cr	24	51.9961	Protactinium	Pa	91	231.036
Cobalt	Co	27	58.9332	Radium	Ra	88	226.025
Copernicium	Cn	112	(285)	Radon	Rn	86	(222)
Copper	Cu	29	63.546	Rhenium	Re	75	186.207
Curium	Cm	96	(247)	Rhodium	Rh	45	102.906
Darmstadtium	Ds	110	(271)	Roentgenium	Rg	111	(272)
Dubnium	Db	105	(262)	Rubidium	Rb	37	85.4678
Dysprosium	Dy	66	162.50	Ruthenium	Ru	44	101.07
Einsteinium	Es	99	(252)	Rutherfordium	Rf	104	(261)
Erbium	Er	68	167.26	Samarium	Sm	62	150.36
Europium	Eu	63	151.965	Scandium	Sc	21	44.9559
Fermium	Fm	100	(257)	Seaborgium	Sg	106	(266)
Fluorine	F	9	18.9984	Selenium	Se	34	78.96
Francium	Fr	87	(223)	Silicon	Si	14	28.0855
Gadolinium	Gd	64	157.25	Silver	Ag	47	107.868
Gallium	Ga	31	69.723	Sodium	Na	11	22.9898
Germanium	Ge	32	72.61	Strontium	Sr	38	87.62
Gold	Au	79	196.967	Sulfur	S	16	32.066
Hafnium	Hf	72	178.49	Tantalum	Ta	73	180.948
Hassium	Hs	108	(269)	Technetium	Tc	43	(98)
Helium	He	2	4.00260	Tellurium	Te	52	127.60
Holmium	Ho	67	164.930	Terbium	Tb	65	158.925
Hydrogen	H	1	1.00794	Thallium	Tl	81	204.383
Indium	In	49	114.818	Thorium	Th	90	232.038
Iodine	I	53	126.904	Thulium	Tm	69	168.934
Iridium	Ir	77	192.22	Tin	Sn	50	118.710
Iron	Fe	26	55.847	Titanium	Ti	22	47.88
Krypton	Kr	36	83.80	Tungsten	W	74	183.84
Lanthanum	La	57	138.906	Uranium	U	92	238.029
Lawrencium	Lr	103	(260)	Vanadium	V	23	50.9415
Lead	Pb	82	207.2	Xenon	Xe	54	131.29
Lithium	Li	3	6.941	Ytterbium	Yb	70	173.04
Lutetium	Lu	71	174.967	Yttrium	Y	39	88.9059
Magnesium	Mg	12	24.3050	Zinc	Zn	30	65.39
Manganese	Mn	25	54.9381	Zirconium	Zr	40	91.224

Fundamentals of General, Organic, and Biological Chemistry

Custom Edition for Kennesaw State University

Taken from:

Fundamentals of General, Organic, and Biological Chemistry, Seventh Edition
by John McMurry, David S. Ballantine, Carl A. Hoeger,
and Virginia E. Peterson

General, Organic, and Biological Chemistry: Structures of Life, Fifth Edition
by Karen C. Timberlake

Taken from:

Fundamentals of General, Organic, and Biological Chemistry, Seventh Edition
by John McMurry, David S. Ballantine, Carl A. Hoeger, and Virginia E. Peterson
Copyright © 2013, 2010, 2007, 2003, 1999, 1996, 1992 by Pearson Education, Inc.
New York, NY 10013

General, Organic, and Biological Chemistry: Structures of Life, Fifth Edition
by Karen C. Timberlake
Copyright © 2015, 2013, 2010, 2007 by Pearson Education, Inc.
New York, NY 10013

This special edition published in cooperation with Pearson Learning Solutions.

Pearson Learning Solutions, 501 Boylston Street, Suite 900, Boston, MA 02116
A Pearson Education Company
www.pearsoned.com

Printed in the United States of America

4

000200010271965463

RD

ISBN 10: 1-323-10562-X
ISBN 13: 978-1-323-10562-7

Brief Contents

Chapters 1-11, 28-29 taken from *Fundamentals of General, Organic, and Biological Chemistry*, Seventh Edition by John McMurry, David S. Ballantine, Carl A. Hoeger, and Virginia E. Peterson

Chapters 12-24 taken from *General, Organic, and Biological Chemistry: Structures of Life*, Fifth Edition by Karen C. Timberlake

Contents

Chapters 1-11, 28-29 taken from *Fundamentals of General, Organic, and Biological Chemistry*, Seventh Edition by John McMurry, David S. Ballantine, Carl A. Hoeger, and Virginia E. Peterson

Chapters 12-24 taken from *General, Organic, and Biological Chemistry: Structures of Life*, Fifth Edition by Karen C. Timberlake

Features

Preface

This textbook and its related digital resources provide students in the allied health sciences with a needed background in chemistry and biochemistry while offering a general context for chemical concepts to ensure that students in other disciplines gain an appreciation of the importance of chemistry in everyday life.

To teach chemistry all the way from "What is an atom?" to "How do we get energy from glucose?" is a challenge. Throughout our general chemistry and organic chemistry coverage, the focus is on concepts fundamental to the chemistry of living things and everyday life. In our biochemistry coverage we strive to meet the further challenge of providing a context for the application of those concepts in biological systems. Our goal is to provide enough detail for thorough understanding while avoiding so much detail that students are overwhelmed. Many practical and relevant examples are included to illustrate the concepts and enhance student learning.

The material covered is ample for a two-term introduction to general, organic, and biological chemistry. While the general and early organic chapters contain concepts that are fundamental to understanding the material in biochemistry, the later chapters can be covered individually and in an order that can be adjusted to meet the needs of the students and the duration of the course.

The writing style is clear and concise and punctuated with practical and familiar examples from students' personal experience. Art work, diagrams, and molecular models are used extensively to provide graphical illustration of concepts to enhance student understanding. Since the true test of knowledge is the ability to apply that knowledge appropriately, we include numerous worked examples that incorporate consistent problem-solving strategies.

Regardless of their career paths, all students will be citizens in an increasingly technological society. When they recognize the principles of chemistry at work not just in their careers but in their daily lives, they are prepared to make informed decisions on scientific issues based on a firm understanding of the underlying concepts.

New to This Edition

The major theme of this revision is *making connections*, which is accomplished in a variety of ways:

- **NEW and updated *Chemistry in Action* boxes** highlight and strengthen the connections between general, organic, and biological chemistry.
- **NEW *Mastering Reactions* boxes** discuss, in some depth, the "how" behind a number of organic reactions.
- **NEW in-chapter questions specifically related to *Chemistry in Action* applications and *Mastering Reactions*** reinforce the connection between the chapter content and practical applications.
- **NEW Concept Maps** added to certain chapters, draw connections between general, organic, and biological chemistry—in particular those chapters dealing with intermolecular forces, chemical reactions and energy, acid–base chemistry, and relationships between functional groups, proteins, and their properties.
- **NEW and updated Concept Links offer** visual reminders for students that indicate when new material builds on concepts from previous chapters. **Updated questions in the End of Chapter section build on Concept Links** and require students to recall information learned in previous chapters.
- **NEW and updated end-of-chapter (EOC) problems:** approximately 20–25% of the end-of-chapter problems have been revised to enhance clarity.
- **All Chapter Goals tied to EOC problem sets:** chapter summaries include a list of EOC problems that correspond to the chapter goals for a greater connection between problems and concepts.

- **Chapters 1 and 2** have been restructured to place a greater emphasis on building math skills.
- **Chapter 6 (Chemical Reactions)** has been reorganized into two chapters: Chapter 5 (Classification and Balancing of Chemical Reactions) and Chapter 6 (Chemical Reactions: Mole and Mass Relationships) to allow student to narrow their focus; Chapter 5 focuses on the qualitative aspect of reactions, while Chapter 6 focuses on calculations.

Organization

General Chemistry: Chapters 1–11 The introduction to elements, atoms, the periodic table, and the quantitative nature of chemistry (Chapters 1 and 2) is followed by chapters that individually highlight the nature of ionic and molecular compounds (Chapters 3 and 4. The next three chapters discuss chemical reactions and their stoichiometry, energies, rates, and equilibria (Chapters 5, 6, and 7). Topics relevant to the chemistry of life follow: Gases, Liquids, and Solids (Chapter 8); Solutions (Chapter 9); and Acids and Bases (Chapter 10). Nuclear Chemistry (Chapter 11) closes the general chemistry sequence.

Organic Chemistry: Chapters 12–17 These chapters concisely focus on what students must know in order to understand biochemistry. The introduction to hydrocarbons (Chapters 12 and 13) includes the basics of nomenclature, which is thereafter kept to a minimum. Discussion of functional groups with single bonds to oxygen, sulfur, or a halogen (Chapter 14) is followed by a short chapter on amines, which are so important to the chemistry of living things and drugs (Chapter 15). After introducing aldehydes and ketones (Chapter 16), the chemistry of carboxylic acids and their derivatives (including amides) is covered (Chapter 17), with a focus on similarities among the derivatives. More attention to the mechanisms by which organic reactions occur and the vernacular used to describe them has been incorporated into this edition.

Biological Chemistry: Chapters 18–29 Rather than proceed through the complexities of protein, carbohydrate, lipid, and nucleic acid structure before getting to the roles of these compounds in the body, structure and function are integrated in this text. Protein structure (Chapter 18) is followed by enzyme and coenzyme chemistry (Chapter 19). With enzymes introduced, the central pathways and themes of biochemical energy production can be described (Chapter 20). If the time you have available to cover biochemistry is limited, stop with Chapter 20 and your students will have an excellent preparation in the essentials of metabolism. The following chapters cover carbohydrate chemistry (Chapters 21 and 22), then lipid chemistry (Chapters 23 and 24). Next we discuss nucleic acids and protein synthesis (Chapter 25) and genomics (Chapter 26). The last three chapters cover protein and amino acid metabolism (Chapter 27), the function of hormones and neurotransmitters, and the action of drugs (Chapter 28), and provide an overview of the chemistry of body fluids (Chapter 29).

Chapter by Chapter Changes

COVERAGE OF GENERAL CHEMISTRY

The major revisions in this section involve reorganization or revision of content to strengthen the connections between concepts and to provide a more focused coverage of specific concepts. In order to reinforce the relationship between topics, Concept Maps have been included in several chapters to illustrate the connections between concepts.

Specific changes to chapters are provided below:

Chapter 1

- Chapters 1 and 2 from the sixth edition have been combined; a greater emphasis is placed on math skills. Goals were revised and updated to reflect the combined chapter.

- The concept of homogeneous and heterogeneous mixtures is introduced (previously in Chapter 9).
- There are several new references to the Application boxes (now titled *Chemistry in Action*), both in the text and in the problems. Four Application boxes were updated to provide more current connections to everyday life and the health fields.

Chapter 2

- Chapter 3 from the sixth edition has become Chapter 2 in the seventh edition: Atoms and the Periodic Table.
- Information on the periodic table has been updated (the 117th element has been discovered, no longer considered a metalloid; 112th element has been named).
- Application boxes (*Chemistry in Action*) have been modified to enhance clarity, relevance to the student, and connection to the text.

Chapter 3

- Chapter 3 in this edition was Chapter 4 in the sixth edition: Ionic Compounds.
- There is a new Application (*Chemistry in Action*) box titled "Ionic Liquids."
- Changes have been made to the boxes to enhance clarity, relevance to the student, and connection to the text.

Chapter 4

- Chapter 4 in this edition was Chapter 5 in the sixth edition: Molecular Compounds.
- Section 11 (Characteristics of Molecular Compounds) has been moved; it is now Section 5.

Chapter 5

- Chapter 5 in this edition, Classification and Balancing of Chemical Reactions, is a portion of Chapter 6 from the sixth edition (6e Sections 6.1–6.2 and 6.8–6.13).
- There are several new references to the Application (*Chemistry in Action*) boxes, both in the text and in the problems.

Chapter 6

- Chapter 6 in this edition, Chemical Reactions: Mole and Mass Relationships, is a portion of Chapter 6 from the sixth edition (6e Sections 6.3 – 6.7).
- There are several new references to the Applications boxes, both in the text and in the problems.
- A new concept map has been added, relating topics in Chapters 3 and 4 to topics in Chapters 5 and 6 and to topics in Chapters 7 and 10.

Chapter 7

- An explanation of bond energies has been added to show how the energy of chemical reactions is related to the covalent bonds in reactants and products.
- Bond and reaction energies in units of both kcal and kJ have been consistently included.
- A new concept map has been added at the end of chapter that shows how energy, rates, and equilibrium are related.
- There is a new *Chemistry in Action* application box titled "Coupled Reactions."

Chapter 8

- Section 8.11 (Intermolecular Forces) has been moved to Section 8.2 to help students make the connection between these forces and the physical states and properties of matter that are discussed in the subsequent sections.
- Chemistry in Action application boxes have been revised to strengthen the connection with chapter content.
- There is a new Concept Map relating molecular shape and polarity (Chapter 4) and the energy of chemical and physical changes (Chapter 7) to intermolecular forces and the physical states of matter.

Chapter 9

- Section 9.7 (Units of Concentration) has been reorganized to add mass/mass units and improve connections between units.
- A new Concept Map has been added to show the relationship between intermolecular forces (Chapter 8) and the formation of solutions and between concentration units of molarity and mole/mass relationships of reactions in solution.

Chapter 10

- Section 10.4 (Water as Both Acid and Base) and Section 10.6 (Dissociation of Water) have been combined to strengthen the connection between these concepts.
- Section 10.11 (Buffer Solutions) and Section 10.12 (Buffers in the Body) have been combined to strengthen the connection between these concepts and reduce redundancy of content in later chapters.
- Content in the *Chemistry in Action* application boxes has been combined and revised to strengthen connections between concepts and practical applications.
- New Concept Map has been added to show the relationships between strong/weak electrolytes (Chapter 9) and the extent of formation of H^+ and OH^- ions in acid/base solutions, and between equilibrium (Chapter 7) and strong/weak acids.

Chapter 11

- One *Chemistry in Action* application box was eliminated and others were revised to strengthen the connections between chapter content and practical applications.

COVERAGE OF ORGANIC CHEMISTRY

A major emphasis in this edition was placed on making the fundamental reactions that organic molecules undergo much clearer to the reader, with particular attention on those reactions encountered again in biochemical transformations. Also new to this edition is the expanded use and evaluation of line-angle structure for organic molecules, which are so important when discussing biomolecules. Most of the Application boxes (*Chemistry in Action*) have been updated to reflect current understanding and research. A number of instructors have asked for an increased discussion of the mechanisms of organic reactions; however, since many that teach this class did not want it to be integrated directly into the text we developed a completely new feature titled *Mastering Reactions*. This boxed feature discusses in relative depth the "how" behind a number of organic reactions. We have designed *Mastering Reactions* so that they may be integrated into an instructor's lecture or simply left out with no detriment to the material in the text itself.

Other specific changes to chapters are provided below:

Chapter 12

- There is a new feature box called *Mastering Reactions* that explains curved-arrow formalism used in organic mechanisms.
- There is a functional group scheme map that will aid in classifying functional groups.
- Table 1 has been substantially reworked to include line structures and sulfur compounds.

Chapter 13

- Sixth edition section 13.7 has been converted into a *Mastering Reactions* box (How Addition Reactions Occur). The content of *Mastering Reactions* box includes expanded discussion of Markovnikov's Rule.
- Chapter 13 now includes in-text references to *Chemistry in Action* boxes, including in-text problems related to them. There are also several cross-references to the *Mastering Reactions* boxes.

Chapter 14

- The language used to describe the classification of alcohols has been adjusted to make it clearer for the reader.
- A *Mastering Reactions* box (How Eliminations Occur) has been added. Discussion of Zaitsev's Rule and its mechanistic explanation are included.

Chapter 15

- A new *Chemistry in Action* box (Knowing What You Work With: Material Safety Data Sheets) has been added.

Chapter 16

- A *Mastering Reactions* box (Carbonyl Additions) has been added, with an emphasis on hemiacetal and acetal formation.
- The discussion of formation of cyclic hemiacetals and acetals has been adjusted to make it more clear to the reader.

Chapter 17

- The colors used in many of the illustrations were corrected and/or modified to allow students to easily follow which atoms come from which starting materials in the formation and degradation of the various carboxylic acid derivatives.

Chapter 18

- There are new references to the Chemistry in Action boxes, both in the text and in the problems.
- There is an expanded discussion of isoelectric points.
- There is a new Concept Map illustrating the organizing principles of protein structure, types of proteins, and amino acids.

Chapter 19

- There is an expanded discussion of minerals, including a new table.
- A clarification of the definition of uncompetitive inhibition (previously noncompetitive inhibition) has been added.

Chapter 20

- A new Concept Map relating biochemical energy to chemical energy concepts discussed in earlier chapters has been added.
- Energy calculations are in both kcalories and kjoules.
- The discussion of "uncouplers" has been integrated into the text.

Chapter 21

- A new *Chemistry in Action* box was added, combining and updating concepts from earlier applications discussing aspects of dietary carbohydrates.
- Many ribbon molecules were made clearer by floating the model on white rather than black backgrounds.
- A new worked example was added to clarify how to analyze a complex molecule for its component structures.

Chapter 22

- The text discussion was made more readable by reducing the jargon present in this chapter.
- The discussion of glucose metabolism in diabetes and metabolic syndrome was freshened.

Chapter 23

- The discussion of cholesterol and bile acids was moved from Chapter 28 to this chapter.
- Dietary and obesity statistics were updated.
- Text information about medical uses of liposomes was added.

Chapter 24

- Jargon was removed and concepts were clarified by a more thorough explanation of reactions.
- A clearer explanation of how triacylglycerides are digested, absorbed, and moved through the body to destination cells was added.
- The discussion of energy yields from fat metabolism was extended for clarity.

Chapter 25

- The retrovirus information has been updated to focus on retroviruses in general.
- The influenza information focuses on the nature of the common influenza viruses and new research directions.

Chapter 26

- This chapter, Genomics, was Chapter 27 in the sixth edition. It has been updated to reflect the current state of genome mapping.
- The *Chemistry In Action* box, DNA Fingerprinting, has been updated to include PCR fingerprinting.

Chapter 27

- This chapter, Protein and Amino Acid Metabolism, was Chapter 28 in the sixth edition.
- Changes have been made to enhance clarity, relevance to the student, and connection to the text.

Chapter 28

- The chapter is now focused only on the messenger aspect of these peptides, amino acid derivatives, and steroids.
- Discussions were made clearer by spelling-out terms instead of defining abbreviations.
- The steroid-abuse section was revamped to increase relevance and enhance clarity for the student.

Chapter 29

- Changes were made to enhance clarity, relevance to the student, and connection to the text.

KEY FEATURES

Focus on Learning

Worked Examples Most Worked Examples include an **Analysis** section that precedes the **Solution**. The Analysis lays out the approach to solving a problem of the given type. When appropriate, a **Ballpark Estimate** gives students an overview of the relationships needed to solve the problem and provides an intuitive approach to arrive at a rough estimate of the answer. The Solution presents the worked-out example using the strategy laid out in the Analysis and, in many cases, includes expanded discussion to enhance student understanding. When applicable, following the Solution there is a Ballpark Check that compares the calculated answer to the Ballpark Estimate and verifies that the answer makes chemical and physical sense.

Worked Example 1.11 Factor Labels: Unit Conversions

A child is 21.5 inches long at birth. How long is this in centimeters?

ANALYSIS This problem calls for converting from inches to centimeters, so we will need to know how many centimeters are in an inch and how to use this information as a conversion factor.

BALLPARK ESTIMATE It takes about 2.5 cm to make 1 in., and so it should take two and a half times as many centimeters to make a distance equal to approximately 20 in., or about 20 in. $\times$ 2.5 = 50 cm.

SOLUTION

STEP 1: **Identify given information.** | Length = 21.5 in.

STEP 2: **Identify answer and units.** | Length = ?? cm

STEP 3: **Identify conversion factor.** | $1 \text{ in.} = 2.54 \text{ cm} \rightarrow \dfrac{2.54 \text{ cm}}{1 \text{ in.}}$

STEP 4: **Solve.** Multiply the known length (in inches) by the conversion factor so that units cancel, providing the answer (in centimeters). | $21.5 \text{ in.} \times \dfrac{2.54 \text{ cm}}{1 \text{ in.}} = 54.6 \text{ cm}$ (Rounded off from 54.61)

BALLPARK CHECK How does this value compare with the ballpark estimate we made at the beginning? Are the final units correct? 54.6 cm is close to our original estimate of 50 cm.

Key Concept Problems are integrated throughout the chapters to focus attention on the use of essential concepts, as do the **Understanding Key Concepts problems** at the end of each chapter. Understanding Key Concepts problems are designed to test students' mastery of the core principles developed in the chapter. Students thus have an opportunity to ask "Did I get it?" before they proceed. Most of these Key Concept Problems use graphics or molecular-level art to illustrate the core principles and will be particularly useful to visual learners.

KEY CONCEPT PROBLEM 6.4

What is the molecular weight of cytosine, a component of DNA (deoxyribonucleic acid)? (black = C, blue = N, red = O, white = H.)

Cytosine

Problems The problems within the chapters, for which brief answers are given in an appendix, cover every skill and topic to be understood. One or more problems follow each Worked Example and others stand alone at the ends of sections.

PROBLEM 1.18

Write appropriate conversion factors and carry out the following conversions:

(a) $16.0 \text{ oz} = ? \text{ g}$ (b) $2500 \text{ mL} = ? \text{ L}$ (c) $99.0 \text{ L} = ? \text{ qt}$

PROBLEM 1.19

Convert 0.840 qt to milliliters in a single calculation using more than one conversion factor.

More Color-Keyed, Labeled Equations It is entirely too easy to skip looking at a chemical equation while reading the text. We have used color extensively to call attention to the aspects of chemical equations and structures under discussion, a continuing feature of this book that has been judged to be very helpful.

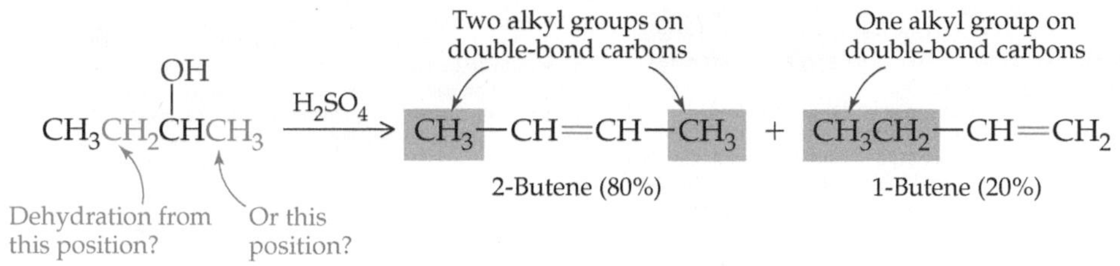

Key Words Every key term is boldfaced on its first use, fully defined in the margin adjacent to that use, and listed at the end of the chapter. These are the terms students must understand to continue with the subject at hand. Definitions of all Key Words are collected in the Glossary.

Focus on Relevancy

Chemistry is often considered to be a difficult and tedious subject. But when students make a connection between a concept in class and an application in their daily lives, the chemistry comes alive, and they get excited about the subject. The applications in this book strive to capture student interest and emphasize the relevance of the scientific concepts. The use of relevant applications makes the concepts more accessible and increases understanding.

Applications—now titled *Chemistry in Action*—are both integrated into the discussions in the text and set off from the text. Each boxed application provides sufficient information for reasonable understanding and, in many cases, extends the concepts discussed in the text in new ways. The boxes end with a cross-reference to end-of-chapter problems that can be assigned by the instructor.

CHEMISTRY IN ACTION

Anemia – A Limiting Reagent Problem?

Anemia is the most commonly diagnosed blood disorder, with symptoms typically including lethargy, fatigue, poor concentration, and sensitivity to cold. Although anemia has many causes, including genetic factors, the most common cause is insufficient dietary intake or absorption of iron.

Hemoglobin (abbreviated Hb), the iron-containing protein found in red blood cells, is responsible for oxygen transport throughout the body. Low iron levels in the body result in decreased production and incorporation of Hb into red blood cells. In addition, blood loss due to injury or to menstruation in women increases the body's demand for iron in order to replace lost Hb. In the United States, nearly 20% of women of childbearing age suffer from iron-deficiency anemia compared to only 2% of adult men.

The recommended minimum daily iron intake is 8 mg for adult men and 18 mg for premenopausal women. One way to ensure sufficient iron intake is a well-balanced diet that includes iron-fortified grains and cereals, red meat, egg yolks, leafy green vegetables, tomatoes, and raisins. Vegetarians should pay extra attention to their diet, because the iron in fruits and vegetables is not as readily absorbed by the body as the iron

▲ Can cooking in cast iron pots decrease anemia?

in meat, poultry, and fish. Vitamin supplements containing folic acid and either ferrous sulfate or ferrous gluconate can decrease iron deficiencies, and vitamin C increases the absorption of iron by the body.

However, the simplest way to increase dietary iron may be to use cast iron cookware. Studies have demonstrated that the iron content of many foods increases when cooked in an iron pot. Other studies involving Ethiopian children showed that those who ate food cooked in iron cookware were less likely to suffer from iron-deficiency anemia than their playmates who ate similar foods prepared in aluminum cookware.

See Chemistry in Action Problems 6.59 and 6.60 at the end of the chapter.

NEW Feature box in this edition—*Mastering Reactions* include How Addition Reactions Occur, How Elimination Reactions Occur, and Carbonyl Additions and discuss how these important organic transformations are believed to occur. This new feature allows instructors to easily introduce discussions of mechanism into their coverage of organic chemistry.

MASTERING REACTIONS

Organic Chemistry and the Curved Arrow Formalism

Starting with this chapter and continuing on through the remainder of this text, you will be exploring the world of organic chemistry and its close relative, biochemistry. Both of these areas of chemistry are much more "visual" than those you have been studying; organic chemists, for example, look at how and why reactions occur by examining the flow of electrons. For example, consider the following reaction of 2-iodopropane with sodium cyanide:

This seemingly simple process (known as a *substitution reaction*, discussed in Chapter 13) is not adequately described by the equation. To help to understand what may really be going on, organic chemists use what is loosely described as "electron pushing" and have adopted what is known as *curved arrow formalism* to represent it. The movement of electrons is depicted using curved arrows, where the number of electrons corresponds to the head of the arrow. Single-headed arrows represent movement of one electron, while a double-headed arrow indicates

The convention is to show the movement *from* an area of high electron density (the start of the arrow) *to* one of lower electron density (the head of the arrow). Using curved arrow formalism, we can examine the reaction of 2-iodopropane with sodium cyanide in more detail. There are two distinct paths by which this reaction can occur:

Path 1

Path 2

Notice that while both pathways lead ultimately to the same product, the curved arrow formalism shows us that they have significantly different ways of occurring. Although it is not important right now to understand which of the two paths

Focus on Making Connections

This can be a difficult course to teach. Much of what students are interested in lies in the last part of the course, but the material they need to understand the biochemistry is found in the first two-thirds. It is easy to lose sight of the connections among general, organic, and biological chemistry, so we use a feature—**Concepts to Review**—to call attention to these connections. From Chapter 4 on, the Concepts to Review section at the beginning of the chapter lists topics covered in earlier chapters that form the basis for what is discussed in the current chapter.

We have also retained the successful Concept Link icons and Looking Ahead notes.

Concept Link icons ▶▶▶ are used extensively to indicate places where previously covered material is relevant to the discussion at hand. These links provide cross-references and also serve to highlight important chemical themes as they are revisited.

LOOKING AHEAD ▶▶▶ notes call attention to connections between just-covered material and discussions in forthcoming chapters. These notes are designed to illustrate to the students why what they are learning will be useful in what lies ahead.

NEW Concept Maps are used to illustrate and reinforce the connections between concepts discussed in each chapter and concepts in previous or later chapters.

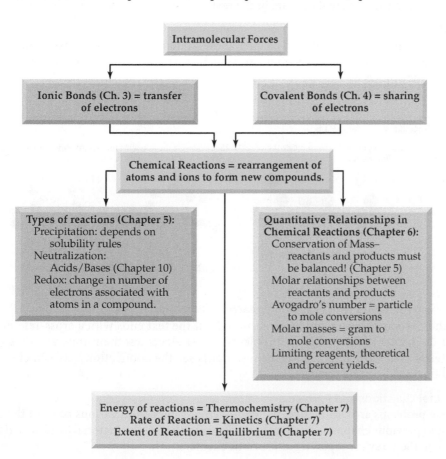

Focus on Studying

End of Chapter Section

Summary: Revisiting the Chapter Goals

The Chapter Summary revisits the Chapter Goals that open the chapter. Each of the questions posed at the start of the chapter is answered by a summary of the essential information needed to attain the corresponding goal.

SUMMARY: REVISITING THE CHAPTER GOALS

1. What are the basic properties of organic compounds? Compounds made up primarily of carbon atoms are classified as organic. Many organic compounds contain carbon atoms that are joined in long chains by a combination of single (C—C), double (C=C), or triple (C≡C) bonds. In this chapter, we focused primarily on *alkanes*, hydrocarbon compounds that contain only single bonds between all C atoms (*see Problems 29, 31, 32*).

is represented by lines and the locations of C and H atoms are understood (*see Problems 22–24, 44, 45, 48, 49–51*).

5. What are alkanes and cycloalkanes, and how are they named? Compounds that contain only carbon and hydrogen are called *hydrocarbons*, and hydrocarbons that have only single bonds are called *alkanes*. A *straight-chain alkane* has all its carbons connected in a row, a *branched-chain alkane* has a

---

Key Words

All of the chapter's boldface terms are listed in alphabetical order and are cross-referenced to the page where it appears in the text.

Understanding Key Concepts

The problems at the end of each chapter allow students to test their mastery of the core principles developed in the chapter. Students have an opportunity to ask "Did I get it?" before they proceed.

UNDERSTANDING KEY CONCEPTS

12.22 How many hydrogen atoms are needed to complete the hydrocarbon formulas for the following carbon backbones?

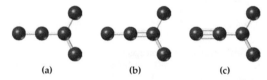

(a)   (b)   (c)

12.23 Convert the following models into condensed structures (black = C; white = H; red = O):

12.25 Convert the following models into line drawings and identify the functional groups in each:

(a)   (b)

12.26 Give systematic names for the following alkanes:

Chemistry in Action and Mastering Reactions Problems

Each boxed application and feature throughout the text ends with a cross-reference to end-of-chapter problems. These problems help students test their understanding of the material and, more importantly, help students see the connection between chemistry and the world around them.

General Questions and Problems

These problems are cumulative, pulling together topics from various parts of the chapter and previous chapters. These help students synthesize the material just learned while helping them review topics from previous chapters.

Acknowledgments

Although this text is now in its seventh edition, each revision has aspired to improve the quality and accuracy of the content and emphasize its relevance to the student users. Achieving this goal requires the coordinated efforts of a dedicated team of editors and media experts. Without them, this textbook would not be possible.

On behalf of all my coauthors, I would like to thank Adam Jaworski (Editor in Chief) and Jeanne Zalesky (Executive Editor) for building an excellent team for this project. Thanks also to Jared Sterzer (Production Manager), Wendy Perez (Project Manager), Eric Schrader (Photo Researcher), Lisa Tarabokjia (Editorial Assistant), and Connie Long (Art Specialist) for their attention to detail as we moved forward. Erica Frost, our developmental editor, deserves special recognition for providing invaluable feedback—her painstaking perusal of each chapter and her eye for details have contributed greatly to the accessibility and relevance of the text. Very special thanks also to Lisa Pierce, Assistant Editor, who patiently guided the process and worked closely with us—thank you for your flexibility and dedication to the success of this project.

The value of this text has also been enhanced by the many individuals who have worked to improve the ancillary materials. Particular thanks to Susan McMurry for her efforts to ensure the accuracy of the answers to problems provided in the text and her revisions of the solutions manuals. Thanks to Ashley Eklund, Miriam Adrianowicz, and Lauren Layn for their work on the media supplements. Thanks also to Margaret Trombley, Kristin Mayo, and Damon Botsakos for their efforts to expand and improve Mastering Chemistry.

Finally, thank you to the many instructors and students who have used the sixth edition and have provided valuable insights and feedback to improve the accuracy of the current edition. We gratefully acknowledge the following reviewers for their contributions to the seventh edition.

Accuracy Reviewers of the Seventh Edition

Sheikh Ahmed, *West Virginia University*
Danae R. Quirk Dorr, *Minnesota State University, Mankato*
Karen Ericson, *Indiana University-Purdue University, Fort Wayne*
Barbara Mowery, *York College of Pennsylvania*
Susan Thomas, *University of Texas, San Antonio*
Richard Triplett, *Des Moines Area Community College*

Reviewers of the Seventh Edition

Francis Burns, *Ferris State University*
Lisa L. Crozier, *Northeast Wisconsin Technical Center*
Robert P. Dixon, *Southern Illinois University, Edwardsville*
Luther Giddings, *Salt Lake Community College*
Arlene Haffa, *University of Wisconsin, Oshkosh*
L. Jaye Hopkins, *Spokane Community College*
Mohammad Mahroof, *Saint Cloud State University*
Gregory Marks, *Carroll University*
Van Quach, *Florida State University*
Douglas Raynie, *South Dakota State University*

Reviewers of the Previous Editions

Sheikh Ahmed, *West Virginia University*
Stanley Bajue, *CUNY-Medgar Evers College*
Daniel Bender, *Sacramento City College*
Dianne A. Bennett, *Sacramento City College*
Alfredo Castro, *Felician College*
Gezahegn Chaka, *Louisiana State University, Alexandria*
Michael Columbia, *Indiana University-Purdue University, Fort Wayne*
Rajeev B. Dabke, *Columbus State University*
Danae R. Quirk Dorr, *Minnesota State University, Mankato*

Pamela S. Doyle, *Essex County College*
Marie E. Dunstan, *York College of Pennsylvania*
Karen L. Ericson, *Indiana University-Purdue University, Fort Wayne*
Charles P. Gibson, *University of Wisconsin, Oshkosh*
Clifford Gottlieb, *Shasta College*
Mildred V. Hall, *Clark State Community College*
Meg Hausman, *University of Southern Maine*
Ronald Hirko, *South Dakota State University*
L. Jaye Hopkins, *Spokane Community College*
Margaret Isbell, *Sacramento City College*
James T. Johnson, *Sinclair Community College*
Margaret G. Kimble, *Indiana University-Purdue University Fort Wayne*
Grace Lasker, *Lake Washington Technical College*
Ashley Mahoney, *Bethel University*
Matthew G. Marmorino, *Indiana University, South Bend*
Diann Marten, *South Central College, Mankato*
Barbara D. Mowery, *York College of Pennsylvania*
Tracey Arnold Murray, *Capital University*
Andrew M. Napper, *Shawnee State University*
Lisa Nichols, *Butte Community College*
Glenn S. Nomura, *Georgia Perimeter College*
Douglas E. Raynie, *South Dakota State University*
Paul D. Root, *Henry Ford Community College*
Victor V. Ryzhov, *Northern Illinois University*
Karen Sanchez, *Florida Community College, Jacksonville-South*
Mir Shamsuddin, *Loyola University, Chicago*
Jeanne A. Stuckey, *University of Michigan*
John Sullivan, *Highland Community College*
Deborah E. Swain, *North Carolina Central University*
Susan T. Thomas, *University of Texas, San Antonio*
Yakov Woldman, *Valdosta State University*

The authors are committed to maintaining the highest quality and accuracy and look forward to comments from students and instructors regarding any aspect of this text and supporting materials. Questions or comments should be directed to the lead co-author.

David S. Ballantine
dballant@niu.edu

Resources in Print and Online

Name of Supplement	Available in Print	Available Online	Instructor or Student Supplement	Description
MasteringChemistry® (www.masteringchemistry.com)		✓	Supplement for Instructors and Students	MasteringChemistry from Pearson has been designed and refined with a single purpose in mind: to help educators create those moments of understanding with their students. The Mastering platform delivers engaging, dynamic learning opportunities—focused on your course objectives and responsive to each student's progress—that are proven to help students absorb course material and understand difficult concepts. By complementing your teaching with our engaging technology and content, you can be confident your students will arrive at those moments—moments of true understanding. The seventh edition will feature 20 new general, organic, and biological (GOB) specific tutorials, totaling over 100 GOB tutorials.
Instructor Resource Manual (isbn: 0321765427)	✓	✓	Supplement for Instructors	The manual features lecture outlines with presentation suggestions, teaching tips, suggested in-class demonstrations, and topics for classroom discussion.
Test Item File (isbn: 0321765435)	✓	✓	Supplement for Instructors	This has been updated to reflect the revisions in this text and contains questions in a bank of more than 2,000 multiple-choice questions.
Instructor Resource Center on DVD (isbn: 0321776119)		✓	Supplement for Instructors	This DVD provides an integrated collection of resources designed to help you make efficient and effective use of your time. The DVD features art from the text, including figures and tables in PDF format for high-resolution printing, as well as pre-built PowerPoint™ presentations. The first presentation contains the images, figures, and tables embedded within the PowerPoint slides, while the second includes a complete, modifiable, lecture outline. The final two presentations contain worked in-chapter sample exercises and questions to be used with Classroom Response Systems. This DVD also contains animations, as well as the TestGen version of the Test Item File, which allows you to create and tailor exams to your needs.
Study Guide and Full Solutions Manual (isbn: 032177616X) Study Guide and Selected Solutions Manual (isbn: 0321776100)	✓		Supplement for Students	**Study Guide and Full Solutions Manual** and **Study Guide and Selected Solutions Manual**, both by Susan McMurry. The selected version provides solutions only to those problems that have a short answer in the text's Selected Answer Appendix. Both versions explain in detail how the answers to the in-text and end-of-chapter problems are obtained. They also contain chapter summaries, study hints, and self-tests for each chapter.
Chemistry and Life in the Laboratory: Experiments, 6e (isbn: 0321751604)	✓		Supplement for Laboratory	***Chemistry and Life in the Laboratory*, sixth edition**, by Victor L. Heasley, Val J. Christensen ,Gene E. Heasley. Written specifically to accompany any fundamentals of general, organic and biological chemistry text, this manual contains 34 comprehensive and accessible experiments specifically for GOB students.
Catalyst: The Pearson Custom Laboratory Program for Chemistry		✓	Supplement for Laboratory	This program allows you to custom-build a chemistry lab manual that matches your content needs and course organization. You can either write your own labs using the Lab Authoring Kit tool or you can select from the hundreds of labs available at http://www.pearsonlearningsolutions.com/custom-library/catalyst. This program also allows you to add your own course notes, syllabi, or other materials.

MasteringChemistry®

MasteringChemistry™ has been designed and refined with a single purpose in mind: to help educators create that moment of understanding with their students. The Mastering platform delivers engaging, dynamic learning opportunities—focused on your course objectives and responsive to each student's progress—that are proven to help students absorb course material and understand difficult concepts.

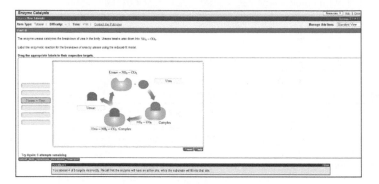

NEW! Chemistry Tutorials

MasteringChemistry® self-paced tutorials are designed to coach students with hints and feedback specific to their individual misconceptions. For the Seventh Edition, new tutorials have been created to guide students through the most challenging General, Organic, and Biological Chemistry topics and help them make connections between different concepts.

Unmatched Gradebook Capability

MasteringChemistry is the only system to capture the step-by-step work of each student in your class, including wrong answers submitted, hints requested, and time taken on every step. This data powers an unprecedented gradebook.

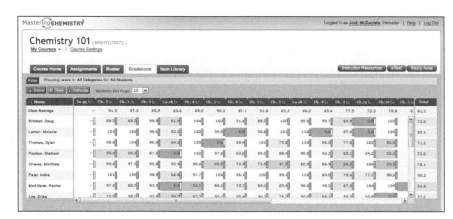

Gradebook Diagnostics

Instructors can identify at a glance students who are having difficulty with the color-coded gradebook. With a single click, charts summarize the most difficult problems in each assignment, vulnerable students, grade distribution, and even score improvement over the course.

Extend Learning Beyond The Classroom

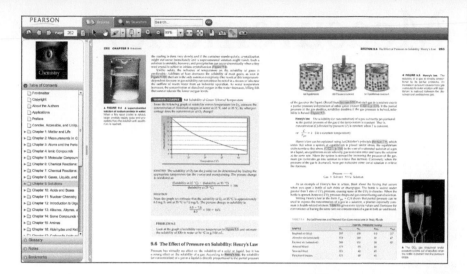

Pearson eText

Pearson eText gives students access to the text whenever and wherever they can access the Internet. The eText pages look exactly like the printed text and include powerful interactive and customization functions.

- Students can create notes, highlight text in different colors, create bookmarks, zoom, click hyperlinked words and phrases to view definitions, and view in single-page or two-page view.
- Students can link directly to associated media files, enabling them to view an animation as they read the text.
- It is possible to perform a full-text search and have the ability to save and export notes.

Instructors can share their notes and highlights with students and can also hide chapters that they do not want their students to read.

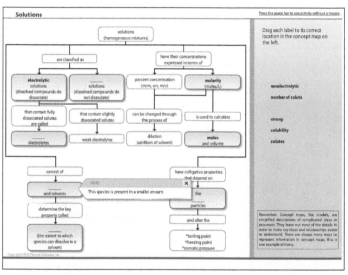

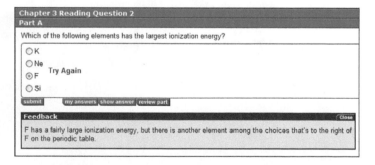

NEW! Concept Map problems

These interactive maps help students synthesize material they learned in previous chapters and demonstrate their understanding of interrelatedness of concepts in general, organic, and biological chemistry.

Reading Quizzes

Chapter-specific quizzes and activities focus on important, hard-to-grasp chemistry concepts.

Matter and Measurements

CONTENTS

◀ Increasing our knowledge of the chemical and physical properties of matter depends on our ability to make measurements that are precise and accurate.

CHAPTER GOALS

1. **What is matter and how is it classified?**
   THE GOAL: Be able to discuss the properties of matter, describe the three states of matter, distinguish between mixtures and pure substances, and distinguish between elements and compounds.

2. **How are chemical elements represented?**
   THE GOAL: Be able to name and give the symbols of common elements.

3. **What kinds of properties does matter have?**
   THE GOAL: Be able to distinguish between chemical and physical properties.

4. **What units are used to measure properties, and how can a quantity be converted from one unit to another?**
   THE GOAL: Be able to name and use the metric and SI units of measurement for mass, length, volume, and temperature and be able to convert quantities from one unit to another using conversion factors.

5. **How good are the reported measurements?**
   THE GOAL: Be able to interpret the number of significant figures in a measurement and round off numbers in calculations involving measurements.

6. **How are large and small numbers best represented?**
   THE GOAL: Be able to interpret prefixes for units of measurement and express numbers in scientific notation.

7. **What techniques are used to solve problems?**
   THE GOAL: Be able to analyze a problem, use the factor-label method to solve the problem, and check the result to ensure that it makes sense chemically and physically.

8. **What are temperature, specific heat, density, and specific gravity?**
   THE GOAL: Be able to define these quantities and use them in calculations.

Earth, air, fire, water—the ancient philosophers believed that all matter was composed of these four fundamental substances. We now know that matter is much more complex, made up of nearly 100 naturally occurring fundamental substances, or elements, in millions of unique combinations. Everything you see, touch, taste, and smell is made of chemicals formed from these elements. Many chemicals occur naturally, but others are synthetic, including the plastics, fibers, and medicines that are so critical to modern life. Just as everything you see is made of chemicals, many of the natural changes you see taking place around you are the result of *chemical reactions*—the change of one chemical into another. The crackling fire of a log burning in the fireplace, the color change of a leaf in the fall, and the changes that a human body undergoes as it grows and ages are all results of chemical reactions. To understand these and other natural processes, you must have a basic understanding of chemistry.

As you might expect, the chemistry of living organisms is complex, and it is not possible to understand all concepts without a proper foundation. Thus, the general plan of this book is to gradually increase in complexity, beginning in the first 11 chapters with a grounding in the scientific fundamentals that govern all of chemistry. In the following six chapters, we look at the nature of the carbon-containing substances, or *organic chemicals*, that compose all living things. In the final 12 chapters, we apply what we have learned in the first part of the book to the study of biological chemistry.

We begin in Chapter 1 with an examination of the states and properties of matter and an introduction to the systems of measurement that are essential to our understanding of matter and its behavior.

1.1 Chemistry: The Central Science

Chemistry is often referred to as "the central science" because it is crucial to nearly all other sciences. In fact, as more and more is learned, the historical dividing lines between chemistry, biology, and physics are fading, and current research is more interdisciplinary. Figure 1.1 diagrams the relationship of chemistry and biological chemistry to other fields of scientific study. Whatever the discipline in which you are most interested, the study of chemistry builds the necessary foundation.

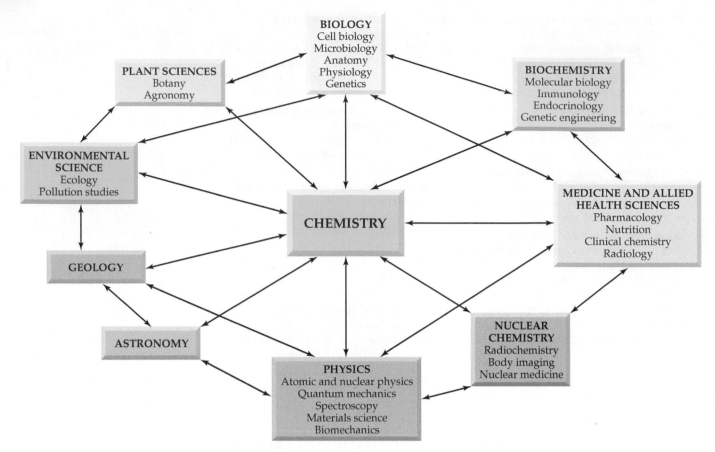

▲ **Figure 1.1**
Some relationships between chemistry—the central science—and other scientific and health-related disciplines.

Chemistry The study of the nature, properties, and transformations of matter.

Matter The physical material that makes up the universe; anything that has mass and occupies space.

Scientific Method The systematic process of observation, hypothesis, and experimentation used to expand and refine a body of knowledge.

Property A characteristic useful for identifying a substance or object.

Physical change A change that does not affect the chemical makeup of a substance or object.

Chemical change A change in the chemical makeup of a substance.

Chemistry is the study of matter—its nature, properties, and transformations. **Matter**, in turn, is a catchall word used to describe anything physically real—anything you can see, touch, taste, or smell. In more scientific terms, matter is anything that has mass and volume. As with our knowledge of all the other sciences, our knowledge of chemistry has developed by application of a process called the **scientific method** (see Chemistry in Action on p. 8). Starting with observations and measurements of the physical world, we form hypotheses to explain what we have observed. These hypotheses can then be tested by more observations and measurements, or experiments, to improve our understanding.

How might we describe different kinds of matter more specifically? Any characteristic that can be used to describe or identify something is called a **property**; size, color, and temperature are all familiar examples. Less familiar properties include *chemical composition*, which describes what matter is made of, and *chemical reactivity*, which describes how matter behaves. Rather than focus on the properties themselves, however, it is often more useful to think about *changes* in properties. Changes are of two types: *physical* and *chemical*. A **physical change** is one that does not alter the chemical makeup of a substance, whereas a **chemical change** is one that *does* alter a substance's chemical makeup. The melting of solid ice to give liquid water, for instance, is a physical change because the water changes only in form but not in chemical makeup. The rusting of an iron bicycle left in the rain, however, is a chemical change because iron combines with oxygen and moisture from the air to give a new substance, rust.

Table 1.1 lists some chemical and physical properties of several familiar substances—water, table sugar (sucrose), and baking soda (sodium bicarbonate). Note in Table 1.1 that the changes occurring when sugar and baking soda are heated are chemical changes, because new substances are produced.

TABLE 1.1 Some Properties of Water, Sugar, and Baking Soda

Water	Sugar (Sucrose)	Baking Soda (Sodium Bicarbonate)
Physical properties		
Colorless liquid	White crystals	White powder
Odorless	Odorless	Odorless
Melting point: 0 °C	Begins to decompose at 160 °C, turning black and giving off water.	Decomposes at 270 °C, giving off water and carbon dioxide.
Boiling point: 100 °C	—	—
Chemical properties		
Composition:*	Composition:*	Composition:*
11.2% hydrogen	6.4% hydrogen	27.4% sodium
88.8% oxygen	42.1% carbon	1.2% hydrogen
	51.5% oxygen	14.3% carbon
		57.1% oxygen
Does not burn.	Burns in air.	Does not burn.

Compositions are given by mass percent.

▲ **Burning of potassium in water is an example of a chemical change.**

PROBLEM 1.1
Identify each of the following as a physical change or a chemical change:
(a) Grinding of a metal   **(b)** Fruit ripening
(c) Wood burning   **(d)** A rain puddle evaporating

1.2 States of Matter

Matter exists in three forms: solid, liquid, and gas. A **solid** has a definite volume and a definite shape that does not change regardless of the container in which it is placed; for example, a wooden block, marbles, or a cube of ice. A **liquid**, by contrast, has a definite volume but an indefinite shape. The volume of a liquid, such as water, does not change when it is poured into a different container, but its shape does. A **gas** is different still, having neither a definite volume nor a definite shape. A gas expands to fill the volume and take the shape of any container it is placed in, such as the helium in a balloon or steam formed by boiling water (Figure 1.2).

Solid A substance that has a definite shape and volume.

Liquid A substance that has a definite volume but assumes the shape of its container.

Gas A substance that has neither a definite volume nor a definite shape.

◀ **Figure 1.2**
The three states of matter—solid, liquid, and gas.

(a) Ice: A solid has a definite volume and a definite shape independent of its container.

(b) Water: A liquid has a definite volume but a variable shape that depends on its container.

(c) Steam: A gas has both variable volume and shape that depend on its container.

State of matter The physical state of a substance as a solid, liquid, or gas.

Change of state The conversion of a substance from one state to another—for example, from liquid to gas.

Many substances, such as water, can exist in all three phases, or **states of matter**—the solid state, the liquid state, and the gaseous state—depending on the temperature. The conversion of a substance from one state to another is known as a **change of state**. The melting of a solid, the freezing or boiling of a liquid, and the condensing of a gas to a liquid are familiar to everyone.

Worked Example 1.1 Identifying States of Matter

Formaldehyde is a disinfectant, a preservative, and a raw material for the manufacturing of plastics. Its melting point is −92 °C and its boiling point is −19.5 °C. Is formaldehyde a gas, a liquid, or a solid at room temperature (25 °C)?

ANALYSIS The state of matter of any substance depends on its temperature. How do the melting point and boiling point of formaldehyde compare with room temperature?

SOLUTION
Room temperature (25 °C) is above the boiling point of formaldehyde (−19.5 °C), and so the formaldehyde is a gas.

▶▶▶ The symbol °C means degrees Celsius and will be discussed in Section 1.13.

PROBLEM 1.2
Acetic acid, which gives the sour taste to vinegar, has a melting point of 16.7 °C and a boiling point of 118 °C. Predict the physical state of acetic acid when the ambient temperature is 10 °C.

1.3 Classification of Matter

The first question a chemist asks about an unknown substance is whether it is a pure substance or a mixture. Every sample of matter is one or the other. Water and sugar alone are pure substances, but stirring some sugar into a glass of water creates a *mixture*.

What is the difference between a pure substance and a mixture? One difference is that a **pure substance** is uniform in its chemical composition and its properties all the way down to the microscopic level. Every sample of water, sugar, or baking soda, regardless of source, has the composition and properties listed in Table 1.1. A **mixture**, however, can vary in both composition and properties, depending on how it is made. A **homogeneous mixture** is a blend of two or more pure substances having a uniform composition at the microscopic level. Sugar dissolved in water is one example. You cannot always distinguish between a pure substance and a homogeneous mixture just by looking. The sugar–water mixture *looks* just like pure water but differs on a molecular level. The amount of sugar dissolved in a glass of water will determine the sweetness, boiling point, and other properties of the mixture. A **heterogeneous mixture**, by contrast, is a blend of two or more pure substances having non-uniform composition, such as a vegetable stew in which each spoonful is different. It is relatively easy to distinguish heterogeneous mixtures from pure substances.

Another difference between a pure substance and a mixture is that the components of a mixture can be separated without changing their chemical identities. Water can be separated from a sugar–water mixture, for example, by boiling the mixture to drive off the steam and then condensing the steam to recover the pure water. Pure sugar is left behind in the container.

Pure substances are themselves classified into two groups: those that can undergo a chemical breakdown to yield simpler substances and those that cannot. A pure substance that cannot be broken down chemically into simpler substances is called an **element**. Examples include hydrogen, oxygen, aluminum, gold, and sulfur. At the time this book was printed, 118 elements had been identified, although only 91 of these occur naturally. All the millions of other substances in the universe are derived from them.

Pure substance A substance that has a uniform chemical composition throughout.

Mixture A blend of two or more substances, each of which retains its chemical identity.

Homogeneous mixture A uniform mixture that has the same composition throughout.

Heterogeneous mixture A nonuniform mixture that has regions of different composition.

▶▶▶ We'll revisit the properties of mixtures in Section 9.1 when we discuss solutions.

Element A fundamental substance that cannot be broken down chemically into any simpler substance.

▶▶▶ Elements are explored in the next section of this chapter (Section 1.4).

Any pure material that *can* be broken down into simpler substances by a chemical change is called a **chemical compound**. The term *compound* implies "more than one" (think "compound fracture"). A chemical compound, therefore, is formed by combining two or more elements to make a new substance. Water, for example, can be chemically changed by passing an electric current through it to produce hydrogen and oxygen. In writing this chemical change, the initial substance, or **reactant** (water), is written on the left; the new substances, or **products** (hydrogen and oxygen), are written on the right; and an arrow connects the two parts to indicate a chemical change, or **chemical reaction**. The conditions necessary to bring about the reaction are written above and below the arrow.

Chemical compound A pure substance that can be broken down into simpler substances by chemical reactions.

Reactant A starting substance that undergoes change during a chemical reaction.

Product A substance formed as the result of a chemical reaction.

Chemical reaction A process in which the identity and composition of one or more substances are changed.

▶▶▶ We will discuss how chemical reactions are represented in more detail in Section 1.6, and how reactions are classified in Chapter 5.

$$\textit{A chemical reaction} \qquad \text{Water} \xrightarrow[\text{current}]{\text{Electric}} \overbrace{\text{Hydrogen } + \text{ Oxygen}}$$

Reactant ⟶ (Water)   Products ⟶ (Hydrogen + Oxygen)

The classification of matter into mixtures, pure compounds, and elements is summarized in Figure 1.3.

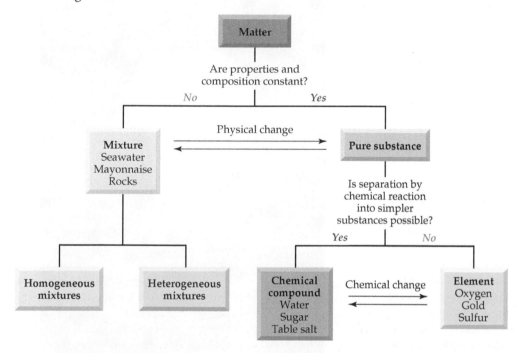

Figure 1.3
◀ A scheme for the classification of matter.

Worked Example 1.2 Classifying Matter

Classify each of the following as a mixture or a pure substance. If a mixture, classify it as heterogeneous or homogeneous. If a pure substance, identify it as an element or a compound.

(a) Vanilla ice cream   **(b)** Sugar

ANALYSIS Refer to the definitions of pure substances and mixtures. Is the substance composed of more than one kind of matter? Is the composition uniform?

SOLUTION

(a) Vanilla ice cream is composed of more than one substance—cream, sugar, and vanilla flavoring. The composition appears to be uniform throughout, so this is a homogeneous mixture.

(b) Sugar is composed of only one kind of matter—pure sugar. This is a pure substance. It can be converted to some other substance by a chemical change (see Table 1.1), so it is not an element. It must be a compound.

PROBLEM 1.3

Classify each of the following as a mixture or a pure substance. If a mixture, classify it as heterogeneous or homogeneous. If a pure substance, identify it as an element or a compound.

(a) Concrete   (b) The helium in a balloon   (c) A lead weight   (d) Wood

PROBLEM 1.4

Classify each of the following as a physical change or a chemical change:

(a) Dissolving sugar in water

(b) Producing carbon dioxide gas and solid lime by heating limestone

(c) Frying an egg

(d) The conversion of salicylic acid to acetylsalicylic acid (see the following Chemistry in Action)

▶▶▶ Prostaglandins are discussed in Section 24.9.

CHEMISTRY IN ACTION

Aspirin—A Case Study

Acetylsalicylic acid, more commonly known as aspirin, is perhaps the first true wonder drug. It is used as an analgesic to reduce fevers and to relieve headaches and body pains. It possesses anticoagulant properties, which in low doses can help prevent heart attacks and minimize the damage caused by strokes. But how was it discovered, and how does it work? The "discovery" of aspirin is a combination of serendipity and a process known as the scientific method: observation, evaluation of data, formation of a hypothesis, and the design of experiments to test the hypothesis and further our understanding.

The origins of aspirin can be traced back to the ancient Greek physician Hippocrates in 400 B.C., who prescribed the bark and leaves of the willow tree to relieve pain and fever. His knowledge of the therapeutic properties of these substances was the result of systematic observations and the evaluation of folklore—knowledge of the common people obtained through trial and error. The development of aspirin took another step forward in 1828 when scientists isolated a bitter-tasting yellow extract, called salicin, from willow bark. Experimental evidence identified salicin as the active ingredient responsible for the observed medical effects. Salicin could be easily converted by chemical reaction to salicylic acid (SA), which by the late 1800s was being mass-produced and marketed. SA had an unpleasant taste, however, and often caused stomach irritation and indigestion.

Further experiments were performed to convert salicylic acid to a substance that retained the therapeutic activity of SA, but without the unpleasant side effects. The discovery of acetylsalicylic acid (ASA), a derivative of SA, has often been attributed to Felix Hoffman, a chemist working for the Bayer pharmaceutical labs, but the first synthesis of ASA was actually reported by a French chemist, Charles Gerhardt, in 1853. Nevertheless, Hoffman obtained a patent for ASA in 1900, and Bayer marketed the new drug, now called aspirin, in water-soluble tablets.

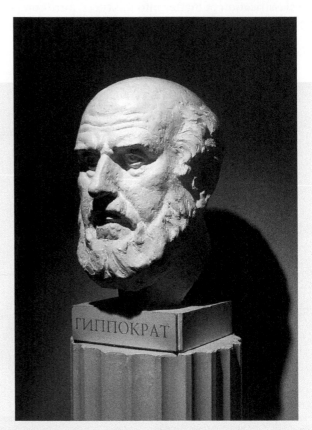

▲ *Hippocrates.* **The ancient Greek physician prescribed a precursor of aspirin found in willow bark to relieve pain.**

But, how does aspirin work? Once again, experimental data provided insights into the therapeutic activity of aspirin. In 1971, the British pharmacologist John Vane discovered that aspirin suppresses the body's production of prostaglandins, which are responsible for the pain and swelling that accompany inflammation. The discovery of this mechanism led to the development of new analgesic drugs.

Research continues to explore aspirin's potential for preventing colon cancer, cancer of the esophagus, and other diseases.

See Chemistry in Action Problem 1.96 at the end of the chapter.

🗝 KEY CONCEPT PROBLEM 1.5

In the image below, red spheres represent element A and blue spheres represent element B. Identify the process illustrated in the image as a chemical change or a physical change. Explain your answer.

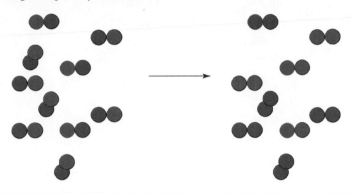

1.4 Chemical Elements and Symbols

As of the date this book was printed, 118 chemical elements have been identified. Some are certainly familiar to you—oxygen, helium, iron, aluminum, copper, and gold, for example—but many others are probably unfamiliar—rhenium, niobium, thulium, and promethium. Rather than write out the full names of elements, chemists use a short-hand notation in which elements are referred to by one- or two-letter symbols. The names and symbols of some common elements are listed in Table 1.2, and a complete alphabetical list is given inside the front cover of this book.

Note that all two-letter symbols have only their first letter capitalized, whereas the second letter is always lowercase. The symbols of most common elements are the first one or two letters of the elements' commonly used names, such as H (hydrogen) and Al (aluminum). Pay special attention, however, to the elements grouped in the last column to the right in Table 1.2. The symbols for these elements are derived from their original Latin names, such as Na for sodium, once known as *natrium*. The only way to learn these symbols is to memorize them; fortunately, they are few in number.

Only 91 of the elements occur naturally; the remaining elements have been produced artificially by chemists and physicists. Each element has its own distinctive properties, and just about all of the first 95 elements have been put to use in some way that takes advantage

▶▶▶ We will discuss the creation of new elements by nuclear bombardment in Chapter 11.

TABLE 1.2 Names and Symbols for Some Common Elements							
Elements with Symbols Based on Modern Names						**Elements with Symbols Based on Latin Names**	
Al	Aluminum	Co	Cobalt	N	Nitrogen	Cu	Copper (*cuprum*)
Ar	Argon	F	Fluorine	O	Oxygen	Au	Gold (*aurum*)
Ba	Barium	He	Helium	P	Phosphorus	Fe	Iron (*ferrum*)
Bi	Bismuth	H	Hydrogen	Pt	Platinum	Pb	Lead (*plumbum*)
B	Boron	I	Iodine	Rn	Radon	Hg	Mercury (*hydrargyrum*)
Br	Bromine	Li	Lithium	Si	Silicon	K	Potassium (*kalium*)
Ca	Calcium	Mg	Magnesium	S	Sulfur	Ag	Silver (*argentum*)
C	Carbon	Mn	Manganese	Ti	Titanium	Na	Sodium (*natrium*)
Cl	Chlorine	Ni	Nickel	Zn	Zinc	Sn	Tin (*stannum*)

TABLE 1.3 Elemental Composition of the Earth's Crust and the Human Body*

Earth's Crust		Human Body	
Oxygen	46.1%	Oxygen	61%
Silicon	28.2%	Carbon	23%
Aluminum	8.2%	Hydrogen	10%
Iron	5.6%	Nitrogen	2.6%
Calcium	4.1%	Calcium	1.4%
Sodium	2.4%	Phosphorus	1.1%
Magnesium	2.3%	Sulfur	0.20%
Potassium	2.1%	Potassium	0.20%
Titanium	0.57%	Sodium	0.14%
Hydrogen	0.14%	Chlorine	0.12%

Mass percent values are given.

Chemical formula A notation for a chemical compound using element symbols and subscripts to show how many atoms of each element are present.

▶▶▶ We'll learn more about the structure of atoms and how they form compounds in Chapter 2.

of those properties. As indicated in Table 1.3, which shows the approximate elemental composition of the earth's crust and the human body, the naturally occurring elements are not equally abundant. Oxygen and silicon together account for nearly 75% of the mass in the earth's crust; oxygen, carbon, and hydrogen account for nearly all the mass of a human body.

Just as elements combine to form chemical compounds, symbols are combined to produce **chemical formulas**, which show by subscripts how many *atoms* (the smallest fundamental units) of each element are in a given chemical compound. For example, the formula H_2O represents water, which contains 2 hydrogen atoms combined with 1 oxygen atom. Similarly, the formula CH_4 represents methane (natural gas), and the formula $C_{12}H_{22}O_{11}$ represents table sugar (sucrose). When no subscript is given for an element, as for carbon in the formula CH_4, a subscript of "1" is understood.

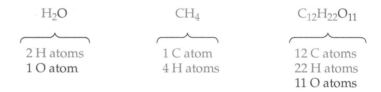

$$H_2O \qquad CH_4 \qquad C_{12}H_{22}O_{11}$$

2 H atoms	1 C atom	12 C atoms
1 O atom	4 H atoms	22 H atoms
		11 O atoms

PROBLEM 1.6

Match the names of the elements described below (a–f) with their elemental symbols (1–6).

(a) Sodium, a major component in table salt

(b) Tungsten, a metal used in light bulb filaments

(c) Strontium, used to produce brilliant red colors in fireworks

(d) Titanium, used in artificial hips and knee-replacement joints

(e) Fluorine, added to municipal water supplies to strengthen tooth enamel

(f) Tin, a metal used in solder

(1) W   (2) Na   (3) Sn   (4) F   (5) Ti   (6) Sr

PROBLEM 1.7

Identify the elements represented in each of the following chemical formulas, and tell the number of atoms of each element:

(a) NH_3 (ammonia)   (b) $NaHCO_3$ (sodium bicarbonate)

(c) C_8H_{18} (octane, a component of gasoline)   (d) $C_6H_8O_6$ (vitamin C)

1.5 Elements and the Periodic Table

The symbols of the known elements are normally presented in a tabular format called the **periodic table**, as shown in Figure 1.4 and the inside front cover of this book. We will have much more to say about the periodic table and how it is numbered later, but will note for now that it is the most important organizing principle in chemistry. An enormous amount of information is embedded in the periodic table, information that gives chemists the ability to explain known chemical behavior of elements and to predict new behavior. The elements can be roughly divided into three groups: *metals*, *nonmetals*, and *metalloids* (sometimes called *semimetals*).

Periodic table A tabular format listing all known elements.

▶▶ The organization of the periodic table will be discussed in Chapter 2.

1A 1	2A 2	3B 3	4B 4	5B 5	6B 6	7B 7	8	8B 9	10	1B 11	2B 12	3A 13	4A 14	5A 15	6A 16	7A 17	8A 18
1 H 1.00794																	2 He 4.00260
3 Li 6.941	4 Be 9.01218											5 B 10.81	6 C 12.011	7 N 14.0067	8 O 15.9994	9 F 18.9984	10 Ne 20.1797
11 Na 22.98977	12 Mg 24.305											13 Al 26.98154	14 Si 28.0855	15 P 30.9738	16 S 32.066	17 Cl 35.4527	18 Ar 39.948
19 K 39.0983	20 Ca 40.078	21 Sc 44.9559	22 Ti 47.88	23 V 50.9415	24 Cr 51.996	25 Mn 54.9380	26 Fe 55.847	27 Co 58.9332	28 Ni 58.69	29 Cu 63.546	30 Zn 65.39	31 Ga 69.72	32 Ge 72.61	33 As 74.9216	34 Se 78.96	35 Br 79.904	36 Kr 83.80
37 Rb 85.4678	38 Sr 87.62	39 Y 88.9059	40 Zr 91.224	41 Nb 92.9064	42 Mo 95.94	43 Tc (98)	44 Ru 101.07	45 Rh 102.9055	46 Pd 106.42	47 Ag 107.8682	48 Cd 112.41	49 In 114.82	50 Sn 118.710	51 Sb 121.757	52 Te 127.60	53 I 126.9045	54 Xe 131.29
55 Cs 132.9054	56 Ba 137.33	57 *La 138.9055	72 Hf 178.49	73 Ta 180.9479	74 W 183.85	75 Re 186.207	76 Os 190.2	77 Ir 192.22	78 Pt 195.08	79 Au 196.9665	80 Hg 200.59	81 Tl 204.383	82 Pb 207.2	83 Bi 208.9804	84 Po (209)	85 At (210)	86 Rn (222)
87 Fr (223)	88 Ra 226.0254	89 †Ac 227.0278	104 Rf (261)	105 Db (262)	106 Sg (266)	107 Bh (264)	108 Hs (269)	109 Mt (268)	110 Ds (271)	111 Rg (272)	112 Cn (285)	113 (284)	114 (289)	115 (288)	116 (292)	117 (293)	118 (294)

58 Ce 140.12	59 Pr 140.9077	60 Nd 144.24	61 Pm (145)	62 Sm 150.36	63 Eu 151.965	64 Gd 157.25	65 Tb 158.9254	66 Dy 162.50	67 Ho 164.9304	68 Er 167.26	69 Tm 168.9342	70 Yb 173.04	71 Lu 174.967
90 Th 232.0381	91 Pa 231.0399	92 U 238.0289	93 Np 237.048	94 Pu (244)	95 Am (243)	96 Cm (247)	97 Bk (247)	98 Cf (251)	99 Es (252)	100 Fm (257)	101 Md (258)	102 No (259)	103 Lr (262)

Metals | Metalloids | Nonmetals

▲ **Figure 1.4**
The periodic table of the elements.
Metals appear on the left, nonmetals on the right, and metalloids in a zigzag band between metals and nonmetals. The numbering system is explained in Section 2.4.

Ninety-four of the currently known elements are metals—aluminum, gold, copper, and zinc, for example. **Metals** are solid at room temperature (except for mercury), usually have a lustrous appearance when freshly cut, are good conductors of heat and electricity, and are malleable rather than brittle. That is, metals can be pounded into different shapes rather than shattering when struck. Note that metals occur on the left side of the periodic table.

Metal A malleable element, with a lustrous appearance, that is a good conductor of heat and electricity.

Eighteen elements are **nonmetals**. All are poor conductors of heat and electricity. Eleven are gases at room temperature, six are brittle solids, and one is a liquid. Oxygen and nitrogen, for example, are gases present in air; sulfur is a solid found in large underground deposits. Bromine is the only liquid nonmetal. Note that nonmetals occur on the right side of the periodic table.

Nonmetal An element that is a poor conductor of heat and electricity.

Only six elements are **metalloids**, so named because their properties are intermediate between those of metals and nonmetals. Boron, silicon, and arsenic are examples. Pure silicon has a lustrous or shiny surface, like a metal, but it is brittle, like a nonmetal, and its electrical conductivity lies between that of metals and nonmetals. Note that metalloids occur in a zigzag band between metals on the left and nonmetals on the right side of the periodic table.

Metalloid An element whose properties are intermediate between those of a metal and a nonmetal.

(a)

(b)

(c)

▲ **Metals: Gold, zinc, and copper.**
(a) Known for its beauty, gold is very unreactive and is used primarily in jewelry and in electronic components. (b) Zinc, an essential trace element in our diets, has industrial uses ranging from the manufacture of brass, to roofing materials, to batteries. (c) Copper is widely used in electrical wiring, in water pipes, and in coins.

(a)

(b)

(c)

▲ **Nonmetals: Nitrogen, sulfur, and iodine.**
(a) Nitrogen, (b) sulfur, and (c) iodine are essential to all living things. Pure nitrogen, which constitutes almost 80% of air, is a gas at room temperature and does not condense to a liquid until it is cooled to −328 °C. Sulfur, a yellow solid, is found in large underground deposits in Texas and Louisiana. Iodine is a dark violet crystalline solid that was first isolated from seaweed.

(a)

(b)

▲ **Metalloids: Boron and silicon.**
(a) Boron is a strong, hard metalloid used in making the composite materials found in military aircraft. (b) Silicon is well known for its use in making computer chips.

Those elements essential for human life are listed in Table 1.4. In addition to the well-known elements carbon, hydrogen, oxygen, and nitrogen, less familiar elements such as molybdenum and selenium are also important.

TABLE 1.4 Elements Essential for Human Life*

Element	Symbol	Function
Carbon	C	These four elements are present in all living organisms
Hydrogen	H	
Oxygen	O	
Nitrogen	N	
Arsenic	As	May affect cell growth and heart function
Boron	B	Aids in the use of Ca, P, and Mg
Calcium*	Ca	Necessary for growth of teeth and bones
Chlorine*	Cl	Necessary for maintaining salt balance in body fluids
Chromium	Cr	Aids in carbohydrate metabolism
Cobalt	Co	Component of vitamin B_{12}
Copper	Cu	Necessary to maintain blood chemistry
Fluorine	F	Aids in the development of teeth and bones
Iodine	I	Necessary for thyroid function
Iron	Fe	Necessary for oxygen-carrying ability of blood
Magnesium*	Mg	Necessary for bones, teeth, and muscle and nerve action
Manganese	Mn	Necessary for carbohydrate metabolism and bone formation
Molybdenum	Mo	Component of enzymes necessary for metabolism
Nickel	Ni	Aids in the use of Fe and Cu
Phosphorus*	P	Necessary for growth of bones and teeth; present in DNA/RNA
Potassium*	K	Component of body fluids; necessary for nerve action
Selenium	Se	Aids vitamin E action and fat metabolism
Silicon	Si	Helps form connective tissue and bone
Sodium*	Na	Component of body fluids; necessary for nerve and muscle action
Sulfur*	S	Component of proteins; necessary for blood clotting
Zinc	Zn	Necessary for growth, healing, and overall health

*C, H, O, and N are present in most foods. Other elements listed vary in their distribution in different foods. Those marked with an asterisk are macronutrients, essential in the diet at more than 100 mg/day; the rest, other than C, H, O, and N, are micronutrients, essential at 15 mg or less per day.

LOOKING AHEAD ▶▶▶ The elements listed in Table 1.4 are not present in our bodies in their free forms. Instead, they are combined into many thousands of different chemical compounds. We will talk about some compounds formed by metals in Chapter 3 and compounds formed by nonmetals in Chapter 4.

PROBLEM 1.8
The six metalloids are boron (B), silicon (Si), germanium (Ge), arsenic (As), antimony (Sb), and tellurium (Te). Locate them in the periodic table, and tell where they appear with respect to metals and nonmetals.

PROBLEM 1.9
Locate the element Hg (discussed in the Chemisty in Action on p. 15) in the periodic table. Is it a metal, nonmetal, or metalloid? What physical and chemical properties contribute to the toxicity of mercury and compounds containing mercury?

1.6 Chemical Reactions: An Example of Chemical Change

If we take a quick look at an example of a chemical reaction, we can reinforce some of the ideas discussed in the previous sections. The element *nickel* is a hard, shiny metal, and the compound *hydrogen chloride* is a colorless gas that dissolves in water to give a solution called *hydrochloric acid*. When pieces of nickel are added to hydrochloric acid in a test tube, the nickel is slowly eaten away, the colorless solution turns green, and a gas bubbles out of the test tube. The change in color, the dissolving of the nickel, and the appearance of gas bubbles are indications that a chemical reaction is taking place, as shown in Figure 1.5.

Overall, the reaction of nickel with hydrochloric acid can be either written in words or represented in a shorthand notation using symbols to represent the elements or compounds involved as reactants and products, as shown below.

Reactants ⎯   ⎯ Products

$$\overbrace{\text{Nickel} + \text{Hydrochloric acid}} \longrightarrow \overbrace{\text{Nickel (II) chloride} + \text{Hydrogen}}$$

$$[\text{Ni} + 2\,\text{HCl} \longrightarrow \text{NiCl}_2 + \text{H}_2]$$

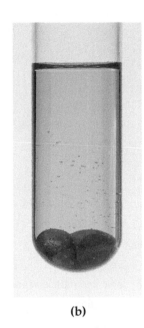

(a)   (b)   (c)

▲ **Figure 1.5**
Reactants and products of a chemical reaction.
(a) The reactants: The flat dish contains pieces of nickel, an element that is a typical lustrous metal. The bottle contains hydrochloric acid, a solution of the chemical compound hydrogen chloride in water. These reactants are about to be combined in the test tube. (b) The reaction: As the chemical reaction occurs, the colorless solution turns green when water-insoluble nickel metal slowly changes into the water-soluble chemical compound nickel (II) chloride. Gas bubbles of the element hydrogen are produced and rise slowly through the green solution. (c) The product: Hydrogen gas can be collected as it bubbles from the solution. Removal of water from the solution leaves behind the other product, a solid green chemical compound known as nickel (II) chloride.

1.7 Physical Quantities

Our understanding of matter depends on our ability to measure the changes in physical properties associated with physical and chemical change. Mass, volume, temperature, density, and other physical properties that can be measured are called **physical quantities** and are described by both a number and a **unit** of defined size:

Physical quantity A physical property that can be measured.

Unit A defined quantity used as a standard of measurement.

Number   Unit

61.2 kilograms

CHEMISTRY IN ACTION

Mercury and Mercury Poisoning

Mercury, the only metallic element that is liquid at room temperature, has fascinated people for millennia. Egyptian kings were buried in their pyramids along with containers of mercury, alchemists during the Middle Ages used mercury to dissolve gold, and Spanish galleons carried loads of mercury to the New World in the 1600s for use in gold and silver mining. Even its symbol, Hg, from the Latin *hydrargyrum,* meaning "liquid silver," hints at mercury's uniqueness.

Much of the recent interest in mercury has concerned its toxicity, but there are some surprises. For example, the mercury compound Hg_2Cl_2 (called *calomel*) is nontoxic and has a long history of medical use as a laxative, yet it is also used as a fungicide and rat poison. Dental amalgam, a solid alloy of approximately 50% elemental mercury, 35% silver, 13% tin, 1% copper, and trace amounts of zinc, has been used by dentists for many years to fill tooth cavities, with little or no adverse effects except in individuals with a hypersensitivity to mercury. Yet exposure to elemental mercury *vapor* for long periods leads to mood swings, headaches, tremors, and loss of hair and teeth. The widespread use of mercuric nitrate, a mercury compound employed to make the felt used in hats, exposed many hatters of the eighteenth and nineteenth centuries to toxic levels of mercury. The eccentric behavior displayed by hatters suffering from mercury poisoning led to the phrase "mad as a hatter."

Why is mercury toxic in some forms but not in others? It turns out that the toxicity of mercury and its compounds is related to solubility. Only soluble mercury compounds are toxic, because they can be transported through the bloodstream to all parts of the body, where they react with different enzymes and interfere with various biological processes. Elemental mercury and insoluble mercury compounds become toxic only when converted

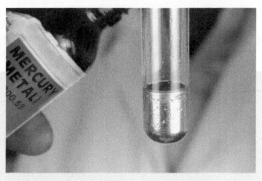

▲ **Elemental Mercury, a liquid at room temperature, forms many toxic compounds.**

into soluble compounds, reactions that are extremely slow in the body. Calomel, for example, is an insoluble mercury compound that passes through the body long before it is converted into any soluble compounds. Mercury alloys were considered safe for dental use because mercury does not evaporate readily from the alloys and it neither reacts with nor dissolves in saliva. Mercury vapor, however, remains in the lungs when breathed, until it is slowly converted into soluble compounds. Soluble organic forms of mercury can be particularly toxic. Trace amounts are found in nearly all seafood, but some larger species such as king mackerel and swordfish contain higher levels of mercury. Because mercury can affect the developing brain and nervous system of a fetus, pregnant women are often advised to avoid consuming them.

Recent events have raised new concerns regarding the safe use of mercury in some other applications. Perhaps the most controversial example is the use of thimerosal, an organic mercury compound, as a preservative in flu vaccines. While there is anecdotal evidence suggesting a link between thimerosal and autism in children, most scientific data seem to refute this claim. In response to these concerns, preservative-free versions of the influenza vaccine are available for use in infants, children, and pregnant women.

See Chemistry in Action Problem 1.97 at the end of the chapter.

The number alone is not much good without a unit. If you asked how much blood an accident victim had lost, the answer "three" would not tell you much. Three drops? Three milliliters? Three pints? Three liters? (By the way, an adult human has only 5–6 liters of blood.)

Any physical quantity can be measured in many different units. For example, a person's height might be measured in inches, feet, yards, centimeters, or many other units. To avoid confusion, scientists from around the world have agreed on a system of standard units, called by the French name *Système International d'Unites* (International System of Units), abbreviated *SI.* **SI units** for some common physical quantities are given in Table 1.5. Mass is measured in *kilograms* (kg), length is measured in *meters* (m), volume is measured in *cubic meters* (m^3), temperature is measured in *kelvins* (K), and time is measured in *seconds* (s, not sec).

SI units are closely related to the more familiar *metric units* used in all industrialized nations of the world except the United States. If you compare the SI and metric units shown in Table 1.5, you will find that the basic metric unit of mass is the *gram* (g) rather than the kilogram (1 g = 1/1000 kg), the metric unit of volume is the *liter* (L) rather than the cubic meter (1 L = 1/1000 m^3), and the metric unit of temperature

SI units Units of measurement defined by the International System of Units.

TABLE 1.5 Some SI and Metric Units and Their Equivalents

Quantity	SI Unit (Symbol)	Metric Unit (Symbol)	Equivalents
Mass	Kilogram (kg)	Gram (g)	1 kg = 1000 g = 2.205 lb
Length	Meter (m)	Meter (m)	1 m = 3.280 ft
Volume	Cubic meter (m^3)	Liter (L)	$1 \, m^3$ = 1000 L = 264.2 gal
Temperature	Kelvin (K)	Celsius degree (°C)	See Section 1.13
Time	Second (s)	Second (s)	—

is the *Celsius degree* (°C) rather than the kelvin. The meter is the unit of length, and the second is the unit of time in both systems. Although SI units are now preferred in scientific research, metric units are still used in some fields. You will probably find yourself working with both.

In addition to the units listed in Table 1.5, many other widely used units are derived from them. For instance, units of *meters per second* (m/s) are often used for *speed*—the distance covered in a given time. Similarly, units of *grams per cubic centimeter* (g/cm^3) are often used for *density*—the mass of substance in a given volume. We will see other such derived units in future chapters.

One problem with any system of measurement is that the sizes of the units often turn out to be inconveniently large or small for the problem at hand. A biologist describing the diameter of a red blood cell (0.000 006 m) would find the meter to be an inconveniently large unit, but an astronomer measuring the average distance from the earth to the sun (150,000,000,000 m) would find the meter to be inconveniently small. For this reason, metric and SI units can be modified by prefixes to refer to either smaller or larger quantities. For instance, the SI unit for mass—the kilogram—differs by the prefix *kilo-* from the metric unit gram. *Kilo-* indicates that a kilogram is 1000 times as large as a gram:

$$1 \, kg = (1000)(1 \, g) = 1000 \, g$$

Small quantities of active ingredients in medications are often reported in *milligrams* (mg). The prefix *milli-* shows that the unit gram has been divided by 1000, which is the same as multiplying by 0.001:

$$1 \, mg = \left(\frac{1}{1000}\right)(1 \, g) = (0.001)(1 \, g) = 0.001 \, g$$

▶▶▶ The use of exponents is reviewed in Section 1.10.

A list of prefixes is given in Table 1.6, with the most common ones displayed in color. Note that the exponents are multiples of 3 for *mega-* (10^6), *kilo-* (10^3), *milli-* (10^{-3}), *micro-* (10^{-6}), *nano-* (10^{-9}), and *pico-* (10^{-12}). The prefixes *centi-*, meaning 1/100, and *deci-*, meaning 1/10, indicate exponents that are not multiples of 3. *Centi-* is seen most often in the length unit *centimeter* (1 cm = 0.01 m), and *deci-* is used most often in clinical chemistry, where the concentrations of blood components are given in milligrams per deciliter (1 dL = 0.1 L). These prefixes allow us to compare the magnitudes of different numbers by noting how the prefixes modify a common unit.

For example,

$$1 \, meter = 10 \, dm = 100 \, cm = 1000 \, mm = 1,000,000 \, \mu m$$

Such comparisons will be useful when we start performing calculations involving units in Section 1.12. Note also in Table 1.6 that numbers having five or more digits to the right of the decimal point are shown with thin spaces every three digits for convenience—0.000 001, for example. This manner of writing numbers is becoming more common and will be used throughout this book.

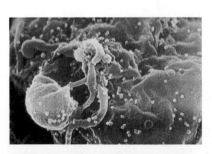

▲ The HIV-1 virus particles (in green) budding from the surface of a lymphocyte have an approximate diameter of 0.000 000 120 m.

TABLE 1.6 Some Prefixes for Multiples of Metric and SI Units

Prefix	Symbol	Base Unit Multiplied By*	Example
mega	M	$1{,}000{,}000 = 10^6$	1 megameter (Mm) $= 10^6$ m
kilo	k	$1000 = 10^3$	1 kilogram (kg) $= 10^3$ g
hecto	h	$100 = 10^2$	1 hectogram (hg) $= 100$ g
deka	da	$10 = 10^1$	1 dekaliter (daL) $= 10$ L
deci	d	$0.1 = 10^{-1}$	1 deciliter (dL) $= 0.1$ L
centi	c	$0.01 = 10^{-2}$	1 centimeter (cm) $= 0.01$ m
milli	m	$0.001 = 10^{-3}$	1 milligram (mg) $= 0.001$ g
micro	μ	$0.000\,001 = 10^{-6}$	1 micrometer (μm) $= 10^{-6}$ m
nano	n	$0.000\,000\,001 = 10^{-9}$	1 nanogram (ng) $= 10^{-9}$ g
pico	p	$0.000\,000\,000\,001 = 10^{-12}$	1 picogram (pg) $= 10^{-12}$ g
femto	f	$0.000\,000\,000\,000\,001 = 10^{-15}$	1 femtogram (fg) $= 10^{-15}$ g

*The scientific notation method of writing large and small numbers (for example, 10^6 for 1,000,000) is explained in Section 1.10.

PROBLEM 1.10

Give the full name of the following units and express the quantities in terms of the basic unit (for example, 1 mL = 1 milliliter = 0.001 L):

(a) 1 cm   (b) 1 dg   (c) 1 km   (d) 1 μs   (e) 1 ng

1.8 Measuring Mass, Length, and Volume

The terms *mass* and *weight*, though often used interchangeably, really have quite different meanings. **Mass** is a measure of the amount of matter in an object, whereas **weight** is a measure of the gravitational pull that the earth, moon, or other large body exerts on an object. Clearly, the amount of matter in an object does not depend on location. Whether you are standing on the earth or standing on the moon, the mass of your body is the same. On the other hand, the weight of an object *does* depend on location. Your weight on earth might be 140 lb, but it would only be 23 lb on the moon because the pull of gravity there is only about one-sixth as great.

At the same location, two objects with identical masses have identical weights; that is, gravity pulls equally on both. Thus, the *mass* of an object can be determined by comparing the *weight* of the object to the weight of a known reference standard. Much of the confusion between mass and weight is simply due to a language problem: We speak of "weighing" when we really mean that we are measuring mass by comparing two weights. Figure 1.6 shows a two-pan balance in which the mass of objects are measured by comparison with the known masses of standard materials, such as brass weights.

Mass A measure of the amount of matter in an object.

Weight A measure of the gravitational force that the earth or other large body exerts on an object.

◄ **Figure 1.6**
The two-pan balance is used to measure the mass of objects, such as the pennies on the left pan, by comparing them with the mass of standard objects, such as the brass weights on the right pan.

One kilogram, the SI unit for mass, is equal to 2.205 lb—too large a quantity for many purposes in chemistry and medicine. Thus, smaller units of mass such as the gram, milligram (mg), and microgram (μg), are more commonly used. Table 1.7 shows the relationships between metric and common units for mass.

The meter is the standard measure of length, or distance, in both the SI and metric systems. One meter is 39.37 inches (about 10% longer than a yard), a length that is much too large for most measurements in chemistry and medicine. Other, more commonly used measures of length are the *centimeter* (cm; 1/100 m) and the *millimeter* (mm; 1/1000 m). One centimeter is a bit less than half an inch—0.3937 inch to be exact. A millimeter, in turn, is 0.03937 inch, or about the thickness of a dime. Table 1.8 lists the relationships of these units.

Volume is the amount of space occupied by an object. The SI unit for volume— the cubic meter, m^3—is so large that the liter (1 L = 0.001 m^3 = 1 dm^3) is much more commonly used in chemistry and medicine. One liter has the volume of a cube 10 cm (1 dm) on edge and is a bit larger than one U.S. quart. Each liter is further divided into

---

TABLE 1.7 Units of Mass

Unit	Equivalent	Unit	Equivalent
1 kilogram (kg)	= 1000 grams = 2.205 pounds	1 ton	= 2000 pounds = 907.03 kilograms
1 gram (g)	= 0.001 kilogram = 1000 milligrams = 0.035 27 ounce	1 pound (lb)	= 16 ounces = 0.454 kilogram = 454 grams
1 milligram (mg)	= 0.001 gram = 1000 micrograms	1 ounce (oz)	= 0.028 35 kilogram = 28.35 grams
1 microgram (μg)	= 0.000 001 gram = 0.001 milligram		= 28,350 milligrams

---

TABLE 1.8 Units of Length

Unit	Equivalent
1 kilometer (km)	= 1000 meters = 0.6214 mile
1 meter (m)	= 100 centimeters = 1000 millimeters = 1.0936 yards = 39.37 inches
1 centimeter (cm)	= 0.01 meter = 10 millimeters = 0.3937 inch
1 millimeter (mm)	= 0.001 meter = 0.1 centimeter
1 mile (mi)	= 1.609 kilometers = 1609 meters
1 yard (yd)	= 0.9144 meter = 91.44 centimeters
1 foot (ft)	= 0.3048 meter = 30.48 centimeters
1 inch (in)	= 2.54 centimeters = 25.4 millimeters

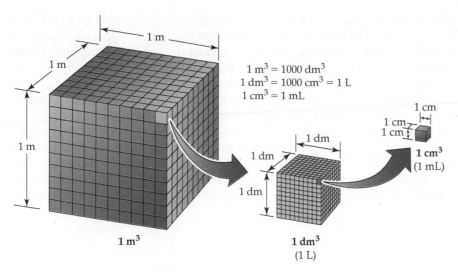

$1 \text{ m}^3 = 1000 \text{ dm}^3$
$1 \text{ dm}^3 = 1000 \text{ cm}^3 = 1 \text{ L}$
$1 \text{ cm}^3 = 1 \text{ mL}$

◄ Figure 1.7
A cubic meter is the volume of a cube
1 m on edge. Each cubic meter contains 1000 cubic decimeters (liters),
and each cubic decimeter contains
1000 cubic centimeters (milliliters).
Thus, there are 1000 mL in a liter and
1000 L in a cubic meter.

TABLE 1.9 Units of Volume

Unit	Equivalent
1 cubic meter (m³)	= 1000 liters = 264.2 gallons
1 liter (L)	= 0.001 cubic meter = 1000 milliliters = 1.057 quarts
1 deciliter (dL)	= 0.1 liter = 100 milliliters
1 milliliter (mL)	= 0.001 liter = 1000 microliters
1 microliter (μL)	= 0.001 milliliter
1 gallon (gal)	= 3.7854 liters
1 quart (qt)	= 0.9464 liter = 946.4 milliliters
1 fluid ounce (fl oz)	= 29.57 milliliters

1000 *milliliters* (mL), with 1 mL being the size of a cube 1 cm on edge, or 1 cm³. In fact, the milliliter is often called a *cubic centimeter* (cm³ or cc) in medical work. Figure 1.7 shows the divisions of a cubic meter, and Table 1.9 shows the relationships among units of volume.

1.9 Measurement and Significant Figures

How much does a tennis ball weigh? If you put a tennis ball on an ordinary bathroom scale, the scale would probably register 0 lb (or 0 kg if you have a metric scale). If you placed the same tennis ball on a common laboratory balance, however, you might get a reading of 54.07 g. Trying again by placing the ball on an expensive analytical balance like those found in clinical and research laboratories, you might find a mass of 54.071 38 g. Clearly, the precision of your answer depends on the equipment used for the measurement.

Every experimental measurement, no matter how precise, has a degree of uncertainty to it because there is always a limit to the number of digits that can be determined. An analytical balance, for example, might reach its limit in measuring mass to the fifth decimal place, and weighing the tennis ball several times might produce

▲ The tennis ball weighs 54.07 g on
this common laboratory balance,
which is capable of determining mass
to about 0.01 g.

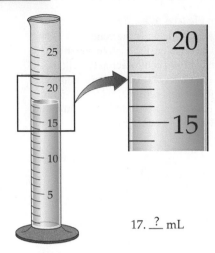

▲ Figure 1.8
What is the volume of liquid in this graduated cylinder?

Significant figures The number of meaningful digits used to express a value.

slightly different readings, such as 54.071 39 g, 54.071 38 g, and 54.071 37 g. Also, different people making the same measurement might come up with slightly different answers. How, for instance, would you record the volume of the liquid shown in Figure 1.8? It is clear that the volume of liquid lies between 17.0 and 18.0 mL, but the exact value of the last digit must be estimated.

To indicate the precision of a measurement, the value recorded should use all the digits known with certainty, plus one additional estimated digit that is usually considered uncertain by plus or minus 1 (written as ±1). The total number of digits used to express such a measurement is called the number of **significant figures**. Thus, the quantity 54.07 g has four significant figures (5, 4, 0, and 7), and the quantity .54.071 38 g has seven significant figures. *Remember*: All but one of the significant figures are known with certainty; the last significant figure is only an estimate accurate to ±1.

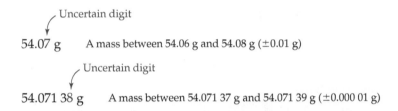

Deciding the number of significant figures in a given measurement is usually simple, but it can be troublesome when zeros are involved. Depending on the circumstances, a zero might be significant or might be just a space-filler to locate the decimal point. For example, how many significant figures does each of the following measurements have?

94.072 g	Five significant figures (9, 4, 0, 7, 2)
0.0834 cm	Three significant figures (8, 3, 4)
0.029 07 mL	Four significant figures (2, 9, 0, 7)
138.200 m	Six significant figures (1, 3, 8, 2, 0, 0)
23,000 kg	*Anywhere* from two (2, 3) to five (2, 3, 0, 0, 0) significant figures

The following rules are helpful for determining the number of significant figures when zeros are present:

RULE 1: Zeros in the middle of a number are like any other digit; they are always significant. Thus, 94.072 g has five significant figures.

RULE 2: Zeros at the beginning of a number are not significant; they act only to locate the decimal point. Thus, 0.0834 cm has three significant figures, and 0.029 07 mL has four.

RULE 3: Zeros at the end of a number and *after* the decimal point are significant. It is assumed that these zeros would not be shown unless they were significant. Thus, 138.200 m has six significant figures. If the value were known to only four significant figures, we would write 138.2 m.

RULE 4: Zeros at the end of a number and *before* an implied decimal point may or may not be significant. We cannot tell whether they are part of the measurement or whether they act only to locate the unwritten but implied decimal point. Thus, 23,000 kg may have two, three, four, or five significant figures. Adding a decimal point at the end would indicate that all five numbers are significant.

Often, however, a little common sense is useful. A temperature reading of 20 °C probably has two significant figures rather than one, because one significant figure would imply a temperature anywhere from 10 °C to 30 °C and would be of little use. Similarly, a volume given as 300 mL probably has three significant figures. On the other hand, a figure of 150,000,000 km for the distance between the earth and the sun has only two or three significant figures because the distance is variable. We will see a better way to deal with this problem in the next section.

One final point about significant figures: some numbers, such as those obtained when counting objects and those that are part of a definition, are *exact* and effectively have an unlimited number of significant figures. Thus, a class might have *exactly* 32 students (not 31.9, 32.0, or 32.1), and 1 foot is defined to have *exactly* 12 inches.

▲ **The number of seats in this auditorium is an exact number with an unlimited number of significant figures.**

Worked Example **1.3** Significant Figures of Measurements

How many significant figures do the following measurements have?

(a) 2730.78 m   (b) 0.0076 mL   (c) 3400 kg   (d) 3400.0 m²

ANALYSIS All nonzero numbers are significant; the number of significant figures will then depend on the status of the zeros in each case. (Hint: which rule applies in each case?)

SOLUTION

(a) Six (rule 1)   (b) Two (rule 2)
(c) Two, three, or four (rule 4)   (d) Five (rule 3)

PROBLEM 1.11
How many significant figures do the following measurements have?
(a) 3.45 m   (b) 0.1400 kg
(c) 10.003 L   (d) 35 cents

 KEY CONCEPT PROBLEM 1.12

How would you record the temperature reading on the following Celsius thermometer? How many significant figures do you have in your answer?

1.10 Scientific Notation

Rather than write very large or very small numbers in their entirety, it is more convenient to express them using *scientific notation*. A number is written in **scientific notation** as the product of a number between 1 and 10, times the number 10 raised to a power. Thus, 215 is written in scientific notation as 2.15×10^2:

$$215 = 2.15 \times 100 = 2.15(10 \times 10) = 2.15 \times 10^2$$

Notice that in this case, where the number is *larger* than 1, the decimal point has been moved *to the left* until it follows the first digit. The exponent on the 10 tells how many places we had to move the decimal point to position it just after the first digit:

$$2\underset{\curvearrowleft}{15.} = 2.15 \times 10^2$$

Decimal point is moved two places to the left, so exponent is 2.

Scientific notation A number expressed as the product of a number between 1 and 10, times the number 10 raised to a power.

To express a number *smaller* than 1 in scientific notation, we have to move the decimal point *to the right* until it follows the first digit. The number of places moved is the negative exponent of 10. For example, the number 0.002 15 can be rewritten as 2.15×10^{-3}:

$$0.002\ 15 = 2.15 \times \frac{1}{1000} = 2.15 \times \frac{1}{10 \times 10 \times 10} = 2.15 \times \frac{1}{10^3} = 2.15 \times 10^{-3}$$

$$0.002\ 15 = 2.15 \times 10^{-3}$$

Decimal point is moved three places to the right, so exponent is −3.

To convert a number written in scientific notation to standard notation, the process is reversed. For a number with a *positive* exponent, the decimal point is moved to the *right* a number of places equal to the exponent:

$$3.7962 \times 10^4 = 37,962$$

Positive exponent of 4, so decimal point is moved to the right four places.

For a number with a *negative* exponent, the decimal point is moved to the *left* a number of places equal to the exponent:

$$1.56 \times 10^{-8} = 0.000\ 000\ 015\ 6$$

Negative exponent of −8, so decimal point is moved to the left eight places.

Scientific notation is particularly helpful for indicating how many significant figures are present in a number that has zeros at the end but to the left of a decimal point. If we read, for instance, that the distance from the earth to the sun is 150,000,000 km, we do not really know how many significant figures are indicated. Some of the zeros might be significant, or they might merely act to locate the decimal point. Using scientific notation, however, we can indicate how many of the zeros are significant. Rewriting 150,000,000 as 1.5×10^8 indicates two significant figures, whereas writing it as 1.500×10^8 indicates four significant figures. Scientific notation is not ordinarily used for numbers that are easily written, such as 10 or 175, although it is sometimes helpful in doing arithmetic.

▶▶▶ Rules for doing arithmetic with numbers written in scientific notation are reviewed in Appendix A.

Worked Example 1.4 Significant Figures and Scientific Notation

There are 1,760,000,000,000,000,000,000 molecules of sucrose (table sugar) in 1 g. Use scientific notation to express this number with four significant figures.

ANALYSIS Because the number is larger than 1, the exponent will be positive. You will have to move the decimal point 21 places to the left.

SOLUTION
The first four digits—1, 7, 6, and 0—are significant, meaning that only the first of the 19 zeros is significant. Because we have to move the decimal point 21 places to the left to put it after the first significant digit, the answer is 1.760×10^{21}.

▲ How many molecules are in this 1 g pile of table sugar?

Worked Example 1.5 Scientific Notation

The rhinovirus responsible for the common cold has a diameter of 20 nm, or 0.000 000 020 m. Express this number in scientific notation.

ANALYSIS The number is smaller than 1, and so the exponent will be negative. You will have to move the decimal point eight places to the right.

SOLUTION
There are only two significant figures, because zeros at the beginning of a number are not significant. We have to move the decimal point 8 places to the right to place it after the first digit, so the answer is 2.0×10^{-8} m.

Worked Example **1.6** Scientific Notation and Unit Conversions

A clinical laboratory found that a blood sample contained 0.0026 g of phosphorus and 0.000 101 g of iron.

(a) Give these quantities in scientific notation.

(b) Give these quantities in the units normally used to report them—milligrams for phosphorus and micrograms for iron.

ANALYSIS Is the number larger or smaller than 1? How many places do you have to move the decimal point?

SOLUTION

(a) 0.0026 g phosphorus $= 2.6 \times 10^{-3}$ g phosphorus

   0.000 101 g iron $= 1.01 \times 10^{-4}$ g iron

(b) We know from Table 1.6 that 1 mg $= 1 \times 10^{-3}$ g, where the exponent is -3. Expressing the amount of phosphorus in milligrams is straightforward because the amount in grams (2.6×10^{-3} g) already has an exponent of -3. Thus, 2.6×10^{-3} g $= 2.6$ mg of phosphorus.

$$(2.6 \times 10^{-3} \cancel{g})\left(\frac{1 \text{ mg}}{1 \times 10^{-3} \cancel{g}}\right) = 2.6 \text{ mg}$$

We know from Table 1.6 that 1 μg $= 1 \times 10^{-6}$ g where the exponent is -6. Expressing the amount of iron in micrograms thus requires that we restate the amount in grams so that the exponent is -6. We can do this by moving the decimal point six places to the right:

$$0.000\,101 \text{ g iron} = 101 \times 10^{-6} \text{ g iron} = 101 \text{ } \mu\text{g iron}$$

PROBLEM 1.13

Convert the following values to scientific notation:

(a) 0.058 g   **(b)** 46,792 m   **(c)** 0.006 072 cm   **(d)** 345.3 kg

PROBLEM 1.14

Convert the following values from scientific notation to standard notation:

(a) 4.885×10^{4} mg   **(b)** 8.3×10^{-6} m   **(c)** 4.00×10^{-2} m

PROBLEM 1.15

Rewrite the following numbers in scientific notation as indicated:

(a) 630,000 with five significant figures

(b) 1300 with three significant figures

(c) 794,200,000,000 with four significant figures

1.11 Rounding Off Numbers

It often happens, particularly when doing arithmetic on a pocket calculator, that a quantity appears to have more significant figures than are really justified. For example, you might calculate the gas mileage of your car by finding that it takes 11.70 gallons of gasoline to drive 278 miles:

$$\text{Mileage} = \frac{\text{Miles}}{\text{Gallons}} = \frac{278 \text{ mi}}{11.70 \text{ gal}} = 23.760\,684 \text{ mi/gal (mpg)}$$

Rounding off A procedure used for deleting nonsignificant figures.

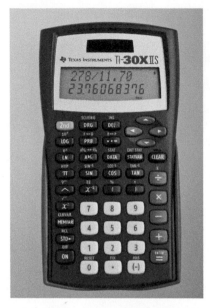

▲ Calculators often display more digits than are justified by the precision of the data.

Although the answer on a calculator has eight digits, your calculated result is really not as precise as it appears. In fact, as we will see below, your answer is good to only three significant figures and should be **rounded off** to 23.8 mi/gal.

How do you decide how many digits to keep? The full answer to this question is a bit complex and involves a mathematical treatment called *error analysis*, but for many purposes, a simplified procedure using just two rules is sufficient:

RULE 1: In carrying out a multiplication or division, the answer cannot have more significant figures than either of the original numbers. This is just a common-sense rule if you think about it. After all, if you do not know the number of miles you drove to better than three significant figures (278 could mean 277, 278, or 279), you certainly cannot calculate your mileage to more than the same number of significant figures.

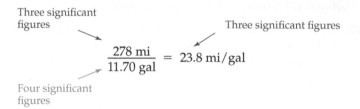

Three significant figures

Three significant figures

$$\frac{278 \text{ mi}}{11.70 \text{ gal}} = 23.8 \text{ mi/gal}$$

Four significant figures

RULE 2: In carrying out an addition or subtraction, the answer cannot have more digits after the decimal point than either of the original numbers. For example, if you have 3.18 L of water and you add 0.013 15 L more, you now have 3.19 L. Again, this rule is just common sense. If you do not know the volume you started with past the second decimal place (it could be 3.17, 3.18, or 3.19), you cannot know the total of the combined volumes past the same decimal place.

Volume of water at start ⟶ 3.18? ?? L ⟵ Two digits after decimal point
Volume of water added ⟶ + 0.013 15 L ⟵ Five digits after decimal point
Total volume of water ⟶ 3.19? ?? L ⟵ Two digits after decimal point

If a calculation has several steps, it is generally best to round off at the end after all the steps have been carried out, keeping the number of significant figures determined by the least precise number in your calculations. Once you decide how many digits to retain for your answer, the rules for rounding off numbers are straightforward:

RULE 1: If the first digit you remove is 4 or less, drop it and all following digits. Thus, 2.4271 becomes 2.4 when rounded off to two significant figures because the first of the dropped digits (a 2) is 4 or less.

RULE 2: If the first digit you remove is 5 or greater, round the number up by adding a 1 to the digit to the left of the one you drop. Thus, 4.5832 becomes 4.6 when rounded off to two significant figures because the first of the dropped digits (an 8) is 5 or greater.

Worked Example 1.7 Significant Figures and Calculations: Addition/Subtraction

Suppose that you weigh 124 lb before dinner. How much will you weigh after dinner if you eat 1.884 lb of food?

ANALYSIS When performing addition or subtraction, the number of significant figures you report in the final answer is determined by the number of digits in the least precise number in the calculation.

SOLUTION

Your after-dinner weight is found by adding your original weight to the weight of the food consumed:

$$
\begin{array}{r}
124\ \ \ \text{lb} \\
\underline{1.884\ \text{lb}} \\
125.884\ \text{lb (Unrounded)}
\end{array}
$$

Because the value of your original weight has no significant figures after the decimal point, your after-dinner weight also must have no significant figures after the decimal point. Thus, 125.884 lb must be rounded off to 126 lb.

Worked Example 1.8 Significant Figures and Calculations: Multiplication/Division

To make currant jelly, 13.75 cups of sugar was added to 18 cups of currant juice. How much sugar was added per cup of juice?

ANALYSIS For calculations involving multiplication or division, the final answer cannot have more significant figures than either of the original numbers.

SOLUTION

The quantity of sugar must be divided by the quantity of juice:

$$
\frac{13.75 \text{ cups sugar}}{18 \text{ cups juice}} = 0.763\ 888\ 89\ \frac{\text{cup sugar}}{\text{cup juice}}\ (\text{Unrounded})
$$

The number of significant figures in the answer is limited to two by the quantity 18 cups in the calculation and must be rounded to 0.76 cup of sugar per cup of juice.

PROBLEM 1.16

Round off the following quantities to the indicated number of significant figures:
(a) 2.304 g (three significant figures)
(b) 188.3784 mL (five significant figures)
(c) 0.008 87 L (one significant figure)
(d) 1.000 39 kg (four significant figures)

PROBLEM 1.17

Carry out the following calculations, rounding each result to the correct number of significant figures:

(a) 4.87 mL + 46.0 mL   **(b)** 3.4 × 0.023 g
(c) 19.333 m − 7.4 m   **(d)** 55 mg − 4.671 mg + 0.894 mg
(e) 62,911 ÷ 611

1.12 Problem Solving: Unit Conversions and Estimating Answers

Many activities in the laboratory and in medicine—measuring, weighing, preparing solutions, and so forth—require converting a quantity from one unit to another. For example: "These pills contain 1.3 grains of aspirin, but I need 200 mg. Is one pill enough?" Converting between units is not mysterious; we all do it every day. If you run 9 laps around a 400-meter track, for instance, you have to convert between the distance unit "lap" and the distance unit "meter" to find that you have run 3600 m (9 laps times

▲ Currency exchange between the US$ and Euros is another activity that requires a unit conversion.

400 m/lap). If you want to find how many miles that is, you have to convert again to find that 3600 m = 2.237 mi.

The simplest way to carry out calculations involving different units is to use the **factor-label method**. In this method, a quantity in one unit is converted into an equivalent quantity in a different unit by using a **conversion factor** that expresses the relationship between units:

Starting quantity × Conversion factor = Equivalent quantity

As an example, we learned from Table 1.8 that 1 km = 0.6214 mi. Writing this relationship as a fraction restates it in the form of a conversion factor, either kilometers per mile or miles per kilometer.

Since 1 km = 0.6214 mi, then:

Conversion factors between kilometers and miles

$$\frac{1 \text{ km}}{0.6214 \text{ mi}} = 1 \quad \text{or} \quad \frac{0.6214 \text{ mi}}{1 \text{ km}} = 1$$

Note that this and all other conversion factors are numerically equal to 1 because the value of the quantity above the division line (the numerator) is equal in value to the quantity below the division line (the denominator). Thus, multiplying by a conversion factor is equivalent to multiplying by 1 and so does not change the value of the quantity being multiplied:

These two quantities are the same.

These two quantities are the same.

$$\frac{1 \text{ km}}{0.6214 \text{ mi}} \quad \text{or} \quad \frac{0.6214 \text{ mi}}{1 \text{ km}}$$

The key to the factor-label method of problem solving is that units are treated like numbers and can thus be multiplied and divided (though not added or subtracted) just as numbers can. When solving a problem, the idea is to set up an equation so that all unwanted units cancel, leaving only the desired units. Usually, it is best to start by writing what you know and then manipulating that known quantity. For example, if you know there are 26.22 mi in a marathon and want to find how many kilometers that is, you could write the distance in miles and multiply by the conversion factor in kilometers per mile. The unit "mi" cancels because it appears both above and below the division line, leaving "km" as the only remaining unit.

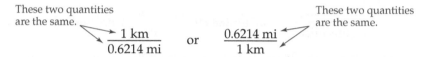

$$26.22 \text{ mi} \times \frac{1 \text{ km}}{0.6214 \text{ mi}} = 42.20 \text{ km}$$

Starting quantity   Conversion factor   Equivalent quantity

The factor-label method gives the right answer only if the equation is set up so that the unwanted unit (or units) cancel. If the equation is set up in any other way, the units will not cancel and you will not get the right answer. Thus, if you selected the incorrect conversion factor (miles per kilometer) for the above problem, you would end up with an incorrect answer expressed in meaningless units:

$$\text{Incorrect } 26.22 \text{ mi} \times \frac{0.6214 \text{ mi}}{1 \text{ km}} = 16.29 \frac{\text{mi}^2}{\text{km}} \text{ Incorrect}$$

The main drawback to using the factor-label method is that it is possible to get an answer without really understanding what you are doing. It is therefore best when solving a problem to first think through a rough estimate, or *ballpark estimate*, as a check on your work. If your ballpark estimate is not close to the final calculated solution, there is a misunderstanding somewhere and you should think the problem through again. If, for example, you came up with the answer 5.3 cm^3 when calculating the volume of a human cell, you should realize that such an answer could not possibly be right. Cells are too tiny to be distinguished with the naked eye, but a volume of 5.3 cm^3 is about the size

Factor-label method A problem-solving procedure in which equations are set up so that unwanted units cancel and only the desired units remain.

Conversion factor An expression of the numerical relationship between two units.

of a walnut. The Worked Examples 1.11, 1.12, and 1.13 at the end of this section show how to estimate the answers to simple unit-conversion problems.

The factor-label method and the use of ballpark estimates are techniques that will help you solve problems of many kinds, not just unit conversions. Problems sometimes seem complicated, but you can usually sort out the complications by analyzing the problem properly:

STEP 1: Identify the information given, including units.

STEP 2: Identify the information needed in the answer, including units.

STEP 3: Find the relationship(s) between the known information and unknown answer, and plan a series of steps, including conversion factors, for getting from one to the other.

STEP 4: Solve the problem.

BALLPARK CHECK Make a ballpark estimate at the beginning and check it against your final answer to be sure the value and the units of your calculated answer are reasonable.

Worked Example 1.9 Factor Labels: Unit Conversions

Write conversion factors for the following pairs of units (use Tables 1.7–1.9):

(a) Deciliters and milliliters

(b) Pounds and grams

ANALYSIS Start with the appropriate equivalency relationship and rearrange to form conversion factors.

SOLUTION

(a) Since 1 dL = 0.1 L and 1 mL = 0.001 L, then 1 dL = $(0.1 \text{ L})\left(\dfrac{1 \text{ mL}}{0.001 \text{ L}}\right)$ =

100 mL. The conversion factors are

$$\frac{1 \text{ dL}}{100 \text{ mL}} \quad \text{and} \quad \frac{100 \text{ mL}}{1 \text{ dL}}$$

(b) $\dfrac{1 \text{ lb}}{454 \text{ g}}$ and $\dfrac{454 \text{ g}}{1 \text{ lb}}$

Worked Example 1.10 Factor Labels: Unit Conversions

(a) Convert 0.75 lb to grams.

(b) Convert 0.50 qt to deciliters.

ANALYSIS Start with conversion factors and set up equations so that units cancel appropriately.

SOLUTION

(a) Select the conversion factor from Worked Example 1.9(b) so that the "lb" units cancel and "g" remains:

$$0.75 \text{ lb} \times \frac{454 \text{ g}}{1 \text{ lb}} = 340 \text{ g}$$

(b) In this, as in many problems, it is convenient to use more than one conversion factor. As long as the unwanted units cancel correctly, two or more conversion factors can be strung together in the same calculation. In this case, we can convert first between quarts and milliliters, and then between milliliters and deciliters:

$$0.50 \text{ qt} \times \frac{946.4 \text{ mL}}{1 \text{ qt}} \times \frac{1 \text{ dL}}{100 \text{ mL}} = 4.7 \text{ dL}$$

Worked Example **1.11** Factor Labels: Unit Conversions

A child is 21.5 inches long at birth. How long is this in centimeters?

ANALYSIS This problem calls for converting from inches to centimeters, so we will need to know how many centimeters are in an inch and how to use this information as a conversion factor.

BALLPARK ESTIMATE It takes about 2.5 cm to make 1 in., and so it should take two and a half times as many centimeters to make a distance equal to approximately 20 in., or about 20 in. × 2.5 = 50 cm.

SOLUTION

STEP 1: **Identify given information.**   Length = 21.5 in.

STEP 2: **Identify answer and units.**   Length = ?? cm

STEP 3: **Identify conversion factor.** $1 \text{ in.} = 2.54 \text{ cm} \rightarrow \dfrac{2.54 \text{ cm}}{1 \text{ in.}}$

STEP 4: **Solve.** Multiply the known length (in inches) by the conversion factor so that units cancel, providing the answer (in centimeters). $21.5 \text{ in.} \times \dfrac{2.54 \text{ cm}}{1 \text{ in.}} = 54.6 \text{ cm}$ (Rounded off from 54.61)

BALLPARK CHECK How does this value compare with the ballpark estimate we made at the beginning? Are the final units correct? 54.6 cm is close to our original estimate of 50 cm.

Worked Example **1.12** Factor Labels: Concentration to Mass

A patient requires an injection of 0.012 g of a pain killer available as a 15 mg/ mL solution. How many milliliters of solution should be administered?

ANALYSIS Knowing the amount of pain killer in 1 mL allows us to use the concentration as a conversion factor to determine the volume of solution that would contain the desired amount.

BALLPARK ESTIMATE One milliliter contains 15 mg of the pain killer, or 0.015 g. Since only 0.012 g is needed, a little less than 1.0 mL should be administered.

▲ **How many milliliters should be injected?**

SOLUTION

STEP 1: **Identify known information.**   Dosage = 0.012 g
                                                            Concentration = 15 mg/mL

STEP 2: **Identify answer and units.**   Volume to administer = ?? mL

STEP 3: **Identify conversion factors.** Two conversion factors are needed. First, g must be converted to mg. Once we have the mass in mg, we can calculate mL using the conversion factor of mL/mg.

$1 \text{ mg} = .001 \text{ g} \Rightarrow \dfrac{1 \text{ mg}}{0.001 \text{ g}}$

$15 \text{ mg/mL} \Rightarrow \dfrac{1 \text{ mL}}{15 \text{ mg}}$

STEP 4: **Solve.** Starting from the desired dosage, we use the conversion factors to cancel units, obtaining the final answer in mL.

$(0.012 \text{ g})\left(\dfrac{1 \text{ mg}}{0.001 \text{ g}}\right)\left(\dfrac{1 \text{ mL}}{15 \text{ mg}}\right) = 0.80 \text{ mL}$

BALLPARK CHECK Consistent with our initial estimate of a little less than 1 mL.

Worked Example **1.13** Factor Labels: Multiple Conversion Calculations

Administration of digitalis to control atrial fibrillation in heart patients must be carefully regulated because even a modest overdose can be fatal. To take differences between patients into account, dosages are sometimes prescribed in micrograms per kilogram of body weight (μg/kg). Thus, two people may differ greatly in weight, but both will receive the proper dosage. At a dosage of 20 μg/kg body weight, how many milligrams of digitalis should a 160 lb patient receive?

ANALYSIS Knowing the patient's body weight (in kg) and the recommended dosage (in μg/kg), we can calculate the appropriate amount of digitalis.

BALLPARK ESTIMATE Since a kilogram is roughly equal to 2 lb, a 160 lb patient has a mass of about 80 kg. At a dosage of 20 μg/kg, an 80 kg patient should receive 80 $\times$ 20 μg, or about 1600 μg of digitalis, or 1.6 mg.

SOLUTION

STEP 1: **Identify known information.**

Patient weight = 160 lb
Prescribed dosage = 20 μg digitalis/kg body weight

STEP 2: **Identify answer and units.**

Delivered dosage = ?? mg digitalis

STEP 3: **Identify conversion factors.** Two conversions are needed. First, convert the patient's weight in pounds to weight in kg. The correct dose can then be determined based on μg digitalis/kg of body weight. Finally, the dosage in μg is converted to mg.

$$1 \text{ kg} = 2.205 \text{ lb} \rightarrow \frac{1 \text{ kg}}{2.205 \text{ lb}}$$

$$1 \text{ mg} = (0.001 \text{ g})\left(\frac{1 \text{ }\mu g}{10^{-6} \text{ g}}\right) = 1000 \text{ }\mu g$$

STEP 4: **Solve.** Use the known information and the conversion factors so that units cancel, obtaining the answer in mg.

$$160 \text{ lb} \times \frac{1 \text{ kg}}{2.205 \text{ lb}} \times \frac{20 \text{ }\mu g \text{ digitalis}}{1 \text{ kg}} \times \frac{1 \text{ mg}}{1000 \text{ }\mu g}$$

$$= 1.5 \text{ mg digitalis (Rounded off)}$$

BALLPARK CHECK Close to our estimate of 1.6 mg.

PROBLEM 1.18
Write appropriate conversion factors and carry out the following conversions:
(a) 16.0 oz = ? g **(b)** 2500 mL = ? L **(c)** 99.0 L = ? qt

PROBLEM 1.19
Convert 0.840 qt to milliliters in a single calculation using more than one conversion factor.

PROBLEM 1.20
One international nautical mile is defined as exactly 6076.1155 ft, and a speed of 1 knot is defined as one international nautical mile per hour. What is the speed in meters per second of a boat traveling at a speed of 14.3 knots? (Hint: what conversion factor is needed to convert from feet to meters? From hours to seconds?)

PROBLEM 1.21
Calculate the dosage in milligrams per kilogram body weight for a 135 lb adult who takes two aspirin tablets containing 0.324 g of aspirin each. Calculate the dosage for a 40 lb child who also takes two aspirin tablets.

1.13 Temperature, Heat, and Energy

All chemical reactions are accompanied by a change in **energy**, which is defined in scientific terms as *the capacity to do work or supply heat* (Figure 1.9). Detailed discussion of the various kinds of energy will be included in Chapter 7, but for now we will look at the various units used to describe energy and heat, and how heat energy can be gained or lost by matter.

Energy The capacity to do work or supply heat.

   Temperature, the measure of the amount of heat energy in an object, is commonly reported either in Fahrenheit (°F) or Celsius (°C) units. The SI unit for reporting temperature, however, is the *kelvin* (K). (Note that we say only "kelvin," not "degrees kelvin".)

Temperature The measure of the amount of heat energy in an object.

   The kelvin and the celsius degree are the same size—both are 1/100 of the interval between the freezing point of water and the boiling point of water at atmospheric pressure.

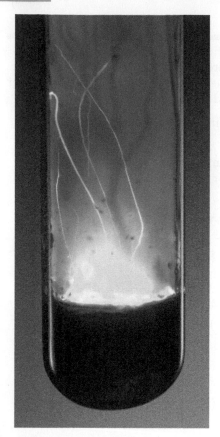

▲ **Figure 1.9**
The reaction of aluminum with bromine releases energy in the form of heat.
When the reaction is complete, the products undergo no further change.

Thus, a change in temperature of 1 °C is equal to a change of 1 K. The only difference between the Kelvin and Celsius temperature scales is that they have different zero points. The Celsius scale assigns a value of 0 °C to the freezing point of water, but the Kelvin scale assigns a value of 0 K to the coldest possible temperature, sometimes called *absolute zero*, which is equal to −273.15 °C. Thus, 0 K = −273.15 °C, and +273.15 K = 0 °C. For example, a warm spring day with a temperature of 25 °C has a Kelvin temperature of 298 K (for most purposes, rounding off to 273 is sufficient):

$$\text{Temperature in K} = \text{Temperature in} \ ^\circ\text{C} + 273.15$$
$$\text{Temperature in} \ ^\circ\text{C} = \text{Temperature in K} - 273.15$$

For practical applications in medicine and clinical chemistry, the Fahrenheit and Celsius scales are used almost exclusively. The Fahrenheit scale defines the freezing point of water as 32 °F and the boiling point of water as 212 °F, whereas 0 °C and 100 °C are the freezing and boiling points of water on the Celsius scale. Thus, it takes 180 Fahrenheit degrees to cover the same range encompassed by only 100 celsius degrees, and a Celsius degree is therefore exactly 180/100 = 9/5 = 1.8 times as large as a Fahrenheit degree. In other words, a change in temperature of 1.0 °C is equal to a change of 1.8 °F. Figure 1.10 gives a comparison of all three scales.

Converting between the Fahrenheit and Celsius scales is similar to converting between different units of length or volume, but is a bit more complex because two corrections need to be made—one to adjust for the difference in degree size and one to adjust for the different zero points. The degree-size correction is made by using the relationship 1 °C = (9/5) °F and 1 °F = (5/9) °C. The zero-point correction is made by remembering that the freezing point is higher by 32 on the Fahrenheit scale than on the Celsius scale. These corrections are incorporated into the following formulas, which show the conversion methods:

Celsius to Fahrenheit:
$$^\circ\text{F} = \left(\frac{9\ ^\circ\text{F}}{5\ ^\circ\text{C}} \times\ ^\circ\text{C} \right) + 32\ ^\circ\text{F}$$

Fahrenheit to Celsius:
$$^\circ\text{C} = \frac{5\ ^\circ\text{C}}{9\ ^\circ\text{F}} \times (^\circ\text{F} - 32\ ^\circ\text{F})$$

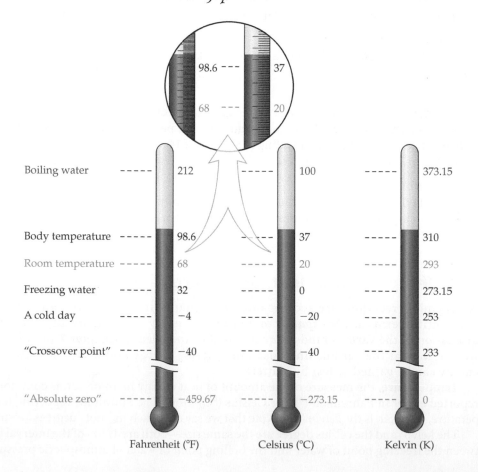

▶ **Figure 1.10**
A comparison of the Fahrenheit, Celsius, and Kelvin temperature scales.
One Fahrenheit degree is 5/9 the size of a kelvin or a celsius degree.

CHEMISTRY IN ACTION

Temperature–Sensitive Materials

Wouldn't it be nice to be able to tell if the baby's formula bottle is too hot without touching it? Or to easily determine if the package of chicken you are buying for dinner has been stored appropriately? Temperature-sensitive materials are already being used in these and other applications. Although these materials have been used previously in many popular "fads," like mood rings or clothes that changed color at different temperatures, more practical applications are emerging.

Most current applications use substances known as thermochromic materials that change color as their temperature increases, and they change from the liquid phase to a semi-crystalline ordered state. These "liquid crystals" can be incorporated into plastics or paints and can be used to monitor the temperature of the products or packages in which they are incorporated. For example, some meat packaging now includes a temperature strip that darkens when the meat is stored above a certain temperature, which makes the meat unsafe to eat. Some beverage containers turn color to indicate when the beverage has reached its optimal temperature for consumption. Hospitals and other medical facilities now routinely use strips that, when placed under the tongue or applied to the forehead, change color to indicate the patient's body temperature. In the future, we may even see road signs that change color to warn us of dangerous icy road conditions.

See Chemistry in Action Problems 1.98 and 1.99 at the end of the chapter.

Energy is represented in SI units by the unit *joule* (J; pronounced "jool"), but the metric unit *calorie* (cal) is still widely used in medicine. In most of this text we will present energy values in both units of calories and joules. One calorie is the amount of heat necessary to raise the temperature of 1 g of water by 1 °C. A *kilocalorie* (kcal), often called a *large calorie (Cal)* or *food calorie* by nutritionists, equals 1000 cal:

$$1000 \text{ cal} = 1 \text{ kcal} \qquad 1000 \text{ J} = 1 \text{ kJ}$$
$$1 \text{ cal} = 4.184 \text{ J} \qquad 1 \text{ kcal} = 4.184 \text{ kJ}$$

Not all substances have their temperatures raised to the same extent when equal amounts of heat energy are added. One calorie raises the temperature of 1 g of water by 1 °C but raises the temperature of 1 g of iron by 10 °C. The amount of heat needed to raise the temperature of 1 g of a substance by 1 °C is called the **specific heat** of the substance. It is measured in units of cal/(g · °C).

$$\text{Specific heat} = \frac{\text{calories}}{\text{grams} \times \text{°C}}$$

Specific heats vary greatly from one substance to another, as shown in Table 1.10. The specific heat of water, 1.00 cal/(g · °C) (or 4.184 J/g °C) is higher than that of most other substances, which means that a large transfer of heat is required to change the temperature of a given amount of water by a given number of degrees. One consequence is that the human body, which is about 60% water, is able to withstand changing outside conditions.

Knowing the mass and specific heat of a substance makes it possible to calculate how much heat must be added or removed to accomplish a given temperature change, as shown in Worked Example 1.15.

$$\text{Heat (cal)} = \text{Mass (g)} \times \text{Temperature change (°C)} \times \text{Specific heat}\left(\frac{\text{cal}}{\text{g} \cdot \text{°C}}\right)$$

Specific heat The amount of heat that will raise the temperature of 1 g of a substance by 1 °C.

TABLE 1.10 Specific Heats of Some Common Substances

Substance	Specific Heat [cal/g °C]; [J/g °C]	
Ethanol	0.59;	2.5
Gold	0.031;	0.13
Iron	0.106;	0.444
Mercury	0.033;	0.14
Sodium	0.293;	1.23
Water	1.00;	4.18

Worked Example 1.14 Temperature Conversions: Fahrenheit to Celsius

A body temperature above 107 °F can be fatal. What does 107 °F correspond to on the Celsius scale?

ANALYSIS Using the temperature (in °F) and the appropriate temperature conversion equation we can convert from the Fahrenheit scale to the Celsius scale.

BALLPARK ESTIMATE Note in Figure 1.10 that normal body temperature is 98.6 °F, or 37 °C. A temperature of 107 °F is approximately 8 °F above normal; since 1 °C is nearly 2 °F, then 8 °F is about 4 °C. Thus, the 107 °F body temperature is 41 °C.

SOLUTION

STEP 1: **Identify known information.**

STEP 2: **Identify answer and units.**

STEP 3: **Identify conversion factors.** We can convert from °F to °C using this equation.

STEP 4: **Solve.** Substitute the known temperature (in °F) into the equation.

$$\text{Temperature} = 107\,°F$$

$$\text{Temperature} = ??\,°C$$

$$°C = \frac{5\,°C}{9\,°F} \times (°F - 32\,°F)$$

$$°C = \frac{5\,°C}{9\,°F} \times (107\,°F - 32\,°F) = 42\,°C^*$$

(Rounded off from 41.666 667 °C)

BALLPARK CHECK Close to our estimate of 41 °C.

*It is worth noting that the 5/9 conversion factor in the equation is an exact conversion, and so does not impact the number of significant figures in the final answer.

Worked Example 1.15 Specific Heat: Mass, Temperature, and Energy

Taking a bath might use about 95 kg of water. How much energy (in calories and Joules) is needed to heat the water from a cold 15 °C to a warm 40 °C?

ANALYSIS From the amount of water being heated (95 kg) and the amount of the temperature change (40 °C − 15 °C = 25 °C), the total amount of energy needed can be calculated by using specific heat $[1.00\,\text{cal}/(g \cdot °C)]$ as a conversion factor.

BALLPARK ESTIMATE The water is being heated 25 °C (from 15 °C to 40 °C), and it therefore takes 25 cal to heat each gram. The tub contains nearly 100,000 g (95 kg is 95,000 g), and so it takes about 25 × 100,000 cal, or 2,500,000 cal, to heat all the water in the tub.

SOLUTION

STEP 1: **Identify known information.**

STEP 2: **Identify answer and units.**

STEP 3: **Identify conversion factors.** The amount of energy (in cal) can be calculated using the specific heat of water (cal/g · °C), and will depend on both the mass of water (in g) to be heated and the total temperature change (in °C). In order for the units in specific heat to cancel correctly, the mass of water must first be converted from kg to g.

STEP 4: **Solve.** Starting with the known information, use the conversion factors to cancel unwanted units.

$$\text{Mass of water} = 95\,kg$$

$$\text{Temperature change} = 40\,°C - 15\,°C = 25\,°C$$

$$\text{Heat} = ??\,\text{cal}$$

$$\text{Specific heat} = \frac{1.0\,\text{cal}}{g \cdot °C}$$

$$1\,kg = 1000\,g \rightarrow \frac{1000\,g}{1\,kg}$$

$$95\,kg \times \frac{1000\,g}{kg} \times \frac{1.00\,\text{cal}}{g \cdot °C} \times 25\,°C = 2,400,000\,\text{cal}$$

$$= 2.4 \times 10^6\,\text{cal (or } 1.0 \times 10^7\,\text{J)}$$

BALLPARK CHECK Close to our estimate of 2.5 × 10⁶ cal.

PROBLEM 1.22
The highest land temperature ever recorded was 136 °F in Al Aziziyah, Libya, on September 13, 1922. What is this temperature on the kelvin scale?

PROBLEM 1.23
The patient in the photo in the Chemistry in Action on page 31 has a temperature of 39 °C. What is the body temperature of the patient in °F?

PROBLEM 1.24
Assuming that Coca-Cola has the same specific heat as water, how much energy in calories is removed when 350 g of Coca-Cola (about the contents of one 12 oz can) is cooled from room temperature (25 °C) to refrigerator temperature (3 °C)?

PROBLEM 1.25
What is the specific heat of aluminum if it takes 161 cal (674 J) to raise the temperature of a 75 g aluminum bar by 10.0 °C?

1.14 Density and Specific Gravity

One further physical quantity that we will take up in this chapter is **density**, which relates the mass of an object to its volume. Density is usually expressed in units of grams per cubic centimeter (g/cm^3) for solids and grams per milliliter (g/mL) for liquids. Thus, if we know the density of a substance, we know both the mass of a given volume and the volume of a given mass. The densities of some common materials are listed in Table 1.11.

Density The physical property that relates the mass of an object to its volume; mass per unit volume.

$$\text{Density} = \frac{\text{Mass (g)}}{\text{Volume (mL or cm}^3)}$$

Although most substances contract when cooled and expand when heated, water behaves differently. Water contracts when cooled from 100 °C to 3.98 °C, but below this temperature it begins to *expand* again. The density of liquid water is at its maximum of 1.0000 g/mL at 3.98 °C but decreases to 0.999 87 g/mL at 0 °C. When freezing occurs, the density drops still further to a value of 0.917 g/cm^3 for ice at 0 °C. Since a less dense substance will float on top of a more dense fluid, ice and any other substance with a density less than that of water will float in water. Conversely, any substance with a density greater than that of water will sink in water.

Knowing the density of a liquid is useful because it is often easier to measure a liquid's volume rather than its mass. Suppose, for example, that you need 1.50 g of

▲ **The Galileo thermometer contains several weighted bulbs which rise or fall as the density of the liquid changes with temperature.**

TABLE **1.11** Densities of Some Common Materials at 25 °C			
Substance	Density*	Substance	Density*
Gases		Solids	
Helium	0.000 194	Ice (0 °C)	0.917
Air	0.001 185	Gold	19.3
		Human fat	0.94
Liquids		Cork	0.22–0.26
Water (3.98 °C)	1.0000	Table sugar	1.59
Urine	1.003–1.030	Balsa wood	0.12
Blood plasma	1.027	Earth	5.54

*Densities are in g/cm³ for solids and g/mL for liquids and gases.

Specific gravity The density of a substance divided by the density of water at the same temperature.

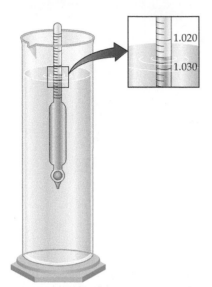

▲ **Figure 1.11**
A hydrometer for measuring specific gravity.
The instrument has a weighted bulb at the end of a calibrated glass tube. The depth to which the hydrometer sinks in a liquid indicates the liquid's specific gravity.

ethanol. Rather than use a dropper to weigh out exactly the right amount, it would be much easier to look up the density of ethanol (0.7893 g/mL at 20 °C) and measure the correct volume (1.90 mL) with a syringe or graduated cylinder. Thus, density acts as a conversion factor between mass (g) and volume (mL).

$$1.50 \text{ g ethanol} \times \frac{1 \text{ mL ethanol}}{0.7893 \text{ g ethanol}} = 1.90 \text{ mL ethanol}$$

For many purposes, ranging from winemaking to medicine, it is more convenient to use *specific gravity* than density. The **specific gravity** (sp gr) of a substance (usually a liquid) is simply the density of the substance divided by the density of water at the same temperature. Because all units cancel, specific gravity is unitless:

$$\text{Specific gravity} = \frac{\text{Density of substance (g/mL)}}{\text{Density of water at the same temperature (g/mL)}}$$

At typical temperatures, the density of water is very close to 1 g/mL. Thus, the specific gravity of a substance is numerically equal to its density and is used in the same way.

The specific gravity of a liquid can be measured using an instrument called a *hydrometer*, which consists of a weighted bulb on the end of a calibrated glass tube, as shown in Figure 1.11. The depth to which the hydrometer sinks when placed in a fluid indicates the fluid's specific gravity: the lower the bulb sinks, the lower the specific gravity of the fluid.

In medicine, a hydrometer called a *urinometer* is used to indicate the amount of solids dissolved in urine. Although the specific gravity of normal urine is about 1.003–1.030, conditions such as diabetes mellitus or a high fever cause an abnormally high urine specific gravity, indicating either excessive elimination of solids or decreased elimination of water. Abnormally low specific gravity is found in individuals using diuretics—drugs that increase water elimination.

Worked Example 1.16 Density: Mass-to-Volume Conversion

What volume of isopropyl alcohol (rubbing alcohol) would you use if you needed 25.0 g? The density of isopropyl alcohol is 0.7855 g/mL at 20 °C.

ANALYSIS The known information is the mass of isopropyl alcohol needed (25.0 g). The density (0.7855 g/mL) acts as a conversion factor between mass and the unknown volume of isopropyl alcohol.

BALLPARK ESTIMATE Because 1 mL of isopropyl alcohol contains only 0.7885 g of the alcohol, obtaining 1 g of alcohol would require almost 20% more than 1 mL, or about 1.2 mL. Therefore, a volume of about 25 × 1.2 mL = 30 mL is needed to obtain 25 g of alcohol.

SOLUTION

STEP 1: Identify known information.

Mass of rubbing alcohol = 25.0 g
Density of rubbing alcohol = 0.7855 g/mL

STEP 2: Identify answer and units.

Volume of rubbing alcohol = ?? mL

STEP 3: Identify conversion factors. Starting with the mass of isopropyl alcohol (in g), the corresponding volume (in mL) can be calculated using density (g/mL) as the conversion factor.

Density = g/mL → 1/density = mL/g

STEP 4: Solve. Starting with the known information, set up the equation with conversion factors so that unwanted units cancel.

$$25.0 \text{ g alcohol} \times \frac{1 \text{ mL alcohol}}{0.7855 \text{ g alcohol}} = 31.8 \text{ mL alcohol}$$

BALLPARK CHECK Our estimate was 30 mL.

CHEMISTRY IN ACTION

A Measurement Example: Obesity and Body Fat

According to the U.S. Centers for Disease Control and Prevention, the U.S. population is suffering from a fat epidemic. Over the last 25 years, the percentage of adults 20 years or older identified as obese increased from 15% in the late 1970s to nearly 33% in 2008. Even children and adolescents are gaining too much weight: The number of overweight children in all age groups increased by nearly a factor of 3, with the biggest increase seen among teenagers (from 5% to 18.1%). Of particular concern is the fact that 80% of children who were overweight as teenagers were identified as obese at age 25. Obesity increases the risk for many adverse health conditions, including type 2 diabetes and heart disease.

How do we define obesity, however, and how is it measured? Obesity is defined by reference to *body mass index* (BMI), which is equal to a person's mass in kilograms divided by the square of his or her height in meters. BMI can also be calculated by dividing a person's weight in pounds by the square of her or his height in inches multiplied by 703. For instance, someone 5 ft 7 in. (67 inches; 1.70 m) tall weighing 147 lb (66.7 kg) has a BMI of 23:

$$BMI = \frac{weight\ (kg)}{[\,height\ (m)\,]^2}, \quad or \quad \frac{weight\ (lb)}{[\,height\ (in.)\,]^2} \times 703$$

A BMI of 25 or above is considered overweight, and a BMI of 30 or above is obese. By these standards, approximately 61% of the U.S. population is overweight. Health professionals are concerned by the rapid rise in obesity in the United States because of the link between BMI and health problems. Many reports have documented the correlation between health and BMI, including a recent study on more than 1 million adults. The

▲ **A person's percentage body fat can be estimated by measuring the thickness of the fat layer under the skin.**

lowest death risk from any cause, including cancer and heart disease, is associated with a BMI between 22 and 24. Risk increases steadily as BMI increases, more than doubling for a BMI above 29.

An individual's percentage of body fat is most easily measured by the skinfold-thickness method. The skin at several locations on the arm, shoulder, and waist is pinched, and the thickness of the fat layer beneath the skin is measured with calipers. Comparing the measured results to those in a standard table gives an estimation of percentage body fat. As an alternative to skinfold measurement, a more accurate assessment of body fat can be made by underwater immersion. The person's underwater body weight is less than her or his weight on land because water gives the body buoyancy. The higher the percentage of body fat, the more buoyant the person and the greater the difference between land weight and underwater body weight. Checking the observed buoyancy on a standard table then gives an estimation of body fat.

See Chemistry in Action Problems 1.100 and 1.101 at the end of the chapter.

Weight (lb)

Height	110	115	120	125	130	135	140	145	150	155	160	165	170	175	180	185	190	195	200
5'0"	21	22	23	24	25	26	27	28	29	30	31	32	33	34	35	36	37	38	39
5'2"	20	21	22	23	24	25	26	27	27	28	29	30	31	32	33	34	35	36	37
5'4"	19	20	21	21	22	23	24	25	26	27	27	28	29	30	31	32	33	33	34
5'6"	18	19	19	20	21	22	23	23	24	25	26	27	27	28	29	30	31	31	32
5'8"	17	17	18	19	20	21	21	22	23	24	24	25	26	27	27	28	29	30	30
5'10"	16	17	17	18	19	19	20	21	22	22	23	24	24	25	26	27	27	28	29
6'0"	15	16	16	17	18	18	19	20	20	21	22	22	23	24	24	25	26	26	27
6'2"	14	15	15	16	17	17	18	19	19	20	21	21	22	22	23	24	24	25	26
6'4"	13	14	15	15	16	16	17	18	18	19	19	20	21	21	22	23	23	24	24

Body Mass Index (numbers in boxes)

▲ The specific gravity of urine, measured by a urinometer, is used to diagnose conditions such as diabetes.

PROBLEM 1.26

A sample of pumice, a porous volcanic rock, weighs 17.4 grams and has a volume of 27.3 cm³. If this sample is placed in a container of water, will it sink or will it float? Explain.

PROBLEM 1.27

Chloroform, once used as an anesthetic agent, has a density of 1.474 g/mL. What volume would you use if you needed 12.37 g?

PROBLEM 1.28

The sulfuric acid solution in an automobile battery typically has a specific gravity of about 1.27. Is battery acid more dense or less dense than pure water?

SUMMARY: REVISITING THE CHAPTER GOALS

1. What is matter and how is it classified? *Matter* is anything that has mass and occupies volume—that is, anything physically real. Matter can be classified by its physical state as *solid, liquid,* or *gas*. A solid has a definite volume and shape, a liquid has a definite volume but indefinite shape, and a gas has neither a definite volume nor a definite shape. Matter can also be classified by composition as being either *pure* or a *mixture*. Every pure substance is either an *element* or a *chemical compound*. Elements are fundamental substances that cannot be chemically changed into anything simpler. A chemical compound, by contrast, can be broken down by chemical change into simpler substances. Mixtures are composed of two or more pure substances and can be separated into component parts by physical means (*see Problems 40–45, 96, 103*).

2. How are chemical elements represented? Elements are represented by one- or two-letter symbols, such as H for hydrogen, Ca for calcium, Al for aluminum, and so on. Most symbols are the first one or two letters of the element name, but some symbols are derived from Latin names—Na (sodium), for example. All the known elements are commonly organized into a form called the *periodic table*. Most elements are *metals*, 18 are *nonmetals*, and 6 are *metalloids* (*see Problems 29–31, 48–57, 96, 102, 103*).

3. What kinds of properties does matter have? A *property* is any characteristic that can be used to describe or identify something: *physical* properties can be seen or measured without changing the chemical identity of the substance (that is, color, melting point), while *chemical* properties can only be seen or measured when the substance undergoes a *chemical change*, such as a chemical reaction (*see Problems 37–39, 42–44, 47, 97, 102, 103*).

4. What units are used to measure properties, and how can a quantity be converted from one unit to another? A property that can be measured is called a *physical quantity* and is described by both a number and a label, or *unit*. The preferred units are either those of the International System of Units (*SI units*) or the *metric system*. Mass, the amount of matter an object contains, is measured in *kilograms* (kg) or *grams* (g). Length is measured in *meters* (m). Volume is measured in *cubic meters* (m³) in the SI system and in *liters* (L) or *milliliters* (mL) in the metric system. Temperature is measured in *kelvins* (K) in the SI system and in *degrees celsius* (°C) in the metric system. A measurement in one unit can be converted to another unit by multiplying by a *conversion factor* that expresses the exact relationship between the units (*see Problems 58–63, 72–82, 100, 101, 104, 105, 107–109, 121*).

5. How good are the reported measurements? When measuring physical quantities or using them in calculations, it is important to indicate the exactness of the measurement by *rounding off* the final answer using the correct number of *significant figures*. All but one of the significant figures in a number is known with certainty; the final digit is estimated to ±1 (*see Problems 32–35, 64–71, 104, 112*).

6. How are large and small numbers best represented? Measurements of small and large quantities are usually written in *scientific notation* as the product of a number between 1 and 10, times a power of 10. Numbers greater than 10 have a positive exponent, and numbers less than 1 have a negative exponent. For example, $3562 = 3.562 \times 10^3$, and $0.003\ 91 = 3.91 \times 10^{-3}$ (*see Problems 64–71, 75, 82, 108*).

7. What techniques are used to solve problems? Problems are best solved by applying the *factor-label method*, in which units can be multiplied and divided just as numbers can. The idea is to set up an equation so that all unwanted units cancel, leaving only the desired units. Usually it is best to start by identifying the known and needed information, then decide how to convert the known information to the answer, and finally check to make sure the answer is reasonable both chemically and physically (*see Problems 76–82, 101, 106, 107, 109, 110–112, 114, 115, 118–123*).

8. What are temperature, specific heat, density, and specific gravity? *Temperature* is a measure of how hot or cold an object is. The *specific heat* of a substance is the amount of heat necessary to raise the temperature of 1 g of the substance by 1 °C (1 cal/g °C or 4.184 J/g °C). Water has an unusually high specific heat, which helps our bodies to maintain an even temperature. *Density*, the physical property that relates mass to volume, is expressed in units of grams per milliliter (g/mL) for a liquid or grams per cubic centimeter (g/cm³) for a solid. The *specific gravity* of a liquid is the density of the liquid divided by the density of water at the same temperature. Because the density of water is approximately 1 g/mL, specific gravity and density have the same numerical value (*see Problems 32, 36, 42, 43, 83–89, 90–95, 98, 99, 106, 109, 113, 118–120, 122, 123*).

KEY WORDS

Change of state, *p. 6*

Chemical change, *p. 4*

Chemical compound, *p. 7*

Chemical formula, *p. 10*

Chemical reaction, *p. 7*

Chemistry, *p. 4*

Conversion factor, *p. 26*

Density, *p. 33*

Element, *p. 6*

Energy, *p. 29*

Factor-label method, *p. 26*

Gas, *p. 5*

Heterogeneous mixture, *p. 6*

Homogeneous mixture, *p. 6*

Liquid, *p. 5*

Mass, *p. 17*

Matter, *p. 4*

Metal, *p. 11*

Metalloid, *p. 11*

Mixture, *p. 6*

Nonmetal, *p. 11*

Periodic table, *p. 11*

Physical change, *p. 4*

Physical quantity, *p. 14*

Product, *p. 7*

Property, *p. 4*

Pure substance, *p. 6*

Reactant, *p. 7*

Rounding off, *p. 24*

Scientific Method, *p. 4*

Scientific notation, *p. 21*

SI units, *p. 15*

Significant figures, *p. 20*

Solid, *p. 5*

Specific gravity, *p. 34*

Specific heat, *p. 31*

State of matter, *p. 6*

Temperature, *p. 29*

Unit, *p. 14*

Weight, *p. 17*

UNDERSTANDING KEY CONCEPTS

The problems in this section are intended as a bridge between the Chapter Summary and the Additional Problems that follow. Primarily visual in nature, they are designed to help you test your grasp of the chapter's most important principles before attempting to solve quantitative problems. Answers to all Key Concept problems are at the end of the book following the appendixes.

1.29   The six elements in blue at the far right of the periodic table are gases at room temperature. The red elements in the middle of the table are the so-called coinage metals. Identify each of these elements using the periodic table inside the front cover of this book.

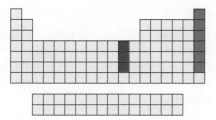

1.30   Identify the three elements indicated on the following periodic table and tell which is a metal, which is a nonmetal, and which is a metalloid.

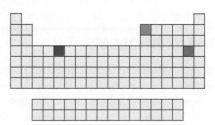

1.31 The radioactive element indicated on the following periodic table is used in smoke detectors. Identify it, and tell whether it is a metal, a nonmetal, or a metalloid.

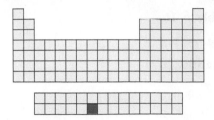

1.32 (a) What is the specific gravity of the following solution?
(b) How many significant figures does your answer have?
(c) Is the solution more dense or less dense than water?

1.33 Assume that you have two graduated cylinders, one with a capacity of 5 mL (a) and the other with a capacity of 50 mL (b). Draw a line in each showing how much liquid you would add if you needed to measure 2.64 mL of water. Which cylinder do you think is more precise? Explain.

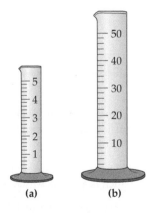

(a)   (b)

1.34 State the length of the pencil depicted in the accompanying figure in both inches and centimeters using appropriate numbers of significant figures.

1.35 Assume that you are delivering a solution sample from a pipette. Figures (a) and (b) show the volume level before and after dispensing the sample, respectively. State the liquid level (in mL) before and after dispensing the sample, and calculate the volume of the sample.

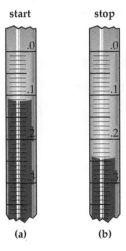

(a)   (b)

1.36 Assume that identical hydrometers are placed in ethanol (sp gr 0.7893) and in chloroform (sp gr 1.4832). In which liquid will the hydrometer float higher? Explain.

ADDITIONAL PROBLEMS

These exercises are divided into sections by topic. Each section begins with review and conceptual questions, followed by numerical problems of varying levels of difficulty. Many of the problems dealing with more difficult concepts or skills are presented in pairs, with each even-numbered problem followed by an odd-numbered one requiring similar skills. The final section consists of unpaired General Questions and Problems that draw on various parts of the chapter and, in future chapters, may even require the use of concepts from previous chapters. Answers to all even-numbered problems are given at the end of the book following the appendixes.

CHEMISTRY AND THE PROPERTIES OF MATTER

1.37 What is the difference between a physical change and a chemical change?

1.38 Which of the following is a physical change and which is a chemical change?

(a) Boiling water

(b) Decomposing water by passing an electric current through it

(c) Exploding of potassium metal when placed in water

(d) Breaking of glass

1.39 Which of the following is a physical change and which is a chemical change?

(a) Making lemonade (lemons + water + sugar)

(b) Frying eggs

(c) Burning a candle

(d) Whipping cream

(e) Leaves changing color

STATES AND CLASSIFICATION OF MATTER

1.40 Name and describe the three states of matter.

1.41 Name two changes of state, and describe what causes each to occur.

1.42 Sulfur dioxide is a compound produced when sulfur burns in air. It has a melting point of $-72.7\,^{\circ}\text{C}$ and a boiling point of $-10\,^{\circ}\text{C}$. In what state does it exist at room temperature (298 K)? (refer to Figure 1.10).

1.43 Butane (C_4H_8) is an easily compressible gas used in cigarette lighters. It has a melting point of $-138.4\,^{\circ}\text{C}$ and a boiling point of $-0.5\,^{\circ}\text{C}$. Would you expect a butane lighter to work in winter when the temperature outdoors is 25 °F? Why or why not? (refer to Figure 1.10).

1.44 Classify each of the following as a mixture or a pure substance:

(a) Pea soup   (b) Seawater

(c) The contents of a propane tank

(d) Urine   (e) Lead

(f) A multivitamin tablet

1.45 Which of these terms, (i) mixture, (ii) solid, (iii) liquid, (iv) gas, (v) chemical element, (vi) chemical compound, applies to the following substances at room temperature?

(a) Gasoline   (b) Iodine

(c) Water   (d) Air

(e) Blood   (f) Sodium bicarbonate

(g) Gaseous ammonia   (h) Silicon

1.46 Hydrogen peroxide, often used in solutions to cleanse cuts and scrapes, breaks down to yield water and oxygen:

Hydrogen peroxide $\longrightarrow$ Water + Oxygen

(a) Identify the reactants and products.

(b) Which of the substances are chemical compounds, and which are elements?

1.47 When sodium metal is placed in water, the following change occurs:

Sodium + Water $\longrightarrow$ Hydrogen + Sodium hydroxide

(a) Identify the reactants and products.

(b) Which of the substances are elements, and which are chemical compounds?

ELEMENTS AND THEIR SYMBOLS

1.48 Describe the general properties of metals, nonmetals, and metalloids.

1.49 What is the most abundant element in the earth's crust? In the human body? List the name and symbol for each.

1.50 What are the symbols for the following elements?

(a) Gadolinium (used in color TV screens)

(b) Germanium (used in semiconductors)

(c) Technetium (used in biomedical imaging)

(d) Arsenic (used in pesticides)

(e) Cadmium (used in rechargeable batteries)

1.51 Supply the missing names or symbols for the elements in the spaces provided:

(a) N _____   (b) K _____

(c) Cl _____   (d) _____ Calcium

(e) _____ Phosphorus   (f) _____ Manganese

1.52 Correct the following statements.

(a) The symbol for bromine is BR.

(b) The symbol for manganese is Mg.

(c) The symbol for carbon is Ca.

(d) The symbol for potassium is Po.

1.53 Correct the following statements.

(a) Carbon dioxide has the formula CO2.

(b) Carbon dioxide has the formula Co_2.

(c) Table salt, NaCl, is composed of nitrogen and chlorine.

1.54 The amino acid glycine has the formula $C_2H_5NO_2$. Which elements are present in glycine? What is the total number of atoms represented by the formula?

1.55 Glucose, a form of sugar, has the formula $C_6H_{12}O_6$. Which elements are included in this compound, and how many atoms of each are present?

1.56 Write the formula for ibuprofen: 13 carbons, 18 hydrogens, and 2 oxygens.

1.57 Given the physical properties of the following elements classify each one as a metal, nonmetal, or metalloid:

(a) a hard, shiny, very dense solid that conducts electricity

(b) a brittle, gray solid that conducts electricity poorly

(c) a brown, crystalline solid that does not conduct electricity

(d) a colorless, odorless gas

PHYSICAL QUANTITIES: DEFINITIONS AND UNITS

1.58 What is the difference between a physical quantity and a number?

1.59   What are the units used in the SI system to measure mass, volume, length, and temperature? In the metric system?

1.60   Give the full name of the following units:

(a) cc   (b) dm   (c) mm

(d) nL   (e) mg   (f) m^3

1.61   Write the symbol for the following units:

(a) nanogram   (b) centimeter

(c) microliter   (d) micrometer

(e) milligram

1.62   How many picograms are in 1 mg? In 35 ng?

1.63   How many microliters are in 1 L? In 20 mL?

SCIENTIFIC NOTATION AND SIGNIFICANT FIGURES

1.64   Express the following numbers in scientific notation with the correct number of significant figures:

(a) 9457   (b) 0.000 07

(c) 20,000,000,000 (four significant figures)

(d) 0.012 345   (e) 652.38

1.65   Convert the following numbers from scientific notation to standard notation:

(a) 5.28×10^3 (b) 8.205×10^{-2}

(c) 1.84×10^{-5} (d) 6.37×10^4

1.66   How many significant figures does each of the following numbers have?

(a) 237,401   (b) 0.300   (c) 3.01

(d) 244.4   (e) 50,000   (f) 660

1.67   How many significant figures are there in each of the following quantities?

(a) Distance from New York City to Wellington, New Zealand, 14,397 km

(b) Average body temperature of a crocodile, 25.6 °C

(c) Melting point of gold, 1064 °C

(d) Diameter of an influenza virus, 0.000 01 mm

(e) Radius of a phosphorus atom, 0.110 nm

1.68   The diameter of the earth at the equator is 7926.381 mi.

(a) Round off the earth's diameter to four significant figures, to two significant figures, and to six significant figures.

(b) Express the earth's diameter in scientific notation.

1.69   Round off each of the numbers in Problem 1.67 to two significant figures, and express them in scientific notation.

1.70   Carry out the following calculations, express each answer to the correct number of significant figures, and include units in the answers.

(a) 9.02 g + 3.1 g   (b) 88.80 cm + 7.391 cm

(c) 362 mL − 99.5 mL

(d) 12.4 mg + 6.378 mg + 2.089 mg

1.71   Carry out the following calculations, express the answers to the correct numbers of significant figures, and include units in the answers.

(a) $5280 \dfrac{\text{ft}}{\text{mi}} \times 6.2 \text{ mi}$

(b) 4.5 m × 3.25 m

(c) $2.50 \text{ g} \div 8.3 \dfrac{\text{g}}{\text{cm}^3}$

(d) 4.70 cm × 6.8 cm × 2.54 cm

UNIT CONVERSIONS AND PROBLEM SOLVING

1.72   Carry out the following conversions:

(a) 3.614 mg to centigrams

(b) 12.0 kL to megaliters

(c) 14.4 μm to millimeters

(d) 6.03×10^{-6} cg to nanograms

(e) 174.5 mL to deciliters

(f) 1.5×10^{-2} km to centimeters

1.73   Carry out the following conversions. Consult Tables 1.7–1.9 as needed.

(a) 56.4 mi to kilometers and to megameters

(b) 2.0 L to quarts and to fluid ounces

(c) 7 ft 2.0 in. to centimeters and to meters

(d) 1.35 lb to kilograms and to decigrams

1.74   Express the following quantities in more convenient units by using SI unit prefixes:

(a) 9.78×10^4 g   (b) 1.33×10^{-4} L

(c) 0.000 000 000 46 g   (d) 2.99×10^8 cm

1.75   Fill in the blanks to complete the equivalencies either with appropriate units prefixes or with the appropriate scientific notation. The first blank is filled in as an example.

(a) 125 km = 1.25×10^5 m

(b) 6.285×10^3 mg = _____? _____ kg

(c) 47.35 dL = 4.735 × _____? _____ mL

(d) 67.4 cm = 6.7×10^{-4} _____? _____

1.76   The speed limit in Canada is 100 km/h.

(a) How many miles per hour is this?

(b) How many feet per second?

1.77   The muzzle velocity of a projectile fired from a 9 mm handgun is 1200 ft/s.

(a) How many miles per hour is this?

(b) How many meters per second?

1.78 The diameter of a red blood cell is 6×10^{-6} m.

   (a) How many centimeters is this?

   (b) How many red blood cells are needed to make a line 1 cm long? 1 in. long?

1.79 The Willis Tower in Chicago has an approximate floor area of 418,000 m^2. How many square feet of floor space is this?

1.80 A normal value for blood cholesterol is 200 mg/dL of blood. If a normal adult has a total blood volume of 5 L, how much total cholesterol is present?

1.81 The recommended daily dose of calcium for an 18-year-old male is 1200 mg. If 1.0 cup of whole milk contains 290 mg of calcium and milk is his only calcium source, how much milk should an 18-year-old male drink each day?

1.82 The white blood cell concentration in normal blood is approximately 12,000 cells/mm^3 of blood. How many white blood cells does a normal adult with 5 L of blood have? Express the answer in scientific notation.

ENERGY, HEAT, AND TEMPERATURE

1.83 The boiling point of liquid nitrogen, used in the removal of warts and in other surgical applications, is -195.8 °C. What is this temperature in kelvins and in degrees Fahrenheit? (3.74 J/g °C)

1.84 Diethyl ether, a substance once used as a general anesthetic, has a specific heat of 0.895 cal/(g °C). How many calories and how many kilocalories of heat are needed to raise the temperature of 30.0 g of diethyl ether from 10.0 °C to 30.0 °C? How many Joules and kiloJoules?

1.85 Aluminum has a specific heat of 0.215 cal/(g °C). When 25.7 cal (108.5 J) of heat is added to 18.4 g of aluminum at 20.0°, what is the final temperature of the aluminum?

1.86 Calculate the specific heat of copper if it takes 23 cal (96 J) to heat a 5.0 g sample from 25 °C to 75 °C.

1.87 The specific heat of fat is 0.45 cal/(g·°C) (1.9 J/g °C) and the density of fat is 0.94 g/cm^3. How much energy (in calories and joules) is needed to heat 10 cm^3 of fat from room temperature (25 °C) to its melting point (35 °C)?

1.88 A 150 g sample of mercury and a 150 g sample of iron are at an initial temperature of 25.0 °C. If 250 cal (1050 J) of heat is applied to each sample, what is the final temperature of each? (See Table 1.10.)

1.89 When 100 cal (418 J) of heat is applied to a 125 g sample, the temperature increases by 28 °C. Calculate the specific heat of the sample and compare your answer to the values in Table 1.10. What is the identity of the sample?

DENSITY AND SPECIFIC GRAVITY

1.90 Aspirin has a density of 1.40 g/cm^3. What is the volume in cubic centimeters of a tablet weighing 250 mg?

1.91 Gaseous hydrogen has a density of 0.0899 g/L at 0 °C. How many liters would you need if you wanted 1.0078 g of hydrogen?

1.92 What is the density of lead (in g/cm^3) if a rectangular bar measuring 0.500 cm in height, 1.55 cm in width, and 25.00 cm in length has a mass of 220.9 g?

1.93 What is the density of lithium metal (in g/cm^3) if a cube measuring 0.82 cm $\times$ 1.45 cm $\times$ 1.25 cm has a mass of 0.794 g?

1.94 Ethanol produced by fermentation has a specific gravity of 0.787 at 25 °C. What is the volume of 125 g of ethanol at this temperature? (The density of water at 25 °C is 0.997 g/mL.)

1.95 Ethylene glycol, commonly used as automobile antifreeze, has a specific gravity of 1.1088 at room temperature (25 °C). What is the mass of 1.00 L of ethylene glycol at this temperature?

CHEMISTRY IN ACTION

1.96 The active ingredient in aspirin, acetylsalicylic acid (ASA), has the formula $C_9H_8O_4$ and melts at 140 °C. Identify the elements and how many atoms of each are present in ASA. Is it a solid or a liquid at room temperature? [*Aspirin—A Case Study, p. 8*]

1.97 Calomel (Hg_2Cl_2) is not toxic but methyl mercury chloride (CH_3HgCl) is highly toxic. What physical property explains this difference in toxicity? [*Mercury and Mercury Poisoning, p. 15*]

1.98 A thermochromic plastic chip included in a shipping container for beef undergoes an irreversible color change if the storage temperature exceeds 28 °F. What is this temperature on the Celsius and Kelvin scales? [*Temperature-Sensitive Materials, p. 31*]

1.99 A temperature-sensitive bath toy undergoes several color changes in the temperature range from 37 °C to 47 °C. What is the corresponding temperature range on the Fahrenheit scale? [*Temperature-Sensitive Materials, p. 31*]

1.100 Calculate the BMI for an individual who is

   (a) 5 ft 1 in. tall and weighs 155 lb

   (b) 5 ft 11 in. tall and weighs 170 lb

   (c) 6 ft 3 in. tall and weighs 195 lb

   Which of these individuals is likely to have increased health risks? [*A Measurement Example: Obesity and Body Fat, p. 35*]

1.101 Liposuction is a technique for removing fat deposits from various areas of the body. How many liters of fat would have to be removed to result in a 5.0 lb weight loss? The density of human fat is 0.94 g/mL. [*A Measurement Example: Obesity and Body Fat, p. 35*]

GENERAL QUESTIONS AND PROBLEMS

1.102 The most recently discovered element is number 117, Ununseptium. Based on its location in the periodic table, classify it as a metal, nonmetal, or metalloid and discuss the physical properties (physical state, conductivity, etc.) you would expect it to exhibit.

1.103 A white solid with a melting point of 730 °C is melted. When electricity is passed through the resultant liquid, a brown gas and a molten metal are produced. Neither the metal nor the gas can be broken down into anything simpler by chemical means. Classify each—the white solid, the molten metal, and the brown gas—as a mixture, a compound, or an element.

1.104 Refer to the pencil in Problem 1.34. Using the equivalent values in Table 1.8 as conversion factors, convert the length measured in inches to centimeters. Compare the calculated length in centimeters to the length in centimeters measured using the metric ruler. How do the two values compare? Explain any differences.

1.105 Gemstones are weighed in carats, where 1 carat = 200 mg exactly. What is the mass in grams of the Hope diamond, the world's largest blue diamond, at 44.4 carats?

1.106 The relationship between the nutritional unit for energy and the metric unit is 1 Calorie = 1 kcal.

(a) One donut contains 350 Calories. Convert this to calories and joules.

(b) If the energy in one donut was used to heat 35.5 kg of water, calculate the increase in temperature of the water (in °C).

1.107 Drug dosages are typically prescribed in units of milligrams per kilogram of body weight. A new drug has a recommended dosage of 9 mg/kg.

(a) How many mgs would a 130 lb woman have to take to obtain this dosage?

(b) How many 125 mg tablets should a 40 lb child take to receive the recommended dosage?

1.108 A clinical report gave the following data from a blood analysis: iron, 39 mg/dL; calcium, 8.3 mg/dL; cholesterol, 224 mg/dL. Express each of these quantities in grams per deciliter, writing the answers in scientific notation.

1.109 The Spirit of America Goodyear blimp has a volume of 2.027×10^5 ft³.

(a) Convert this volume to L.

(b) When in operation it is filled with helium gas. If the density of helium at room temperature is 0.179 g/L, calculate the mass of helium in the blimp.

(c) What is the mass of air occupying the same volume? The density of air at room temperature is 1.20 g/L.

1.110 Approximately 75 mL of blood is pumped by a normal human heart at each beat. Assuming an average pulse of 72 beats per minute, how many milliliters of blood are pumped in one day?

1.111 A doctor has ordered that a patient be given 15 g of glucose, which is available in a concentration of 50.00 g glucose/1000.0 mL of solution. What volume of solution should be given to the patient?

1.112 Reconsider the volume of the sample dispensed by pipette in Problem 1.35. Assuming that the solution in the pipette has a density of 0.963 g/mL, calculate the mass of solution dispensed in the problem to the correct number of significant figures.

1.113 Today, thermometers containing mercury are used less frequently than in the past because of concerns regarding the toxicity of mercury and because of its relatively high melting point (−39 °C). This means that mercury thermometers cannot be used in very cold environments because the mercury is a solid under such conditions. Alcohol thermometers, however, can be used over a temperature range from −115 °C (the melting point of alcohol) to 78.5 °C (the boiling point of alcohol).

(a) What is the effective temperature range of the alcohol thermometer in °F?

(b) The densities of alcohol and mercury are 0.79 g/mL and 13.6 g/mL, respectively. If the volume of liquid in a typical laboratory thermometer is 1.0 mL, what mass of alcohol is contained in the thermometer? What mass of mercury?

1.114 In a typical person, the level of blood glucose (also known as blood sugar) is about 85 mg/100 mL of blood. If an average body contains about 11 pints of blood, how many grams and how many pounds of glucose are present in the blood?

1.115 A patient is receiving 3000 mL/day of a solution that contains 5 g of dextrose (glucose) per 100 mL of solution. If glucose provides 4 kcal/g of energy, how many kilocalories per day is the patient receiving from the glucose?

1.116 A rough guide to fluid requirements based on body weight is 100 mL/kg for the first 10 kg of body weight, 50 mL/kg for the next 10 kg, and 20 mL/kg for weight over 20 kg. What volume of fluid per day is needed by a 55 kg woman? Give the answer with two significant figures.

1.117 Chloral hydrate, a sedative and sleep-inducing drug, is available as a solution labeled 10.0 gr/fluidram. What volume in milliliters should be administered to a patient who is meant to receive 7.5 gr per dose? (1 gr = 64.8 mg ; 1 fluidram = 3.72 mL)

1.118 When 1.0 tablespoon of butter is burned or used by our body, it releases 100 kcal (100 food Calories or 418. 4 kJ) of energy. If we could use all the energy provided, how many tablespoons of butter would have to be burned to raise the temperature of 3.00 L of water from 18.0 °C to 90.0 °C?

1.119 An archeologist finds a 1.62 kg goblet that she believes to be made of pure gold. When 1350 cal (5650 J) of heat is added to the goblet, its temperature increases by 7.8 °C. Calculate the specific heat of the goblet. Is it made of gold? Explain.

1.120 In another test, the archeologist in Problem 1.119 determines that the volume of the goblet is 205 mL. Calculate the density of the goblet and compare it with the density of gold (19.3 g/mL), lead (11.4 g/mL), and iron (7.86 g/mL). What is the goblet probably made of?

1.121 Sulfuric acid (H_2SO_4, density = 1.83 g/mL) is produced in larger amounts than any other chemical: 2.01×10^{11} lb worldwide in 2004. What is the volume of this amount in liters?

1.122 Imagine that you place a piece of cork measuring 1.30 cm $\times$ 5.50 cm $\times$ 3.00 cm in a pan of water and that on top of the cork you place a small cube of lead measuring 1.15 cm on each edge. The density of cork is 0.235 g/cm^3 and the density of lead is 11.35 g/cm^3. Will the combination of cork plus lead float or sink?

1.123 At a certain point, the Celsius and Fahrenheit scales "cross," and at this point the numerical value of the Celsius temperature is the same as the numerical value of the Fahrenheit temperature. At what temperature does this crossover occur?

Atoms and the Periodic Table

CONTENTS

◄ These basaltic columns at the
Devil's Post-pile National Monument
in northern California are one
example of repeating patterns
that can be found in nature.

1. **What is the modern theory of atomic structure?**
   THE GOAL: Be able to explain the major assumptions of atomic theory.

2. **How do atoms of different elements differ?**
   THE GOAL: Be able to explain the composition of different atoms according to the number of protons, neutrons, and electrons they contain.

3. **What are isotopes, and what is atomic weight?**
   THE GOAL: Be able to explain what isotopes are and how they affect an element's atomic weight.

4. **How is the periodic table arranged?**
   THE GOAL: Be able to describe how elements are arranged in the periodic table, name the subdivisions of the periodic table, and relate the position of an element in the periodic table to its electronic structure.

5. **How are electrons arranged in atoms?**
   THE GOAL: Be able to explain how electrons are distributed in shells and subshells around the nucleus of an atom, how valence electrons can be represented as electron-dot symbols, and how the electron configurations can help explain the chemical properties of the elements.

Chemistry must be studied on two levels. In the previous chapter we dealt with chemistry on the large-scale, or *macroscopic*, level, looking at the properties and transformations of matter that we can see and measure. Now we are ready to look at the sub-microscopic, or atomic level, studying the behavior and properties of individual atoms. Although scientists have long been convinced of their existence, only within the past 20 years have powerful new instruments made it possible to see individual atoms. In this chapter, we will look at modern atomic theory and how the structure of atoms influences macroscopic properties.

2.1 Atomic Theory

Take a piece of aluminum foil, and cut it in two. Then, take one of the pieces and cut *it* in two, and so on. Assuming that you have extremely small scissors and extraordinary dexterity, how long can you keep dividing the foil? Is there a limit, or is matter infinitely divisible into ever smaller and smaller pieces? Historically, this argument can be traced as far back as the ancient Greek philosophers. Aristotle believed that matter could be divided infinitely, while Democritus argued (correctly) that there is a limit. The smallest and simplest bit that aluminum (or any other element) can be divided and still be identifiable as aluminum is called an **atom**, a word derived from the Greek *atomos*, meaning "indivisible."

Chemistry is founded on four fundamental assumptions about atoms and matter, which together make up modern **atomic theory**:

- All matter is composed of atoms.
- The atoms of a given element differ from the atoms of all other elements.
- Chemical compounds consist of atoms combined in specific ratios. That is, only whole atoms can combine—one A atom with one B atom, or one A atom with two B atoms, and so on. The enormous diversity in the substances we see around us is based on the vast number of ways that atoms can combine with one another.
- Chemical reactions change only the way that atoms are combined in compounds. The atoms themselves are unchanged.

Atoms are extremely small, ranging from about 7.4×10^{-11} m in diameter for a hydrogen atom to 5.24×10^{-10} m for a cesium atom. In mass, atoms vary from 1.67×10^{-24} g for hydrogen to 3.95×10^{-22} g for uranium, one of the heaviest naturally occurring atoms. It is difficult to appreciate just how small atoms are, although it might help if you realize that a fine pencil line is about 3 million atoms across and that even the smallest speck of dust contains about 10^{16} atoms. Our current understanding

Atom The smallest and simplest particle of an element.

Atomic theory A set of assumptions proposed by the English scientist John Dalton to explain the chemical behavior of matter.

▶▶▶ We will further explore the topics of chemical compounds in Chapters 3 and 4, and chemical reactions in Chapters 5 and 6.

TABLE 2.1 A Comparison of Subatomic Particles				
		Mass		
Name	Symbol	(Grams)	(amu)	Charge (Charge Units)
Proton	p	$1.672\,622 \times 10^{-24}$	$1.007\,276$	+1
Neutron	n	$1.674\,927 \times 10^{-24}$	$1.008\,665$	0
Electron	e^-	$9.109\,328 \times 10^{-28}$	$5.485\,799 \times 10^{-4}$	−1

Subatomic particles Three kinds of fundamental particles from which atoms are made: protons, neutrons, and electrons.

Proton A positively charged subatomic particle.

Neutron An electrically neutral subatomic particle.

Electron A negatively charged subatomic particle.

Atomic mass unit (amu) A convenient unit for describing the mass of an atom; 1 amu $= \frac{1}{12}$ the mass of a carbon-12 atom.

▲ The relative size of a nucleus in an atom is the same as that of a pea in the middle of this stadium.

Nucleus The dense, central core of an atom that contains protons and neutrons.

of atomic structure is the result of many experiments performed in the late 1800s and early 1900s (see Chemistry in Action on p. 48).

Atoms are composed of tiny **subatomic particles** called *protons, neutrons,* and *electrons.* A **proton** has a mass of $1.672\,622 \times 10^{-24}$ g and carries a positive (+) electrical charge; a **neutron** has a mass similar to that of a proton ($1.674\,927 \times 10^{-24}$ g) but is electrically neutral; and an **electron** has a mass that is only $1/1836$ that of a proton ($9.109\,328 \times 10^{-28}$ g) and carries a negative (−) electrical charge. In fact, electrons are so much lighter than protons and neutrons that their mass is usually ignored. Table 2.1 compares the properties of the three fundamental subatomic particles.

The masses of atoms and their constituent subatomic particles are so small when measured in grams that it is more convenient to express them on a *relative* mass scale. That is, one atom is assigned a mass, and all others are measured relative to it. The process is like deciding that a golf ball (46.0 g) will be assigned a mass of 1. A baseball (149 g), which is $149/46.0 = 3.24$ times heavier than a golf ball, would then have a mass of about 3.24; a volleyball (270 g) would have a mass of $270/46.0 = 5.87$; and so on.

The basis for the relative atomic mass scale is an atom of carbon that contains 6 protons and 6 neutrons. Such an atom is assigned a mass of exactly 12 **atomic mass units** (**amu**; also called a *dalton* in honor of the English scientist John Dalton, who proposed most of atomic theory as we know it), where 1 amu $= 1.660\,539 \times 10^{-24}$ g. Thus, for all practical purposes, both a proton and a neutron have a mass of 1 amu (Table 2.1). Hydrogen atoms are only about $\frac{1}{12}$th as heavy as carbon atoms and have a mass close to 1 amu, magnesium atoms are about twice as heavy as carbon atoms and have a mass close to 24 amu, and so forth.

Subatomic particles are not distributed at random throughout an atom. Rather, the protons and neutrons are packed closely together in a dense core called the **nucleus**. Surrounding the nucleus, the electrons move about rapidly through a large, mostly empty volume of space (Figure 2.1). Measurements show that the diameter of a nucleus is only about 10^{-15} m, whereas that of the atom itself is about 10^{-10} m. For comparison, if an atom were the size of a large domed stadium, the nucleus would be approximately the size of a small pea in the center of the playing field.

▶ **Figure 2.1**

The structure of an atom. Protons and neutrons are packed together in the nucleus, whereas electrons move about in the large surrounding volume. Virtually all the mass of an atom is concentrated in the nucleus.

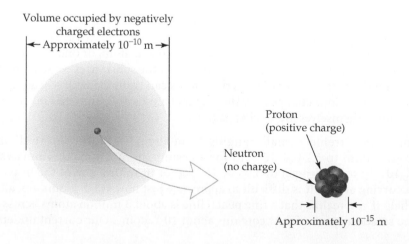

Volume occupied by negatively charged electrons
← Approximately 10^{-10} m →

Proton (positive charge)

Neutron (no charge)

Approximately 10^{-15} m

The structure of the atom is determined by an interplay of different attractive and repulsive forces. Because unlike charges attract one another, the negatively charged electrons are held near the positively charged nucleus. But because like charges repel one another, the electrons also try to get as far away from one another as possible, accounting for the relatively large volume they occupy. The positively charged protons in the nucleus also repel one another, but are nevertheless held together by a unique attraction called the *nuclear strong force*, which we will discuss further in Chapter 11.

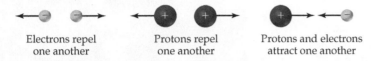

Electrons repel   Protons repel   Protons and electrons
one another   one another   attract one another

Worked Example 2.1 Atomic Mass Units: Gram-to-Atom Conversions

How many atoms are in a small piece of aluminum foil with a mass of 0.100 g? The mass of an atom of aluminum is 27.0 amu.

ANALYSIS We know the sample mass in grams and the mass of one atom in atomic mass units. To find the number of atoms in the sample, two conversions are needed, the first between grams and atomic mass units and the second between atomic mass units and the number of atoms. The conversion factor between atomic mass units and grams is $1 \text{ amu} = 1.660\ 539 \times 10^{-24}$ g.

BALLPARK ESTIMATE An atom of aluminum has a mass of 27.0 amu; since 1 amu $\sim 10^{-24}$ g, the mass of a single aluminum atom is very small ($\approx 10^{-23}$ g). A very *large* number of atoms, therefore, (10^{22} ?) is needed to obtain a mass of 0.100 g.

SOLUTION

STEP 1: Identify known information.

Mass of aluminum foil $= 0.100$ g
1 Al atom $= 27.0$ amu

STEP 2: Identify unknown answer and units.

Number of Al atoms $= ?$

STEP 3: Identify needed conversion factors. Knowing the mass of foil (in g) and the mass of individual atoms (in amu) we need to convert from atoms/amu to atoms/g.

$1 \text{ amu} = 1.660\ 539 \times 10^{-24}$ g

$$\rightarrow \frac{1 \text{ amu}}{1.660\ 539 \times 10^{-24} \text{ g}}$$

STEP 4: Solve. Set up an equation using known information and conversion factors so that unwanted units cancel.

$$(0.100 \cancel{g})\left(\frac{1 \cancel{amu}}{1.660\ 539 \times 10^{-24} \cancel{g}}\right)\left(\frac{1 \text{ Al atom}}{27.0 \cancel{amu}}\right)$$
$$= 2.23 \times 10^{21} \text{ Al atoms}$$

BALLPARK CHECK Our estimate was 10^{22}, which is within a factor of 10.

PROBLEM 2.1
What is the mass in grams of 150×10^{12} iron atoms, each having a mass of 56 amu?

PROBLEM 2.2
How many atoms are in each of the following?
(a) 1.0 g of hydrogen atoms, each of mass 1.0 amu
(b) 12.0 g of carbon atoms, each of mass 12.0 amu
(c) 23.0 g of sodium atoms, each of mass 23.0 amu

PROBLEM 2.3
What pattern do you see in your answers to Problem 2.2? (We will return to this very important pattern in Chapter 6.)

PROBLEM 2.4
The atoms in the gold foil used in Rutherford's experiments have an estimated radius of 1.44×10^{-10} m (see Chemistry in Action on p. 48). If we assume that the radius of the nucleus of a gold atom is 1.5×10^{-15} m, what fraction of the volume of the atom is occupied by the nucleus? (Volume $= 4/3\ \pi r^3$)

CHEMISTRY IN ACTION

Are Atoms Real?

Chemistry rests on the premise that matter is composed of the tiny particles we call atoms. Every chemical reaction and every physical law that governs the behavior of matter is explained by chemists in terms of atomic theory. But how do we know that atoms are real and not just an imaginary concept? And how do we know the structure of the atom? The development of our understanding of atomic structure is another example of the scientific method at work.

Dalton's atomic theory was originally published in 1808, but many prominent scientists dismissed it. Over the next century, however, several unrelated experiments provided insight into the nature of matter and the structure of the atom. Nineteenth-century investigations into electricity, for example, demonstrated that matter was composed of charged particles—rubbing a glass rod with a silk cloth would generate "static electricity," the same phenomenon that shocks you when you walk across a carpet and then touch a metal surface. It was also known that passing electricity through certain substances, such as water, decomposed the compounds into their constituent elements (hydrogen and oxygen, in the case of water). Several hypotheses were proposed to explain the nature and origin of these charged particles, but our current understanding of atomic structure developed incrementally from several key experiments.

Experiments performed in 1897 by J. J. Thomson demonstrated that matter contained negatively charged particles that were 1000 times lighter than H^+, the lightest positively charged particles found in aqueous solution, and that the mass-to-charge ratio of these particles was the same regardless of the material used to produce the particles (Section 6.10 and Chapter 10). This result implied that atoms were not the smallest particles of matter but that they could be divided into even smaller particles. In 1909, Robert Millikan determined that the charge associated with the "electron," as these particles were now called, was 1.6×10^{-19} coulombs.

But where did the electron fit in the overall structure of matter? The pieces to this puzzle fell into place as a result of experiments performed in 1910 by Ernest Rutherford. He bombarded a gold foil with positively charged "alpha" particles emitted from radium during radioactive decay. The majority of these particles

▲ STM image of the Kanji characters for "atom" formed by iron atoms (radius = 126 pm) deposited on a copper metal surface.

passed straight through the foil, but a small fraction of them were deflected, and a few even bounced back. From these results, Rutherford deduced that an atom consists mostly of empty space (occupied by the negatively charged electrons) and that most of the mass and all of the positive charges are contained in a relatively small, dense region that he called the "nucleus."

We can now actually "see" and manipulate individual atoms through the use of a device called a *scanning tunneling microscope*, or STM. With the STM, invented in 1981 by a research team at the IBM Corporation, magnifications of up to 10 million have been achieved, allowing chemists to look directly at atoms. The accompanying photograph shows a computer-enhanced representation of iron atoms that have been deposited on a copper surface.

Most present uses of the STM involve studies of surface chemistry, such as the events accompanying the corrosion of metals and the ordering of large molecules in polymers. Work is also underway using the STM to determine the structures of complex biological molecules, such as immunoglobulin G and streptavidin.

See Chemistry in Action Problems 2.84 and 2.85 at the end of the chapter.

2.2 Elements and Atomic Number

Atomic number (Z) The number of protons in atoms of a given element; the number of electrons in atoms of a given element.

Atoms of different elements differ from one another according to how many protons they contain, a value called the element's **atomic number (Z)**. Thus, if we know the number of protons in an atom, we can identify the element. Any atom with 6 protons, for example, is a carbon atom because the atomic number for carbon is 6 ($Z = 6$).

Atoms are neutral overall and have no net charge because the number of positively charged protons in an atom is the same as the number of negatively charged electrons. Thus, the atomic number also equals the number of electrons in every atom of a given element. Hydrogen, $Z = 1$, has only 1 proton and 1 electron; carbon, $Z = 6$, has 6 protons and 6 electrons; sodium, $Z = 11$, has 11 protons and 11 electrons; and so on, up to the element with the largest known atomic number ($Z = 118$). In a periodic table, elements are listed in order of increasing atomic number, beginning at the upper left and ending at the lower right.

The sum of the protons and neutrons in an atom is called the atom's **mass number** (A). Hydrogen atoms with 1 proton and no neutrons have mass number 1, carbon atoms with 6 protons and 6 neutrons have mass number 12, sodium atoms with 11 protons and 12 neutrons have mass number 23, and so on. Except for hydrogen, atoms generally contain at least as many neutrons as protons and frequently contain more. There is no simple way to predict how many neutrons a given atom will have.

Mass number (A) The total number of protons and neutrons in an atom.

Worked Example 2.2 Atomic Structure: Protons, Neutrons, and Electrons

Phosphorus has the atomic number $Z = 15$. How many protons, electrons, and neutrons are there in phosphorus atoms, which have mass number $A = 31$?

ANALYSIS The atomic number gives the number of protons, which is the same as the number of electrons, and the mass number gives the total number of protons plus neutrons.

SOLUTION
Phosphorus atoms, with $Z = 15$, have 15 protons and 15 electrons. To find the number of neutrons, subtract the atomic number from the mass number:

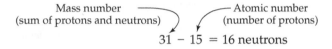

Mass number
(sum of protons and neutrons)
Atomic number
(number of protons)
$$31 - 15 = 16 \text{ neutrons}$$

Worked Example 2.3 Atomic Structure: Atomic Number and Atomic Mass

An atom contains 28 protons and has $A = 60$. Give the number of electrons and neutrons in the atom, and identify the element.

ANALYSIS The number of protons and the number of electrons are the same and are equal to the atomic number Z, 28 in this case. Subtracting the number of protons (28) from the total number of protons plus neutrons (60) gives the number of neutrons.

SOLUTION
The atom has 28 electrons and $60 - 28 = 32$ neutrons. The list of elements inside the front cover shows that the element with atomic number 28 is nickel (Ni).

PROBLEM 2.5
Use the list inside the front cover to identify the following elements:
(a) $A = 186$, with 111 neutrons
(b) $A = 59$, with 21 neutrons
(c) $A = 127$, with 75 neutrons

PROBLEM 2.6
The cobalt used in cancer treatments has $Z = 27$ and $A = 60$. How many protons, neutrons, and electrons are in these cobalt atoms?

2.3 Isotopes and Atomic Weight

Isotopes Atoms with identical atomic numbers but different mass numbers.

▶▶▶ We will see that isotopes of the same element have the same *chemical* behavior (Chapter 5), but very different *nuclear* behavior (Chapter 11).

All atoms of a given element have the same number of protons, equal to the atomic number (*Z*) characteristic of that element. But, different atoms of an element can have different numbers of neutrons and therefore different mass numbers. Atoms with identical atomic numbers but different mass numbers are called **isotopes**. Hydrogen, for example, has three isotopes. The most abundant hydrogen isotope, called *protium*, has no neutrons and thus has a mass number of 1. A second hydrogen isotope, called *deuterium*, has one neutron and a mass number of 2; and a third isotope, called *tritium*, has two neutrons and a mass number of 3. Tritium is unstable and does not occur naturally in significant amounts, although it can be made in nuclear reactors.

  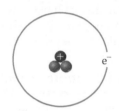

Protium—one proton
(●) and no neutrons;
mass number = 1

Deuterium—one proton
(●) and one neutron (●);
mass number = 2

Tritium—one proton
(●) and two neutrons (●);
mass number = 3

A specific isotope is represented by showing its mass number (*A*) as a superscript and its atomic number (*Z*) as a subscript in front of the atomic symbol, for example, $^{A}_{Z}X$, where X represents the symbol for the element. Thus, protium is $^{1}_{1}H$, deuterium is $^{2}_{1}H$, and tritium is $^{3}_{1}H$.

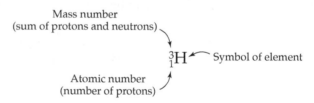

Mass number
(sum of protons and neutrons)

$^{3}_{1}H$ ← Symbol of element

Atomic number
(number of protons)

▶▶▶ We will discuss nuclear reactors in Section 11.11.

Unlike the three isotopes of hydrogen, the isotopes of most elements do not have distinctive names. Instead, the mass number of the isotope is given after the name of the element. The $^{235}_{92}U$ isotope used in nuclear reactors, for example, is usually referred to as uranium-235, or U-235.

Most naturally occurring elements are mixtures of isotopes. In a large sample of naturally occurring hydrogen atoms, for example, 99.985% have mass number *A* = 1 (protium) and 0.015% have mass number *A* = 2 (deuterium). Therefore, it is useful to know the *average* mass of the atoms in a large sample, a value called the element's **atomic weight**. For hydrogen, the atomic weight is 1.008 amu. Atomic weights for all elements are given on the inside of the front cover of this book.

Atomic weight The weighted average mass of an element's atoms.

To calculate the atomic weight of an element, the individual masses of the naturally occurring isotopes and the percentage of each must be known. The atomic weight can then be calculated as the sum of the masses of the individual isotopes for that element, or

$$\text{Atomic weight} = \sum[(\text{isotopic abundance}) \times (\text{isotopic mass})]$$

where the Greek symbol $\sum$ indicates the mathematical summing of terms.

Chlorine, for example, occurs on earth as a mixture of 75.77% Cl-35 atoms (mass = 34.97 amu) and 24.23% Cl-37 atoms (mass = 36.97 amu). The atomic weight is found by calculating the percentage of the mass contributed by each isotope. For chlorine, the calculation is done in the following way (to four significant figures), giving an atomic weight of 35.45 amu:

Contribution from ^{35}Cl: $(0.7577)(34.97 \text{ amu}) = 26.4968 \text{ amu}$

Contribution from ^{37}Cl: $(0.2423)(36.97 \text{ amu}) = \underline{8.9578 \text{ amu}}$

Atomic weight = 35.4546 = 35.45　amu

(rounded to four significant figures)

The final number of significant figures in this case (four) was determined by the atomic masses. Note that the final rounding to four significant figures was not done until *after* the final answer was obtained.

Worked Example 2.4 Average Atomic Mass: Weighted-Average Calculation

Gallium is a metal with a very low melting point—it will melt in the palm of your hand. It has two naturally occurring isotopes: 60.4% is Ga-69 (mass = 68.9257 amu), and 39.6% is Ga-71 (mass = 70.9248 amu). Calculate the atomic weight for gallium.

ANALYSIS We can calculate the average atomic mass for the element by summing up the contributions from each of the naturally occurring isotopes.

BALLPARK ESTIMATE The masses of the two naturally occurring isotopes of gallium differ by 2 amu (68.9 and 70.9 amu). Since slightly more than half of the Ga atoms are the lighter isotope (Ga-69), the average mass will be slightly less than halfway between the two isotopic masses; estimate = 69.8 amu.

SOLUTION

STEP 1: **Identify known information.**	Ga-69 (60.4% at 68.9257 amu) Ga-71 (39.6% at 70.9248 amu)
STEP 2: **Identify the unknown answer and units.**	Atomic weight for Ga (in amu) = ?
STEP 3: **Identify conversion factors or equations.** This equation calculates the average atomic weight as a weighted average of all naturally occurring isotopes.	Atomic weight = Σ [(isotopic abundance) × (isotopic mass)]
STEP 4: **Solve.** Substitute known information and solve.	Atomic weight = (0.604) × (68.9257 amu) = 41.6311 amu + (0.396) × (70.9248 amu) = 28.0862 amu Atomic weight = 69.7 amu (3 significant figures)
	BALLPARK CHECK Our estimate (69.8 amu) is close!

Worked Example 2.5 Identifying Isotopes from Atomic Mass and Atomic Number

Identify element X in the symbol $^{194}_{78}$X, and give its atomic number, mass number, number of protons, number of electrons, and number of neutrons.

ANALYSIS The identity of the atom corresponds to the atomic number—78.

SOLUTION

Element X has Z = 78, which shows that it is platinum. (Look inside the front cover for the list of elements.) The isotope $^{194}_{78}$Pt has a mass number of 194, and we can subtract the atomic number from the mass number to get the number of neutrons. This platinum isotope therefore has 78 protons, 78 electrons, and $194 - 78 = 116$ neutrons.

PROBLEM 2.7

Potassium (K) has two naturally occurring isotopes: K-39 (93.12%; mass = 38.9637 amu) and K-41 (6.88%; 40.9618 amu). Calculate the atomic weight for potassium. How does your answer compare with the atomic weight given in the list inside the front cover of this book?

PROBLEM 2.8

Bromine, an element present in compounds used as sanitizers and fumigants (for example, ethylene bromide), has two naturally occurring isotopes, with mass numbers 79 and 81. Write the symbols for both, including their atomic numbers and mass numbers.

PROBLEM 2.9

An element used to sanitize water supplies has two naturally occurring isotopes with mass numbers of 35 and 37, and 17 electrons. Write the symbols for both isotopes, including their atomic numbers and mass numbers.

2.4 The Periodic Table

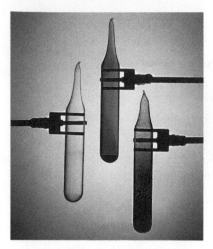

▲ Samples of chlorine, bromine, and iodine, one of Döbereiner's triads of elements with similar chemical properties.

Ten elements have been known since the beginning of recorded history: antimony (Sb), carbon (C), copper (Cu), gold (Au), iron (Fe), lead (Pb), mercury (Hg), silver (Ag), sulfur (S), and tin (Sn). It is worth noting that the symbols for many of these elements are derived from their Latin names, a reminder that they have been known since the time when Latin was the language used for all scholarly work. The first "new" element to be found in several thousand years was arsenic (As), discovered in about 1250. In fact, only 24 elements were known up to the time of the American Revolution in 1776.

As the pace of discovery quickened in the late 1700s and early 1800s, chemists began to look for similarities among elements that might make it possible to draw general conclusions. Particularly important was Johann Döbereiner's observation in 1829 that there were several *triads*, or groups of three elements, that appeared to have similar chemical and physical properties. For example, lithium, sodium, and potassium were all known to be silvery metals that react violently with water; chlorine, bromine, and iodine were all known to be colored nonmetals with pungent odors.

Numerous attempts were made in the mid-1800s to account for the similarities among groups of elements, but the great breakthrough came in 1869 when the Russian chemist Dmitri Mendeleev organized the elements in order of increasing mass and then grouped elements into columns based on similarities in chemical behavior. His table is a forerunner of the modern periodic table, introduced previously in Section 1.5 and shown again in Figure 2.2. The table has boxes for each element that give the symbol, atomic number, and atomic mass of the element:

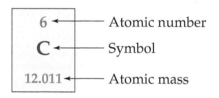

Beginning at the upper left corner of the periodic table, elements are arranged by increasing atomic number into seven horizontal rows, called **periods**, and 18 vertical columns, called **groups**. When organized in this way, *the elements in a given group have similar chemical properties.* Lithium, sodium, potassium, and the other elements in group 1A behave similarly. Chlorine, bromine, iodine, and the other elements in group 7A behave similarly, and so on throughout the table.

Note that different periods (rows) contain different numbers of elements. The first period contains only 2 elements, hydrogen and helium; the second and third periods each contain 8 elements; the fourth and fifth periods each contain 18; the sixth and seventh periods contain 32. Note also that the 14 elements following lanthanum (the *lanthanides*) and the 14 following actinium (the *actinides*) are pulled out and shown below the others.

Groups are numbered in two ways, both shown in Figure 2.2. The 2 large groups on the far left and the 6 on the far right are called the **main group elements** and are numbered 1A through 8A. The 10 smaller groups in the middle of the table are called the **transition metal elements** and are numbered 1B through 8B. Alternatively, all 18 groups are numbered sequentially from 1 to 18. The 14 groups shown separately at the bottom of the table are called the **inner transition metal elements** and are not numbered.

Period One of the 7 horizontal rows of elements in the periodic table.

Group One of the 18 vertical columns of elements in the periodic table.

Main group element An element in one of the 2 groups on the left or the 6 groups on the right of the periodic table.

Transition metal element An element in one of the 10 smaller groups near the middle of the periodic table.

Inner transition metal element An element in one of the 14 groups shown separately at the bottom of the periodic table.

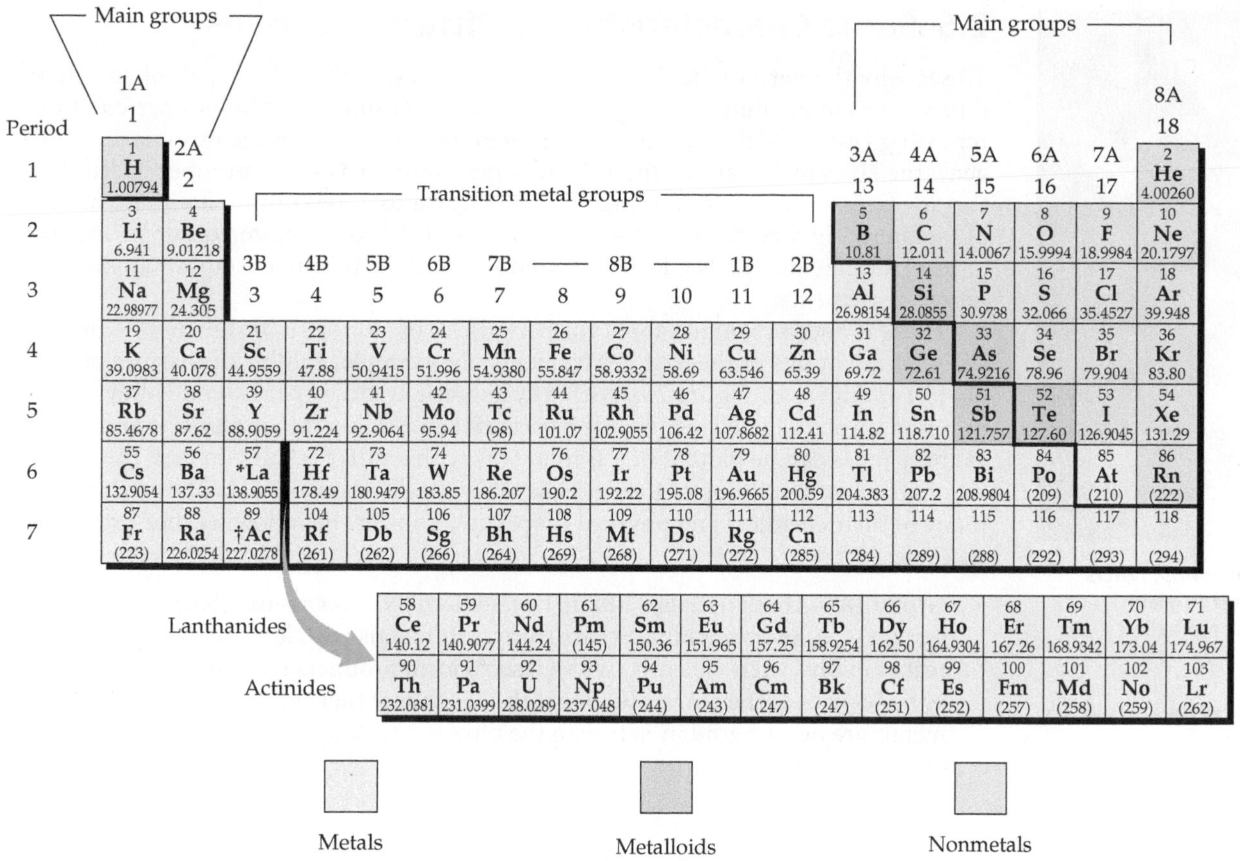

Main groups

Main groups

Period	1A 1	2A 2	Transition metal groups										3A 13	4A 14	5A 15	6A 16	7A 17	8A 18
1	1 **H** 1.00794																	2 **He** 4.00260
2	3 **Li** 6.941	4 **Be** 9.01218	3B 3	4B 4	5B 5	6B 6	7B 7	―― 8	8B 9	―― 10	1B 11	2B 12	5 **B** 10.81	6 **C** 12.011	7 **N** 14.0067	8 **O** 15.9994	9 **F** 18.9984	10 **Ne** 20.1797
3	11 **Na** 22.98977	12 **Mg** 24.305											13 **Al** 26.98154	14 **Si** 28.0855	15 **P** 30.9738	16 **S** 32.066	17 **Cl** 35.4527	18 **Ar** 39.948
4	19 **K** 39.0983	20 **Ca** 40.078	21 **Sc** 44.9559	22 **Ti** 47.88	23 **V** 50.9415	24 **Cr** 51.996	25 **Mn** 54.9380	26 **Fe** 55.847	27 **Co** 58.9332	28 **Ni** 58.69	29 **Cu** 63.546	30 **Zn** 65.39	31 **Ga** 69.72	32 **Ge** 72.61	33 **As** 74.9216	34 **Se** 78.96	35 **Br** 79.904	36 **Kr** 83.80
5	37 **Rb** 85.4678	38 **Sr** 87.62	39 **Y** 88.9059	40 **Zr** 91.224	41 **Nb** 92.9064	42 **Mo** 95.94	43 **Tc** (98)	44 **Ru** 101.07	45 **Rh** 102.9055	46 **Pd** 106.42	47 **Ag** 107.8682	48 **Cd** 112.41	49 **In** 114.82	50 **Sn** 118.710	51 **Sb** 121.757	52 **Te** 127.60	53 **I** 126.9045	54 **Xe** 131.29
6	55 **Cs** 132.9054	56 **Ba** 137.33	57 ***La** 138.9055	72 **Hf** 178.49	73 **Ta** 180.9479	74 **W** 183.85	75 **Re** 186.207	76 **Os** 190.2	77 **Ir** 192.22	78 **Pt** 195.08	79 **Au** 196.9665	80 **Hg** 200.59	81 **Tl** 204.383	82 **Pb** 207.2	83 **Bi** 208.9804	84 **Po** (209)	85 **At** (210)	86 **Rn** (222)
7	87 **Fr** (223)	88 **Ra** 226.0254	89 **†Ac** 227.0278	104 **Rf** (261)	105 **Db** (262)	106 **Sg** (266)	107 **Bh** (264)	108 **Hs** (269)	109 **Mt** (268)	110 **Ds** (271)	111 **Rg** (272)	112 **Cn** (285)	113 (284)	114 (289)	115 (288)	116 (292)	117 (293)	118 (294)

Lanthanides	58 **Ce** 140.12	59 **Pr** 140.9077	60 **Nd** 144.24	61 **Pm** (145)	62 **Sm** 150.36	63 **Eu** 151.965	64 **Gd** 157.25	65 **Tb** 158.9254	66 **Dy** 162.50	67 **Ho** 164.9304	68 **Er** 167.26	69 **Tm** 168.9342	70 **Yb** 173.04	71 **Lu** 174.967
Actinides	90 **Th** 232.0381	91 **Pa** 231.0399	92 **U** 238.0289	93 **Np** 237.048	94 **Pu** (244)	95 **Am** (243)	96 **Cm** (247)	97 **Bk** (247)	98 **Cf** (251)	99 **Es** (252)	100 **Fm** (257)	101 **Md** (258)	102 **No** (259)	103 **Lr** (262)

Metals   Metalloids   Nonmetals

▲ Figure 2.2

The periodic table of the elements.

Each element is identified by a one- or two-letter symbol and is characterized by an *atomic number*. The table begins with hydrogen (H, atomic number 1) in the upper left-hand corner and continues to the yet unnamed element with atomic number 118. The 14 elements following lanthanum (La, atomic number 57) and the 14 elements following actinium (Ac, atomic number 89) are pulled out and shown below the others.

Elements are organized into 18 vertical columns, or *groups*, and 7 horizontal rows, or *periods*. The 2 groups on the left and the 6 on the right are the *main groups*; the 10 in the middle are the *transition metal groups*. The 14 elements following lanthanum are the *lanthanides*, and the 14 elements following actinium are the *actinides*; together these are known as the *inner transition metals*. Two systems for numbering the groups are explained in the text.

Those elements (except hydrogen) on the left-hand side of the black zigzag line running from boron (B) to tellurium (Te) are *metals* (yellow), those elements to the right of the line are *nonmetals* (blue), and most elements abutting the line are *metalloids* (purple).

PROBLEM 2.10

Locate aluminum in the periodic table, and give its group number and period number.

PROBLEM 2.11

Identify the group 1B element in period 5 and the group 2A element in period 4.

PROBLEM 2.12

There are five elements in group 5A of the periodic table. Identify them, and give the period of each.

▲ **Sodium, an alkali metal, reacts violently with water to yield hydrogen gas and an alkaline (basic) solution.**

Alkali metal   An element in group 1A of the periodic table.

2.5 Some Characteristics of Different Groups

To see why the periodic table has the name it does, look at the graph of atomic radius versus atomic number in Figure 2.3. The graph shows an obvious *periodicity*—a repeating rise-and-fall pattern. Beginning on the left with atomic number 1 (hydrogen), the sizes of the atoms increase to a maximum at atomic number 3 (lithium), then decrease to a minimum, then increase again to a maximum at atomic number 11 (sodium), then decrease, and so on. It turns out that the maxima occur for atoms of group 1A elements—Li, Na, K, Rb, Cs, and Fr—and the minima occur for atoms of the group 7A elements.

There is nothing unique about the periodicity of atomic radii shown in Figure 2.3. The melting points of the first 100 elements, for example, exhibit similar periodic behavior, as shown in Figure 2.4, with a systematic trend of peaks and valleys as you progress through the elements in the periodic table. Many other physical and chemical properties can be plotted in a similar way with similar results. In fact, the various elements in a given group of the periodic table usually show remarkable similarities in many of their chemical and physical properties. Look at the following four groups, for example:

- **Group 1A—Alkali metals:** Lithium (Li), sodium (Na), potassium (K), rubidium (Rb), cesium (Cs), and francium (Fr) are shiny, soft metals with low melting points. All react rapidly (often violently) with water to form products that are highly alkaline, or basic—hence the name *alkali metals*. Because of their high reactivity, the alkali metals are never found in nature in the pure state but only in combination with other elements.

▶ **Figure 2.3**

A graph of atomic radius in picometers (pm) versus atomic number shows a periodic rise-and-fall pattern.

The maxima occur for atoms of the group 1A elements (Li, Na, K, Rb, Cs, Fr, in red); the minima occur for atoms of the group 7A elements (blue). Accurate data are not available for the group 8A elements.

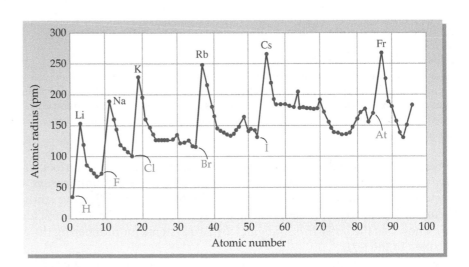

▶ **Figure 2.4**

A graph of melting point versus atomic number shows periodic properties similar to the trend in Figure 2.3.

While the maxima and minima are not as sharp as in Figure 2.3, the change in melting points of the elements still show a similar periodic trend.

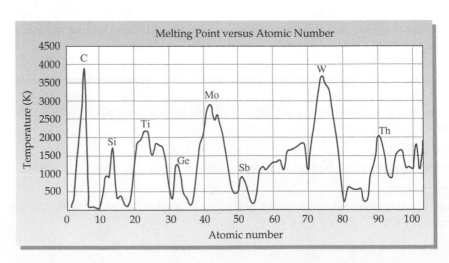

- **Group 2A—Alkaline earth metals:** Beryllium (Be), magnesium (Mg), calcium (Ca), strontium (Sr), barium (Ba), and radium (Ra) are also lustrous, silvery metals, but are less reactive than their neighbors in group 1A. Like the alkali metals, the alkaline earths are never found in nature in the pure state.
- **Group 7A—Halogens:** Fluorine (F), chlorine (Cl), bromine (Br), iodine (I), and astatine (At) are colorful and corrosive nonmetals. All are found in nature only in combination with other elements, such as with sodium in table salt (sodium chloride, NaCl). In fact, the group name **halogen** is taken from the Greek word *hals*, meaning salt.
- **Group 8A—Noble gases:** Helium (He), neon (Ne), argon (Ar), krypton (Kr), xenon (Xe), and radon (Rn) are colorless gases. The elements in this group were labeled the "noble" gases because of their lack of chemical reactivity—helium, neon, and argon don't combine with any other elements, whereas krypton and xenon combine with a very few.

Although the resemblances are not as pronounced as they are within a single group, *neighboring* elements often behave similarly as well. Thus, as noted in Section 1.5 and indicated in Figure 2.2, the periodic table can be divided into three major classes of elements—*metals*, *nonmetals*, and *metalloids* (metal-like). Metals, the largest category of elements, are found on the left side of the periodic table, bounded on the right by a zigzag line running from boron (B) at the top to astatine (At) at the bottom. Nonmetals are found on the right side of the periodic table, and six of the elements adjacent to the zigzag boundary between metals and nonmetals are metalloids.

Alkaline earth metal An element in group 2A of the periodic table.

Halogen An element in group 7A of the periodic table.

Noble gas An element in group 8A of the periodic table.

▶▶▶ The reason for the similarity in chemical properties of elements within each group will be explained in Section 2.8.

LOOKING AHEAD ▶▶▶ Carbon, the element on which life is based, is a group 4A nonmetal near the top right of the periodic table. Clustered near carbon are other elements often found in living organisms, including oxygen, nitrogen, phosphorus, and sulfur. We will look at the subject of *organic chemistry*—the chemistry of carbon compounds—in Chapters 12–17, and move on to *biochemistry*—the chemistry of living things—in Chapters 18–29.

PROBLEM 2.13

Identify the following elements as metals, nonmetals, or metalloids:

(a) Ti   (b) Te

(c) Se   (d) Sc

(e) At   (f) Ar

PROBLEM 2.14

Locate (a) krypton, (b) strontium, (c) nitrogen, and (d) cobalt in the periodic table. Indicate which categories apply to each: (i) metal, (ii) nonmetal, (iii) transition element, (iv) main group element, (v) noble gas.

PROBLEM 2.15

Heavier elements were formed in stars by the fusion of hydrogen and helium nuclei (see Chemistry in Action on p. 56). How many He-4 nuclei would be needed to form a Fe-56 nucleus? What additional particles would be needed?

🔑 KEY CONCEPT PROBLEM 2.16

Identify the elements whose nuclei are shown below. For each, tell its group number, its period number, and whether it is a metal, nonmetal, or metalloid.

○ Neutron

● Proton

(a)   (b)

CHEMISTRY IN ACTION

The Origin of Chemical Elements

Astronomers believe that the universe began some 15 billion years ago in an extraordinary moment they call the "big bang." Initially, the temperature must have been inconceivably high, but after 1 second, it had dropped to about 10^{10} K and subatomic particles began to form: protons, neutrons, and electrons. After 3 minutes, the temperature had dropped to 10^9 K, and protons began fusing with neutrons to form helium nuclei, $^4_2$He.

Matter remained in this form for many millions of years, until the expanding universe had cooled to about 10,000 K and electrons were then able to bind to protons and to helium nuclei, forming stable hydrogen and helium atoms.

The attractive force of gravity acting on regions of higher-than-average density of hydrogen and helium atoms slowly produced massive local concentrations of matter and ultimately formed billions of galaxies, each with many billions of stars. As the gas clouds of hydrogen and helium condensed under gravitational attraction and stars formed, their temperatures reached 10^7 K, and their densities reached 100 g/cm^3. Protons and neutrons again fused to yield helium nuclei, generating vast amounts of heat and light.

Most of these early stars probably burned out after a few billion years, but a few were so massive that, as their nuclear fuel diminished, gravitational attraction caused a rapid contraction leading to still higher core temperatures and higher densities—up to 5×10^8 K and 5×10^5 g/cm^3. Under such extreme conditions, larger nuclei were formed, including carbon, oxygen, silicon, magnesium, and iron. Ultimately, the stars underwent a gravitational collapse resulting in the synthesis of still heavier

▲ "Light echoes" illuminate dust around the supergiant star V838 monocerotis, as seen from the Hubble telescope.

elements and an explosion visible throughout the universe as a *supernova*.

Matter from exploding supernovas was blown throughout the galaxy, forming a new generation of stars and planets. Our own sun and solar system formed about 4.5 billion years ago from matter released by former supernovas. Except for hydrogen and helium, all the atoms in our bodies and our entire solar system were created more than 5 billion years ago in exploding stars. We and our world are made from the ashes of dying stars.

See Chemistry in Action Problems 2.86 and 2.87 at the end of this chapter.

2.6 Electronic Structure of Atoms

Why does the periodic table have the shape it does, with periods of different length? Why are periodic variations observed in atomic radii and in so many other characteristics of the elements? And why do elements in a given group of the periodic table show similar chemical behavior? These questions occupied the thoughts of chemists for more than 50 years after Mendeleev, and it was not until well into the 1920s that the answers were established. Today, we know that *the properties of the elements are determined by the arrangement of electrons in their atoms.*

Our current understanding of the electronic structure of atoms is based on the now accepted *quantum mechanical model*, developed by Austrian physicist Erwin Schrödinger in 1926. One of the fundamental assumptions of the model is that electrons have both particle-like and wave-like properties, and that the behavior of electrons can be described using a mathematical equation called a wave function. One consequence of this assumption is that electrons are not perfectly free to move about in an atom. Instead, each electron is restricted to a certain region of space within the atom, depending on the energy level of the electron. Different electrons have different amounts of energy and thus occupy different regions within the atom.

Furthermore, the energies of electrons are *quantized*, or restricted to having only certain values.

To understand the idea of quantization, think about the difference between stairs and a ramp. A ramp is *not* quantized because it changes height continuously. Stairs, by contrast, *are* quantized because they change height only by a fixed amount. You can climb one stair or two stairs, but you cannot climb 1.5 stairs. In the same way, the energy values available to electrons in an atom change only in steps rather than continuously.

The wave functions derived from the quantum mechanical model also provide important information about the location of electrons in an atom. Just as a person can be found by giving his or her address within a state, an electron can be found by giving its "address" within an atom. Furthermore, just as a person's address is composed of several successively narrower categories—city, street, and house number—an electron's address is also composed of successively narrower categories—*shell, subshell*, and *orbital*, which are defined by the quantum mechanical model.

The electrons in an atom are grouped around the nucleus into **shells**, roughly like the layers in an onion, according to the energy of the electrons. The farther a shell is from the nucleus, the larger it is, the more electrons it can hold, and the higher the energies of those electrons. The first shell (the one nearest the nucleus) can hold only 2 electrons, the second shell can hold 8, the third shell can hold 18, and the fourth shell can hold 32 electrons.

Shell number:	1	2	3	4
Electron capacity:	2	8	18	32

Within shells, electrons are further grouped into **subshells** of four different types, identified in order of increasing energy by the letters *s*, *p*, *d*, and *f*. The first shell has only one subshell, of the *s* type. The second shell has two subshells: an *s* subshell and a *p* subshell. The third shell has an *s*, a *p*, and a *d* subshell. The fourth shell has an *s*, a *p*, a *d*, and an *f* subshell. Of the four types, we will be concerned mainly with *s* and *p* subshells because most of the elements found in living organisms use only these. A specific subshell is symbolized by writing the number of the shell, followed by the letter for the subshell. For example, the designation 3*p* refers to the *p* subshell in the third shell. Note that the number of subshells in a given shell is equal to the shell number. For example, shell number 3 has 3 subshells.

Finally, within each subshell, electrons are grouped into **orbitals**, regions of space within an atom where the specific electrons are most likely to be found. There are different numbers of orbitals within the different kinds of subshells. A given *s* subshell has only 1 orbital, a *p* subshell has 3 orbitals, a *d* subshell has 5 orbitals, and an *f* subshell has 7 orbitals. Each orbital can hold only two electrons, which differ in a property known as *spin*. If one electron in an orbital has a clockwise spin, the other electron in the same orbital must have a counterclockwise spin. The configuration of shells, subshells, and orbitals is summarized in the figure below.

Shell number:	1	2	3	4
Subshell designation:	s	s , p	s , p , d	s , p , d , f
Number of orbitals:	1	1 , 3	1 , 3 , 5	1 , 3 , 5 , 7

Different orbitals have different shapes and orientations, which are described by the quantum mechanical model. Orbitals in *s* subshells are spherical regions centered about the nucleus, whereas orbitals in *p* subshells are roughly dumbbell-shaped regions (Figure 2.5). As shown in Figure 2.5(b), the three *p* orbitals in a given subshell are oriented at right angles to one another.

The overall electron distribution within an atom is summarized in Table 2.2 and in the following list:

- The first shell holds only 2 electrons. The 2 electrons have different spins and are in a single 1*s* orbital.

▲ Stairs are *quantized* because they change height in discrete amounts. A ramp, by contrast, is not quantized because it changes height continuously.

Shell (electron) A grouping of electrons in an atom according to energy.

Subshell (electron) A grouping of electrons in a shell according to the shape of the region of space they occupy.

Orbital A region of space within an atom where an electron in a given subshell can be found.

▶ **Figure 2.5**
The shapes of *s* and *p* orbitals.
(a) The *s* orbitals and (b) the *p* orbitals.
The three *p* orbitals in a given subshell
are oriented at right angles to one another. Each orbital can hold only two
electrons.

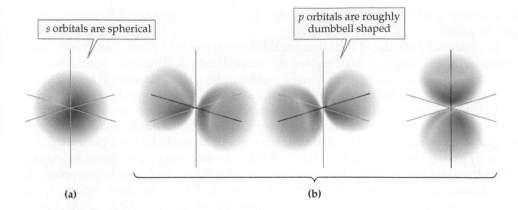

s orbitals are spherical

p orbitals are roughly
dumbbell shaped

(a)

(b)

- The second shell holds 8 electrons. Two are in a 2*s* orbital, and 6 are in the three different 2*p* orbitals (two per 2*p* orbital).
- The third shell holds 18 electrons. Two are in a 3*s* orbital, 6 are in three 3*p* orbitals, and 10 are in five 3*d* orbitals.
- The fourth shell holds 32 electrons. Two are in a 4*s* orbital, 6 are in three 4*p* orbitals, 10 are in five 4*d* orbitals, and 14 are in seven 4*f* orbitals.

Worked Example 2.6 Atomic Structure: Electron Shells

How many electrons are present in an atom that has its first and second shells filled and has 4 electrons in its third shell? Name the element.

ANALYSIS The number of electrons in the atom is calculated by adding the total electrons in each shell. We can identify the element from the number of protons in the nucleus, which is equal to the number of electrons in the atom.

SOLUTION
The first shell of an atom holds 2 electrons in its 1*s* orbital, and the second shell holds 8 electrons (2 in a 2*s* orbital and 6 in three 2*p* orbitals). Thus, the atom has a total of $2 + 8 + 4 = 14$ electrons and must be silicon (Si).

PROBLEM 2.17
How many electrons are present in an atom in which the first and second shells and the 3*s* subshell are filled? Name the element.

PROBLEM 2.18
An element has completely filled $n = 1$ and $n = 2$ shells and has 6 electrons in the $n = 3$ shell. Identify the element and its major group (i.e., main group, transition, etc.). Is it a metal or a nonmetal? Identify the orbital in which the last electron is found.

TABLE 2.2 Electron Distribution in Atoms				
SHELL NUMBER:	1	2	3	4
Subshell designation:	*s*	*s* , *p*	*s* , *p* , *d*	*s* , *p* , *d* , *f*
Number of orbitals:	1	1 , 3	1 , 3 , 5	1 , 3 , 5 , 7
Number of electrons:	2	2 , 6	2 , 6 , 10	2 , 6 , 10 , 14
Total electron capacity:	2	8	18	32

2.7 Electron Configurations

The exact arrangement of electrons in an atom's shells and subshells is called the atom's **electron configuration** and can be predicted by applying three rules:

RULE 1: Electrons occupy the lowest-energy orbitals available, beginning with 1s and continuing in the order shown in Figure 2.6a. Within each shell, the orbital energies increase in the order *s, p, d, f.* The overall ordering is complicated, however, by the fact that some "crossover" of energies occurs between orbitals in different shells above the 3p level. For example, the 4s orbital is lower in energy than the 3d orbitals, and is therefore filled first. The energy level diagram can be used to predict the order in which orbitals are filled, but it may be hard to remember. The schematic in Figure 2.6b may also be used and is easier to remember.

RULE 2: Each orbital can hold only two electrons, which must be of opposite spin.

RULE 3: Two or more orbitals with the same energy—the three *p* orbitals or the five *d* orbitals in a given shell, for example—are each half-filled by one electron before any one orbital is completely filled by addition of the second electron.

Electron configurations of the first 20 elements are shown in Table 2.3. Notice that the number of electrons in each subshell is indicated by a superscript. For example, the notation $1s^2\, 2s^2\, 2p^6\, 3s^2$ for magnesium means that magnesium atoms have 2 electrons in the first shell, 8 electrons in the second shell, and 2 electrons in the third shell.

Electron configuration The specific arrangement of electrons in an atom's shells and subshells.

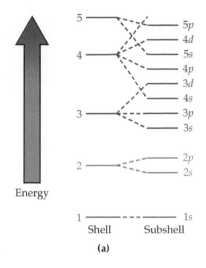

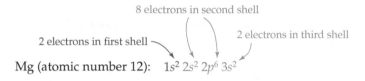

8 electrons in second shell

2 electrons in first shell

2 electrons in third shell

Mg (atomic number 12): $1s^2\, 2s^2\, 2p^6\, 3s^2$

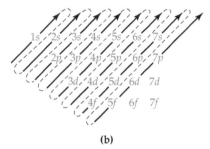

(b)

▲ **Figure 2.6**
Order of orbital energy levels.
(a) An energy-level diagram shows the order in which orbitals will be filled within each shell. Above the 3p level, there is some crossover of energies among orbitals in different shells.
(b) A simple scheme to remember the order in which the orbitals are filled.

TABLE 2.3 Electron Configurations of the First 20 Elements

	Element	Atomic Number	Electron Configuration
H	Hydrogen	1	$1s^1$
He	Helium	2	$1s^2$
Li	Lithium	3	$1s^2\, 2s^1$
Be	Beryllium	4	$1s^2\, 2s^2$
B	Boron	5	$1s^2\, 2s^2\, 2p^1$
C	Carbon	6	$1s^2\, 2s^2\, 2p^2$
N	Nitrogen	7	$1s^2\, 2s^2\, 2p^3$
O	Oxygen	8	$1s^2\, 2s^2\, 2p^4$
F	Fluorine	9	$1s^2\, 2s^2\, 2p^5$
Ne	Neon	10	$1s^2\, 2s^2\, 2p^6$
Na	Sodium	11	$1s^2\, 2s^2\, 2p^6\, 3s^1$
Mg	Magnesium	12	$1s^2\, 2s^2\, 2p^6\, 3s^2$
Al	Aluminum	13	$1s^2\, 2s^2\, 2p^6\, 3s^2\, 3p^1$
Si	Silicon	14	$1s^2\, 2s^2\, 2p^6\, 3s^2\, 3p^2$
P	Phosphorus	15	$1s^2\, 2s^2\, 2p^6\, 3s^2\, 3p^3$
S	Sulfur	16	$1s^2\, 2s^2\, 2p^6\, 3s^2\, 3p^4$
Cl	Chlorine	17	$1s^2\, 2s^2\, 2p^6\, 3s^2\, 3p^5$
Ar	Argon	18	$1s^2\, 2s^2\, 2p^6\, 3s^2\, 3p^6$
K	Potassium	19	$1s^2\, 2s^2\, 2p^6\, 3s^2\, 3p^6\, 4s^1$
Ca	Calcium	20	$1s^2\, 2s^2\, 2p^6\, 3s^2\, 3p^6\, 4s^2$

As you read through the following electron configurations, check the atomic number and the location of each element in the periodic table (Figure 2.2). See if you can detect the relationship between electron configuration and position in the table.

- **Hydrogen ($Z = 1$):** The single electron in a hydrogen atom is in the lowest-energy, $1s$, level. The configuration can be represented in either of two ways:

$$\text{H} \quad 1s^1 \quad \text{or} \quad \frac{\uparrow}{1s^1}$$

In the written representation, the superscript in the notation $1s^1$ means that the $1s$ orbital is occupied by one electron. In the graphic representation, the $1s$ orbital is indicated by a line and the single electron in this orbital is shown by an up arrow ($\uparrow$). A single electron in an orbital is often referred to as being *unpaired*.

- **Helium ($Z = 2$):** The two electrons in helium are both in the lowest-energy, $1s$, orbital, and their spins are *paired*, as represented by up and down arrows ($\uparrow\downarrow$):

$$\text{He} \quad 1s^2 \quad \text{or} \quad \frac{\uparrow\downarrow}{1s^2}$$

- **Lithium ($Z = 3$):** With the first shell full, the second shell begins to fill. The third electron goes into the $2s$ orbital:

$$\text{Li} \quad 1s^2\, 2s^1 \quad \text{or} \quad \frac{\uparrow\downarrow}{1s^2}\ \frac{\uparrow}{2s^1}$$

Because [He] has the configuration of a filled $1s^2$ orbital, it is sometimes substituted for the $1s^2$ orbital in depictions of electron pairing. Using this alternative shorthand notation, the electron configuration for Li is written [He] $2s^1$.

- **Beryllium ($Z = 4$):** An electron next pairs up to fill the $2s$ orbital:

$$\text{Be} \quad 1s^2\, 2s^2 \quad \text{or} \quad \frac{\uparrow\downarrow}{1s^2}\ \frac{\uparrow\downarrow}{2s^2} \quad \text{or} \quad [\text{He}]\, 2s^2$$

- **Boron ($Z = 5$), Carbon ($Z = 6$), Nitrogen ($Z = 7$):** The next three electrons enter the three $2p$ orbitals, one at a time. Note that representing the configurations with lines and arrows gives more information than the alternative written notations because the filling and pairing of electrons in individual orbitals within the p subshell is shown.

$$\text{B} \quad 1s^2\, 2s^2\, 2p^1 \quad \text{or} \quad \frac{\uparrow\downarrow}{1s^2}\ \frac{\uparrow\downarrow}{2s^2}\ \underbrace{\frac{\uparrow}{\ }\ \_\ \_}_{2p^1} \quad \text{or} \quad [\text{He}]\, 2s^2\, 2p^1$$

$$\text{C} \quad 1s^2\, 2s^2\, 2p^2 \quad \text{or} \quad \frac{\uparrow\downarrow}{1s^2}\ \frac{\uparrow\downarrow}{2s^2}\ \underbrace{\frac{\uparrow}{\ }\ \frac{\uparrow}{\ }\ \_}_{2p^2} \quad \text{or} \quad [\text{He}]\, 2s^2\, 2p^2$$

$$\text{N} \quad 1s^2\, 2s^2\, 2p^3 \quad \text{or} \quad \frac{\uparrow\downarrow}{1s^2}\ \frac{\uparrow\downarrow}{2s^2}\ \underbrace{\frac{\uparrow}{\ }\ \frac{\uparrow}{\ }\ \frac{\uparrow}{\ }}_{2p^3} \quad \text{or} \quad [\text{He}]\, 2s^2\, 2p^3$$

- **Oxygen ($Z = 8$), Fluorine ($Z = 9$), Neon ($Z = 10$):** Electrons now pair up one by one to fill the three $2p$ orbitals and fully occupy the second shell:

$$\text{O} \quad 1s^2\, 2s^2\, 2p^4 \quad \text{or} \quad \frac{\uparrow\downarrow}{1s^2}\ \frac{\uparrow\downarrow}{2s^2}\ \underbrace{\frac{\uparrow\downarrow}{\ }\ \frac{\uparrow}{\ }\ \frac{\uparrow}{\ }}_{2p^4} \quad \text{or} \quad [\text{He}]\, 2s^2\, 2p^4$$

$$\text{F} \quad 1s^2\, 2s^2\, 2p^5 \quad \text{or} \quad \frac{\uparrow\downarrow}{1s^2}\ \frac{\uparrow\downarrow}{2s^2}\ \underbrace{\frac{\uparrow\downarrow}{\ }\ \frac{\uparrow\downarrow}{\ }\ \frac{\uparrow}{\ }}_{2p^5} \quad \text{or} \quad [\text{He}]\, 2s^2\, 2p^5$$

$$\text{Ne} \quad 1s^2\, 2s^2\, 2p^6 \quad \text{or} \quad \frac{\uparrow\downarrow}{1s^2}\ \frac{\uparrow\downarrow}{2s^2}\ \underbrace{\frac{\uparrow\downarrow}{\ }\ \frac{\uparrow\downarrow}{\ }\ \frac{\uparrow\downarrow}{\ }}_{2p^6}$$

At this point, we may use the shorthand notation [Ne] to represent the electron configuration for a completely filled set of orbitals in the second shell.

- **Sodium to Calcium** $(Z = 11 - 20)$**:** The pattern seen for lithium through neon is seen again for sodium $(Z = 11)$ through argon $(Z = 18)$ as the $3s$ and $3p$ sub-shells fill up. For elements having a third filled shell, we may use $[\,\text{Ar}\,]$ to represent a completely filled third shell. After argon, however, the first crossover in subshell energies occurs. As indicated in Figure 2.6, the $4s$ subshell is lower in energy than the $3d$ subshell and is filled first. Potassium $(Z = 19)$ and calcium $(Z = 20)$ therefore have the following electron configurations:

$$\textbf{K}\quad 1s^2\,2s^2\,2p^6\,3s^2\,3p^6\,4s^1 \text{ or } [\,\text{Ar}\,]4s^1 \qquad \textbf{Ca}\quad 1s^2\,2s^2\,2p^6\,3s^2\,3p^6\,4s^2 \text{ or } [\,\text{Ar}\,]4s^2$$

Worked Example 2.7 Atomic Structure: Electron Configurations

Show how the electron configuration of magnesium can be assigned.

ANALYSIS Magnesium, $Z = 12$, has 12 electrons to be placed in specific orbitals. Assignments are made by putting 2 electrons in each orbital, according to the order shown in Figure 2.6.

- The first 2 electrons are placed in the $1s$ orbital $(1s^2)$.
- The next 2 electrons are placed in the $2s$ orbital $(2s^2)$.
- The next 6 electrons are placed in the three available $2p$ orbitals $(2p^6)$.
- The remaining 2 electrons are both put in the $3s$ orbital $(3s^2)$.

SOLUTION
Magnesium has the configuration $1s^2\,2s^2\,2p^6\,3s^2$ or $[\,\text{Ne}\,]3s^2$.

Worked Example 2.8 Electron Configurations: Orbital-Filling Diagrams

Write the electron configuration of phosphorus, $Z = 15$, using up and down arrows to show how the electrons in each orbital are paired.

ANALYSIS Phosphorus has 15 electrons, which occupy orbitals according to the order shown in Figure 2.6.

- The first 2 are paired and fill the first shell $(1s^2)$.
- The next 8 fill the second shell $(2s^2\,2p^6)$. All electrons are paired.
- The remaining 5 electrons enter the third shell, where 2 fill the $3s$ orbital $(3s^2)$ and 3 occupy the $3p$ subshell, one in each of the three p orbitals.

SOLUTION

$$\text{P}\quad \underset{1s^2}{\uparrow\downarrow}\quad \underset{2s^2}{\uparrow\downarrow}\quad \underset{2p^6}{\underbrace{\uparrow\downarrow\ \uparrow\downarrow\ \uparrow\downarrow}}\quad \underset{3s^2}{\uparrow\downarrow}\quad \underset{3p^3}{\underbrace{\uparrow\ \uparrow\ \uparrow}}$$

PROBLEM 2.19
Write electron configurations for the following elements. (You can check your answers in Table 2.3.)
(a) C   **(b)** P   **(c)** Cl   **(d)** K

PROBLEM 2.20
For an atom containing 33 electrons, identify the incompletely filled subshell, and show the paired and/or unpaired electrons in this subshell using up and down arrows.

KEY CONCEPT PROBLEM 2.21

Identify the atom with the following orbital-filling diagram.

$$1s^2\,2s^2\,2p^6\,3s^2\,3p^6\quad \underset{4s}{\updownarrow}\qquad \underset{3d}{\updownarrow\ \ \updownarrow\ \ \updownarrow\ \ \updownarrow\ \ \updownarrow}\qquad \underset{4p}{\uparrow\ \ \underline{\ \ }\ \ \underline{\ \ }}$$

2.8 Electron Configurations and the Periodic Table

How is an atom's electron configuration related to its chemical behavior, and why do elements with similar behavior occur in the same group of the periodic table? As shown in Figure 2.7, the periodic table can be divided into four regions, or *blocks*, of elements according to the electron shells and subshells occupied by *the subshell filled last.*

s-Block element A main group element that results from the filling of an *s* orbital.

p-Block element A main group element that results from the filling of *p* orbitals.

d-Block element A transition metal element that results from the filling of *d* orbitals.

f-Block element An inner transition metal element that results from the filling of *f* orbitals.

- The main group 1A and 2A elements on the left side of the table (plus He) are called the **s-block elements** because an *s* subshell is filled last in these elements.
- The main group 3A–8A elements on the right side of the table (except He) are the **p-block elements** because a *p* subshell is filled last in these elements.
- The transition metals in the middle of the table are the **d-block elements** because a *d* subshell is filled last in these elements.
- The inner transition metals detached at the bottom of the table are the **f-block elements** because an *f* subshell is filled last in these elements.

Thinking of the periodic table as outlined in Figure 2.7 provides a simple way to remember the order of orbital filling shown previously in Figure 2.6. Beginning at the top left corner of the periodic table, the first row contains only two elements (H and He) because only two electrons are required to fill the *s* orbital in the first shell, $1s^2$. The second row begins with two *s*-block elements (Li and Be) and continues with six *p*-block elements (B through Ne), so electrons fill the next available *s* orbital ($2s$) and then the first available *p* orbitals ($2p$). The third row is similar to the second row, so the $3s$ and $3p$ orbitals are filled next. The fourth row again starts with 2 *s*-block elements (K and Ca) but is then followed by 10 *d*-block elements (Sc through Zn) and 6 *p*-block elements (Ga through Kr). Thus, the order of orbital filling is $4s$ followed by the first available *d* orbitals ($3d$) followed by $4p$. Continuing through successive rows of the periodic table gives the entire filling order, identical to that shown in Figure 2.6.

$$1s \rightarrow 2s \rightarrow 2p \rightarrow 3s \rightarrow 3p \rightarrow 4s \rightarrow 3d \rightarrow 4p \rightarrow 5s \rightarrow$$
$$4d \rightarrow 5p \rightarrow 6s \rightarrow 4f \rightarrow 5d \rightarrow 6p \rightarrow 7s \rightarrow 5f \rightarrow 6d \rightarrow 7p$$

But why do the elements in a given group of the periodic table have similar properties? The answer emerges when you look at Table 2.4, which gives electron configurations for elements in the main groups 1A, 2A, 7A, and 8A. Focusing only on the

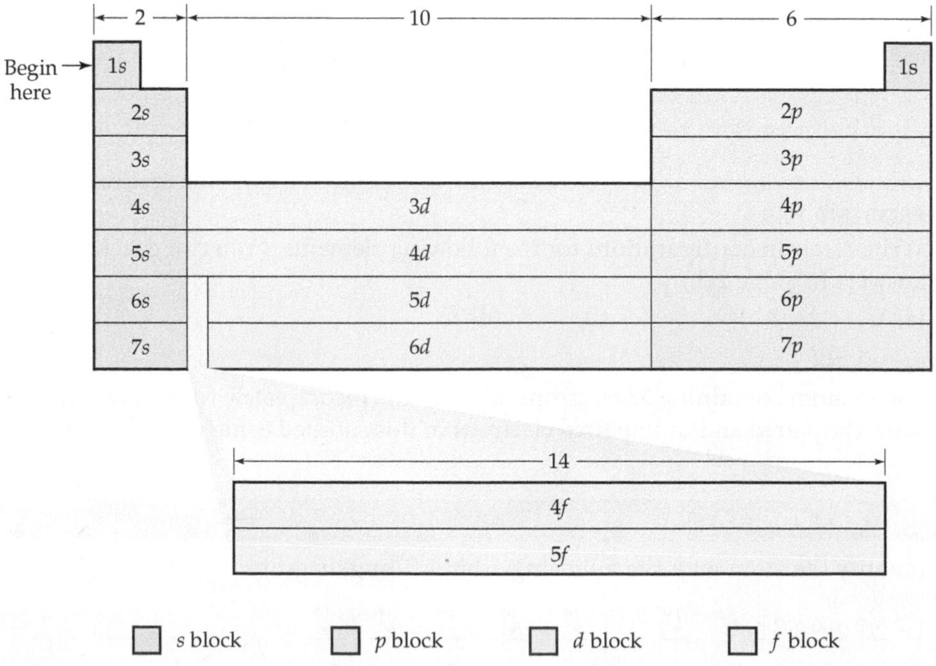

▶ **Figure 2.7**
The blocks of elements in the periodic table correspond to filling the different types of subshells.
Beginning at the top left and going across successive rows of the periodic table provides a method for remembering the order of orbital filling: $1s \rightarrow 2s \rightarrow 2p \rightarrow 3s \rightarrow 3p \rightarrow 4s \rightarrow 3d \rightarrow 4p$, and so on.

Table 2.4 Valence-Shell Electron Configurations for Group 1A, 2A, 7A, and 8A Elements

Group	Element	Atomic Number	Valence-Shell Electron Configuration
1A	Li (lithium)	3	$2s^1$
	Na (sodium)	11	$3s^1$
	K (potassium)	19	$4s^1$
	Rb (rubidium)	37	$5s^1$
	Cs (cesium)	55	$6s^1$
2A	Be (beryllium)	4	$2s^2$
	Mg (magnesium)	12	$3s^2$
	Ca (calcium)	20	$4s^2$
	Sr (strontium)	38	$5s^2$
	Ba (barium)	56	$6s^2$
7A	F (fluorine)	9	$2s^2\,2p^5$
	Cl (chlorine)	17	$3s^2\,3p^5$
	Br (bromine)	35	$4s^2\,4p^5$
	I (iodine)	53	$5s^2\,5p^5$
8A	He (helium)	2	$1s^2$
	Ne (neon)	10	$2s^2\,2p^6$
	Ar (argon)	18	$3s^2\,3p^6$
	Kr (krypton)	36	$4s^2\,4p^6$
	Xe (xenon)	54	$5s^2\,5p^6$

electrons in the outermost shell, or **valence shell**, *elements in the same group of the periodic table have similar electron configurations in their valence shells.* The group 1A elements, for example, all have one **valence electron**, ns^1 (where n represents the number of the valence shell: $n = 2$ for Li; $n = 3$ for Na; $n = 4$ for K; and so on). The group 2A elements have two valence electrons (ns^2); the group 7A elements have seven valence electrons ($ns^2\,np^5$); and the group 8A elements (except He) have eight valence electrons ($ns^2\,np^6$). You might also notice that the group numbers from 1A through 8A give the numbers of valence electrons for the elements in each main group. It is worth noting that the valence electrons are those in the outermost shell—not necessarily in the orbitals that were filled last!

What is true for the main group elements is also true for the other groups in the periodic table: atoms within a given group have the same number of valence electrons and have similar electron configurations. *Because the valence electrons are the most loosely held, they are the most important in determining an element's properties.* Similar electron configurations thus explain why the elements in a given group of the periodic table have similar chemical behavior.

Valence shell The outermost electron shell of an atom.

Valence electron An electron in the valence shell of an atom.

LOOKING AHEAD ▶▶▶ We have seen that elements in a given group have similar chemical behavior because they have similar valence electron configurations, and that many chemical properties exhibit periodic trends across the periodic table. The *chemical* behavior of nearly all the elements can be predicted based on their position in the periodic table, and this will be examined in more detail in Chapters 3 and 4. Similarly, the *nuclear* behavior of the different isotopes of a given element is related to the configuration of the nucleus (that is, the number of neutrons and protons) and will be examined in Chapter 11.

Worked Example 2.9 Electron Configurations: Valence Electrons

Write the electron configuration for the following elements, using both the complete and the shorthand notations. Indicate which electrons are the valence electrons.

(a) Na   **(b)** Cl   **(c)** Zr

ANALYSIS Locate the row and the block in which each of the elements is found in Figure 2.7. The location can be used to determine the complete electron configuration and to identify the valence electrons.

SOLUTION

(a) Na (sodium) is located in the third row and in the first column of the s-block. Therefore, all orbitals up to the $3s$ are completely filled, and there is one electron in the $3s$ orbital.

$$\text{\textbf{Na:} } 1s^2\, 2s^2\, 2p^6\, \underline{3s^1} \quad \text{or} \quad [\text{Ne}]\, \underline{3s^1} \quad \text{(valence electrons are underlined)}$$

(b) Cl (chlorine) is located in the third row and in the fifth column of the p-block.

$$\text{\textbf{Cl:} } 1s^2\, 2s^2\, 2p^6\, \underline{3s^2\, 3p^5} \quad \text{or} \quad [\text{Ne}]\, \underline{3s^2\, 3p^5}$$

(c) Zr (zirconium) is located in the fifth row and in the second column of the d-block. All orbitals up to the $4d$ are completely filled, and there are 2 electrons in the $4d$ orbitals. Note that the $4d$ orbitals are filled after the $5s$ orbitals in both Figures 2.6 and 2.7.

$$\text{\textbf{Zr:} } 1s^2\, 2s^2\, 2p^6\, 3s^2\, 3p^6\, 4s^2\, 3d^{10}\, 4p^6\, \underline{5s^2\, 4d^2} \quad \text{or} \quad [\text{Kr}]\, \underline{5s^2\, 4d^2}$$

Worked Example 2.10 Electron Configurations: Valence-Shell Configurations

Using n to represent the number of the valence shell, write a general valence-shell configuration for the elements in group 6A.

ANALYSIS The elements in group 6A have 6 valence electrons. In each element, the first two of these electrons are in the valence s subshell, giving ns^2, and the next four electrons are in the valence p subshell, giving np^4.

SOLUTION
For group 6A, the general valence-shell configuration is $ns^2\, np^4$.

Worked Example 2.11 Electron Configurations: Inner Shells versus Valence Shell

How many electrons are in a tin atom? Give the number of electrons in each shell. How many valence electrons are there in a tin atom? Write the valence-shell configuration for tin.

ANALYSIS The total number of electrons will be the same as the atomic number for tin ($Z = 50$). The number of valence electrons will equal the number of electrons in the valence shell.

SOLUTION
Checking the periodic table shows that tin has atomic number 50 and is in group 4A. The number of electrons in each shell is

Shell number:	1	2	3	4	5
Number of electrons:	2	8	18	18	4

As expected from the group number, tin has 4 valence electrons. They are in the $5s$ and $5p$ subshells and have the configuration $5s^2\, 5p^2$.

PROBLEM 2.22

Write the electron configuration for the following elements, using both the complete and the shorthand notations. Indicate which electrons are the valence electrons.

(a) F **(b)** Al **(c)** As

PROBLEM 2.23

Identify the group in which all the elements have the valence-shell configuration ns^2.

PROBLEM 2.24

For chlorine, identify the group number, give the number of electrons in each occupied shell, and write its valence-shell configuration.

KEY CONCEPT PROBLEM 2.25

Identify the group number, and write the general valence-shell configuration (for example, ns^1 for group 1A elements) for the elements indicated in red in the following periodic table.

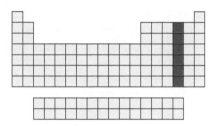

2.9 Electron-Dot Symbols

Valence electrons play such an important role in the behavior of atoms that it is useful to have a method for including them with atomic symbols. In an **electron-dot symbol**, dots are placed around the atomic symbol to indicate the number of valence electrons present. A group 1A atom, such as sodium, has a single dot; a group 2A atom, such as magnesium, has two dots; a group 3A atom, such as boron, has three dots; and so on.

Table 2.5 gives electron-dot symbols for atoms of the first few elements in each main group. As shown, the dots are distributed around the four sides of the element symbol, singly at first until each of the four sides has one dot. As more electron dots are added they will form pairs, with no more than two dots on a side. Note that helium differs from other noble gases in having only two valence electrons rather than eight. Nevertheless, helium is considered a member of group 8A because its properties resemble those of the other noble gases and because its highest occupied subshell is filled $(1s^2)$.

Electron-dot symbol An atomic symbol with dots placed around it to indicate the number of valence electrons.

TABLE 2.5 Electron-Dot Symbols for Some Main Group Elements

1A	2A	3A	4A	5A	6A	7A	NOBLE GASES
H·							He:
Li·	·Be·	·B·	·C·	·N:	·O:	·F:	:Ne:
Na·	·Mg·	·Al·	·Si·	·P:	·S:	·Cl:	:Ar:
K·	·Ca·	·Ga·	·Ge·	·As:	·Se:	·Br:	:Kr:

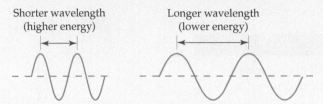

Atoms and Light

What we see as *light* is really a wave of energy moving through space. The shorter the length of the wave (the *wavelength*), the higher the energy; the longer the wavelength, the lower the energy.

Shorter wavelength
(higher energy)

Longer wavelength
(lower energy)

▲ **The brilliant colors of fireworks are due to the release of the energy from excited atoms as electrons fall from higher to lower energy levels.**

Visible light has wavelengths in the range 400–800 nm, but that is just one small part of the overall *electromagnetic spectrum*, shown in the accompanying figure. Although we cannot see the other wavelengths of electromagnetic energy, we use them for many purposes and their names may be familiar to you: gamma rays, X rays, ultraviolet (UV) rays, infrared (IR) rays, microwaves, and radio waves.

What happens when a beam of electromagnetic energy collides with an atom? Remember that electrons are located in orbitals based on their energy levels. An atom with its electrons in their usual, lowest-energy locations is said to be in its *ground state*. If the amount of electromagnetic energy is just right, an electron can be kicked up from its usual energy level to a higher one. Energy from an electrical discharge or in the form of heat can also boost electrons to higher energy levels. With one of its electrons promoted to a higher energy, an atom is said to be *excited*. The excited state does not last long, though, because the electron quickly drops back to its more stable, ground-state energy level, releasing its extra energy in the process. If the released energy falls in the range of visible

light, we can see the result. Many practical applications, from neon lights to fireworks, are the result of this phenomenon.

In "neon" lights, noble gas atoms are excited by an electric discharge, giving rise to a variety of colors that depend on the gas—red from neon, white from krypton, and blue from argon—as electrons release energy and return to their ground states. Similarly, mercury or sodium atoms excited by electrical energy are responsible for the intense bluish or yellowish light, respectively, provided by some street lamps. In the same manner, metal atoms excited by heat are responsible for the spectacular colors of fireworks—red from strontium, green from barium, and blue from copper, for example.

The concentration of certain biologically important metals in body fluids, such as blood or urine, is measured by sensitive instruments relying on the same principle of electron excitation that we see in fireworks. These instruments measure the intensity of color produced in a flame by lithium (red), sodium (yellow), and potassium (violet), to determine the concentrations of these metals, which are included in most clinical lab reports.

See Chemistry in Action Problems 2.88 and 2.89 at the end of the chapter.

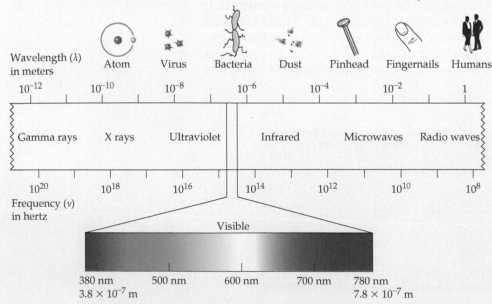

◄ **The electromagnetic spectrum consists of a continuous range of wavelengths, with the familiar visible region accounting for only a small portion near the middle of the range.**

Worked Example **2.12** Electron Configurations: Electron-Dot Symbols

Write the electron-dot symbol for any element X in group 5A.

ANALYSIS The group number, 5A, indicates 5 valence electrons. The first four are distributed singly around the four sides of the element symbol, and any additional are placed to form electron pairs.

SOLUTION

·$\overset{\cdot}{\underset{\cdot}{X}}$:   (5 electrons)

PROBLEM 2.26
Write the electron-dot symbol for any element X in group 3A.

PROBLEM 2.27
Write electron-dot symbols for radon, lead, xenon, and radium.

PROBLEM 2.28
When an electron in a strontium atom drops from the excited state to the ground state, it emits red light, as explained in the Chemistry in Action on p. 66. When an electron in a copper atom drops from the excited state to the ground state, it emits blue light. What are the approximate wavelengths of the red light and the blue light? Which color is associated with higher energy?

SUMMARY: REVISITING THE CHAPTER GOALS

1. What is the modern theory of atomic structure? All matter is composed of *atoms*. An atom is the smallest and simplest unit into which a sample of an element can be divided while maintaining the properties of the element. Atoms are made up of subatomic particles called *protons, neutrons*, and *electrons*. Protons have a positive electrical charge, neutrons are electrically neutral, and electrons have a negative electrical charge. The protons and neutrons in an atom are present in a dense, positively charged central region called the *nucleus*. Electrons are situated a relatively large distance away from the nucleus, leaving most of the atom as empty space (*see Problems 34, 42, 43*).

2. How do atoms of different elements differ? Elements differ according to the number of protons their atoms contain, a value called the element's *atomic number* (*Z*). All atoms of a given element have the same number of protons and an equal number of electrons. The number of neutrons in an atom is not predictable but is generally as great or greater than the number of protons. The total number of protons plus neutrons in an atom is called the atom's *mass number* (*A*) (*see Problems 35, 44, 46, 86, 87, 92*).

3. What are isotopes, and what is atomic weight? Atoms with identical numbers of protons and electrons but different numbers of neutrons are called *isotopes*. The atomic weight of an element is the weighted average mass of atoms of the element's naturally occurring isotopes measured in *atomic mass units* (amu) (*see Problems 36–41, 45–53, 92, 96, 97*).

4. How is the periodic table arranged? Elements are organized into the *periodic table*, consisting of 7 rows, or *periods*, and 18 columns, or *groups*. The 2 groups on the left side of the table and the 6 groups on the right are called the *main group elements*. The 10 groups in the middle are the *transition metal groups*, and the 14 groups pulled out and displayed below the main part of the table are called the *inner transition metal groups*. Within a given group in the table, elements have the same number of valence electrons in their valence shell and similar electron configurations (*see Problems 29, 30, 54–65, 90, 91, 93*).

5. How are electrons arranged in atoms? The electrons surrounding an atom are grouped into layers, or *shells*. Within each shell, electrons are grouped into *subshells*, and within each subshell into *orbitals*—regions of space in which electrons are most likely to be found. The *s* orbitals are spherical, and the *p* orbitals are dumbbell-shaped.

Each shell can hold a specific number of electrons. The first shell can hold 2 electrons in an *s* orbital ($1s^2$); the second shell can hold 8 electrons in one *s* and three *p* orbitals ($2s^2\ 2p^6$); the third shell can hold 18 electrons in one *s*, three *p*, and five *d* orbitals ($3s^2\ 3p^6\ 3d^{10}$); and so on. The *electron configuration* of an element is predicted by assigning the element's electrons into orbitals, beginning with the lowest-energy orbital. The electrons in the outermost shell, or *valence shell*, can be represented using electron-dot symbols (*see Problems 31–33, 54, 55, 57, 66–83, 91, 94, 95, 98–100, 102–106*).

KEY WORDS

Alkali metal, *p. 54*	Main group element, *p. 52*
Alkaline earth metal, *p. 55*	Mass number (*A*), *p. 49*
Atom, *p. 45*	Neutron, *p. 46*
Atomic mass unit (amu), *p. 46*	Noble gas, *p. 55*
Atomic number (*Z*), *p. 48*	Nucleus, *p. 46*
Atomic theory, *p. 45*	Orbital, *p. 57*
Atomic weight, *p. 50*	*p*-Block element, *p. 62*
d-Block element, *p. 62*	Period, *p. 52*
Electron, *p. 46*	Proton, *p. 46*
Electron configuration, *p. 59*	*s*-Block element, *p. 62*
Electron-dot symbol, *p. 65*	Shell (electron), *p. 57*
f-Block element, *p. 62*	Subatomic particles, *p. 46*
Group, *p. 52*	Subshell (electron), *p. 57*
Halogen, *p. 55*	Transition metal element, *p. 52*
Inner transition metal element, *p. 52*	Valence electron, *p. 63*
Isotopes, *p. 50*	Valence shell, *p. 63*

UNDERSTANDING KEY CONCEPTS

2.29 Where on the following outline of a periodic table do the indicated elements or groups of elements appear?

- **(a)** Alkali metals
- **(b)** Halogens
- **(c)** Alkaline earth metals
- **(d)** Transition metals
- **(e)** Hydrogen
- **(f)** Helium
- **(g)** Metalloids

2.30 Is the element marked in red on the following periodic table likely to be a gas, a liquid, or a solid? What is the atomic number of the element in blue? Name at least one other element that is likely to be similar to the element in green.

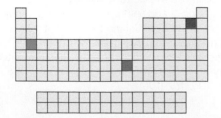

2.31 Use the blank periodic table below to show where the elements matching the following descriptions appear.

- **(a)** Elements with the valence-shell electron configuration $ns^2 np^5$
- **(b)** An element whose third shell contains two *p* electrons
- **(c)** Elements with a completely filled valence shell

2.32 What atom has the following orbital-filling diagram?

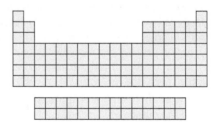

$1s^2 2s^2 2p^6 3s^2 3p^6$

2.33 Use the orbital-filling diagram below to show the electron configuration for As:

$1s^2 2s^2 2p^6 3s^2 3p^6$ — — — — — — — — —

4s   3d   4p

ADDITIONAL PROBLEMS

ATOMIC THEORY AND THE COMPOSITION OF ATOMS

2.34 What four fundamental assumptions about atoms and matter make up modern atomic theory?

2.35 How do atoms of different elements differ?

2.36 Find the mass in grams of one atom of the following elements:

(a) Bi, atomic weight 208.9804 amu

(b) Xe, atomic weight 131.29 amu

(c) He, atomic weight 4.0026 amu

2.37 Find the mass in atomic mass units of the following:

(a) 1 O atom, with a mass of 2.66×10^{-23} g

(b) 1 Br atom, with a mass of 1.31×10^{-22} g

2.38 What is the mass in grams of 6.022×10^{23} N atoms of mass 14.01 amu?

2.39 What is the mass in grams of 6.022×10^{23} O atoms of mass 16.00 amu?

2.40 How many O atoms of mass 15.99 amu are in 15.99 g of oxygen?

2.41 How many C atoms of mass 12.00 amu are in 12.00 g of carbon?

2.42 What are the names of the three subatomic particles? What are their approximate masses in atomic mass units, and what electrical charge does each have?

2.43 Where within an atom are the three types of subatomic particles located?

2.44 Give the number of neutrons in each naturally occurring isotope of argon: argon-36, argon-38, argon-40.

2.45 Give the number of protons, neutrons, and electrons in the following isotopes:

(a) Al-27 **(b)** $^{28}_{14}Si$

(c) B-11 **(d)** $^{115}_{47}Ag$

2.46 Which of the following symbols represent isotopes of the same element?

(a) $^{19}_{9}X$ **(b)** $^{19}_{10}X$

(c) $^{21}_{9}X$ **(d)** $^{21}_{12}X$

2.47 Give the name and the number of neutrons in each isotope listed in Problem 2.46.

2.48 Write the symbols for the following isotopes:

(a) Its atoms contain 6 protons and 8 neutrons.

(b) Its atoms have mass number 39 and contain 19 protons.

(c) Its atoms have mass number 20 and contain 10 electrons.

2.49 Write the symbols for the following isotopes:

(a) Its atoms contain 50 electrons and 70 neutrons.

(b) Its atoms have $A = 56$ and $Z = 26$.

(c) Its atoms have $A = 226$ and contain 88 electrons.

2.50 There are three naturally occurring isotopes of carbon, with mass numbers of 12, 13, and 14. How many neutrons does each have? Write the symbol for each isotope, indicating its atomic number and mass number.

2.51 One of the most widely used isotopes in medical diagnostics is technicium-99*m* (the *m* indicates that it is a *metastable* isotope). Write the symbol for this isotope, indicating both mass number and atomic number.

2.52 Naturally occurring copper is a mixture of 69.17% Cu-63 with a mass of 62.93 amu and 30.83% Cu-65 with a mass of 64.93 amu. What is the atomic weight of copper?

2.53 Naturally occurring lithium is a mixture of 92.58% Li-7 with a mass of 7.016 amu and 7.42% Li-6 with a mass of 6.015 amu. What is the atomic weight of lithium?

THE PERIODIC TABLE

2.54 Why does the third period in the periodic table contain eight elements?

2.55 Why does the fourth period in the periodic table contain 18 elements?

2.56 Americium, atomic number 95, is used in household smoke detectors. What is the symbol for americium? Is americium a metal, a nonmetal, or a metalloid?

2.57 What subshell is being filled for the metalloid elements?

2.58 Answer the following questions for the elements from scandium through zinc:

(a) Are they metals or nonmetals?

(b) To what general class of elements do they belong?

(c) What subshell is being filled by electrons in these elements?

2.59 Answer the following questions for the elements from cerium through lutetium:

(a) Are they metals or nonmetals?

(b) To what general class of elements do they belong?

(c) What subshell is being filled by electrons in these elements?

2.60 For **(a)** rubidium **(b)** tungsten, **(c)** germanium, and **(d)** krypton, which of the following terms apply? (i) metal, (ii) nonmetal, (iii) metalloid (iv) transition element, (v) main group element, (vi) noble gas, (vii) alkali metal, (viii) alkaline earth metal.

2.61 For **(a)** calcium, **(b)** palladium, **(c)** carbon, and **(d)** radon, which of the following terms apply? (i) metal, (ii) nonmetal, (iii) metalloid (iv) transition element, (v) main group element, (vi) noble gas, (vii) alkali metal, (viii) alkaline earth metal.

2.62 Name an element in the periodic table that you would expect to be chemically similar to sulfur.

2.63 Name an element in the periodic table that you would expect to be chemically similar to potassium.

2.64 What elements in addition to lithium make up the alkali metal family?

2.65 What elements in addition to fluorine make up the halogen family?

ELECTRON CONFIGURATIONS

2.66 What is the maximum number of electrons that can go into an orbital?

2.67 What are the shapes and locations within an atom of s and p orbitals?

2.68 What is the maximum number of electrons that can go into the first shell? The second shell? The third shell?

2.69 What is the total number of orbitals in the third shell? The fourth shell?

2.70 How many subshells are there in the third shell? The fourth shell? The fifth shell?

2.71 How many orbitals would you expect to find in the last subshell of the fifth shell? How many electrons would you need to fill this subshell?

2.72 How many electrons are present in an atom with its $1s$, $2s$, and $2p$ subshells filled? What is this element?

2.73 How many electrons are present in an atom with its $1s$, $2s$, $2p$, $3s$, $3p$, and $4s$ subshells filled and with two electrons in the $3d$ subshell? What is this element?

2.74 Use arrows to show electron pairing in the valence p subshell of

(a) Sulfur

(b) Bromine

(c) Silicon

2.75 Use arrows to show electron pairing in the $5s$ and $4d$ orbitals of

(a) Rubidum

(b) Niobium

(c) Rhodium

2.76 Determine the number of unpaired electrons for each of the atoms in Problems 2.74 and 2.75.

2.77 Without looking back in the text, write the electron configurations for the following:

(a) Titanium $Z = 22$ (b) Phosphorus, $Z = 15$

(c) Argon, $Z = 18$ (d) Lanthanum, $Z = 57$

2.78 How many electrons does the element with $Z = 12$ have in its valence shell? Write the electron-dot symbol for this element.

2.79 How many valence electrons do group 4A elements have? Explain. Write a generic electron-dot symbol for elements in this group.

2.80 Identify the valence subshell occupied by electrons in beryllium and arsenic atoms.

2.81 What group in the periodic table has the valence-shell configuration $ns^2\,np^3$?

2.82 Give the number of valence electrons and draw electron-dot symbols for atoms of the following elements:

(a) Kr   (b) C

(c) Ca   (d) K

(e) B   (f) Cl

2.83 Using n for the number of the valence shell, write a general valence-shell configuration for the elements in group 6A and in group 2A.

CHEMISTRY IN ACTION

2.84 What is the advantage of using a scanning tunneling microscope rather than a normal light microscope? [*Are Atoms Real? p. 48*]

2.85 For the Kanji character in the lower portion of the figure on p. 48: (a) How wide is the character in terms of iron atoms? (b) Given the radius of an iron atom is 126 pm, calculate the width of this character in centimeters. [*Are Atoms Real? p. 48*]

2.86 What are the first two elements that are made in stars? [*The Origin of Chemical Elements, p. 56*]

2.87 How are elements heavier than iron made? [*The Origin of Chemical Elements, p. 56*]

2.88 Which type of electromagnetic energy in the following pairs is of higher energy? [*Atoms and Light, p. 66*]

(a) Infrared, ultraviolet

(b) Gamma waves, microwaves

(c) Visible light, X rays

2.89 Why do you suppose ultraviolet rays from the sun are more damaging to the skin than visible light? [*Atoms and Light, p. 66*]

GENERAL QUESTIONS AND PROBLEMS

2.90 What elements in addition to helium make up the noble gas family?

2.91 Hydrogen is placed in group 1A on many periodic charts, even though it is not an alkali metal. On other periodic charts, however, hydrogen is included with group 7A even though it is not a halogen. Explain. (Hint: draw electron-dot symbols for H and for the 1A and 7A elements.)

2.92 Tellurium ($Z = 52$) has a *lower* atomic number than iodine ($Z = 53$), yet it has a *higher* atomic weight (127.60 amu for Te versus 126.90 amu for I). How is this possible?

2.93 What is the atomic number of the yet-undiscovered element directly below francium (Fr) in the periodic table?

2.94 Give the number of electrons in each shell for lead.

2.95 Identify the highest-energy occupied subshell in atoms of the following elements:

(a) Iodine   (b) Scandium

(c) Arsenic   (d) Aluminum

2.96 What is the atomic weight of naturally occurring bromine, which contains 50.69% Br-79 of mass 78.92 amu and 49.31% Br-81 of mass 80.91 amu?

2.97 (a) What is the mass (in amu and in grams) of a single atom of Carbon-12?

(b) What is the mass (in grams) of 6.02×10^{23} atoms of Carbon-12?

(c) Based on your answer to part (b), what would be the mass of 6.02×10^{23} atoms of Sodium-23?

2.98 An unidentified element is found to have an electron configuration by shell of 2 8 18 8 2. To what group and period does this element belong? Is the element a metal or a nonmetal? How many protons does an atom of the element have? What is the name of the element? Write its electron-dot symbol.

2.99 Germanium, atomic number 32, is used in building semiconductors for microelectronic devices, and has an electron configuration by shell of 2 8 18 4.

(a) Write the electronic configuration for germanium.

(b) In what shell and orbitals are the valence electrons?

2.100 Tin, atomic number 50, is directly beneath germanium (Problem 2.99) in the periodic table. What electron configuration by shell would you expect tin to have? Is tin a metal or a nonmetal?

2.101 A blood sample is found to contain 8.6 mg/dL of Ca. How many atoms of Ca are present in 8.6 mg? The atomic weight of Ca is 40.08 amu.

2.102 What is wrong with the following electron configurations?

(a) Ni $1s^2\,2s^2\,2p^6\,3s^2\,3p^6\,3d^{10}$

(b) N $1s^2\,2p^5$

(c) Si $1s^2\,2s^2\,2p$ $\underline{\uparrow\downarrow}$ $\underline{}$ $\underline{}$

(d) Mg $1s^2\,2s^2\,2p^6\,3s$ $\underline{\uparrow\uparrow}$

2.103 Not all elements follow exactly the electron-filling order described in Figure 2.7. Atoms of which elements are represented by the following electron configurations?

(a) $1s^2\,2s^2\,2p^6\,3s^2\,3p^6\,3d^5\,4s^1$

(b) $1s^2\,2s^2\,2p^6\,3s^2\,3p^6\,3d^{10}\,4s^1$

(c) $1s^2\,2s^2\,2p^6\,3s^2\,3p^6\,3d^{10}\,4s^2\,4p^6\,4d^5\,5s^1$

(d) $1s^2\,2s^2\,2p^6\,3s^2\,3p^6\,3d^{10}\,4s^2\,4p^6\,4d^{10}\,5s^1$

2.104 What similarities do you see in the electron configurations for the atoms in Problem 2.103? How might these similarities explain their anomalous electron configurations?

2.105 Based on the identity of the elements whose electron configurations are given in Problem 2.103, write the electron configurations for the element with atomic number $Z = 79$.

2.106 What orbital is filled last in the most recently discovered element 117?

Ionic Compounds

CONTENTS

◄ Stalagmites and stalactites, such as these in a cave in the Nangu Stone Forest in China, are composed of the ionic compounds calcium carbonate, $CaCO_3$, and magnesium carbonate, $MgCO_3$.

There are more than 19 million known chemical compounds, ranging in size from small *diatomic* (two-atom) substances like carbon monoxide, CO, to deoxyribonucleic acid (DNA), which can contain several *billion* atoms linked together in a precise way. Clearly, there must be some force that holds atoms together in compounds; otherwise, the atoms would simply drift apart and no compounds could exist. The forces that hold atoms together in compounds are called *chemical bonds* and are of two major types: *ionic bonds* and *covalent bonds*. In this chapter, we look at ionic bonds and at the substances formed by them. In the next chapter, we will look at covalent bonds.

All chemical bonds result from the electrical attraction between opposite charges—between positively charged nuclei and negatively charged electrons. As a result, the way that different elements form bonds is related to their different electron configurations and the changes that take place as each atom tries to achieve a more stable electron configuration.

3.1 Ions

A general rule noted by early chemists is that metals, on the left side of the periodic table, tend to form compounds with nonmetals, on the right side of the table. The alkali metals of group 1A, for instance, react with the halogens of group 7A to form a variety of compounds. Sodium chloride (table salt), formed by the reaction of sodium with chlorine, is a familiar example. The names and chemical formulas of some other compounds containing elements from groups 1A and 7A include:

Potassium iodide, KI	Added to table salt to provide the iodide ion that is needed by the thyroid gland
Sodium fluoride, NaF	Added to many municipal water supplies to provide fluoride ion for the prevention of tooth decay
Sodium iodide, NaI	Used in laboratory scintillation counters to detect radiation (See Section 11.8)

The compositions and the properties of these alkali metal–halogen compounds are similar. For instance, the two elements always combine in a 1:1 ratio: one alkali metal atom for every halogen atom. Each compound has a high melting point (all are over 500 °C); each is a stable, white, crystalline solid; and each is soluble in water.

▲ A solution of sodium chloride in water conducts electricity, allowing the bulb to light.

Ion An electrically charged atom or group of atoms.

Cation A positively charged ion.

Anion A negatively charged ion.

Furthermore, a water solution containing each compound conducts electricity, a property that gives a clue to the kind of chemical bond holding the atoms together.

Electricity can only flow through a medium containing charged particles that are free to move. The electrical conductivity of metals, for example, results from the movement of negatively charged electrons through the metal. But what charged particles might be present in the water solutions of alkali metal–halogen compounds? To answer this question, think about the composition of atoms. Atoms are electrically neutral because they contain equal numbers of protons and electrons. By gaining or losing one or more electrons, however, an atom can be converted into a charged particle called an **ion**.

The *loss* of one or more electrons from a neutral atom gives a *positively* charged ion called a **cation** (**cat**-ion). As we saw in Section 2.8, sodium and other alkali metal atoms have a single electron in their valence shell and an electron configuration symbolized as ns^1, where n represents the shell number. By losing this electron, an alkali metal is converted to a positively charged cation.

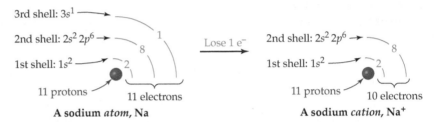

A sodium *atom*, Na   **A sodium *cation*, Na$^+$**

Conversely, the *gain* of one or more electrons by a neutral atom gives a *negatively* charged ion called an **anion** (**an**-ion). Chlorine and other halogen atoms have ns^2np^5 valence electrons and can easily gain an additional electron to fill out their valence subshell, thereby forming negatively charged anions.

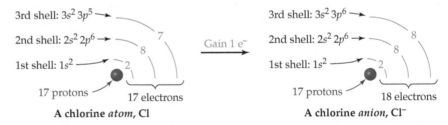

A chlorine *atom*, Cl   **A chlorine *anion*, Cl$^-$**

The symbol for a cation is written by adding the positive charge as a superscript to the symbol for the element; an anion symbol is written by adding the negative charge as a superscript. If one electron is lost or gained, the charge is $+1$ or -1 but the number 1 is omitted in the notation, as in Na$^+$ and Cl$^-$. If two or more electrons are lost or gained, however, the charge is ± 2 or greater and the number *is* used, as in Ca^{2+} and N^{3-}.

PROBLEM 3.1
Magnesium atoms lose two electrons when they react. Write the symbol of the ion that is formed. Is it a cation or an anion?

PROBLEM 3.2
Sulfur atoms gain two electrons when they react. Write the symbol of the ion that is formed. Is it a cation or an anion?

🔑 **KEY CONCEPT PROBLEM 3.3**

Write the symbol for the ion depicted here. Is it a cation or an anion?

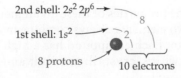

3.2 Periodic Properties and Ion Formation

The ease with which an atom loses an electron to form a positively charged cation is measured by a property called the atom's **ionization energy**, defined as the energy required to remove one electron from a single atom in the gaseous state. Conversely, the ease with which an atom *gains* an electron to form a negatively charged anion is measured by a property called **electron affinity**, defined as the energy released on adding an electron to a single atom in the gaseous state.

Ionization energy The energy required to remove one electron from a single atom in the gaseous state.

Electron affinity The energy released on adding an electron to a single atom in the gaseous state.

Ionization energy
(energy is added)
$$\text{Atom} + \text{Energy} \xrightarrow{\text{Gain } e^-} \text{Cation} + \text{Electron}$$

Electron affinity
(energy is relased)
$$\text{Atom} + \text{Electron} \xrightarrow{\text{Lose } e^-} \text{Anion} + \text{Energy}$$

The relative magnitudes of ionization energies and electron affinities for elements in the first four rows of the periodic table are shown in Figure 3.1. Because ionization energy measures the amount of energy that must be *added* to pull an electron away from a neutral atom, the small values shown in Figure 3.1 for alkali metals (Li, Na, K) and other elements on the left side of the periodic table mean that these elements lose an electron easily. Conversely, the large values shown for halogens (F, Cl, Br) and noble gases (He, Ne, Ar, Kr) on the right side of the periodic table mean that these elements do not lose an electron easily. Electron affinities, however, measure the amount of energy *released* when an atom gains an electron. Although electron affinities are small compared to ionization energies, the halogens nevertheless have the largest values and therefore gain an electron most easily, whereas metals have the smallest values and do not gain an electron easily:

Alkali metal
{
Small ionization energy—electron easily lost
Small electron affinity—electron not easily gained
Net result: Cation formation is favored
}

Halogen
{
Large ionization energy—electron not easily lost
Large electron affinity—electron easily gained
Net result: Anion formation is favored
}

You might also note in Figure 3.1 that main group elements near the *middle* of the periodic table—boron $(Z = 5,$ group 3A) carbon $(Z = 6,$ group 4A), and nitrogen $(Z = 7,$ group 5A) —neither lose nor gain electrons easily and thus do not form ions easily. In the next chapter, we will see that these elements tend not to form ionic bonds but form covalent bonds instead.

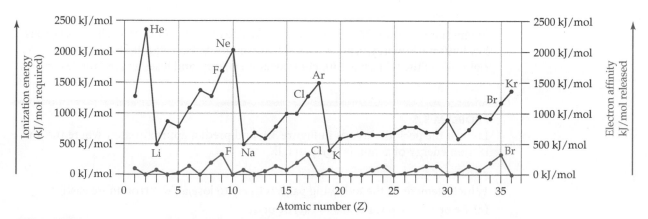

▲ **Figure 3.1**
Relative ionization energies (red) and electron affinities (blue) for elements in the first four rows of the periodic table.
Those elements having a value of zero for electron affinity do not accept an electron. Note that the alkali metals (Li, Na, K) have the lowest ionization energies and lose an electron most easily, whereas the halogens (F, Cl, Br) have the highest electron affinities and gain an electron most easily. The noble gases (He, Ne, Ar, Kr) neither gain nor lose an electron easily.

Because alkali metals such as sodium tend to lose an electron, and halogens such as chlorine tend to gain an electron, these two elements (sodium and chlorine) will react with each other by transfer of an electron from the metal to the halogen (Figure 3.2). The product that results—sodium chloride (NaCl)—is electrically neutral because the positive charge of each Na^+ ion is balanced by the negative charge of each Cl^- ion.

▶ **Figure 3.2**
(a) Chlorine is a toxic green gas, sodium is a reactive metal, and sodium chloride is a harmless white solid. (b) Sodium metal burns with an intense yellow flame when immersed in chlorine gas, yielding white sodium chloride "smoke."

(a)   (b)

Worked Example 3.1 Periodic Trends: Ionization Energy

Look at the periodic trends in Figure 3.1, and predict where the ionization energy of rubidium is likely to fall on the chart.

ANALYSIS Identify the group number of rubidium (group 1A), and find where other members of the group appear in Figure 3.1.

SOLUTION
Rubidium (Rb) is the alkali metal below potassium (K) in the periodic table. Since the alkali metals Li, Na, and K all have ionization energies near the bottom of the chart, the ionization energy of rubidium is probably similar.

Worked Example 3.2 Periodic Trends: Formation of Anions and Cations

Which element is likely to lose an electron more easily, Mg or S?

ANALYSIS Identify the group numbers of the elements, and find where members of those groups appear in Figure 3.1.

SOLUTION
Magnesium, a group 2A element on the left side of the periodic table, has a relatively low ionization energy, and loses an electron easily. Sulfur, a group 6A element on the right side of the table, has a higher ionization energy, and loses an electron less easily.

PROBLEM 3.4
Look at the periodic trends in Figure 3.1, and predict approximately where the ionization energy of xenon is likely to fall.

PROBLEM 3.5
Which element in the following pairs is likely to lose an electron more easily?
(a) Be or B   **(b)** Ca or Co   **(c)** Sc or Se

PROBLEM 3.6
Which element in the following pairs is likely to gain an electron more easily?
(a) H or He   **(b)** S or Si   **(c)** Cr or Mn

3.3 Ionic Bonds

When sodium reacts with chlorine, the product is sodium chloride, a compound completely unlike either of the elements from which it is formed. Sodium is a soft, silvery metal that reacts violently with water, and chlorine is a corrosive, poisonous, green gas (Figure 3.2a). When chemically combined, however, they produce our familiar table salt containing Na^+ ions and Cl^- ions. Because opposite electrical charges attract each other, the positive Na^+ ion and negative Cl^- ion are said to be held together by an **ionic bond**.

When a vast number of sodium atoms transfer electrons to an equally vast number of chlorine atoms, a visible crystal of sodium chloride results. In this crystal, equal numbers of Na^+ and Cl^- ions are packed together in a regular arrangement. Each positively charged Na^+ ion is surrounded by six negatively charged Cl^- ions, and each Cl^- ion is surrounded by six Na^+ ions (Figure 3.3). This packing arrangement allows each ion to be stabilized by the attraction of unlike charges on its six nearest-neighbor ions, while being as far as possible from ions of like charge.

Ionic bond The electrical attractions between ions of opposite charge in a crystal.

◄ **Figure 3.3**
The arrangement of Na^+ and Cl^- ions in a sodium chloride crystal. Each positively charged Na^+ ion is surrounded by six negatively charged Cl^- ions, and each Cl^- ion is surrounded by six Na^+ ions. The crystal is held together by ionic bonds—the attraction between oppositely charged ions.

Because of the three-dimensional arrangement of ions in a sodium chloride crystal, we cannot speak of specific ionic bonds between specific pairs of ions. Rather, there are many ions attracted by ionic bonds to their nearest neighbors. We therefore speak of the whole NaCl crystal as being an **ionic solid** and of such compounds as being **ionic compounds**. The same is true of all compounds composed of ions.

Ionic solid A crystalline solid held together by ionic bonds.

Ionic compound A compound that contains ionic bonds.

3.4 Some Properties of Ionic Compounds

Like sodium chloride, ionic compounds are usually crystalline solids. Different ions vary in size and charge, therefore, they are packed together in crystals in different ways. The ions in each compound settle into a pattern that efficiently fills space and maximizes ionic bonding.

Because the ions in an ionic solid are held rigidly in place by attraction to their neighbors, they cannot move about. Once an ionic solid is dissolved in water, however, the ions can move freely, thereby accounting for the electrical conductivity of these compounds in solution.

The high melting points and boiling points observed for ionic compounds are also accounted for by ionic bonding. The attractive force between oppositely charged particles is extremely strong, and the ions need to gain a large amount of energy by being heated to high temperatures for them to loosen their grip on one another. Sodium chloride, for example, melts at 801 °C and boils at 1413 °C; potassium iodide melts at 681 °C and boils at 1330 °C.

▲ **The melting point of sodium chloride is 801 °C.**

Despite the strength of ionic bonds, ionic solids shatter if struck sharply. A blow disrupts the orderly arrangement of cations and anions, forcing particles of like electrical charge closer together. The close proximity of like charges creates repulsive energies that split the crystal apart.

Ionic compounds dissolve in water if the attraction between water and the ions overcomes the attraction of the ions for one another. Compounds like sodium chloride are very soluble in water and can be dissolved to make solutions of high concentration. Do not be misled, however, by the ease with which sodium chloride and other familiar ionic compounds dissolve in water. Many other ionic compounds, such as magnesium hydroxide or barium sulfate, are not water-soluble, because the attractive forces between these ions and water is not sufficient to overcome the ionic attractions in the crystals.

PROBLEM 3.7
Consider the ionic liquids described in the Chemistry in Action below. How are the properties of these ionic liquids different from other common ionic substances?

CHEMISTRY IN ACTION

Ionic Liquids

Imagine a substance that could help solve the problems of nuclear waste, make solar energy more efficient, revolutionize the development of biomass-based renewable energies, serve as a solvent for enzyme-based biochemical transformations, and act as a major component in a spinning-liquid mirror telescope stationed on the moon. Ionic liquids can do all that—and more! When discussing ionic substances, most of us think of hard, crystalline materials like common table salt (see Chemistry in Action, p. 83), with high melting points. But ionic liquids have very different properties, including low melting points, high viscosity, low-to-moderate electrical conductivity, and low volatility, which make them suitable for the widely varied uses described previously.

Although the details of the discovery of ionic liquids are in dispute, one of the first *room temperature ionic liquids* (or RTILs), ethylammonium nitrate, was synthesized in 1914 by Paul Walden. Most RTILs developed since then consist of a bulky, asymmetric organic cation (see Organic Chemistry in Chapters 12–19), combined with a variety of anions. The bulky cations cannot pack together in an ordered fashion, and so these substances do not condense into a solid at ambient temperatures. Rather, they tend to form highly viscous liquids that exhibit low volatility, ideal properties for a large-diameter spinning liquid mirror in a low-pressure environment like the moon. The viscous liquid can be covered

with a thin metallic film that will form a parabolic reflective surface to collect long-wavelength infrared light. And the cost of the spinning-liquid mirror is about 1% of a conventional lens, which must be ground and polished.

The bulky cations also provide unique solvent properties, enabling them to dissolve substances that are not very soluble in more conventional solvents. Their low volatility also makes them attractive as "green," or environmentally friendly, solvents. Consider the practice of using biomass as a fuel source. One common approach is to convert sugar or starch (from corn, beets, or cane sugar) into ethanol by the process of fermentation. But the major component of these and most other plants is cellulose. Cellulose is a polymer (see Chemistry in Action on pp. 118 and 538) composed of many sugars joined together in a long chain. Cellulose is chemically similar to starch but is neither highly soluble in most solvents nor subject to fermentation. RTILs, however, such as that illustrated in the figure below, can be used to dissolve cellulose at moderate temperatures and facilitate its breakdown into simple fermentable sugars. At a volume of nearly 700 billion tons of the earth's biomass, cellulose represents an important renewable energy source. The ability to convert cellulose into fuel will certainly help meet our expanding energy needs.

See Chemistry in Action Problems 3.80 and 3.81 at the end of the chapter.

Benzylmethylimidazolium chloride

◄ **Pine wood fibers dissolving in an ionic liquid solvent consisting of benzyl methyl imidazolium chloride, whose structural formula is shown.**

3.5 Ions and the Octet Rule

We have seen that alkali metal atoms have a single valence-shell electron, ns^1. The electron-dot symbol X· is consistent with this valence electron configuration. Halogens, having seven valence electrons, ns^2np^5, can be represented using $:\ddot{X}·$ as the electron-dot symbol. Noble gases can be represented as $:\ddot{X}:$, since they have eight valence electrons, ns^2np^6. Both the alkali metals and the halogens are extremely reactive, undergoing many chemical reactions and forming many compounds. The noble gases, however, are quite different. They are the least reactive of all elements.

Now look at sodium chloride and similar ionic compounds. When sodium or any other alkali metal reacts with chlorine or any other halogen, the metal transfers an electron from its valence shell to the valence shell of the halogen. Sodium thereby changes its valence-shell electron configuration from $2s^22p^63s^1$ in the atom to $2s^22p^6(3s^0)$ in the Na^+ ion, and chlorine changes from $3s^23p^5$ in the atom to $3s^23p^6$ in the Cl^- ion. *As a result, both sodium and chlorine gain noble gas electron configurations, with 8 valence electrons.* The Na^+ ion has 8 electrons in the $n = 2$ shell, matching the electron configuration of neon. The Cl^- ion has 8 electrons in the $n = 3$ shell, matching the electron configuration of argon.

$$\underset{1s^2\,2s^2\,2p^6\,3s^1}{Na} + \underset{1s^2\,2s^2\,2p^6\,3s^2\,3p^5}{Cl} \longrightarrow \underset{\underbrace{1s^2\,2s^2\,2p^63s^0}_{\substack{\text{Neon}\\\text{configuration}}}}{Na^+} + \underset{\underbrace{1s^2\,2s^2\,2p^6\,3s^2\,3p^6}_{\substack{\text{Argon}\\\text{configuration}}}}{Cl^-}$$

$$Na· \quad + \quad ·\ddot{\underset{..}{Cl}}: \quad \longrightarrow \quad Na^+ \quad + \quad :\ddot{\underset{..}{Cl}}:^-$$

Evidently there is something special about having 8 valence electrons (filled s and p subshells) that leads to stability and lack of chemical reactivity. In fact, observations of many chemical compounds have shown that main group elements frequently combine in such a way that each winds up with 8 valence electrons, a so-called *electron octet*. This conclusion is summarized in a statement called the **octet rule**:

Octet rule Main group elements tend to undergo reactions that leave them with 8 valence electrons.

Put another way, main group *metals* tend to lose electrons when they react so that they attain an electron configuration like that of the noble gas just *before* them in the periodic table, and reactive main group *nonmetals* tend to gain electrons when they react so that they attain an electron configuration like that of the noble gas just *after* them in the periodic table. In both cases, the product ions have filled s and p subshells in their valence electron shell.

Worked Example 3.3 Electron Configurations: Octet Rule for Cations

Write the electron configuration of magnesium $(Z = 12)$. Show how many electrons a magnesium atom must lose to form an ion with a filled shell (8 electrons), and write the configuration of the ion. Explain the reason for the ion's charge, and write the ion's symbol.

ANALYSIS Write the electron configuration of magnesium as described in Section 2.7 and count the number of electrons in the valence shell.

SOLUTION
Magnesium has the electron configuration $1s^22s^22p^63s^2$. Since the second shell contains an octet of electrons $(2s^22p^6)$ and the third shell is only partially filled $(3s^2)$, magnesium can achieve a valence-shell octet by losing the 2 electrons in the

3*s* subshell. The result is formation of a doubly charged cation, Mg^{2+}, with the neon configuration:

$$Mg^{2+} \qquad 1s^2 2s^2 2p^6 \text{ (Neon configuration, or } [\text{Ne}])$$

A neutral magnesium atom has 12 protons and 12 electrons. With the loss of 2 electrons, there is an excess of 2 protons, accounting for the +2 charge of the ion, Mg^{2+}.

Worked Example 3.4 Electron Configurations: Octet Rule for Anions

How many electrons must a nitrogen atom, $Z = 7$, gain to attain a noble gas configuration? Write the electron-dot and ion symbols for the ion formed.

ANALYSIS Write the electron configuration of nitrogen, and identify how many more electrons are needed to reach a noble gas configuration.

SOLUTION
Nitrogen, a group 5A element, has the electron configuration $1s^2 2s^2 2p^3$. The second shell contains 5 electrons $(2s^2 2p^3)$ and needs 3 more to reach an octet. The result is formation of a triply charged anion, N^{3-}, with 8 valence electrons, matching the neon configuration:

$$N^{3-} \qquad 1s^2 2s^2 2p^6 \quad \text{(Neon configuration)} \quad :\underset{\cdot\cdot}{\ddot{N}}:^{3-}$$

PROBLEM 3.8
Write the electron configuration of potassium, $Z = 19$, and show how a potassium atom can attain a noble gas configuration.

PROBLEM 3.9
How many electrons must an aluminum atom, $Z = 13$, lose to attain a noble gas configuration? Write the symbol for the ion formed.

KEY CONCEPT PROBLEM 3.10

Which atom in the reaction depicted here gains electrons, and which loses electrons? Draw the electron-dot symbols for the resulting ions.

$$X: + \cdot\underset{\cdot\cdot}{\ddot{Y}}\cdot \rightarrow ?$$

3.6 Ions of Some Common Elements

The periodic table is the key to understanding and remembering which elements form ions and which do not. As shown in Figure 3.4, atoms of elements in the same group tend to form ions of the same charge. The metals of groups 1A and 2A, for example, form only +1 and +2 ions, respectively. The ions of these elements

1A	2A											3A	4A	5A	6A	7A	8A
1 H^+																	2
3 Li^+	4 Be^{2+}											5	6	7	8 O^{2-}	9 F^-	10
11 Na^+	12 Mg^{2+}	Transition metals										13 Al^{3+}	14	15	16 S^{2-}	17 Cl^-	18
19 K^+	20 Ca^{2+}	21 Sc^{3+}	22 Ti^{4+}	23 V^{2+}	24 Cr^{2+} Cr^{3+}	25 Mn^{2+}	26 Fe^{2+} Fe^{3+}	27 Co^{2+}	28 Ni^{2+}	29 Cu^{2+}	30 Zn^{2+}	31	32	33	34 Se^{2-}	35 Br^-	36

▸ **Figure 3.4**
Common ions formed by elements in the first four periods.
Ions important in biological chemistry are shown in red.

all have noble gas configurations as a result of electron loss from their valence *s* subshells. (Note in the following equations that the electrons being lost are shown as products.)

Group 1A: $M \cdot \rightarrow M^+ + e^-$
$(M = Li, Na, K, Rb, or Cs)$

Group 2A: $M : \rightarrow M^{2+} + 2e^-$
$(M = Be, Mg, Ca, Sr, Ba, or Ra)$

Four of these ions, Na^+, K^+, Mg^{2+}, and Ca^{2+}, are present in body fluids, where they play extremely important roles in biochemical processes.

The only group 3A element commonly encountered in ionic compounds is aluminum, which forms Al^{3+} by loss of three electrons from its valence *s* and *p* subshells. Aluminum is not thought to be an essential element in the human diet, although it is known to be present in some organisms.

The first three elements in groups 4A (C, Si, Ge) and 5A (N, P, As) do not ordinarily form cations or anions, because either too much energy is required to remove an electron or not enough energy is released by adding an electron to make the process energetically favorable. The bonding of these elements is largely covalent and will be described in the next chapter. Carbon, in particular, is the key element on which life is based. Together with hydrogen, nitrogen, phosphorus, and oxygen, carbon is present in all the essential biological compounds that we will be describing throughout the latter half of this book.

The group 6A elements, oxygen and sulfur, form large numbers of compounds, some of which are ionic and some of which are covalent. Their ions have noble gas configurations, achieved by gaining two electrons:

Group 6A: $\cdot \ddot{O} \cdot + 2 e^- \longrightarrow \; : \ddot{O} :^{2-}$

$\cdot \ddot{S} \cdot + 2 e^- \longrightarrow \; : \ddot{S} :^{2-}$

The halogens are present in many compounds as ions formed by gaining one electron:

Group 7A: $\cdot \ddot{X} : + \; e^- \longrightarrow \; : \ddot{X} :^{-}$
$(X = F, Cl, Br, I)$

Transition metals lose electrons to form cations, some of which are present in the human body. The charges of transition metal cations are not as predictable as those of main group elements, however, because many transition metal atoms can lose one or more *d* electrons in addition to losing valence *s* electrons. For example, iron $(\ldots 3s^2 3p^6 3d^6 4s^2)$ forms Fe^{2+} by losing two electrons from the 4*s* subshell and also forms Fe^{3+} by losing an additional electron from the 3*d* subshell. Looking at the electron configuration for iron shows why the octet rule is limited to main group elements: transition metal cations generally do not have noble gas configurations because they would have to lose *all* their *d* electrons.

Important Points about Ion Formation and the Periodic Table:

- **Metals form cations by losing one or more electrons.**
  - Group 1A and 2A metals form +1 and +2 ions, respectively (for example, Li^+ and Mg^{2+}) to achieve a noble gas configuration.
  - Transition metals can form cations of more than one charge (for example, Fe^{2+} and Fe^{3+}) by losing a combination of valence-shell *s* electrons and inner-shell *d* electrons.

- **Reactive nonmetals form anions by gaining one or more electrons to achieve a noble gas configuration.**
  - Group 6A nonmetals oxygen and sulfur form the anions O^{2-} and S^{2-}.
  - Group 7A elements (the halogens) form −1 ions; for example, F^- and Cl^-.

- **Group 8A elements (the noble gases) are unreactive.**
- **Ionic charges of main group elements can be predicted using the group number and the octet rule.**
  - For 1A and 2A metals: cation charge = group number
  - For nonmetals in groups 5A, 6A, and 7A: anion charge = 8 − (group number)

Worked Example 3.5 Formation of Ions: Gain/Loss of Valence Electrons

Which of the following ions is likely to form?

(a) S^{3-} **(b)** Si^{2+} **(c)** Sr^{2+}

ANALYSIS Count the number of valence electrons in each ion. For main group elements, only ions with a valence octet of electrons are likely to form.

SOLUTION

(a) Sulfur is in group 6A, has 6 valence electrons, and needs only 2 more to reach an octet. Gaining 2 electrons gives an S^{2-} ion with a noble gas configuration, but gaining 3 electrons does not. The S^{3-} ion is, therefore, unlikely to form.

(b) Silicon is a nonmetal in group 4A. Like carbon, it does not form ions because it would have to gain or lose too many electrons (4) to reach a noble gas electron configuration. The Si^{2+} ion does not have an octet and will not form.

(c) Strontium, a metal in group 2A, has only 2 outer-shell electrons and can lose both to reach a noble gas configuration. The Sr^{2+} ion has an octet and, therefore, forms easily.

PROBLEM 3.11
Is molybdenum more likely to form a cation or an anion? Why?

PROBLEM 3.12
Write symbols, both with and without electron dots, for the ions formed by the following processes:
(a) Gain of 2 electrons by selenium   **(b)** Loss of 2 electrons by barium
(c) Gain of 1 electron by bromine

PROBLEM 3.13
By mass, seawater contains 3.5% NaCl, or table salt (see Chemistry in Action, p. 83). If one liter of seawater contains 35 g of NaCl, how many gallons of water must be evaporated to produce one pound of NaCl?

3.7 Naming Ions

Main group metal cations in groups 1A, 2A, and 3A are named by identifying the metal, followed by the word "ion," as in the following examples:

$$K^+ \qquad Mg^{2+} \qquad Al^{3+}$$
Potassium ion   Magnesium ion   Aluminum ion

It is sometimes a little confusing to use the same name for both a metal and its ion, and you may occasionally have to stop and think about what is meant. For example, it is common practice in nutrition and health-related fields to talk about sodium or potassium in the bloodstream. Because both sodium and potassium *metals* react violently with water, however, they cannot possibly be present in blood. The references are to dissolved sodium and potassium *ions*.

Transition metals, such as iron or chromium, and many metals found in the *p*-block, such as tin and lead, can form more than one type of cation. To avoid confusion, a method is needed to differentiate between ions of these metals. Two systems are used. The first is an old system that gives the ion with the smaller charge the word ending *-ous* and the ion with the larger charge the ending *-ic*.

CHEMISTRY IN ACTION

Salt

If you are like most people, you feel a little guilty about reaching for the salt shaker at mealtime. The notion that high salt intake and high blood pressure go hand in hand is surely among the most highly publicized pieces of nutritional lore ever to appear.

Salt has not always been held in such disrepute. Historically, salt has been prized since the earliest recorded times as a seasoning and a food preservative. Words and phrases in many languages reflect the importance of salt as a life-giving and life-sustaining substance. We refer to a kind and generous person as "the salt of the earth," for instance, and we speak of being "worth one's salt." In Roman times, soldiers were paid in salt; the English word "salary" is derived from the Latin word for paying salt wages (*salarium*).

Salt is perhaps the easiest of all minerals to obtain and purify. The simplest method, used for thousands of years throughout the world in coastal climates where sunshine is abundant and rainfall is scarce, is to evaporate seawater. Though the exact amount varies depending on the source, seawater contains an average of about 3.5% by mass of dissolved substances, most of which is sodium chloride. It has been estimated that evaporation of all the world's oceans would yield approximately *4.5 million cubic miles* of NaCl.

Only about 10% of current world salt production comes from evaporation of seawater. Most salt is obtained by mining the vast deposits of *halite*, or *rock salt,* formed by evaporation of ancient inland seas. These salt beds vary in thickness up to hundreds of meters and vary in depth from a few meters to thousands of meters below the earth's surface. Salt mining has gone on for at least 3400 years, and the Wieliczka mine in Galicia, Poland, has been worked continuously from A.D. 1000 to the present.

What about the link between dietary salt intake and high blood pressure? Although sodium is a macronutrient that we need—it plays a critical role in charge balance and ion transport in cell membranes—too much sodium has been linked to both hypertension and kidney ailments. The recommended daily intake (RDI) for sodium is 2300 mg, which translates to roughly 4 g of salt. However, the average adult in most industrialized countries consumes over twice this amount, with most of it coming from processed foods.

What should an individual do? The best answer, as in so many things, is to use moderation and common sense. People with hypertension should make a strong effort to lower their

▲ **In many areas of the world, salt is still harvested by evaporation of ocean or tidal waters.**

■ 5% added while cooking

■ 6% added while eating

□ 12% from natural sources

□ 77% from processed and prepared foods

sodium intake; others might be well advised to choose unsalted snacks, monitor their consumption of processed food, and read nutrition labels for sodium content.

See Chemistry in Action Problem 3.82 at the end of the chapter.

The second is a newer system in which the charge on the ion is given as a Roman numeral in parentheses right after the metal name. For example:

	Cr^{2+}	Cr^{3+}
Old name:	Chrom*ous* ion	Chrom*ic* ion
New name:	Chromium(II) ion	Chromium(III) ion

We will generally emphasize the new system in this book, but it is important to understand both systems because the old system is often found on labels of commercially supplied chemicals. The small differences between the names in either system illustrate the importance of reading a name very carefully before using a chemical. There are significant differences between compounds consisting of the same two elements but having different charges on the cation. In treating iron-deficiency anemia, for example, iron(II) compounds are preferable because the body absorbs them considerably better than iron(III) compounds.

The names of some common transition metal cations are listed in Table 3.1. Notice that the old names of the copper, iron, and tin ions are derived from their Latin names (*cuprum, ferrum,* and *stannum*).

TABLE 3.1 Names of Some Transition Metal Cations

Element	Symbol	Old Name	New Name
Chromium	Cr^{2+}	Chromous	Chromium(II)
	Cr^{3+}	Chromic	Chromium(III)
Copper	Cu^+	Cuprous	Copper(I)
	Cu^{2+}	Cupric	Copper(II)
Iron	Fe^{2+}	Ferrous	Iron(II)
	Fe^{3+}	Ferric	Iron(III)
Mercury	*Hg_2^{2+}	Mercurous	Mercury(I)
	Hg^{2+}	Mercuric	Mercury(II)
Tin	Sn^{2+}	Stannous	Tin(II)
	Sn^{4+}	Stannic	Tin(IV)

*This cation is composed of two mercury atoms, each of which has an average charge of +1.

Anions are named by replacing the ending of the element name with *-ide*, followed by the word "ion" (Table 3.2). For example, the anion formed by fluor*ine* is the fluor*ide* ion, and the anion formed by sulf*ur* is the sulf*ide* ion.

TABLE 3.2 Names of Some Common Anions

Element	Symbol	Name
Bromine	Br^-	Bromide ion
Chlorine	Cl^-	Chloride ion
Fluorine	F^-	Fluoride ion
Iodine	I^-	Iodide ion
Oxygen	O^{2-}	Oxide ion
Sulfur	S^{2-}	Sulfide ion

PROBLEM 3.14
Name the following ions:

(a) Cu^{2+} (b) F^- (c) Mg^{2+} (d) S^{2-}

PROBLEM 3.15
Write the symbols for the following ions:

(a) Silver(I) ion   (b) Iron(II) ion   (c) Cuprous ion   (d) Telluride ion

PROBLEM 3.16
Ringer's solution, which is used intravenously to adjust ion concentrations in body fluids, contains the ions of sodium, potassium, calcium, and chlorine. Give the names and symbols of these ions.

3.8 Polyatomic Ions

Ions that are composed of more than one atom are called **polyatomic ions**. Most polyatomic ions contain oxygen and another element, and their chemical formulas include subscripts to show how many of each type of atom are present. Sulfate ion, for example, is composed of 1 sulfur atom and 4 oxygen atoms and has a -2 charge: $SO_4{}^{2-}$. The atoms in a polyatomic ion are held together by covalent bonds of the sort discussed in the next chapter, and the entire group of atoms acts as a single unit. A polyatomic ion is charged because it contains a total number of electrons different from the total number of protons in the combined atoms.

The most common polyatomic ions are listed in Table 3.3. Note that the ammonium ion, $NH_4{}^+$, and the hydronium ion, H_3O^+, are the only cations; all the others are anions. These ions are encountered so frequently in chemistry, biology, and medicine that there is no alternative but to memorize their names and formulas. Fortunately, there are only a few of them.

Polyatomic ion An ion that is composed of more than one atom.

TABLE 3.3 Some Common Polyatomic Ions

Name	Formula	Name	Formula
Hydronium ion	H_3O^+	Nitrate ion	$NO_3{}^-$
Ammonium ion	$NH_4{}^+$	Nitrite ion	$NO_2{}^-$
Acetate ion	$CH_3CO_2{}^-$	Oxalate ion	$C_2O_4{}^{2-}$
Carbonate ion	$CO_3{}^{2-}$	Permanganate ion	$MnO_4{}^-$
Hydrogen carbonate ion (bicarbonate ion)	$HCO_3{}^-$	Phosphate ion	$PO_4{}^{3-}$
Chromate ion	$CrO_4{}^{2-}$	Hydrogen phosphate ion (biphosphate ion)	$HPO_4{}^{2-}$
Dichromate ion	$Cr_2O_7{}^{2-}$	Dihydrogen phosphate ion	$H_2PO_4{}^-$
Cyanide ion	CN^-	Sulfate ion	$SO_4{}^{2-}$
Hydroxide ion	OH^-	Hydrogen sulfate ion (bisulfate ion)	$HSO_4{}^-$
Hypochlorite ion	OCl^-	Sulfite ion	$SO_3{}^{2-}$

Note in Table 3.3 that several pairs of ions—$CO_3{}^{2-}$ and $HCO_3{}^-$, for example—are related by the presence or absence of a hydrogen ion, H^+. In such instances, the ion with the hydrogen is sometimes named using the prefix *bi-*. Thus, $CO_3{}^{2-}$ is the carbonate ion, and $HCO_3{}^-$ is the bicarbonate ion; similarly, $SO_4{}^{2-}$ is the sulfate ion, and $HSO_4{}^-$ is the bisulfate ion.

PROBLEM 3.17

Name the following ions:

(a) $NO_3{}^-$
(b) CN^-
(c) OH^-
(d) $HPO_4{}^{2-}$

PROBLEM 3.18

Which of the biologically important ions (see Chemistry in Action, p. 86) belong to Group 1A? To Group 2A? To the transition metals? To the halogens?

CHEMISTRY IN ACTION

Biologically Important Ions

The human body requires many different ions for proper functioning. Several of these ions, such as Ca^{2+}, Mg^{2+}, and HPO_4^{2-}, are used as structural materials in bones and teeth in addition to having other essential functions. Although 99% of Ca^{2+} is contained in bones and teeth, small amounts in body fluids play a vital role in transmission of nerve impulses. Other ions, including essential transition metal ions such as Fe^{2+}, are required for specific chemical reactions in the body. And still others, such as K^+, Na^+, and Cl^-, are present in fluids throughout the body.

In order to maintain charge neutrality in solution, the total negative charge (from anions) must balance the total positive charge (from cations). Several monatomic anions, and several polyatomic anions, especially HCO_3^- and HPO_4^{2-}, are present in body fluids where they help balance the cation charges. Some of the most important ions and their functions are shown in the accompanying table.

See Chemistry in Action Problems 3.83, 3.84, and 3.85 at the end of the chapter.

Some Biologically Important Ions

Ion	Location	Function	Dietary source
Ca^{2+}	Outside cell; 99% of Ca^{2+} is in bones and teeth as $Ca_3(PO_4)_2$ and $CaCO_3$	Bone and tooth structure; necessary for blood clotting, muscle contraction, and transmission of nerve impulses	Milk, whole grains, leafy vegetables
Fe^{2+}	Blood hemoglobin	Transports oxygen from lungs to cells	Liver, red meat, leafy green vegetables
K^+	Fluids inside cells	Maintain ion concentrations in cells; regulate insulin release and heartbeat	Milk, oranges, bananas, meat
Na^+	Fluids outside cells	Protect against fluid loss; necessary for muscle contraction and transmission of nerve impulses	Table salt, seafood
Mg^{2+}	Fluids inside cells; bone	Present in many enzymes; needed for energy generation and muscle contraction	Leafy green plants, seafood, nuts
Cl^-	Fluids outside cells; gastric juice	Maintain fluid balance in cells; help transfer CO_2 from blood to lungs	Table salt, seafood
HCO_3^-	Fluids outside cells	Control acid–base balance in blood	By-product of food metabolism
HPO_4^{2-}	Fluids inside cells; bones and teeth	Control acid–base balance in cells	Fish, poultry, milk

3.9 Formulas of Ionic Compounds

Since all chemical compounds are neutral, it is relatively easy to figure out the formulas of ionic compounds. Once the ions are identified, all we need to do is decide how many ions of each type give a total charge of zero. Thus, the chemical formula of an ionic compound tells the ratio of anions and cations.

If the ions have the same charge, only one of each ion is needed:

$$K^+ \text{ and } F^- \text{ form } KF$$
$$Ca^{2+} \text{ and } O^{2-} \text{ form } CaO$$

This makes sense when we look at how many electrons must be gained or lost by each atom in order to satisfy the octet rule:

$$K\cdot \; + \; \cdot \ddot{\underset{\cdot\cdot}{F}}: \; \longrightarrow \; K^+ \; + \; :\ddot{\underset{\cdot\cdot}{F}}:^-$$
$$\cdot Ca\cdot \; + \; \cdot \ddot{O} \cdot \; \longrightarrow \; Ca^{2+} \; + \; :\ddot{\underset{\cdot\cdot}{O}}:^{2-}$$

If the ions have different charges, however, unequal numbers of anions and cations must combine in order to have a net charge of zero. When potassium and oxygen combine, for example, it takes two K^+ ions to balance the -2 charge of the O^{2-} ion. Put another way, it takes two K atoms to provide the two electrons needed in order to complete the octet for the O atom:

$$2\,K\cdot \; + \; \cdot\ddot{O}\cdot \; \longrightarrow \; 2\,K^+ + \; :\ddot{O}:^{2-}$$

$$2\,K^+ \quad \text{and} \quad O^{2-} \quad \text{form} \quad K_2O$$

The situation is reversed when a Ca^{2+} ion reacts with a Cl^- ion. One Ca atom can provide two electrons; each Cl atom requires only one electron to achieve a complete octet. Thus, there is one Ca^{2+} cation for every two Cl^- anions:

$$\cdot Ca\cdot \; + \; 2\cdot\ddot{Cl}: \; \longrightarrow \; Ca^{2+} + \; 2\,:\ddot{Cl}:^-$$

$$Ca^{2+} \quad \text{and} \quad 2Cl^- \quad \text{form} \quad CaCl_2$$

It sometimes helps when writing the formulas for an ionic compound to remember that, when the two ions have different charges, the number of one ion is equal to the charge on the other ion. In magnesium phosphate, for example, the charge on the magnesium ion is +2 and the charge on the polyatomic phosphate ion is −3. Thus, there must be 3 magnesium ions with a total charge of 3 × (+2) = +6, and 2 phosphate ions with a total charge of 2 × (−3) = −6 for overall neutrality:

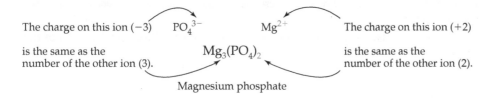

The charge on this ion (−3) $PO_4{}^{3-}$ Mg^{2+} The charge on this ion (+2)

is the same as the number of the other ion (3). $Mg_3(PO_4)_2$ is the same as the number of the other ion (2).

Magnesium phosphate

The formula of an ionic compound shows the lowest possible ratio of atoms in the compound and is thus known as a *simplest formula*. Because there is no such thing as a single neutral *particle* of an ionic compound, however, we use the term **formula unit** to identify the smallest possible neutral *unit* (Figure 3.5). For NaCl, the formula unit is 1 Na^+ ion and 1 Cl^- ion; for K_2SO_4, the formula unit is 2 K^+ ions and 1 $SO_4{}^{2-}$ ion; for CaF_2, the formula unit is 1 Ca^{2+} ion and 2 F^- ions; and so on.

Formula unit The formula that identifies the smallest neutral unit of an ionic compound.

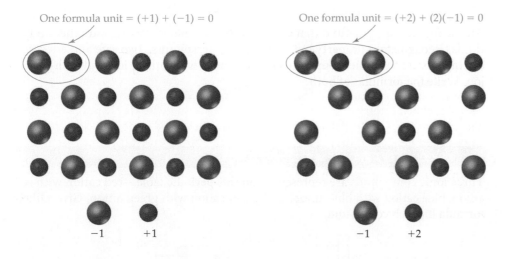

One formula unit = (+1) + (−1) = 0   One formula unit = (+2) + (2)(−1) = 0

−1   +1   −1   +2

Figure 3.5
Formula units of ionic compounds.
The sum of charges on the ions in a formula unit equals zero.

Once the numbers and kinds of ions in a compound are known, the formula is written using the following rules:

- List the cation first and the anion second; for example, NaCl rather than ClNa.
- Do not write the charges of the ions; for example, KF rather than K^+F^-.
- Use parentheses around a polyatomic ion formula if it has a subscript; for example, $Al_2(SO_4)_3$ rather than Al_2SO_{43}.

Worked Example **3.6** Ionic Compounds: Writing Formulas

Write the formula for the compound formed by calcium ions and nitrate ions.

ANALYSIS Knowing the formula and charges on the cation and anion (Figure 3.4), we determine how many of each are needed to yield a neutral formula for the ionic compound.

SOLUTION
The two ions are Ca^{2+} and NO_3^-. Two nitrate ions, each with a -1 charge, will balance the $+2$ charge of the calcium ion.

$$Ca^{2+} \qquad \text{Charge} = 1 \times (+2) = +2$$
$$2NO_3^- \qquad \text{Charge} = 2 \times (-1) = -2$$

Since there are 2 ions, the nitrate formula must be enclosed in parentheses:

$$Ca(NO_3)_2 \qquad \text{Calcium nitrate}$$

PROBLEM 3.19
Write the formulas for the ionic compounds that silver(I) forms with each of the following:
(a) Iodide ion   **(b)** Oxide ion   **(c)** Phosphate ion

PROBLEM 3.20
Write the formulas for the ionic compounds that sulfate ion forms with the following:
(a) Sodium ion   **(b)** Iron(II) ion   **(c)** Chromium(III) ion

PROBLEM 3.21
The ionic compound containing ammonium ion and carbonate ion gives off the odor of ammonia, a property put to use in smelling salts for reviving someone who has fainted. Write the formula for this compound.

PROBLEM 3.22
An *astringent* is a compound that causes proteins in blood, sweat, and other body fluids to coagulate, a property put to use in antiperspirants. Two safe and effective astringents are the ionic compounds of aluminum with sulfate ion and with acetate ion. Write the formulas of both.

🔑 **KEY CONCEPT PROBLEM 3.23**

Three ionic compounds are represented on this periodic table—red cation with red anion, blue cation with blue anion, and green cation with green anion. Give a likely formula for each compound.

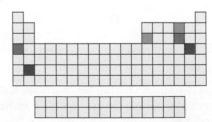

The ionic compound calcium nitride is represented here. What is the formula for calcium nitride, and what are the charges on the calcium and nitride ions?

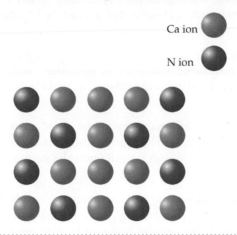

Ca ion

N ion

3.10 Naming Ionic Compounds

Just as in writing formulas for ionic compounds, these compounds are named by citing first the cation and then the anion, with a space between words. There are two kinds of ionic compounds, and the rules for naming them are slightly different.

Type I: Ionic compounds containing cations of main group elements (1A, 2A, aluminum). Since the charges on these cations do not vary, we do not need to specify the charge on the cation as discussed in Section 3.7. For example, NaCl is sodium chloride and $MgCO_3$ is magnesium carbonate.

Type II: Ionic compounds containing metals that can exhibit more than one charge. Since some metals, including the transition metals, often form more than one ion, we need to specify the charge on the cation in these compounds. Either the old (-ous, -ic) or the new (Roman numerals) system described in Section 3.7 can be used. Thus, $FeCl_2$ is called iron(II) chloride (or ferrous chloride), and $FeCl_3$ is called iron(III) chloride (or ferric chloride). Note that we do *not* name these compounds iron *di*chloride or iron *tri*chloride—once the charge on the metal is known, the number of anions needed to yield a neutral compound is also known and does not need to be included as part of the compound name. Table 3.4 lists some common ionic compounds and their uses.

TABLE 3.4 Some Common Ionic Compounds and Their Applications

Chemical Name (Common Name)	Formula	Applications
Ammonium carbonate	$(NH_4)_2CO_3$	Smelling salts
Calcium hydroxide (hydrated lime)	$Ca(OH)_2$	Mortar, plaster, whitewash
Calcium oxide (lime)	CaO	Lawn treatment, industrial chemical
Lithium carbonate ("lithium")	Li_2CO_3	Treatment of bipolar disorder
Magnesium hydroxide (milk of magnesia)	$Mg(OH)_2$	Antacid
Magnesium sulfate (Epsom salts)	$MgSO_4$	Laxative, anticonvulsant
Potassium permanganate	$KMnO_4$	Antiseptic, disinfectant*
Potassium nitrate (saltpeter)	KNO_3	Fireworks, matches, and desensitizer for teeth
Silver nitrate	$AgNO_3$	Antiseptic, germicide
Sodium bicarbonate (baking soda)	$NaHCO_3$	Baking powder, antacid, mouthwash, deodorizer
Sodium hypochlorite	NaOCl	Disinfectant; active ingredient in household bleach
Zinc oxide	ZnO	Skin protection, in calamine lotion

*Antiseptics and disinfectants can also be harmful/toxic to non-harmful microorganisms, but are used specifically to prevent infection from harmful microorganisms.

LOOKING AHEAD ▶▶▶ Because the formula unit for an ionic compound must be neutral, we can unambiguously write the formula from the name of the compound, and vice versa. As we shall see in Chapter 4, covalent bonding between atoms can produce a much greater variety of compounds. The rules for naming covalent compounds must be able to accommodate multiple combinations of elements (for example, CO and CO_2).

Worked Example 3.7 Ionic Compounds: Formulas Involving Polyatomic Ions

Magnesium carbonate is used as an ingredient in Bufferin (buffered aspirin) tablets. Write its formula.

ANALYSIS Since magnesium is a main group metal, we can determine its ionic compound formula by identifying the charges and formulas for the anion and the cation, remembering that the overall formula must be neutral.

SOLUTION
Look at the cation and the anion parts of the name separately. Magnesium, a group 2A element, forms the doubly positive Mg^{2+} cation; carbonate anion is doubly negative, CO_3^{2-} Because the charges on the anion and cation are equal, a formula of $MgCO_3$ will be neutral.

Worked Example 3.8 Ionic Compounds: Formulas and Ionic Charges

Sodium and calcium both form a wide variety of ionic compounds. Write formulas for the following compounds:

(a) Sodium bromide and calcium bromide
(b) Sodium sulfide and calcium sulfide
(c) Sodium phosphate and calcium phosphate

ANALYSIS Using the formulas and charges for the cations and the anions (from Tables 3.2 and 3.3), we determine how many of each cation and anion are needed to yield a formula that is neutral.

SOLUTION
(a) Cations = Na^+ and Ca^{2+}; anion = Br^-: NaBr and $CaBr_2$
(b) Cations = Na^+ and Ca^{2+}; anion = S^{2-}: Na_2S and CaS
(c) Cations = Na^+ and Ca^{2+}; anion = PO_4^{3-}: Na_3PO_4 and $Ca_2(PO_4)_2$

Worked Example 3.9 Naming Ionic Compounds

Name the following compounds, using Roman numerals to indicate the charges on the cations where necessary:

(a) KF   **(b)** $MgCl_2$ **(c)** $AuCl_3$ **(d)** Fe_2O_3

ANALYSIS For main group metals, the charge is determined from the group number, and no Roman numerals are necessary. For transition metals, the charge on the metal can be determined from the total charge(s) on the anion(s).

SOLUTION
(a) Potassium fluoride. No Roman numeral is necessary because a group 1A metal forms only one cation.
(b) Magnesium chloride. No Roman numeral is necessary because magnesium (group 2A) forms only Mg^{2+}.

(c) Gold(III) chloride. The 3 Cl$^-$ ions require a +3 charge on the gold for a neutral formula. Since gold is a transition metal that can form other ions, the Roman numeral is necessary to specify the +3 charge.

(d) Iron(III) oxide. Because the 3 oxide anions (O^{2-}) have a total negative charge of -6, the 2 iron cations must have a total charge of +6. Thus, each is Fe^{3+}, and the charge on each is indicated by the Roman numeral (III).

PROBLEM 3.25
The compound Ag$_2$S is responsible for much of the tarnish found on silverware. Name this compound, and give the charge on the silver ion.

PROBLEM 3.26
Name the following compounds:

(a) SnO$_2$ (b) Ca(CN)$_2$ (c) Na$_2$CO$_3$
(d) Cu$_2$SO$_4$ (e) Ba(OH)$_2$ (f) Fe(NO$_3$)$_2$

PROBLEM 3.27
Write formulas for the following compounds:

(a) Lithium phosphate   (b) Copper(II) carbonate
(c) Aluminum sulfite   (d) Cuprous fluoride
(e) Ferric sulfate   (f) Ammonium chloride

KEY CONCEPT PROBLEM 3.28

The ionic compound, formed between chromium and oxygen is shown here. Name the compound, and write its formula.

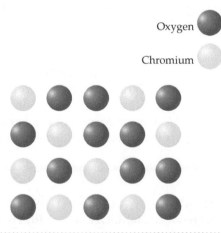

Oxygen

Chromium

3.11 H$^+$ and OH$^-$ Ions: An Introduction to Acids and Bases

Two of the most important ions we will be discussing in the remainder of this book are the hydrogen cation (H^+) and the hydroxide anion (OH^-). Since a hydrogen *atom* contains one proton and one electron, a hydrogen *cation* is simply a proton. When an acid dissolves in water, the proton typically attaches to a molecule of water to form the hydronium ion (H_3O^+), but chemists routinely use the H$^+$ and H$_3$O$^+$ ions interchangeably. A hydroxide anion, by contrast, is a polyatomic ion in which an oxygen atom is covalently bonded to a hydrogen atom. Although much of Chapter 10 is devoted to the chemistry of H$^+$ and OH$^-$ ions, it is worth taking a preliminary look now.

◀◀◀ In Chapter 10 we will look at the chemical behavior of acids and bases and their importance in many areas of chemistry.

Acid A substance that provides H^+ ions in water;

Base A substance that provides OH^- ions in water

The importance of the H^+ cation and the OH^- anion is that they are fundamental to the concepts of *acids* and *bases*. In fact, one definition of an **acid** is a substance that provides H^+ ions when dissolved in water; for example, HCl, HNO_3, H_2SO_4, H_3PO_4. One definition of a **base** is a substance that provides OH^- ions when dissolved in water; for example, NaOH, KOH, $Ba(OH)_2$.

Hydrochloric acid (HCl), nitric acid (HNO_3) sulfuric acid (H_2SO_4), and phosphoric acid (H_3PO_4) are among the most common acids. When any of these substances is dissolved in water, H^+ ions are formed along with the corresponding anion (Table 3.5).

TABLE 3.5 Some Common Acids and the Anions Derived from Them

Acids		Anions	
Acetic acid	CH_3COOH	Acetate ion	*CH_3COO^-
Carbonic acid	H_2CO_3	Hydrogen carbonate ion (bicarbonate ion) Carbonate ion	CO_3^{2-}
Hydrochloric acid	HCl	Chloride ion	Cl^-
Nitric acid	HNO_3	Nitrate ion	NO_3^-
Nitrous acid	HNO_2	Nitrite ion	NO_2^-
Phosphoric acid	H_3PO_4	Dihydrogen phosphate ion Hydrogen phosphate ion Phosphate ion	$H_2PO_4^-$ HPO_4^{2-} PO_4^{3-}
Sulfuric acid	H_2SO_4	Hydrogen sulfate ion Sulfate ion	HSO_4^- SO_4^{2-}

*Sometimes written $C_2H_3O_2^-$ or as $CH_3CO_2^-$.

Different acids can provide different numbers of H^+ ions per acid molecule. Hydrochloric acid, for instance, provides one H^+ ion per acid molecule; sulfuric acid can provide two H^+ ions per acid molecule; and phosphoric acid can provide three H^+ ions per acid molecule.

▶▶▶ The behavior of polyprotic acids, or acids that provide more than one H^+ ion per acid molecule, will be discussed in more detail in Chapter 10.

Sodium hydroxide (NaOH; also known as *lye* or *caustic soda*), potassium hydroxide (KOH; also known as *caustic potash*), and barium hydroxide $[Ba(OH)_2]$ are examples of bases. When any of these compounds dissolves in water, OH^- anions go into solution along with the corresponding metal cation. Sodium hydroxide and potassium hydroxide provide one OH^- ion per formula unit; barium hydroxide provides two OH^- ions per formula unit, as indicated by its formula, $Ba(OH)_2$.

PROBLEM 3.29
Which of the following compounds are acids, and which are bases? Explain.
(a) HF   (b) $Ca(OH)_2$ (c) LiOH   (d) HCN

KEY CONCEPT PROBLEM 3.30

One of these pictures represents a solution of HCl, and one represents a solution of H_2SO_4. Which is which?

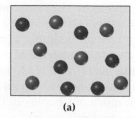

(a)

(b)

CHEMISTRY IN ACTION

Osteoporosis

Bone consists primarily of two components, one mineral and one organic. About 70% of bone is the ionic compound *hydroxyapatite,* $Ca_{10}(PO_4)_6(OH)_2$, called the *trabecular,* or spongy, bone. This mineral component is intermingled in a complex matrix with about 30% by mass of fibers of the protein *collagen,* called the *cortical,* or compact, bone. Hydroxyapatite gives bone its hardness and strength, whereas collagen fibers add flexibility and resistance to breaking.

Total bone mass in the body increases from birth until reaching a maximum in the mid-30s. By the early 40s, however, an age-related decline in bone mass begins to occur in both sexes. Bone density decreases, and the microarchitecture of bones is disrupted, resulting in weakening of bone structure, particularly in the wrists, hips, and spine. Should this thinning of bones become too great and the bones become too porous and brittle, a clinical condition called *osteoporosis* can result. Osteoporosis is, in fact, the most common of all bone diseases, affecting approximately 25 million people in the United States. Approximately 1.5 million bone fractures each year are caused by osteoporosis, at an estimated healthcare cost of $14 billion.

Although both sexes are affected by osteoporosis, the condition is particularly common in postmenopausal women, who undergo bone loss at a rate of 2–3% per year over and above that of the normal age-related loss. The cumulative lifetime bone loss, in fact, may approach 40–50% in women versus 20–30% in men. It has been estimated that half of all women over age 50 will have an osteoporosis-related bone fracture at some point in their life. Other risk factors, in addition to sex,

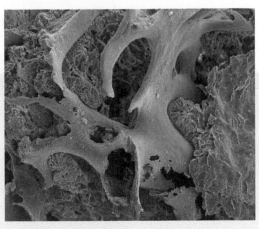

▲ **Normal bone is strong and dense; a bone affected by osteoporosis, shown here, is weak and spongy in appearance.**

include being thin, being sedentary, having a family history of osteoporosis, smoking, and having a diet low in calcium.

No cure exists for osteoporosis, but treatment for its prevention and management includes estrogen-replacement therapy for postmenopausal women as well as several approved medications called *bisphosphonates* that bind to the calcium in bone, slowing down bone loss by inhibiting the action of *osteoclasts,* or cells that break down bone tissue. Calcium supplements are also recommended, as is appropriate weight-bearing exercise. In addition, treatment with sodium fluoride is under active investigation and shows considerable promise. Fluoride ion reacts with hydroxyapatite to give *fluorapatite,* in which OH^- ions are replaced by F^-, increasing both bone strength and density.

$$Ca_{10}(PO_4)_6(OH)_2 + 2\ F^- \longrightarrow Ca_{10}(PO_4)_6F_2$$
Hydroxyapatite   Fluorapatite

See Chemistry in Action Problems 3.86 and 3.87 at the end of the chapter.

SUMMARY: REVISITING THE CHAPTER GOALS

1. What is an ion, what is an ionic bond, and what are the general characteristics of ionic compounds? Atoms are converted into *cations* by the loss of one or more electrons and into *anions* by the gain of one or more electrons. Ionic compounds are composed of cations and anions held together by *ionic bonds,* which result from the attraction between opposite electrical charges. Ionic compounds conduct electricity when dissolved in water, and they are generally crystalline solids with high melting points and high boiling points (*see Problems 33, 35, 38–41, 80, 81, 95–97*).

2. What is the octet rule, and how does it apply to ions? A valence-shell electron configuration of 8 electrons in filled *s* and *p* subshells leads to stability and lack of reactivity, as typified by the noble gases in group 8A. According to the *octet rule,*

atoms of main group elements tend to form ions in which they have gained or lost the appropriate number of electrons to reach a noble gas configuration (*see Problems 42–49, 88, 89*).

3. What is the relationship between an element's position in the periodic table and the formation of its ion? Periodic variations in *ionization energy,* the amount of energy that must be supplied to remove an electron from an atom, show that metals lose electrons more easily than nonmetals. As a result, metals usually form cations. Similar periodic variations in *electron affinity,* the amount of energy released on adding an electron to an atom, show that reactive nonmetals gain electrons more easily than metals. As a result, reactive nonmetals usually form anions. The ionic charge can be predicted from the group number and the octet rule. For main group metals, the charge on the cation is equal to the group number. For nonmetals, the charge on the anion is equal to 8 − (group number) (see Problems 31, 32, 36, 40, 41, 50–57, 88, 89, 96).

4. What determines the chemical formula of an ionic compound? Ionic compounds contain appropriate numbers of anions and cations to maintain overall neutrality, thereby providing a means of determining their chemical formulas (see Problems 36, 37, 64, 65, 68, 69, 86, 87, 90, 92, 94).

5. How are ionic compounds named? Cations have the same name as the metal from which they are derived. Monatomic anions have the name ending -ide. For metals that form more than one ion, a Roman numeral equal to the charge on the ion is added to the name of the cation. Alternatively, the

ending -ous is added to the name of the cation with the lesser charge and the ending -ic is added to the name of the cation with the greater charge. To name an ionic compound, the cation name is given first, with the charge of the metal ion indicated if necessary, and the anion name is given second (see Problems 36, 58-63, 66, 68, 70–75, 93, 94).

6. What are acids and bases? The hydrogen ion (H^+) and the hydroxide ion (OH^-) are among the most important ions in chemistry because they are fundamental to the idea of acids and bases. According to one common definition, an *acid* is a substance that yields H^+ ions when dissolved in water, and a *base* is a substance that yields OH^- ions when dissolved in water (see Problems 76–79, 91).

KEY WORDS

Acid, *p. 92*

Anion, *p. 74*

Base, *p. 92*

Cation, *p. 74*

Electron affinity, *p. 75*

Formula unit, *p. 87*

Ion, *p. 74*

Ionic bond, *p. 77*

Ionic compound, *p. 77*

Ionic solid, *p. 77*

Ionization energy, *p. 75*

Octet rule, *p. 79*

Polyatomic ion, *p. 85*

UNDERSTANDING KEY CONCEPTS

3.31 Where on the blank outline of the periodic table are the following elements found?

    (a) Elements that commonly form only one type of cation

    (b) Elements that commonly form anions

    (c) Elements that can form more than one type of cation

    (d) Elements that do not readily form either anions or cations

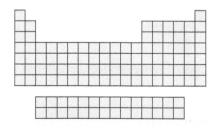

3.32 Where on the blank outline of the periodic table are the following elements found?

    (a) Elements that commonly form +2 ions

    (b) Elements that commonly form −2 ions

    (c) An element that forms a +3 ion

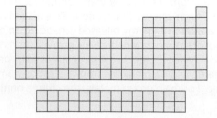

3.33 Write the symbols for the ions represented in the following drawings.

    (a)   (b)   (c)   (d)

3.34 One of these drawings represents an Na atom, and one represents an Na^+ ion. Tell which is which, and explain why there is a difference in size.

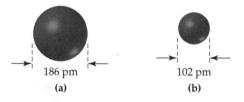

    186 pm   102 pm

    (a)   (b)

3.35 One of these drawings represents a Cl atom, and one represents a Cl^- ion. Tell which is which, and explain why there is a difference in size.

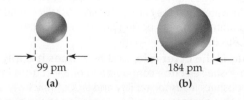

    99 pm   184 pm

    (a)   (b)

3.36   The elements in red in the periodic table can form cations having more than one charge. Write the formulas and names of the compounds that are formed between the red cations and the blue anions depicted in the periodic table.

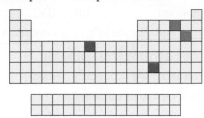

3.37   Each of these drawings (a)–(d) represents one of the following ionic compounds: $PbBr_2$, ZnS, CrF_3, Al_2O_3. Which is which?

(a)   (b)   (c)

(d)

ADDITIONAL PROBLEMS

IONS AND IONIC BONDING

3.38   Write equations for loss or gain of electrons by atoms that result in formation of the following ions:

(a) Ca^{2+} (b) Au^+

(c) F^- (d) Cr^{3+}

3.39   Write electronic configurations and symbols for the ions formed by the following:

(a) Gain of 3 electrons by phosphorus

(b) Loss of 1 electron by lithium

(c) Loss of 2 electrons by cobalt

(d) Loss of 3 electrons by thallium

3.40   Tell whether each statement about ions is true or false. If a statement is false, explain why.

(a) A cation is formed by addition of one or more electrons to an atom.

(b) Group 4A elements tend to lose 4 electrons to yield ions with a +4 charge.

(c) Group 4A elements tend to gain 4 electrons to yield ions with a −4 charge.

(d) The individual atoms in a polyatomic ion are held together by covalent bonds.

3.41   Tell whether each statement about ionic solids is true or false. If a statement is false, explain why.

(a) Ions are randomly arranged in ionic solids.

(b) All ions are the same size in ionic solids.

(c) Ionic solids can often be shattered by a sharp blow.

(d) Ionic solids have low boiling points.

IONS AND THE OCTET RULE

3.42   What is the *octet rule*?

3.43   Why do H and He not obey the octet rule?

3.44   Write the symbol for an ion that contains 34 protons and 36 electrons.

3.45   What is the charge of an ion that contains 21 protons and 19 electrons?

3.46   Identify the element X in the following ions, and tell which noble gas has the same electron configuration.

(a) X^{2+}, a cation with 36 electrons

(b) X^-, an anion with 36 electrons

3.47   Element Z forms an ion Z^{3+}, which contains 31 protons. What is the identity of Z, and how many electrons does Z^{3+} have?

3.48   Write the electron configuration for the following ions:

(a) Rb^+ (b) Br^-

(c) S^{2-} (d) Ba^{2+}

(e) Al^{3+}

3.49   Based on the following atomic numbers and electronic configurations, write the symbols for the following ions:

(a) Z = 20; $1s^2\ 2s^2\ 2p^6\ 3s^2\ 3p^6$

(b) Z = 8; $1s^2\ 2s^2\ 2p^6$

(c) Z = 22; $1s^2\ 2s^2\ 2p^6\ 3s^2\ 3p^6\ 3d^2$

(d) Z = 19; $1s^2\ 2s^2\ 2p^6\ 3s^2\ 3p^6$

(e) Z = 13; $1s^2\ 2s^2\ 2p^6$

PERIODIC PROPERTIES AND ION FORMATION

3.50   Looking only at the periodic table, tell which member of each pair of atoms has the larger ionization energy and thus loses an electron less easily:

(a) Li and O   (b) Li and Cs

(c) K and Zn   (d) Mg and N

3.51   Looking only at the periodic table, tell which member of each pair of atoms has the larger electron affinity and thus gains an electron more easily:

(a) Li and S

(b) Ba and I

(c) Ca and Br

3.52 Which of the following ions are likely to form? Explain.

(a) Li^{2+} (b) K^-

(c) Mn^{3+} (d) Zn^{4+}

(e) Ne^+

3.53 What is the charge on the cation formed from the following elements? For those elements that form more than one cation, indicate the ionic charges most commonly observed.

(a) Magnesium   (b) Tin

(c) Mercury   (d) Aluminum

3.54 Write the electron configurations of Cr^{2+} and Cr^{3+}.

3.55 Write the electron configurations of Co, Co^{2+} and Co^{3+}.

3.56 Would you expect the ionization energy of Li^+ to be less than, greater than, or the same as the ionization energy of Li? Explain.

3.57 (a) Write equations for the loss of an electron by a K atom and the gain of an electron by a K^+ ion.

(b) What is the relationship between the equations?

(c) What is the relationship between the ionization energy of a K atom and the electron affinity of a K^+ ion?

SYMBOLS, FORMULAS, AND NAMES FOR IONS

3.58 Name the following ions:

(a) S^{2-} (b) Sn^{2+} (c) Sr^{2+}

(d) Mg^{2+} (e) Au^+

3.59 Name the following ions in both the old and the new systems:

(a) Cr^{2+} (b) Fe^{3+} (c) Hg^{2+}

3.60 Write symbols for the following ions:

(a) Selenide ion   (b) Oxide ion

(c) Silver(I) ion

3.61 Write symbols for the following ions:

(a) Ferrous ion   (b) Tin(IV) ion

(c) Lead(II) ion   (d) Chromic ion

3.62 Write formulas for the following ions:

(a) Hydroxide ion   (b) Bisulfate ion

(c) Acetate ion   (d) Permanganate ion

(e) Hypochlorite ion   (f) Nitrate ion

(g) Carbonate ion   (h) Dichromate ion

3.63 Name the following ions:

(a) NO_2^- (b) CrO_4^{2-} (c) NH_4^+ (d) HPO_4^{2-}

NAMES AND FORMULAS FOR IONIC COMPOUNDS

3.64 Write formulas for the compounds formed by the sulfate ion with the following cations:

(a) Aluminum   (b) Silver(I)

(c) Zinc   (d) Barium

3.65 Write formulas for the compounds formed by the carbonate ion with the following cations:

(a) Strontium   (b) Fe(III)

(c) Ammonium   (d) Sn(IV)

3.66 Write the formula for the following substances:

(a) Sodium bicarbonate (baking soda)

(b) Potassium nitrate (a backache remedy)

(c) Calcium carbonate (an antacid)

(d) Ammonium nitrate (first aid cold packs)

3.67 Write the formula for the following compounds:

(a) Calcium hypochlorite, used as a swimming pool disinfectant

(b) Copper(II) sulfate, used to kill algae in swimming pools

(c) Sodium phosphate, used in detergents to enhance cleaning action

3.68 Complete the table by writing in the formula of the compound formed by each pair of ions:

	S^{2-}	Cl^-	PO_4^{3-}	CO_3^{2-}
Copper(II)	CuS			
Ca^{2+}				
NH_4^+				
Ferric ion				

3.69 Complete the table by writing in the formula of the compound formed by each pair of ions:

	O^{2-}	HSO_4^-	HPO_4^{2-}	$C_2O_4^{2-}$
K^+	K_2O			
Ni^{2+}				
NH_4^+				
Chromous				

3.70 Write the name of each compound in the table for Problem 3.68.

3.71 Write the name of each compound in the table for Problem 3.69.

3.72 Name the following substances:

(a) $MgCO_3$ (b) $Ca(CH_3CO_2)_2$

(c) AgCN   (d) $Na_2Cr_2O_7$

3.73 Name the following substances:

(a) $Fe(OH)_2$ (b) $KMnO_4$

(c) Na_2CrO_4 (d) $Ba_3(PO_4)_2$

3.74 Which of the following formulas is most likely to be correct for calcium phosphate?

(a) Ca_2PO_4 (b) $CaPO_4$

(c) $Ca_2(PO_4)_3$ (d) $Ca_2(PO_4)_2$

3.75 Fill in the missing information to give the correct formula for each compound:

(a) $Al_?(SO_4)_?$ (b) $(NH_4)_?(PO_4)_?$

(c) $Rb_?(SO_4)_?$

ACIDS AND BASES

3.76 What is the difference between an acid and a base?

3.77 Identify the following substances as either an acid or a base:

(a) H_2CO_3 (b) HCN

(c) $Mg(OH)_2$ (d) KOH

3.78 Write equations to show how the substances listed in Problem 3.77 give ions when dissolved in water.

3.79 Name the anions that result when the acids in Problem 3.77 are dissolved in water.

CHEMISTRY IN ACTION

3.80 Most ionic substances are solids at room temperature. Explain why the RTILs discussed in this application are liquids rather than solids. [*Ionic Liquids, p. 78*]

3.81 Ionic liquids are being evaluated for use in a moon-based spinning-liquid telescope. Which properties of ionic liquids make them particularly well-suited for this application? [*Ionic Liquids, p. 78*]

3.82 What is the RDI for sodium for adults, and what amount of table salt (in grams) contains this quantity of sodium? [*Salt, p. 83*]

3.83 Where are most of the calcium ions found in the body? [*Biologically Important Ions, p. 86*]

3.84 Excess sodium ion is considered hazardous, but a certain amount is necessary for normal body functions. What is the purpose of sodium in the body? [*Biologically Important Ions, p. 86*]

3.85 Before a person is allowed to donate blood, a drop of the blood is tested to be sure that it contains a sufficient amount of iron (men, 41 μg/dL; women, 38 μg/dL). What is the biological role of iron, and which ion of iron is involved? [*Biologically Important Ions, p. 86*]

3.86 Name each ion in hydroxyapatite, $Ca_{10}(PO_4)_6(OH)_2$; give its charge; and show that the formula represents a neutral compound. [*Osteoporosis, p. 93*]

3.87 Sodium fluoride reacts with hydroxyapatite to give fluorapatite. What is the formula of fluorapatite? [*Osteoporosis, p. 93*]

GENERAL QUESTIONS AND PROBLEMS

3.88 Explain why the hydride ion, H^-, has a noble gas configuration.

3.89 The H^- ion (Problem 3.88) is stable, but the Li^- ion is not. Explain.

3.90 Many compounds containing a metal and a nonmetal are not ionic, yet they are named using the Roman numeral system for ionic compounds described in Section 3.7. Write the chemical formulas for the following such compounds.

(a) Chromium(VI) oxide

(b) Vanadium(V) chloride

(c) Manganese(IV) oxide

(d) Molybdenum(IV) sulfide

3.91 The arsenate ion has the formula AsO_4^{3-}. Write the formula of the corresponding acid that contains this anion.

3.92 One commercially available calcium supplement contains calcium gluconate, a compound that is also used as an anticaking agent in instant coffee.

(a) If this compound contains 1 calcium ion for every 2 gluconate ions, what is the charge on a gluconate ion?

(b) What is the ratio of iron ions to gluconate ions in iron(III) gluconate, a commercial iron supplement?

3.93 The names given for the following compounds are incorrect. Write the correct name for each compound.

(a) Cu_3PO_4, copper(III) phosphate

(b) Na_2SO_4, sodium sulfide

(c) MnO_2, manganese(II) oxide

(d) $AuCl_3$, gold chloride

(e) $Pb(CO_3)_2$, lead(II) acetate

(f) Ni_2S_3, nickel(II) sulfide

3.94 The formulas given for the following compounds are incorrect. Write the correct formula for each compound.

(a) Cobalt(II) cyanide, $CoCN_2$

(b) Uranium(VI) oxide, UO_6

(c) Tin(II) sulfate, $Ti(SO_4)_2$

(d) Manganese(IV) oxide; MnO_4

(e) Potassium phosphate, K_2PO_4

(f) Calcium phosphide, CaP

(g) Lithium bisulfate, $Li(SO_4)_2$

(h) Aluminum hydroxide; $Al_2(OH)_3$

3.95 How many protons, electrons, and neutrons are in each of these ions?

(a) $^{16}O^{2-}$ (b) $^{89}Y^{3+}$ (c) $^{133}Cs^+$ (d) $^{81}Br^-$

3.96 Element X reacts with element Y to give a product containing X^{3+} ions and Y^{2-} ions.

(a) Is element X likely to be a metal or a nonmetal?

(b) Is element Y likely to be a metal or a nonmetal?

(c) What is the formula of the product?

(d) What groups of the periodic table are elements X and Y likely to be in?

3.97 Identify each of the ions having the following charges and electron configurations:

(a) X^{4+}; $[Ar] 4s^0 3d^3$ (b) X^+; $[Ar] 4s^0 3d^{10}$

(c) X^{4+}; $[Ar] 4s^0 3d^0$

Molecular Compounds

CONTENTS

◄ The Atomium monument in Brussels, Belgium, provides an artistic image of the binding forces between atoms.

1. **What is a covalent bond?**
   THE GOAL: Be able to describe the nature of covalent bonds and how they are formed. (◀◀◀ A, B, C.)

2. **How does the octet rule apply to covalent bond formation?**
   THE GOAL: Be able to use the octet rule to predict the numbers of covalent bonds formed by common main group elements. (◀◀◀ B, C.)

3. **What are the major differences between ionic and molecular compounds?**
   THE GOAL: Be able to compare the structures, compositions, and properties of ionic and molecular compounds.

4. **How are molecular compounds represented?**
   THE GOAL: Be able to interpret molecular formulas and draw Lewis structures for molecules. (◀◀◀ D.)

5. **What is the influence of valence-shell electrons on molecular shape?**
   THE GOAL: Be able to use Lewis structures to predict molecular geometry. (◀◀◀ D.)

6. **When are bonds and molecules polar?**
   THE GOAL: Be able to use electronegativity and molecular geometry to predict bond and molecular polarity. (◀◀◀ A, D.)

A. The Periodic Table
(Sections 2.4 and 2.5)

B. Electron Configurations
(Sections 2.7 and 2.8)

C. The Octet Rule
(Section 3.5)

D. Electron-Dot Symbols
(Section 2.9)

We saw in the preceding chapter that ionic compounds are crystalline solids composed of positively and negatively charged ions. Not all substances, however, are ionic. In fact, with the exception of table salt (NaCl), baking soda ($NaHCO_3$), lime for the garden (CaO), and a few others, most of the compounds around us are *not* crystalline, brittle, high-melting ionic solids. We are much more likely to encounter gases (like those in air), liquids (such as water), low-melting solids (such as butter), and flexible solids (like plastics). All these materials are composed of *molecules* rather than ions, all contain *covalent* bonds rather than ionic bonds, and all consist primarily of nonmetal atoms rather than metals.

4.1 Covalent Bonds

How do we describe the bonding in carbon dioxide, water, polyethylene, and the many millions of nonionic compounds that make up our bodies and much of the world around us? Simply put, the bonds in such compounds are formed by the *sharing* of electrons between atoms (in contrast to ionic bonds, which involve the complete transfer of electrons from one atom to another). The bond formed when atoms share electrons is called a **covalent bond**, and the group of atoms held together by covalent bonds is called a **molecule**. A single molecule of water, for example, contains 2 hydrogen atoms and 1 oxygen atom covalently bonded to one another. We might visualize a water molecule using a space-filling model as shown here:

Covalent bond A bond formed by sharing electrons between atoms.

Molecule A group of atoms held together by covalent bonds.

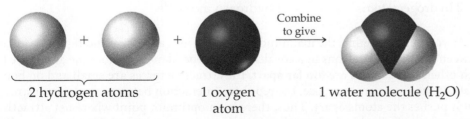

2 hydrogen atoms   +   1 oxygen atom   Combine to give →   1 water molecule (H_2O)

Recall that according to the *octet rule* (Section 3.5), main group elements tend to undergo reactions that leave them with completed outer subshells with 8 valence electrons (or 2 for hydrogen), so that they have a noble gas electron configuration. Although metals and reactive nonmetals can achieve an electron octet by gaining or losing an appropriate number of electrons to form ions, the nonmetals can also achieve an electron octet by *sharing* an appropriate number of electrons in covalent bonds.

As an example of how covalent bond formation occurs, let us look first at the bond between 2 hydrogen atoms in a hydrogen molecule, H_2. Recall that a hydrogen *atom* consists of a positively charged nucleus and a single, negatively charged 1s valence electron, which we represent as H· using the electron-dot symbol. When 2 hydrogen atoms come together, electrical interactions occur. Some of these interactions are repulsive—the 2 positively charged nuclei repel each other, and the 2 negatively charged electrons repel each other. Other interactions, however, are attractive—each nucleus attracts both electrons, and each electron attracts both nuclei (Figure 4.1). Because the attractive forces are stronger than the repulsive forces, a covalent bond is formed, and the hydrogen atoms stay together.

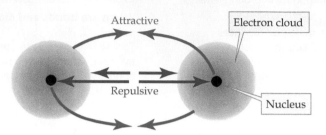

▲ **Figure 4.1**

A covalent H—H bond is the net result of attractive and repulsive forces.
The nucleus–electron attractions (blue arrows) are greater than the nucleus–nucleus and electron–electron repulsions (red arrows), resulting in a net attractive force that holds the atoms together to form an H_2 molecule.

In essence, the electrons act as a kind of "glue" to bind the 2 nuclei together into an H_2 molecule. Both nuclei are simultaneously attracted to the same electrons and are held together, much as two tug-of-war teams pulling on the same rope are held together.

Covalent bond formation in the H—H molecule can be visualized by imagining that the spherical 1s orbitals from the two individual atoms blend together and *overlap* to give an egg-shaped region in the H_2 molecule. The 2 electrons in the H—H covalent bond occupy the central region between the nuclei, giving both atoms a share in 2 valence electrons and the $1s^2$ electron configuration of the noble gas helium. For simplicity, the shared pair of electrons in a covalent bond is often represented as a line between atoms. Thus, the symbols H—H, H:H, and H_2 all represent a hydrogen molecule.

▲ The two teams are joined together because both are holding onto the same rope. In a similar way, two atoms are bonded together when both hold onto the same electrons.

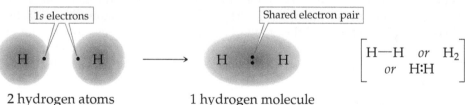

2 hydrogen atoms   1 hydrogen molecule

As you might imagine, the magnitudes of the various attractive and repulsive forces between nuclei and electrons in a covalent bond depend on how close the atoms are to each other. If the atoms are too far apart, the attractive forces are small and no bond exists. If the atoms are too close, the repulsive interaction between nuclei is so strong that it pushes the atoms apart. Thus, there is an optimum point where net attractive forces are maximized and where the H_2 molecule is most stable. This optimum distance between nuclei is called the **bond length** and is 74 pm (7.4×10^{-11} m) in the H_2 molecule.

Bond length The optimum distance between nuclei in a covalent bond.

As another example of covalent bond formation, look at the chlorine molecule, Cl_2. An individual chlorine atom has 7 valence electrons and the valence-shell electron configuration $3s^2 3p^5$. Using the electron-dot symbols for the valence electrons, each Cl atom can be represented as :C̈l·. The 3s orbital and 2 of the three 3p orbitals are filled by 2 electrons each, but the third $3p$ orbital holds only 1 electron. When 2 chlorine atoms approach each other, the unpaired $3p$ electrons are shared by both atoms in a covalent bond. Each chlorine atom in the resultant Cl_2 molecule now "owns" 6 outer-shell electrons and "shares" 2 more, giving each a valence-shell octet like that of the noble gas argon. We can represent the formation of a covalent bond between chlorine atoms as

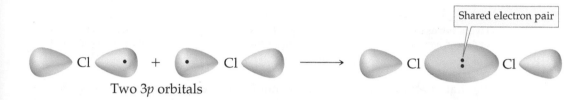

Such bond formation can also be pictured as the overlap of the $3p$ orbitals containing the single electrons, with resultant formation of a region of high electron density between the nuclei:

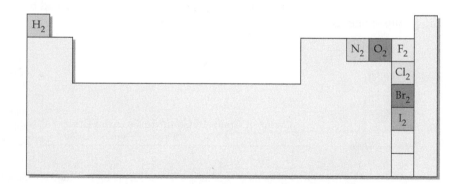

Shared electron pair

Two $3p$ orbitals

In addition to H_2 and Cl_2, five other elements always exist as *diatomic* (2-atom) molecules (Figure 4.2): nitrogen (N_2) and oxygen (O_2) are colorless, odorless, nontoxic gases present in air; fluorine (F_2) is a pale yellow, highly reactive gas; bromine (Br_2) is a dark red, toxic liquid; and iodine (I_2) is a violet crystalline solid.

H_2			
	N_2	O_2	F_2
			Cl_2
			Br_2
			I_2

◄ **Figure 4.2**
Diatomic elements in the periodic table.

PROBLEM 4.1
Draw the iodine molecule using electron-dot symbols, and indicate the shared electron pair. What noble gas configuration do the iodine atoms have in an (I_2) molecule?

4.2 Covalent Bonds and the Periodic Table

Covalent bonds can form between unlike atoms as well as between like atoms, making possible a vast number of **molecular compounds**. Water molecules, for example, consist of 2 hydrogen atoms joined by covalent bonds to an oxygen atom, H_2O; ammonia molecules consist of 3 hydrogen atoms covalently bonded to a nitrogen atom, NH_3; and methane molecules consist of 4 hydrogen atoms covalently bonded to a carbon atom, CH_4.

Molecular compound A compound that consists of molecules rather than ions.

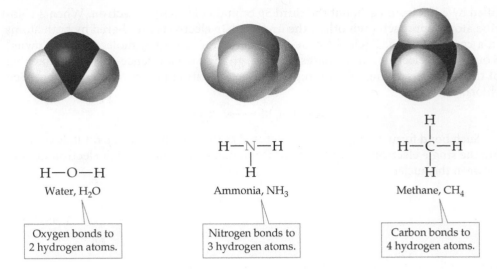

H—O—H
Water, H_2O

Oxygen bonds to 2 hydrogen atoms.

H—N—H
|
H
Ammonia, NH_3

Nitrogen bonds to 3 hydrogen atoms.

H
|
H—C—H
|
H
Methane, CH_4

Carbon bonds to 4 hydrogen atoms.

Note that in all these examples, each atom shares enough electrons to achieve a noble gas configuration: 2 electrons for hydrogen and octets for oxygen, nitrogen, and carbon. Hydrogen, with 1 valence electron (H·), needs one more electron to achieve a noble gas configuration (that of helium, $1s^2$) and thus forms 1 covalent bond. Oxygen, with 6 valence electrons (·Ö·), needs two more electrons to have an octet; this happens when oxygen forms 2 covalent bonds. Nitrogen, with 5 valence electrons (·Ṅ·), needs three more electrons to achieve an octet and thus forms 3 covalent bonds. Carbon, with 4 valence electrons (·Ċ·), needs four more electrons and thus forms 4 covalent bonds. Figure 4.3 summarizes the number of covalent bonds typically formed by common main group elements.

▶ **Figure 4.3**
Numbers of covalent bonds typically formed by main group elements to achieve octet configurations.
For P, S, Cl, and other elements in the third period and below, the number of covalent bonds may vary. Numbers in parentheses indicate other possible numbers of bonds that result in exceptions to the octet rule, as explained in the text.

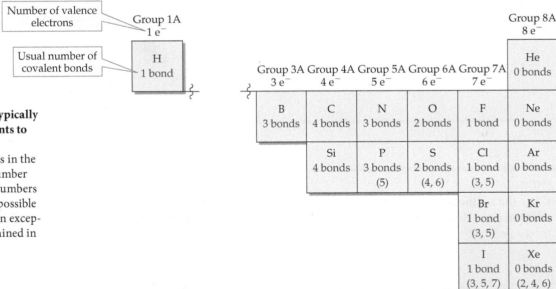

The octet rule is a useful guideline, but it has numerous exceptions. Boron, for example, has only 3 valence electrons it can share (·Ḃ·) and thus forms compounds in which it has only 3 covalent bonds and 6 electrons, such as BF_3. Exceptions to the octet rule are also seen with elements in the third row of the periodic table and below because these elements have vacant *d* orbitals that can be used for bonding. Phosphorus sometimes forms 5 covalent bonds (using 10 bonding electrons); sulfur sometimes forms 4 or 6 covalent bonds (using 8 and 12 bonding electrons, respectively); and chlorine, bromine, and iodine sometimes form 3, 5, or 7 covalent bonds. Phosphorus and sulfur, for example, form molecules such as PCl_5, SF_4, and SF_6.

BF$_3$

Boron trifluoride
(6 valence electrons on B)

PCl$_5$

Phosphorus pentachloride
(10 valence electrons on P)

SF$_6$

Sulfur hexafluoride
(12 valence electrons on S)

Worked Example 4.1 Molecular Compounds: Octet Rule and Covalent Bonds

Look at Figure 4.3 and tell whether the following molecules are likely to exist.

(a)
$$Br-\underset{\underset{CBr_3}{|}}{\overset{\overset{Br}{|}}{C}}-Br$$

(b) $I-Cl$
ICl

(c)
$$H-\underset{\underset{FH_4}{|}}{\overset{\overset{H}{|}}{F}}-H$$

(d) $H-S-H$
H_2S

ANALYSIS Count the number of covalent bonds formed by each element and see if the numbers correspond to those shown in Figure 4.3.

SOLUTION

(a) No. Carbon needs 4 covalent bonds but has only 3 in CBr_3.

(b) Yes. Both iodine and chlorine have 1 covalent bond in ICl.

(c) No. Fluorine only needs 1 covalent bond to achieve an octet. It cannot form more than 1 covalent bond because it is in the second period and does not have valence *d* orbitals to use for bonding.

(d) Yes. Sulfur, which is in group 6A like oxygen, often forms 2 covalent bonds.

Worked Example 4.2 Molecular Compounds: Electron-Dot Symbols

Using electron-dot symbols, show the reaction between a hydrogen atom and a fluorine atom.

ANALYSIS The electron-dot symbols show the valence electrons for the hydrogen and fluorine atoms. A covalent bond is formed by the sharing of unpaired valence electrons between the 2 atoms.

SOLUTION
Draw the electron-dot symbols for the H and F atoms, showing the covalent bond as a shared electron pair.

$$H\cdot \; + \; \cdot\ddot{\underset{..}{F}}: \; \longrightarrow \; H\!:\!\ddot{\underset{..}{F}}:$$

Worked Example **4.3** Molecular Compounds: Predicting Number of Bonds

What are likely formulas for the following molecules?

(a) SiH₂Cl?   (b) HBr?   (c) PBr?

ANALYSIS The numbers of covalent bonds formed by each element should be those shown in Figure 4.3.

SOLUTION

(a) Silicon typically forms 4 bonds: SiH_2Cl_2
(b) Hydrogen forms only 1 bond: HBr
(c) Phosphorus typically forms 3 bonds: PBr_3

PROBLEM 4.2

How many covalent bonds are formed by each atom in the following molecules? Draw molecules using the electron-dot symbols and lines to show the covalent bonds.

(a) PH_3 (b) H_2Se (c) HCl   (d) SiF_4

PROBLEM 4.3

Lead forms both ionic and molecular compounds. Using Figure 4.3, the periodic table, and electronic configurations, predict which of the following lead compounds is more likely to be ionic and which is more likely to be molecular: $PbCl_2$, $PbCl_4$.

PROBLEM 4.4

What are likely formulas for the following molecules?

(a) CH_2Cl?   (b) BH?   (c) NI?   (d) SiCl?

4.3 Multiple Covalent Bonds

The bonding in some molecules cannot be explained by the sharing of only 2 electrons between atoms. For example, the carbon and oxygen atoms in carbon dioxide (CO_2) and the nitrogen atoms in the N_2 molecule cannot have electron octets if only 2 electrons are shared:

UNSTABLE—Carbon has only 6 electrons; each oxygen has only 7.

UNSTABLE—Each nitrogen has only 6 electrons.

The only way the atoms in CO_2 and N_2 can have outer-shell electron octets is by sharing *more* than 2 electrons, resulting in the formation of *multiple* covalent bonds. Only if the carbon atom shares 4 electrons with each oxygen atom do all atoms in CO_2 have electron octets, and only if the 2 nitrogen atoms share 6 electrons do both have electron octets. A bond formed by sharing 2 electrons (one pair) is a **single bond**, a bond formed by sharing 4 electrons (two pairs) is a **double bond**, and a bond formed by sharing 6 electrons (three pairs) is a **triple bond**. Just as a single bond is represented by a single line between atoms, a double bond is represented by two lines between atoms and a triple bond by three lines:

Single bond A covalent bond formed by sharing one electron pair.

Double bond A covalent bond formed by sharing two electron pairs.

Triple bond A covalent bond formed by sharing three electron pairs.

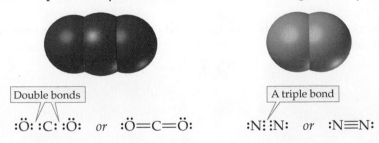

The carbon atom in CO_2 has 2 double bonds (4e⁻ each) for a total of 8 electrons. Each oxygen atom also has a complete octet: a double bond (4e⁻) plus two sets of lone pairs. Similarly, formation of a triple bond in N_2 allows each nitrogen to obtain a complete octet: 6 electrons from the triple bond plus a lone pair.

Carbon, nitrogen, and oxygen are the elements most often present in multiple bonds. Carbon and nitrogen form both double and triple bonds; oxygen forms double bonds. Multiple covalent bonding is particularly common in *organic* molecules, which consist predominantly of the element carbon. For example, ethylene, a simple compound used commercially to induce ripening in fruit, has the formula C_2H_4. The only way for the 2 carbon atoms to have octets is for them to share 4 electrons in a carbon-carbon double bond:

Ethylene—the carbon atoms share
4 electrons in a double bond.

As another example, acetylene, the gas used in welding, has the formula C_2H_2. To achieve octets, the 2 acetylene carbons share 6 electrons in a carbon-carbon triple bond:

Acetylene—the carbon atoms share
6 electrons in a triple bond.

Note that in compounds with multiple bonds like ethylene and acetylene, each carbon atom still forms a total of 4 covalent bonds.

Worked Example 4.4 Molecular Compounds: Multiple Bonds

The compound 1-butene contains a multiple bond. In the following representation, however, only the connections between atoms are shown; the multiple bond is not specifically indicated. Identify the position of the multiple bond.

$$\begin{array}{cccc} H & H & H & H \\ | & | & | & | \\ H-C-C-C-C-H \\ | & | \\ H & H \end{array}$$

1-Butene

ANALYSIS Look for 2 adjacent atoms that appear to have fewer than the typical number of covalent bonds, and connect those atoms by a double or triple bond. Refer to Figure 4.3 to see how many bonds will typically be formed by hydrogen and carbon atoms.

SOLUTION

$$\left[\begin{array}{cccc} H & H & H & H \\ | & | & | & | \\ H-C-C-C-C-H \\ | & | \\ H & H \end{array}\right] \qquad \begin{array}{cccc} H & H & H & H \\ | & | & | & | \\ H-C=C-C-C-H \\ | & | \\ H & H \end{array}$$

Only 3 bonds here   Double bond here

Worked Example 4.5 Multiple Bonds: Electron-Dot and Line Structures

Draw the oxygen molecule (a) using the electron-dot symbols, and (b) using lines rather than dots to indicate covalent bonds.

ANALYSIS Each oxygen atom has 6 valence electrons and will tend to form 2 covalent bonds to reach an octet. Thus, each oxygen will need to share 4 electrons to form a double bond.

SOLUTION

$$:\ddot{O}::\ddot{O}: \quad \text{or} \quad :\ddot{O}=\ddot{O}:$$

PROBLEM 4.5

Acetic acid, the organic constituent of vinegar, can be drawn using electron-dot symbols as shown below. How many outer-shell electrons are associated with each atom? Draw the structure using lines rather than dots to indicate covalent bonds.

$$\begin{array}{c} \quad\;\; :\ddot{O}: \\ H\;\; \| \\ H:\ddot{C}:\ddot{C}:\ddot{O}:H \\ \ddot{H} \end{array}$$

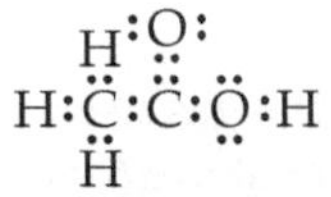

PROBLEM 4.6

Identify the positions of all double bonds in caffeine, a stimulant found in coffee and many soft drinks and as an additive in several over-the-counter drugs, such as aspirin.

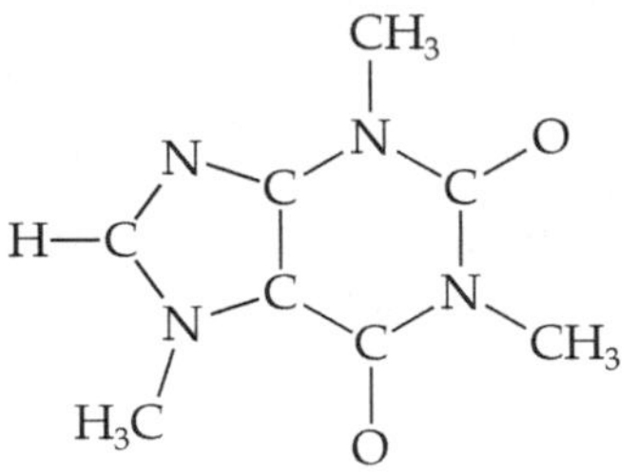

4.4 Coordinate Covalent Bonds

In the covalent bonds we have seen thus far, the shared electrons have come from different atoms. That is, the bonds result from the overlap of 2 singly occupied valence orbitals, 1 from each atom. Sometimes, though, a bond is formed by the overlap of a filled orbital on 1 atom with a vacant orbital on another atom so that both electrons come from the *same* atom. The bond that results in this case is called a **coordinate covalent bond**.

Coordinate covalent bond The covalent bond that forms when both electrons are donated by the same atom.

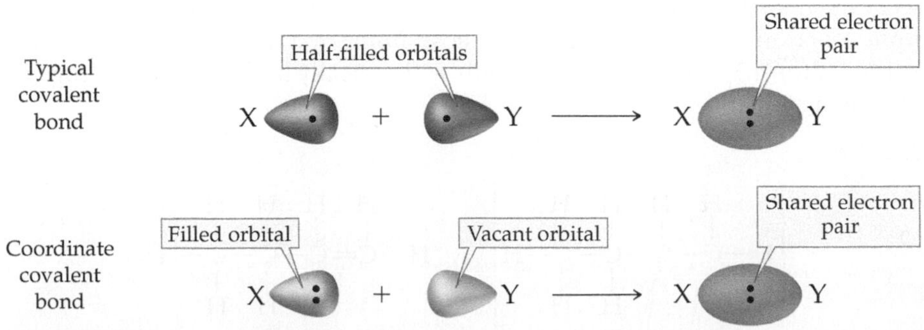

The ammonium ion, NH_4^+, is an example of a species with a coordinate covalent bond. When ammonia reacts in water solution with a hydrogen ion, H^+, the nitrogen atom donates 2 electrons from a filled valence orbital to form a coordinate covalent bond to the hydrogen ion, which has a vacant $1s$ orbital.

$$H^+ + H—\underset{..}{N}—H \longrightarrow \left[H—\underset{\underset{|}{H}}{\overset{\overset{|}{H}}{N}}—H \right]^+$$

Once formed, a coordinate covalent bond contains two shared electrons and is no different from any other covalent bond. All four covalent bonds in NH_4^+ are identical, for example. Note, however, that formation of a coordinate covalent bond often results in unusual bonding patterns, such as an N atom with four covalent bonds rather than the usual three, or an oxygen atom with three bonds rather than the usual two (H_3O^+). An entire class of substances is based on the ability of transition metals to form coordinate covalent bonds with nonmetals. Called *coordination compounds*, many of these substances have important roles in living organisms. For example, toxic metals can be removed from the bloodstream by the formation of water-soluble coordination compounds.

▶▶▶ As another example, we will see in Chapter 19 that essential metal ions are held in enzyme molecules by coordinate covalent bonds.

4.5 Characteristics of Molecular Compounds

We saw in Section 3.4 that ionic compounds have high melting and boiling points because the attractive forces between oppositely charged ions are so strong that the ions are held tightly together. But *molecules* are neutral, so there is no strong electrostatic attraction between molecules. There are, however, several weaker forces between molecules, called *intermolecular forces*, which we will look at in more detail in Chapter 8.

When intermolecular forces are very weak, molecules of a substance are so weakly attracted to one another that the substance is a gas at ordinary temperatures. If the forces are somewhat stronger, the molecules are pulled together into a liquid; and if the forces are still stronger, the substance becomes a molecular solid. Even so, the melting points and boiling points of molecular solids are usually lower than those of ionic solids.

In addition to having lower melting points and boiling points, molecular compounds differ from ionic compounds in other ways. Most molecular compounds are insoluble in water, for instance, because they have little attraction to the strongly polar water molecules. In addition, they do not conduct electricity when melted because they have no charged particles. Table 4.1 provides a comparison of the properties of ionic and molecular compounds.

TABLE 4.1 A Comparison of Ionic and Molecular Compounds

Ionic Compounds	Molecular Compounds
Smallest components are ions (e.g., Na^+, Cl^-)	Smallest components are molecules (e.g., CO_2, H_2O)
Usually composed of metals combined with nonmetals	Usually composed of nonmetals with nonmetals
Crystalline solids	Gases, liquids, or low-melting-point solids
High melting points (e.g., NaCl = 801 °C)	Low melting points (H_2O = 0.0 °C)
High boiling points (above 700 °C) (e.g., NaCl = 1413 °C)	Low boiling points (e.g., H_2O = 100 °C; CH_3CH_2OH = 76 °C)
Conduct electricity when molten or dissolved in water	Do not conduct electricity
Many are water-soluble	Relatively few are water-soluble
Not soluble in organic liquids	Many are soluble in organic liquids

4.6 Molecular Formulas and Lewis Structures

Molecular formula A formula that shows the numbers and kinds of atoms in 1 molecule of a compound.

Structural formula A molecular representation that shows the connections among atoms by using lines to represent covalent bonds.

Lewis structure A molecular representation that shows both the connections among atoms and the locations of lone-pair valence electrons.

Lone pair A pair of electrons that is not used for bonding.

Formulas such as H_2O, NH_3, and CH_4, which show the numbers and kinds of atoms in one molecule of a compound, are called **molecular formulas**. Though important, molecular formulas are limited in their use because they do not provide information about how the atoms in a given molecule are connected.

Much more useful are **structural formulas**, which use lines to show how atoms are connected, and **Lewis structures**, which show both the connections among atoms and the placement of unshared valence electrons. In a water molecule, for instance, the oxygen atom shares two electron pairs in covalent bonds with 2 hydrogen atoms and has two other pairs of valence electrons that are not shared in bonds. Such unshared pairs of valence electrons are called **lone pairs**. In an ammonia molecule, three electron pairs are used in bonding, and there is one lone pair. In methane, all four electron pairs are bonding.

Lewis structures

Electron lone pairs

H—Ö—H   H—N̈—H   H—C—H
   Water | |
                  H   H

                Ammonia   Methane

Note how a molecular formula differs from an ionic formula, described previously in Section 3.9. A *molecular* formula gives the number of atoms that are combined in one molecule of a compound, whereas an *ionic* formula gives only a ratio of ions (Figure 4.4). The formula C_2H_4 for ethylene, for example, says that every ethylene molecule consists of 2 carbon atoms and 4 hydrogen atoms. The formula NaCl for sodium chloride, however, says only that there are equal numbers of Na^+ and Cl^- ions in the crystal; the formula says nothing about how the ions interact with one another.

▶ **Figure 4.4**
The distinction between ionic and molecular compounds.
In ionic compounds, the smallest particle is an ion. In molecular compounds, the smallest particle is a molecule.

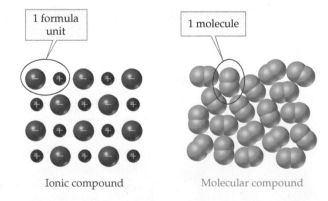

1 formula unit

1 molecule

Ionic compound

Molecular compound

4.7 Drawing Lewis Structures

To draw a Lewis structure, you first need to know the connections among atoms. Sometimes the connections are obvious. Water, for example, can only be H—O—H because only oxygen can be in the middle and form 2 covalent bonds. Other times, you will have to be told how the atoms are connected.

Two approaches are used for drawing Lewis structures once the connections are known. The first is particularly useful for organic molecules like those found in living organisms because the atoms follow common bonding patterns. The second approach is a more general, stepwise procedure that works for all molecules.

Lewis Structures for Molecules Containing C, N, O, X (Halogen), and H

As summarized in Figure 4.3, carbon, nitrogen, oxygen, halogen, and hydrogen atoms usually maintain consistent bonding patterns:

- C forms 4 covalent bonds and often bonds to other carbon atoms.
- N forms 3 covalent bonds and has one lone pair of electrons.
- O forms 2 covalent bonds and has two lone pairs of electrons.
- Halogens (X = F, Cl, Br, I) form 1 covalent bond and have three lone pairs of electrons.
- H forms 1 covalent bond.

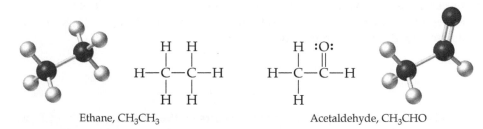

| Carbon 4 bonds | Nitrogen 3 bonds | Oxygen 2 bonds | Halogen 1 bond | Hydrogen 1 bond |

Relying on these common bonding patterns simplifies the writing of Lewis structures. In ethane (C_2H_6), a constituent of natural gas, for example, 3 of the 4 covalent bonds of each carbon atom are used in bonds to hydrogen, and the fourth is a carbon-carbon bond. There is no other arrangement in which all 8 atoms can have their usual bonding patterns. In acetaldehyde (C_2H_4O), a substance used in manufacturing perfumes, dyes, and plastics, 1 carbon has 3 bonds to hydrogen, while the other has 1 bond to hydrogen and a double bond to oxygen.

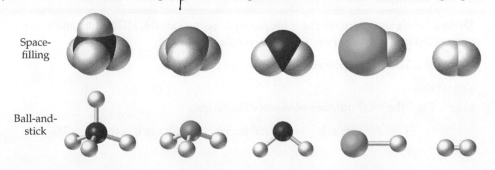

Ethane, CH_3CH_3 Acetaldehyde, CH_3CHO

Because Lewis structures are awkward for larger organic molecules, ethane is more frequently written as a **condensed structure** in which the bonds are not specifically shown. In its condensed form, ethane is CH_3CH_3, meaning that each carbon atom has 3 hydrogen atoms bonded to it (CH_3) and the 2 (CH_3) units are bonded to each other. In the same way, acetaldehyde can be written as CH_3CHO. Note that neither the lone-pair electrons nor the C=O double bond in acetaldehyde is shown explicitly. You will get a lot more practice with such condensed structures in later chapters.

Many of the computer-generated pictures we will be using from now on will be *ball-and-stick models* rather than the space-filling models used previously. Space-filling models are more realistic, but ball-and-stick models do a better job of showing connections and molecular geometry. All models, regardless of type, use a consistent color code in which C is dark gray or black, H is white or ivory, O is red, N is blue, S is yellow, P is dark blue, F is light green, Cl is green, Br is brownish red, and I is purple.

Condensed structure A molecular representation in which bonds are not specifically shown but rather are understood by the order in which atoms are written.

▶▶▶ Condensed structures are used extensively to represent molecular structures in organic chemistry (Chapters 12–17).

Space-filling

Ball-and-stick

A General Method for Drawing Lewis Structures

A Lewis structure can be drawn for any molecule or polyatomic ion by following a five-step procedure. Take PCl_3, for example, a substance in which 3 chlorine atoms surround the central phosphorus atom.

STEP 1: **Find the total number of valence electrons of all atoms in the molecule or ion.** In PCl_3, for example, phosphorus (group 5A) has 5 valence electrons and chlorine (group 7A) has 7 valence electrons, giving a total of 26:

$$P + (3 \times Cl) = PCl_3$$
$$5e^- + (3 \times 7e^-) = 26e^-$$

For a polyatomic ion, add 1 electron for each negative charge or subtract 1 for each positive charge. In OH^-, the total is 8 electrons (6 from oxygen, 1 from hydrogen, plus 1 for the negative charge). In NH_4^+, the total is 8 (5 from nitrogen, 1 from each of 4 hydrogens, minus 1 for the positive charge).

STEP 2: **Draw a line between each pair of connected atoms to represent the two electrons in a covalent bond.** Remember that elements in the second row of the periodic table form the number of bonds discussed earlier in this section, whereas elements in the third row and beyond can use more than 8 electrons and form more than the "usual" number of bonds (Figure 4.3). A particularly common pattern is that an atom in the third row (or beyond) occurs as the central atom in a cluster. In PCl_3, for example, the phosphorus atom is in the center with the 3 chlorine atoms bonded to it:

$$\begin{array}{c} Cl \\ | \\ Cl-P-Cl \end{array}$$

STEP 3: **Using the remaining electrons, add lone pairs so that each atom connected to the central atom (except H) gets an octet.** In PCl_3, 6 of the 26 valence electrons were used to make the covalent bonds. From the remaining 20 electrons, each Cl atom needs three lone pairs to complete the octet:

$$\begin{array}{c} :\ddot{C}l: \\ | \\ :\ddot{C}l-P-\ddot{C}l: \end{array}$$

STEP 4: **Place any remaining electrons in lone pairs on the central atom.** In PCl_3, we have used 24 of the 26 available electrons—6 in three single bonds and 18 in the three lone pairs on each chlorine atom. This leaves 2 electrons for one lone pair on phosphorus:

$$\begin{array}{c} :\ddot{C}l: \\ | \\ :\ddot{C}l-\ddot{P}-\ddot{C}l: \end{array}$$

STEP 5: **If the central atom does not yet have an octet after all electrons have been assigned, take a lone pair from a neighboring atom, and form a multiple bond to the central atom.** In PCl_3, each atom has an octet, all 26 available electrons have been used, and the Lewis structure is finished.

Worked Examples 4.6–4.8 shows how to deal with cases where this fifth step is needed.

Worked Example 4.6 Multiple Bonds: Electron Dots and Valence Electrons

Draw a Lewis structure for the toxic gas hydrogen cyanide, HCN. The atoms are connected in the order shown in the preceding sentence.

ANALYSIS Follow the procedure outlined in the text.

SOLUTION

STEP 1: Find the total number of valence electrons:

H = 1, C = 4, N = 5   Total number of valence electrons = 10

STEP 2: Draw a line between each pair of connected atoms to represent bonding electron pairs:

$$H—C—N \quad 2 \text{ bonds} = 4 \text{ electrons}; 6 \text{ electrons remaining}$$

STEP 3: Add lone pairs so that each atom (except H) has a complete octet:

$$H—C—\ddot{\underset{..}{N}}:$$

STEP 4: All valence electrons have been used, and so step 4 is not needed. H and N have filled valence shells, but C does not.

STEP 5: If the central atom (C in this case) does not yet have an octet, use lone pairs from a neighboring atom (N) to form multiple bonds. This results in a triple bond between the C and N atoms, as shown in the electron dot and ball-and-stick representations below:

$$H—C≡N:$$

We can check the structure by noting that all 10 valence electrons have been used (in 4 covalent bonds and one lone pair) and that each atom has the expected number of bonds (1 bond for H, 3 for N, and 4 for C).

Worked Example 4.7 Lewis Structures: Location of Multiple Bonds

Draw a Lewis structure for vinyl chloride, C_2H_3Cl, a substance used in making polyvinyl chloride, or PVC, plastic.

ANALYSIS Since H and Cl form only 1 bond each, the carbon atoms must be bonded to each other, with the remaining atoms bonded to the carbons. With only 4 atoms available to bond with them, the carbon atoms cannot have 4 covalent bonds each unless they are joined by a double bond.

SOLUTION

STEP 1: The total number of valence electrons is 18; 4 from each of the 2 C atoms, 1 from each of the 3 H atoms, and 7 from the Cl atom.

STEP 2: Place the 2 C atoms in the center, and divide the 4 other atoms between them:

$$\begin{array}{cc} H & Cl \\ \backslash & / \\ C—C \\ / & \backslash \\ H & H \end{array}$$

The 5 bonds account for 10 valence electrons, with 8 remaining.

STEP 3: Place 6 of the remaining valence electrons around the Cl atom so that it has a complete octet, and place the remaining 2 valence electrons on one of the C atoms (either C, it does not matter):

$$\begin{array}{cc} H & :\ddot{C}l: \\ \backslash & / \\ C—\ddot{C}: \\ / & \backslash \\ H & H \end{array}$$

When all the valence electrons are distributed, the C atoms still do not have a complete octet; they each need 4 bonds but have only 3.

STEP 5: The lone pair of electrons on the C atom can be used to form a double bond between the C atoms, giving each a total of 4 bonds (8 electrons). Placement of the double bond yields the Lewis structure and ball-and-stick model for vinyl chloride shown below:

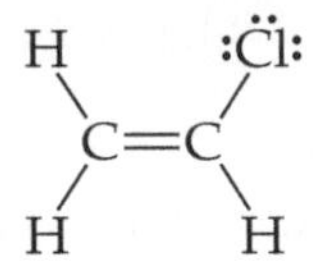

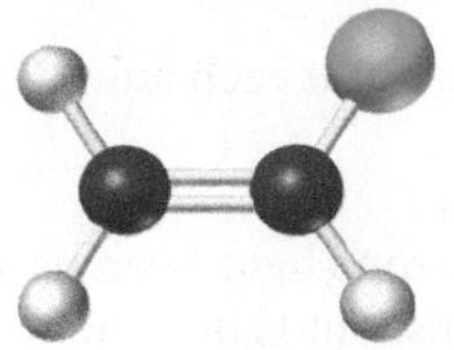

$$\begin{array}{ccc} H & & :\ddot{\underset{..}{Cl}}: \\ \diagdown & & \diagup \\ & C{=}C & \\ \diagup & & \diagdown \\ H & & H \end{array}$$

All 18 valence electrons are accounted for in 6 covalent bonds and three lone pairs, and each atom has the expected number of bonds.

Worked Example **4.8** Lewis Structures: Octet Rule and Multiple Bonds

Draw a Lewis structure for sulfur dioxide, SO_2. The connections are $O{-}S{-}O$.

ANALYSIS Follow the procedure outlined in the text.

SOLUTION

STEP 1: The total number of valence electrons is 18, 6 from each atom:

$$S + (2 \times O) = SO_2$$
$$6e^- + (2 + 6e^-) = 18e^-$$

STEP 2: $O{-}S{-}O$ Two covalent bonds use 4 valence electrons.

STEP 3: $:\ddot{O}{-}S{-}\ddot{O}:$ Adding three lone pairs to each oxygen to give each an octet uses 12 additional valence electrons.

STEP 4: $:\ddot{O}{-}\underset{..}{S}{-}\ddot{O}:$ The remaining 2 valence electrons are placed on sulfur, but sulfur still does not have an octet.

STEP 5: Moving one lone pair from a neighboring oxygen to form a double bond with the central sulfur gives sulfur an octet (it does not matter on which side the $S{=}O$ bond is written):

$$:\ddot{O}{-}\underset{..}{S}{=}\ddot{O}:$$

NOTE: The Lewis structure for SO_2 includes a single bond to one O and a double bond to the other O. It doesn't matter which O has the double bond—both structures are equally acceptable. In reality, however, the $S{-}O$ bonds in this molecule are actually closer to 1.5, an average between the two possible structures we could draw. This is an example of *resonance structures*, or different Lewis structures that could be used to represent the same molecule.

▶▶▶ Aromatic compounds, a class of organic compounds discussed in Section 13.9, are an important example of resonance structures.

PROBLEM 4.8
Methylamine, CH_5N, is responsible for the characteristic odor of decaying fish. Draw a Lewis structure of methylamine.

PROBLEM 4.9
Add lone pairs where appropriate to the following structures:

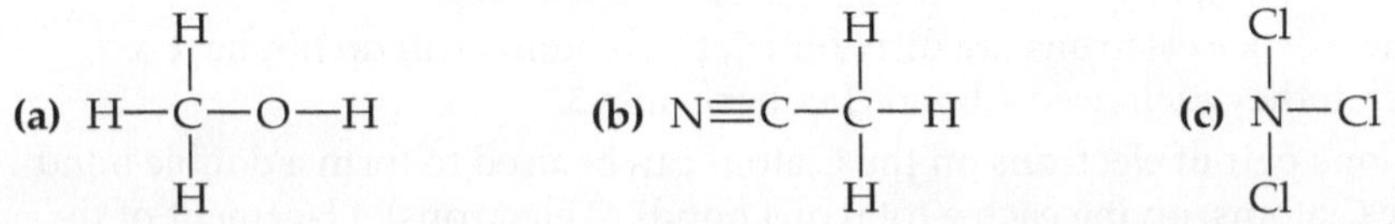

(a)
$$\begin{array}{c} H \\ | \\ H{-}C{-}O{-}H \\ | \\ H \end{array}$$

(b)
$$\begin{array}{c} H \\ | \\ N{\equiv}C{-}C{-}H \\ | \\ H \end{array}$$

(c)
$$\begin{array}{c} Cl \\ | \\ N{-}Cl \\ | \\ Cl \end{array}$$

PROBLEM 4.10

Draw Lewis structures for the following:

(a) Phosgene, $COCl_2$, a poisonous gas

(b) Hypochlorite ion, OCl^-, present in many swimming pool chemicals

(c) Hydrogen peroxide, H_2O_2

(d) Sulfur dichloride, SCl_2

PROBLEM 4.11

Draw a Lewis structure for nitric acid, HNO_3. The nitrogen atom is in the center, and the hydrogen atom is bonded to an oxygen atom.

CHEMISTRY IN ACTION

CO and NO: Pollutants or Miracle Molecules?

Carbon monoxide (CO) is a killer; everyone knows that. It is to blame for an estimated 3500 accidental deaths and suicides each year in the United States and is the number one cause of all deaths by poisoning. Nitric oxide (NO) is formed in combustion engines and reacts with oxygen to form nitrogen dioxide (NO_2), the reddish-brown gas associated with urban smog. What most people do not know, however, is that our bodies cannot function without these molecules. A startling discovery made in 1992 showed that CO and NO are key chemical messengers in the body, used by cells to regulate critical metabolic processes.

The toxicity of CO in moderate concentration is due to its ability to bind to hemoglobin molecules in the blood, thereby preventing the hemoglobin from carrying oxygen to tissues. The high reactivity of NO leads to the formation of compounds that are toxic irritants. However, low concentrations of CO and NO are produced in cells throughout the body. Both CO and NO are highly soluble in water and can diffuse from one cell to another, where they stimulate production of a substance called *guanylyl cyclase*. Guanylyl cyclase, in turn, controls the production of another substance called *cyclic GMP*, which regulates many cellular functions.

Levels of CO production are particularly high in certain regions of the brain, including those associated with long-term memory. Evidence from experiments with rat brains suggests that a special kind of cell in the brain's hippocampus is signaled by transfer of a molecular messenger from a neighboring cell. The receiving cell responds back to the signaling cell by releasing CO, which causes still more messenger molecules to be sent. After several rounds of this back-and-forth communication, the receiving cell undergoes some sort of change that becomes a memory. When CO production is blocked, possibly in response to a medical condition or exposure to certain toxic metals, long-term memories are no longer stored, and those memories that previously existed are erased. When CO production is stimulated, however, memories are again laid down.

▲ **Los Angeles at sunset. Carbon monoxide is a major component of photochemical smog, but it also functions as an essential chemical messenger in our bodies.**

NO controls a seemingly limitless range of functions in the body. The immune system uses NO to fight infections and tumors. It is also used to transmit messages between nerve cells and is associated with the processes involved in learning and memory, sleeping, and depression. Its most advertised role, however, is as a *vasodilator*, a substance that allows blood vessels to relax and dilate. This discovery led to the development of a new class of drugs that stimulate production of enzymes called nitric oxide synthases (NOS). These drugs can be used to treat conditions from erectile dysfunction (Viagra) to hypertension. Given the importance of NO in the fields of neuroscience, physiology, and immunology, it is not surprising that it was named "Molecule of the Year" in 1992.

See Chemistry in Action Problems 4.89 and 4.90 at the end of the chapter.

KEY CONCEPT PROBLEM 4.12

The molecular model shown here is a representation of methyl methacrylate, a starting material used to prepare Lucite plastic. Only the connections between atoms are shown; multiple bonds are not indicated.

(a) What is the molecular formula of methyl methacrylate?

(b) Indicate the positions of the multiple bonds and lone pairs in methyl methacrylate.

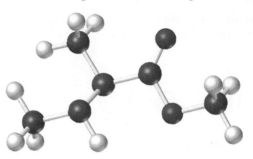

PROBLEM 4.13

Draw the Lewis dot structures for the molecules CO and NO discussed in the Chemistry in Action box on page 113. How do the Lewis structures provide insight into the reactivity of these molecules?

4.8 The Shapes of Molecules

Look back at the computer-generated drawings of molecules in the preceding section, and you will find that the molecules are shown with specific shapes. Acetylene is *linear*, water is *bent*, ammonia is *pyramid-shaped*, methane is *tetrahedral*, and ethylene is flat, or *planar*. What determines such shapes? Why, for example, are the 3 atoms in water connected at an angle of (104.5°) rather than in a straight line? Like so many properties, molecular shapes are related to the numbers and locations of the valence electrons around atoms.

Molecular shapes can be predicted by noting how many bonds and electron pairs surround individual atoms and applying what is called the **valence-shell electron-pair repulsion (VSEPR) model**. The basic idea of the VSEPR model is that the constantly moving valence electrons in bonds and lone pairs make up negatively charged clouds of electrons, which electrically repel one another. The clouds therefore tend to keep as far apart as possible, causing molecules to assume specific shapes. There are three steps to applying the VSEPR model:

STEP 1: Draw a Lewis structure of the molecule, and identify the atom whose geometry is of interest. In a simple molecule like PCl_3 or CO_2, this is usually the central atom.

STEP 2: Count the number of electron charge clouds surrounding the atom of interest. The number of charge clouds is simply the total number of lone pairs plus connections to other atoms. It does not matter whether a connection is a single bond or a multiple bond because we are interested only in the *number* of charge clouds, not in how many electrons each cloud contains. The carbon atom in carbon dioxide, for instance, has 2 double bonds to oxygen $(O{=}C{=}O)$, and thus has two charge clouds.

STEP 3: Predict molecular shape by assuming that the charge clouds orient in space so that they are as far away from one another as possible. How they achieve this favorable orientation depends on their number, as summarized in Table 4.2.

If there are only two charge clouds, as occurs on the central atom of CO_2 (2 double bonds) and HCN (1 single bond and 1 triple bond), the clouds are farthest apart when

Valence-shell electron-pair repulsion (VSEPR) model A method for predicting molecular shape by noting how many electron charge clouds surround atoms and assuming that the clouds orient as far away from one another as possible.

TABLE 4.2 Molecular Geometry Around Atoms with 2, 3, and 4 Charge Clouds

NUMBER OF BONDS	NUMBER OF LONE PAIRS	TOTAL NUMBER OF CHARGE CLOUDS	MOLECULAR GEOMETRY		EXAMPLE
2	0	2		Linear	$O{=}C{=}O$
3	0	3		Trigonal planar	$\begin{matrix} H \\ H \end{matrix} \!\!> C{=}O$
2	1			Bent	$\begin{matrix} O \\ O \end{matrix} \!\!> S$
4	0	4		Tetrahedral	$H{-}C(H)(H){-}H$
3	1			Pyramidal	$H{-}N(H){-}H$
2	2			Bent	$H{-}O{-}H$

they point in opposite directions. Thus, both HCN and CO_2 are linear molecules, with **bond angles** of 180°:

These molecules are linear, with bond angles of 180°.

$$H{-}C{\equiv}N\!: \qquad 180°$$

$$\ddot{O}{=}C{=}\ddot{O} \qquad 180°$$

Bond angle The angle formed by 3 adjacent atoms in a molecule.

When there are three charge clouds, as occurs on the central atom in formaldehyde (1 single bond and 1 double bond) and SO_2 (1 single bond, 1 double bond, and one lone pair), the clouds will be farthest apart if they lie in a plane and point to the corners of an equilateral triangle. Thus, a formaldehyde molecule is trigonal planar, with all bond angles near 120°. In the same way, an SO_2 molecule has a trigonal planar arrangement of its three electron clouds, but one point of the triangle is occupied by a lone pair. The connection between the 3 atoms is therefore bent rather than linear, with an O—S—O bond angle of approximately 120°:

A formaldehyde molecule is planar triangular, with bond angles of roughly 120°.

$$\begin{matrix} H & \overset{117°}{\leftarrow} \\ 126° & C{=}O \\ H & \end{matrix}$$

Top view

Side view

An SO_2 molecule is bent, with a bond angle of approximately 120°.

Top view

Side view

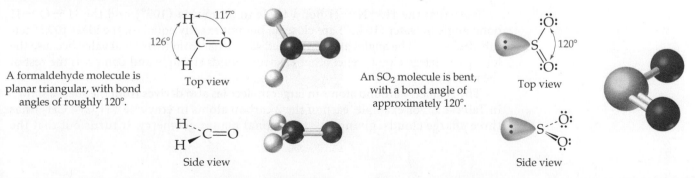

Note how the three-dimensional shapes of molecules like formaldehyde and SO_2 are shown. Solid lines are assumed to be in the plane of the paper; a dashed line recedes behind the plane of the paper away from the viewer; and a dark wedged line protrudes out of the paper toward the viewer. This standard method for showing three-dimensionality will be used throughout the rest of the book.

When there are four charge clouds, as occurs on the central atom in CH_4 (4 single bonds), NH_3 (3 single bonds and one lone pair), and H_2O (2 single bonds and two lone pairs), the clouds can be farthest apart when they extend to the corners of a *regular tetrahedron*. As illustrated in Figure 4.5, a **regular tetrahedron** is a geometric solid whose four identical faces are equilateral triangles. The central atom is at the center of the tetrahedron, the charge clouds point to the corners, and the angle between lines drawn from the center to any two corners is 109.5°.

Regular tetrahedron A geometric figure with four identical triangular faces.

▶ **Figure 4.5**
The tetrahedral geometry of an atom surrounded by four charge clouds. The atom is located at the center of the regular tetrahedron, and the four charge clouds point toward the corners. The bond angle between the center and any two corners is 109.5°.

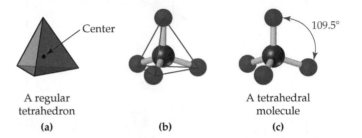

A regular tetrahedron
(a)

(b)

A tetrahedral molecule
(c)

Because valence-shell electron octets are so common, a great many molecules have geometries based on the tetrahedron. In methane (CH_4), for example, the carbon atom has tetrahedral geometry with H—C—H bond angles of exactly 109.5°. In ammonia (NH_3), the nitrogen atom has a tetrahedral arrangement of its four charge clouds, but one corner of the tetrahedron is occupied by a lone pair, resulting in an overall pyramidal shape for the molecule. Similarly, water, which has two corners of the tetrahedron occupied by lone pairs, has an overall bent shape.

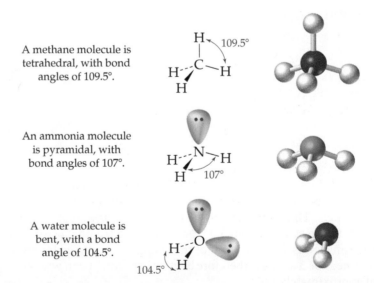

A methane molecule is tetrahedral, with bond angles of 109.5°.

An ammonia molecule is pyramidal, with bond angles of 107°.

A water molecule is bent, with a bond angle of 104.5°.

Note that the H—N—H bond angle in ammonia (107°) and the H—O—H bond angle in water (104.5°) are close to, but not exactly equal to, the ideal 109.5° tetrahedral value. The angles are diminished somewhat from their ideal value because the lone-pair charge clouds repel other electron clouds strongly and compress the rest of the molecule.

The geometry around atoms in larger molecules also derives from the shapes shown in Table 4.2. For example, each of the 2 carbon atoms in ethylene ($H_2C{=}CH_2$) has three charge clouds, giving rise to trigonal planar geometry. It turns out that the molecule as a whole is also planar, with H—C—C and H—C—H bond angles of approximately 120°:

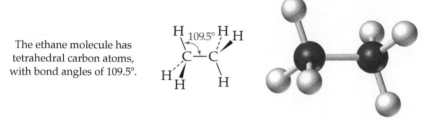

The ethylene molecule is planar, with bond angles of 120°.

Top view

Side view

Carbon atoms bonded to 4 other atoms are each at the center of a tetrahedron, as shown here for ethane, H_3C—CH_3:

The ethane molecule has tetrahedral carbon atoms, with bond angles of 109.5°.

Worked Example 4.9 Lewis Structures: Molecular Shape

What shape would you expect for the hydronium ion, H_3O^+?

ANALYSIS Draw the Lewis structure for the molecular ion, and count the number of charge clouds around the central oxygen atom; imagine the clouds orienting as far away from one another as possible.

SOLUTION
The Lewis structure for the hydronium ion shows that the oxygen atom has four charge clouds (3 single bonds and one lone pair). The hydronium ion is therefore pyramidal with bond angles of approximately 109.5°.

Worked Example 4.10 Lewis Structures: Charge Cloud Geometry

Predict the geometry around each of the carbon atoms in an acetaldehyde molecule, CH_3CHO.

ANALYSIS Draw the Lewis structure and identify the number of charge clouds around each of the central carbon atoms.

SOLUTION
The Lewis structure of acetaldehyde shows that the CH_3 carbon has four charge clouds (4 single bonds) and the CHO carbon atom has three charge clouds (2 single bonds, 1 double bond). Table 4.2 indicates that the CH_3 carbon is tetrahedral, but the CHO carbon is trigonal planar.

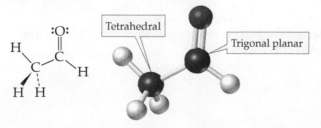

Tetrahedral

Trigonal planar

CHEMISTRY IN ACTION

VERY Big Molecules

How big can a molecule be? The answer is very, *very* big. The really big molecules in our bodies and in many items we buy are all *polymers*. Like a string of beads, a polymer is formed of many repeating units connected in a long chain. Each "bead" in the chain comes from a simple molecule that has formed chemical bonds at both ends, linking it to other molecules. The repeating units can be the same:

$$-a-a-a-a-a-a-a-a-a-a-a-a-$$

or they can be different. If different, they can be connected in an ordered pattern:

$$-a-b-a-b-a-b-a-b-a-b-a-b-$$

or in a random pattern:

$$-a-b-b-a-b-a-a-a-b-a-b-b-$$

Furthermore, the polymer chains can have branches, and the branches can have either the same repeating unit as the main chain or a different one:

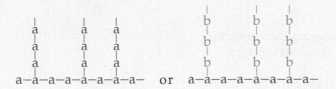

Still other possible variations include complex, three-dimensional networks of "cross-linked" chains. The rubber used in tires, for example, contains polymer chains connected by cross-linking atoms of sulfur to impart greater rigidity.

We all use synthetic polymers every day—we usually call them "plastics." Common synthetic polymers are made by connecting up to several hundred thousand smaller molecules together, producing giant polymer molecules with masses up to several million atomic mass units. Polyethylene, for example, is made by

▲ **The protective gear worn by motor-cyclists (shown above), firefighters, and security forces are composed of advanced composite materials based on polymers.**

combining as many as 50,000 ethylene molecules ($H_2C = CH_2$) to give a polymer with repeating $-CH_2CH-$ units:

$$\text{Many } H_2C = CH_2 \longrightarrow -CH_2CH_2CH_2CH_2CH_2CH_2-$$

Ethylene   Polyethlene

The product is used in such items as chairs, toys, drain pipes, milk bottles, and packaging films. Other examples of polymers include the nylon used in clothing and pantyhose, molded hardware (nuts and bolts), and the Kevlar used in bulletproof vests (see Chemistry in Action on p. 538).

Nature began to exploit the extraordinary variety of polymer properties long before humans did. In fact, despite great progress in recent years, there is still much to be learned about the polymers in living things. Carbohydrates and proteins are polymers, as are the giant molecules of deoxyribonucleic acid (DNA) that govern many cellular processes, including reproduction, in all organisms. Nature's polymer molecules, though, are more complex than any that chemists have yet created.

▶▶▶ Carbohydrates are polymers composed of sugar molecules linked together in long chains (Chapter 21), while proteins are polymers of smaller molecules called amino acids (Chapter 18). DNA, a polymer of repeating nucleotide subunits, is discussed in Chapter 25.

See Chemistry in Action Problems 4.91 and 4.92 at the end of the chapter.

PROBLEM 4.14
Boron typically only forms 3 covalent bonds because it only has 3 valence electrons, but can form coordinate covalent bonds. Draw the Lewis structure for BF_4^- and predict the molecular shape of the ion.

PROBLEM 4.15
Predict shapes for the organic molecules chloroform, $CHCl_3$, and 1,1-dichloroethylene, $Cl_2C = CH_2$.

PROBLEM 4.16

Polycarbonate, also known as plexiglass, has the basic repeating unit shown below. What is the geometry of the electron clouds for the carbon atoms labeled "a" and "b" in this structure?

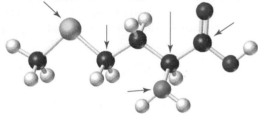

PROBLEM 4.17

Hydrogen selenide (H_2Se) resembles hydrogen sulfide (H_2S) in that both compounds have terrible odors and are poisonous. What are their shapes?

🔑 KEY CONCEPT PROBLEM 4.18

Draw a structure corresponding to the molecular model of the amino acid methionine shown here, and describe the geometry around the indicated atoms. (Remember the color key discussed in Section 4.7: black = carbon; white = hydrogen; red = oxygen; blue = nitrogen; yellow = sulfur.)

Methionine

4.9 Polar Covalent Bonds and Electronegativity

Electrons in a covalent bond occupy the region between the bonded atoms. If the atoms are identical, as in H_2 and Cl_2, the electrons are attracted equally to both atoms and are shared equally. If the atoms are *not* identical, however, as in HCl, the bonding electrons may be attracted more strongly by one atom than by the other and may be shared unequally. Such bonds are said to be **polar covalent bonds**. In hydrogen chloride, for example, electrons spend more time near the chlorine atom than near the hydrogen atom. Although the molecule as a whole is neutral, the chlorine is more negative than the hydrogen, resulting in *partial* charges on the atoms. These partial charges are represented by placing a $\delta-$ (Greek lowercase *delta*) on the more negative atom and a $\delta+$ on the more positive atom.

A particularly helpful way of visualizing this unequal distribution of bonding electrons is to look at what is called an *electrostatic potential map*, which uses color to portray the calculated electron distribution in a molecule. In HCl, for example, the electron-poor hydrogen is blue, and the electron-rich chlorine is reddish-yellow:

Polar covalent bond A bond in which the electrons are attracted more strongly by one atom than by the other.

This end of the molecule is electron-poor and has a partial positive charge ($\delta+$).

This end of the molecule is electron-rich and has a partial negative charge ($\delta-$).

$\delta+$ $\delta-$
$$H-Cl$$

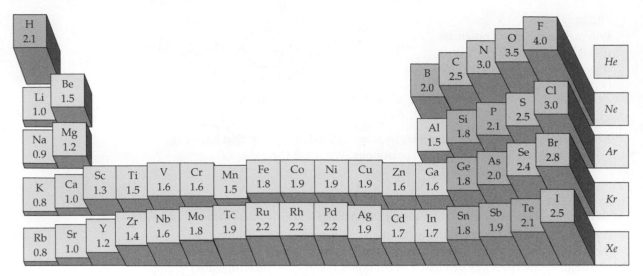

▲ **Figure 4.6**

Electronegativities of several main group and transition metal elements.
Reactive nonmetals at the top right of the periodic table are the most electronegative, and metals at the lower left are the least electronegative. The noble gases are not assigned values.

Electronegativity The ability of an atom to attract electrons in a covalent bond.

The ability of an atom to attract electrons in a covalent bond is called the atom's **electronegativity**. Fluorine, the most electronegative element, is assigned a value of 4, and less electronegative atoms are assigned lower values, as shown in Figure 4.6. Metallic elements on the left side of the periodic table attract electrons only weakly and have lower electronegativities, whereas the halogens and other reactive nonmetal elements on the upper right side of the table attract electrons strongly and have higher electronegativities. Note in Figure 4.6 that electronegativity generally decreases going down the periodic table within a group.

Comparing the electronegativities of bonded atoms makes it possible to compare the polarities of bonds and to predict the occurrence of ionic bonding. Both oxygen (electronegativity 3.5) and nitrogen (3.0), for instance, are more electronegative than carbon (2.5). As a result, both C—O and C—N bonds are polar, with carbon at the positive end. The larger difference in electronegativity values shows that the C—O bond is the more polar of the two:

Less polar
$^{\delta+}C$—$N^{\delta-}$
Electronegativity difference:
$3.0 - 2.5 = 0.5$

More polar
$^{\delta+}C$—$O^{\delta-}$
Electronegativity difference:
$3.5 - 2.5 = 1.0$

As a rule of thumb, electronegativity differences of less than 0.5 result in nonpolar covalent bonds, differences up to 1.9 indicate increasingly polar covalent bonds, and differences of 2 or more indicate ionic bonds. The electronegativity differences show, for example, that the bond between carbon and fluorine is highly polar covalent, the bond between sodium and chlorine is largely ionic, and the bond between rubidium and fluorine is almost completely ionic:

E.N difference		Type of bond
0 — 0.4	~	Covalent
0.5 — 1.9	~	Polar covalent
2.0 and above	~	Ionic

$^{\delta+}C$—$F^{\delta-}$ Na^+Cl^- Rb^+F^-

Electronegativity difference: 1.5 2.1 3.2

Note, though, that there is no sharp dividing line between covalent and ionic bonds; most bonds fall somewhere between two extremes.

LOOKING AHEAD ▶▶▶ The values given in Figure 4.6 indicate that carbon and hydrogen have similar electronegativities. As a result, C—H bonds are nonpolar. We will see in Chapters 12–25 how this fact helps explain the properties of organic and biological compounds, all of which have carbon and hydrogen as their principal constituents.

Worked Example 4.11 Electronegativity: Ionic, Nonpolar, and Polar Covalent Bonds

Predict whether each of the bonds between the following atoms would be ionic, polar covalent, or nonpolar covalent. If polar covalent, which atom would carry the partial positive and negative charges?

(a) C and Br   (b) Li and Cl

(c) N and H   (d) Si and I

ANALYSIS Compare the electronegativity values for the atoms and classify the nature of the bonding based on the electronegativity difference.

SOLUTION

(a) The electronegativity for C is 2.5, and for Br is 2.8; the difference is 0.3, indicating nonpolar covalent bonding would occur between these atoms.

(b) The electronegativity for Li is 1.0, and for Cl is 3.0; the difference is 2.0, indicating that ionic bonding would occur between these atoms.

(c) The electronegativity for N is 3.0, and for H is 2.5; the difference is 0.5. Bonding would be polar covalent, with $N = \delta-$ and $H = \delta+$.

(d) The electronegativity for Si is 1.8, and for I is 2.5; the difference is 0.7. Bonding would be polar covalent, with $I = \delta-$, and $Si = \delta+$.

PROBLEM 4.19
The elements H, N, O, P, and S are commonly bonded to carbon in organic compounds. Arrange these elements in order of increasing electronegativity.

PROBLEM 4.20
Use electronegativity differences to classify bonds between the following pairs of atoms as ionic, nonpolar covalent, or polar covalent. For those that are polar, use the symbols $\delta+$ and $\delta-$ to identify the location of the partial charges on the polar covalent bond.

(a) I and Cl   (b) Li and O

(c) Br and Br   (d) P and Br

4.10 Polar Molecules

Just as individual bonds can be polar, entire *molecules* can be polar if electrons are attracted more strongly to one part of the molecule than to another. Molecular polarity is due to the sum of all individual bond polarities and lone-pair contributions in the molecule and is often represented by an arrow pointing in the direction that electrons are displaced. The arrow is pointed at the negative end and is crossed at the positive end to resemble a plus sign, $(\delta+) \longmapsto (\delta-)$.

Molecular polarity depends on the shape of the molecule as well as the presence of polar covalent bonds and lone pairs. In water, for example, electrons are displaced away from the less electronegative hydrogen atoms toward the more electronegative oxygen atom so that the net polarity points between the two O—H bonds. In chloromethane, CH_3Cl, electrons are attracted from the carbon/hydrogen part of the molecule toward the electronegative chlorine atom so that the net polarity points along the C—Cl bond. Electrostatic potential maps show these polarities clearly, with electron-poor regions in blue and electron-rich regions in red.

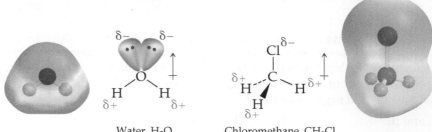

Water, H₂O   Chloromethane, CH₃Cl

Furthermore, just because a molecule has polar covalent bonds, it does not mean that the molecule is necessarily polar overall. Carbon dioxide (CO_2) and tetrachloromethane (CCl_4) molecules, for instance, have no net polarity because their symmetrical shapes cause the individual C=O and C—Cl bond polarities to cancel.

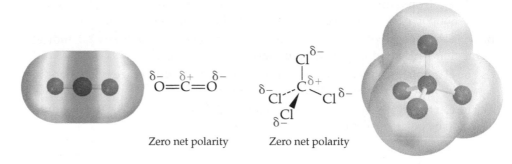

Zero net polarity   Zero net polarity

Polarity has a dramatic effect on the physical properties of molecules, particularly on melting points, boiling points, and solubilities. We will see numerous examples of such effects in subsequent chapters.

Worked Example 4.12 Electronegativity: Polar Bonds and Polar Molecules

Look at the structures of (a) hydrogen cyanide (HCN) and (b) vinyl chloride ($H_2C=CHCl$), described in Worked Examples 4.6 and 4.7, decide whether or not the molecules are polar, and show the direction of net polarity in each.

ANALYSIS Draw a Lewis structure for each molecule to find its shape, and identify any polar bonds using the electronegativity values in Figure 4.6. Then, decide on net polarity by adding the individual contributions.

SOLUTION

(a) The carbon atom in hydrogen cyanide has two charge clouds, making HCN a linear molecule. The C—H bond is relatively nonpolar, but the C≡N bonding electrons are pulled toward the electronegative nitrogen atom. In addition, a lone pair protrudes from nitrogen. Thus, the molecule has a net polarity:

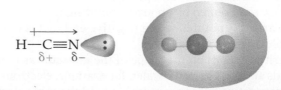

(b) Vinyl chloride, like ethylene, is a planar molecule. The C—H and C=C bonds are nonpolar, but the C—Cl bonding electrons are displaced toward the electronegative chlorine. Thus, the molecule has a net polarity:

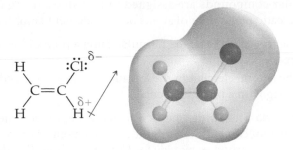

PROBLEM 4.21
Look at the molecular shape of formaldehyde (CH_2O) described on page 115, decide whether or not the molecule is polar, and show the direction of net polarity.

PROBLEM 4.22
Draw a Lewis structure for dimethyl ether (CH_3OCH_3), predict its shape, and tell whether or not the molecule is polar.

🔑 **KEY CONCEPT PROBLEM 4.23**

From this electrostatic potential map of methyllithium, identify the direction of net polarity in the molecule. Explain this polarity based on electronegativity values.

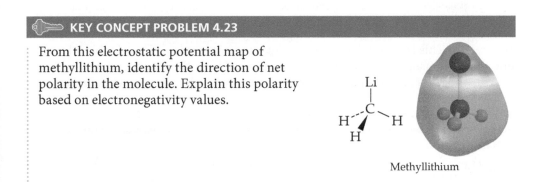

Methyllithium

4.11 Naming Binary Molecular Compounds

When two different elements combine, they form what is called a **binary compound**. The formulas of binary molecular compounds are usually written with the less electronegative element first. Thus, metals are always written before nonmetals, and a nonmetal farther left on the periodic table generally comes before a nonmetal farther right. For example,

Binary compound A compound formed by combination of two different elements.

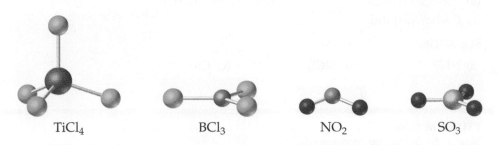

TiCl$_4$ BCl$_3$ NO$_2$ SO$_3$

As we learned in Section 3.9, the formulas of ionic compounds indicate the number of anions and cations necessary for a neutral formula unit, which depends on the charge on each of the ions. With molecular compounds, however, many combinations of atoms are possible, since nonmetals are capable of forming multiple covalent bonds.

TABLE 4.3 Numerical Prefixes Used in Chemical Names

Number	Prefix
1	mono-
2	di-
3	tri-
4	tetra-
5	penta-
6	hexa-
7	hepta-
8	octa-
9	nona-
10	deca-

When naming binary molecular compounds, therefore, we must identify exactly how many atoms of each element are included in the molecular formula. The names of binary molecular compounds are assigned in two steps, using the prefixes listed in Table 4.3 to indicate the number of atoms of each element combined.

STEP 1: Name the first element in the formula, using a prefix if needed to indicate the number of atoms.

STEP 2: Name the second element in the formula, using an *-ide* ending like for anions (Section 3.7), along with a prefix if needed.

The prefix *mono-*, meaning one, is omitted except where needed to distinguish between two different compounds with the same elements. For example, the two oxides of carbon are named carbon *mon*oxide for CO and carbon *di*oxide for CO_2. (Note that we say *mon*oxide rather than *mono*oxide.) Some other examples are:

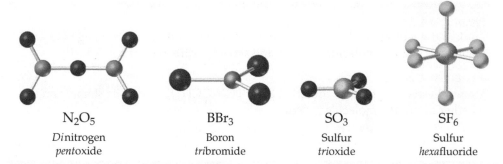

N_2O_5	BBr_3	SO_3	SF_6
*Di*nitrogen *pent*oxide	Boron *tri*bromide	Sulfur trioxide	Sulfur *hexa*fluoride

Naming of molecular compounds can get complicated when more than two elements are present. This is particularly true for *organic compounds*, a class of molecular compounds composed largely of carbon (see examples in the Chemistry in Action on p. 125). The rules for naming these compounds will be discussed in later chapters.

Worked Example 4.13 Naming Molecular Compounds

Name the following compounds:

(a) N_2O_3 (b) $GeCl_4$ (c) PCl_5

SOLUTION

(a) Dinitrogen trioxide   (b) Germanium tetrachloride
(c) Phosphorus pentachloride

Worked Example 4.14 Writing Formulas for Molecular Compounds

Write molecular formulas for the following compounds:

(a) Nitrogen triiodide   (b) Silicon tetrachloride
(c) Carbon disulfide

SOLUTION

(a) NI_3 (b) $SiCl_4$ (c) CS_2

PROBLEM 4.24
Name the following compounds:

(a) S_2Cl_2 (b) ICl   (c) ICl_3

PROBLEM 4.25
Write formulas for the following compounds:
(a) Selenium tetrafluoride   (b) Diphosphorus pentoxide   (c) Bromine trifluoride

PROBLEM 4.26
Geraniol, one of the components of rose oil (see the following Chemistry in Action). has the basic structure represented below. Draw the structural formula for geraniol to include any multiple bonds, and then write the condensed structure for geraniol.

$$CH_3-\underset{\underset{H}{|}}{\overset{\overset{CH_3}{|}}{C}}-\underset{\underset{H}{|}}{\overset{\overset{H}{|}}{C}}-\underset{\underset{H}{|}}{\overset{\overset{H}{|}}{C}}-\underset{\underset{H}{|}}{\overset{\overset{CH_3}{|}}{C}}-\underset{\underset{H}{|}}{C}-\underset{\underset{H}{|}}{\overset{\overset{H}{|}}{C}}-OH$$

CHEMISTRY IN ACTION

Damascenone by Any Other Name Would Smell as Sweet

What's in a name? According to Shakespeare's *Romeo and Juliet,* a rose by any other name would smell as sweet. Chemical names, however, often provoke less favorable responses: "It's unpronounceable." "It's too complicated." "It must be something bad."

But why are chemical names so complicated? The reason is obvious once you realize that there are more than 19 *million* known chemical compounds. The full name of a chemical compound has to include enough information to tell chemists the composition and structure of the compound. It is as if every person on earth had to have his or her own unique name that described height, hair color, and other identifying characteristics in sufficient detail to distinguish him or her from every other person. Consider, also, that subtle differences in structure can result in significant differences in chemical or physical properties. Geraniol, for example, is used as a flavor additive in the food industry, while citronellol is used in perfumes and insect repellants, such as citronella candles. The common names for these substances are easier to remember, but their *chemical* names give us precise information about their structural differences and similarities. Geraniol ($C_{10}H_{18}O$), also known as *3,7-dimethylocta-2, 6-dien-1-ol* differs from citronellol ($C_{10}H_{20}O$ or *3,7-dimethyloct-6-en-1-ol*) by only one C—C double bond.

Unfortunately, people sometimes conclude that everything with a chemical name is unnatural and dangerous. Neither is true, of course. Acetaldehyde, for instance, is present naturally in most tart, ripe fruits and is often added in small amounts to artificial flavorings. When *pure*, however, acetaldehyde

▲ The scent of these roses contains β-damascenone, β-ionone, citronellol, geraniol, nerol, eugenol, methyl eugenol, β-phenylethyl, alcohol, farnesol, linalool, terpineol, rose oxide, carvone, and many other natural substances.

is also a flammable gas that is toxic and explosive in high concentrations.

Similar comparisons of desirable and harmful properties can be made for almost all chemicals, including water, sugar, and salt. The properties of a substance and the conditions surrounding its use must be evaluated before judgments are made. Damascenone, geraniol, and citronellol, by the way, are chemicals that contribute to the wonderful aroma of roses.

See Chemistry in Action Problems 4.93 and 4.94 at the end of the chapter.

SUMMARY: REVISITING THE CHAPTER GOALS

1. What is a covalent bond? A *covalent bond* is formed by the sharing of electrons between atoms rather than by the complete transfer of electrons from one atom to another. Atoms that share 2 electrons are joined by a *single bond* (such as C—C), atoms that share 4 electrons are joined by a *double bond* (such as C=C), and atoms that share 6 electrons are joined by a *triple* bond (such as C≡C). The group of atoms held together by covalent bonds is called a *molecule.*

Electron sharing typically occurs when a singly occupied valence orbital on one atom *overlaps* a singly occupied valence orbital on another atom. The 2 electrons occupy both overlapping orbitals and belong to both atoms, thereby bonding the atoms together. Alternatively, electron sharing can occur when a filled orbital containing an unshared, *lone pair* of electrons on one atom overlaps a vacant orbital on another atom to form a *coordinate covalent bond* (see Problems 33–35, 40, 41, 44, 45, 89, 92).

2. How does the octet rule apply to covalent bond formation? Depending on the number of valence electrons, different atoms form different numbers of covalent bonds. In general, an atom shares enough electrons to reach a noble gas configuration. Hydrogen, for instance, forms 1 covalent bond because it needs to share 1 more electron to achieve the helium configuration ($1s^2$). Carbon and other group 4A elements form 4 covalent bonds because they need to share 4 more electrons to reach an octet. In the same way, nitrogen and other group 5A elements form 3 covalent bonds, oxygen and other group 6A elements form 2 covalent bonds, and halogens (group 7A elements) form 1 covalent bond (see Problems 38, 39, 50, 51, 95).

3. What are the major differences between ionic and molecular compounds? *Molecular compounds* can be gases, liquids, or low-melting solids. They usually have lower melting points and boiling points than ionic compounds, many are water insoluble, and they do not conduct electricity when melted or dissolved (see Problems 33, 35–37, 42, 43, 47, 99, 102, 103).

4. How are molecular compounds represented? Formulas such as H_2O, NH_3, and CH_4, which show the numbers and kinds of atoms in a molecule, are called *molecular formulas*. More useful are *Lewis structures*, which show how atoms are connected in molecules. Covalent bonds are indicated as lines between atoms, and valence electron lone pairs are shown as dots. Lewis struc-

tures are drawn by counting the total number of valence electrons in a molecule or polyatomic ion and then placing shared pairs (bonding) and lone pairs (nonbonding) so that all electrons are accounted for (see Problems 30, 46–66, 94–100, 104–109).

5. What is the influence of valence-shell electrons on molecular shape? Molecules have specific shapes that depend on the number of electron charge clouds (bonds and lone pairs) surrounding the various atoms. These shapes can often be predicted using the *valence-shell electron-pair repulsion* (*VSEPR*) model. Atoms with two electron charge clouds adopt linear geometry, atoms with three charge clouds adopt trigonal planar geometry, and atoms with four charge clouds adopt tetrahedral geometry (see Problems 27, 28–31, 67–72, 81, 96, 100, 109).

6. When are bonds and molecules polar? Bonds between atoms are *polar covalent* if the bonding electrons are not shared equally between the atoms. The ability of an atom to attract electrons in a covalent bond is the atom's *electronegativity* and is highest for reactive nonmetal elements on the upper right of the periodic table and lowest for metals on the lower left. Comparing electronegativities allows prediction of whether a given bond is covalent, polar covalent, or ionic. Just as individual bonds can be polar, entire molecules can be polar if electrons are attracted more strongly to one part of the molecule than to another. Molecular polarity is due to the sum of all individual bond polarities and lone-pair contributions in the molecule (see Problems 32, 73–84, 96, 97, 101).

CONCEPT MAP: ELECTROSTATIC FORCES

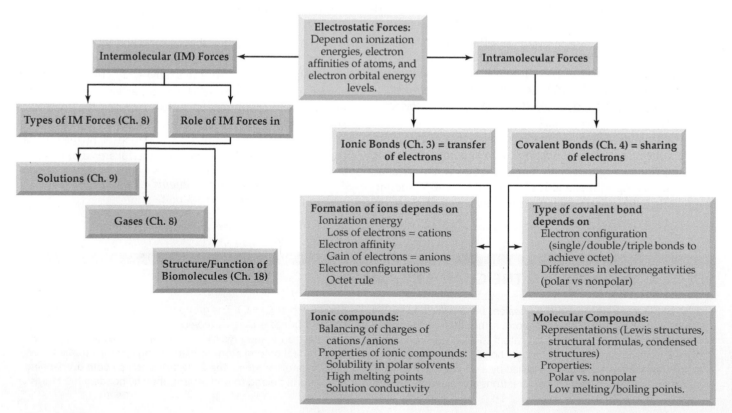

▲ **Figure 4.7**

Concept Maps. Chemistry, like most subjects, makes more sense when presented in context. When we understand the connections between concepts, or how one idea leads to another, it becomes easier to see the "big picture" and to appreciate why a certain concept is important. A concept map is one way of illustrating those connections and providing a context for what we have learned and what we will be learning in later chapters.

As you can see from the concept map in Figure 4.7, the electronic structure of atoms discussed in Chapter 2 plays a critical role in the chemical behavior of an element, specifically in terms of its tendency to form ionic compounds (Chapter 3) or molecular compounds (Chapter 4). Furthermore, the nature of the attractive forces between particles (intermolecular versus intramolecular) plays a role in the physical and chemical behavior of substances discussed in later chapters.

As we continue exploring new topics, we will expand certain areas of this concept map or add new branches as needed.

KEY WORDS

Binary compound, *p. 123*

Bond angle, *p. 115*

Bond length, *p. 100*

Condensed structure, *p. 109*

Coordinate covalent bond, *p. 106*

Covalent bond, *p. 99*

Double bond, *p. 104*

Electronegativity, *p. 120*

Lewis structure, *p. 108*

Lone pair, *p. 108*

Molecular compound, *p. 101*

Molecular formula, *p. 108*

Molecule, *p. 99*

Polar covalent bond, *p. 119*

Regular tetrahedron, *p. 116*

Single bond, *p. 104*

Structural formula, *p. 108*

Triple bond, *p. 104*

Valence-shell electron-pair repulsion (VSEPR) model, *p. 114*

UNDERSTANDING KEY CONCEPTS

4.27 What is the geometry around the central atom in the following molecular models? (There are no "hidden" atoms; all atoms in each model are visible.)

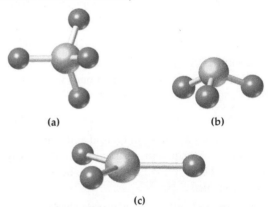

(a)   (b)

(c)

4.28 Three of the following molecular models have a tetrahedral central atom, and one does not. Which is the odd one?

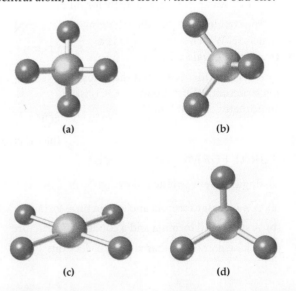

(a)   (b)

(c)   (d)

4.29 The ball-and-stick molecular model shown here is a representation of acetaminophen, the active ingredient in over-the-counter headache remedies such as Tylenol. The lines indicate only the connections between atoms, not whether the bonds are single, double, or triple (red = O, gray = C, blue = N, ivory = H).

(a) What is the molecular formula of acetaminophen?

(b) Indicate the positions of the multiple bonds in acetaminophen.

(c) What is the geometry around each carbon and each nitrogen?

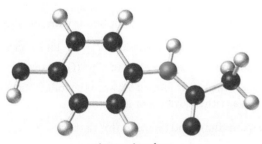

Acetaminophen

4.30 The atom-to-atom connections in vitamin C (ascorbic acid) are as shown here. Convert this skeletal drawing to a Lewis electron-dot structure for vitamin C by showing the positions of any multiple bonds and lone pairs of electrons.

Vitamin C

4.31   The ball-and-stick molecular model shown here is a representation of thalidomide, a drug that has been approved for treating leprosy, but causes severe birth defects when taken by expectant mothers. The lines indicate only the connections between atoms, not whether the bonds are single, double, or triple (red = O, gray = C, blue = N, ivory = H).

   (a) What is the molecular formula of thalidomide?

   (b) Indicate the positions of the multiple bonds in thalidomide.

   (c) What is the geometry around each carbon and each nitrogen?

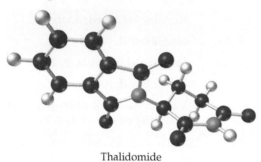

Thalidomide

4.32   Show the position of any electron lone pairs in this structure of acetamide, and indicate the electron-rich and electron-poor regions.

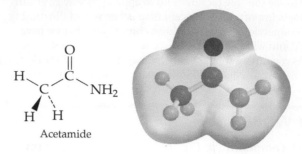

Acetamide

ADDITIONAL PROBLEMS

COVALENT BONDS

4.33   What is a covalent bond, and how does it differ from an ionic bond?

4.34   What is a coordinate covalent bond, and how does it differ from a covalent bond?

4.35   Which of the following elements would you expect to form (i) diatomic molecules, (ii) mainly covalent bonds, (iii) mainly ionic bonds, (iv) both covalent and ionic bonds? (More than one answer may apply; remember that some nonmetals can form ionic bonds with metals.)

   (a) Oxygen   **(b)** Potassium   **(c)** Phosphorus

   (d) Iodine   **(e)** Hydrogen   **(f)** Cesium

4.36   Identify the bonds formed between the following pairs of atoms as either covalent or ionic.

   (a) Aluminum and bromine   **(b)** Carbon and fluorine

   (c) Cesium and iodine   **(d)** Zinc and fluorine

   (e) Lithium and chlorine

4.37   Write electron-dot symbols to show the number of covalent bonds and the lone pairs of electrons in the molecules that are formed by reactions between the atoms in Problem 4.36.

4.38   Look up tellurium ($Z = 52$) in the periodic table and predict how many covalent bonds it is likely to form. Explain.

4.39   Look up antimony in the periodic table ($Z = 51$). How many covalent bonds would you expect it to form? Based on this information, which of the following antimony compounds is covalent and which is ionic: $SbCl_3$ or $SbCl_5$?

4.40   Which of the following contains a coordinate covalent bond? (Hint: how many covalent bonds would you expect the central atom (underlined) to form?)

   (a) $\underline{Pb}Cl_2$ **(b)** $\underline{Cu}(NH_3)_4^{2+}$ **(c)** $\underline{N}H_4^+$

4.41   Which of the following contains a coordinate covalent bond? (Hint: how many covalent bonds would you expect the central atom (underlined) to form?)

   (a) $H_2\underline{O}$ **(b)** $\underline{B}F_4^-$ **(c)** $H_3\underline{O}^+$

4.42   Tin forms both an ionic compound and a covalent compound with chlorine. The ionic compound is $SnCl_2$. Is the covalent compound more likely to be $SnCl_3$, $SnCl_4$, or $SnCl_5$? Explain.

4.43   A compound of gallium with chlorine has a melting point of 77 °C and a boiling point of 201 °C. Is the compound ionic or covalent? What is a likely formula?

4.44   Nitrous oxide, N_2O, has the following structure. Which bond in N_2O is a coordinate covalent bond?

$:N\equiv N-\ddot{O}:$

Nitrous oxide

4.45   Thionyl chloride, $SOCl_2$ has the following structure. Which bond in $SOCl_2$ is a coordinate covalent bond?

Thionyl chloride

STRUCTURAL FORMULAS

4.46   Distinguish between the following:

   (a) A molecular formula and a structural formula

   (b) A structural formula and a condensed structure

   (c) A lone pair and a shared pair of electrons

4.47 Assume that you are given samples of two white crystalline compounds, one of them ionic and one covalent. Describe how you might tell which is which.

4.48 Determine the total number of valence electrons in the following molecules. If the molecule contains multiple bonds, indicate where the multiple bonds are located and whether they are double or triple bonds.

(a) N_2 (b) NOCl

(c) CH_3CH_2CHO (d) OF_2

4.49 Add lone pairs where appropriate to the following structures:

(a) $C\equiv O$ (b) CH_3SH

(c) $\left[H-\underset{\overset{|}{H}}{O}-H \right]^+$ (d) $H_3C-\underset{\overset{|}{H}}{N}-CH_3$

4.50 If a research paper appeared reporting the structure of a new molecule with formula C_2H_8 most chemists would be highly skeptical. Why?

4.51 Consider the following possible structural formulas for $C_3H_6O_2$. If a structure is not reasonable, explain what changes could be made to convert it to a reasonable structure.

(a) $H-\overset{\overset{H}{|}}{\underset{\overset{|}{H}}{C}}-\overset{\overset{H}{|}}{\underset{\overset{|}{H}}{C}}-\overset{\overset{O}{\|}}{C}-OH$

(b) $H-\overset{\overset{H}{|}}{\underset{\overset{|}{H}}{C}}-\overset{\overset{OH}{|}}{\underset{\overset{|}{OH}}{C}}-\overset{\overset{H}{|}}{C}-H$ (c) $H-\overset{\overset{H}{|}}{\underset{\overset{|}{H}}{C}}-O-\overset{\overset{H}{|}}{\underset{\overset{|}{H}}{C}}-C=O$

4.52 Convert the following Lewis structures into structural formulas in which lines replace the bonding electrons. Include the lone pairs.

(a) $H:\ddot{O}:\ddot{N}::\ddot{O}:$ (b) $H:\overset{\overset{H}{..}}{\underset{\overset{..}{H}}{C}}:C:::N:$ (c) $H:\ddot{\underset{..}{F}}:$

4.53 Convert the following Lewis structure for the nitrate ion into a line structure that includes the lone pairs. Why does the nitrate ion have a −1 charge? $\left[:\ddot{O}:\overset{\overset{:O:}{..}}{\underset{..}{N}}:\ddot{O}: \right]^-$

4.54 Convert the following structural formulas into condensed structures.

(a) $H-\overset{\overset{H}{|}}{\underset{\overset{|}{H}}{C}}-\overset{\overset{H}{|}}{\underset{\overset{|}{H}}{C}}-\overset{\overset{H}{|}}{\underset{\overset{|}{H}}{C}}-H$ (b) $\underset{\overset{|}{H}}{\overset{\overset{H}{\diagdown}}{}}C=C\underset{\overset{|}{H}}{\overset{\overset{H}{\diagup}}{}}$ (with extra H's)

(c) $H-\overset{\overset{H}{|}}{\underset{\overset{|}{H}}{C}}-\overset{\overset{H}{|}}{\underset{\overset{|}{H}}{C}}-Cl$

4.55 Expand the following condensed structures into the correct structural formulas.

(a) $CH_3CH_2COCH(CH_3)_2$ (b) $CH_3CH_2COOCH_3$

(c) $CH_3CH_2OCH_2Cl$

4.56 Acetic acid is the major organic constituent of vinegar. Convert the following structural formula of acetic acid into a condensed structure similar to those shown in Problem 4.55.

$$ H-\overset{\overset{H}{|}}{\underset{\overset{|}{H}}{C}}-\overset{\overset{O}{\|}}{C}-O-H $$

DRAWING LEWIS STRUCTURES

4.57 Draw a Lewis structure for the following molecules:

(a) SF_6 (b) $AlCl_3$ (c) CS_2 (d) SeF_4

(e) $BeCl_2$ (Note: this molecule does not follow the octet rule.)

(f) N_2O_4

4.58 Draw a Lewis structure for the following molecules:

(a) Nitrous acid, HNO_2 (H is bonded to an O atom)

(b) Ozone, O_3

(c) Acetaldehyde, CH_3CHO

4.59 Ethanol, or "grain alcohol," has the formula C_2H_6O and contains an O—H bond. Propose a structure for ethanol that is consistent with common bonding patterns.

4.60 Dimethyl ether has the same molecular formula as ethanol (Problem 4.59) but very different properties. Propose a structure for dimethyl ether in which the oxygen is bonded to two carbons.

4.61 Hydrazine, a substance used to make rocket fuel, has the formula N_2H_4. Propose a structure for hydrazine.

4.62 Tetrachloroethylene, C_2Cl_4, is used commercially as a dry-cleaning solvent. Propose a structure for tetrachloroethylene based on the common bonding patterns expected in organic molecules. What kind of carbon-carbon bond is present?

4.63 Dimethyl sulfoxide, also known as DMSO, is an important organic solvent often used for drug delivery since it readily penetrates the skin. The formula for DMSO is $(CH_3)_2SO$. Draw a Lewis structure of DMSO; both C atoms are attached to the S atom.

4.64 Draw a Lewis structure for hydroxylamine, NH_2OH.

4.65 The carbonate ion, CO_3^{2-}, contains a double bond. Draw a Lewis structure for the ion and show why it has a charge of −2.

4.66 Draw a Lewis structure for the following polyatomic ions:

(a) Formate, HCO_2^- (b) Sulfite, SO_3^{2-}

(c) Thiocyanate, SCN^- (d) Phosphate, PO_4^{3+}

(e) Chlorite, ClO_2^- (chlorine is the central atom)

MOLECULAR GEOMETRY

4.67 Predict the geometry and bond angles around atom A for molecules with the general formulas AB_3 and AB_2E, where B represents another atom and E represents an electron pair.

4.68 Predict the geometry and bond angles around atom A for molecules with the general formulas AB_4, AB_3E, and AB_2E_2, where B represents another atom and E represents an electron pair.

4.69 Sketch the three-dimensional shape of the following molecules:

(a) Methylamine, CH_3NH_2 (b) Iodoform, CHI_3

(c) Ozone, O_3

(d) Phosphorus pentachloride, PCl_5

(e) Chloric acid, $HClO_3$.

4.70 Predict the three-dimensional shape of the following molecules:

(a) SiF_4 (b) CF_2Cl_2 (c) SO_3

(d) BBr_3 (e) NF_3

4.71 Predict the geometry around each carbon atom in the amino acid alanine.

$$CH_3CHCOH$$
with O double bonded above C and NH_2 below the second carbon

Alanine

4.72 Predict the geometry around each carbon atom in vinyl acetate, a precursor of the polyvinyl alcohol polymer used in automobile safety glass.

$$H_2C=CH-O-C-CH_3$$
with O double bonded above the C

Vinyl acetate

POLARITY OF BONDS AND MOLECULES

4.73 Where in the periodic table are the most electronegative elements found, and where are the least electronegative elements found?

4.74 Predict the electronegativity of the yet-undiscovered element with $Z = 119$.

4.75 Look at the periodic table, and then order the following elements according to increasing electronegativity: K, Si, Be, O, B.

4.76 Look at the periodic table, and then order the following elements according to decreasing electronegativity: C, Ca, Cs, Cl, Cu.

4.77 Which of the following bonds are polar? If a bond is polar, identify the negative and positive ends of each bond by using $\delta+$ and $\delta-$.

(a) I—Br   (b) O—H

(c) C—F   (d) N—C

(e) C—C

4.78 Which of the following bonds are polar? If a bond is polar, identify the negative and positive ends of each bond by using $\delta+$ and $\delta-$.

(a) O—Cl   (b) N—Cl

(c) P—H   (d) C—I

(e) C—O

4.79 Based on electronegativity differences, would you expect bonds between the following pairs of atoms to be largely ionic or largely covalent?

(a) Be and F   (b) Ca and Cl

(c) O and H   (d) Be and Br

4.80 Arrange the following molecules in order of the increasing polarity of their bonds:

(a) HCl   (b) PH_3

(c) H_2O (d) CF_4

4.81 Ammonia, NH_3, and phosphorus trihydride, PH_3, both have a trigonal pyramid geometry. Which one is more polar? Explain.

4.82 Decide whether each of the compounds listed in Problem 4.80 is polar, and show the direction of polarity.

4.83 Carbon dioxide is a nonpolar molecule, whereas sulfur dioxide is polar. Draw Lewis structures for each of these molecules to explain this observation.

4.84 Water (H_2O) is more polar than hydrogen sulfide (H_2S). Explain.

NAMES AND FORMULAS OF MOLECULAR COMPOUNDS

4.85 Name the following binary compounds:

(a) PI_3 (b) $AsCl_3$ (c) P_4S_3

(d) Al_2F_6 (e) N_2O_5 (f) $AsCl_5$

4.86 Name the following compounds:

(a) SeO_2 (b) XeO_4

(c) N_2S_5 (d) P_3Se_4

4.87 Write formulas for the following compounds:

(a) Nitrogen dioxide   (b) Sulfur hexafluoride

(c) Bromine triiodide   (d) Dinitrogen trioxide

(e) Nitrogen triiodide   (f) Iodine heptafluoride

4.88 Write formulas for the following compounds:

(a) Silicon tetrachloride   (b) Sodium hydride

(c) Antimony pentafluoride   (d) Osmium tetroxide

CHEMISTRY IN ACTION

4.89 The CO molecule is highly reactive and will bind to the Fe^{2+} ion in hemoglobin and interfere with O_2 transport. What type of bond is formed between the CO molecule and the Fe^{2+} ion? [*CO and NO: Pollutants or Miracle Molecules?*, p. 113]

4.90 What is a vasodilator, and why would it be useful in treating hypertension (high blood pressure)? [*CO and NO: Pollutants or Miracle Molecules?, p. 113*]

4.91 How is a polymer formed? [*VERY Big Molecules, p. 118*]

4.92 Do any polymers exist in nature? Explain. [*VERY Big Molecules, p. 118*]

4.93 Why are many chemical names so complex? [*Damascenone by Any Other Name, p. 125*]

4.94 Citronellol, one of the compounds found in the scent of roses, is also used in perfumes and in insect repellent products. Write the condensed formula from the structural formula of citronellol shown below. [*Damascenone by Any Other Name, p. 125*]

$$CH_3-\underset{\underset{H}{|}}{\overset{\overset{CH_3}{|}}{C}}=\underset{\underset{H}{|}}{\overset{\overset{H}{|}}{C}}-\underset{\underset{H}{|}}{\overset{\overset{H}{|}}{C}}-\underset{\underset{H}{|}}{\overset{\overset{CH_3}{|}}{C}}-\underset{\underset{H}{|}}{\overset{\overset{H}{|}}{C}}-\underset{\underset{H}{|}}{\overset{\overset{H}{|}}{C}}-OH$$

GENERAL QUESTIONS AND PROBLEMS

4.95 The discovery in the 1960s that xenon and fluorine react to form a molecular compound was a surprise to most chemists, because it had been thought that noble gases could not form bonds.

(a) Why was it thought that noble gases could not form bonds?

(b) Draw a Lewis structure of XeF_4 in which Xe is the central atom. How many electron clouds are there on the central atom?

(c) What type of bonds are the Xe—F bonds? Explain.

4.96 Acetone, a common solvent used in some nail polish removers, has the molecular formula C_3H_6O and contains a carbon-oxygen double bond.

(a) Propose two Lewis structures for acetone.

(b) What is the geometry around the carbon atoms in each of the structures?

(c) Which of the bonds in each structure are polar?

4.97 Draw the structural formulas for two compounds having the molecular formula C_2H_4O. What is the molecular geometry around the carbon atoms in each of these molecules? Would these molecules be polar or nonpolar? (Hint: there is one double bond.)

4.98 The following formulas are unlikely to be correct. What is wrong with each?

(a) CCl_3 (b) N_2H_5

(c) H_3S (d) C_2OS

4.99 Which of the compounds (a) through (d) contain ionic bonds? Which contain covalent bonds? Which contain coordinate covalent bonds? (A compound may contain more than one type of bond.)

(a) $BaCl_2$ (b) $Ca(NO_3)_2$

(c) BCl_4^- (d) $TiBr_4$

4.100 The phosphonium ion, PH_4^+, is formed by reaction of phosphine, PH_3, with an acid.

(a) Draw the Lewis structure of the phosphonium ion.

(b) Predict its molecular geometry.

(c) Describe how a fourth hydrogen can be added to PH_3.

(d) Explain why the ion has a +1 charge.

4.101 Compare the trend in electronegativity seen in Figure 4.6 (p. 120) with the trend in electron affinity shown in Figure 3.1 (p. 75). What similarities do you see? What differences? Explain.

4.102 Name the following compounds. Be sure to determine whether the compound is ionic or covalent so that you use the proper rules.

(a) $CaCl_2$ (b) $TeCl_2$ (c) BF_3

(d) $MgSO_4$ (e) K_2O (f) FeF_3

(g) PF_3

4.103 Titanium forms both molecular and ionic compounds with nonmetals, as, for example, $TiBr_4$ and TiO_2. One of these compounds has a melting point of 39 °C, and the other has a melting point of 1825 °C. Which is ionic and which is molecular? Explain your answer in terms of electronegativities of the atoms involved in each compound.

4.104 Draw a Lewis structure for chloral hydrate, known in detective novels as "knockout drops." Indicate all lone pairs.

$$Cl-\underset{\underset{Cl}{|}}{\overset{\overset{Cl}{|}}{C}}-\underset{\underset{H}{|}}{\overset{\overset{O-H}{|}}{C}}-O-H \qquad \text{Chloral hydrate}$$

4.105 The dichromate ion, $Cr_2O_7{}^{2-}$, has neither Cr—Cr nor O—O bonds. Draw a Lewis structure.

4.106 Oxalic acid, $H_2C_2O_4$, is a substance found in uncooked spinach leaves and other greens that can be poisonous at high concentrations (for example, in raw rhubarb leaves). If oxalic acid has a C—C single bond and the H atoms are both connected to O atoms, draw its Lewis structure.

4.107 Identify the fourth row elements represented by "X" in the following compounds.

(a) $\ddot{\text{O}}=\ddot{\text{X}}=\ddot{\text{O}}$ (b) $:\!\ddot{\text{F}}\!\diagdown_{\!\!\ddot{\text{X}}\!:}\!\diagup\!\ddot{\text{F}}\!:$

4.108 Write Lewis structures for molecules with the following connections, showing the positions of any multiple bonds and lone pairs of electrons.

(a) $Cl-\underset{}{\overset{\overset{O}{\|}}{C}}-O-\underset{\underset{H}{|}}{\overset{\overset{H}{|}}{C}}-H$ (b) $H-\underset{\underset{H}{|}}{\overset{\overset{H}{|}}{C}}-C-\underset{}{\overset{\overset{H}{|}}{C}}-H$

4.109 Electron-pair repulsion influences the shapes of polyatomic ions in the same way it influences neutral molecules. Draw electron-dot symbols and predict the shape of the ammonium ion, NH_4^+, the sulfate ion, $SO_4{}^{2-}$, and the phosphite ion, $PO_3{}^{3-}$.

CHAPTER 5

Classification and Balancing of Chemical Reactions

CONTENTS

◄ Water reclamation and purification plants utilize the many different types of chemical reactions discussed in this chapter.

1. **How are chemical reactions written?**
   THE GOAL: Given the identities of reactants and products, be able to write a balanced chemical equation or net ionic equation.

2. **How are chemical reactions of ionic compounds classified?**
   THE GOAL: Be able to recognize precipitation, acid–base neutralization, and redox reactions.

3. **What are oxidation numbers, and how are they used?**
   THE GOAL: Be able to assign oxidation numbers to atoms in compounds and identify the substances oxidized and reduced in a given reaction. (◀◀ A.)

4. **What is a net ionic equation?**
   THE GOAL: Be able to recognize spectator ions and write the net ionic equation for reactions involving ionic compounds. (◀◀ A, B.)

A log burns in the fireplace, an oyster makes a pearl, a seed grows into a plant—these and almost all the other changes you see taking place around you are the result of chemical reactions. The study of how and why chemical reactions happen is a major part of chemistry, providing information that is both fascinating and practical. In this chapter, we will begin to look at chemical reactions, starting with a discussion of how to represent them in writing. We will then examine how to balance reactions and how to recognize different types or classes of chemical reactions.

5.1 Chemical Equations

One way to view chemical reactions is to think of them as "recipes." Like recipes, all the "ingredients" in a chemical equation and their relative amounts are given, as well as the amount of product that would be obtained. Take, for example, a recipe for making S'mores, a concoction of chocolate, marshmallows, and graham crackers, which could be written as:

Graham crackers + Roasted marshmallows + Chocolate bars $\longrightarrow$ S'mores

This recipe, however, is simply a list of ingredients and gives no indication of the relative amounts of each ingredient, or how many s'mores we would obtain. A more detailed recipe would be:

2 Graham crackers + 1 Roasted marshmallow + $\frac{1}{4}$ Chocolate bar $\longrightarrow$ 1 S'more

In this case, the relative amounts of each ingredient are given, as well as the amount of the final product.

Let us extend this analogy to a typical chemical reaction. When sodium bicarbonate is heated in the range 50–100 °C, sodium carbonate, water, and carbon dioxide are produced. In words, we might write the reaction as:

Sodium bicarbonate $\xrightarrow{\text{Heat}}$ Sodium carbonate + Water + Carbon dioxide

Just as in the recipe, the starting materials and final products are listed. Replacing the chemical names with formulas converts the word description of this reaction into a **chemical equation:**

$$2\,\underbrace{NaHCO_3}_{\text{Reactant}} \xrightarrow{\text{Heat}} \underbrace{Na_2CO_3 + H_2O + CO_2}_{\text{Products}}$$

Look at how this equation is written. The **reactants** are written on the left, the **products** are written on the right, and an arrow is placed between them to indicate a chemical change. Conditions necessary for the reaction to occur—heat in this particular instance—are often specified above the arrow.

Why is the number 2 placed before $NaHCO_3$ in the equation? The 2 is necessary because of a fundamental law of nature called the **law of conservation of mass**, which states that matter can neither be created nor destroyed in a chemical reaction.

Chemical equation An expression in which symbols and formulas are used to represent a chemical reaction.

Reactant A substance that undergoes change in a chemical reaction and is written on the left side of the reaction arrow in a chemical equation.

Product A substance that is formed in a chemical reaction and is written on the right side of the reaction arrow in a chemical equation.

Balanced equation A chemical equation in which the numbers and kinds of atoms are the same on both sides of the reaction arrow.

Coefficient A number placed in front of a formula to balance a chemical equation.

The bonds between atoms in the reactants are rearranged to form new compounds in chemical reactions, but none of the atoms disappear and no new ones are formed. As a consequence, chemical equations must be **balanced**, meaning that *the numbers and kinds of atoms must be the same on both sides of the reaction arrow.*

Law of conservation of mass Matter is neither created nor destroyed in chemical reactions.

The numbers placed in front of formulas to balance equations are called **coefficients**, and they multiply all the atoms in a formula. Thus, the symbol "2 NaHCO$_3$" indicates two units of sodium bicarbonate, which contain 2 Na atoms, 2 H atoms, 2 C atoms, and 6 O atoms ($2 \times 3 = 6$, the coefficient times the subscript for O). Count the numbers of atoms on the right side of the equation to convince yourself that it is indeed balanced.

The substances that take part in chemical reactions may be solids, liquids, or gases, or they may be dissolved in a solvent. Ionic compounds, in particular, frequently undergo reactions in *aqueous solution*—that is, when they are dissolved in water. Sometimes this information is added to an equation by placing the appropriate abbreviations after the formulas:

$$(s) \qquad (l) \qquad (g) \qquad (aq)$$

Solid   Liquid   Gas   Aqueous solution

Thus, the decomposition of solid sodium bicarbonate can be written as

$$2\,NaHCO_3(s) \xrightarrow{\text{Heat}} Na_2CO_3(s) + H_2O(l) + CO_2(g)$$

Worked Example 5.1 Balancing Chemical Reactions

Use words to explain the following equation for the reaction used in extracting lead metal from its ores. Show that the equation is balanced.

$$2\,PbS(s) + 3\,O_2(g) \longrightarrow 2\,PbO(s) + 2\,SO_2(g)$$

SOLUTION

The equation can be read as, "Solid lead(II) sulfide plus gaseous oxygen yields solid lead(II) oxide plus gaseous sulfur dioxide."

To show that the equation is balanced, count the atoms of each element on each side of the arrow:

On the left: 2 Pb   2 S $(3 \times 2)\,O = 6\,O$

On the right: 2 Pb   2 S $2\,O + (2 \times 2)\,O = 6\,O$

From 2 PbO   From 2 SO$_2$

The numbers of atoms of each element are the same in the reactants and products, so the equation is balanced.

PROBLEM 5.1

Interpret the following equations using words:

(a) $CoCl_2(s) + 2\,HF(g) \longrightarrow CoF_2(s) + 2\,HCl(g)$

(b) $Pb(NO_3)_2(aq) + 2\,KI(aq) \longrightarrow PbI_2(s) + 2\,KNO_3(aq)$

PROBLEM 5.2

Which of the following equations are balanced?

(a) $HCl + KOH \longrightarrow H_2O + KCl$

(b) $CH_4 + Cl_2 \longrightarrow CH_2Cl_2 + HCl$

(c) $H_2O + MgO \longrightarrow Mg(OH)_2$

(d) $Al(OH)_3 + H_3PO_4 \longrightarrow AlPO_4 + 2\,H_2O$

5.2 Balancing Chemical Equations

Just as a recipe indicates the appropriate amounts of each ingredient needed to make a given dish, a balanced chemical equation indicates the appropriate amounts of reactants needed to generate a given amount of product. Although balancing chemical equations often involves some trial and error, most reactions can be balanced by the following four-step approach:

STEP 1: **Write an unbalanced equation, using the correct formulas for all given reactants and products.** For example, hydrogen and oxygen must be written as H_2 and O_2, rather than as H and O, since we know that both elements exist as diatomic molecules. Remember that *the subscripts in chemical formulas cannot be changed in balancing an equation because doing so would change the identity of the substances in the reaction.*

STEP 2: **Add appropriate coefficients to balance the numbers of atoms of each element.** It helps to begin with elements that appear in only one compound or formula on each side of the equation, leaving elements that exist in elemental forms, such as oxygen and hydrogen, until last. For example, in the reaction of sulfuric acid with sodium hydroxide to give sodium sulfate and water, we might balance first for sodium. We could do this by adding a coefficient of 2 for NaOH:

$$H_2SO_4 + NaOH \longrightarrow Na_2SO_4 + H_2O \quad \text{(Unbalanced)}$$
$$H_2SO_4 + 2\,NaOH \longrightarrow Na_2SO_4 + H_2O \quad \text{(Balanced for Na)}$$

Add this coefficient . . .   . . . to balance these 2 Na.

If a polyatomic ion appears on both sides of an equation, it is treated as a single unit. For example, the sulfate ion (SO_4^{2-}) in our example is balanced because there is one on the left and one on the right:

$$H_2SO_4 + 2\,NaOH \longrightarrow Na_2SO_4 + H_2O \quad \text{(Balanced for Na and sulfate)}$$

One sulfate here . . .   . . . and one here.

At this point, the equation can be balanced for H and O by adding a coefficient of 2 for H_2O:

$$H_2SO_4 + 2\,NaOH \longrightarrow Na_2SO_4 + 2\,H_2O \quad \text{(Completely balanced)}$$

4 H and 2 O here.   4 H and 2 O here.

STEP 3: **Check the equation to make sure the numbers and kinds of atoms on both sides of the equation are the same.**

STEP 4: **Make sure the coefficients are reduced to their lowest whole-number values.** For example, the equation:

$$2\,H_2SO_4 + 4\,NaOH \longrightarrow 2\,Na_2SO_4 + 4\,H_2O$$

is balanced but can be simplified by dividing all coefficients by 2:

$$H_2SO_4 + 2\,NaOH \longrightarrow Na_2SO_4 + 2\,H_2O$$

Worked Example 5.2 Balancing Chemical Equations

Write a balanced chemical equation for the Haber process, an important industrial reaction in which elemental nitrogen and hydrogen combine to form ammonia.

SOLUTION

STEP 1: Write an unbalanced equation, using the correct formulas for all reactants and products.

$$N_2(g) + H_2(g) \longrightarrow NH_3(g)$$

By examination, we see that only two elements, N and H, need to be balanced. Both these elements exist in nature as diatomic gases, as indicated on the reactant side of the unbalanced equation.

STEP 2: Add appropriate coefficients to balance the numbers of atoms of each element. Remember that the subscript 2 in N_2 and H_2 indicates that these are diatomic molecules (that is, 2 N atoms or 2 H atoms per molecule). Since there are 2 nitrogen atoms on the left, we must add a coefficient of 2 in front of the NH_3 on the right side of the equation to balance the equation with respect to N:

$$N_2(g) + H_2(g) \longrightarrow 2\,NH_3(g)$$

Now we see that there are 2 H atoms on the left, but 6 H atoms on the right. We can balance the equation with respect to hydrogen by adding a coefficient of 3 in front of the $H_2(g)$ on the left side:

$$N_2(g) + 3\,H_2(g) \longrightarrow 2\,NH_3(g)$$

STEP 3: Check the equation to make sure the numbers and kinds of atoms on both sides of the equation are the same.

On the left:	$(1 \times 2)\,N = 2\,N$	$(3 \times 2)\,H = 6\,H$
On the right:	$(2 \times 1)\,N = 2\,N$	$(2 \times 3)\,H = 6\,H$

STEP 4: Make sure the coefficients are reduced to their lowest whole-number values. In this case, the coefficients already represent the lowest whole-number values.

Worked Example 5.3 Balancing Chemical Equations

Natural gas (methane, CH_4) burns in oxygen to yield water and carbon dioxide (CO_2). Write a balanced equation for the reaction.

SOLUTION

STEP 1: Write the unbalanced equation, using correct formulas for all substances:

$$CH_4 + O_2 \longrightarrow CO_2 + H_2O \quad \text{(Unbalanced)}$$

STEP 2: Since carbon appears in one formula on each side of the arrow, let us begin with that element. In fact, there is only 1 carbon atom in each formula, so the equation is already balanced for that element. Next, note that there are 4 hydrogen atoms on the left (in CH_4) and only 2 on the right (in H_2O). Placing a coefficient of 2 before H_2O gives the same number of hydrogen atoms on both sides:

$$CH_4 + O_2 \longrightarrow CO_2 + 2\,H_2O \quad \text{(Balanced for C and H)}$$

Finally, look at the number of oxygen atoms. There are 2 on the left (in O_2) but 4 on the right (2 in CO_2 and 1 in each H_2O). If we place a 2 before the O_2, the number of oxygen atoms will be the same on both sides, but the numbers of other elements will not change:

$$CH_4 + 2\,O_2 \longrightarrow CO_2 + 2\,H_2O \quad \text{(Balanced for C, H, and O)}$$

STEP 3: Check to be sure the numbers of atoms on both sides are the same.

On the left:	1 C	4 H	$(2 \times 2)\,O = 4\,O$
On the right:	1 C	$(2 \times 2)\,H = 4\,H$	$2\,O + 2\,O = 4\,O$

From CO_2 From 2 H_2O

STEP 4: Make sure the coefficients are reduced to their lowest whole-number values. In this case, the answer is already correct.

Worked Example **5.4** Balancing Chemical Equations

Sodium chlorate ($NaClO_3$) decomposes when heated to yield sodium chloride and oxygen, a reaction used to provide oxygen for the emergency breathing masks in airliners. Write a balanced equation for this reaction.

The oxygen in emergency breathing masks comes from heating sodium chlorate.

SOLUTION

STEP 1: The unbalanced equation is:

$$NaClO_3 \longrightarrow NaCl + O_2$$

STEP 2: Both the Na and the Cl are already balanced, with only one atom of each on the left and right sides of the equation. There are 3 O atoms on the left, but only 2 on the right. The O atoms can be balanced by placing a coefficient of 1½ in front of O_2 on the right side of the equation:

$$NaClO_3 \longrightarrow NaCl + 1½ O_2$$

STEP 3: Checking to make sure the same number of atoms of each type occurs on both sides of the equation, we see 1 atom of Na and Cl on both sides, and 3 O atoms on both sides.

STEP 4: In this case, obtaining all coefficients in their smallest whole-number values requires that we multiply all coefficients by 2 to obtain:

$$2 NaClO_3 \longrightarrow 2 NaCl + 3 O_2$$

Checking gives

> *On the left:* $2 Na \; 2 Cl \; (2 \times 3) O = 6 O$
>
> *On the right:* $2 Na \; 2 Cl \; (3 \times 2) O = 6 O$

PROBLEM 5.3

Ozone (O_3) is formed in the earth's upper atmosphere by the action of solar radiation on oxygen molecules (O_2). Write a balanced equation for the formation of ozone from oxygen.

PROBLEM 5.4

Balance the following equations:

(a) $Ca(OH)_2 + HCl \longrightarrow CaCl_2 + H_2O$

(b) $Al + O_2 \longrightarrow Al_2O_3$

(c) $CH_3CH_3 + O_2 \longrightarrow CO_2 + H_2O$

(d) $AgNO_3 + MgCl_2 \longrightarrow AgCl + Mg(NO_3)_2$

🔑 **KEY CONCEPT PROBLEM 5.5**

The following diagram represents the reaction of A (red spheres) with B_2 (blue spheres). Write a balanced equation for the reaction.

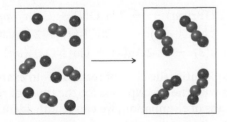

5.3 Classes of Chemical Reactions

One of the best ways to understand any subject is to look for patterns that help us categorize large amounts of information. When learning about chemical reactions, for instance, it is helpful to group the reactions of ionic compounds into three general classes: *precipitation reactions, acid–base neutralization reactions*, and *oxidation–reduction reactions*. This is not the only possible way of categorizing reactions but it is useful nonetheless. Let us look briefly at examples of each of these three reaction classes before studying them in more detail in subsequent sections.

Precipitate An insoluble solid that forms in solution during a chemical reaction.

- **Precipitation reactions** are processes in which an insoluble solid called a **precipitate** forms when reactants are combined in aqueous solution. Most precipitations take place when the anions and cations of two ionic compounds change partners. For example, an aqueous solution of lead(II) nitrate reacts with an aqueous solution of potassium iodide to yield an aqueous solution of potassium nitrate plus an insoluble yellow precipitate of lead iodide:

$$Pb(NO_3)_2(aq) + 2\,KI(aq) \longrightarrow 2\,KNO_3(aq) + PbI_2(s)$$

Salt An ionic compound formed from reaction of an acid with a base.

▶▶▶ See Section 3.11 for more discussion of acids and bases.

- **Acid–base neutralization reactions** are processes in which an acid reacts with a base to yield water plus an ionic compound called a **salt**. We will look at both acids and bases in more detail in Chapter 10, but you might recall for the moment that we previously defined acids as compounds that produce H^+ ions and bases as compounds that produce OH^- ions when dissolved in water. Thus, a neutralization reaction removes H^+ and OH^- ions from solution and yields neutral H_2O. The reaction between hydrochloric acid and sodium hydroxide is a typical example:

$$HCl(aq) + NaOH(aq) \longrightarrow H_2O(l) + NaCl(aq)$$

Note that in this reaction, the "salt" produced is sodium chloride, or common table salt. In a general sense, however, *any* ionic compound produced in an acid–base reaction is also called a salt. Other examples include potassium nitrate (KNO_3), magnesium bromide ($MgBr_2$), and sodium sulfate (Na_2SO_4).

Oxidation–reduction (redox) reaction A reaction in which electrons are transferred from one atom to another.

- **Oxidation–reduction reactions**, or **redox reactions**, are processes in which one or more electrons are transferred between reaction partners (atoms, molecules, or ions). As a result of this transfer, the number of electrons assigned to individual atoms in the various reactants change. When metallic magnesium reacts with iodine vapor, for instance, a magnesium atom gives an electron to each of 2 iodine atoms, forming a Mg^{2+} ion and 2 I^- ions. The charge on the magnesium changes from 0 to +2, and the charge on each iodine changes from 0 to −1:

$$Mg(s) + I_2(g) \longrightarrow MgI_2(s)$$

Fundamentally, all reactions involving covalent compounds are classified as redox reactions, because electrons are rearranged as bonds are broken and new bonds are formed. The discussion here, however, will focus mainly on reactions involving ionic substances.

▲ Reaction of aqueous $Pb(NO_3)_2$ with aqueous KI gives a yellow precipitate of PbI_2.

Worked Example 5.5 Classifying Chemical Reactions

Classify the following as a precipitation, an acid–base neutralization, or a redox reaction.

(a) $Ca(OH)_2(aq) + 2\,HBr(aq) \longrightarrow 2\,H_2O(l) + CaBr_2(aq)$
(b) $Pb(ClO_4)_2(aq) + 2\,NaCl(aq) \longrightarrow PbCl_2(s) + 2\,NaClO_4(aq)$
(c) $2\,AgNO_3(aq) + Cu(s) \longrightarrow 2\,Ag(s) + Cu(NO_3)_2(aq)$

ANALYSIS One way to identify the class of reaction is to examine the products that form and match them with the descriptions for the types of reactions provided in this section. By a process of elimination, we can readily identify the appropriate reaction classification.

SOLUTION

(a) The products of this reaction are water and an ionic compound, or salt ($CaBr_2$). This is consistent with the description of an acid–base neutralization reaction.

(b) This reaction involves two aqueous reactants, $Pb(ClO_4)_2$ and $NaCl$, which combine to form a solid product, $PbCl_2$. This is consistent with a precipitation reaction.

(c) The products of this reaction are a solid, $Ag(s)$, and an aqueous ionic compound, $Cu(NO_3)_2$. This does not match the description of a neutralization reaction, which would form *water* and an ionic compound. One of the products *is* a solid, but the reactants are not both aqueous compound; one of the reactants is *also* a solid (Cu). Therefore, this reaction would not be classified as a precipitation reaction. By the process of elimination, then, it must be a redox reaction.

PROBLEM 5.6

Classify each of the following as a precipitation, an acid–base neutralization, or a redox reaction.

(a) $AgNO_3(aq) + KCl(aq) \longrightarrow AgCl(s) + KNO_3(aq)$

(b) $2\,Al(s) + 3\,Br_2(l) \longrightarrow 2\,AlBr_3(s)$

(c) $Ca(OH)_2(aq) + 2\,HNO_3(aq) \longrightarrow 2\,H_2O(l) + Ca(NO_3)_2(aq)$

PROBLEM 5.7

The reaction involved in photosynthesis combines carbon dioxide and water to create simple sugars:

$$CO_2(g) + H_2O(l) \xrightarrow{\text{Sunlight}} C_6H_{12}O_6(s)$$

Balance the equation and classify the reaction.

5.4 Precipitation Reactions and Solubility Guidelines

Now let us look at precipitation reactions in more detail. To predict whether a precipitation reaction will occur upon mixing aqueous solutions of two ionic compounds, you must know the **solubilities** of the potential products—how much of each compound will dissolve in a given amount of solvent at a given temperature. If a substance has a low solubility in water, then it is likely to precipitate from an aqueous solution. If a substance has a high solubility in water, then no precipitate will form.

Solubility The amount of a compound that will dissolve in a given amount of solvent at a given temperature.

Solubility is a complex matter, and it is not always possible to make correct predictions. As a rule of thumb, though, the following solubility guidelines for ionic compounds are useful.

General Rules on Solubility

RULE 1: **A compound is probably soluble if it contains one of the following cations:**
- Group 1A cation: Li^+, Na^+, K^+, Rb^+, Cs^+
- Ammonium ion: $NH_4{}^+$

RULE 2: **A compound is probably soluble if it contains one of the following anions:**
- Halide: Cl^-, Br^-, I^- except Ag^+, $Hg_2{}^{2+}$, and Pb^{2+} compounds
- Nitrate ($NO_3{}^-$), perchlorate ($ClO_4{}^-$), acetate ($CH_3CO_2{}^-$), sulfate ($SO_4{}^{2-}$) except Ba^{2+}, $Hg_2{}^{2+}$, and Pb^{2+} sulfates

If a compound does *not* contain at least one of the ions listed above, it is probably *not* soluble. Thus, Na_2CO_3 is soluble because it contains a group 1A cation, and $CaCl_2$ is soluble because it contains a halide anion. The compound $CaCO_3$, however, is probably *insoluble* because it contains none of the ions listed above. These same guidelines are presented in table form in Table 5.1.

TABLE 5.1 General Solubility Guidelines for Ionic Compounds in Water

Soluble	Exceptions
Ammonium compounds (NH_4^+)	None
Lithium compounds (Li^+)	None
Sodium compounds (Na^+)	None
Potassium compounds (K^+)	None
Nitrates (NO_3^-)	None
Perchlorates (ClO_4^-)	None
Acetates ($CH_3CO_2^-$)	None
Chlorides (Cl^-)	
Bromides (Br^-)	Ag^+, Hg_2^{2+}, and Pb^{2+} compounds
Iodides (I^-)	
Sulfates (SO_4^{2-})	Ba^{2+}, Hg_2^{2+}, and Pb^{2+} compounds

CHEMISTRY IN ACTION

Gout and Kidney Stones: Problems in Solubility

One of the major pathways in the body for the breakdown of the nucleic acids DNA and RNA is by conversion to a substance called *uric acid*, $C_5H_4N_4O_3$, so named because it was first isolated from urine in 1776. Most people excrete about 0.5 g of uric acid every day in the form of sodium urate, the salt that results from an acid–base reaction of uric acid. Unfortunately, the amount of sodium urate that dissolves in water (or urine) is fairly low—only about 0.07 mg/mL at the normal body temperature of 37 °C. When too much sodium urate is produced or mechanisms for its elimination fail, its concentration in blood and urine rises, and the excess sometimes precipitates in the joints and kidneys.

Gout is a disorder of nucleic acid metabolism that primarily affects middle-aged men (only 5% of gout patients are women). It is characterized by an increased sodium urate concentration in blood, leading to the deposit of sodium urate crystals in soft tissue around the joints, particularly in the hands and at the base of the big toe. Deposits of the sharp, needlelike crystals cause an extremely painful inflammation that can lead ultimately to arthritis and even to bone destruction.

Just as increased sodium urate concentration in blood can lead to gout, increased concentration in urine can result in the formation of one kind of *kidney stones*, small crystals that precipitate in the kidney. Although often quite small, kidney stones cause excruciating pain when they pass through the ureter, the duct that carries urine from the kidney to the bladder. In some cases, complete blockage of the ureter occurs.

Treatment of excessive sodium urate production involves both dietary modification and drug therapy. Foods such as liver, sardines, and asparagus should be avoided, and drugs such as allopurinol can be taken to lower production of sodium urate. Allopurinol functions by inhibiting the action of an enzyme called *xanthine oxidase*, thereby blocking a step in nucleic acid metabolism.

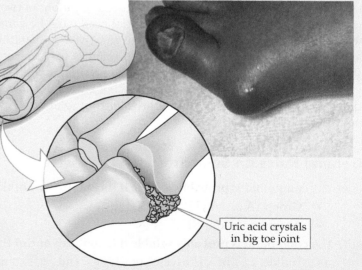

Uric acid crystals in big toe joint

▲ **Excess production of uric acid can cause gout, a painful condition characterized by the accumulation of sodium urate crystals in joints.**

See Chemistry in Action Problems 5.63 and 5.64 at the end of the chapter.

Let us try a problem. What will happen if aqueous solutions of sodium nitrate $(NaNO_3)$ and potassium sulfate (K_2SO_4) are mixed? To answer this question, look at the guidelines to find the solubilities of the two possible products, Na_2SO_4 and KNO_3. Because both have group 1A cations (Na^+ and K^+), both are water-soluble and no precipitation will occur. If aqueous solutions of silver nitrate $(AgNO_3)$ and sodium carbonate (Na_2CO_3) are mixed, however, the guidelines predict that a precipitate of insoluble silver carbonate (Ag_2CO_3) will form.

$$2\,AgNO_3(aq) + Na_2CO_3(aq) \longrightarrow Ag_2CO_3(s) + 2\,NaNO_3(aq)$$

Worked Example 5.6 Chemical Reactions: Solubility Rules

Will a precipitation reaction occur when aqueous solutions of $CdCl_2$ and $(NH_4)_2S$ are mixed?

SOLUTION
Identify the two potential products, and predict the solubility of each using the guidelines in the text. In this instance, $CdCl_2$ and $(NH_4)_2S$ might give CdS and NH_4Cl. Since the guidelines predict that CdS is insoluble, a precipitation reaction will occur:

$$CdCl_2(aq) + (NH_4)_2S(aq) \longrightarrow CdS(s) + 2\,NH_4Cl(aq)$$

PROBLEM 5.8
Predict the solubility of the following compounds:
(a) $CdCO_3$ (b) Na_2S
(c) $PbSO_4$ (d) $(NH_4)_3PO_4$
(e) Hg_2Cl_2

PROBLEM 5.9
Predict whether a precipitation reaction will occur in the following situations. If a precipitation reaction occurs, write the balanced chemical equation for the reaction.
(a) $NiCl_2(aq) + (NH_4)_2S(aq) \longrightarrow$
(b) $AgNO_3(aq) + CaBr_2(aq) \longrightarrow$

PROBLEM 5.10
In addition to kidney stone formation by sodium urate (See Chemistry in Action on p. 140), many kidney stones are formed by precipitation of oxalate by calcium. Oxalates are found in many foods, including spinach, blueberries, and chocolate. Show the balanced chemical equation for the precipitation of calcium oxalate, starting with calcium chloride $(CaCl_2)$ and sodium oxalate $(Na_2C_2O_4)$.

5.5 Acids, Bases, and Neutralization Reactions

When acids and bases are mixed in the correct proportion, both acidic and basic properties disappear because of a **neutralization reaction**. The most common kind of neutralization reaction occurs between an acid (generalized as HA), and a metal hydroxide (generalized as MOH), to yield water and a salt. The H^+ ion from the acid combines with the OH^- ion from the base to give neutral H_2O, whereas the anion from the acid (A^-) combines with the cation from the base (M^+) to give the salt:

Neutralization reaction The reaction of an acid with a base.

$$\text{A neutralization reaction:} \quad \underset{\text{Acid}}{HA(aq)} + \underset{\text{Base}}{MOH(aq)} \longrightarrow \underset{\text{Water}}{H_2O(l)} + \underset{\text{A salt}}{MA(aq)}$$

The reaction of hydrochloric acid with potassium hydroxide to produce potassium chloride is an example:

$$HCl(aq) + KOH(aq) \longrightarrow H_2O(l) + KCl(aq)$$

Another kind of neutralization reaction occurs between an acid and a carbonate (or bicarbonate) to yield water, a salt, and carbon dioxide. Hydrochloric acid reacts with potassium carbonate, for example, to give H_2O, KCl, and CO_2:

$$2\,HCl(aq) + K_2CO_3(aq) \longrightarrow H_2O(l) + 2\,KCl(aq) + CO_2(g)$$

The reaction occurs because the carbonate ion $(CO_3{}^{2-})$ reacts initially with H^+ to yield H_2CO_3, which is unstable and immediately decomposes to give CO_2 plus H_2O.

We will defer a more complete discussion of carbonates as bases until Chapter 10, but note for now that they yield OH^- ions when dissolved in water just as KOH and other bases do.

$$K_2CO_3(s) + H_2O(l) \xrightarrow{\text{Dissolve in water}} 2\,K^+(aq) + HCO_3{}^-(aq) + OH^-(aq)$$

LOOKING AHEAD ▶▶▶ Acids and bases are enormously important in biological chemistry. We will see in Chapter 18, for instance, how acids and bases affect the structure and properties of proteins.

Worked Example **5.7** Chemical Reactions: Acid–Base Neutralization

Write an equation for the neutralization reaction of aqueous HBr and aqueous $Ba(OH)_2$.

SOLUTION
The reaction of HBr with $Ba(OH)_2$ involves the combination of a proton (H^+) from the acid with OH^- from the base to yield water and a salt $(BaBr_2)$.

$$2\,HBr(aq) + Ba(OH)_2(aq) \longrightarrow 2\,H_2O(l) + BaBr_2(aq)$$

PROBLEM 5.11
Write and balance equations for the following acid–base neutralization reactions:
(a) $CsOH(aq) + H_2SO_4(aq) \longrightarrow$
(b) $Ca(OH)_2(aq) + CH_3CO_2H(aq) \longrightarrow$
(c) $NaHCO_3(aq) + HBr(aq) \longrightarrow$

5.6 Redox Reactions

Oxidation–reduction (redox) reactions, the third and final category of reactions that we will discuss here, are more complex than precipitation and neutralization reactions. Look, for instance, at the following examples and see if you can tell what they have in common. Copper metal reacts with aqueous silver nitrate to form silver metal and aqueous copper(II) nitrate; iron rusts in air to form iron(III) oxide; the zinc metal container on the outside of a battery reacts with manganese dioxide and ammonium chloride inside the battery to generate electricity and give aqueous zinc chloride plus manganese(III) oxide. Although these and many thousands of other reactions appear unrelated, all are examples of redox reactions.

$$Cu(s) + 2\,AgNO_3(aq) \longrightarrow 2\,Ag(s) + Cu(NO_3)_2(aq)$$
$$2\,Fe(s) + 3\,O_2(g) \longrightarrow Fe_2O_3(s)$$
$$Zn(s) + 2\,MnO_2(s) + 2\,NH_4Cl(s) \longrightarrow$$
$$ZnCl_2(aq) + Mn_2O_3(s) + 2\,NH_3(aq) + H_2O(l)$$

Historically, the word *oxidation* referred to the combination of an element with oxygen to yield an oxide, and the word *reduction* referred to the removal of oxygen from an oxide to yield the element. Today, though, the words have taken on a much broader meaning. An **oxidation** is now defined as the loss of one or more electrons by an atom,

Oxidation The loss of one or more electrons by an atom.

and a **reduction** is the gain of one or more electrons. Thus, an oxidation–reduction reaction, or redox reaction, is one in which *electrons are transferred from one atom to another.*

Reduction The gain of one or more electrons by an atom.

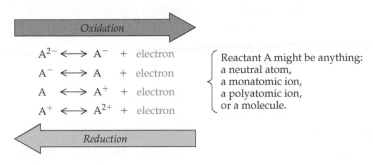

$$A^{2-} \longleftrightarrow A^- + \text{electron}$$
$$A^- \longleftrightarrow A + \text{electron}$$
$$A \longleftrightarrow A^+ + \text{electron}$$
$$A^+ \longleftrightarrow A^{2+} + \text{electron}$$

Reactant A might be anything: a neutral atom, a monatomic ion, a polyatomic ion, or a molecule.

Take the reaction of copper with aqueous Ag^+ as an example, as shown in Figure 5.1. Copper metal gives an electron to each of 2 Ag^+ ions, forming Cu^{2+} and silver metal. Copper is oxidized in the process, and Ag^+ is reduced. You can follow the transfer of the electrons by noting that the charge on the copper increases from 0 to +2 when it loses 2 electrons, whereas the charge on Ag^+ decreases from +1 to 0 when it gains an electron.

+2 electrons = reduced!

$$Cu(s) + 2\,Ag^+(aq) \longrightarrow Cu^{2+}(aq) + 2\,Ag(s)$$

0 charge   +1 charge   +2 charge   0 charge

−2 electrons = oxidized!

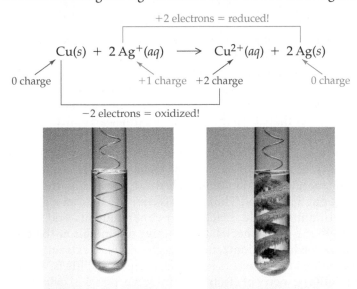

◄ Figure 5.1
The copper wire reacts with aqueous Ag^+ ion and becomes coated with metallic silver. At the same time, copper(II) ions go into solution, producing the blue color.

Similarly, in the reaction of aqueous iodide ion with bromine, iodide ion gives an electron to bromine, forming iodine and bromide ion. Iodide ion is oxidized as its charge increases from −1 to 0, and bromine is reduced as its charge decreases from 0 to −1.

+2 electrons = reduced!

$$2\,I^-(aq) + Br_2(aq) \longrightarrow I_2(aq) + 2\,Br^-(aq)$$

−1 charge   0 charge   0 charge   −1 charge

−2 electrons = oxidized!

As these examples show, oxidation and reduction always occur together. Whenever one substance loses an electron (is oxidized), another substance must gain that electron (be reduced). The substance that gives up an electron and causes the reduction—the copper atom in the reaction of Cu with Ag^+ and the iodide ion in the reaction of I^- with Br_2—is called a **reducing agent**. The substance that gains an electron and causes the oxidation—the silver ion in the reaction of Cu with Ag^+ and the bromine molecule in the reaction of I^- with Br_2—is called an **oxidizing agent**. The charge on the reducing agent increases during the reaction, and the charge on the oxidizing agent decreases.

Reducing agent A reactant that causes a reduction in another reactant by giving up electron to it.

Oxidizing agent A reactant that causes an oxidation by taking electrons from another reactant.

Reducing agent	Loses one or more electrons
	Causes reduction
	Undergoes oxidation
	Becomes more positive (less negative)
	(May gain oxygen atoms)
Oxidizing agent	Gains one or more electrons
	Causes oxidation
	Undergoes reduction
	Becomes more negative (less positive)
	(May lose oxygen atoms)

Among the simplest of redox processes is the reaction of an element, usually a metal, with an aqueous cation to yield a different element and a different ion. Iron metal reacts with aqueous copper(II) ion, for example, to give iron(II) ion and copper metal. Similarly, magnesium metal reacts with aqueous acid to yield magnesium ion and hydrogen gas. In both cases, the reactant element (Fe or Mg) is oxidized, and the reactant ion (Cu^{2+} or H^+) is reduced.

$$Fe(s) + Cu^{2+}(aq) \longrightarrow Fe^{2+}(aq) + Cu(s)$$
$$Mg(s) + 2\,H^+(aq) \longrightarrow Mg^{2+}(aq) + H_2(g)$$

The reaction of a metal with water or aqueous acid (H^+) to release H_2 gas is a particularly important process. As you might expect based on the periodic properties discussed in Section 3.2, the alkali metals and alkaline earth metals (on the left side of the periodic table) are the most powerful reducing agents (electron donors), so powerful that they even react with pure water, in which the concentration of H^+ is very low. This is due in part to the fact that alkali metals and alkaline earth metals have low ionization energies. Ionization energy, which is a measure of how easily an element will lose an electron, tends to decrease as we move to the left and down in the periodic table. Thus, metals toward the middle of the periodic table, such as iron and chromium, have higher ionization energies and do not lose electrons as readily; they react only with aqueous acids but not with water. Those metals near the bottom right of the periodic table, such as platinum and gold, react with neither aqueous acid nor water. At the other extreme from the alkali metals, the reactive nonmetals at the top right of the periodic table have the highest ionization energies and are extremely weak reducing agents but powerful oxidizing agents (electron acceptors). This is, again, predictable based on the periodic property of electron affinity (Section 3.2), which becomes more energetically favored as we move up and to the right in the periodic table.

We can make a few generalizations about the redox behavior of metals and nonmetals.

1. In reactions involving metals and nonmetals, metals tend to lose electrons while nonmetals tend to gain electrons. The number of electrons lost or gained can often be predicted based on the position of the element in the periodic table. (Section 3.5)

2. In reactions involving nonmetals, the "more metallic" element (farther down and/or to the left in the periodic table) tends to lose electrons, and the "less metallic" element (up and/or to the right) tends to gain electrons.

   Redox reactions involve almost every element in the periodic table, and they occur in a vast number of processes throughout nature, biology, and industry. Here are just a few examples:

   • **Corrosion** is the deterioration of a metal by oxidation, such as the rusting of iron in moist air. The economic consequences of rusting are enormous: it has been estimated that up to one-fourth of the iron produced in the United States is used to replace bridges, buildings, and other structures that have been destroyed by corrosion. (The raised dot in the formula $Fe_2O_3 \cdot H_2O$ for rust indicates that one water molecule is associated with each Fe_2O_3 in an undefined way.)

▶▶▶ The relationship between formation of ions and ionization energy/electronegativity was discussed in Chapter 3.

- **Combustion** is the burning of a fuel by rapid oxidation with oxygen in air. Gasoline, fuel oil, natural gas, wood, paper, and other organic substances of carbon and hydrogen are the most common fuels that burn in air. Even some metals, though, will burn in air. Magnesium and calcium are examples.

$$CH_4(g) + 2\,O_2(g) \longrightarrow CO_2(g) + 2\,H_2O(l)$$

Methane
(natural gas)

$$2\,Mg(s) + O_2(g) \longrightarrow 2\,MgO(s)$$

- **Respiration** is the process of breathing and using oxygen for the many biological redox reactions that provide the energy required by living organisms. We will see in Chapters 21–22 that in the respiration process, energy is released from food molecules slowly and in complex, multistep pathways, but that the overall result is similar to that of the simpler combustion reactions. For example, the simple sugar glucose $(C_6H_{12}O_6)$ reacts with O_2 to give CO_2 and H_2O according to the following equation:

$$C_6H_{12}O_6 + 6\,O_2 \longrightarrow 6\,CO_2 + 6\,H_2O + Energy$$

Glucose
(a carbohydrate)

- **Bleaching** makes use of redox reactions to decolorize or lighten colored materials. Dark hair is bleached to turn it blond, clothes are bleached to remove stains, wood pulp is bleached to make white paper, and so on. The oxidizing agent used depends on the situation: hydrogen peroxide (H_2O_2) is used for hair, sodium hypochlorite $(NaOCl)$ for clothes, and elemental chlorine for wood pulp, but the principle is always the same. In all cases, colored organic materials are destroyed by reaction with strong oxidizing agents.
- **Metallurgy,** the science of extracting and purifying metals from their ores, makes use of numerous redox processes. Worldwide, approximately 800 million tons of iron are produced each year by reduction of the mineral hematite, Fe_2O_3, with carbon monoxide.

$$Fe_2O_3(s) + 3\,CO(g) \longrightarrow 2\,Fe(s) + 3\,CO_2(g)$$

Worked Example 5.8 Chemical Reactions: Redox Reactions

For the following reactions, indicate which atom is oxidized and which is reduced, based on the definitions provided in this section. Identify the oxidizing and reducing agents.

(a) $Cu(s) + Pt^{2+}(aq) \longrightarrow Cu^{2+}(aq) + Pt(s)$
(b) $2\,Mg(s) + CO_2(g) \longrightarrow 2\,MgO(s) + C(s)$

ANALYSIS The definitions for oxidation include a loss of electrons, an increase in charge, and a gain of oxygen atoms; reduction is defined as a gain of electrons, a decrease in charge, and a loss of oxygen atoms.

SOLUTION

(a) In this reaction, the charge on the Cu atom increases from 0 to 2+. This corresponds to a loss of 2 electrons. The Cu is therefore oxidized and acts as the reducing agent. Conversely, the Pt^{2+} ion undergoes a decrease in charge from 2+ to 0, corresponding to a gain of 2 electrons for the Pt^{2+} ion. The Pt^{2+} is reduced, and acts as the oxidizing agent.

(b) In this case, the gain or loss of oxygen atoms is the easiest way to identify which atoms are oxidized and reduced. The Mg atom is gaining oxygen to form MgO; therefore, the Mg is being oxidized and acts as the reducing agent. The C atom in CO_2 is losing oxygen. Therefore, the C atom in CO_2 is being reduced, and so CO_2 acts as the oxidizing agent.

Worked Example 5.9 Chemical Reactions: Identifying Oxidizing/Reducing Agents

For the respiration and metallurgy examples discussed previously, identify the atoms being oxidized and reduced, and label the oxidizing and reducing agents.

ANALYSIS Again, using the definitions of oxidation and reduction provided in this section, we can determine which atom(s) are gaining/losing electrons or gaining/losing oxygen atoms.

SOLUTION

$$\textit{Respiration:} \quad C_6H_{12}O_6 + 6\,O_2 \longrightarrow 6\,CO_2 + 6\,H_2O$$

Because the charge associated with the individual atoms is not evident, we will use the definition of oxidation/reduction as the gaining/losing of oxygen atoms. In this reaction, there is only one reactant besides oxygen $(C_6H_{12}O_6)$, so we must determine *which* atom in the compound is changing. The ratio of carbon to oxygen in $C_6H_{12}O_4$ is 1:1, while the ratio in CO_2 is 1:2. Therefore, the C atoms are gaining oxygen and are oxidized; the $C_6H_{12}O_{16}$ is the reducing agent and O_2 is the oxidizing agent. Note that the ratio of hydrogen to oxygen in $C_6H_{12}O_6$ and in H_2O is 2:1. The H atoms are neither oxidized nor reduced.

$$\textit{Metallurgy:} \quad Fe_2O_3(s) + 3\,CO(g) \longrightarrow 2\,Fe(s) + 3\,CO_2(g)$$

The Fe_2O_3 is losing oxygen to form Fe(s); it is being reduced and acts as the oxidizing agent. In contrast, the CO is gaining oxygen to form CO_2; it is being oxidized and acts as the reducing agent.

Worked Example 5.10 Chemical Reactions: Identifying Redox Reactions

For the following reactions, identify the atom(s) being oxidized and reduced:

(a) $2\,Al(s) + 3\,Cl_2(g) \longrightarrow 2\,AlCl_3(s)$ **(b)** $C(s) + 2\,Cl_2(g) \longrightarrow CCl_4(l)$

ANALYSIS Again, there is no obvious increase or decrease in charge to indicate a gain or loss of electrons. Also, the reactions do not involve a gain or loss of oxygen. We can, however, evaluate the reactions in terms of the typical behavior of metals and nonmetals in reactions.

SOLUTION

(a) In this case, we have the reaction of a metal (Al) with a nonmetal (Cl_2). Because metals tend to lose electrons and nonmetals tend to gain electrons, we can assume that the Al atom is oxidized (loses electrons) and the Cl_2 is reduced (gains electrons).

(b) The carbon atom is the less electronegative element (farther to the left) and is less likely to gain an electron. The more electronegative element (Cl) will tend to gain electrons (be reduced).

PROBLEM 5.12

Identify the oxidized reactant, the reduced reactant, the oxidizing agent, and the reducing agent in the following reactions:

(a) $Fe(s) + Cu^{2+}(aq) \longrightarrow Fe^{2+}(aq) + Cu(s)$
(b) $Mg(s) + Cl_2(g) \longrightarrow MgCl_2(s)$
(c) $2\,Al(s) + Cr_2O_3(s) \longrightarrow 2\,Cr(s) + Al_2O_3(s)$

PROBLEM 5.13

Potassium, a silvery metal, reacts with bromine, a corrosive, reddish liquid, to yield potassium bromide, a white solid. Write the balanced equation, and identify the oxidizing and reducing agents.

PROBLEM 5.14

The redox reaction that provides energy for the lithium battery described in the Chemistry in Action on p. 147 is $2\,Li(s) + I_2(s) \rightarrow 2\,LiI(aq)$. Identify which reactant is being oxidized and which is being reduced in this reaction.

CHEMISTRY IN ACTION

Batteries

Imagine life without batteries: no cars (they do not start very easily without their batteries!), no heart pacemakers, no flashlights, no hearing aids, no laptops, no radios, no cell phones, nor thousands of other things. Modern society could not exist without batteries.

Although they come in many types and sizes, all batteries work using redox reactions. In a typical redox reaction carried out in the laboratory—say, the reaction of zinc metal with Ag^+ to yield Zn^{2+} and silver metal—the reactants are simply mixed in a flask and electrons are transferred by direct contact between the reactants. In a battery, however, the two reactants are kept in separate compartments and the electrons are transferred through a wire running between them.

The common household battery used for flashlights and radios is the *dry cell*, developed in 1866. One reactant is a can of zinc metal, and the other is a paste of solid manganese dioxide. A graphite rod sticks into the MnO_2 paste to provide electrical contact, and a moist paste of ammonium chloride separates the two reactants. If the zinc can and the graphite rod are connected by a wire, zinc sends electrons flowing through the wire toward the MnO_2 in a redox reaction. The resultant electrical current can then be used to power a lightbulb or a radio. The accompanying figure shows a cutaway view of a dry-cell battery.

$$Zn(s) + 2\,MnO_2(s) + 2\,NH_4Cl(s) \longrightarrow$$
$$ZnCl_2(aq) + Mn_2O_3(s) + 2\,NH_3(aq) + H_2O(l)$$

▲ **Think of all the devices we use every day—laptop computers, cell phones, iPods—that depend on batteries.**

Closely related to the dry-cell battery is the familiar *alkaline* battery, in which the ammonium chloride paste is replaced by an alkaline, or basic, paste of NaOH or KOH. The alkaline battery has a longer life than the standard dry-cell battery because the zinc container corrodes less easily under basic conditions. The redox reaction is:

$$Zn(s) + 2\,MnO_2(s) \longrightarrow ZnO(aq) + Mn_2O_3(s)$$

The batteries used in implanted medical devices such as pacemakers must be small, corrosion-resistant, reliable, and able to last up to 10 years. Nearly all pacemakers being implanted today—about 750,000 each year—use titanium-encased, lithium–iodine batteries, whose redox reaction is:

$$2\,Li(s) + I_2(s) \longrightarrow 2\,LiI(aq)$$

See Chemistry in Action Problems 5.65 and 5.66 at the end of the chapter.

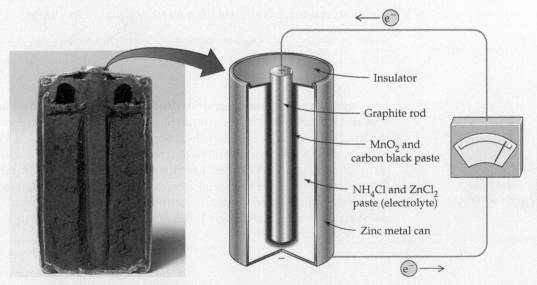

Insulator
Graphite rod
MnO_2 and carbon black paste
NH_4Cl and $ZnCl_2$ paste (electrolyte)
Zinc metal can

▲ **A dry-cell battery. The cutaway view shows the two reactants that make up the redox reaction.**

5.7 Recognizing Redox Reactions

How can you tell when a redox reaction is taking place? When ions are involved, it is simply a matter of determining whether there is a change in the charges. For reactions involving metals and nonmetals, we can predict the gain or loss of electrons as discussed previously. When molecular substances are involved, though, it is not as obvious. Is the combining of sulfur with oxygen a redox reaction? If so, which partner is the oxidizing agent and which is the reducing agent?

$$S(s) + O_2(g) \longrightarrow SO_2(g)$$

One way to evaluate this reaction is in terms of the oxygen gain by sulfur, indicating that S atoms are oxidized and O atoms are reduced. But can we also look at this reaction in terms of the gain or loss of electrons by the S and O atoms? Because oxygen is more electronegative than sulfur, the oxygen atoms in SO_2 attract the electrons in the S—O bonds more strongly than sulfur does, giving the oxygen atoms a larger share of the electrons than sulfur. By extending the ideas of oxidation and reduction to an increase or decrease in electron *sharing* instead of complete electron *transfer*, we can say that the sulfur atom is oxidized in its reaction with oxygen because it loses a share in some electrons, whereas the oxygen atoms are reduced because they gain a share in some electrons.

A formal system has been devised for keeping track of changes in electron sharing, and thus for determining whether atoms are oxidized or reduced in reactions. To each atom in a substance, we assign a value called an **oxidation number** (or *oxidation state*), which indicates whether the atom is neutral, electron-rich, or electron-poor. By comparing the oxidation number of an atom before and after a reaction, we can tell whether the atom has gained or lost shares in electrons. Note that *oxidation numbers do not necessarily imply ionic charges*. They are simply a convenient device for keeping track of electrons in redox reactions.

The rules for assigning oxidation numbers are straightforward:

- **An atom in its elemental state has an oxidation number of 0.**

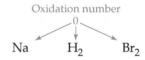

- **A monatomic ion has an oxidation number equal to its charge.**

Oxidation number +1   Na$^+$ Oxidation number +2   Ca^{2+} Oxidation number −1   Cl$^-$ Oxidation number −2   O^{2-}

- **In a molecular compound, an atom usually has the same oxidation number it would have if it were a monatomic ion.** Recall from Chapters 3 and 4 that the less electronegative elements (hydrogen and metals) on the left side of the periodic table tend to form cations, and the more electronegative elements (oxygen, nitrogen, and the halogens) near the top right of the periodic table tend to form anions. Hydrogen and metals therefore have positive oxidation numbers in most compounds, whereas reactive nonmetals generally have negative oxidation numbers. Hydrogen is usually +1, oxygen is usually −2, nitrogen is usually −3, and halogens are usually −1:

▶▶▶ Electronegativity, or the propensity of an atom in a covalent bond to attract electrons, was introduced in Section 4.9.

Oxidation number A number that indicates whether an atom is neutral, electron-rich, or electron-poor.

▶▶▶ Review the Important Points about Ion Formation and the Periodic Table listed in Section 3.6.

For compounds with more than one nonmetal element, such as SO_2, NO, or CO_2, the more electronegative element—oxygen in these examples—has a negative oxidation number and the less electronegative element has a positive oxidation number. Thus, in answer to the question posed at the beginning of this section, combining sulfur with oxygen to form SO_2 is a redox reaction because the oxidation number of sulfur increases from 0 to +4 and that of oxygen decreases from 0 to −2.

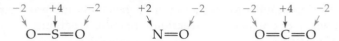

- **The sum of the oxidation numbers in a neutral compound is 0.** Using this rule, the oxidation number of any atom in a compound can be found if the oxidation numbers of the other atoms are known. In the SO_2 example just mentioned, each of the 2 O atoms has an oxidation number of −2, so the S atom must have an oxidation number of +4. In HNO_3, the H atom has an oxidation number of +1 and the strongly electronegative O atom has an oxidation number of −2, so the N atom must have an oxidation number of +5. In a polyatomic ion, the sum of the oxidation numbers equals the charge on the ion.

$$\overset{+1}{H}-\overset{-2}{O}-\overset{+5}{N}=\overset{-2}{O} \qquad Total = 1 + 5 + 3(-2) = 0$$
$$\underset{\underset{O}{|}}{} \overset{-2}{}$$

Worked Examples 5.11 and 5.12 show further instances of assigning and using oxidation numbers.

Worked Example 5.11 Redox Reactions: Oxidation Numbers

What is the oxidation number of the titanium atom in $TiCl_4$? Name the compound using a Roman numeral (Section 3.10).

SOLUTION
Chlorine, a reactive nonmetal, is more electronegative than titanium and has an oxidation number of −1. Because there are 4 chlorine atoms in $TiCl_4$, the oxidation number of titanium must be +4. The compound is named titanium(IV) chloride. Note that the Roman numeral IV in the name of this molecular compound refers to the oxidation number +4 rather than to a true ionic charge.

Worked Example 5.12 Redox Reactions: Identifying Redox Reactions

Use oxidation numbers to show that the production of iron metal from its ore (Fe_2O_3) by reaction with charcoal (C) is a redox reaction. Which reactant has been oxidized, and which has been reduced? Which reactant is the oxidizing agent, and which is the reducing agent?

$$2\,Fe_2O_3(s) + 3\,C(s) \longrightarrow 4\,Fe(s) + 3\,CO_2(g)$$

SOLUTION
The idea is to assign oxidation numbers to both reactants and products and see if there has been a change. In the production of iron from Fe_2O_3, the oxidation number of Fe changes from +3 to 0, and the oxidation number of C changes from 0 to +4. Iron has thus been reduced (decrease in oxidation number), and carbon has been oxidized (increase in oxidation number). Oxygen is neither oxidized nor reduced because its oxidation number does not change. Carbon is the reducing agent, and Fe_2O_3 is the oxidizing agent.

$$\overset{+3\ \ -2}{2\,Fe_2O_3} + \overset{0}{3\,C} \longrightarrow \overset{0}{4\,Fe} + \overset{+4\ -2}{3\,CO_2}$$

PROBLEM 5.15

What are the oxidation numbers of the metal atoms in the following compounds? Name each, using the oxidation number as a Roman numeral.

(a) VCl_3 (b) $SnCl_4$ (c) CrO_3 (d) $Cu(NO_3)_2$ (e) $NiSO_4$

PROBLEM 5.16

Assign an oxidation number to each atom in the reactants and products shown here to determine which of the following reactions are redox reactions:

(a) $Na_2S(aq) + NiCl_2(aq) \longrightarrow 2\,NaCl(aq) + NiS(s)$

(b) $2\,Na(s) + 2\,H_2O(l) \longrightarrow 2\,NaOH(aq) + H_2(g)$

(c) $C(s) + O_2(g) \longrightarrow CO_2(g)$

(d) $CuO(s) + 2\,HCl(aq) \longrightarrow CuCl_2(aq) + H_2O(l)$

(e) $2\,MnO_4^-(aq) + 5\,SO_2(g) + 2\,H_2O(l) \longrightarrow$
$2\,Mn^{2+}(aq) + 5\,SO_4^{2-}(aq) + 4\,H^+(aq)$

PROBLEM 5.17

For each of the reactions you identified as redox reactions in Problem 5.16, identify the oxidizing agent and the reducing agent.

5.8 Net Ionic Equations

In the equations we have been writing up to this point, all the substances involved in reactions have been written using their full formulas. In the precipitation reaction of lead(II) nitrate with potassium iodide mentioned in Section 5.3, for example, only the parenthetical *aq* indicated that the reaction actually takes place in aqueous solution, and nowhere was it explicitly indicated that ions are involved:

$$Pb(NO_3)_2(aq) + 2\,KI(aq) \longrightarrow 2\,KNO_3(aq) + PbI_2(s)$$

In fact, lead(II) nitrate, potassium iodide, and potassium nitrate dissolve in water to yield solutions of ions. Thus, it is more accurate to write the reaction as an **ionic equation**, in which all the ions are explicitly shown:

Ionic equation An equation in which ions are explicitly shown.

An ionic equation: $Pb^{2+}(aq) + 2\,NO_3^-(aq) + 2\,K^+(aq) + 2\,I^-(aq) \longrightarrow$
$2\,K^+(aq) + 2\,NO_3^-(aq) + PbI_2(s)$

A look at this ionic equation shows that the NO_3^- and K^+ ions undergo no change during the reaction. They appear on both sides of the reaction arrow and act merely as **spectator ions**, that is, they are present but play no role. The actual reaction, when stripped to its essentials, can be described more simply by writing a **net ionic equation**, which includes only the ions that undergo change and ignores all spectator ions:

Spectator ion An ion that appears unchanged on both sides of a reaction arrow.

Net ionic equation An equation that does not include spectator ions.

Ionic equation: $Pb^{2+}(aq) + 2\,\cancel{NO_3^-}(aq) + 2\,\cancel{K^+(aq)} + 2\,I^-(aq) \longrightarrow$
$2\,\cancel{K^+(aq)} + 2\,\cancel{NO_3^-}(aq) + PbI_2(s)$

Net ionic equation: $Pb^{2+}(aq) + 2\,I^-(aq) \longrightarrow PbI_2(s)$

Note that a net ionic equation, like all chemical equations, must be balanced both for atoms and for charge, with all coefficients reduced to their lowest whole numbers. Note also that all compounds that do *not* give ions in solution—all insoluble compounds and all molecular compounds—are represented by their full formulas.

We can apply the concept of ionic equations to acid–base neutralization reactions and redox reactions as well. Consider the neutralization reaction between KOH and HNO_3:

$$KOH(aq) + HNO_3(aq) \longrightarrow H_2O(l) + KNO_3(aq)$$

Since acids and bases are identified based on the ions they form when dissolved in aqueous solutions, we can write an ionic equation for this reaction:

Ionic equation: $\cancel{K^+(aq)} + OH^-(aq) + H^+(aq) + \cancel{NO_3^-(aq)} \longrightarrow$
$H_2O(l) + \cancel{K^+(aq)} + \cancel{NO_3^-(aq)}$

Eliminating the spectator ions (K^+ and NO_3^-), we obtain the net ionic equation for the neutralization reaction:

Net ionic equation: $OH^-(aq) + H^+(aq) \longrightarrow H_2O(l)$

The net ionic equation confirms the basis of the acid–base neutralization; the OH^- from the base and the H^+ from the acid neutralize each other to form water.

Similarly, many redox reactions can be viewed in terms of ionic equations. Consider the reaction between $Cu(s)$ and $AgNO_3$ from Section 5.6:

$$Cu(s) + 2\,AgNO_3(aq) \longrightarrow 2\,Ag^+(aq) + Cu(NO_3)_2(aq)$$

The aqueous products and reactants can be written as dissolved ions:

Ionic equation: $Cu(s) + 2\,Ag^+(aq) + 2\,\cancel{NO_3^-(aq)} \longrightarrow$
$$2\,Ag(s) + Cu^{2+}(aq) + 2\,\cancel{NO_3^-(aq)}$$

Again, eliminating the spectator ions (NO_3^-), we obtain the net ionic equation for this redox reaction:

Net ionic equation: $Cu(s) + 2\,Ag^+(aq) \longrightarrow 2\,Ag(s) + Cu^{2+}(aq)$

It is now clear that the $Cu(s)$ loses 2 electrons and is oxidized, whereas each Ag^+ ion gains an electron and is reduced.

Worked Example 5.13 Chemical Reactions: Net Ionic Reactions

Write balanced net ionic equations for the following reactions:

(a) $AgNO_3(aq) + ZnCl_2(aq) \longrightarrow$
(b) $HCl(aq) + Ca(OH)_2(aq) \longrightarrow$
(c) $6\,HCl(aq) + 2\,Al(s) \longrightarrow 2\,AlCl_3(aq) + 3\,H_2(g)$

SOLUTION

(a) The solubility guidelines discussed in Section 5.4 predict that a precipitate of insoluble AgCl forms when aqueous solutions of Ag^+ and Cl^- are mixed. Writing all the ions separately gives an ionic equation, and eliminating spectator ions Zn^{2+} and NO_3^- gives the net ionic equation.

Ionic equation: $2\,Ag^+(aq) + 2\,\cancel{NO_3^-(aq)} + \cancel{Zn^{2+}(aq)} + 2\,Cl^-(aq) \longrightarrow$
$$2\,AgCl(s) + \cancel{Zn^{2+}(aq)} + 2\,\cancel{NO_3(aq)}$$

Net ionic equation: $2\,Ag^+(aq) + 2\,Cl^-(aq) \longrightarrow 2\,AgCl(s)$

The coefficients can all be divided by 2 to give:

Net ionic equation: $Ag^+(aq) + Cl^+(aq) \longrightarrow AgCl(s)$

A check shows that the equation is balanced for atoms and charge (zero on each side).

(b) Allowing the acid HCl to react with the base $Ca(OH)_2$ leads to a neutralization reaction. Writing the ions separately, and remembering to write a complete formula for water, gives an ionic equation. Then eliminating the spectator ions and dividing the coefficients by 2 gives the net ionic equation.

Ionic equation: $2\,H^+(aq) + 2\,\cancel{Cl^-(aq)} + \cancel{Ca^{2+}(aq)} + 2\,OH^-(aq) \longrightarrow$
$$2\,H_2O(l) + \cancel{Ca^{2+}(aq)} + 2\,\cancel{Cl^-(aq)}$$

Net ionic equation: $H^+(aq) + OH^-(aq) \longrightarrow H_2O(l)$

A check shows that atoms and charges are the same on both sides of the equation.

(c) The reaction of Al metal with acid (HCl) is a redox reaction. The Al is oxidized, since the oxidation number increases from $0 \rightarrow +3$, whereas the H in HCl is reduced from $+1 \rightarrow 0$. We write the ionic equation by showing the ions that are formed for each aqueous ionic species. Eliminating the spectator ions yields the net ionic equation.

Ionic equation: $6\,H^+(aq) + 6\,Cl^-(aq) + 2\,Al(s) \longrightarrow$
$$2\,Al^{3+}(aq) + 6\,Cl^-(aq) + 3\,H_2(g)$$

Net ionic equation: $6\,H^+(aq) + 2\,Al(s) \longrightarrow 2\,Al^{3+}(aq) + 3\,H_2(g)$

A check shows that atoms and charges are the same on both sides of the equation.

PROBLEM 5.18
Write net ionic equations for the following reactions:
(a) $Zn(s) + Pb(NO_3)_2(aq) \longrightarrow Zn(NO_3)_2(aq) + Pb(s)$
(b) $2\,KOH(aq) + H_2SO_4(aq) \longrightarrow K_2SO_4(aq) + 2\,H_2O(l)$
(c) $2\,FeCl_3(aq) + SnCl_2(aq) \longrightarrow 2\,FeCl_2(aq) + SnCl_4(aq)$

PROBLEM 5.19
Identify each of the reactions in Problem 5.18 as an acid–base neutralization, a precipitation, or a redox reaction.

SUMMARY: REVISITING THE CHAPTER GOALS

1. How are chemical reactions written? Chemical equations must be *balanced*; that is, the numbers and kinds of atoms must be the same in both the reactants and the products. To balance an equation, *coefficients* are placed before formulas but the formulas themselves cannot be changed (*see Problems 21–23, 26–37, 59, 60, 64, 67, 68, 71, 72, 75, 76, 79, 80*).

2. How are chemical reactions of ionic compounds classified? There are three common types of reactions of ionic compounds (*see Problems 38–50, 65, 70, 79, 81*).

Precipitation reactions are processes in which an insoluble solid called a *precipitate* is formed. Most precipitations take place when the anions and cations of two ionic compounds change partners. Solubility guidelines for ionic compounds are used to predict when precipitation will occur (*see Problems 24, 25, 43–46, 49, 69, 76–78*).

Acid–base neutralization reactions are processes in which an acid reacts with a base to yield water plus an ionic compound called a *salt*. Since acids produce H⁺ ions and bases produce OH⁻ ions when dissolved in water, a neutralization reaction removes H⁺ and OH⁻ ions from solution and yields neutral H_2O (*see Problems 37, 39, 75, 81*).

Oxidation–reduction (redox) reactions are processes in which one or more electrons are transferred between reaction partners.

An *oxidation* is defined as the loss of one or more electrons by an atom, and a *reduction* is the gain of one or more electrons. An *oxidizing agent* causes the oxidation of another reactant by accepting electrons, and a *reducing agent* causes the reduction of another reactant by donating electrons (*see Problems 51–54, 57–62, 65, 66, 68, 82*).

3. What are oxidation numbers, and how are they used? *Oxidation numbers* are assigned to atoms in reactants and products to provide a measure of whether an atom is neutral, electron-rich, or electron-poor. By comparing the oxidation number of an atom before and after reaction, we can tell whether the atom has gained or lost shares in electrons and thus whether a redox reaction has occurred (*see Problems 51–62, 65, 66, 70–74, 82*).

4. What is a net ionic equation? The *net ionic equation* only includes those ions that are directly involved in the ionic reaction. These ions can be identified because they are found in different phases or compounds on the reactant and product sides of the chemical equation. The net ionic equation does not include *spectator ions*, which appear in the same state on both sides of the chemical equation (*see Problems 39, 47, 48, 50, 69, 76–78, 81*).

KEY WORDS

Balanced equation, *p. 134*

Chemical equation, *p. 133*

Coefficient, *p. 134*

Ionic equation, *p. 150*

Law of conservation of mass, *p. 133*

Net ionic equation, *p. 150*

Neutralization reaction, *p. 141*

Oxidation, *p. 143*

Oxidation number, *p. 148*

Oxidation–reduction (redox) reaction, *p. 138*

Oxidizing agent, *p. 143*

Precipitate, *p. 138*

Product, *p. 133*

Reactant, *p. 133*

Reducing agent, *p. 143*

Reduction, *p. 143*

Salt, *p. 138*

Solubility, *p. 139*

Spectator ion, *p. 150*

UNDERSTANDING KEY CONCEPTS

5.20 Assume that the mixture of substances in drawing (a) undergoes a reaction. Which of the drawings (b)–(d) represents a product mixture consistent with the law of conservation of mass?

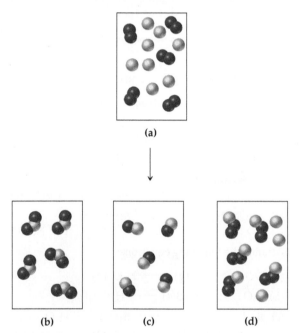

5.21 Reaction of A (green spheres) with B (blue spheres) is shown in the following diagram:

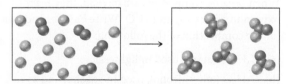

Which equation best describes the reaction?

(a) $A_2 + 2\,B \longrightarrow A_2B_2$

(b) $10\,A + 5\,B_2 \longrightarrow 5\,A_2B_2$

(c) $2\,A + B_2 \longrightarrow A_2B_2$

(d) $5\,A + 5\,B_2 \longrightarrow 5\,A_2B_2$

5.22 If blue spheres represent nitrogen atoms and red spheres represent oxygen atoms in the following diagrams, which box

represents reactants and which represents products for the reaction $2\,NO(g) + O_2(g) \longrightarrow 2\,NO_2(g)$?

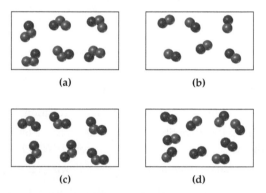

5.23 Assume that an aqueous solution of a cation (represented as red spheres in the diagram) is allowed to mix with a solution of an anion (represented as yellow spheres). Three possible outcomes are represented by boxes (1)–(3):

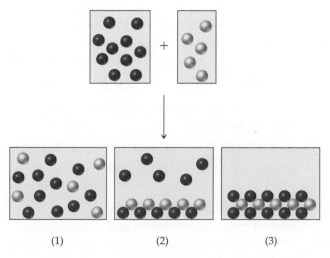

Which outcome corresponds to each of the following reactions?

(a) $2\,Na^+(aq) + CO_3{}^{2-}(aq) \longrightarrow$

(b) $Ba^{2+}(aq) + CrO_4{}^{2-}(aq) \longrightarrow$

(c) $2\,Ag^+(aq) + SO_3{}^{2-}(aq) \longrightarrow$

5.24 An aqueous solution of a cation (represented as blue spheres in the diagram) is allowed to mix with a solution of an anion (represented as green spheres) and the following result is obtained:

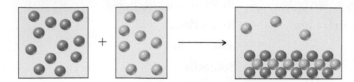

Which combinations of cation and anion, chosen from the following lists, are compatible with the observed results? Explain.

Cations: Na^+, Ca^{2+}, Ag^+, Ni^{2+}

Anions: Cl^-, $CO_3{}^{2-}$, $CrO_4{}^{2-}$, $NO_3{}^-$

5.25 A molecular view of two ionic solutions is presented right:

(a) Which compound is most likely dissolved in beaker A: KBr, $CaCl_2$, PbI_2, Na_2SO_4?

(b) Which compound is most likely dissolved in beaker B: Na_2CO_3, $BaSO_4$, $Cu(NO_3)_2$, $FeCl_3$?

(c) Identify the precipitate and spectator ions for any reaction that will result when beakers A and B are mixed.

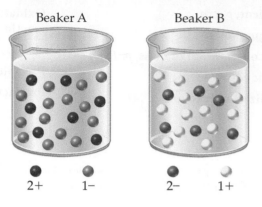

ADDITIONAL PROBLEMS

BALANCING CHEMICAL EQUATIONS

5.26 What is meant by the term "balanced equation"?

5.27 Why is it not possible to balance an equation by changing the subscript on a substance, say from H_2O to H_2O_2?

5.28 Write balanced equations for the following reactions:

(a) Gaseous sulfur dioxide reacts with water to form aqueous sulfurous acid (H_2SO_3).

(b) Liquid bromine reacts with solid potassium metal to form solid potassium bromide.

(c) Gaseous propane (C_3H_8) burns in oxygen to form gaseous carbon dioxide and water vapor.

5.29 Balance the following equation for the synthesis of hydrazine, N_2H_4, a substance used as rocket fuel.

$$NH_3(g) + Cl_2(g) \longrightarrow N_2H_4(l) + NH_4Cl(s)$$

5.30 Which of the following equations are balanced? Balance those that need it.

(a) $2\,C_2H_6(g) + 5\,O_2(g) \longrightarrow 2\,CO_2(g) + 6\,H_2O(l)$

(b) $3\,Ca(OH)_2(aq) + 2\,H_3PO_4(aq) \longrightarrow$
$$Ca_3(PO_4)_2(aq) + 6\,H_2O(l)$$

(c) $Mg(s) + O_2(g) \longrightarrow 2\,MgO(s)$

(d) $K(s) + H_2O(l) \longrightarrow KOH(aq) + H_2(g)$

5.31 Which of the following equations are balanced? Balance those that need it.

(a) $CaC_2 + 2\,H_2O \longrightarrow Ca(OH)_2 + C_2H_2$

(b) $C_2H_8N_2 + 2\,N_2O_4 \longrightarrow 2\,N_2 + 2\,CO_2 + 4\,H_2O$

(c) $3\,MgO + 2\,Fe \longrightarrow Fe_2O_3 + 3\,Mg$

(d) $N_2O \longrightarrow N_2 + O_2$

5.32 Balance the following equations:

(a) $Hg(NO_3)_2(aq) + LiI(aq) \longrightarrow$
$$LiNO_3(aq) + HgI_2(s)$$

(b) $I_2(s) + Cl_2(g) \longrightarrow ICl_5(s)$

(c) $Al(s) + O_2(g) \longrightarrow Al_2O_3(s)$

(d) $CuSO_4(aq) + AgNO_3(aq) \longrightarrow$
$$Ag_2SO_4(s) + Cu(NO_3)_2(aq)$$

(e) $Mn(NO_3)_3(aq) + Na_2S(aq) \longrightarrow$
$$Mn_2S_3(s) + NaNO_3(aq)$$

5.33 Balance the following equations:

(a) $NO_2(g) + O_2(g) \longrightarrow N_2O_5(g)$

(b) $P_4O_{10}(s) + H_2O(l) \longrightarrow H_3PO_4(aq)$

(c) $B_2H_6(l) + O_2(g) \longrightarrow B_2O_3(s) + H_2O(l)$

(d) $Cr_2O_3(s) + CCl_4(l) \longrightarrow CrCl_3(s) + COCl_2(aq)$

(e) $Fe_3O_4(s) + O_2(g) \longrightarrow Fe_2O_3(s)$.

5.34 When organic compounds are burned, they react with oxygen to form CO_2 and H_2O. Write balanced equations for the combustion of the following:

(a) C_4H_{10} (butane, used in lighters)

(b) C_2H_6O (ethyl alcohol, used in gasohol and as race car fuel)

(c) C_8H_{18} (octane, a component of gasoline)

5.35 When organic compounds are burned without enough oxygen, carbon monoxide is formed as a product instead of carbon dioxide. Write and balance the combustion reactions from Problem 5.34 using CO as a product instead of CO_2.

5.36 Hydrofluoric acid (HF) is used to etch glass (SiO_2). The products of the reaction are silicon tetrafluoride and water. Write the balanced chemical equation.

5.37 Write a balanced equation for the reaction of aqueous sodium carbonate (Na_2CO_3) with aqueous nitric acid (HNO_3) to yield CO_2, $NaNO_3$, and H_2O.

TYPES OF CHEMICAL REACTIONS

5.38 Identify each of the following reactions as a precipitation, neutralization, or redox reaction:

(a) $Mg(s) + 2 HCl(aq) \longrightarrow MgCl_2(aq) + H_2(g)$

(b) $KOH(aq) + HNO_3(aq) \longrightarrow KNO_3(aq) + H_2O(l)$

(c) $Pb(NO_3)_2(aq) + 2 HBr(aq) \longrightarrow$
$$PbBr_2(s) + 2 HNO_3(aq)$$

(d) $Ca(OH)_2(aq) + 2 HCl(aq) \longrightarrow$
$$2 H_2O(l) + CaCl_2(aq)$$

5.39 Write balanced ionic equations and net ionic equations for the following reactions:

(a) Aqueous sulfuric acid is neutralized by aqueous potassium hydroxide.

(b) Aqueous magnesium hydroxide is neutralized by aqueous hydrochloric acid.

5.40 Write balanced ionic equations and net ionic equations for the following reactions:

(a) A precipitate of barium sulfate forms when aqueous solutions of barium nitrate and potassium sulfate are mixed.

(b) Zinc ion and hydrogen gas form when zinc metal reacts with aqueous sulfuric acid.

5.41 Identify each of the reactions in Problem 5.30 as a precipitation, neutralization, or redox reaction.

5.42 Identify each of the reactions in Problem 5.32 as a precipitation, neutralization, or redox reaction.

5.43 Which of the following substances are likely to be soluble in water?

(a) $ZnSO_4$ (b) $NiCO_3$

(c) $PbCl_2$ (d) $Ca_3(PO_4)_2$

5.44 Which of the following substances are likely to be soluble in water?

(a) Ag_2O (b) $Ba(NO_3)_2$

(c) $SnCO_3$ (d) Al_2S_3

5.45 Use the solubility guidelines in Section 5.4 to predict whether a precipitation reaction will occur when aqueous solutions of the following substances are mixed.

(a) $NaOH + HClO_4$

(b) $FeCl_2 + KOH$

(c) $(NH_4)_2SO_4 + NiCl_2$

5.46 Use the solubility guidelines in Section 5.4 to predict whether precipitation reactions will occur between the listed pairs of reactants. Write balanced equations for those reactions that should occur.

(a) NaBr and $Hg_2(NO_3)_2$

(b) $CuCl_2$ and K_2SO_4

(c) $LiNO_3$ and $Ca(CH_3CO_2)_2$

(d) $(NH_4)_2CO_3$ and $CaCl_2$

(e) KOH and $MnBr_2$

(f) Na_2S and $Al(NO_3)_3$

5.47 Write net ionic equations for the following reactions:

(a) $Mg(s) + CuCl_2(aq) \longrightarrow MgCl_2(aq) + Cu(s)$

(b) $2 KCl(aq) + Pb(NO_3)_2(aq) \longrightarrow$
$$PbCl_2(s) + 2 KNO_3(aq)$$

(c) $2 Cr(NO_3)_3(aq) + 3 Na_2S(aq) \longrightarrow$
$$Cr_2S_3(s) + 6 NaNO_3(aq)$$

5.48 Write net ionic equations for the following reactions:

(a) $2 AuCl_3(aq) + 3 Sn(s) \longrightarrow 3 SnCl_2(aq) + 2 Au(s)$

(b) $2 NaI(aq) + Br_2(l) \longrightarrow 2 NaBr(aq) + I_2(s)$

(c) $2 AgNO_3(aq) + Fe(s) \longrightarrow Fe(NO_3)_2(aq) + 2 Ag(s)$

5.49 Complete the following precipitation reactions using balanced chemical equations:

(a) $FeSO_4(aq) + Sr(OH)_2(aq) \longrightarrow$

(b) $Na_2S(aq) + ZnSO_4(aq) \longrightarrow$

5.50 Write net ionic equations for each of the reactions in Problem 5.49.

REDOX REACTIONS AND OXIDATION NUMBERS

5.51 Where in the periodic table are the best reducing agents found? The best oxidizing agents?

5.52 Where in the periodic table are the most easily reduced elements found? The most easily oxidized?

5.53 In each of the following, tell whether the substance gains electrons or loses electrons in a redox reaction:

(a) An oxidizing agent

(b) A reducing agent

(c) A substance undergoing oxidation

(d) A substance undergoing reduction

5.54 For the following substances, tell whether the oxidation number increases or decreases in a redox reaction:

(a) An oxidizing agent

(b) A reducing agent

(c) A substance undergoing oxidation

(d) A substance undergoing reduction

5.55 Assign an oxidation number to each element in the following compounds or ions:

(a) N_2O_5 (b) $SO_3{}^{2-}$

(c) CH_2O (d) $HClO_3$

5.56 Assign an oxidation number to the metal in the following compounds:

(a) $CoCl_3$ (b) $FeSO_4$

(c) UO_3 (d) CuF_2

(e) TiO_2 (f) SnS

5.57 Which element is oxidized and which is reduced in the following reactions?

(a) $Si(s) + 2\,Cl_2(g) \longrightarrow SiCl_4(l)$

(b) $Cl_2(g) + 2\,NaBr(aq) \longrightarrow Br_2(aq) + 2\,NaCl(aq)$

(c) $SbCl_3(s) + Cl_2(g) \longrightarrow SbCl_5(s)$

5.58 Which element is oxidized and which is reduced in the following reactions?

(a) $2\,SO_2(g) + O_2(g) \longrightarrow 2\,SO_3(g)$

(b) $2\,Na(s) + Cl_2(g) \longrightarrow 2\,NaCl(s)$

(c) $CuCl_2(aq) + Zn(s) \longrightarrow ZnCl_2(aq) + Cu(s)$

(d) $2\,NaCl(aq) + F_2(g) \longrightarrow 2\,NaF(aq) + Cl_2(g)$

5.59 Balance each of the following redox reactions:

(a) $Al(s) + H_2SO_4(aq) \longrightarrow Al_2(SO_4)_3(aq) + H_2(g)$

(b) $Fe(s) + Cl_2(g) \longrightarrow FeCl_3(s)$

(c) $CO(g) + I_2O_5(s) \longrightarrow I_2(s) + CO_2(g)$

5.60 Balance each of the following redox reactions:

(a) $N_2O_4(l) + N_2H_4(l) \longrightarrow N_2(g) + H_2O(g)$

(b) $CaH_2(s) + H_2O(l) \longrightarrow Ca(OH)_2(aq) + H_2(g)$

(c) $Al(s) + H_2O(l) \longrightarrow Al(OH)_3(s) + H_2(g)$

5.61 Identify the oxidizing agent and the reducing agent in Problem 5.59.

5.62 Identify the oxidizing agent and the reducing agent in Problem 5.60.

CHEMISTRY IN ACTION

5.63 Sodium urate, the principal constituent of some kidney stones and the substance responsible for gout, has the formula $NaC_5H_3N_4O_3$. In aqueous solution, the solubility of sodium urate is only 0.067 g/L. How many grams of sodium urate could be dissolved in the blood before precipitation might occur? (The average adult has a blood capacity of about 5 L.) [*Gout and Kidney Stones, p. 140*]

5.64 Uric acid is formed in the body by the metabolism of purines. The reaction can be represented as $C_5H_4N_4$ (purine) + $O_2 \rightarrow C_5H_4N_4O_3$ (uric acid).

(a) Balance the reaction.

(b) What type of reaction is this? [*Gout and Kidney Stones, p. 140*]

5.65 The rechargeable NiCd battery uses the following reaction:

$$2\,NiO(OH) + Cd + 2\,H_2O \longrightarrow 2\,Ni(OH)_2 + Cd(OH)_2.$$

Which reactant is being oxidized and which is being reduced in this reaction? [*Batteries, p. 147*]

5.66 Identify the oxidizing and reducing agents in a typical dry-cell battery. [*Batteries, p. 147*]

GENERAL QUESTIONS AND PROBLEMS

5.67 Balance the following equations.

(a) The thermite reaction, used in welding:
$Al(s) + Fe_2O_3(s) \longrightarrow Al_2O_3(l) + Fe(l)$

(b) The explosion of ammonium nitrate:
$NH_4NO_3(s) \longrightarrow N_2(g) + O_2(g) + H_2O(g)$

5.68 Lithium oxide is used aboard the space shuttle to remove water from the atmosphere according to the equation:

$$Li_2O(s) + H_2O(g) \longrightarrow LiOH(s)$$

(a) Balance the chemical equation.

(b) Is this a redox reaction? Why or why not?

5.69 Look at the solubility guidelines in Section 5.4 and predict whether a precipitate forms when $CuCl_2(aq)$ and $Na_2CO_3(aq)$ are mixed. If so, write both the balanced equation and the net ionic equation for the process.

5.70 Balance the following equations and classify each as a precipitation, neutralization, or redox reaction:

(a) $Al(OH)_3(aq) + HNO_3(aq) \longrightarrow$
$ Al(NO_3)_3(aq) + H_2O(l)$

(b) $AgNO_3(aq) + FeCl_3(aq) \longrightarrow$
$ AgCl(s) + Fe(NO_3)_3(aq)$

(c) $(NH_4)_2Cr_2O_7(s) \longrightarrow Cr_2O_3(s) + H_2O(g) + N_2(g)$

(d) $Mn_2(CO_3)_3(s) \longrightarrow Mn_2O_3(s) + CO_2(g)$

5.71 White phosphorus (P_4) is a highly reactive form of elemental phosphorus that reacts with oxygen to form a variety of molecular compounds, including diphosphorus pentoxide.

(a) Write the balanced chemical equation for this reaction.

(b) Calculate the oxidation number for P and O on both sides of the reaction, and identify the oxidizing and reducing agents.

5.72 The combustion of fossil fuels containing sulfur contributes to the phenomenon known as acid rain. The combustion process releases sulfur in the form of sulfur dioxide, which is converted to sulfuric acid in a process involving two reactions.

(a) In the first reaction, sulfur dioxide reacts with molecular oxygen to form sulfur trioxide. Write the balanced chemical equation for this reaction.

(b) In the second reaction, sulfur trioxide reacts with water in the atmosphere to form sulfuric acid. Write the balanced chemical equation for this reaction.

(c) Calculate the oxidation number for the S atom in each compound in these reactions.

5.73 The transition metals form compounds with oxygen in which the metals have different oxidation states. Calculate the oxidation number for the transition metal in the following sets of compounds:

(a) Mn in MnO_2, Mn_2O_3, and $KMnO_4$

(b) Cr in CrO_2, CrO_3, and Cr_2O_3.

5.74 In the Breathalyzer test, blood alcohol is determined by reaction of the alcohol with potassium dichromate:

$$16H^+(aq) + 2Cr_2O_7^{2-}(aq) + C_2H_5OH(aq) \longrightarrow$$
$$4Cr^{3+}(aq) + 2CO_2(g) + 11H_2O(l)$$

(a) Calculate the oxidation number of Cr in $Cr_2O_7^{2-}$.

(b) Calculate the oxidation number of C in C_2H_5OH and in CO_2.

(c) Identify the oxidizing agent and the reducing agent in this reaction.

5.75 Milk of magnesia is a suspension of magnesium hydroxide in water that is used to neutralize excess stomach acid. Write the balanced chemical equation for this neutralization reaction.

5.76 Iron in drinking water is removed by precipitation of the Fe^{3+} ion by reaction with NaOH to produce iron(III) hydroxide. Write the balanced chemical equation and the net ionic equation for this reaction.

5.77 Hard water contains magnesium and calcium ions (Mg^{2+}, Ca^{2+}), which can precipitate out in hot water pipes and water heaters as carbonates. Write the net ionic equation for this reaction.

5.78 Pepto-Bismol™, an antacid and antidiarrheal, contains bismuth subsalicylate, $C_7H_5BiO_4$. Some users of this product can experience a condition known as "black tongue," which is caused by the reaction of bismuth(III) ions with trace amounts of S^{2-} in saliva to form a black precipitate. Write the balanced net ionic equation for this precipitation reaction.

5.79 Iron is produced from iron ore by reaction with carbon monoxide:

$$Fe_2O_3(s) + CO(g) \longrightarrow Fe(s) + CO_2(g)$$

(a) Balance the chemical equation.

(b) Classify the reaction as a precipitation, neutralization, or redox reaction.

5.80 Balance the reaction for the synthesis of urea, commonly used as a fertilizer:

$$CO_2(g) + NH_3(g) \longrightarrow NH_2CONH_2(s) + H_2O(l)$$

5.81 Geologists identify carbonate minerals by reaction with acids. Dolomite, for example, contains magnesium carbonate, which reacts with hydrochloric acid by the following reaction:

$$MgCO_3(s) + HCl(aq) \longrightarrow MgCl_2(aq) + CO_2(g) + H_2O(l)$$

(a) Balance the reaction and write the net ionic equation.

(b) Classify the reaction as a precipitation, neutralization, or redox reaction.

5.82 Iodine, used as an antiseptic agent, can be prepared in the laboratory by the following reaction:

$$2NaI(s) + 2H_2SO_4(aq) + MnO_2(s) \longrightarrow$$
$$Na_2SO_4(aq) + MnSO_4(aq) + I_2(g) + 2H_2O(l)$$

(a) Determine the oxidation number for the Mn and I on both sides of the equation.

(b) Identify the oxidizing and reducing agents.

CHAPTER 6

Chemical Reactions: Mole and Mass Relationships

CONTENTS

◄ The amount of CO_2 and H_2O produced by the fuel combustion of airplanes and automobiles can be calculated using mole ratios and mole-to-mass conversions.

1. **What is the mole, and why is it useful in chemistry?**
    THE GOAL: Be able to explain the meaning and uses of the mole and Avogadro's number.

2. **How are molar quantities and mass quantities related?**
    THE GOAL: Be able to convert between molar and mass quantities of an element or compound. (◀◀◀ A.)

3. **What are the limiting reagent, theoretical yield, and percent yield of a reaction?**
    THE GOAL: Be able to take the amount of product actually formed in a reaction, calculate the amount that could form theoretically, and express the results as a percent yield. (◀◀◀ A, B.)

CONCEPTS
TO REVIEW

A. Problem Solving: Unit Conversions and Estimating Answers
(Section 1.12)

B. Balancing Chemical Equations
(Section 5.2)

When chefs prepare to cook a rice pudding, they don't count out individual grains of rice, or individual raisins, or individual sugar crystals. Rather, they measure out appropriate amounts of the necessary ingredients using more convenient units—such as cups, or tablespoons. When chemists prepare chemical reactions, they use the same approach. In this chapter we introduce the concept of the mole and how chemists use it when studying the quantitative relationships between reactants and products.

6.1 The Mole and Avogadro's Number

In the previous chapter, we learned how to use the balanced chemical equation to indicate what is happening at the molecular level during a reaction. Now, let us imagine a laboratory experiment: the reaction of ethylene (C_2H_4) with hydrogen chloride (HCl) to prepare ethyl chloride (C_2H_5Cl), a colorless, low-boiling liquid used by doctors and athletic trainers as a spray-on anesthetic. The reaction is represented as

$$C_2H_4(g) + HCl(g) \rightarrow C_2H_5Cl(g)$$

In this reaction, 1 molecule of ethylene reacts with 1 molecule of hydrogen chloride to produce 1 molecule of ethyl chloride.

How, though, can you be sure you have a 1 to 1 ratio of reactant molecules in your reaction flask? Since it is impossible to hand-count the number of molecules correctly, you must weigh them instead. (This is a common method for dealing with all kinds of small objects: Nails, nuts, and grains of rice are all weighed rather than counted.) But the weighing approach leads to another problem. How many molecules are there in 1 gram of ethylene, hydrogen chloride, or any other substance? The answer depends on the identity of the substance, because different molecules have different masses.

To determine how many molecules of a given substance are in a certain mass, it is helpful to define a quantity called *molecular weight*. Just as the *atomic weight* of an element is the average mass of the element's *atoms*, the **molecular weight (MW)** of a molecule is the average mass of a substance's *molecules*. Numerically, a substance's molecular weight (or **formula weight** for an ionic compound) is equal to the sum of the atomic weights for all the atoms in the molecule or formula unit.

For example, the molecular weight of ethylene (C_2H_4) is 28.0 amu, the molecular weight of HCl is 36.5 amu, and the molecular weight of ethyl chloride (C_2H_5Cl) is 64.5 amu. (The actual values are known more precisely but are rounded off here for convenience.)

> **Molecular weight** The sum of atomic weights of all atoms in a molecule.

> ◀◀◀ See Section 2.3 for discussion of atomic weight.

> **Formula weight** The sum of atomic weights of all atoms in one formula unit of any compound, whether molecular or ionic.

For ethylene, C_2H_4:

$$\text{Atomic weight of 2 C} = 2 \times 12.0 \text{ amu} = 24.0 \text{ amu}$$

$$\underline{\text{Atomic weight of 4 H} = 4 \times 1.0 \text{ amu} = 4.0 \text{ amu}}$$

$$\text{MW of } C_2H_4 = 28.0 \text{ amu}$$

▲ These samples of sulfur, copper, mercury, and helium each contain 1 mol. Do they all have the same mass?

For hydrogen chloride, **HCl:**

$$
\begin{array}{ll}
\text{Atomic weight of H} & = 1.0 \text{ amu} \\
\underline{\text{Atomic weight of Cl} = 35.5 \text{ amu}} \\
\text{MW of HCl} & = 36.5 \text{ amu}
\end{array}
$$

For ethyl chloride, C_2H_5Cl:

$$
\begin{array}{lll}
\text{Atomic weight of 2 C} = 2 \times 12.0 \text{ amu} & = 24.0 \text{ amu} \\
\text{Atomic weight of 5 H} = 5 \times 1.0 \text{ amu} & = 5.0 \text{ amu} \\
\underline{\text{Atomic weight of Cl}} & = 35.5 \text{ amu} \\
\text{MW of } C_2H_5Cl & = 64.5 \text{ amu}
\end{array}
$$

How are molecular weights used? Since the mass ratio of 1 ethylene molecule to 1 HCl molecule is 28.0 to 36.5, the mass ratio of *any* given number of ethylene molecules to the same number of HCl molecules is also 28.0 to 36.5. In other words, a 28.0 to 36.5 *mass* ratio of ethylene and HCl always guarantees a 1 to 1 *number* ratio. *Samples of different substances always contain the same number of molecules or formula units whenever their mass ratio is the same as their molecular or formula weight ratio* (Figure 6.1).

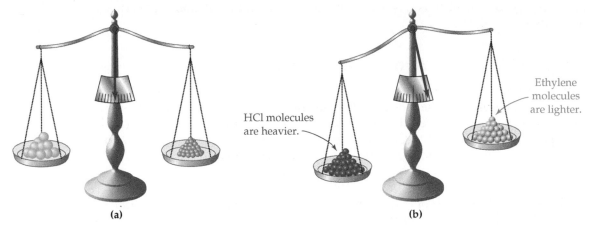

HCl molecules are heavier.

Ethylene molecules are lighter.

(a)   (b)

▲ **Figure 6.1**
(a) Because the yellow balls (left pan) are bigger than the green balls (right pan), you cannot get an equal number by taking equal weights. The same is true for atoms or molecules of different substances. (b) Equal numbers of ethylene and HCl molecules always have a mass ratio equal to the ratio of their molecular weights, 28.0 to 36.5.

A particularly convenient way to use this mass/number relationship for molecules is to measure amounts in grams that are numerically equal to molecular weights. If, for instance, you were to carry out your experiment with 28.0 g of ethylene and 36.5 g of HCl, you could be certain that you would have a 1 to 1 ratio of reactant molecules.

When referring to the vast numbers of molecules or formula units that take part in a visible chemical reaction, it is convenient to use a counting unit called a **mole**, abbreviated *mol*. One mole of any substance is the amount whose mass in grams—its **molar mass** —is numerically equal to its molecular or formula weight in amu. One mole of ethylene has a mass of 28.0 g, one mole of HCl has a mass of 36.5 g, and one mole of ethyl chloride has a mass of 64.5 g.

Just how many molecules are there in a mole? Think back to Chapter 2 where we learned to calculate the number of atoms in a sample of an element given its weight in grams, the atomic mass of the atom, and a gram/amu conversion factor. In Problem 2.2, you (hopefully!) found that a 1 gram sample of hydrogen (atomic mass 1 amu) and a 12 gram sample of carbon (atomic mass 12 amu) each contain 6.022×10^{23} atoms. One mole of any substance, therefore, contains 6.022×10^{23} formula units, a value called **Avogadro's number** (abbreviated N_A) after the Italian scientist who first recognized the importance of the mass/number relationship in molecules. Avogadro's

Mole The amount of a substance whose mass in grams is numerically equal to its molecular or formula weight.

Molar mass The mass in grams of 1 mole of a substance, numerically equal to molecular weight.

number of formula units of any substance—that is, one mole—has a mass in grams numerically equal to the molecular weight of the substance.

Avogadro's number (N_A) The number of formula units in 1 mole of anything; 6.022×10^{23}.

$$1 \text{ mol HCl} = 6.022 \times 10^{23} \text{ HCl molecules} = 36.5 \text{ g HCl}$$

$$1 \text{ mol C}_2\text{H}_4 = 6.022 \times 10^{23} \text{ C}_2\text{H}_4 \text{ molecules} = 28.0 \text{ g C}_2\text{H}_4$$

$$1 \text{ mol C}_2\text{H}_5\text{Cl} = 6.022 \times 10^{23} \text{ C}_2\text{H}_5\text{Cl molecules} = 64.5 \text{ g C}_2\text{H}_5\text{Cl}$$

How big is Avogadro's number? Our minds cannot really conceive of the magnitude of a number like 6.022×10^{23}, but the following comparisons will give you a sense of the scale:

Amount of water in world's oceans (liters)

Age of earth in (seconds)

Population of earth

Avogadro's number: 602,200,000,000,000,000,000,000

Distance from earth to sun (centimeters)

Average college tuition (U.S. dollars)

Worked Example 6.1 Molar Mass and Avogadro's Number: Number of Molecules

Pseudoephedrine hydrochloride ($C_{10}H_{16}ClNO$) is a nasal decongestant commonly found in cold medication. (a) What is the molar mass of pseudoephedrine hydrochloride? (b) How many molecules of pseudoephedrine hydrochloride are in a tablet that contains 30.0 mg of this decongestant?

ANALYSIS We are given a mass and need to convert to a number of molecules. This is most easily accomplished by using the molar mass of pseudoephedrine hydrochloride calculated in part (a) as the conversion factor from mass to moles and realizing that this mass (in grams) contains Avogadro's number of molecules (6.022×10^{23}).

BALLPARK ESTIMATE The formula for pseudoephedrine contains 10 carbon atoms (each one of atomic weight 12.0 amu), so the molecular weight is greater than 120 amu, probably near 200 amu. Thus, the molecular weight should be near 200 g/mol. The mass of 30 mg of pseudoepinephrine HCl is less than the mass of 1 mol of this compound by a factor of roughly 10^4 (0.03 g versus 200 g), which means that the number of molecules should also be smaller by a factor of 10^4 (on the order of 10^{19} in the tablet versus 10^{23} in 1 mol).

SOLUTION

(a) The molecular weight of pseudoephedrine is found by summing the atomic weights of all atoms in the molecule:

Atomic Weight of 10 atoms of C:	10×12.011 amu =	120.11 amu
16 atoms of H:	16×1.00794 amu =	16.127 amu
1 atom of Cl:	1×35.4527 amu =	35.4527 amu
1 atom of N:	1×14.0067 amu =	14.0067 amu
1 atom of O:	1×15.9994 amu =	15.9994 amu

MW of $C_{10}H_{16}ClNO$ = 201.6958 amu $\longrightarrow$ 201.70 g/mol

Remember that atomic mass in amu converts directly to molar mass in g/mol. Also, following the rules for significant figures from Sections 1.9 and 1.11, our final answer is rounded to the second decimal place.

(b) Since this problem involves unit conversions, we can use the step-wise solution introduced in Chapter 1.

STEP 1: Identify known information. We are given the mass of pseudoephedrine hydrochloride (in mg).	30.0 mg pseudoephedrine hydrochloride
STEP 2: Identify answer and units. We are looking for the number of molecules of pseudoephedrine hydrochloride in a 30 mg tablet.	?? = molecules
STEP 3: Identify conversion factors. Since the molecular weight of pseudoephedrine hydrochloride is 201.70 amu, 201.70 g contains 6.022×10^{23} molecules. We can use this ratio as a conversion factor to convert from mass to molecules. We will also need to convert 30 mg to g.	$\dfrac{6.022 \times 10^{23} \text{ molecules}}{201.70 \text{ g}}$ $\dfrac{.001 \text{ g}}{1 \text{ mg}}$

STEP 4: **Solve.** Set up an equation so that unwanted units cancel.	$(30.0 \text{ mg pseudoephedrine hydrochloride}) \times \left(\dfrac{.001 \text{ g}}{1 \text{ mg}}\right) \times \left(\dfrac{6.022 \times 10^{23} \text{ molecules}}{201.70 \text{ g}}\right)$ $= 8.96 \times 10^{19}$ molecules of pseudoephedrine hydrochloride

BALLPARK CHECK Our estimate for the number of molecules was on the order of 10^{19}, which is consistent with the calculated answer.

Worked Example **6.2** Avogadro's Number: Atom to Mass Conversions

A tiny pencil mark just visible to the naked eye contains about 3×10^{17} atoms of carbon. What is the mass of this pencil mark in grams?

ANALYSIS We are given a number of atoms and need to convert to mass. The conversion factor can be obtained by realizing that the atomic weight of carbon in grams contains Avogadro's number of atoms (6.022×10^{23}).

BALLPARK ESTIMATE Since we are given a number of atoms that is six orders of magnitude less than Avogadro's number, we should get a corresponding mass that is six orders of magnitude less than the molar mass of carbon, which means a mass for the pencil mark of about 10^{-6} g.

SOLUTION

STEP 1: **Identify known information.** We know the number of carbon atoms in the pencil mark.	3×10^{17} atoms of carbon
STEP 2: **Identify answer and units.**	Mass of carbon = ?? g
STEP 3: **Identify conversion factors.** The atomic weight of carbon is 12.01 amu, so 12.01 g of carbon contains 6.022×10^{23} atoms.	$\dfrac{12.01 \text{ g carbon}}{6.022 \times 10^{23} \text{ atoms}}$
STEP 4: **Solve.** Set up an equation using the conversion factors so that unwanted units cancel.	$(3 \times 10^{17} \text{ atoms})\left(\dfrac{12.01 \text{ g carbon}}{6.022 \times 10^{23} \text{ atoms}}\right) = 6 \times 10^{-6} \text{ g carbon}$

BALLPARK CHECK The answer is of the same magnitude as our estimate and makes physical sense.

PROBLEM 6.1
Calculate the molecular weight of the following substances:
(a) Ibuprofen, $C_{13}H_{18}O_2$ (b) Phenobarbital, $C_{12}H_{12}N_2O_3$

PROBLEM 6.2
How many molecules of ascorbic acid $(\text{vitamin C, } C_6H_8O_6)$ are in a 500 mg tablet?

PROBLEM 6.3
What is the mass in grams of 5.0×10^{20} molecules of aspirin $(C_9H_8O_4)$?

⟢ **KEY CONCEPT PROBLEM 6.4**

What is the molecular weight of cytosine, a component of DNA (deoxyribonucleic acid)? (black = C, blue = N, red = O, white = H.)

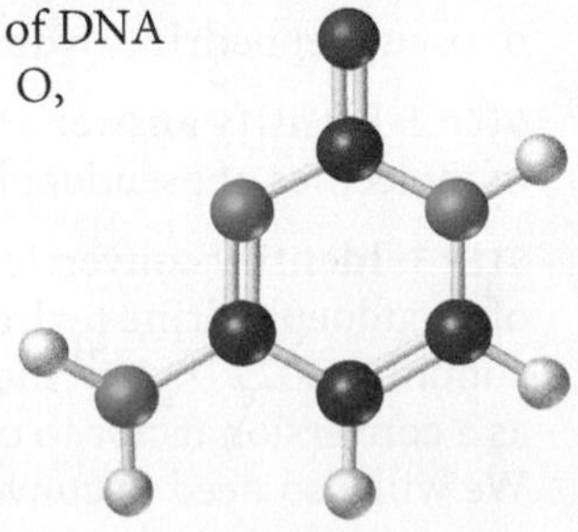

Cytosine

6.2 Gram–Mole Conversions

To ensure that we have the correct molecule to molecule (or mole to mole) relationship between reactants as specified by the balanced chemical equation, we can take advantage of the constant mass ratio between reactants. The mass in grams of 1 mol of any substance (that is, Avogadro's number of molecules or formula units) is called the molar mass of the substance.

Molar mass = Mass of 1 mol of substance

= Mass of 6.022×10^{23} molecules (formula units) of substance

= Molecular (formula) weight of substance in grams

In effect, molar mass serves as a conversion factor between numbers of moles and mass. If you know how many moles you have, you can calculate their mass; if you know the mass of a sample, you can calculate the number of moles. Suppose, for example, we need to know how much 0.25 mol of water weighs. The molecular weight of H_2O is $(2 \times 1.0 \text{ amu}) + 16.0 \text{ amu} = 18.0 \text{ amu}$, so the molar mass of water is 18.0 g/mol. Thus, the conversion factor between moles of water and mass of water is 18.0 g/mol:

$$0.25 \text{ mol } H_2O \times \frac{\boxed{\text{Molar mass used as conversion factor}}}{} $$

$$0.25 \text{ mol } H_2O \times \frac{18.0 \text{ g } H_2O}{1 \text{ mol } H_2O} = 4.5 \text{ g } H_2O$$

Alternatively, suppose we need to know how many moles of water are in 27 g of water. The conversion factor is 1 mol/18.0 g:

$$27 \text{ g } H_2O \times \frac{\boxed{\text{Molar mass used as conversion factor}}}{}$$

$$27 \text{ g } H_2O \times \frac{1 \text{ mol } H_2O}{18.0 \text{ g } H_2O} = 1.5 \text{ mol } H_2O$$

Note that the 1 mol in the numerator is an exact number, so the number of significant figures in the final answer is based on the 27 g H_2O (2 sig figs.). Worked Examples 6.3 and 6.4 give more practice in gram–mole conversions.

Worked Example 6.3 Molar Mass: Mole to Gram Conversion

The nonprescription pain relievers Advil and Nuprin contain ibuprofen $(C_{13}H_{18}O_2)$, whose molecular weight is 206.3 amu (Problem 6.1a). If all the tablets in a bottle of pain reliever together contain 0.082 mol of ibuprofen, what is the number of grams of ibuprofen in the bottle?

ANALYSIS We are given a number of moles and asked to find the mass. Molar mass is the conversion factor between the two.

BALLPARK ESTIMATE Since 1 mol of ibuprofen has a mass of about 200 g, 0.08 mol has a mass of about $0.08 \times 200 \text{ g} = 16 \text{ g}$.

SOLUTION

STEP 1: **Identify known information.**	0.082 mol ibuprofen in bottle
STEP 2: **Identify answer and units.**	mass ibuprofen in bottle = ?? g
STEP 3: **Identify conversion factor.** We use the molecular weight of ibuprofen to convert from moles to grams.	1 mol ibuprofen = 206.3 g $$\frac{206.3 \text{ g ibuprofen}}{1 \text{ mol ibuprofen}}$$
STEP 4: **Solve.** Set up an equation using the known information and conversion factor so that unwanted units cancel.	$$0.082 \text{ mol } C_{13}H_{18}O_2 \times \frac{206.3 \text{ g ibuprofen}}{1 \text{ mol ibuprofen}} = 17 \text{ g } C_{13}H_{18}O_2$$

BALLPARK CHECK The calculated answer is consistent with our estimate of 16 g.

CHEMISTRY IN ACTION

Did Ben Franklin Have Avogadro's Number? A Ballpark Calculation

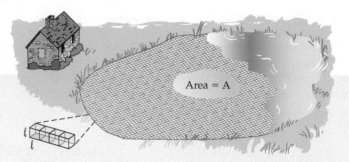

"At" length being at Clapham, where there is on the common a large pond . . . I fetched out a cruet of oil and dropped a little of it on the water. I saw it spread itself with surprising swiftness upon the surface. The oil, though not more than a teaspoonful, produced an instant calm over a space several yards square which spread amazingly and extended itself gradually . . . making all that quarter of the pond, perhaps half an acre, as smooth as a looking glass. *Excerpt from a letter of Benjamin Franklin to William Brownrigg, 1773.*

▲ **What did these two have in common? [Benjamin Franklin (left), Amedeo Avogadro (right)]**

Benjamin Franklin, author and renowned statesman, was also an inventor and a scientist. Every school-child knows of Franklin's experiment with a kite and a key, demonstrating that lightning is electricity. Less well known is that his measurement of the extent to which oil spreads on water makes possible a simple estimate of molecular size and Avogadro's number.

The calculation goes like this: Avogadro's number is the number of molecules in 1 mole of any substance. So, if we can estimate both the number of molecules and the number of moles in Franklin's teaspoon of oil, we can calculate Avogadro's number. Let us start by calculating the number of molecules in the oil.

1. The volume (V) of oil Franklin used was 1 tsp = 4.9 cm^3, and the area (A) covered by the oil was 1/2 acre = $2.0 \times 10^7 \text{ cm}^2$. We will assume that the oil molecules are tiny cubes that pack closely together and form a layer only one molecule thick. As shown in the accompanying figure, the volume of the oil is equal to the surface area of the layer times the

length (l) of the side of one molecule: $V = A \times l$. Rearranging this equation to find the length then gives us an estimate of molecular size:

$$l = \frac{V}{A} = \frac{4.9 \text{ cm}^3}{2.0 \times 10^7 \text{ cm}^2} = 2.5 \times 10^{-7} \text{ cm}$$

2. The area of the oil layer is the area of the side of one molecule (l^2) times the number of molecules (N) of oil: $A = l^2 \times N$. Rearranging this equation gives us the number of molecules:

$$N = \frac{A}{l^2} = \frac{2 \times 10^7 \text{ cm}^2}{(2.5 \times 10^{-7} \text{ cm})^2} = 3.2 \times 10^{20} \text{ molecules}$$

3. To calculate the number of moles, we first need to know the mass (M) of the oil. This could have been determined by weighing the oil, but Franklin neglected to do so. Let us therefore estimate the mass by multiplying the volume (V) of the oil by the density (D) of a typical oil, 0.95 g/cm^3. (Since oil floats on water, it is not surprising that the density of oil is a bit less than the density of water, which is 1.00 g/cm^3.)

$$M = V \times D = 4.9 \text{ cm}^3 \times 0.95 \frac{\text{g}}{\text{cm}^3} = 4.7 \text{ g}$$

4. We now have to make one final assumption about the molecular weight of the oil before we complete the calculation. Assuming that a typical oil has MW = 200 amu, then the mass of 1 mol of oil is 200 g. Dividing the mass of the oil (M) by the mass of 1 mol gives the number of moles of oil:

$$\text{Moles of oil} = \frac{4.7 \text{ g}}{200 \text{ g/mol}} = 0.024 \text{ mol}$$

5. Finally, the number of molecules per mole—Avogadro's number—can be obtained by dividing the estimated number of molecules (step 2) by the estimated moles (step 4):

$$\text{Avogadro's number} = \frac{3.2 \times 10^{20} \text{ molecules}}{0.024 \text{ mol}} = 1.3 \times 10^{22}$$

The calculation is not very accurate, of course, but Ben was not really intending for us to calculate Avogadro's number when he made a rough estimate of how much his oil spread out. Nevertheless, the result is not too bad for such a simple experiment.

See Chemistry in Action Problem 6.58 at the end of the chapter.

Worked Example 6.4 Molar Mass: Gram to Mole Conversion

The maximum dose of sodium hydrogen phosphate (Na_2HPO_4, MW = 142.0 molar mass) that should be taken in one day for use as a laxative is 3.8 g. How many moles of sodium hydrogen phosphate, how many moles of Na^+ ions, and how many total moles of ions are in this dose?

ANALYSIS Molar mass is the conversion factor between mass and number of moles. The chemical formula Na_2HPO_4 shows that each formula unit contains 2 Na^+ ions and 1 HPO_4^{2-} ion.

BALLPARK ESTIMATE The maximum dose is about two orders of magnitude smaller than the molecular weight (approximately 4 g compared to 142 g). Thus, the number of moles of sodium hydrogen phosphate in 3.8 g should be about two orders of magnitude less than one mole. The number of moles of Na_2HPO_4 and total moles of ions, then, should be on the order of 10^{-2}.

SOLUTION

STEP 1: Identify known information. We are given the mass and molecular weight of Na_2HPO_4.

3.8 g Na_2HPO_4; MW = 142.0 amu

STEP 2: Identify answer and units. We need to find the number of moles of Na_2HPO_4, and the total number of moles of ions.

Moles of Na_2HPO_4 = ?? mol
Moles of Na^+ ions = ?? mol
Total moles of ions = ?? mol

STEP 3: Identify conversion factor. We can use the molecular weight of Na_2HPO_4 to convert from grams to moles.

$$\frac{1 \text{ mol } Na_2HPO_4}{142.0 \text{ g } Na_2HPO_4}$$

STEP 4: Solve. We use the known information and conversion factor to obtain moles of Na_2HPO_4; since 1 mol of Na_2HPO_4 contains 2 mol of Na^+ ions and 1 mol of HPO_4^{2-} ions, we multiply these values by the number of moles in the sample.

$$3.8 \text{ g } Na_2HPO_4 \times \frac{1 \text{ mol } Na_2HPO_4}{142.0 \text{ g } Na_2HPO_4} = 0.027 \text{ mol } Na_2HPO_4$$

$$\frac{2 \text{ mol } Na^+}{1 \text{ mol } Na_2HPO_4} \times 0.027 \text{ mol } Na_2HPO_4 = 0.054 \text{ mol } Na^+$$

$$\frac{3 \text{ mol ions}}{1 \text{ mol } Na_2HPO_4} \times 0.027 \text{ mol } Na_2HPO_4 = 0.081 \text{ mol ions}$$

BALLPARK CHECK: The calculated answers (0.027 mol Na_2HPO_4, 0.081 mol ions) are on the order of 10^{-2}, consistent with our estimate.

PROBLEM 6.5
How many moles of ethyl alcohol, C_2H_6O, are in a 10.0 g sample? How many grams are in a 0.10 mol sample of ethyl alcohol?

PROBLEM 6.6
Which weighs more, 5.00 g or 0.0225 mol of acetaminophen ($C_8H_9NO_2$)?

PROBLEM 6.7
How would our estimate of Avogadro's number be affected if we were to assume that Benjamin Franklin's oil molecules were spherical rather than cubes (see Chemistry in Action on p. 164)? If the density of the oil was 0.90 g/mL? If the molar mass was 150 g/mol rather than 200 g/mol?

6.3 Mole Relationships and Chemical Equations

In a typical recipe, the amounts of ingredients needed are specified using a variety of units: the amount of flour, for example, is usually specified in cups, whereas the amount of salt or vanilla flavoring might be indicated in teaspoons. In chemical reactions, the appropriate unit to specify the relationship between reactants and products is the mole.

The coefficients in a balanced chemical equation tell how many *molecules*, and thus, how many *moles*, of each reactant are needed and how many molecules, and thus, moles, of each product are formed. You can then use molar mass to calculate reactant and product masses. If, for example, you saw the following balanced equation for the industrial synthesis of ammonia, you would know that 3 mol of H_2 (3 mol $\times$ 2.0 g/mol = 6.0 g) are required for reaction with 1 mol of N_2 (28.0 g) to yield 2 mol of NH_3 (2 mol $\times$ 17.0 g/mol = 34.0 g).

This number of moles of hydrogen . . .   . . . reacts with this number of moles of nitrogen . . .   to yield this number of moles of ammonia.

$$3\,H_2 \;+\; 1\,N_2 \longrightarrow 2\,NH_3$$

The coefficients can be put in the form of *mole ratios*, which act as conversion factors when setting up factor-label calculations. In the ammonia synthesis, for example, the mole ratio of H_2 to N_2 is 3:1, the mole ratio of H_2 to NH_3 is 3:2, and the mole ratio of N_2 to NH_3 is 1:2:

$$\frac{3\ \text{mol}\ H_2}{1\ \text{mol}\ N_2} \qquad \frac{3\ \text{mol}\ H_2}{2\ \text{mol}\ NH_3} \qquad \frac{1\ \text{mol}\ N_2}{2\ \text{mol}\ NH_3}$$

Worked Example 6.5 shows how to set up and use mole ratios.

Worked Example 6.5 Balanced Chemical Equations: Mole Ratios

Rusting involves the reaction of iron with oxygen to form iron(III) oxide, Fe_2O_3:

$$4\,Fe(s) + 3\,O_2(g) \longrightarrow 2\,Fe_2O_3(s)$$

(a) What are the mole ratios of the product to each reactant and of the reactants to each other?

(b) How many moles of iron(III) oxide are formed by the complete oxidation of 6.2 mol of iron?

ANALYSIS AND SOLUTION

(a) The coefficients of a balanced equation represent the mole ratios:

$$\frac{2\ \text{mol}\ Fe_2O_3}{4\ \text{mol}\ Fe} \qquad \frac{2\ \text{mol}\ Fe_2O_3}{3\ \text{mol}\ O_2} \qquad \frac{4\ \text{mol}\ Fe}{3\ \text{mol}\ O_2}$$

(b) To find how many moles of Fe_2O_3 are formed, write down the known information—6.2 mol of iron—and select the mole ratio that allows the quantities to cancel, leaving the desired quantity:

$$6.2\ \cancel{\text{mol Fe}} \times \frac{2\ \text{mol}\ Fe_2O_3}{4\ \cancel{\text{mol Fe}}} = 3.1\ \text{mol}\ Fe_2O_3$$

Note that mole ratios are exact numbers and therefore do not limit the number of significant figures in the result of a calculation.

PROBLEM 6.8

(a) Balance the following equation, and tell how many moles of nickel will react with 9.81 mol of hydrochloric acid.

$$Ni(s) + HCl(aq) \longrightarrow NiCl_2(aq) + H_2(g)$$

(b) How many moles of $NiCl_2$ can be formed in the reaction of 6.00 mol of Ni and 12.0 mol of HCl?

PROBLEM 6.9

Plants convert carbon dioxide and water to glucose $(C_6H_{12}O_6)$ and oxygen in the process of photosynthesis. Write a balanced equation for this reaction, and determine how many moles of CO_2 are required to produce 15.0 mol of glucose.

6.4 Mass Relationships and Chemical Equations

It is important to remember that the coefficients in a balanced chemical equation represent molecule to molecule (or mole to mole) relationships between reactants and products. Mole ratios make it possible to calculate the molar amounts of reactants and products, but actual amounts of substances used in the laboratory are weighed out in grams. Regardless of what units we use to specify the amount of reactants and/or products (mass, volume, number of molecules, and so on), the reaction always takes place on a mole to mole basis. Thus, we need to be able to carry out three kinds of conversions when doing chemical arithmetic:

* **Mole to mole conversions** are carried out using *mole ratios* as conversion factors. Worked Example 6.5 at the end of the preceding section is an example of this kind of calculation.

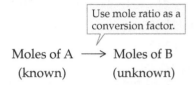

* **Mole to mass and mass to mole conversions** are carried out using *molar mass* as a conversion factor. Worked Examples 6.3 and 6.4 at the end of Section 6.2 are examples of this kind of calculation.

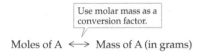

* **Mass to mass conversions** are frequently needed but cannot be carried out directly. If you know the mass of substance A and need to find the mass of substance B, you must first convert the mass of A into moles of A, then carry out a mole to mole conversion to find moles of B, and then convert moles of B into the mass of B (Figure 6.2).

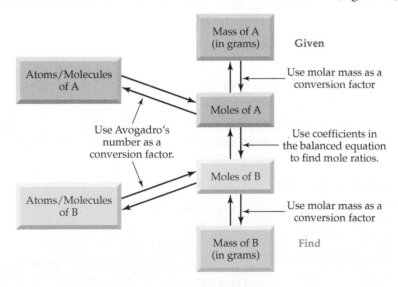

◄ **Figure 6.2**

A summary of conversions between moles, grams, and number of atoms or molecules for substances in a chemical reaction.

The numbers of moles tell how many molecules of each substance are needed, as given by the coefficients in the balanced equation; the numbers of grams tell what mass of each substance is needed.

Overall, there are four steps for determining mass relationships among reactants and products:

STEP 1: Write the balanced chemical equation.

STEP 2: Choose molar masses and mole ratios to convert the known information into the needed information.

STEP 3: Set up the factor-label expressions.

STEP 4: Calculate the answer and check the answer against the ballpark estimate you made before you began your calculations.

Worked Example 6.6 Mole Ratios: Mole to Mass Conversions

In the atmosphere, nitrogen dioxide reacts with water to produce NO and nitric acid, which contributes to pollution by acid rain:

$$3\, NO_2(g) + H_2O(l) \longrightarrow 2\, HNO_3(aq) + NO(g)$$

How many grams of HNO_3 are produced for every 1.0 mol of NO_2 that reacts? The molecular weight of HNO_3 is 63.0 amu.

ANALYSIS We are given the number of moles of a reactant and are asked to find the mass of a product. Problems of this sort always require working in moles and then converting to mass, as outlined in Figure 6.2.

BALLPARK ESTIMATE The molar mass of nitric acid is approximately 60 g/mol, and the coefficients in the balanced equation say that 2 mol of HNO_3 are formed for each 3 mol of NO_2 that undergo reaction. Thus, 1 mol of NO_2 should give about $2/3$ mol HNO_3, or $2/3$ mol $\times$ 60 g/mol = 40 g.

SOLUTION

STEP 1: **Write balanced equation.**

$$3\, NO_2(g) + H_2O(l) \longrightarrow 2\, HNO_3(aq) + NO(g)$$

STEP 2: **Identify conversion factors.** We need a mole to mole conversion to find the number of moles of product, and then a mole to mass conversion to find the mass of product. For the first conversion we use the mole ratio of HNO_3 to NO_2 as a conversion factor, and for the mole to mass calculation, we use the molar mass of HNO_3 (63.0 g/mol) as a conversion factor.

$$\frac{2\ mol\ HNO_3}{3\ mol\ NO_2}$$

$$\frac{63.0\ g\ HNO_3}{1\ mol\ HNO_3}$$

STEP 3: **Set up factor labels.** Identify appropriate mole ratio factor labels to convert moles NO_2 to moles HNO_3, and moles HNO_3 to grams.

$$1.0\ \cancel{mol\ NO_2} \times \frac{2\ \cancel{mol\ HNO_3}}{3\ \cancel{mol\ NO_2}} \times \frac{63.0\ g\ HNO_3}{1\ \cancel{mol\ HNO_3}} = 42\ g\ HNO_3$$

STEP 4: **Solve.**

BALLPARK CHECK Our estimate was 40 g!

Worked Example 6.7 Mole Ratios: Mass to Mole/Mole to Mass Conversions

The following reaction produced 0.022 g of calcium oxalate (CaC_2O_4). What mass of calcium chloride was used as reactant? (The molar mass of CaC_2O_4 is 128.1 g/mol, and the molar mass of $CaCl_2$ is 111.0 g/mol.)

$$CaCl_2(aq) + Na_2C_2O_4(aq) \longrightarrow CaC_2O_4(s) + 2\, NaCl(aq)$$

ANALYSIS Both the known information and that to be found are masses, so this is a mass to mass conversion problem. The mass of CaC_2O_4 is first converted into moles, a mole ratio is used to find moles of $CaCl_2$, and the number of moles of $CaCl_2$ is converted into mass.

BALLPARK ESTIMATE The balanced equation says that 1 mol of CaC_2O_4 is formed for each mole of $CaCl_2$ that reacts. Because the formula weights of the two substances are similar, it should take about 0.02 g of $CaCl_2$ to form 0.02 g of CaC_2O_4.

SOLUTION

STEP 1: **Write the balanced equation.**

$$CaCl_2(aq) + Na_2C_2O_4(aq) \longrightarrow CaC_2O_4(s) + 2\, NaCl(aq)$$

STEP 2: **Identify conversion factors.** Convert the mass of CaC_2O_4 into moles, use a mole ratio to find moles of $CaCl_2$, and convert the number of moles of $CaCl_2$ to mass. We will need three conversion factors.

mass CaC_2O_4 to moles: $\dfrac{1\ mol\ CaC_2O_4}{128.1\ g}$

moles CaC_2O_4 to moles $CaCl_2$: $\dfrac{1\ mol\ CaCl_2}{1\ mol\ CaC_2O_4}$

moles $CaCl_2$ to mass: $\dfrac{111.0\ g\ CaCl_2}{1\ mol\ CaCl_2}$

STEP 3: **Set up factor-labels.** We will need to perform gram to mole and mole to mole conversions to get from grams CaC_2O_4 to grams $CaCl_2$.

$$0.022\ g\ \cancel{CaC_2O_4} \times \frac{1\ \cancel{mol\ CaC_2O_4}}{128.1\ g\ \cancel{CaC_2O_4}} \times$$

$$\frac{1\ \cancel{mol\ CaCl_2}}{1\ \cancel{mol\ CaC_2O_4}} \times \frac{111.0\ g\ CaCl_2}{1\ \cancel{mol\ CaCl_2}} = 0.019\ g\ CaCl_2$$

STEP 4: **Solve.**

BALLPARK CHECK The calculated answer (0.019 g) is consistent with our estimate (0.02 g).

PROBLEM 6.10

Hydrogen fluoride is one of the few substances that react with glass (which is made of silicon dioxide, SiO_2).

$$4\,HF(g) + SiO_2(s) \longrightarrow SiF_4(g) + 2\,H_2O(l)$$

(a) How many moles of HF will react completely with 9.90 mol of SiO_2?

(b) What mass of water (in grams) is produced by the reaction of 23.0 g of SiO_2?

PROBLEM 6.11

The tungsten metal used for filaments in light bulbs is made by reaction of tungsten trioxide with hydrogen:

$$WO_3(s) + 3\,H_2(g) \longrightarrow W(s) + 3\,H_2O(g)$$

How many grams of tungsten trioxide, and how many grams of hydrogen must you start with to prepare 5.00 g of tungsten? (For WO_3, MW = 231.8 amu.)

6.5 Limiting Reagent and Percent Yield

All the calculations we have done in the last several sections have assumed that 100% of the reactants are converted to products. Only rarely is this the case in practice, though. Let us return to the recipe for s'mores presented in the previous chapter:

2 Graham crackers + 1 Roasted marshmallow + $\frac{1}{4}$ Chocolate bar $\longrightarrow$ 1 S'more

When you check your supplies, you find that you have 20 graham crackers, 8 marshmallows, and 3 chocolate bars. How many s'mores can you make? (Answer = 8!) You have enough graham crackers and chocolate bars to make more, but you will run out of marshmallows after you have made eight s'mores. In a similar way, when running a chemical reaction we don't always have the exact amounts of reagents to allow all of them to react completely. The reactant that is exhausted first in such a reaction is called the **limiting reagent**. The amount of product you obtain if the limiting reagent is completely consumed is called the **theoretical yield** of the reaction.

Suppose that, while you are making s'mores, one of your eight marshmallows gets burned to a crisp. If this happens, the actual number of s'mores produced will be less than what you predicted based on the amount of starting materials. Similarly, chemical reactions do not always yield the exact amount of product predicted by the initial amount of reactants. More frequently, a majority of the reactant molecules behave as written, but other processes, called *side reactions*, also occur. In addition, some of the product may be lost in handling. As a result, the amount of product actually formed—the reaction's **actual yield**—is somewhat less than the theoretical yield. The amount of product actually obtained in a reaction is usually expressed as a **percent yield**:

$$\text{Percent yield} = \frac{\text{Actual yield}}{\text{Theoretical yield}} \times 100\%$$

A reaction's actual yield is found by weighing the amount of product obtained. The theoretical yield is found by using the amount of limiting reagent in a mass to mass calculation like those illustrated in the preceding section (see Worked Example 6.7). Worked Examples 6.8–6.10 involve limiting reagent, percent yield, actual yield, and theoretical yield calculations.

Limiting reagent The reactant that runs out first in any given reaction.

Theoretical yield The amount of product formed, assuming complete reaction of the limiting reagent.

Actual yield The amount of product actually formed in a reaction.

Percent yield The percent of the theoretical yield actually obtained from a chemical reaction.

Worked Example 6.8 Percent Yield

The combustion of acetylene gas (C_2H_2) produces carbon dioxide and water, as indicated in the following reaction:

$$2\,C_2H_2(g) + 5\,O_2(g) \longrightarrow 4\,CO_2(g) + 2\,H_2O(g)$$

When 26.0 g of acetylene is burned in sufficient oxygen for complete reaction, the theoretical yield of CO_2 is 88.0 g. Calculate the percent yield for this reaction if the actual yield is only 72.4 g CO_2.

ANALYSIS The percent yield is calculated by dividing the actual yield by the theoretical yield and multiplying by 100.

BALLPARK ESTIMATE The theoretical yield (88.0 g) is close to 100 g. The actual yield (72.4 g) is about 15 g less than the theoretical yield. The actual yield is thus about 15% less than the theoretical yield, so the percent yield is about 85%.

SOLUTION

$$\text{Percent yield} = \frac{\text{Actual yield}}{\text{Theoretical yield}} \times 100 = \frac{72.4\ \text{g}\ CO_2}{88.0\ \text{g}\ CO_2} \times 100 = 82.3\%$$

BALLPARK CHECK The calculated percent yield agrees very well with our estimate of 85%.

Worked Example 6.9 Mass to Mole Conversions: Limiting Reagent and Theoretical Yield

The element boron is produced commercially by the reaction of boric oxide with magnesium at high temperature:

$$B_2O_3(l) + 3\,Mg(s) \longrightarrow 2\,B(s) + 3\,MgO(s)$$

What is the theoretical yield of boron when 2350 g of boric oxide is reacted with 3580 g of magnesium? The molar masses of boric oxide and magnesium are 69.6 g/mol and 24.3 g/mol, respectively.

ANALYSIS To calculate theoretical yield, we first have to identify the limiting reagent. The theoretical yield in grams is then calculated from the amount of limiting reagent used in the reaction. The calculation involves the mass to mole and mole to mass conversions discussed in the preceding section.

SOLUTION

STEP 1: Identify known information. We have the masses and molar masses of the reagents.

2350 g B_2O_3, molar mass 69.6 g/mol
3580 g Mg, molar mass 24.3 g/mol

STEP 2: Identify answer and units. We are solving for the theoretical yield of boron.

Theoretical mass of B = ?? g

STEP 3: Identify conversion factors. We can use the molar masses to convert from masses to moles of reactants (B_2O_3, Mg). From moles of reactants, we can use mole ratios from the balanced chemical equation to find the number of moles of B produced, assuming complete conversion of a given reactant. B_2O_3 is the limiting reagent, since complete conversion of this reagent yields less product (67.6 mol B formed) than does complete conversion of Mg (98.0 mol B formed).

$$(2350\ \text{g}\ B_2O_3) \times \frac{1\ \text{mol}\ B_2O_3}{69.6\ \text{g}\ B_2O_3} = 33.8\ \text{mol}\ B_2O_3$$

$$(3580\ \text{g}\ Mg) \times \frac{1\ \text{mol}\ Mg}{24.3\ \text{g}\ Mg} = 147\ \text{mol}\ Mg$$

$$33.8\ \text{mol}\ B_2O_3 \times \frac{2\ \text{mol}\ B}{1\ \text{mol}\ B_2O_3} = 67.6\ \text{mol}\ B^*$$

$$147\ \text{mol}\ Mg \times \frac{2\ \text{mol}\ B}{3\ \text{mol}\ Mg} = 98.0\ \text{mol}\ B$$

(*B_2O_3 is the limiting reagent because it yields fewer moles of B!)

STEP 4: Solve. Once the limiting reagent has been identified (B_2O_3), the theoretical amount of B that should be formed can be calculated using a mole to mass conversion.

$$67.6\ \text{mol}\ B \times \frac{10.8\ \text{g}\ B}{1\ \text{mol}\ B} = 730\ \text{g}\ B$$

Worked Example 6.10 Mass to Mole Conversion: Percent Yield

The reaction of ethylene with water to give ethyl alcohol (CH_3CH_2OH) occurs with 78.5% actual yield. How many grams of ethyl alcohol are formed by reaction of 25.0 g of ethylene? (For ethylene, MW = 28.0 amu; for ethyl alcohol, MW = 46.0 amu.)

$$H_2C=CH_2 + H_2O \longrightarrow CH_3CH_2OH$$

ANALYSIS Treat this as a typical mass relationship problem to find the amount of ethyl alcohol that can theoretically be formed from 25.0 g of ethylene, and then multiply the answer by 0.785 (the fraction of the theoretical yield actually obtained) to find the amount actually formed.

BALLPARK ESTIMATE The 25.0 g of ethylene is a bit less than 1 mol; since the percent yield is about 78%, a bit less than 0.78 mol of ethyl alcohol will form— perhaps about 3/4 mol, or $3/4 \times 46 g = 34 g$.

SOLUTION
The theoretical yield of ethyl alcohol is:

$$25.0 \text{ g ethylene} \times \frac{1 \text{ mol ethylene}}{28.0 \text{ g ethylene}} \times \frac{1 \text{ mol ethyl alc.}}{1 \text{ mol ethylene}} \times \frac{46.0 \text{ g ethyl alc.}}{1 \text{ mol ethyl alc.}}$$

$$= 41.1 \text{ g ethyl alcohol}$$

and so the actual yield is:

$$41.1 \text{ g ethyl alc.} \times 0.785 = 32.3 \text{ g ethyl alcohol}$$

BALLPARK CHECK The calculated result (32.3 g) is close to our estimate (34 g).

PROBLEM 6.12
What is the theoretical yield of ethyl chloride in the reaction of 19.4 g of ethylene with 50 g of hydrogen chloride? What is the percent yield if 25.5 g of ethyl chloride is actually formed? (For ethylene, MW = 28.0 amu; for hydrogen chloride, MW = 36.5 amu; for ethyl chloride, MW = 64.5 amu.)

$$H_2C=CH_2 + HCl \longrightarrow CH_3CH_2Cl$$

PROBLEM 6.13
The reaction of ethylene oxide with water to give ethylene glycol (automobile antifreeze) occurs in 96.0% actual yield. How many grams of ethylene glycol are formed by reaction of 35.0 g of ethylene oxide? (For ethylene oxide, MW = 44.0 amu; for ethylene glycol, MW = 62.0 amu.)

Ethylene oxide   Ethylene glycol

PROBLEM 6.14
The recommended daily intake of iron is 8 mg for adult men and 18 mg for premenopausal women (see Chemistry in Action on p. 172). Convert these masses of iron into moles.

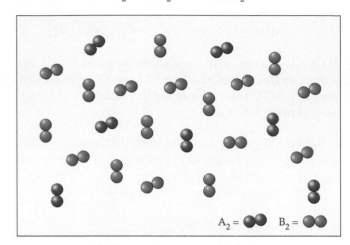

🔑 **KEY CONCEPT PROBLEM 6.15**

Identify the limiting reagent in the reaction mixture shown below. The balanced reaction is:

$$A_2 + 2\,B_2 \longrightarrow 2\,AB_2$$

CHEMISTRY IN ACTION

Anemia – A Limiting Reagent Problem?

Anemia is the most commonly diagnosed blood disorder, with symptoms typically including lethargy, fatigue, poor concentration, and sensitivity to cold. Although anemia has many causes, including genetic factors, the most common cause is insufficient dietary intake or absorption of iron.

Hemoglobin (abbreviated Hb), the iron-containing protein found in red blood cells, is responsible for oxygen transport throughout the body. Low iron levels in the body result in decreased production and incorporation of Hb into red blood cells. In addition, blood loss due to injury or to menstruation in women increases the body's demand for iron in order to replace lost Hb. In the United States, nearly 20% of women of childbearing age suffer from iron-deficiency anemia compared to only 2% of adult men.

The recommended minimum daily iron intake is 8 mg for adult men and 18 mg for premenopausal women. One way to ensure sufficient iron intake is a well-balanced diet that includes iron-fortified grains and cereals, red meat, egg yolks, leafy green vegetables, tomatoes, and raisins. Vegetarians should pay extra attention to their diet, because the iron in fruits and vegetables is not as readily absorbed by the body as the iron

▲ **Can cooking in cast iron pots decrease anemia?**

in meat, poultry, and fish. Vitamin supplements containing folic acid and either ferrous sulfate or ferrous gluconate can decrease iron deficiencies, and vitamin C increases the absorption of iron by the body.

However, the simplest way to increase dietary iron may be to use cast iron cookware. Studies have demonstrated that the iron content of many foods increases when cooked in an iron pot. Other studies involving Ethiopian children showed that those who ate food cooked in iron cookware were less likely to suffer from iron-deficiency anemia than their playmates who ate similar foods prepared in aluminum cookware.

See Chemistry in Action Problems 6.59 and 6.60 at the end of the chapter.

▶▶▶ We'll explore the role of hemoglobin in oxygen transport in greater detail in Chapter 9.

CONCEPT MAP: CHEMICAL REACTIONS (CHAPTERS 5, 6)

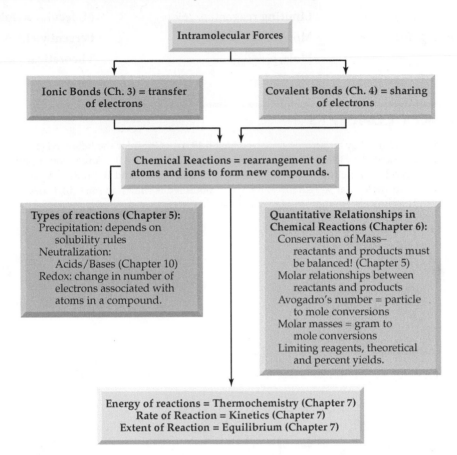

▶ **Figure 6.3**

Concept Maps. In Chapters 5 and 6, we examined chemical reactions. As shown in the concept map above, chemical reactions represent a rearrangement of the intermolecular forces within compounds as bonds in the reactants are broken and new bonds are formed to generate products. Ionic reactions can be classified as precipitation reactions, neutralization reactions, or redox reactions. One class of reactions (acid–base neutralization) will be examined in further detail in Chapter 10. Other characteristics of reactions will be examined in Chapter 7.

SUMMARY: REVISITING THE CHAPTER GOALS

1. What is the mole, and why is it useful in chemistry?
A *mole* refers to *Avogadro's number* (6.022×10^{23}) of formula units of a substance. One mole of any substance has a mass (*molar mass*) equal to the molecular or formula weight of the substance in grams. Because equal numbers of moles contain equal numbers of formula units, molar masses act as conversion factors between numbers of moles and masses in grams (*see Problems 16, 21–25, 27, 28, 32, 33, 38, 41, 62, 63*).

2. How are molar quantities and mass quantities related?
The coefficients in a balanced chemical equation represent the numbers of moles of reactants and products in a reaction. Thus, the ratios of coefficients act as *mole ratios* that relate amounts of reactants and/or products. By using molar masses and mole ratios in factor-label calculations, unknown masses or molar amounts can be found from known masses or molar amounts (*see Problems 17, 20, 25, 26, 29–31, 34–57, 59–61, 63–76*).

3. What are the limiting reagent, theoretical yield, and percent yield of a reaction? The *limiting reagent* is the reactant that runs out first. The *theoretical yield* is the amount of product that would be formed based on the amount of the limiting reagent. The *actual yield* of a reaction is the amount of product obtained. The *percent yield* is the amount of product obtained divided by the amount theoretically possible and multiplied by 100% (*see Problems 18, 19, 52–57, 71, 72*).

KEY WORDS

Actual yield, *p. 169*
Avogadro's number (N_A), *p. 161*
Formula weight, *p. 159*

Limiting reagent, *p. 169*
Molar mass, *p. 160*
Mole, *p. 160*

Molecular weight (MW), *p. 159*
Percent yield, *p. 169*
Theoretical yield, *p. 169*

UNDERSTANDING KEY CONCEPTS

6.16   Methionine, an amino acid used by organisms to make proteins, can be represented by the following ball-and-stick molecular model. Write the formula for methionine, and give its molecular weight (red = O, black = C, blue = N, yellow = S, white = H).

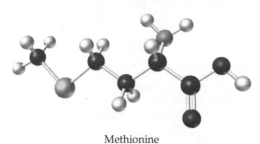

Methionine

6.17   The following diagram represents the reaction of A_2 (red spheres) with B_2 (blue spheres):

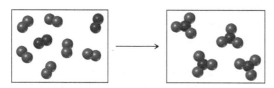

(a) Write a balanced equation for the reaction.

(b) How many moles of product can be made from 1.0 mol of A_2? From 1.0 mol of B_2?

6.18   Consider the balanced chemical equation: $2A + B_2 \longrightarrow 2AB$. Given the reaction vessel below, determine the theoretical yield of product.

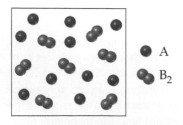

6.19   Consider the balanced chemical equation: $A_2 + 2 B_2 \longrightarrow 2 AB_2$. A reaction is performed with the initial amounts of A_2 and B_2 shown in part (a). The amount of product obtained is shown in part (b). Calculate the percent yield.

(a)

(b)

6.20   The following drawing represents the reaction of ethylene oxide with water to give ethylene glycol, a compound used as automobile antifreeze. What mass in grams of ethylene oxide is needed to react with 9.0 g of water, and what mass in grams of ethylene glycol is formed?

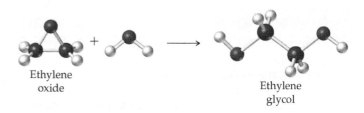

Ethylene
oxide

Ethylene
glycol

ADDITIONAL PROBLEMS

MOLAR MASSES AND MOLES

6.21   What is a mole of a substance? How many molecules are in 1 mol of a molecular compound?

6.22   What is the difference between molecular weight and formula weight? Between molecular weight and molar mass?

6.23   How many Na^+ ions are in a mole of Na_2SO_4? How many $SO_4{}^{2-}$ ions?

6.24   How many moles of ions are in 1.75 mol of K_2SO_4?

6.25   How many calcium atoms are in 16.2 g of calcium?

6.26 What is the mass in grams of 2.68×10^{22} atoms of uranium?

6.27 Calculate the molar mass of each of the following compounds:

(a) Calcium carbonate, $CaCO_3$

(b) Urea, $CO(NH_2)_2$

(c) Ethylene glycol, $C_2H_6O_2$

6.28 How many moles of carbon atoms are there in 1 mol of each compound in Problem 6.27?

6.29 How many atoms of carbon, and how many grams of carbon are there in 1 mol of each compound in Problem 6.27?

6.30 Caffeine has the formula $C_8H_{10}N_4O_2$. If an average cup of coffee contains approximately 125 mg of caffeine, how many moles of caffeine are in one cup?

6.31 How many moles of aspirin, $C_9H_8O_4$, are in a 500 mg tablet?

6.32 What is the molar mass of diazepam (Valium), $C_{16}H_{13}ClN_2O$?

6.33 Calculate the molar masses of the following substances:

(a) Aluminum sulfate, $Al_2(SO_4)_3$

(b) Sodium bicarbonate, $NaHCO_3$

(c) Diethyl ether, $(C_2H_5)_2O$

(d) Penicillin V, $C_{16}H_{18}N_2O_5S$

6.34 How many moles are present in a 4.50 g sample of each compound listed in Problem 6.33?

6.35 The recommended daily dietary intake of calcium for adult men and premenopausal women is 1000 mg/day. Calcium citrate, $Ca_3(C_6H_5O_7)_2$ (MW = 498.5 amu), is a common dietary supplement. What mass of calcium citrate would be needed to provide the recommended daily intake of calcium?

6.36 What is the mass in grams of 0.0015 mol of aspirin, $C_9H_8O_4$? How many aspirin molecules are there in this 0.0015 mol sample?

6.37 How many grams are present in a 0.075 mol sample of each compound listed in Problem 6.33?

6.38 The principal component of many kidney stones is calcium oxalate, CaC_2O_4. A kidney stone recovered from a typical patient contains 8.5×10^{20} formula units of calcium oxalate. How many moles of CaC_2O_4 are present in this kidney stone? What is the mass of the kidney stone in grams?

MOLE AND MASS RELATIONSHIPS FROM CHEMICAL EQUATIONS

6.39 At elevated temperatures in an automobile engine, N_2 and O_2 can react to yield NO, an important cause of air pollution.

(a) Write a balanced equation for the reaction.

(b) How many moles of N_2 are needed to react with 7.50 mol of O_2?

(c) How many moles of NO can be formed when 3.81 mol of N_2 reacts?

(d) How many moles of O_2 must react to produce 0.250 mol of NO?

6.40 Ethyl acetate reacts with H_2 in the presence of a catalyst to yield ethyl alcohol:

$$C_4H_8O_2(l) + H_2(g) \longrightarrow C_2H_6O(l)$$

(a) Write a balanced equation for the reaction.

(b) How many moles of ethyl alcohol are produced by reaction of 1.5 mol of ethyl acetate?

(c) How many grams of ethyl alcohol are produced by reaction of 1.5 mol of ethyl acetate with H_2?

(d) How many grams of ethyl alcohol are produced by reaction of 12.0 g of ethyl acetate with H_2?

(e) How many grams of H_2 are needed to react with 12.0 g of ethyl acetate?

6.41 The active ingredient in Milk of Magnesia (an antacid) is magnesium hydroxide, $Mg(OH)_2$. A typical dose (one tablespoon) contains 1.2 g of $Mg(OH)_2$. Calculate (a) the molar mass of magnesium hydroxide, and (b) the amount of magnesium hydroxide (in moles) in one teaspoon.

6.42 Ammonia, NH_3, is prepared for use as a fertilizer by reacting N_2 with H_2.

(a) Write a balanced equation for the reaction.

(b) How many moles of N_2 are needed for reaction to make 16.0 g of NH_3?

(c) How many grams of H_2 are needed to react with 75.0 g of N_2?

6.43 Hydrazine, N_2H_4, a substance used as rocket fuel, reacts with oxygen as follows:

$$N_2H_4(l) + O_2(g) \longrightarrow NO_2(g) + H_2O(g)$$

(a) Balance the equation.

(b) How many moles of oxygen are needed to react with 165 g of hydrazine?

(c) How many grams of oxygen are needed to react with 165 g of hydrazine?

6.44 One method for preparing pure iron from Fe_2O_3 is by reaction with carbon monoxide:

$$Fe_2O_3(s) + CO(g) \longrightarrow Fe(s) + CO_2(g)$$

(a) Balance the equation.

(b) How many grams of CO are needed to react with 3.02 g of Fe_2O_3?

(c) How many grams of CO are needed to react with 1.68 mol of Fe_2O_3?

6.45 Magnesium metal burns in oxygen to form magnesium oxide, MgO.

(a) Write a balanced equation for the reaction.

(b) How many grams of oxygen are needed to react with 25.0 g of Mg? How many grams of MgO will result?

(c) How many grams of Mg are needed to react with 25.0 g of O_2? How many grams of MgO will result?

6.46 Titanium metal is obtained from the mineral rutile, TiO_2. How many kilograms of rutile are needed to produce 95 kg of Ti?

6.47 In the preparation of iron from hematite (Problem 6.44), how many moles of carbon monoxide are needed to react completely with 105 kg of Fe_2O_3?

6.48 The eruption of Mount St. Helens volcano in 1980 injected 4×10^8 kg of SO_2 into the atmosphere. If all this SO_2 was converted to sulfuric acid, how many moles of H_2SO_4 would be produced? How many kg?

6.49 The thermite reaction was used to produce molten iron for welding applications before arc welding was available. The thermite reaction is:

$$Fe_2O_3(s) + 2\,Al(s) \longrightarrow Al_2O_3(s) + 2\,Fe(l)$$

How many moles of molten iron can be produced from 1.5 kg of iron(III) oxide?

6.50 Pyrite, also known as fool's gold, is composed of iron disulfide, FeS_2. It is used commercially to produce SO_2 used in the production of paper products. How many moles of SO_2 can be produced from 1.0 kg of pyrite?

6.51 Diborane (B_2H_6) is a gas at room temperature that forms explosive mixtures with air. It reacts with oxygen according to the following equation:

$$B_2H_6(g) + 3\,O_2(g) \longrightarrow B_2O_3(s) + 3\,H_2O(l)$$

How many grams of diborane will react with 7.5 mol of O_2?

LIMITING REAGENT AND PERCENT YIELD

6.52 Once made by heating wood in the absence of air, methanol (CH_3OH) is now made by reacting carbon monoxide and hydrogen at high pressure:

$$CO(g) + 2\,H_2(g) \longrightarrow CH_3OH(l)$$

(a) If 25.0 g of CO is reacted with 6.00 g of H_2, which is the limiting reagent?

(b) How many grams of CH_3OH can be made from 10.0 g of CO if it all reacts?

(c) If 9.55 g of CH_3OH is recovered when the amounts in part (b) are used, what is the percent yield?

6.53 In Problem 6.43, hydrazine reacted with oxygen according to the (unbalanced) equation:

$$N_2H_4(l) + O_2(g) \longrightarrow NO_2(g) + H_2O(g)$$

(a) If 75.0 kg of hydrazine are reacted with 75.0 kg of oxygen, which is the limiting reagent?

(b) How many kilograms of NO_2 are produced from the reaction of 75.0 kg of the limiting reagent?

(c) If 59.3 kg of NO_2 are obtained from the reaction in part (a), what is the percent yield?

6.54 Dichloromethane, CH_2Cl_2, the solvent used to decaffeinate coffee beans, is prepared by reaction of CH_4 with Cl_2.

(a) Write the balanced equation. (HCl is also formed.)

(b) How many grams of Cl_2 are needed to react with 50.0 g of CH_4?

(c) How many grams of dichloromethane are formed from 50.0 g of CH_4 if the percent yield for the reaction is 76%?

6.55 Cisplatin $[Pt(NH_3)_2Cl_2]$, a compound used in cancer treatment, is prepared by reaction of ammonia with potassium tetrachloroplatinate:

$$K_2PtCl_4 + 2\,NH_3 \longrightarrow 2\,KCl + Pt(NH_3)_2Cl_2$$

(a) How many grams of NH_3 are needed to react with 55.8 g of K_2PtCl_4?

(b) How many grams of cisplatin are formed from 55.8 g of K_2PtCl_4 if the percent yield for the reaction is 95%?

6.56 Nitrobenzene $(C_6H_5NO_2)$ is used in small quantities as a flavoring agent or in perfumes, but can be toxic in large amounts. It is produced by reaction of benzene (C_6H_6) with nitric acid:

$$C_6H_6(l) + HNO_3(aq) \longrightarrow C_6H_5NO_2(l) + H_2O(l).$$

(a) Identify the limiting reagent in the reaction of 27.5 g of nitric acid with 75 g of benzene.

(b) Calculate the theoretical yield for this reaction.

6.57 Calculate the percent yield if 48.2 g of nitrobenzene is obtained from the reaction described in Problem 6.56.

CHEMISTRY IN ACTION

6.58 What do you think might be some of the errors involved in calculating Avogadro's number by spreading oil on a pond? [*Did Ben Franklin Have Avogadro's Number?* p. 164]

6.59 Dietary iron forms a 1:1 complex with hemoglobin (Hb), which is responsible for O_2 transport in the body based on the following equation:

$$Hb + 4\,O_2 \longrightarrow Hb(O_2)_4$$

How many moles of oxygen could be transported by the hemoglobin complex formed from 8 mg of dietary iron? [*Anemia—A Limiting Reagent Problem?* p. 172]

6.60 Ferrous sulfate is one dietary supplement used to treat iron-deficiency anemia. What are the molecular formula and molecular weight of this compound? How many milligrams of iron are in 250 mg of ferrous sulfate?

GENERAL QUESTIONS AND PROBLEMS

6.61 Zinc metal reacts with hydrochloric acid (HCl) according to the equation:

$$Zn(s) + 2\,HCl(aq) \longrightarrow ZnCl_2(aq) + H_2(g)$$

(a) How many grams of hydrogen are produced if 15.0 g of zinc reacts?

(b) Is this a redox reaction? If so, tell what is reduced, what is oxidized, and identify the reducing and oxidizing agents.

6.62 Batrachotoxin, $C_{31}H_{42}N_2O_6$, an active component of South American arrow poison, is so toxic that 0.05 μg can kill a person. How many molecules is this?

6.63 Lovastatin, a drug used to lower serum cholesterol, has the molecular formula of $C_{24}H_{36}O_5$.

(a) Calculate the molar mass of lovastatin.

(b) How many moles of lovastatin are present in a typical dose of one 10 mg tablet?

6.64 When table sugar $(\text{sucrose, } C_{12}H_{22}O_{11})$ is heated, it decomposes to form C and H_2O.

(a) Write a balanced equation for the process.

(b) How many grams of carbon are formed by the breakdown of 60.0 g of sucrose?

(c) How many grams of water are formed when 6.50 g of carbon are formed?

6.65 Although Cu is not sufficiently active to react with acids, it can be dissolved by concentrated nitric acid, which functions as an oxidizing agent according to the following equation:

$$Cu(s) + 4\,HNO_3(aq) \longrightarrow$$
$$Cu(NO_3)_2(aq) + 2\,NO_2(g) + 2\,H_2O(l)$$

(a) Write the net ionic equation for this process.

(b) Is 35.0 g of HNO_3 sufficient to dissolve 5.00 g of copper?

6.66 The net ionic equation for the Breathalyzer test used to indicate alcohol concentration in the body is

$$16\,H^+(aq) + 2\,Cr_2O_7^{2-}(aq) + 3\,C_2H_6O(aq) \longrightarrow$$
$$3\,C_2H_4O_2(aq) + 4\,Cr^{3+}(aq) + 11\,H_2O(l)$$

(a) How many grams of $K_2Cr_2O_7$ must be used to consume 1.50 g of C_2H_6O?

(b) How many grams of $C_2H_4O_2$ can be produced from 80.0 g of C_2H_6O?

6.67 Ethyl alcohol is formed by enzyme action on sugars and starches during fermentation:

$$C_6H_{12}O_6 \longrightarrow 2\,CO_2 + 2\,C_2H_6O$$

If the density of ethyl alcohol is 0.789 g/mL, how many quarts can be produced by the fermentation of 100.0 lb of sugar?

6.68 Gaseous ammonia reacts with oxygen in the presence of a platinum catalyst to produce nitrogen monoxide and water vapor.

(a) Write a balanced chemical equation for this reaction.

(b) What mass of nitrogen monoxide would be produced by complete reaction of 17.0 g of ammonia?

6.69 Sodium hypochlorite, the primary component in commercial bleach, is prepared by bubbling chlorine gas through solutions of sodium hydroxide:

$$NaOH(aq) + Cl_2(g) \longrightarrow NaOCl(aq) + H_2O(l)$$

How many moles of sodium hypochlorite can be prepared from 32.5 g of NaOH?

6.70 Barium sulfate is an insoluble ionic compound swallowed by patients before having an X-ray of their gastrointestinal tract.

(a) Write the balanced chemical equation for the precipitation reaction between barium chloride and sodium sulfate.

(b) What mass of barium sulfate can be produced by complete reaction of 27.4 g of Na_2SO_4?

6.71 The last step in the production of nitric acid is the reaction of nitrogen dioxide with water:

$$NO_2(g) + H_2O(l) \longrightarrow HNO_3(aq) + NO(g)$$

(a) Balance the chemical equation.

(b) If 65.0 g of nitrogen dioxide is reacted with excess water, calculate the theoretical yield.

(c) If only 43.8 g of nitric acid is obtained, calculate the percent yield.

6.72 Acetylsalicylic acid, the active ingredient in aspirin, is prepared from salicylic acid by reaction with acetic anhydride:

$$C_7H_6O_3 \quad + \quad C_4H_6O_3 \longrightarrow C_9H_8O_4 \quad + \quad C_2H_4O_2$$
$$\text{(salicylic acid) (acetic anhydride) (acetylsalicylic acid) (acetic acid)}$$

(a) Calculate the theoretical yield if 47 g of salicylic acid is reacted with 25 g of acetic anhydride.

(b) What is the percent yield if only 35 g is obtained?

6.73 Jewelry and tableware can be silver-plated by reduction of silver ions from a solution of silver nitrate. The net ionic equation is $Ag^+(aq) + e^- \longrightarrow Ag(s)$. How many grams of silver nitrate would be needed to plate 15.2 g of silver on a piece of jewelry?

6.74 Elemental phosphorus exists as molecules of P_4. It reacts with $Cl_2(g)$ to produce phosphorus pentachloride.

(a) Write the balanced chemical equation for this reaction.

(b) What mass of phosphorus pentachloride would be produced by the complete reaction of 15.2 g of P_4?

6.75 Lithium oxide is used aboard the space shuttle to remove water from the atmosphere according to the equation

$$Li_2O(s) + H_2O(g) \longrightarrow 2\,LiOH(s)$$

How many grams of Li_2O must be carried on board to remove 80.0 kg of water?

6.76 One of the reactions used to provide thrust for space shuttle launch involves the reaction of ammonium perchlorate with aluminum to produce $AlCl_3(s)$, $H_2O(g)$, and $NO(g)$.

(a) Write the balanced chemical equation for this reaction.

(b) How many moles of gas are produced by the reaction of 14.5 kg of ammonium perchlorate?

CHAPTER 7

Chemical Reactions: Energy, Rates, and Equilibrium

▲ Many spontaneous chemical reactions are accompanied by the release of energy, in some cases explosively.

CONTENTS

CHAPTER GOALS

1. **What energy changes take place during reactions?**
   THE GOAL: Be able to explain the factors that influence energy changes in chemical reactions. (◀◀◀ A, B, and C)

2. **What is "free energy," and what is the criterion for spontaneity in chemistry?**
   THE GOAL: Be able to define enthalpy, entropy, and free-energy changes, and explain how the values of these quantities affect chemical reactions.

3. **What determines the rate of a chemical reaction?**
   THE GOAL: Be able to explain activation energy and other factors that determine reaction rate. (◀◀◀ D)

4. **What is chemical equilibrium?**
   THE GOAL: Be able to describe what occurs in a reaction at equilibrium, and write the equilibrium equation for a given reaction. (◀◀◀ D)

5. **What is Le Châtelier's principle?**
   THE GOAL: Be able to state Le Châtelier's principle, and use it to predict the effect of changes in temperature, pressure, and concentration on reactions.

We have yet to answer many questions about reactions. Why, for instance, do reactions occur? Just because a balanced equation can be written it does not mean it will take place. We can write a balanced equation for the reaction of gold with water, for example, but the reaction does not occur in practice—so your gold jewelry is safe in the shower.

Balanced, but does not occur $\quad 2\,Au(s) + 3\,H_2O(l) \longrightarrow Au_2O_3(s) + 3\,H_2(g)$

To describe reactions more completely, several fundamental questions are commonly asked: Is energy released or absorbed when a reaction occurs? Is a given reaction fast or slow? Does a reaction continue until all reactants are converted to products, or is there a point beyond which no additional product forms?

7.1 Energy and Chemical Bonds

There are two fundamental and interconvertible kinds of energy: *potential* and *kinetic*. **Potential energy** is stored energy. The water in a reservoir behind a dam, an automobile poised to coast downhill, and a coiled spring have potential energy waiting to be released. **Kinetic energy**, by contrast, is the energy of motion. When the water falls over the dam and turns a turbine, when the car rolls downhill, or when the spring uncoils and makes the hands on a clock move, the potential energy in each is converted to kinetic energy. Of course, once all the potential energy is converted, nothing further occurs. The water at the bottom of the dam, the car at the bottom of the hill, and the uncoiled spring no longer have potential energy and thus, undergo no further change.

In chemical compounds, the attractive forces between ions or atoms are a form of potential energy, similar to the attractive forces between the poles of a magnet. When these attractive forces result in the formation of ionic or covalent bonds between ions or atoms, the potential energy is often converted into **heat**—a measure of the kinetic energy of the particles that make up the molecule. Breaking these bonds requires an input of energy.

In chemical reactions, some of the chemical bonds in the reactants must break (energy in) so that new bonds can form in the products (energy out). If the reaction products have less potential energy than the reactants, we say that the products are *more stable* than the reactants. The term "stable" is used in chemistry to describe a substance that has little remaining potential energy and consequently little tendency to undergo further change. Whether a reaction occurs, and how much energy or heat

Potential energy Stored energy.

Kinetic energy The energy of an object in motion.

Heat A measure of the transfer of thermal energy.

is associated with the reaction, depends on the difference in the amount of potential energy contained in the reactants and products.

7.2 Heat Changes during Chemical Reactions

Why does chlorine react so easily with many elements and compounds, but nitrogen does not? What difference between Cl_2 molecules and N_2 molecules accounts for their different reactivities? The answer is that the nitrogen–nitrogen triple bond is much *stronger* than the chlorine–chlorine single bond and cannot be broken as easily in chemical reactions.

Bond dissociation energy The amount of energy that must be supplied to break a bond and separate the atoms in an isolated gaseous molecule.

The strength of a covalent bond is measured by its **bond dissociation energy**, defined as the amount of energy that must be supplied to break the bond and separate the atoms in an isolated gaseous molecule. The greater the bond dissociation energy, the more stable the chemical bond between the atoms or ions. The triple bond in N_2, for example, has a bond dissociation energy of 226 kcal/mol (946 kJ/mol), whereas the single bond in chlorine has a bond dissociation energy of only 58 kcal/mol (243 kJ/mol):

$$:N:::N: \xrightarrow{\text{226 kcal/mol}} \cdot\ddot{N}\cdot \; + \; \cdot\ddot{N}: \qquad N_2 \text{ bond dissociation energy } = 226 \text{ kcal/mol (946 kJ/mol)}$$

$$:\ddot{C}l:\ddot{C}l: \xrightarrow{\text{58 kcal/mol}} :\ddot{C}l\cdot \; + \; \cdot\ddot{C}l: \qquad Cl_2 \text{ bond dissociation energy } = 58 \text{ kcal/mol (243 kJ/mol)}$$

The greater stability of the triple bond in N_2 explains why nitrogen molecules are less reactive than Cl_2 molecules. Some typical bond dissociation energies are given in Table 7.1

TABLE 7.1 Average Bond Dissociation Energies

Bond	Bond Dissociation Energy (kcal/mol, kJ/mol)	Bond	Bond Dissociation Energy (kcal/mol, kJ/mol)	Bond	Bond Dissociation Energy (kcal/mol, kJ/mol)
C—H	99, 413	N—H	93, 391	C=C	147, 614
C—C	83, 347	N—N	38, 160	C≡C	201, 839
C—N	73, 305	N—Cl	48, 200	C=O*	178, 745
C—O	86, 358	N—O	48, 201	O=O	119, 498
C—Cl	81, 339	H—H	103, 432	N=O	145, 607
Cl—Cl	58, 243	O—H	112, 467	C≡N	213, 891
H—Cl	102, 427	O—Cl	49, 203	N≡N	226, 946

*The C=O bond dissociation energies in CO_2 are 191 kcal/mol (799 kJ/mol).

Endothermic A process or reaction that absorbs heat.

Exothermic A process or reaction that releases heat.

A chemical change that absorbs heat, like the breaking of bonds, is said to be **endothermic**, from the Greek words *endon* (within) and *therme* (heat), meaning that *heat is put in*. The reverse of bond breaking is bond formation, a process that *releases* heat and is described as **exothermic**, from the Greek *exo* (outside), meaning that heat goes out. The amount of energy released in forming a bond is numerically the same as that absorbed in breaking it. When nitrogen atoms combine to give N_2, 226 kcal/mol (946 kJ/mol) of heat is released. Similarly, when chlorine atoms combine to give Cl_2, 58 kcal/mol (243 kJ/mol) of heat is released. We indicate the direction of energy flow in a chemical change by the sign associated with the number. If heat is absorbed (endothermic) then the sign is positive to indicate energy is *gained* by the substance. If heat is released (exothermic) then the sign is negative to indicate energy is *lost* by the substance during the change.

$$\cdot\ddot{N}\cdot \; + \; \cdot\ddot{N}: \longrightarrow :N:::N: \; + \; 226 \text{ kcal/mol (946 kJ/mol) heat released}$$

$$:\ddot{C}l\cdot \; + \; \cdot\ddot{C}l: \longrightarrow :\ddot{C}l:\ddot{C}l: \; + \; 58 \text{ kcal/mol (243 kJ/mol) heat released}$$

The same energy relationships that govern bond breaking and bond formation apply to every physical or chemical change. That is, the amount of heat transferred during a change in one direction is numerically equal to the amount of heat transferred during the change in the opposite direction. Only the *direction* of the heat transfer is different. This relationship reflects a fundamental law of nature called the *law of conservation of energy*:

Law of conservation of energy Energy can be neither created nor destroyed in any physical or chemical change.

If more energy could be released by an exothermic reaction than was consumed in its reverse, the law would be violated, and we could "manufacture" energy out of nowhere by cycling back and forth between forward and reverse reactions—a clear impossibility.

In every chemical reaction, some bonds in the reactants are broken, and new bonds are formed in the products. The difference between the heat energy absorbed in breaking bonds and the heat energy released in forming bonds is called the **heat of reaction** and is a quantity that we can measure. Heats of reaction that are measured when a reaction is held at constant pressure are represented by the abbreviation ΔH, where Δ (the Greek capital letter delta) is a general symbol used to indicate "a change in," and H is a quantity called **enthalpy**. Thus, the value of ΔH represents the **enthalpy change** that occurs during a reaction. The terms *enthalpy change* and *heat of reaction* are often used interchangeably, but we will generally use the latter term in this book.

Heat of reaction, or Enthalpy change (ΔH) The difference between the energy of bonds broken in reactants and the energy of bonds formed in products.

Enthalpy (H) A measure of the amount of energy associated with substances involved in a reaction.

7.3 Exothermic and Endothermic Reactions

When the total strength of the bonds formed in the products is *greater* than the total strength of the bonds broken in the reactants, the net result is that energy is released and a reaction is exothermic. All combustion reactions are exothermic; for example, burning 1 mol of methane releases 213 kcal (891 kJ) of energy in the form of heat. The heat released in an exothermic reaction can be thought of as a reaction product, and the heat of reaction ΔH is assigned a *negative* value, because overall, heat is *lost* during the reaction.

An exothermic reaction—negative ΔH

Heat is a product.

$$CH_4(g) \ + \ 2\,O_2(g) \ \longrightarrow \ CO_2(g) \ + \ 2\,H_2O(l) \ + \ 213 \text{ kcal (891 kJ)}$$

or

$$CH_4(g) \ + \ 2\,O_2(g) \ \longrightarrow \ CO_2(g) \ + \ 2\,H_2O(l) \qquad \Delta H = -213 \text{ kcal/mol} \ (-891 \text{ kJ/mol})$$

The heat of reaction can be calculated as the difference between the bond dissociation energies in the products and the bond dissociation energies of the reactants:

$$\Delta H = \Sigma(\text{Bond dissociation energies})_{\text{reactants}} - \Sigma(\text{Bond dissociation energies})_{\text{products}}$$

Look again at the reaction involving the combustion of methane. By counting the number of bonds on each side of the chemical equation, we can use the average bond dissociation energies from Table 7.1 to estimate ΔH for the reaction.

Reactants	Bond Dissociation Energies (kcal/mol)	Products	Bond Dissociation Energies (kcal/mol)
(C—H) × 4	99 × 4 = 396 kcal	(C=O) × 2	191 × 2 = 382 kcal
(O=O) × 2	119 × 2 = 238 kcal	(H—O) × 4	112 × 4 = 448 kcal
Total:	= 634 kcal		= 830 kcal

$$\Delta H = (634 \text{ kcal})_{\text{reactants}} - (830 \text{ kcal})_{\text{products}} = -196 \text{ kcal}(-820 \text{ kJ})$$

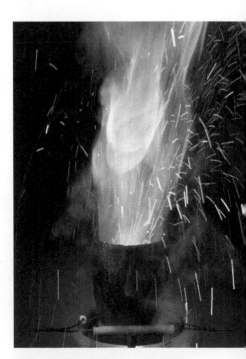

▲ The reaction between aluminum metal and iron(III) oxide, called the *thermite reaction*, is so strongly exothermic that it melts iron.

In this reaction, the input of energy needed to break the bonds in the reactants is less than the amount of energy released when forming bonds in the products. The excess energy is released as heat, and the reaction is exothermic (ΔH = negative).

It should be noted that the bond energies in Table 7.1 are average values, and that actual bond energies may vary depending on the chemical environment in which the bond is found. The average C=O bond energy, for example, is 178 kcal/mol, but the actual value for the C=O bonds in the CO_2 molecule is 191 kcal/mol. The average C—H bond energy is 99 kca/mol (413 kJ/mol), but in CH_3CH_3 the C—H bond dissociation energy is actually 101 kcal/mol (423 kJ/mol). Thus, the calculated ΔH for a reaction using average bond energies may differ slightly from the value obtained by experiment. For the combustion of methane, for example, the ΔH estimated from bond energies is −196 kcal/mol (−820 kJ/mol), while the value measured experimentally is −213 kcal/mol (−891 kJ/mol), a difference of about 9%.

Note that ΔH is given in units of kilocalories or kilojoules per mole, where "per mole" means the reaction of *molar amounts of products and reactants as represented by the coefficients of the balanced equation*. Thus, the experimental value ΔH = −213 kcal/mol (−891 kJ/mol) refers to the amount of heat released when 1 mol (16.0 g) of methane reacts with 2 mol of O_2 to give 1 mol of CO_2 gas and 2 mol of liquid H_2O. If we were to double the amount of methane from 1 mol to 2 mol, the amount of heat released would also double.

The quantities of heat released in the combustion of several fuels, including natural gas (which is primarily methane), are compared in Table 7.2. The values are given in kilocalories and kilojoules per gram to make comparisons easier. You can see from the table why there is interest in the potential of hydrogen as a fuel.

TABLE 7.2 Energy Values of Some Common Fuels	
Fuel	**Energy Value (kcal/g, kJ/g)**
Wood (pine)	4.3, 18.0
Ethyl alcohol	7.1, 29.7
Coal (anthracite)	7.4, 31.0
Crude oil (Texas)	10.5, 43.9
Gasoline	11.5, 48.1
Natural gas	11.7, 49.0
Hydrogen	34.0, 142

When the total energy released upon bond formation in the products is *less* than the total energy added to break the bonds in the reactants, the net result is that energy is absorbed and a reaction is endothermic. The combination of nitrogen and oxygen to give nitrogen oxide (also known as nitric oxide), a gas present in automobile exhaust, is such a reaction. The heat added in an endothermic reaction is like a reactant, and ΔH is assigned a *positive* value because heat is *added*.

An endothermic reaction—positive ΔH

Heat is a reactant.

$$N_2(g) + O_2(g) + 43 \text{ kcal (180 kJ)} \longrightarrow 2\,NO(g)$$

or

$$N_2(g) + O_2(g) \longrightarrow 2\,NO(g) \qquad \Delta H = +43 \text{ kcal/mol} (+180 \text{ kJ/mol})$$

Important Points about Heat Transfers and Chemical Reactions

- An exothermic reaction releases heat to the surroundings; ΔH is negative.
- An endothermic reaction absorbs heat from the surroundings; ΔH is positive.
- The reverse of an exothermic reaction is endothermic.
- The reverse of an endothermic reaction is exothermic.
- The amount of heat absorbed or released in the reverse of a reaction is equal to that released or absorbed in the forward reaction, but ΔH has the opposite sign.

Worked Examples 7.1–7.4 show how to calculate the amount of heat absorbed or released for reaction of a given amount of reactant. All that is needed is the balanced equation and its accompanying ΔH or the bond dissociation energies to permit calculation of ΔH. Mole ratios and molar masses are used to convert between masses and moles of reactants or products, as discussed in Sections 6.3 and 6.4.

Worked Example 7.1 Heat of Reaction from Bond Energies

Estimate the ΔH (in kcal/mol) for the reaction of hydrogen and oxygen to form water:

$$2\,H_2 + O_2 \longrightarrow 2\,H_2O \quad \Delta H = ?$$

ANALYSIS The individual bond energies from Table 7.1 can be used to calculate the total bond energies of reactants and products. ΔH can then be calculated as

$$\Delta H = \Sigma(\text{Bond dissociation energies})_{\text{reactants}} - \Sigma(\text{Bond dissociation energies})_{\text{products}}$$

BALLPARK ESTIMATE The average H—H bond energy is ~100 kcal/mol and the O=O bond energy is ~120 kcal/mol. Thus, the total energy needed to break reactant bonds is ~$(200 + 120) = 320$ kcal/mol. The O—H bonds are ~110 kcal/mol, so the total energy released when product bonds are formed is ~440 kcal/mol. Based on these estimates, $\Delta H \sim -120$ kcal/mol.

SOLUTION

$$\begin{aligned}
\Delta H &= \Sigma(\text{Bond dissociation energies})_{\text{reactants}} - \Sigma(\text{Bond dissociation energies})_{\text{products}} \\
&= (2(\text{H—H}) + (\text{O=O})) - (4(\text{O—H})) \\
&= (2(103\,\text{kcal/mol}) + (119\,\text{kcal/mol})) - (4(112\,\text{kcal/mol})) = -123\,\text{kcal/mol}
\end{aligned}$$

BALLPARK CHECK Our estimate was −120 kcal/mol, within 3% of the calculated answer.

Worked Example 7.2 Heat of Reaction: Moles

Methane undergoes combustion with O_2 according to the following equation:

$$CH_4(g) + 2\,O_2(g) \longrightarrow CO_2(g) + 2\,H_2O(l) \quad \Delta H = -213\,\frac{\text{kcal}}{\text{mol CH}_4}$$

How much heat (in kcal and kJ) is released during the combustion of 0.35 mol of methane?

ANALYSIS Since the value of ΔH for the reaction (213 kcal/mol) is negative, it indicates the amount of heat released when 1 mol of methane reacts with O_2. We need to find the amount of heat released when an amount other than 1 mol reacts, using appropriate factor-label calculations to convert from our known or given units to kilocalories, and then to kilojoules.

BALLPARK ESTIMATE Since 213 kcal is released for each mole of methane that reacts, 0.35 mol of methane should release about one-third of 213 kcal, or about 70 kcal. There are about 4 kJ per kcal, so 70 kcal is about 280 kJ.

SOLUTION

To find the amount of heat released (in kilocalories) by combustion of 0.35 mol of methane, we use a conversion factor of kcal/mol, and then we can convert to kilojoules using a kJ/kcal conversion factor (see Section 1.13):

$$0.35 \text{ mol CH}_4 \times \frac{-213 \text{ kcal}}{1 \text{ mol CH}_4} = -75 \text{ kcal}$$

$$-75 \text{ kcal} \times \left(\frac{4.184 \text{ kJ}}{\text{kcal}}\right) = -314 \text{ kJ}$$

The negative sign indicates that the 75 kcal (314 kJ) of heat is released.

BALLPARK CHECK The calculated answer is consistent with our estimate (70 kcal or 280 kJ).

Worked Example 7.3 Heat of Reaction: Mass to Mole Conversion

How much heat is released during the combustion of 7.50 g of methane (molar mass = 16.0 g/mol)?

$$CH_4(g) + 2\,O_2(g) \longrightarrow CO_2(g) + 2\,H_2O(l) \quad \Delta H = -213\,\frac{\text{kcal}}{\text{mol CH}_4} = -891\,\frac{\text{kJ}}{\text{mol CH}_4}$$

ANALYSIS We can find the moles of methane involved in the reaction by using the molecular weight in a mass to mole conversion, and then use ΔH to find the heat released.

BALLPARK ESTIMATE Since 1 mol of methane (molar mass = 16.0 g/mol) has a mass of 16.0 g, 7.50 g of methane is a little less than 0.5 mol. Thus, less than half of 213 kcal, or about 100 kcal (418 kJ), is released from combustion of 7.50 g.

SOLUTION

Going from a given mass of methane to the amount of heat released in a reaction requires that we first find the number of moles of methane by including molar mass (in mol/g) in the calculation and then converting moles to kilocalories or kilojoules:

$$7.50 \text{ g CH}_4 \times \frac{1 \text{ mol CH}_4}{16.0 \text{ g CH}_4} \times \frac{-213 \text{ kcal}}{1 \text{ mol CH}_4} = -99.8 \text{ kcal}$$

or

$$7.50 \text{ g CH}_4 \times \frac{1 \text{ mol CH}_4}{16.0 \text{ g CH}_4} \times \frac{-891 \text{ kJ}}{1 \text{ mol CH}_4} = -418 \text{ kJ}$$

The negative sign indicates that the 99.8 kcal (418 kJ) of heat is released.

BALLPARK CHECK Our estimate was −100 kcal (−418 kJ)!

Worked Example 7.4 Heat of Reaction: Mole Ratio Calculations

How much heat is released in kcal and kJ when 2.50 mol of O_2 reacts completely with methane?

$$CH_4(g) + 2\,O_2(g) \longrightarrow CO_2(g) + 2\,H_2O(l) \quad \Delta H = -213\,\frac{\text{kcal}}{\text{mol CH}_4} = -891\,\frac{\text{kJ}}{\text{mol CH}_4}$$

ANALYSIS Since the ΔH for the reaction is based on the combustion of 1 mol of methane, we will need to perform a mole ratio calculation.

BALLPARK ESTIMATE The balanced equation shows that 213 kcal (891 kJ) is released for each 2 mol of oxygen that reacts. Thus, 2.50 mol of oxygen should release a bit more than 213 kcal, perhaps about 250 kcal (1050 kJ).

SOLUTION

To find the amount of heat released by combustion of 2.50 mol of oxygen, we include in our calculation a mole ratio based on the balanced chemical equation:

$$2.50 \ \text{mol} \ O_2 \times \frac{1 \ \text{mol} \ CH_4}{2 \ \text{mol} \ O_2} \times \frac{-213 \ \text{kcal}}{1 \ \text{mol} \ CH_4} = -266 \ \text{kcal}$$

or

$$2.50 \ \text{mol} \ O_2 \times \frac{1 \ \text{mol} \ CH_4}{2 \ \text{mol} \ O_2} \times \frac{-891 \ \text{kJ}}{1 \ \text{mol} \ CH_4} = -1110 \ \text{kJ}$$

The negative sign indicates that the 266 kcal (1110 kJ) of heat is released.

BALLPARK CHECK The calculated answer is close to our estimate (-250 kcal or -1050 kJ).

CHEMISTRY IN ACTION

Energy from Food

Any serious effort to lose weight usually leads to studying the caloric values of foods. Have you ever wondered how the numbers quoted on food labels are obtained?

Food is "burned" in the body to yield H_2O, CO_2, and energy, just as natural gas is burned in furnaces to yield the same products. In fact, the "caloric value" of a food is just the heat of reaction for complete combustion of the food (minus a small correction factor). The value is the same whether the food is burned in the body or in the laboratory. One gram of protein releases 4 kcal, 1 g of table sugar (a carbohydrate) releases 4 kcal, and 1 g of fat releases 9 kcal (see Table).

Caloric Values of Some Foods

Substance, Sample Size	Caloric Value (kcal, kJ)
Protein, 1 g	4, 17
Carbohydrate, 1 g	4, 17
Fat, 1 g	9, 38
Alcohol, 1 g	7.1, 29.7
Cola drink, 12 fl oz (369 g)	160, 670
Apple, one medium (138 g)	80, 330
Iceberg lettuce, 1 cup shredded (55 g)	5, 21
White bread, 1 slice (25 g)	65, 270
Hamburger patty, 3 oz (85 g)	245, 1030
Pizza, 1 slice (120 g)	290, 1200
Vanilla ice cream, 1 cup (133 g)	270, 1130

The caloric value of a food is usually given in "Calories" (note the capital C), where 1 Cal = 1000 cal = 1 kcal = 4.184 kJ. To determine these values experimentally, a carefully dried and weighed food sample is placed together with oxygen in an instrument called a *calorimeter*, the food is ignited, the temperature change is measured, and the amount of heat given off is

▲ This frosted donut provides your body with 330 Calories. Burning this donut in a calorimeter releases 330 kcal (1380 kJ) as heat.

calculated from the temperature change. In the calorimeter, the heat from the food is released very quickly and the temperature rises dramatically. Clearly, though, something a bit different goes on when food is burned in the body, otherwise we would burst into flames after a meal!

It is a fundamental principle of chemistry that the total heat released or absorbed in going from reactants to products is the same, no matter how many reactions are involved. The body applies this principle by withdrawing energy from food a bit at a time in a long series of interconnected reactions rather than all at once in a single reaction. These and other reactions that are continually taking place in the body—called the body's *metabolism*—will be examined in later chapters.

See Chemistry in Action Problems 7.70 and 7.71 at the end of the chapter.

PROBLEM 7.1

In photosynthesis, green plants convert carbon dioxide and water into glucose ($C_6H_{12}O_6$) according to the following equation:

$$6\,CO_2(g) + 6\,H_2O(l) \longrightarrow C_6H_{12}O_6(aq) + 6\,O_2(g)$$

(a) Estimate ΔH for the reaction using bond dissociation energies from Table 7.1. Give your answer in kcal/mol and kJ/mol. $C_6H_{12}O_6$ has five C—C bonds, seven C—H bonds, seven C—O bonds, and five O—H bonds).

(b) Is the reaction endothermic or exothermic?

PROBLEM 7.2

The following equation shows the conversion of aluminum oxide (from the ore bauxite) to aluminum:

$$2\,Al_2O_3(s) \longrightarrow 4\,Al(s) + 3\,O_2(g) \quad \Delta H = +801\ \text{kcal/mol}\ (+3350\ \text{kJ/mol})$$

(a) Is the reaction exothermic or endothermic?

(b) How many kilocalories are required to produce 1.00 mol of aluminum? How many kilojoules?

(c) How many kilocalories are required to produce 10.0 g of aluminum? How many kilojoules?

PROBLEM 7.3

How much heat is absorbed (in kilocalories and kilojoules) during production of 127 g of NO by the combination of nitrogen and oxygen?

$$N_2(g) + O_2(g) \longrightarrow 2\,NO(g) \quad \Delta H = +43\ \text{kcal/mol}\ (+180\ \text{kJ/mol})$$

PROBLEM 7.4

Once consumed, the body metabolizes alcohol (ethanol, CH_3CH_2OH; MW = 46 g/mol) to carbon dioxide and water. The balanced reaction is: $CH_3CH_2OH + 3\,O_2 \longrightarrow 2\,CO_2 + 3\,H_2O$. Using the bond energies in Table 7.1, estimate the ΔH for this reaction in kcal/mol. How does it compare to the caloric value of alcohol (in Cal/g) given in Chemistry in Action: Energy from Food on p. 185)?

7.4 Why Do Chemical Reactions Occur? Free Energy

Events that lead to lower energy states tend to occur spontaneously. Water falls downhill, for instance, releasing its stored (potential) energy and reaching a lower-energy, more stable position. Similarly, a wound-up spring uncoils when set free. Applying this lesson to chemistry, the obvious conclusion is that exothermic processes—those that release heat energy—should be spontaneous. A log burning in a fireplace is just one example of a spontaneous reaction that releases heat. At the same time, endothermic processes, which absorb heat energy, should not be spontaneous. Often, these conclusions are correct, but not always. Many, but not all, exothermic processes take place spontaneously, and many, but not all, endothermic processes are nonspontaneous.

Before exploring the situation further, it is important to understand what the word "spontaneous" means in chemistry, which is not quite the same as in everyday language. A **spontaneous process** is one that, once started, proceeds on its own without any external influence. The change does not necessarily happen quickly, like a spring suddenly uncoiling or a car coasting downhill. It can also happen slowly, like the gradual rusting away of an abandoned bicycle. A *nonspontaneous process*, by contrast, takes place only in the presence of a continuous external influence. Energy must be continually expended to rewind a spring or push a car uphill. The reverse of a spontaneous process is always nonspontaneous.

As an example of a process that takes place spontaneously yet absorbs heat, think about what happens when you take an ice cube out of the freezer. The ice spontaneously

▲ Events that lead to lower energy tend to occur spontaneously. Thus, water always flows *down* a waterfall, not up.

Spontaneous process A process or reaction that, once started, proceeds on its own without any external influence.

melts to give liquid water above 0 °C, even though it *absorbs* heat energy from the surroundings. What this and other spontaneous endothermic processes have in common is *an increase in molecular disorder, or randomness.* When the solid ice melts, the H_2O molecules are no longer locked in position but are now free to move around randomly in the liquid water.

The amount of disorder in a system is called the system's **entropy**, symbolized by S and expressed in units of calories (or Joules) per mole-kelvin $[\text{cal}/(\text{mol} \cdot \text{K}) \text{ or J}/(\text{mol} \cdot \text{K})]$. The greater the disorder, or randomness, of the particles in a substance or mixture, the larger the value of S (Figure 7.1). Gases have more disorder and therefore higher entropy than liquids because particles in the gas move around more freely than particles in the liquid. Similarly, liquids have higher entropy than solids. In chemical reactions, entropy increases when, for example, a gas is produced from a solid or when 2 mol of reactants split into 4 mol of products.

Entropy (S) A measure of the amount of molecular disorder in a system.

Entropy increases ⟶

Solid ⟶ Liquid ⟶ Gas

Fewer moles ⟶ More moles

⟵ Entropy decreases

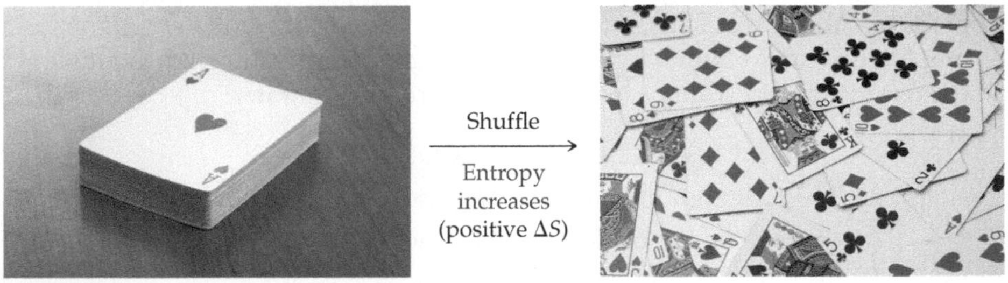

▲ **Figure 7.1**
Entropy and values of S.
A new deck of cards, neatly stacked, has more order and lower entropy than the randomly shuffled and strewn cards on the right. The value of the entropy change, ΔS, for converting the system on the left to that on the right is positive because entropy increases.

The **entropy change** for a process, ΔS, has a *positive* value if disorder increases because the process adds disorder to the system. The melting of ice to give water is an example. Conversely, ΔS has a *negative* value if the disorder of a system decreases. The freezing of water to give ice is an example.

Entropy change ΔS A measure of the increase in disorder $(\Delta S = +)$ or decrease in disorder $(\Delta S = -)$ as a chemical reaction or physical change occurs.

It thus appears that two factors determine the spontaneity of a chemical or physical change: the release or absorption of heat, ΔH, and the increase or decrease in entropy, ΔS. *To decide whether a process is spontaneous, both the enthalpy change and the entropy change must be taken into account.* We have already seen that a negative ΔH favors spontaneity, but what about ΔS? The answer is that an increase in molecular disorder (ΔS positive) favors spontaneity. A good analogy is the bedroom or office that seems to spontaneously become more messy over time (an increase in disorder, ΔS positive); to clean it up (a decrease in disorder, ΔS negative) requires an input of energy, a nonspontaneous process. Using our chemical example, the combustion of a log spontaneously converts large, complex molecules like lignin and cellulose (high molecular order, low entropy) into CO_2 and H_2O (a large number of small molecules with higher entropy). For this process, the level of disorder increases, and so ΔS is positive. The reverse process—turning CO_2 and H_2O back into cellulose—does occur in photosynthesis, but it requires a significant input of energy in the form of sunlight.

When enthalpy and entropy are both favorable (ΔH negative, ΔS positive), a process is spontaneous; when both are unfavorable, a process is nonspontaneous. Clearly,

Free-energy change ΔG A measure of the change in free energy as a chemical reaction or physical change occurs.

however, the two factors do not have to operate in the same direction. It is possible for a process to be *unfavored* by enthalpy (the process absorbs heat, and so, has a positive ΔH) and yet be *favored* by entropy (there is an increase in disorder, and so, ΔS is positive). The melting of an ice cube above 0 °C, for which $\Delta H = +1.44$ kcal/mol ($+6.02$ kJ/mol) and $\Delta S = +5.26$ cal/(mol·K)($+22.0$ J/(mol·K)) is such a process. To take both heat of reaction (ΔH) and change in disorder (ΔS) into account when determining the spontaneity of a process, a quantity called the **free-energy change** (ΔG) is needed:

Free-energy change

$$\underset{\text{Heat of reaction}}{\Delta G} = \underset{}{\Delta H} - \underset{\substack{\text{Temperature} \\ \text{(in kelvins)}}}{T}\underset{\text{Entropy change}}{\Delta S}$$

Exergonic A spontaneous reaction or process that releases free energy and has a negative ΔG.

Endergonic A nonspontaneous reaction or process that absorbs free energy and has a positive ΔG.

The value of the free-energy change, ΔG, determines spontaneity. A negative value for ΔG means that free energy is released and the reaction or process is spontaneous. Such events are said to be **exergonic**. A positive value for ΔG means that free energy must be added and the process is nonspontaneous. Such events are said to be **endergonic**.

The equation for the free-energy change shows that spontaneity also depends on temperature (T). At low temperatures, the value of $T \Delta S$ is often small so that ΔH is the dominant factor. At a high enough temperature, however, the value of $T \Delta S$ can become larger than ΔH. Thus, an endothermic process that is nonspontaneous at a low temperature can become spontaneous at a higher temperature. An example is the industrial synthesis of hydrogen by reaction of carbon with water:

$$C(s) + H_2O(l) \longrightarrow CO(g) + H_2(g)$$
$$\Delta H = +31.3 \text{ kcal/mol} \, (+131.0 \text{ kJ/mol}) \qquad \text{(Unfavorable)}$$
$$\Delta S = +32 \text{ cal/(mol·K)}(+134 \text{ J/(mol·K))} \qquad \text{(Favorable)}$$

The reaction has an unfavorable (positive) ΔH term but a favorable (positive) ΔS term because disorder increases when a solid and a liquid are converted into two gases. No reaction occurs if carbon and water are mixed together at 25 °C (298 K) because the unfavorable ΔH is larger than the favorable $T \Delta S$. Above about 700 °C (973 K), however, the favorable $T \Delta S$ becomes larger than the unfavorable ΔH, so the reaction becomes spontaneous.

Important Points about Spontaneity and Free Energy

- A spontaneous process, once begun, proceeds without any external assistance and is exergonic; that is, free energy is released and it has a negative value of ΔG.
- A nonspontaneous process requires continuous external influence and is endergonic; that is, free energy is added and it has a positive value of ΔG.
- The value of ΔG for the reverse of a reaction is numerically equal to the value of ΔG for the forward reaction, but has the opposite sign.
- Some nonspontaneous processes become spontaneous with a change in temperature.

LOOKING AHEAD ▶▶▶ In later chapters, we will see that a knowledge of free-energy changes is especially important for understanding how metabolic reactions work. Living organisms cannot raise their temperatures to convert nonspontaneous reactions into spontaneous reactions, so they must resort to other strategies, which we will explore in Chapter 20.

Worked Example 7.5 Entropy Change of Processes

Does entropy increase or decrease in the following processes?

(a) Smoke from a cigarette disperses throughout a room rather than remaining in a cloud over the smoker's head.

(b) Water boils, changing from liquid to vapor.

(c) A chemical reaction occurs: $3\,H_2(g) + N_2(g) \longrightarrow 2\,NH_3(g)$

ANALYSIS Entropy is a measure of molecular disorder. Entropy increases when the products are more disordered than the reactants; entropy decreases when the products are less disordered than the reactants.

SOLUTION

(a) Entropy increases because smoke particles are more disordered when they are randomly distributed in the larger volume.

(b) Entropy increases because H_2O molecules have more freedom and disorder in the gas phase than in the liquid phase.

(c) Entropy decreases because 4 mol of reactant gas particles become 2 mol of product gas particles, with a consequent decrease in freedom and disorder.

Worked Example 7.6 Spontaneity of Reactions: Enthalpy, Entropy, and Free Energy

The industrial method for synthesizing hydrogen by reaction of carbon with water has $\Delta H = +31.3\ \text{kcal/mol}\ (+131\ \text{kJ/mol})$ and $\Delta S = +32\ \text{cal/}[\text{mol}\cdot\text{K}]\ (+134\ \text{J/}[\text{mol}\cdot\text{K}])$. What is the value of ΔG (in kcal and kJ) for the reaction at 27 °C (300 K)? Is the reaction spontaneous or nonspontaneous at this temperature?

$$C(s) + H_2O(l) \longrightarrow CO(g) + H_2(g)$$

ANALYSIS The reaction is endothermic (ΔH positive) and does not favor spontaneity, whereas the ΔS indicates an increase in disorder (ΔS positive), which *does* favor spontaneity. Calculate ΔG to determine spontaneity.

BALLPARK ESTIMATE The unfavorable ΔH ($+31.3\ \text{kcal/mol}$) is 1000 times greater than the favorable ΔS ($+32\ \text{cal/mol}\cdot\text{K}$), so the reaction will be spontaneous (ΔG negative) only when the temperature is high enough to make the $T\,\Delta S$ term in the equation for ΔG larger than the ΔH term. This happens at $T \geq 1000\ \text{K}$. Since $T = 300\ \text{K}$, expect ΔG to be positive and the reaction to be nonspontaneous.

SOLUTION
Use the free-energy equation to determine the value of ΔG at this temperature. (Remember that ΔS has units of *calories* per mole-kelvin or *joules* per mole-kelvin, not kilocalories per mole-kelvin or kilojoules per mole-kelvin.)

$$\Delta G = \Delta H - T\,\Delta S$$

$$\Delta G = +31.3\frac{\text{kcal}}{\text{mol}} - (300\ \cancel{K})\left(+32\frac{\cancel{\text{cal}}}{\text{mol}\cdot\cancel{K}}\right)\left(\frac{1\ \text{kcal}}{1000\ \cancel{\text{cal}}}\right) = +21.7\frac{\text{kcal}}{\text{mol}}$$

$$\Delta G = +131\frac{\text{kJ}}{\text{mol}} - (300\ \cancel{K})\left(+134\frac{\cancel{J}}{\text{mol}\cdot\cancel{K}}\right)\left(\frac{1\ \text{kJ}}{1000\ \cancel{J}}\right) = +90.8\frac{\text{kJ}}{\text{mol}}$$

BALLPARK CHECK Because ΔG is positive, the reaction is nonspontaneous at 300 K, consistent with our estimate.

PROBLEM 7.5
Does entropy increase or decrease in the following processes?

(a) Complex carbohydrates are metabolized by the body, converted into simple sugars.

(b) Steam condenses on a glass surface.

(c) $2\,SO_2(g) + O_2(g) \longrightarrow 2\,SO_3(g)$

PROBLEM 7.6

Lime (CaO) is prepared by the decomposition of limestone ($CaCO_3$).

$$CaCO_3(s) \longrightarrow CaO(s) + CO_2(g) \quad \Delta H = +42.6 \text{ kcal/mol} (+178.3 \text{ kJ/mol});$$
$$\Delta S = +38.0 \text{ cal/(mol} \cdot \text{K)}(+159 \text{ J/(mol} \cdot \text{K))} \text{ at } 25 \text{ °C}$$

(a) Calculate ΔG at 25 °C. Give your answer in kcal/mol and kJ/mol. Does the reaction occur spontaneously?

(b) Would you expect the reaction to be spontaneous at higher or lower temperatures?

PROBLEM 7.7

The melting of solid ice to give liquid water has $\Delta H = +1.44 \text{ kcal/mol} (+6.02 \text{ kJ/mol})$ and $\Delta S = +5.26 \text{ cal/(mol} \cdot \text{K)}(+22.0 \text{ J/(mol} \cdot \text{K))}$. What is the value of ΔG for the melting process at the following temperatures? Give your answer in kcal/mol and kJ/mol. Is the melting spontaneous or nonspontaneous at these temperatures?

(a) −10 °C (263 K)   (b) 0 °C (273 K)   (c) +10 °C (283 K)

KEY CONCEPT PROBLEM 7.8

The following diagram portrays a reaction of the type $A(s) \longrightarrow B(s) + C(g)$, where the different colored spheres represent different molecular structures. Assume that the reaction has $\Delta H = -23.5 \text{ kcal/mol} (-98.3 \text{ kJ/mol})$.

(a) What is the sign of ΔS for the reaction?

(b) Is the reaction likely to be spontaneous at all temperatures, nonspontaneous at all temperatures, or spontaneous at some but nonspontaneous at others?

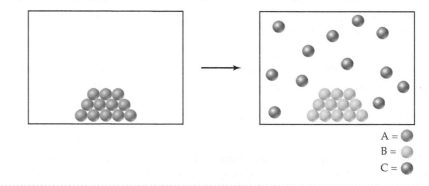

A =
B =
C =

7.5 How Do Chemical Reactions Occur? Reaction Rates

Just because a chemical reaction has a favorable free-energy change does not mean that it occurs rapidly. The value of ΔG tells us only whether a reaction *can* occur; it says nothing about how *fast* the reaction will occur or about the details of the molecular changes that take place during the reaction. It is now time to look into these other matters.

For a chemical reaction to occur, reactant particles must collide, some chemical bonds have to break, and new bonds have to form. Not all collisions lead to products, however. One requirement for a productive collision is that the colliding molecules must approach with the correct orientation so that the atoms about to form new bonds can connect. In the reaction of ozone (O_3) with nitric oxide (NO) to give oxygen (O_2) and nitrogen dioxide (NO_2), for example, the two reactants must collide so that the nitrogen atom of NO strikes a terminal oxygen atom of O_3 (Figure 7.2).

Another requirement for a reaction to occur is that the collision must take place with enough energy to break the appropriate bonds in the reactant. If the reactant particles are moving slowly, collisions might be too gentle to overcome the repulsion between electrons in the different reactants, and the particles will simply bounce apart. A reaction will only occur if the collisions between reactant molecules are sufficiently energetic.

Effective collision:

Bond can form

Ineffective collision:

No bond can form

◄ **Figure 7.2**
How do chemical reactions occur?
For a collision between NO and O_3 molecules to give O_2 and NO_2, the molecules must collide so that the correct atoms come into contact. No bond forms if the molecules collide with the wrong orientation.

For this reason, many reactions with a favorable free-energy change do not occur at room temperature. To get such a reaction started, energy (heat) must be added. The heat causes the reactant particles to move faster, thereby increasing both the frequency and the force of the collisions. We all know that matches burn, for instance, but we also know that they do not burst into flame until struck. The heat of friction provides enough energy for a few molecules to react. Once started, the reaction sustains itself as the energy released by reacting molecules gives other molecules enough energy to react.

The energy change that occurs during the course of a chemical reaction can be visualized in an energy diagram like that in Figure 7.3. At the beginning of the reaction (left side of the diagram), the reactants are at the energy level indicated. At the end of the reaction (right side of the diagram), the products are at a lower energy level than the reactants if the reaction is exergonic (Figure 7.3a) but higher than the reactants if the reaction is endergonic (Figure 7.3b).

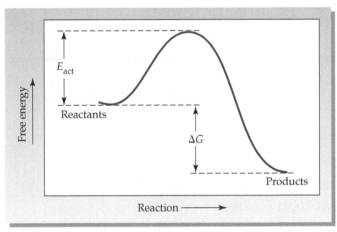

(a) An exergonic reaction

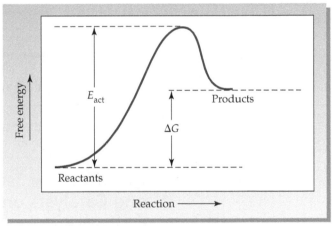

(b) An endergonic reaction

▲ **Figure 7.3**
Reaction energy diagrams show energy changes during a chemical reaction.
A reaction begins on the left and proceeds to the right. (a) In an exergonic reaction, the product energy level is lower than that of reactants. (b) In an endergonic reaction, the situation is reversed. The height of the barrier between reactant and product energy levels is the activation energy, E_{act}. The difference between reactant and product energy levels is the free-energy change, ΔG.

Lying between the reactants and the products is an energy "barrier" that must be surmounted. The height of this barrier represents the amount of energy the colliding particles must have for productive collisions to occur, an amount called the **activation energy (E_{act})** of the reaction. The size of the activation energy determines the **reaction rate**, or how fast the reaction occurs. The lower the activation energy, the greater the number of productive collisions in a given amount of time, and the faster the reaction. Conversely, the higher the activation energy, the lower the number of productive collisions, and the slower the reaction.

Activation energy (E_{act}) The amount of energy necessary for reactants to surmount the energy barrier to reaction; determines reaction rate.

Reaction rate A measure of how rapidly a reaction occurs; determined by E_{act}.

Note that the size of the activation energy and the size of the free-energy change are unrelated. A reaction with a large E_{act} takes place very slowly even if it has a large negative ΔG. Every reaction is different; each has its own characteristic activation energy and free-energy change.

Worked Example **7.7** Energy of Reactions: Energy Diagrams

Draw an energy diagram for a reaction that is very fast but has a small negative free-energy change.

ANALYSIS A very fast reaction has a small E_{act}. A reaction with a small negative free-energy change is a favorable reaction with a small energy difference between starting materials and products.

SOLUTION

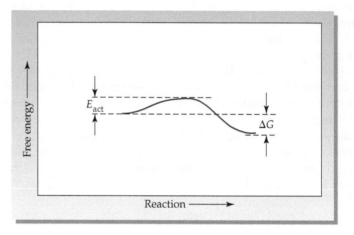

PROBLEM 7.9
Draw an energy diagram for a reaction that is very slow but highly favorable.

PROBLEM 7.10
Draw an energy diagram for a reaction that is slightly unfavorable.

7.6 Effects of Temperature, Concentration, and Catalysts on Reaction Rates

Several things can be done to help reactants over an activation energy barrier and thereby speed up a reaction. Let us look at some possibilities.

Temperature

One way to increase reaction rate is to add energy to the reactants by raising the temperature. With more energy in the system, the reactants move faster, so the frequency of collisions increases. Furthermore, the force with which collisions occur increases, making them more likely to overcome the activation barrier. As a rule of thumb, a 10 °C rise in temperature causes a reaction rate to double.

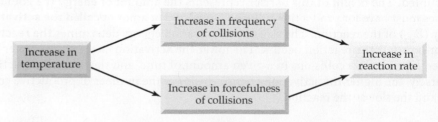

Concentration

A second way to speed up a reaction is to increase the **concentrations** of the reactants. As the concentration increases, reactants are crowded together, and collisions between reactant molecules become more frequent. As the frequency of collisions increases, reactions between molecules become more likely. Flammable materials burn more rapidly in pure oxygen than in air, for instance, because the concentration of O_2 molecules is higher (air is approximately 21% oxygen). Hospitals must therefore take extraordinary precautions to ensure that no flames are used near patients receiving oxygen. Although different reactions respond differently to concentration changes, doubling or tripling a reactant concentration often doubles or triples the reaction rate.

Concentration A measure of the amount of a given substance in a mixture.

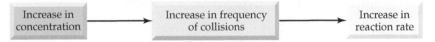

Catalysts

A third way to speed up a reaction is to add a **catalyst**—a substance that accelerates a chemical reaction but is itself unchanged in the process. For example, metals such as nickel, palladium, and platinum catalyze the addition of hydrogen to the carbon–carbon double bonds in vegetable oils to yield semisolid margarine. Without the metal catalyst, the reaction does not occur.

Catalyst A substance that speeds up the rate of a chemical reaction but is itself unchanged.

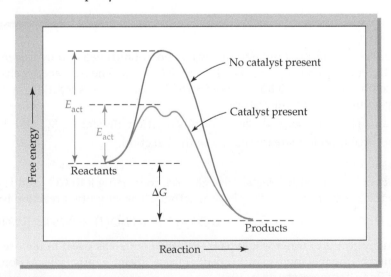

A catalyst does not affect the energy level of either reactants or products. Rather, it increases reaction rate either by letting a reaction take place through an alternative pathway with a lower energy barrier, or by orienting the reacting molecules appropriately. In a reaction energy diagram, the catalyzed reaction has a lower activation energy (Figure 7.4). It is worth noting that the free-energy change for a reaction depends *only* on the difference in the energy levels of the reactants and products, and *not* on the pathway of the reaction. Therefore, a catalyzed reaction releases (or absorbs) the same amount of energy as an uncatalyzed reaction. It simply occurs more rapidly.

◄ Figure 7.4
A reaction energy diagram for a reaction in the presence (green curve) and absence (blue curve) of a catalyst. The catalyzed reaction has a lower (E_{act}) because it uses an alternative pathway (represented by the multiple bumps in the green line) with a lower energy barrier. The free-energy change, ΔG, is unaffected by the presence of a catalyst.

In addition to their widespread use in industry, we also rely on catalysts to reduce the air pollution created by exhaust from automobile engines. The catalytic converters in most automobiles are tubes packed with catalysts of two types (Figure 7.5). One catalyst accelerates the complete combustion of hydrocarbons and CO in the exhaust to give CO_2 and H_2O, and the other decomposes NO to N_2 and O_2.

▶ **Figure 7.5**

A catalytic converter.
The exhaust gases from an automobile pass through a two-stage catalytic converter. In one stage, carbon monoxide and unburned hydrocarbons are converted to CO_2 and H_2O. In the second stage, NO is converted to N_2 and O_2.

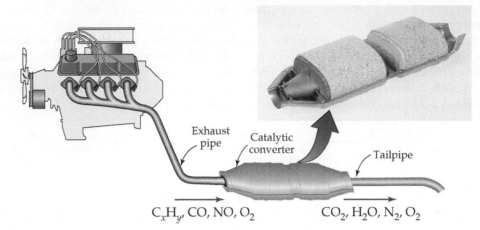

Exhaust pipe   Catalytic converter   Tailpipe

C_xH_y, CO, NO, O_2 CO_2, H_2O, N_2, O_2

Table 7.3 summarizes the effects of changing conditions on reaction rates.

TABLE 7.3 Effects of Changes in Reaction Conditions on Reaction Rates

Change	Effect
Concentration	Increase in reactant concentration increases rate. Decrease in reactant concentration decreases rate.
Temperature	Increase in temperature increases rate. Decrease in temperature decreases rate.
Catalyst added	Increases reaction rate.

LOOKING AHEAD ▶▶▶ The thousands of biochemical reactions continually taking place in our bodies are catalyzed by large protein molecules called *enzymes*, which promote reactions by controlling the orientation of the reacting molecules. Since almost every reaction is catalyzed by its own specific enzyme, the study of enzyme structure, activity, and control is a central part of biochemistry. We will look more closely at enzymes and how they work in Chapter 19.

PROBLEM 7.11

Ammonia is synthesized industrially by reaction of nitrogen and hydrogen according to the equation $3\,H_2(g) + N_2(g) \longrightarrow 2\,NH_3(g)$. The free-energy change for this reaction is $\Delta G = -3.8\,\text{kcal/mol}\,(-16\,\text{kJ/mol})$, yet this reaction does not readily occur at room temperature.

(a) Draw a reaction energy diagram for this reaction, indicating E_{act} and ΔG.

(b) List three ways to increase the rate of this reaction.

PROBLEM 7.12

As we exercise, our bodies metabolize glucose, converting it to CO_2 and H_2O, to supply the energy necessary for physical activity. The simplified reaction is:

$$C_6H_{12}O_6(aq) + 6\,O_2(g) \longrightarrow 6\,CO_2(g) + 6\,H_2O(l) + 678\,\text{kcal}(2840\,\text{kJ})$$

How many grams of water would have to be evaporated as sweat to remove the heat generated by the metabolism of 1 mol of glucose? (See Chemistry in Action: Regulation of Body Temperature on p. 195).

CHEMISTRY IN ACTION

Regulation of Body Temperature

Maintaining normal body temperature is crucial. If the body's thermostat is unable to maintain a temperature of 37 °C, the rates of the many thousands of chemical reactions that take place constantly in the body will change accordingly, with potentially disastrous consequences.

If, for example, a skater fell through the ice of a frozen lake, *hypothermia* could soon result. Hypothermia is a dangerous state that occurs when the body is unable to generate enough heat to maintain normal temperature. All chemical reactions in the body slow down because of the lower temperature, energy production drops, and death can result. Slowing the body's reactions can also be used to advantage, however. During open-heart surgery, the heart is stopped and maintained at about 15 °C, while the body, which receives oxygenated blood from an external pump, is cooled to 25–32 °C.

In this case, the body is receiving oxygenated blood from an external pump in an operating chamber under medical supervision. If hypothermia occurred due to some other environmental condition, the heart would slow down, respiration would decrease, and the body would not receive sufficient oxygen and death would result.

Conversely, a marathon runner on a hot, humid day might become overheated, and *hyperthermia* could result. Hyperthermia, also called *heat stroke*, is an uncontrolled rise in temperature as the result of the body's inability to lose sufficient heat. Chemical reactions in the body are accelerated at higher temperatures, the heart struggles to pump blood faster to supply increased oxygen, and brain damage can result if the body temperature rises above 41 °C.

Body temperature is maintained both by the thyroid gland and by the hypothalamus region of the brain, which act together to regulate metabolic rate. When the body's environment changes, temperature receptors in the skin, spinal cord, and abdomen send signals to the hypothalamus, which contains both heat-sensitive and cold-sensitive neurons.

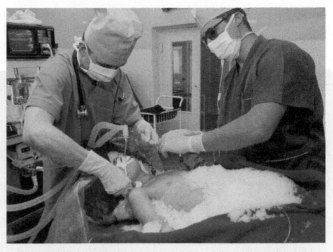

▲ The body is cooled to 25–32°C by immersion in ice prior to open-heart surgery to slow down metabolism.

Stimulation of the heat-sensitive neurons on a hot day causes a variety of effects: Impulses are sent to stimulate the sweat glands, dilate the blood vessels of the skin, decrease muscular activity, and reduce metabolic rate. Sweating cools the body through evaporation; approximately 540 cal (2260 J) is removed by evaporation of 1.0 g of sweat. Dilated blood vessels cool the body by allowing more blood to flow close to the surface of the skin, where heat is removed by contact with air. Decreased muscular activity and a reduced metabolic rate cool the body by lowering internal heat production.

Stimulation of the cold-sensitive neurons on a cold day also causes a variety of effects: The hormone epinephrine is released to stimulate metabolic rate; peripheral blood vessels contract to decrease blood flow to the skin and prevent heat loss; and muscular contractions increase to produce more heat, resulting in shivering and "goosebumps."

One further comment: Drinking alcohol to warm up on a cold day actually has the opposite effect. Alcohol causes blood vessels to dilate, resulting in a warm feeling as blood flow to the skin increases. Although the warmth feels good temporarily, body temperature ultimately drops as heat is lost through the skin at an increased rate.

See Chemistry in Action Problems 7.72 and 7.73 at the end of the chapter.

7.7 Reversible Reactions and Chemical Equilibrium

Many chemical reactions result in the virtually complete conversion of reactants into products. When sodium metal reacts with chlorine gas, for example, both are entirely consumed. The sodium chloride product is so much more stable than the reactants that, once started, the reaction keeps going until it is complete.

What happens, though, when the reactants and products are of approximately equal stability? This is the case, for example, in the reaction of acetic acid (the main organic constituent of vinegar) with ethyl alcohol to yield ethyl acetate, a solvent used in nail-polish remover and glue.

$$\underset{\text{Acetic acid}}{CH_3\overset{\displaystyle O}{\overset{\|}{C}}OH} + \underset{\text{Ethyl alcohol}}{HOCH_2CH_3} \underset{\text{Or this direction?}}{\overset{\text{This direction?}}{\rightleftharpoons}} \underset{\text{Ethyl acetate}}{CH_3\overset{\displaystyle O}{\overset{\|}{C}}OCH_2CH_3} + \underset{\text{Water}}{H_2O}$$

Reversible reaction A reaction that can go in either direction, from products to reactants or reactants to products.

Chemical equilibrium A state in which the rates of forward and reverse reactions are the same.

Imagine the situation if you mix acetic acid and ethyl alcohol. The two begin to form ethyl acetate and water. But as soon as ethyl acetate and water form, they begin to go back to acetic acid and ethyl alcohol. Such a reaction, which easily goes in either direction, is said to be **reversible** and is indicated by a double arrow ($\rightleftharpoons$) in equations. The reaction read from left to right as written is referred to as the *forward reaction*, and the reaction from right to left is referred to as the *reverse reaction*.

Now suppose you mix some ethyl acetate and water. The same thing occurs: As soon as small quantities of acetic acid and ethyl alcohol form, the reaction in the other direction begins to take place. No matter which pair of reactants is mixed together, both reactions occur until ultimately the concentrations of reactants and products reach constant values and undergo no further change. At this point, the reaction vessel contains all four substances—acetic acid, ethyl acetate, ethyl alcohol, and water—and the reaction is said to be in a state of **chemical equilibrium**.

Since the reactant and product concentrations undergo no further change once equilibrium is reached, you might conclude that the forward and reverse reactions have stopped. That is not the case, however. The forward reaction takes place rapidly at the beginning of the reaction but then slows down as reactant concentrations decrease. At the same time, the reverse reaction takes place slowly at the beginning but then speeds up as product concentrations increase (Figure 7.6). Ultimately, the forward and reverse rates become equal and change no further.

▶ **Figure 7.6**
Reaction rates in an equilibrium reaction.
The forward rate is large initially but decreases as the concentrations of reactants drop. The reverse rate is small initially but increases as the concentrations of products increase. At equilibrium, the forward and reverse reaction rates are equal.

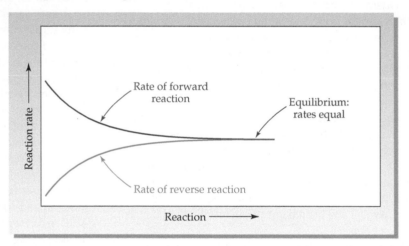

▲ When the number of people moving up is the same as the number of people moving down, the number of people on each floor remains constant, and the two populations are in equilibrium.

Chemical equilibrium is an active, dynamic condition. All substances present are continuously being made and unmade at the same rate, so their concentrations are constant at equilibrium. As an analogy, think of two floors of a building connected by up and down escalators. If the number of people moving up is the same as the number of people moving down, the numbers of people on each floor remain constant. *Individual people* are continuously changing from one floor to the other, but the *total populations* of the two floors are in equilibrium.

Note that it is not necessary for the concentrations of reactants and products at equilibrium to be equal (just as it is not necessary for the numbers of people on two floors connected by escalators to be equal). Equilibrium can be reached at any point between pure products and pure reactants. The extent to which the forward or reverse reaction is favored over the other is a characteristic property of a given reaction under given conditions.

7.8 Equilibrium Equations and Equilibrium Constants

Remember that the rate of a reaction depends on the number of collisions between molecules (Section 7.5), and that the number of collisions in turn depends on concentration, i.e., the number of molecules in a given volume (Section 7.6). For a reversible reaction, then, the rates of both the forward *and* the reverse reactions must depend on the concentration of reactants and products, respectively. When a reaction reaches equilibrium, the rates of the forward and reverse reactions are equal, and the concentrations of reactants and products remain constant. We can use this fact to obtain useful information about a reaction.

Let us look at the details of a specific equilibrium reaction. Suppose that you allow various mixtures of sulfur dioxide and oxygen to come to equilibrium with sulfur trioxide at a temperature of 727 °C and then measure the concentrations of all three gases in the mixtures.

$$2 SO_2(g) + O_2(g) \rightleftharpoons 2 SO_3(g)$$

In one experiment, we start with only 1.00 mol of SO_2 and 1.00 mol of O_2 in a 1.00 L container. In other words, the initial concentrations of reactants are 1.00 mol/L. When the reaction reaches equilibrium, we have 0.0620 mol/L of SO_2, 0.538 mol/L of O_2, and 0.938 mol/L of SO_3. In another experiment, we start with 1.00 mol/L of SO_3. When this reaction reaches equilibrium, we have 0.150 mol/L of SO_2, 0.0751 mol/L of O_2, and 0.850 mol/L of SO_3. In both cases, we see that there is substantially more product (SO_3) than reactants when the reaction reaches equilibrium, regardless of the starting conditions. Is it possible to predict what the equilibrium conditions will be for any given reaction?

As it turns out, the answer is YES! No matter what the original concentrations were, and no matter what concentrations remain at equilibrium, we find that a constant numerical value is obtained if the equilibrium concentrations are substituted into the expression

$$\frac{[SO_3]^2}{[SO_2]^2[O_2]} = \text{constant at a given T}$$

The square brackets in this expression indicate the concentration of each substance expressed as moles per liter. Using the equilibrium concentrations for each of the experiments described above, we can calculate the value and verify that it is constant:

Experiment 1. $\dfrac{[SO_3]^2}{[SO_2]^2[O_2]} = \dfrac{(0.938 \text{ mol/L})^2}{(0.0620 \text{ mol/L})^2(0.538 \text{ mol/L})} = 425$

Experiment 2. $\dfrac{[SO_3]^2}{[SO_2]^2[O_2]} = \dfrac{(0.850 \text{ mol/L})^2}{(0.150 \text{ mol/L})^2(0.0751 \text{ mol/L})} = 428$

At a temperature of 727 °C, the actual value of the constant is 429. Within experimental error, the ratios of product and reactant concentrations for the two experiments at equilibrium yield the same result. Numerous experiments like those just described have led to a general equation that is valid for any reaction. Consider a general reversible reaction:

$$aA + bB + \ldots \rightleftharpoons mM + nN + \ldots$$

where A, B, ... are reactants; M, N, ... are products; and a, b, ..., m, n, ... are coefficients in the balanced equation. At equilibrium, the composition of the reaction mixture obeys the following *equilibrium equation*, where K is the **equilibrium constant**.

Equilibrium equation $K = \dfrac{[M]^m[N]^n \cdots}{[A]^a[B]^b \cdots}$ ⟵Product concentrations

⟵Reactant concentrations

Equilibrium constant

Equilibrium constant (K) Value obtained at a given temperature from the ratio of the concentrations of products and reactants, each raised to a power equal to its coefficient in the balanced equation.

The equilibrium constant K is the number obtained by multiplying the equilibrium concentrations of the products and dividing by the equilibrium concentrations of the reactants, with the concentration of each substance raised to a power equal to its coefficient in the balanced equation. If we take another look at the reaction between sulfur dioxide and oxygen, we can now see how the equilibrium constant was obtained:

$$2\,SO_2\,(g) + O_2\,(g) \rightleftharpoons 2\,SO_3\,(g)$$

$$K = \frac{[SO_3]^2}{[SO_2]^2\,[O_2]}$$

Note that if there is no coefficient for a reactant or product in the reaction equation, it is assumed to be 1. The value of K varies with temperature (25 °C) is assumed unless otherwise specified—and units are usually omitted.

For reactions that involve pure solids or liquids, these pure substances are omitted when writing the equilibrium constant expression. To explain why, consider the decomposition of limestone from Problem 7.6:

▶▶▶ The practice of omitting pure substances in the equilibrium constant expression will be utilized in Chapter 10 when we discuss equilibria involving acids and bases.

$$CaCO_3(s) \longrightarrow CaO(s) + CO_2(g)$$

Writing the equilibrium constant expression for this reaction as the concentration of products over the concentration of reactions would yield

$$K = \frac{[CaO][CO_2]}{[CaCO_3]}$$

Consider the solids CaO and $CaCO_3$. Their concentrations (in moles/L) can be calculated from their molar masses and densities at a given temperature. For example, the concentration of CaO at 25 °C can be calculated as

$$\frac{\left(3.25\,\frac{g\,CaO}{cm^3}\right) \cdot \left(\frac{1000\,cm^3}{L}\right)}{56.08\,\frac{g\,CaO}{mol\,CaO}} = 58.0\,\frac{mol\,CaO}{L}$$

The ratio of products over reactants would change if CO_2 was added to or removed from the reaction. The concentration of CaO, however, is the same whether we have 10 grams or 500 grams. Adding solid CaO will not change the ratio of products over reactants. Since the concentration of solids is independent of the amount of solid present, these concentrations are omitted and the expression for K becomes

$$K = \frac{[CaO][CO_2]}{[CaCO_3]} = [CO_2]$$

The value of the equilibrium constant indicates the position of a reaction at equilibrium. If the forward reaction is favored, the product term $[M]^m[N]^n$ is larger than the reactant term $[A]^a[B]^b$, and the value of K is larger than 1. If instead the reverse reaction is favored, $[M]^m[N]^n$ is smaller than $[A]^a[B]^b$ at equilibrium, and the value of K is smaller than 1.

For a reaction such as the combination of hydrogen and oxygen to form water vapor, the equilibrium constant is enormous (3.1×10^{81}), showing how greatly the formation of water is favored. Equilibrium is effectively nonexistent for such reactions, and the reaction is described as *going to completion*.

On the other hand, the equilibrium constant is very small for a reaction such as the combination of nitrogen and oxygen at 25 °C to give NO (4.7×10^{-31}), showing what we know from observation—that N_2 and O_2 in the air do not combine noticeably at room temperature:

$$N_2(g) + O_2(g) \rightleftharpoons 2\,NO(g) \quad K = \frac{[NO]^2}{[N_2][O_2]} = 4.7 \times 10^{-31}$$

When K is close to 1, say between 10^3 and 10^{-3}, significant amounts of both reactants and products are present at equilibrium. An example is the reaction of acetic acid with ethyl alcohol to give ethyl acetate (Section 7.7). For this reaction, $K = 3.4$.

$$CH_3CO_2H + CH_3CH_2OH \rightleftharpoons CH_3CO_2CH_2CH_3 + H_2O$$

$$K = \frac{[CH_3CO_2CH_2CH_3][H_2O]}{[CH_3CO_2H][CH_3CH_2OH]} = 3.4$$

We can summarize the meaning of equilibrium constants in the following way:

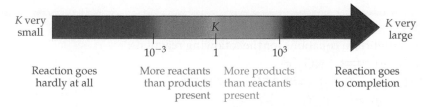

| K very small | | K | | K very large |

| 10^{-3} | 1 | 10^3 |

| Reaction goes hardly at all | More reactants than products present | More products than reactants present | Reaction goes to completion |

K much smaller than 0.001   Only reactants are present at equilibrium; essentially no reaction occurs.

K between 0.001 and 1   More reactants than products are present at equilibrium.

K between 1 and 1000   More products than reactants are present at equilibrium.

K much larger than 1000   Only products are present at equilibrium; reaction goes essentially to completion.

Worked Example 7.8 Writing Equilibrium Equations

The first step in the industrial synthesis of hydrogen is the reaction of steam with methane to give carbon monoxide and hydrogen. Write the equilibrium equation for the reaction.

$$H_2O(g) + CH_4(g) \rightleftharpoons CO(g) + 3\,H_2(g)$$

ANALYSIS The equilibrium constant K is the number obtained by multiplying the equilibrium concentrations of the products (CO and H_2) and dividing by the equilibrium concentrations of the reactants (H_2O and CH_4), with the concentration of each substance raised to the power of its coefficient in the balanced equation.

SOLUTION

$$K = \frac{[CO][H_2]^3}{[H_2O][CH_4]}$$

Worked Example 7.9 Equilibrium Equations: Calculating K

In the reaction of Cl_2 with PCl_3, the concentrations of reactants and products were determined experimentally at equilibrium and found to be 7.2 mol/L for PCl_3, 7.2 mol/L for Cl_2, and 0.050 mol/L for PCl_5.

$$PCl_3(g) + Cl_2(g) \rightleftharpoons PCl_5(g)$$

Write the equilibrium equation, and calculate the equilibrium constant for the reaction. Which reaction is favored, the forward one or the reverse one?

ANALYSIS All the coefficients in the balanced equation are 1, so the equilibrium constant equals the concentration of the product, PCl_5, divided by the product of the concentrations of the two reactants, PCl_3 and Cl_2. Insert the values given for each concentration, and calculate the value of K.

BALLPARK ESTIMATE At equilibrium, the concentration of the reactants (7.2 mol/L for each reactant) is higher than the concentration of the product (0.05 mol/L), so we expect a value of K less than 1.

SOLUTION

$$K = \frac{[PCl_5]}{[PCl_3][Cl_2]} = \frac{0.050 \text{ mol/L}}{(7.2 \text{ mol/L})(7.2 \text{ mol/L})} = 9.6 \times 10^{-4}$$

The value of K is less than 1, so the reverse reaction is favored. Note that units for K are omitted.

BALLPARK CHECK Our calculated value of K is just as we predicted: $K < 1$.

PROBLEM 7.13

Write equilibrium equations for the following reactions:
(a) $N_2O_4(g) \rightleftharpoons 2 NO_2(g)$
(b) $2 H_2S(g) + O_2(g) \rightleftharpoons 2 S(s) + 2 H_2O(g)$
(c) $2 BrF_5(g) \rightleftharpoons Br_2(g) + 5 F_2(g)$

PROBLEM 7.14

Do the following reactions favor reactants or products at equilibrium? Give relative concentrations at equilibrium.
(a) Sucrose(aq) + $H_2O(l) \rightleftharpoons$ Glucose(aq) + Fructose(aq) $K = 1.4 \times 10^5$
(b) $NH_3(aq) + H_2O(l) \rightleftharpoons NH_4^+(aq) + OH^-(aq)$ $K = 1.6 \times 10^{-5}$
(c) $Fe_2O_3(s) + 3 CO(g) \rightleftharpoons 2 Fe(s) + 3 CO_2(g)$ K (at 727 °C) = 24.2

PROBLEM 7.15

For the reaction $H_2(g) + I_2(g) \rightleftharpoons 2 HI(g)$, equilibrium concentrations at 25 °C are $[H_2] = 0.0510$ mol/L, $[I_2] = 0.174$ mol/L, and $[HI] = 0.507$ mol/L. What is the value of K at 25 °C?

KEY CONCEPT PROBLEM 7.16

The following diagrams represent two similar reactions that have achieved equilibrium:

   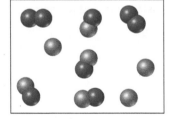

$$A_2 + B_2 \longrightarrow 2 AB \qquad\qquad A_2 + 2B \longrightarrow 2 AB$$

(a) Write the expression for the equilibrium constant for each reaction.
(b) Calculate the value for the equilibrium constant for each reaction.

7.9 Le Châtelier's Principle: The Effect of Changing Conditions on Equilibria

The effect of a change in reaction conditions on chemical equilibrium is predicted by a general rule called *Le Châtelier's principle*:

Le Châtelier's principle When a stress is applied to a system at equilibrium, the equilibrium shifts to relieve the stress.

The word "stress" in this context means any change in concentration, pressure, volume, or temperature that disturbs the original equilibrium and causes the rates of the forward and reverse reactions to become temporarily unequal.

We saw in Section 7.6 that reaction rates are affected by changes in temperature and concentration, and by addition of a catalyst. But what about equilibria? Are they similarly affected? The answer is that changes in concentration, temperature, and pressure *do* affect equilibria, but that addition of a catalyst does not (except to reduce the time it takes to reach equilibrium). The change caused by a catalyst affects forward and reverse reactions equally so that equilibrium concentrations are the same in both the presence and the absence of the catalyst.

Effect of Changes in Concentration

Let us look at the effect of a concentration change by considering the reaction of CO with H_2 to form CH_3OH (methanol). Once equilibrium is reached, the concentrations of the reactants and product are constant, and the forward and reverse reaction rates are equal.

$$CO(g) + 2 H_2(g) \rightleftharpoons CH_3OH(g)$$

What happens if the concentration of CO is increased? To relieve the "stress" of added CO, according to Le Châtelier's principle, the extra CO must be used up. In other words, the rate of the forward reaction must increase to consume CO. Think of the CO added on the left as "pushing" the equilibrium to the right:

$$\overset{[CO \longrightarrow]}{CO(g) + 2 H_2(g) \rightleftharpoons CH_3OH(g)}$$

Of course, as soon as more CH_3OH forms, the reverse reaction also speeds up, some CH_3OH converts back to CO and H_2. Ultimately, the forward and reverse reaction rates adjust until they are again equal, and equilibrium is reestablished. At this new equilibrium state, the value of $[H_2]$ is lower because some of the H_2 reacted with the added CO and the value of $[CH_3OH]$ is higher because CH_3OH formed as the reaction was driven to the right by the addition of CO. The changes offset each other, however, so that the value of the equilibrium constant K remains constant.

$$CO(g) + 2 H_2(g) \rightleftharpoons CH_3OH(g)$$

If this increases . . .   . . . then this decreases . . .   . . . and this increases . . .

. . . but this remains constant. $K = \dfrac{[CH_3OH]}{[CO][H_2]^2}$

What happens if CH_3OH is added to the reaction at equilibrium? Some of the methanol reacts to yield CO and H_2, making the values of $[CO]$, $[H_2]$, and $[CH_3OH]$ higher when equilibrium is reestablished. As before, the value of K does not change.

If this increases . . .

$$CO(g) + 2 H_2(g) \rightleftharpoons CH_3OH(g)$$

. . . then this increases . . .   . . . and this increases . . .

. . . but this remains constant. $K = \dfrac{[CH_3OH]}{[CO][H_2]^2}$

Alternatively, we can view chemical equilibrium as a *balance* between the free energy of the reactants (on the left) and the free energy of the products (on the right). Adding more reactants tips the balance in favor of the reactants. In order to restore the balance, reactants must be converted to products, or the reaction must shift to the right. If, instead, we remove reactants, then the balance is too heavy on the product side and the reaction must shift left, generating more reactants to restore balance.

▶ Equilibrium represents a balance between the free energy of reactants and products. Adding reactants (or products) to one side upsets the balance, and the reaction will proceed in a direction to restore the balance.

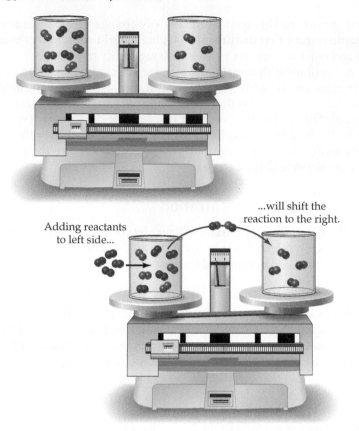

Adding reactants to left side...

...will shift the reaction to the right.

Finally, what happens if a reactant is continuously supplied or a product is continuously removed? Because the concentrations are continuously changing, equilibrium can never be reached. As a result, it is sometimes possible to force a reaction to produce large quantities of a desirable product even when the equilibrium constant is unfavorable. Take the reaction of acetic acid with ethanol to yield ethyl acetate, for example. As discussed in the preceding section, the equilibrium constant K for this reaction is 3.4, meaning that substantial amounts of reactants and products are both present at equilibrium. If, however, the ethyl acetate is removed as soon as it is formed, the production of more and more product is forced to occur, in accord with Le Châtelier's principle.

Continuously removing this product from the reaction forces more of it to be produced.

$$\underset{\text{Acetic acid}}{CH_3\overset{\overset{\displaystyle O}{\|}}{C}OH} + \underset{\text{Ethyl alcohol}}{CH_3CH_2OH} \rightleftharpoons \underset{\text{Ethyl acetate}}{CH_3\overset{\overset{\displaystyle O}{\|}}{C}OCH_2CH_3} + H_2O$$

Metabolic reactions sometimes take advantage of this effect, with one reaction prevented from reaching equilibrium by the continuous consumption of its product in a further reaction.

Effect of Changes in Temperature and Pressure

We noted in Section 7.2 that the reverse of an exothermic reaction is always endothermic. Equilibrium reactions are therefore exothermic in one direction and endothermic in the other. Le Châtelier's principle predicts that an increase in temperature will cause an equilibrium to shift in favor of the endothermic reaction so the additional heat is absorbed. Conversely, a decrease in temperature will cause an equilibrium to shift in favor of the exothermic reaction so additional heat is released. In other words, you can think of heat as a reactant or product whose increase or decrease stresses an equilibrium just as a change in reactant or product concentration does.

Endothermic reaction   Favored by increase in temperature
(Heat is absorbed)

Exothermic reaction   Favored by decrease in temperature
(Heat is released)

In the exothermic reaction of N_2 with H_2 to form NH_3, for example, raising the temperature favors the reverse reaction, which absorbs the heat:

$$[\xleftarrow{\hspace{4cm}} \text{Heat}]$$
$$N_2(g) \ + \ 3\,H_2(g) \ \rightleftharpoons \ 2\,NH_3(g) \ + \ \text{Heat}$$

We can also use the balance analogy to predict the effect of temperature on an equilibrium mixture; this time, we think of heat as a reactant or product. Increasing the temperature of the reaction is the same as adding heat to the left side (for an endothermic reaction) or to the right side (for an exothermic reaction). The reaction then proceeds in the appropriate direction to restore "balance" to the system.

What about changing the pressure? Pressure influences an equilibrium only if one or more of the substances involved is a gas. As predicted by Le Châtelier's principle, decreasing the volume to increase the pressure in such a reaction shifts the equilibrium in the direction that decreases the number of molecules in the gas phase and thus, decreases the pressure. For the ammonia synthesis, decreasing the volume *increases* the concentration of reactants and products, but has a greater effect on the reactant side of the equilibrium since there are more moles of gas phase reactants. Increasing the pressure, therefore, favors the forward reaction because 4 mol of gas is converted to 2 mol of gas.

$$[\text{Pressure} \xrightarrow{\hspace{2cm}}]$$
$$\underbrace{N_2(g) \ + \ 3\,H_2(g)}_{\text{4 mol of gas}} \ \rightleftharpoons \ \underbrace{2\,NH_3(g)}_{\text{2 mol of gas}}$$

The effects of changing reaction conditions on equilibria are summarized in Table 7.4

TABLE 7.4 Effects of Changes in Reaction Conditions on Equilibria

Change	Effect
Concentration	Increase in reactant concentration or decrease in product concentration favors forward reaction. Increase in product concentration or decrease in reactant concentration favors reverse reaction.
Temperature	Increase in temperature favors endothermic reaction. Decrease in temperature favors exothermic reaction.
Pressure	Increase in pressure favors side with fewer moles of gas. Decrease in pressure favors side with more moles of gas.
Catalyst added	Equilibrium reached more quickly; value of K unchanged.

LOOKING AHEAD ▶▶▶ In Chapter 20, we will see how Le Châtelier's principle is exploited to keep chemical "traffic" moving through the body's metabolic pathways. It often happens that one reaction in a series is prevented from reaching equilibrium because its product is continuously consumed in another reaction.

CHEMISTRY IN ACTION

Coupled Reactions

Living organisms are highly complex systems that use chemical reactions to produce the energy needed for daily activity. Many of these reactions occur very slowly—if at all—at normal body temperature, so organisms use several different strategies discussed in this chapter to obtain the energy they need and to function optimally. For example, the rates of slow reactions are increased by using biocatalysts, otherwise known as enzymes (Chapter 19). Le Châtelier's principle is used for regulation of critical processes, including oxygen transport (Chemistry in Action: Breathing and O_2 Transport, p. 263) and blood pH (Chemistry in Action: Buffers in the Body, p. 312). But what about reactions that do not occur spontaneously? One useful strategy is to "couple" a nonspontaneous reaction with a spontaneous one.

Coupling of reactions is a common strategy in both biochemical and industrial applications. Consider the following reaction for the recovery of copper metal from the smelting of ore containing Cu_2S:

$$Cu_2S(s) \longrightarrow 2\,Cu(s) + S(s) \quad \Delta G = +86.2\,kJ\,(+21.6\,kcal)$$

Since ΔG for this process is positive (endergonic), this reaction will not proceed spontaneously. But when the smelting process is performed at elevated temperatures in the presence of oxygen, this reaction can be "coupled" with another reaction:

$$Cu_2S(s) \longrightarrow 2\,Cu(s) + S(s) \quad \Delta G = +86.2\,kJ\,(+21.6\,kcal)$$
$$S(s) + O_2(g) \longrightarrow SO_2(g) \quad \Delta G = -300.1\,kJ\,(-71.7\,kcal)$$

Net Reaction: $Cu_2S(s) + O_2(g) \longrightarrow 2\,Cu(s) + SO_2(g)$
$$\Delta G = -213.9\,kJ\,(-51.1\,kcal)$$

The overall reaction has a negative ΔG (exergonic) to produce pure copper spontaneously.

Coupled Reactions in Biochemistry

An important example of coupled reactions in biochemistry is the endergonic phosphorylation of glucose (Section 22.6), which is the essential first step in the metabolism of glucose. It is combined with the hydrolysis of adenosine triphosphate (ATP) to form adenosine diphosphate (ADP), an exergonic process:

Glucose + $HOPO_3^{2-} \longrightarrow$ Glucose-6-phosphate + H_2O
$$\Delta G = +13.8\,kJ/mol$$
$ATP + H_2O \longrightarrow ADP + HOPO_3^{2-} + H^+ \quad \Delta G = -30.5\,kJ/mol$

Net Reaction: Glucose + ATP $\longrightarrow$ ADP + Glucose-6-phosphate
$$\Delta G = -16.7\,kJ/mol$$

In addition to the production of glucose-6-phosphate, which is critical for metabolic activity, any heat that is generated by the coupled reactions can be used to maintain body temperature.

See Chemistry in Action Problems 7.74 and 7.75 at the end of the chapter.

Worked Example **7.10** Le Châtelier's Principle and Equilibrium Mixtures

Nitrogen reacts with oxygen to give NO:

$$N_2(g) + O_2(g) \rightleftharpoons 2\,NO(g) \quad \Delta H = +43\,kcal/mol\,(+180\,kJ/mol)$$

Explain the effects of the following changes on reactant and product concentrations:

(a) Increasing temperature   **(b)** Increasing the concentration of NO
(c) Adding a catalyst

SOLUTION

(a) The reaction is endothermic (positive ΔH), so increasing the temperature favors the forward reaction. The concentration of NO will be higher at equilibrium.

(b) Increasing the concentration of NO, a product, favors the reverse reaction. At equilibrium, the concentrations of both N_2 and O_2, as well as that of NO, will be higher.

(c) A catalyst accelerates the rate at which equilibrium is reached, but the concentrations at equilibrium do not change.

PROBLEM 7.17

Is the yield of SO_3 at equilibrium favored by a higher or lower pressure? By a higher or lower temperature?

$$2\,SO_2(g) + O_2(g) \rightleftharpoons 2\,SO_3(g) \quad \Delta H = -47\,\text{kcal/mol}$$

PROBLEM 7.18

What effect do the listed changes have on the position of the equilibrium in the reaction of carbon with hydrogen?

$$C(s) + 2\,H_2(g) \rightleftharpoons CH_4(g) \quad \Delta H = -18\,\text{kcal/mol}\ (-75\,\text{kJ/mol})$$

(a) Increasing temperature
(b) Increasing pressure by decreasing volume
(c) Allowing CH_4 to escape continuously from the reaction vessel

PROBLEM 7.19

Another example of a coupled reaction used in the smelting of copper ore (Chemistry in Action: Coupled Reactions, p. 204) involves the following two reactions performed at 375 °C:

(1) $Cu_2O(s) \longrightarrow 2\,Cu(s) + \frac{1}{2}O_2(g) \quad \Delta G\ (\text{at }375\,°C) = +140.0\,\text{kJ}\ (+33.5\,\text{kcal})$
(2) $C(s) + \frac{1}{2}O_2(g) \longrightarrow CO(g) \quad \Delta G\ (\text{at }375\,°C) = -143.8\,\text{kJ}\ (-34.5\,\text{kcal})$

Derive the overall reaction and calculate the net free-energy change for the coupled reaction.

SUMMARY: REVISITING THE CHAPTER GOALS

1. What energy changes take place during reactions? The strength of a covalent bond is measured by its *bond dissociation energy*, the amount of energy that must be supplied to break the bond in an isolated gaseous molecule. For any reaction, the heat released or absorbed by changes in bonding is called the *heat of reaction*, or *enthalpy change* (ΔH). If the total strength of the bonds formed in a reaction is greater than the total strength of the bonds broken, then heat is released (negative ΔH) and the reaction is said to be *exothermic*. If the total strength of the bonds formed in a reaction is less than the total strength of the bonds broken, then heat is absorbed (positive ΔH) and the reaction is said to be *endothermic* (see Problems 26–33, 40, 62, 63, 70, 71, 76–78, 80, 81, 83, 85).

2. What is "free-energy," and what is the criterion for spontaneity in chemistry? *Spontaneous reactions* are those that, once started, continue without external influence; nonspontaneous reactions require a continuous external influence. Spontaneity depends on two factors, the amount of heat absorbed or released in a reaction (ΔH) and the *entropy change* (ΔS), which measures the change in molecular disorder in a reaction. Spontaneous reactions are favored by a release of heat (negative ΔH) and an increase in disorder (positive ΔS). The *free-energy change* (ΔG) takes both factors into account, according to the equation $\Delta G = \Delta H - T\Delta S$. A negative value for ΔG indicates spontaneity, and a positive value for ΔG indicates nonspontaneity (see Problems 20–22, 25, 34–43, 46, 50, 51, 73, 84).

3. What determines the rate of a chemical reaction? A chemical reaction occurs when reactant particles collide with proper orientation and sufficient energy. The exact amount of

collision energy necessary is called the *activation energy* (E_{act}). A high activation energy results in a slow reaction because few collisions occur with sufficient force, whereas a low activation energy results in a fast reaction. Reaction rates can be increased by raising the temperature, by raising the concentrations of reactants, or by adding a *catalyst*, which accelerates a reaction without itself undergoing any change (see Problems 23, 24, 44–51, 75).

4. What is chemical equilibrium? A reaction that can occur in either the forward or reverse direction is *reversible* and will ultimately reach a state of *chemical equilibrium*. At equilibrium, the forward and reverse reactions occur at the same rate, and the concentrations of reactants and products are constant. Every reversible reaction has a characteristic *equilibrium constant* (K), given by an *equilibrium equation* (see Problems 52–63, 78, 82).

For the reaction: $aA + bB + \cdots \rightleftharpoons mM + nN + \cdots$

Product concentrations raised to powers equal to coefficients

$$K = \frac{[M]^m[N]^n\cdots}{[A]^a[B]^b\cdots}$$

Reactant concentrations raised to powers equal to coefficients

5. What is Le Châtelier's principle? *Le Châtelier's principle* states that when a stress is applied to a system in equilibrium, the equilibrium shifts so that the stress is relieved. Applying this principle allows prediction of the effects of changes in temperature, pressure, and concentration (see Problems 62–69, 79, 82).

CONCEPT MAP: CHEMICAL REACTIONS: ENERGY, RATES, AND EQUILIBRIUM

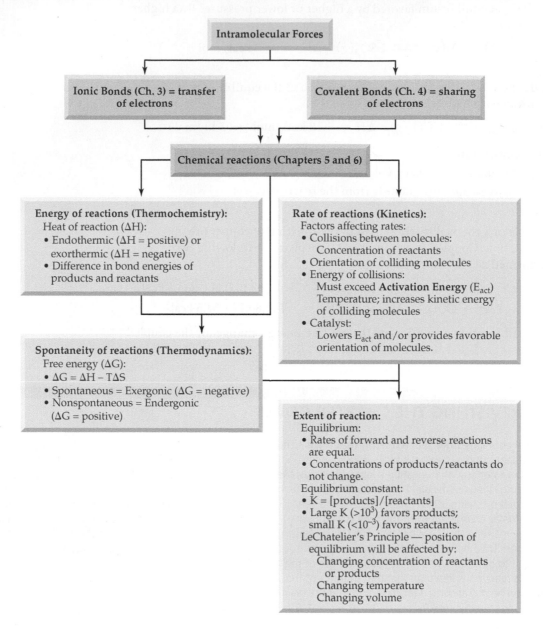

▶**Figure 7.7**

Concept Map: We discussed the fundamentals of chemical reactions in Chapters 5 and 6. In Chapter 7 we looked at the heats of reaction, rates of reaction, spontaneity of reactions, and the extent of reaction as indicated by the equilibrium constant, *K*. These concepts, and the connections between them and previous concepts, are shown here in Figure 7.7.

KEY WORDS

Activation energy (E_{act}), *p. 191*

Bond dissociation energy, *p. 180*

Catalyst, *p. 193*

Chemical equilibrium, *p. 196*

Concentration, *p. 193*

Endergonic, *p. 188*

Endothermic, *p. 180*

Enthalpy (*H*), *p. 181*

Enthalpy change (ΔH), *p. 181*

Entropy (*S*), *p. 187*

Entropy change (ΔS), *p. 187*

Equilibrium constant (*K*), *p. 197*

Exergonic, *p. 188*

Exothermic, *p. 180*

Free-energy change (ΔG), *p. 188*

Heat, *p. 179*

Heat of reaction, *p. 181*

Kinetic energy, *p. 179*

Law of conservation of energy, *p. 181*

Le Châtelier's principle, *p. 200*

Potential energy, *p. 179*

Reaction rate, *p. 191*

Reversible reaction, *p. 196*

Spontaneous process, *p. 186*

UNDERSTANDING KEY CONCEPTS

7.20 What are the signs of ΔH, ΔS, and ΔG for the spontaneous conversion of a crystalline solid into a gas? Explain.

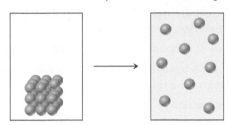

7.21 What are the signs of ΔH, ΔS, and ΔG for the spontaneous condensation of a vapor to a liquid? Explain.

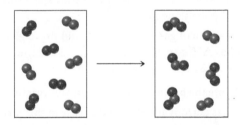

7.22 Consider the following spontaneous reaction of A_2 molecules (red) and B_2 molecules (blue):

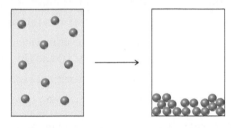

(a) Write a balanced equation for the reaction.

(b) What are the signs of ΔH, ΔS, and ΔG for the reaction? Explain.

7.23 Two curves are shown in the following energy diagram:

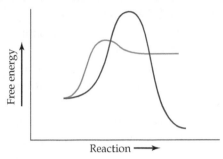

(a) Which curve represents the faster reaction, and which the slower?

(b) Which curve represents the spontaneous reaction, and which the nonspontaneous?

7.24 Draw energy diagrams for the following situations:

(a) A slow reaction with a large negative ΔG

(b) A fast reaction with a small positive ΔG

7.25 The following diagram portrays a reaction of the type $A(s) \longrightarrow B(g) + C(g)$, where the different colored spheres represent different molecular structures. Assume that the reaction has $\Delta H = +9.1$ kcal/mol ($+38.1$ kJ/mol).

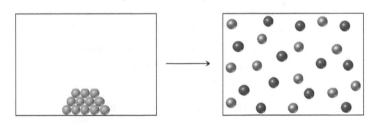

(a) What is the sign of ΔS for the reaction?

(b) Is the reaction likely to be spontaneous at all temperatures, nonspontaneous at all temperatures, or spontaneous at some but nonspontaneous at others?

ADDITIONAL PROBLEMS

ENTHALPY AND HEAT OF REACTION

7.26 Is the total enthalpy (H) of the reactants for an endothermic reaction greater than or less than the total enthalpy of the products?

7.27 What is meant by the term *heat of reaction*? What other name is a synonym for this term?

7.28 The vaporization of Br_2 from the liquid to the gas state requires 7.4 kcal/mol (31.0 kJ/mol).

(a) What is the sign of ΔH for this process? Write a reaction showing heat as a product or reactant.

(b) How many kilocalories are needed to vaporize 5.8 mol of Br_2?

(c) How many kilojoules are needed to evaporate 82 g of Br_2?

7.29 Converting liquid water to solid ice releases 1.44 kcal/mol (6.02 kJ/mol).

(a) What is the sign of ΔH for this process? Write a reaction showing heat as a product or reactant.

(b) How many kilojoules are released by freezing 2.5 mol of H_2O?

(c) How many kilocalories are released by freezing 32 g of H_2O?

(d) How many kilocalories are absorbed by melting 1 mol of ice?

7.30 Acetylene $(H-C\equiv C-H)$ is the fuel used in welding torches.

(a) Write the balanced chemical equation for the combustion reaction of 1 mol of acetylene with $O_2(g)$ to produce $CO_2(g)$ and water vapor.

(b) Estimate ΔH for this reaction (in kJ/mol) using the bond energies listed in Table 7.1

(c) Calculate the energy value (in kJ/g) for acetylene. How does it compare to the energy values for other fuels in Table 7.2?

7.31 Nitrogen in air reacts at high temperatures to form NO_2 according to the following reaction: $N_2 + 2\,O_2 \longrightarrow 2\,NO_2$

(a) Draw structures for the reactant and product molecules indicating single, double, and triple bonds.

(b) Estimate ΔH for this reaction (in kcal and kJ) using the bond energies from Table 7.1.

7.32 Glucose, also known as "blood sugar" when measured in blood, has the formula $C_6H_{12}O_6$.

(a) Write the equation for the combustion of glucose with O_2 to give CO_2 and H_2O.

(b) If 3.8 kcal (16 kJ) is released by combustion of each gram of glucose, how many kilocalories are released by the combustion of 1.50 mol of glucose? How many kilojoules?

(c) What is the minimum amount of energy (in kJ) a plant must absorb to produce 15.0 g of glucose?

7.33 During the combustion of 5.00 g of octane, C_8H_{18}, 239.5 kcal (1002 kJ) is released.

(a) Write a balanced equation for the combustion reaction.

(b) What is the sign of ΔH for this reaction?

(c) How much energy (in kJ) is released by the combustion of 1.00 mol of C_8H_{18}?

(d) How many grams and how many moles of octane must be burned to release 450.0 kcal?

(e) How many kilojoules are released by the combustion of 17.0 g of C_8H_{18}?

ENTROPY AND FREE ENERGY

7.34 Which of the following processes results in an increase in entropy of the system?

(a) A drop of ink spreading out when it is placed in water

(b) Steam condensing into drops on windows

(c) Constructing a building from loose bricks

7.35 For each of the following processes, specify whether entropy increases or decreases. Explain each of your answers.

(a) Assembling a jigsaw puzzle

(b) $I_2(s) + 3\,F_2(g) \longrightarrow 2\,IF_3(g)$

(c) A precipitate forming when two solutions are mixed

(d) $C_6H_{12}O_6(aq) + 6\,O_2(g) \longrightarrow 6\,CO_2(g) + 6\,H_2O(g)$

(e) $CaCO_3(s) \longrightarrow CaO(s) + CO_2(g)$

(f) $Pb(NO_3)_2(aq) + 2\,NaCl(aq) \longrightarrow$
$$PbCl_2(s) + 2\,NaNO_3(aq)$$

7.36 What two factors affect the spontaneity of a reaction?

7.37 What is the difference between an exothermic reaction and an exergonic reaction?

7.38 Why are most spontaneous reactions exothermic?

7.39 Under what conditions might a reaction be endothermic, but exergonic? Explain.

7.40 For the reaction
$$NaCl(s) \xrightarrow{Water} Na^+(aq) + Cl^-(aq),$$
$$\Delta H = +1.00\,\text{kcal/mol}\;(+4.184\,\text{kJ/mol})$$

(a) Is this process endothermic or exothermic?

(b) Does entropy increase or decrease in this process?

(c) Table salt (NaCl) readily dissolves in water. Explain, based on your answers to parts (a) and (b).

7.41 For the reaction $2\,Hg(l) + O_2(g) \longrightarrow 2\,HgO(s)$,
$$\Delta H = -43\,\text{kcal/mol}\;(-180\,\text{kJ/mol}).$$

(a) Does entropy increase or decrease in this process? Explain.

(b) Under what conditions would you expect this process to be spontaneous?

7.42 The reaction of gaseous H_2 and liquid Br_2 to give gaseous HBr has $\Delta H = -17.4\,\text{kcal/mol}\;(-72.8\,\text{kJ/mol})$ and $\Delta S = 27.2\,\text{cal/(mol}\cdot\text{K)}\,(114\,\text{J/(mol}\cdot\text{K)})$.

(a) Write the balanced equation for this reaction.

(b) Does entropy increase or decrease in this process?

(c) Is this process spontaneous at all temperatures? Explain.

(d) What is the value of ΔG (in kcal and kJ) for the reaction at 300 K?

7.43 The following reaction is used in the industrial synthesis of PVC polymer:
$$Cl_2(g) + H_2C=CH_2(g) \longrightarrow$$
$$ClCH_2CH_2Cl(l)\quad \Delta H = -52\,\text{kcal/mol}\;(-218\,\text{kJ/mol})$$

(a) Is ΔS positive or negative for this process?

(b) Is this process spontaneous at all temperatures? Explain.

RATES OF CHEMICAL REACTIONS

7.44 What is the activation energy of a reaction?

7.45 Which reaction is faster, one with $E_{act} = +10\,\text{kcal/mol}\;(+41.8\,\text{kJ/mol})$ or one with $E_{act} = +5\,\text{kcal/mol}\;(+20.9\,\text{kJ/mol})$? Explain.

7.46 Draw energy diagrams for exergonic reactions that meet the following descriptions:

(a) A slow reaction that has a small free-energy change

(b) A fast reaction that has a large free-energy change

7.47 Why does increasing concentration generally increase the rate of a reaction?

7.48 What is a catalyst, and what effect does it have on the activation energy of a reaction?

7.49 If a catalyst changes the activation energy of a forward reaction from 28.0 kcal/mol to 23.0 kcal/mol, what effect does it have on the reverse reaction?

7.50 For the reaction C(s, diamond) $\longrightarrow$ C(s, graphite),

$$\Delta G = -0.693 \text{ kcal/mol} (-2.90 \text{ kJ/mol}) \text{ at } 25 \text{ °C}.$$

(a) According to this information, do diamonds spontaneously turn into graphite?

(b) In light of your answer to part (a), why can diamonds be kept unchanged for thousands of years?

7.51 The reaction between hydrogen gas and carbon to produce the gas known as ethylene is

$$2 H_2(g) + 2 C(s) \longrightarrow H_2C=CH_2(g),$$
$$\Delta G = +16.3 \text{ kcal/mol} (+68.2 \text{ kJ/mol}) \text{ at } 25 \text{ °C}.$$

(a) Is this reaction spontaneous at 25 °C?

(b) Would it be reasonable to try to develop a catalyst for the reaction run at 25 °C? Explain.

CHEMICAL EQUILIBRIA

7.52 What is meant by the term "chemical equilibrium"? Must amounts of reactants and products be equal at equilibrium?

7.53 Why do catalysts not alter the amounts of reactants and products present at equilibrium?

7.54 Write the equilibrium constant expressions for the following reactions:

(a) $2 CO(g) + O_2(g) \rightleftharpoons 2 CO_2(g)$

(b) $Mg(s) + HCl(aq) \rightleftharpoons MgCl_2(aq) + H_2(g)$

(c) $HF(aq) + H_2O(l) \rightleftharpoons H_3O^+(aq) + F^-(aq)$

(d) $S(s) + O_2(g) \rightleftharpoons SO_2(g)$

7.55 Write the equilibrium constant expressions for the following reactions.

(a) $S_2(g) + 2 H_2(g) \rightleftharpoons 2 H_2S(g)$

(b) $H_2S(aq) + Cl_2(aq) \rightleftharpoons S(s) + 2 HCl(aq)$

(c) $Br_2(g) + Cl_2(g) \rightleftharpoons 2 BrCl(g)$

(d) $C(s) + H_2O(g) \rightleftharpoons CO(g) + H_2(g)$

7.56 For the reaction $N_2O_4(g) \rightleftharpoons 2 NO_2(g)$, the equilibrium concentrations at 25 °C are $[NO_2] = 0.0325 \text{ mol/L}$ and $[N_2O_4] = 0.147 \text{ mol/L}$.

(a) What is the value of K at 25 °C? Are reactants or products favored?

7.57 For the reaction $2 CO(g) + O_2(g) \rightleftharpoons 2 CO_2(g)$, the equilibrium concentrations at a certain temperature are $[CO_2] = 0.11 \text{ mol/L}$, $[O_2] = 0.015 \text{ mol/L}$, $[CO] = 0.025 \text{ mol/L}$.

(a) Write the equilibrium constant expression for the reaction.

(b) What is the value of K at this temperature? Are reactants or products favored?

7.58 Use your answer from Problem 7.56 to calculate the following:

(a) $[N_2O_4]$ at equilibrium when $[NO_2] = 0.0250 \text{ mol/L}$

(b) $[NO_2]$ at equilibrium when $[N_2O_4] = 0.0750 \text{ mol/L}$

7.59 Use your answer from Problem 7.57 to calculate the following:

(a) $[O_2]$ at equilibrium when $[CO_2] = 0.18 \text{ mol/L}$ and $[CO] = 0.0200 \text{ mol/L}$

(b) $[CO_2]$ at equilibrium when $[CO] = 0.080 \text{ mol/L}$ and $[O_2] = 0.520 \text{ mol/L}$

7.60 Would you expect to find relatively more reactants or more products for the reaction in Problem 7.56 if the pressure is raised? Explain.

7.61 Would you expect to find relatively more reactants or more products for the reaction in Problem 7.57 if the pressure is lowered?

LE CHÂTELIER'S PRINCIPLE

7.62 Oxygen can be converted into ozone by the action of lightning or electric sparks:

$$3 O_2(g) \rightleftharpoons 2 O_3(g)$$

For this reaction, $\Delta H = +68 \text{ kcal/mol} (+285 \text{ kJ/mol})$ and $K = 2.68 \times 10^{-29}$ at 25 °C.

(a) Is the reaction exothermic or endothermic?

(b) Are the reactants or the products favored at equilibrium?

(c) Explain the effect on the equilibrium of

(1) increasing pressure by decreasing volume.

(2) increasing the concentration of $O_2(g)$.

(3) increasing the concentration of $O_3(g)$.

(4) adding a catalyst.

(5) increasing the temperature.

7.63 Hydrogen chloride can be made from the reaction of chlorine and hydrogen:

$$Cl_2(g) + H_2(g) \longrightarrow 2 HCl(g)$$

For this reaction, $K = 26 \times 10^{33}$ and $\Delta H = -44 \text{ kcal/mol} (-184 \text{ kJ/mol})$ at 25 °C.

(a) Is the reaction endothermic or exothermic?

(b) Are the reactants or the products favored at equilibrium?

(c) Explain the effect on the equilibrium of

  (1) Increasing pressure by decreasing volume
  (2) Increasing the concentration of $HCl(g)$
  (3) Decreasing the concentration of $Cl_2(g)$
  (4) Increasing the concentration of $H_2(g)$
  (5) Adding a catalyst

7.64 When the following equilibria are disturbed by increasing the pressure, does the concentration of reaction products increase, decrease, or remain the same?

  (a) $2 CO_2(g) \rightleftharpoons 2 CO(g) + O_2(g)$
  (b) $N_2(g) + O_2(g) \rightleftharpoons 2 NO(g)$
  (c) $Si(s) + 2 Cl_2(g) \rightleftharpoons SiCl_4(g)$

7.65 For the following equilibria, use Le Châtelier's principle to predict the direction of the reaction when the pressure is increased by decreasing the volume of the equilibrium mixture.

  (a) $C(s) + H_2O(g) \rightleftharpoons CO(g) + H_2(g)$
  (b) $2 H_2(g) + O_2(g) \rightleftharpoons 2 H_2O(g)$
  (c) $2 Fe(s) + 3 H_2O(g) \rightleftharpoons Fe_2O_3(s) + 3 H_2(g)$

7.66 The reaction $CO(g) + H_2O(g) \rightleftharpoons CO_2(g) + H_2(g)$ has $\Delta H = -9.8$ kcal/mol $(-41$ kJ/mol$)$. Does the amount of H_2 in an equilibrium mixture increase or decrease when the temperature is decreased?

7.67 The reaction $3 O_2(g) \rightleftharpoons 2 O_3(g)$ has $\Delta H = +68$ kcal/mol $(+285$ kJ/mol$)$. Does the equilibrium constant for the reaction increase or decrease when the temperature increases?

7.68 The reaction $H_2(g) + I_2(g) \rightleftharpoons 2 HI(g)$ has $\Delta H = -2.2$ kcal/mol $(-9.2$kJ/mol$)$. Will the equilibrium concentration of HI increase or decrease when

  (a) I_2 is added?
  (b) H_2 is removed?
  (c) a catalyst is added?
  (d) the temperature is increased?

7.69 The reaction $Fe^{3+}(aq) + Cl^-(aq) \rightleftharpoons FeCl^{2+}(aq)$ is endothermic. How will the equilibrium concentration of $FeCl^{2+}$ change when

  (a) $Fe(NO_3)_3$ is added?
  (b) Cl^- is precipitated by addition of $AgNO_3$?
  (c) the temperature is increased?
  (d) a catalyst is added?

CHEMISTRY IN ACTION

7.70 Which provides more energy, 1 g of carbohydrate or 1 g of fat? [*Energy from Food, p. 185*]

7.71 How many Calories (that is, kilocalories) are in a 45.0 g serving of potato chips if we assume that they are essentially 50% carbohydrate and 50% fats? [*Energy from Food, p. 185*]

7.72 Which body organs help to regulate body temperature? [*Regulation of Body Temperature, p. 195*]

7.73 What is the purpose of blood vessel dilation? [*Regulation of Body Temperature, p. 195*]

7.74 The ATP required for the production of glucose-6-phosphate is regenerated by another coupled reaction:

$ADP + HOPO_3^{2-} \longrightarrow ATP + H_2O \quad \Delta G = +30.5$ kJ/mol

Phosphoenolpyruvate $+ H_2O \longrightarrow$ pyruvate $+ HOPO_3^{2-}$
$\Delta G = -61.9$ kJ/mol

Derive the net reaction and calculate ΔG for the coupled reaction. [*Coupled Reactions, p. 204*]

7.75 The coupling of reactions in the smelting of copper at elevated temperatures yields an overall reaction that is energetically favorable. Why is the use of elevated temperature not feasible for most living organisms, and what other strategies do they use to make reactions occur at normal body temperatures? [*Coupled Reactions, p. 204*]

GENERAL QUESTIONS AND PROBLEMS

7.76 For the unbalanced combustion reaction shown below, 1 mol of ethanol, C_2H_5OH, releases 327 kcal (1370 kJ).

$$C_2H_5OH + O_2 \longrightarrow CO_2 + H_2O$$

  (a) Write a balanced equation for the combustion reaction.
  (b) What is the sign of ΔH for this reaction?
  (c) How much heat (in kilocalories) is released from the combustion of 5.00 g of ethanol?
  (d) How many grams of C_2H_5OH must be burned to raise the temperature of 500.0 mL of water from 20.0 °C to 100.0 °C? (The specific heat of water is 1.00 cal/g·°C or 4.184 J/g·°C. See Section 1.13.)
  (e) If the density of ethanol is 0.789 g/mL, calculate the combustion energy of ethanol in kilocalories/milliliter and kilojoules/milliliter

7.77 For the production of ammonia from its elements, $\Delta H = -22$ kcal/mol $(-92$ kJ/mol$)$.

  (a) Is this process endothermic or exothermic?
  (b) How much energy (in kilocalories and kilojoules) is involved in the production of 0.700 mol of NH_3?

7.78 Magnetite, an iron ore with formula Fe_3O_4, can be reduced by treatment with hydrogen to yield iron metal and water vapor.

  (a) Write the balanced equation.
  (b) This process requires 36 kcal (151 kJ) for every 1.00 mol of Fe_3O_4 reduced. How much energy (in kilocalories and kilojoules) is required to produce 55 g of iron?
  (c) How many grams of hydrogen are needed to produce 75 g of iron?
  (d) This reaction has $K = 2.3 \times 10^{-18}$. Are the reactants or the products favored?

7.79 Hemoglobin (Hb) reacts reversibly with O_2 to form HbO_2, a substance that transfers oxygen to tissues:

$$Hb(aq) + O_2(aq) \rightleftharpoons HbO_2(aq)$$

Carbon monoxide (CO) is attracted to Hb 140 times more strongly than O_2 and establishes another equilibrium.

(a) Explain, using Le Châtelier's principle, why inhalation of CO can cause weakening and eventual death.

(b) Still another equilibrium is established when both O_2 and CO are present:

$$Hb(CO)(aq) + O_2(aq) \rightleftharpoons HbO_2(aq) + CO(aq)$$

Explain, using Le Châtelier's principle, why pure oxygen is often administered to victims of CO poisoning.

7.80 Urea is a metabolic waste product that decomposes to ammonia and water according to the following reaction:

$$NH_2CONH_2 + H_2O \longrightarrow 2\,NH_3 + CO_2.$$

(a) Draw the Lewis structure for urea.

(b) Estimate ΔH (in kcal and kJ) for this reaction using the bond energies from Table 7.1.

7.81 For the evaporation of water, $H_2O(l) \longrightarrow H_2O(g)$, at $100\,°C$, $\Delta H = +9.72\,kcal/mol$ ($+40.7\,kJ/mol$).

(a) How many kilocalories are needed to vaporize 10.0 g of $H_2O(l)$?

(b) How many kilojoules are released when 10.0 g of $H_2O(g)$ is condensed?

7.82 Ammonia reacts slowly in air to produce nitrogen monoxide and water vapor:

$$NH_3(g) + O_2(g) \rightleftharpoons NO(g) + H_2O(g) + Heat$$

(a) Balance the equation.

(b) Write the equilibrium equation.

(c) Explain the effect on the equilibrium of

(1) raising the pressure.
(2) adding $NO(g)$.
(3) decreasing the concentration of NH_3.
(4) lowering the temperature.

7.83 Methanol, CH_3OH, is used as race car fuel.

(a) Write the balanced equation for the combustion reaction of methanol with O_2 to form CO_2 and H_2O.

(b) $\Delta H = -174\,kcal/mol$ ($-728\,kJ/mol$) methanol for the process. How many kilocalories are released by burning 1.85 mol of methanol?

(c) How many kilojoules are released by burning 50.0 g of methanol?

7.84 Sketch an energy diagram for a system in which the forward reaction has $E_{act} = +25\,kcal/mol$ ($+105\,kJ/mol$) and the reverse reaction has $E_{act} = +35\,kcal/mol$ ($+146\,kJ/mol$).

(a) Is the forward process endergonic or exergonic?

(b) What is the value of ΔG for the reaction?

7.85 The thermite reaction (photograph, p. 181), in which aluminum metal reacts with iron(III) oxide to produce a spectacular display of sparks, is so exothermic that the product (iron) is in the molten state:

$$2\,Al(s) + Fe_2O_3(s) \longrightarrow 2\,Al_2O_3(s) + 2\,Fe(l)$$
$$\Delta H = -202.9\,kcal/mol\ (-848.9\,kJ/mol)$$

(a) How much heat is released (in kilojoules) when 0.255 mol of Al is used in this reaction?

(b) How much heat (in kilocalories) is released when 5.00 g of Al is used in the reaction?

7.86 How much heat (in kilocalories) is evolved or absorbed in the reaction of 1.00 g of Na with H_2O? Is the reaction exothermic or endothermic?

$$2\,Na(s) + 2\,H_2O(l) \longrightarrow 2\,NaOH(aq) + H_2(g)$$
$$\Delta H = -88.0\,kcal/mol\ (-368\,kJ/mol)$$

CHAPTER 8

Gases, Liquids, and Solids

CONTENTS

◀ This winter scene in Yellowstone National Park shows the three states of matter for water—solid (snow/ice), liquid (water), and gas (steam/water vapor)—all present at the same time.

The previous seven chapters dealt with matter at the atomic level. We have seen that all matter is composed of atoms, ions, or molecules; that these particles are in constant motion; that atoms combine to make compounds using chemical bonds; and that physical and chemical changes are accompanied by the release or absorption of energy. Now it is time to look at a different aspect of matter, concentrating not on the properties and small-scale behavior of individual atoms but on the properties and large-scale behavior of visible amounts of matter and the factors that affect those properties.

8.1 States of Matter and Their Changes

Matter exists in any of three phases, or *states*—solid, liquid, or gas. The state in which a compound exists under a given set of conditions depends on the relative strength of the attractive forces between particles compared to the kinetic energy of the particles. Kinetic energy (Section 7.1) is energy associated with motion and is related to the temperature of the substance. In gases, the attractive forces between particles are very weak compared to their kinetic energy, so the particles move about freely, are far apart, and have almost no influence on one another. In liquids, the attractive forces between particles are stronger, pulling the particles close together but still allowing them considerable freedom to move about. In solids, the attractive forces are much stronger than the kinetic energy of the particles, so the atoms, molecules, or ions are held in a specific arrangement and can only wiggle around in place (Figure 8.1).

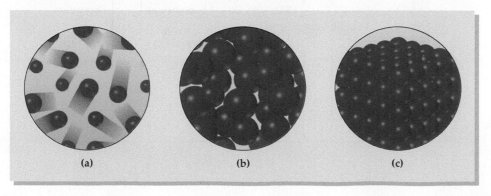

(a)   (b)   (c)

◀ **Figure 8.1**
A molecular comparison of gases, liquids, and solids.
(a) In gases, the particles feel little attraction for one another and are free to move about randomly. (b) In liquids, the particles are held close together by attractive forces but are free to slide over one another. (c) In solids, the particles are strongly attracted to one another. They can move slightly, but are held in a fairly rigid arrangement with respect to one another.

Change of state The change of a substance from one state of matter (gas, liquid, or solid) to another.

▶▶▶ You might want to reread Section 7.4 to brush up on these concepts.

The transformation of a substance from one state to another is called a *phase change*, or a **change of state**. Every change of state is reversible and, like all chemical and physical processes, is characterized by a free-energy change, ΔG. A change of state that is spontaneous in one direction (exergonic, negative ΔG) is nonspontaneous in the other direction (endergonic, positive ΔG). As always, the free-energy change ΔG has both an enthalpy term ΔH and a temperature-dependent entropy term ΔS, according to the equation $\Delta G = \Delta H - T\Delta S$.

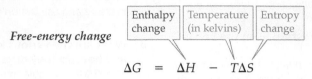

Free-energy change

$$\Delta G = \Delta H - T\Delta S$$

The enthalpy change ΔH is a measure of the heat absorbed or released during a given change of state. In the melting of a solid to a liquid, for example, heat is absorbed and ΔH is positive (endothermic). In the reverse process—the freezing of a liquid to a solid—heat is released and ΔH is negative (exothermic). Look at the change between ice and water for instance:

Melting: $H_2O(s) \longrightarrow H_2O(l)$ $\Delta H = +1.44$ kcal/mol or $+6.02$ kJ/mol
Freezing: $H_2O(l) \longrightarrow H_2O(s)$ $\Delta H = -1.44$ kcal/mol or -6.02 kJ/mol

The entropy change ΔS is a measure of the change in molecular disorder or freedom that occurs during a process. In the melting of a solid to a liquid, for example, disorder increases because particles gain freedom of motion, so ΔS is positive. In the reverse process—the freezing of a liquid to a solid—disorder decreases as particles are locked into position, so ΔS is negative. Look at the change between ice and water:

Melting: $H_2O(s) \longrightarrow H_2O(l)$ $\Delta S = +5.26$ cal/(mol·K) or $+22.0$ J/(mol·K)
Freezing: $H_2O(l) \longrightarrow H_2O(s)$ $\Delta S = -5.26$ cal/(mol·K) or -22.0 J/(mol·K)

As with all processes that are unfavored by one term in the free-energy equation but favored by the other, the sign of ΔG depends on the temperature (Section 7.4). The melting of ice, for instance, is unfavored by a positive ΔH but favored by a positive ΔS. Thus, at a low temperature, the unfavorable ΔH is larger than the favorable $T\Delta S$, so ΔG is positive and no melting occurs. At a higher temperature, however, $T\Delta S$ becomes larger than ΔH, so ΔG is negative and melting *does* occur. The exact temperature at

▶ **Figure 8.2**
Changes of state.
The changes are endothermic from bottom to top and exothermic from top to bottom. Solid and liquid states are in equilibrium at the melting point; liquid and gas states are in equilibrium at the boiling point.

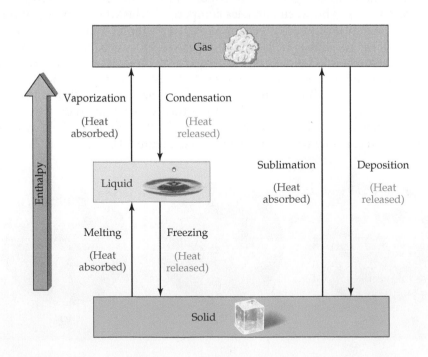

which the changeover in behavior occurs is called the **melting point (mp)** and represents the temperature at which solid and liquid coexist in equilibrium. In the corresponding change from a liquid to a gas, the two states are in equilibrium at the **boiling point (bp)**.

The names and enthalpy changes associated with the different changes of state are summarized in Figure 8.2. Note that a solid can change directly to a gas without going through the liquid state—a process called *sublimation*. Dry ice (solid CO_2) at atmospheric pressure, for example, changes directly to a gas without melting.

Melting point (mp) The temperature at which solid and liquid are in equilibrium.

Boiling point (bp) The temperature at which liquid and gas are in equilibrium.

Worked Example 8.1 Change of State: Enthalpy, Entropy, and Free Energy

The change of state from liquid to gas for chloroform, formerly used as an anesthetic, has $\Delta H = +6.98$ kcal/mol $(+29.2$ kJ/mol$)$ and a $\Delta S = +20.9$ cal/(mol $\cdot$ K) $[+87.4$ J/(mol $\cdot$ K)$]$.

(a) Is the change of state from liquid to gas favored or unfavored by ΔH? by ΔS?

(b) Is the change of state from liquid to gas favored or unfavored at 35 °C?

(c) Is this change of state spontaneous at 65 °C?

ANALYSIS A process will be favored if energy is released $(\Delta H =$ negative$)$ and if there is a decrease in disorder $(\Delta S =$ positive$)$. In cases in which one factor is favorable and the other is unfavorable, then we can calculate the free-energy change to determine if the process is favored:

$$\Delta G = \Delta H - T\Delta S$$

When ΔG is negative, the process is favored.

SOLUTION

(a) The ΔH does NOT favor this change of state $(\Delta H =$ positive$)$, but the ΔS does favor the process. Since the two factors are not in agreement, we must use the equation for free-energy change to determine if the process is favored at a given temperature.

(b) Substituting the values for ΔH and ΔS into the equation for free-energy change we can determine if ΔG is positive or negative at 35 °C (308 K). Note that we must first convert degrees celsius to kelvins and convert the ΔS from cal to kcal so the units can be added together.

$$\Delta G = \Delta H - T\Delta S = \left(\frac{6.98 \text{ kcal}}{\text{mol}}\right) - (308 \text{ K})\left(\frac{20.9 \text{ cal}}{\text{mol} \cdot \text{K}}\right)\left(\frac{1 \text{ kcal}}{1000 \text{ cal}}\right)$$

$$= 6.98 \frac{\text{kcal}}{\text{mol}} - 6.44 \frac{\text{kcal}}{\text{mol}} = +0.54 \frac{\text{kcal}}{\text{mol}}$$

$$\left(+0.54 \frac{\text{kcal}}{\text{mol}}\right)\left(\frac{4.184 \text{ kJ}}{\text{kcal}}\right) = +2.26 \frac{\text{kJ}}{\text{mol}}$$

Since the $\Delta G =$ positive, this change of state is not favored at 35 °C.

(c) Repeating the calculation using the equation for free-energy change at 65 °C (338 K):

$$\Delta G = \Delta H - T\Delta S = \left(\frac{6.98 \text{ kcal}}{\text{mol}}\right) - (338 \text{ K})\left(\frac{20.9 \text{ cal}}{\text{mol} \cdot \text{K}}\right)\left(\frac{1 \text{ kcal}}{1000 \text{ cal}}\right)$$

$$= 6.98 \frac{\text{kcal}}{\text{mol}} - 7.06 \frac{\text{kcal}}{\text{mol}} = -0.08 \frac{\text{kcal}}{\text{mol}} \left(\text{or } -0.33 \frac{\text{kJ}}{\text{mol}}\right)$$

Because ΔG is negative in this case, the change of state is favored at this temperature.

> **PROBLEM 8.1**
> The change of state from liquid H_2O to gaseous H_2O has $\Delta H = +9.72$ kcal/mol $(+40.7$ kJ/mol$)$ and $\Delta S = 26.1$ cal/$(\text{mol} \cdot \text{K})$ $[109$ J/$(\text{mol} \cdot \text{K})]$.
> **(a)** Is the change from liquid to gaseous H_2O favored or unfavored by ΔH? By ΔS?
> **(b)** What is the value of ΔG (in kcal/mol and kJ/mol) for the change from liquid to gaseous H_2O at 373 K?
> **(c)** What are the values of ΔH and ΔS (in kcal/mol and kJ/mol) for the change from gaseous to liquid H_2O?

8.2 Intermolecular Forces

What determines whether a substance is a gas, a liquid, or a solid at a given temperature? Why does rubbing alcohol evaporate much more readily than water? Why do molecular compounds have lower melting points than ionic compounds? To answer these and a great many other such questions, we need to look into the nature of **intermolecular forces**—the forces that act *between different molecules* rather than within an individual molecule.

In gases, the intermolecular forces are negligible, so the gas molecules act independently of one another. In liquids and solids, however, intermolecular forces are strong enough to hold the molecules in close contact. As a general rule, the stronger the intermolecular forces in a substance, the more difficult it is to separate the molecules, and the higher the melting and boiling points of the substance.

There are three major types of intermolecular forces: *dipole–dipole, London dispersion*, and *hydrogen bonding*. We will discuss each in turn.

Dipole–Dipole Forces

Many molecules contain polar covalent bonds and may therefore have a net molecular polarity. In such cases, the positive and negative ends of different molecules are attracted to one another by what is called a **dipole–dipole force** (Figure 8.3).

Dipole–dipole forces are weak, with strengths on the order of 1 kcal/mol (4 kJ/mol) compared to the 70–100 kcal/mol (300–400 kJ/mol) typically found for the strength of a covalent bond (see Table 7.1). Nevertheless, the effects of dipole–dipole forces are important, as can be seen by looking at the difference in boiling points between polar and nonpolar molecules. Butane, for instance, is a nonpolar molecule with a molecular weight of 58 amu and a boiling point of –0.5 °C, whereas acetone has the same molecular weight yet boils 57 °C higher because it is polar.

Intermolecular force A force that acts between molecules and holds molecules close to one another.

▶▶▶ Recall from Sections 4.9 and 4.10 that a polar covalent bond is one in which the electrons are attracted more strongly by one atom than by the other.

Dipole–dipole force The attractive force between positive and negative ends of polar molecules.

▶▶▶ Recall from Section 4.9 how molecular polarities can be visualized using electrostatic potential maps.

▲ **Figure 8.3**
Dipole–dipole forces.
The positive and negative ends of polar molecules are attracted to one another by dipole–dipole forces. As a result, polar molecules have higher boiling points than nonpolar molecules of similar size.

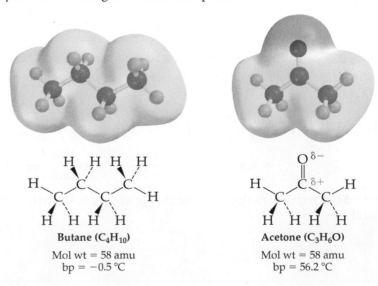

Butane (C_4H_{10})
Mol wt = 58 amu
bp = –0.5 °C

Acetone (C_3H_6O)
Mol wt = 58 amu
bp = 56.2 °C

London Dispersion Forces

Only polar molecules experience dipole–dipole forces, but all molecules, regardless of structure, experience *London dispersion forces*. **London dispersion forces** are caused by the constant motion of electrons within molecules. Take even a simple nonpolar molecule like Br_2, for example. Averaged over time, the distribution of electrons throughout the molecule is uniform, but at any given *instant* there may be more electrons at one end of the molecule than at the other (Figure 8.4). At that instant, the molecule has a short-lived polarity. Electrons in neighboring molecules are attracted to the positive end of the polarized molecule, resulting in a polarization of the neighbor and creation of an attractive London dispersion force that holds the molecules together. As a result, Br_2 is a liquid at room temperature rather than a gas.

London dispersion force The short-lived attractive force due to the constant motion of electrons within molecules.

$\delta-$ $\qquad$ $\delta+$ $\delta-$ $\qquad$ $\delta+$

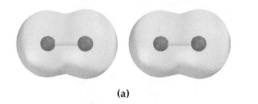

(a) $\qquad\qquad\qquad\qquad$ (b)

◄ **Figure 8.4**
(a) Averaged over time, the electron distribution in a Br_2 molecule is symmetrical. (b) At any given instant, however, the electron distribution may be unsymmetrical, resulting in a temporary polarity that induces a complementary polarity in neighboring molecules.

London dispersion forces are weak—in the range 0.5–2.5 kcal/mol (2–10 kJ/mol)—but they increase with molecular weight and amount of surface area available for interaction between molecules. The larger the molecular weight, the more electrons there are moving about and the greater the temporary polarization of a molecule. The larger the amount of surface contact, the greater the close interaction between different molecules.

The effect of surface area on the magnitude of London dispersion forces can be seen by comparing a roughly spherical molecule with a flatter, more linear one having the same molecular weight. Both 2,2-dimethylpropane and pentane, for instance, have the same formula (C_5H_{12}), but the nearly spherical shape of 2,2-dimethylpropane allows for less surface contact with neighboring molecules than does the more linear shape of pentane (Figure 8.5). As a result, London dispersion forces are smaller for 2,2-dimethylpropane, molecules are held together less tightly, and the boiling point is correspondingly lower: 9.5 °C for 2,2-dimethylpropane versus 36 °C for pentane.

◄ **Figure 8.5**
London dispersion forces.
More compact molecules like 2,2-dimethylpropane have smaller surface areas, weaker London dispersion forces, and lower boiling points. By comparison, flatter, less compact molecules like pentane have larger surface areas, stronger London dispersion forces, and higher boiling points.

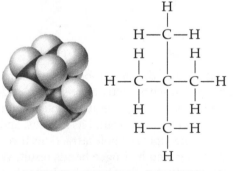

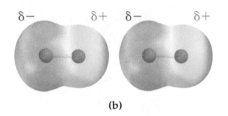

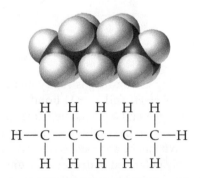

(a) 2,2-Dimethylpropane (bp = 9.5 °C) $\qquad\qquad$ (b) Pentane (bp = 36 °C)

Hydrogen Bonds

In many ways, hydrogen bonding is responsible for life on earth. It causes water to be a liquid rather than a gas at ordinary temperatures, and it is the primary intermolecular force that holds huge biomolecules in the shapes needed to play their essential roles in biochemistry. Deoxyribonucleic acid (DNA) and keratin (Figure 8.6), for instance, are long molecular chains that form a α-helix, held in place largely due to hydrogen bonding.

A **hydrogen bond** is an attractive interaction between an unshared electron pair on an electronegative O, N, or F atom and a positively polarized hydrogen atom bonded to

Hydrogen bond The attraction between a hydrogen atom bonded to an electronegative O, N, or F atom and another nearby electronegative O, N, or F atom.

▶ **Figure 8.6**
The α-helical structure of keratin results from hydrogen bonding along the amino acid backbone of the molecule. Hydrogen bonding is represented by gray dots in the ball and stick model on the left and red dots in the molecular structure on the right.

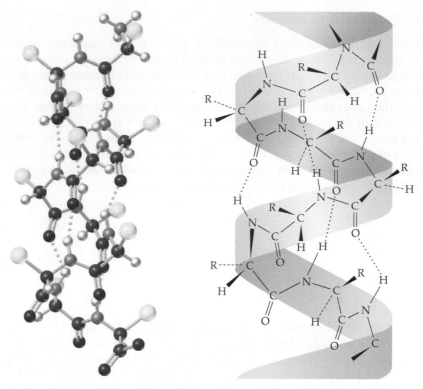

another electronegative O, N, or F. For example, hydrogen bonds occur in both water and ammonia:

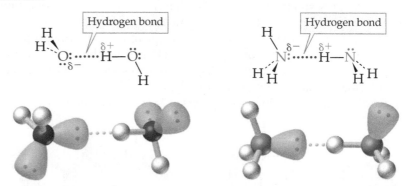

Hydrogen bonding is really just a special kind of dipole–dipole interaction. The O—H, N—H, and F—H bonds are highly polar, with a partial positive charge on the hydrogen and a partial negative charge on the electronegative atom. In addition, the hydrogen atom has no inner-shell electrons to act as a shield around its nucleus, and it is small, so it can be approached closely. As a result, the dipole–dipole attractions involving positively polarized hydrogens are unusually strong, and hydrogen bonds result. Water, in particular, is able to form a vast three-dimensional network of hydrogen bonds because each H_2O molecule has two hydrogens and two electron pairs (Figure 8.7).

▶ **Figure 8.7**
Hydrogen bonding in water.
The intermolecular attraction in water is especially strong because each oxygen atom has two lone pairs and two hydrogen atoms, allowing the formation of as many as four hydrogen bonds per molecule. Individual hydrogen bonds are constantly being formed and broken.

Hydrogen bonds can be quite strong, with energies up to 10 kcal/mol (40 kJ/mol). To see the effect of hydrogen bonding, look at Table 8.1, which compares the boiling points of binary hydrogen compounds of second-row elements with their third-row counterparts. Because NH_3, H_2O, and HF molecules are held tightly together by hydrogen bonds, an unusually large amount of energy must be added to separate them in the boiling process. As a result, the boiling points of NH_3, H_2O, and HF are much higher than the boiling points of their second-row neighbor CH_4 and of related third-row compounds.

TABLE 8.1 Boiling Points for Binary Hydrogen Compounds of Some Second-row and Third-row Elements

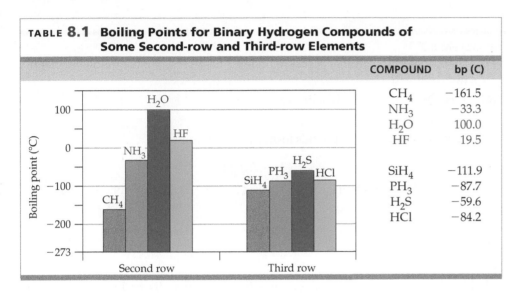

COMPOUND	bp (C)
CH_4	−161.5
NH_3	−33.3
H_2O	100.0
HF	19.5
SiH_4	−111.9
PH_3	−87.7
H_2S	−59.6
HCl	−84.2

A summary and comparison of the various kinds of intermolecular forces is shown in Table 8.2.

TABLE 8.2 A Comparison of Intermolecular Forces

Force	Strength	Characteristics
Dipole–dipole	Weak (1 kcal/mol, 4 kJ/mol))	Occurs between polar molecules
London dispersion	Weak (0.5–2.5 kcal/mol, 2–10 kJ/mol)	Occurs between all molecules; strength depends on size
Hydrogen bond	Moderate (2–10 kcal/mol, 8–40 kJ/mol)	Occurs between molecules with O—H, N—H, and F—H bonds

LOOKING AHEAD ▶▶▶ Dipole–dipole forces, London dispersion forces, and hydrogen bonds are traditionally called "intermolecular forces" because of their influence on the properties of molecular compounds. But these same forces can also operate between different parts of a very large molecule. In this context, they are often referred to as "noncovalent interactions." In later chapters, we will see how noncovalent interactions determine the shapes of biologically important molecules such as proteins and nucleic acids.

Worked Example 8.2 Identifying Intermolecular Forces: Polar versus Nonpolar

Identify the intermolecular forces that influence the properties of the following compounds:

(a) Methane, CH_4 (b) HCl   (c) CH_3COOH

ANALYSIS The intermolecular forces will depend on the molecular structure, what type of bonds are in the molecule (polar or non-polar), and how the bonds are arranged.

SOLUTION

(a) Since methane contains only C—H bonds, it is a nonpolar molecule; it has only London dispersion forces.

(b) The H—Cl bond is polar, so this is a polar molecule; it has both dipole–dipole forces and London dispersion forces.

(c) Acetic acid is a polar molecule with an O—H bond. Thus, it has dipole–dipole forces, London dispersion forces, and hydrogen bonds.

PROBLEM 8.2

Would you expect the boiling points to increase or decrease in the following series? Explain.

(a) Kr, Ar, Ne   (b) Cl_2, Br_2, I_2

PROBLEM 8.3

Which of the following compounds form hydrogen bonds?

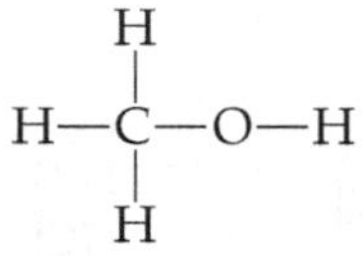

Methyl alcohol   Ethylene   Methylamine
      (a)   (b)   (c)

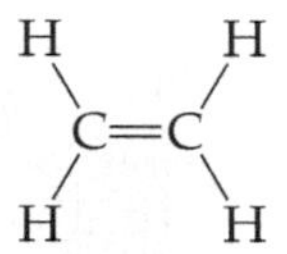

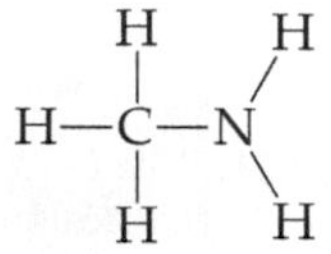

PROBLEM 8.4

Identify the intermolecular forces (dipole–dipole, London dispersion, hydrogen bonding) that influence the properties of the following compounds:

(a) Ethane, CH_3CH_3

(b) Ethyl alcohol, CH_3CH_2OH

(c) Ethyl chloride, CH_3CH_2Cl

8.3 Gases and the Kinetic–Molecular Theory

Gases behave quite differently from liquids and solids. Gases, for instance, have low densities and are easily compressed to a smaller volume when placed under pressure, a property that allows them to be stored in large tanks. Liquids and solids, by contrast, are much more dense and much less compressible. Furthermore, gases undergo a far larger expansion or contraction when their temperature is changed than do liquids and solids.

The behavior of gases can be explained by a group of assumptions known as the **kinetic–molecular theory of gases**. We will see in the next several sections how the following assumptions account for the observable properties of gases:

Kinetic–molecular theory of gases A group of assumptions that explain the behavior of gases.

- **A gas consists of many particles, either atoms or molecules, moving about at random with no attractive forces between them.** Because of this random motion, different gases mix together quickly.
- **The amount of space occupied by the gas particles themselves is much smaller than the amount of space between particles.** Most of the volume taken up by gases is empty space, accounting for the ease of compression and low densities of gases.
- **The average kinetic energy of gas particles is proportional to the Kelvin temperature.** Thus, gas particles have more kinetic energy and move faster as the temperature increases. (In fact, gas particles move much faster than you might suspect. The average speed of a helium atom at room temperature and atmospheric pressure is approximately 1.36 km/s, or 3000 mi/hr, nearly that of a rifle bullet.)

- **Collisions of gas particles, either with other particles or with the wall of their container, are elastic; that is, the total kinetic energy of the particles is constant.** The pressure of a gas against the walls of its container is the result of collisions of the gas particles with the walls. The more collisions and the more forceful each collision, the higher the pressure.

A gas that obeys all the assumptions of the kinetic–molecular theory is called an **ideal gas**. In practice, though, there is no such thing as a perfectly ideal gas. All gases behave somewhat differently than predicted when, at very high pressures or very low temperatures, their particles get closer together and interactions between particles become significant. As a rule, however, most real gases display nearly ideal behavior under normal conditions.

8.4 Pressure

We are all familiar with the effects of air pressure. When you fly in an airplane, the change in air pressure against your eardrums as the plane climbs or descends can cause a painful "popping." When you pump up a bicycle tire, you increase the pressure of air against the inside walls of the tire until the tire feels hard.

In scientific terms, **pressure** (P) is defined as a force (F) per unit area (A) pushing against a surface; that is, $P = F/A$. In the bicycle tire, for example, the pressure you feel is the force of air molecules colliding with the inside walls of the tire. The units you probably use for tire pressure are pounds per square inch (psi), where 1 psi is equal to the pressure exerted by a 1-pound object resting on a 1-square inch surface.

We on earth are under pressure from the atmosphere, the blanket of air pressing down on us (Figure 8.8). Atmospheric pressure is not constant, however; it varies slightly from day to day depending on the weather, and it also varies with altitude. Due to gravitational forces, the density of air is greatest at the earth's surface and decreases with increasing altitude. As a result, air pressure is greatest at the surface: it is about 14.7 psi at sea level but only about 4.7 psi on the summit of Mt. Everest.

One of the most commonly used units of pressure is the *millimeter of mercury*, abbreviated *mmHg* and often called a *torr* (after the Italian physicist Evangelista Torricelli). This unusual unit dates back to the early 1600s when Torricelli made the first mercury *barometer*. As shown in Figure 8.9, a barometer consists of a long, thin tube that is sealed at one end, filled with mercury, and then inverted into a dish of mercury. Some mercury runs from the tube into the dish until the downward pressure of the mercury in the column is exactly balanced by the outside atmospheric pressure, which presses down on the mercury in the dish and pushes it up into the column. The height of the mercury column varies depending on the altitude and weather conditions, but standard atmospheric pressure at sea level is defined to be exactly 760 mm.

Gas pressure inside a container is often measured using an open-ended *manometer*, a simple instrument similar in principle to the mercury barometer. As shown in Figure 8.10, an open-ended manometer consists of a U-tube filled with mercury, with one end connected to a gas-filled container and the other end open to the atmosphere. The difference between the heights of the mercury levels in the two arms of the U-tube indicates the difference between the pressure of the gas in the container and the pressure of the atmosphere. If the gas pressure inside the container is less than atmospheric, the mercury level is higher in the arm connected to the container (Figure 8.10a). If the gas pressure inside the container is greater than atmospheric, the mercury level is higher in the arm open to the atmosphere (Figure 8.10b).

Pressure is given in the SI system (Section 2.1) by a unit named the *pascal* (Pa), where 1 Pa = 0.007500 mmHg (or 1 mmHg = 133.32 Pa). Measurements in pascals are becoming more common, and many clinical laboratories have made the switchover. Higher pressures are often still given in *atmospheres* (atm), where 1 atm = 760 mmHg exactly.

Pressure units: 1 atm = 760 mmHg = 14.7 psi = 101,325 Pa
1 mmHg = 1 torr = 133.32 Pa

Ideal gas A gas that obeys all the assumptions of the kinetic–molecular theory.

Pressure (*P*) The force per unit area pushing against a surface.

▲ **Figure 8.8**
Atmospheric pressure.
A column of air weighing 14.7 lb presses down on each square inch of the earth's surface at sea level, resulting in what we call atmospheric pressure.

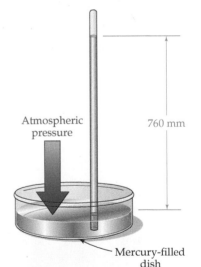

▲ **Figure 8.9**
Measuring atmospheric pressure.
A mercury barometer measures atmospheric pressure by determining the height of a mercury column in a sealed glass tube. The downward pressure of the mercury in the column is exactly balanced by the outside atmospheric pressure, which presses down on the mercury in the dish and pushes it up into the column.

▶ **Figure 8.10**
Open-ended manometers for measuring pressure in a gas-filled bulb.
(a) When the pressure in the gas-filled container is lower than atmospheric, the mercury level is higher in the arm open to the container. (b) When the pressure in the container is higher than atmospheric, the mercury level is higher in the arm open to the atmosphere.

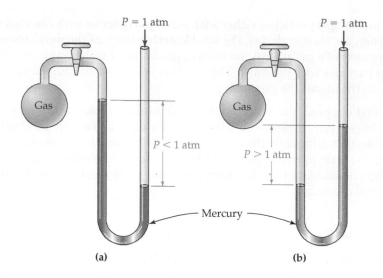

(a)   (b)

Worked Example 8.3 Unit Conversions (Pressure): psi, Atmospheres, and Pascals

A typical bicycle tire is inflated with air to a pressure of 55 psi. How many atmospheres is this? How many pascals?

ANALYSIS Using the starting pressure in psi, the pressure in atm and pascals can be calculated using the equivalent values in appropriate units as conversion factors.

SOLUTION

STEP 1: **Identify known information.**

STEP 2: **Identify answer and units.**

STEP 3: **Identify conversion factors.** Using equivalent values in appropriate units, we can obtain conversion factors to convert to atm and pascals.

STEP 4: **Solve.** Use the appropriate conversion factors to set up an equation in which unwanted units cancel.

Pressure = 55 psi

Pressure = ?? atm = ?? pascals

$$14.7 \text{ psi} = 1 \text{ atm} \rightarrow \frac{1 \text{ atm}}{14.7 \text{ psi}}$$

$$14.7 \text{ psi} = 101{,}325 \text{ Pa} \rightarrow \frac{101{,}325 \text{ Pa}}{14.7 \text{ psi}}$$

$$(55 \text{ psi}) \times \left(\frac{1 \text{ atm}}{14.7 \text{ psi}}\right) = 3.7 \text{ atm}$$

$$(55 \text{ psi}) \times \left(\frac{101{,}325 \text{ Pa}}{14.7 \text{ psi}}\right) = 3.8 \times 10^5 \text{ Pa}$$

Worked Example 8.4 Unit Conversions (Pressure): mmHg to Atmospheres

The pressure in a closed flask is measured using a manometer. If the mercury level in the arm open to the sealed vessel is 23.6 cm higher than the level of mercury in the arm open to the atmosphere, what is the gas pressure (in atm) in the closed flask?

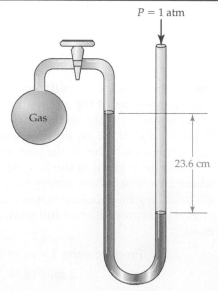

ANALYSIS Since the mercury level is higher in the arm open to the flask, the gas pressure in the flask is lower than atmospheric pressure (1 atm = 760 mmHg). We can convert the difference in the level of mercury in the two arms of the manometer from mmHg to atmospheres to determine the difference in pressure.

BALLPARK ESTIMATE The height difference (23.6 cm) is about one-third the height of a column of Hg that is equal to 1 atm (or 76 cm Hg). Therefore, the pressure in the flask should be about 0.33 atm lower than atmospheric pressure, or about 0.67 atm.

SOLUTION
Since the height difference is given in cm Hg, we must first convert to mmHg, and then to atm. The result is the difference in gas pressure between the flask and the open atmosphere (1 atm).

$$(23.6 \ \cancel{cm \ Hg})\left(\frac{10 \ \cancel{mmHg}}{\cancel{cm \ Hg}}\right)\left(\frac{1 \ atm}{760 \ \cancel{mmHg}}\right) = 0.311 \ atm$$

The pressure in the flask is calculated by subtracting this difference from 1 atm:

$$1 \ atm - 0.311 \ atm = 0.689 \ atm$$

BALLPARK CHECK This result agrees well with our estimate of 0.67 atm.

PROBLEM 8.5
The air pressure outside a jet airliner flying at 35,000 ft is about 0.289 atm. Convert this pressure to mmHg, psi, and pascals.

PROBLEM 8.6
The increase in atmospheric CO_2 levels has been correlated with the combustion of fossil fuels (see Chemistry in Action: Greenhouse Gases and Global Warming on p. 224). How would the atmospheric CO_2 levels be affected by a shift to corn-based ethanol or some other biomass-based fuel? Explain.

KEY CONCEPT PROBLEM 8.7

What is the pressure of the gas inside the following manometer (in mmHg) if outside pressure is 750 mmHg?

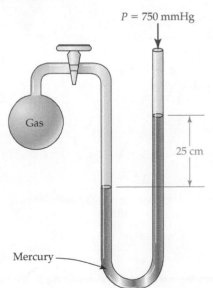

P = 750 mmHg

Gas

25 cm

Mercury

CHEMISTRY IN ACTION

Greenhouse Gases and Global Warming

The mantle of gases surrounding the earth is far from the uniform mixture you might expect, consisting of layers that vary in composition and properties at different altitudes. The ability of the gases in these layers to absorb radiation is responsible for life on earth as we know it.

The *stratosphere*—the layer extending from about 12 km up to 50 km altitude—contains the ozone layer that is responsible for absorbing harmful UV radiation. The *troposphere* is the layer extending from the surface up to about 12 km altitude. It should not surprise you to learn that the troposphere is the layer most easily disturbed by human activities and that this layer has the greatest impact on the earth's surface conditions. Among those impacts, a process called the *greenhouse effect* is much in the news today.

The greenhouse effect refers to the warming that occurs in the troposphere as gases absorb radiant energy. Much of the radiant energy reaching the Earth's surface from the sun is reflected back into space, but some is absorbed by atmospheric gases, particularly those referred to as *greenhouse gases* (GHGs)—water vapor, carbon dioxide, and methane. This absorbed radiation warms the atmosphere and acts to maintain a relatively stable temperature of 15 °C (59 °F) at the Earth's surface. Without the greenhouse effect, the average surface temperature would be about −18 °C (0 °F)—a temperature so low that Earth would be frozen and unable to sustain life.

The basis for concern about the greenhouse effect is the fear that human activities over the past century have disturbed the earth's delicate thermal balance. Should increasing amounts of radiation be absorbed, increased atmospheric heating will result, and global temperatures will continue to rise.

Measurements show that the concentration of atmospheric CO_2 has been rising in the last 150 years, from an estimated 290 parts per million (ppm) in 1850 to current levels approaching 400 ppm. The increase in CO_2 levels is largely because of the increased burning of fossil fuels and correlates with a concurrent increase in average global temperatures. The latest Assessment Report of the Intergovernmental Panel on Climate Change published in November 2007 concluded that "[W]arming of the climate system is unequivocal, as is now evident from observations of increases in global average air and ocean temperatures, widespread melting of snow and ice and rising global average sea level. . . . Continued GHG emissions at or above current rates would cause further warming and induce many changes in the global climate system during the 21st century that would *very likely* be larger than those observed during the 20th century."

Increased international concerns about the political and economic impacts of global climate change prompted development of the Kyoto Protocol to the United Nations Framework Convention on Climate Change (UNFCCC). Under the protocol, countries commit to a reduction in the production and emission of greenhouse gases, including CO_2, methane, and chlorofluorocarbons (CFCs). As of April 2010, 191 countries have signed and ratified the protocol. These concerns have also resulted in market pressures to develop sustainable and renewable energy sources, as well as more efficient technologies, such as hybrid electric vehicles.

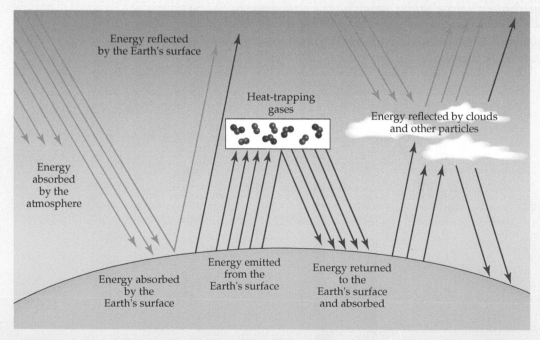

▲ **Greenhouse gases (GHG) trap heat reflected from the earth's surface, resulting in the increase in surface temperatures known as global warming.**

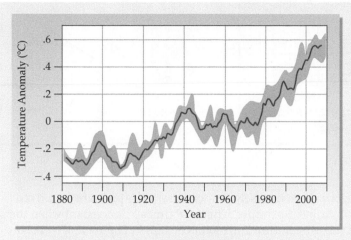

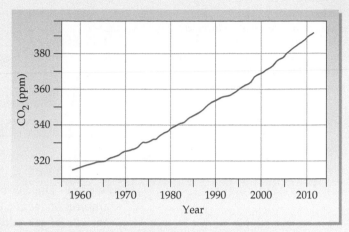

▲ Concentrations of atmospheric CO_2 and global average temperatures have increased dramatically in the last 150 years because of increased fossil fuel use, causing serious changes in earth's climate system.
© NASA, GISS Surface Temperature Analysis.

See Chemistry in Action Problems 8.100 and 8.101 at the end of the chapter.

8.5 Boyle's Law: The Relation between Volume and Pressure

The physical behavior of all gases is much the same, regardless of identity. Helium and chlorine, for example, are completely different in their *chemical* behavior, but are very similar in many of their physical properties. Observations of many different gases by scientists in the 1700s led to the formulation of what are now called the **gas laws**, which make it possible to predict the influence of pressure (P), volume (V), temperature (T), and molar amount (n) on any gas or mixture of gases. We will begin by looking at *Boyle's law*, which describes the relation between volume and pressure.

Imagine that you have a sample of gas inside a cylinder that has a movable plunger at one end (Figure 8.11). What happens if you double the pressure on the gas by pushing the plunger down, while keeping the temperature constant? Since the gas particles are forced closer together, the volume of the sample decreases.

Gas laws A series of laws that predict the influence of pressure (P), volume (V), and temperature (T) on any gas or mixture of gases.

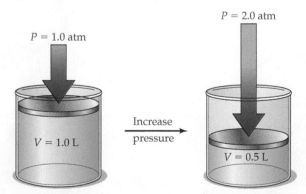

$P = 1.0$ atm

$P = 2.0$ atm

$V = 1.0$ L

Increase pressure

$V = 0.5$ L

◄ **Figure 8.11**
Boyle's law.
The volume of a gas decreases proportionately as its pressure increases. For example, if the pressure of a gas sample is doubled, the volume is halved.

According to **Boyle's law**, the volume of a fixed amount of gas at a constant temperature is inversely proportional to its pressure, meaning that volume and pressure change in opposite directions. As pressure goes up, volume goes down; as pressure goes down, volume goes up (Figure 8.12). This observation is consistent with the kinetic–molecular theory. Since most of the volume occupied by gases is empty space, gases are easily compressed into smaller volumes. Since the average kinetic energy remains constant, the number of collisions must increase as the interior surface area of the container decreases, leading to an increase in pressure.

▶ **Figure 8.12**
Boyle's law.
Pressure and volume are inversely related. Graph (a) demonstrates the decrease in volume as pressure increases, whereas graph (b) shows the linear relationship between V and $1/P$.

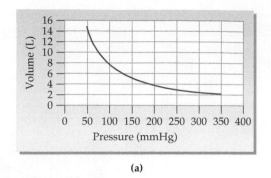

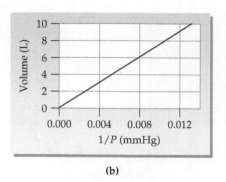

(a)

(b)

Boyle's law The volume of a gas is inversely proportional to its pressure for a fixed amount of gas at a constant temperature. That is, P times V is constant when the amount of gas n and the temperature T are kept constant. (The symbol $\propto$ means "is proportional to," and k denotes a constant value.)

$$\text{Volume }(V) \propto \frac{1}{\text{Pressure }(P)}$$

$$\text{or} \quad PV = k \quad (\text{A constant value})$$

Because $P \times V$ is a constant value for a fixed amount of gas at a constant temperature, the starting pressure (P_1) times the starting volume (V_1) must equal the final pressure (P_2) times the final volume (V_2). Thus, Boyle's law can be used to find the final pressure or volume when the starting pressure or volume is changed.

$$\text{Since} \quad P_1V_1 = k \quad \text{and} \quad P_2V_2 = k$$

$$\text{then} \quad P_1V_1 = P_2V_2$$

$$\text{so} \quad P_2 = \frac{P_1V_1}{V_2} \quad \text{and} \quad V_2 = \frac{P_1V_1}{P_2}$$

As an example of Boyle's law behavior, think about what happens every time you breathe. Between breaths, the pressure inside your lungs is equal to atmospheric pressure. When inhalation takes place, your diaphragm lowers and the rib cage expands, increasing the volume of the lungs and thereby decreasing the pressure inside them (Figure 8.13). Air

▶ **Figure 8.13**
Boyle's law in breathing.
During inhalation, the diaphragm moves down and the rib cage moves up and out, thus increasing lung volume, decreasing pressure, and drawing in air. During exhalation, the diaphragm moves back up, lung volume decreases, pressure increases, and air moves out.

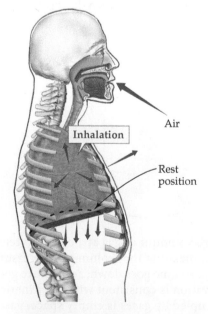

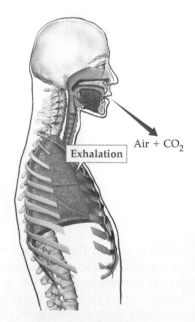

Lung volume increases, causing pressure in lungs to *decrease*. Air flows *in*.

Lung volume decreases, causing pressure in lungs to *increase*. Air flows *out*.

must then move into the lungs to equalize their pressure with that of the atmosphere. When exhalation takes place, the diaphragm rises and the rib cage contracts, decreasing the volume of the lungs and increasing pressure inside them. Now gases move out of the lungs until pressure is again equalized with the atmosphere.

Worked Example 8.5 Using Boyle's Law: Finding Volume at a Given Pressure

In a typical automobile engine, the fuel/air mixture in a cylinder is compressed from 1.0 atm to 9.5 atm. If the uncompressed volume of the cylinder is 750 mL, what is the volume when fully compressed?

ANALYSIS This is a Boyle's law problem because the volume and pressure in the cylinder change but the amount of gas and the temperature remain constant. According to Boyle's law, the pressure of the gas times its volume is constant:

$$P_1 V_1 = P_2 V_2$$

Knowing three of the four variables in this equation, we can solve for the unknown.

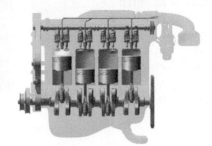

◄ A cut-away diagram of an internal combustion engine shows movement of pistons during expansion and compression cycles.

BALLPARK ESTIMATE Since the pressure *increases* approximately 10-fold (from 1.0 atm to 9.5 atm), the volume must *decrease* to approximately 1/10, from 750 mL to about 75 mL.

SOLUTION

STEP 1: Identify known information. Of the four variables in Boyle's law, we know P_1, V_1, and P_2.

$P_1 = 1.0$ atm
$V_1 = 750$ mL
$P_2 = 9.5$ atm

STEP 2: Identify answer and units.

$V_2 = ??$ mL

STEP 3: Identify equation. In this case, we simply substitute the known variables into Boyle's law and rearrange to isolate the unknown.

$$P_1 V_1 = P_2 V_2 \implies V_2 = \frac{P_1 V_1}{P_2}$$

STEP 4: Solve. Substitute the known information into the equation. Make sure units cancel so that the answer is given in the units of the unknown variable.

$$V_2 = \frac{P_1 V_1}{P_2} = \frac{(1.0 \text{ atm})(750 \text{ mL})}{(9.5 \text{ atm})} = 79 \text{ mL}$$

BALLPARK CHECK Our estimate was 75 mL.

PROBLEM 8.8

An oxygen cylinder used for breathing has a volume of 5.0 L at 90 atm pressure. What is the volume of the same amount of oxygen at the same temperature if the pressure is 1.0 atm? (Hint: Would you expect the volume of gas at this pressure to be greater than or less than the volume at 90 atm?)

PROBLEM 8.9

A sample of hydrogen gas at 273 K has a volume of 3.2 L at 4.0 atm pressure. What is the volume if the pressure is increased to 10.0 atm? If the pressure is decreased to 0.70 atm?

PROBLEM 8.10

A typical blood pressure measured using a sphygmomanometer is reported as 112/75 (see Chemistry in Action: Blood Pressure on p. 228). How would this pressure be recorded if the sphygmomanometer used units of psi instead of mmHg?

CHEMISTRY IN ACTION

Blood Pressure

Having your blood pressure measured is a quick and easy way to get an indication of the state of your circulatory system. Although blood pressure varies with age, a normal adult male has a reading near 120/80 mmHg, and a normal adult female has a reading near 110/70 mmHg. Abnormally high values signal an increased risk of heart attack and stroke.

Pressure varies greatly in different types of blood vessels. Usually, though, measurements are carried out on arteries in the upper arm as the heart goes through a full cardiac cycle. *Systolic pressure* is the maximum pressure developed in the artery just after contraction, as the heart forces the maximum amount of blood into the artery. *Diastolic pressure* is the minimum pressure that occurs at the end of the heart cycle.

Blood pressure is most often measured by a *sphygmomanometer*, a device consisting of a squeeze bulb, a flexible cuff, and a mercury manometer. (1) The cuff is placed around the upper arm over the brachial artery and inflated by the squeeze bulb to about 200 mmHg pressure, an amount great enough to squeeze the artery shut and prevent blood flow. Air is then slowly released from the cuff, and pressure drops (2). As cuff pressure reaches the systolic pressure, blood spurts through the artery, creating a turbulent tapping sound that can be heard through a stethoscope. The pressure registered on the manometer at the moment the first sounds are heard is the systolic blood pressure.

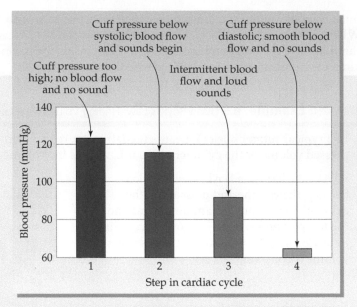

▲ The sequence of events during blood pressure measurement, including the sounds heard.

(3) Sounds continue until the pressure in the cuff becomes low enough to allow diastolic blood flow. (4) At this point, blood flow becomes smooth, no sounds are heard, and a diastolic blood pressure reading is recorded on the manometer. Readings are usually recorded as systolic/diastolic, for example, 120/80. The accompanying figure shows the sequence of events during measurement.

See Chemistry in Action Problems 8.102 and 103 at the end of the chapter.

8.6 Charles's Law: The Relation between Volume and Temperature

Imagine that you again have a sample of gas inside a cylinder with a plunger at one end. What happens if you double the sample's kelvin temperature while letting the plunger move freely to keep the pressure constant? The gas particles move with twice as much energy and collide twice as forcefully with the walls. To maintain a constant pressure, the volume of the gas in the cylinder must double (Figure 8.14).

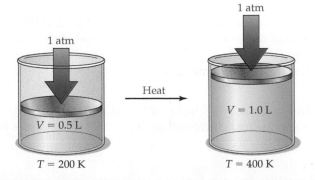

▲ The volume of the gas in the balloon increases as it is heated, causing a decrease in density and allowing the balloon to rise.

▲ **Figure 8.14**
Charles's law.
The volume of a gas is directly proportional to its kelvin temperature at constant n and P. If the kelvin temperature of the gas is doubled, its volume doubles.

According to **Charles's law**, the volume of a fixed amount of gas at constant pressure is directly proportional to its kelvin temperature. Note the difference between *directly* proportional in Charles's law and *inversely* proportional in Boyle's law. Directly proportional quantities change in the same direction: as temperature goes up or down, volume also goes up or down (Figure 8.15).

Charles's law The volume of a gas is directly proportional to its kelvin temperature for a fixed amount of gas at a constant pressure. That is, V divided by T is constant when n and P are held constant.

$$V \propto T \quad \text{(In kelvins)}$$

$$\text{or } \frac{V}{T} = k \quad \text{(A constant value)}$$

$$\text{or } \frac{V_1}{T_1} = \frac{V_2}{T_2}$$

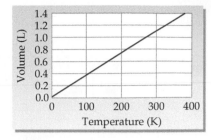

▲ **Figure 8.15**
Charles's law.
Volume is directly proportional to the kelvin temperature for a fixed amount of gas at a constant pressure. As the temperature goes up, the volume also goes up.

This observation is consistent with the kinetic–molecular theory. As temperature increases, the average kinetic energy of the gas molecules increases, as does the energy of molecular collisions with the interior surface of the container. The volume of the container must increase to maintain a constant pressure. As an example of Charles's law, think about what happens when a hot-air balloon is inflated. Heating causes the air inside to expand and fill the balloon. The air inside the balloon is less dense than the air outside the balloon, creating the buoyancy effect.

Worked Example 8.6 Using Charles's Law: Finding Volume at a Given Temperature

An average adult inhales a volume of 0.50 L of air with each breath. If the air is warmed from room temperature (20 °C = 293 K) to body temperature (37 °C = 310 K) while in the lungs, what is the volume of the air exhaled?

ANALYSIS This is a Charles's law problem because the volume and temperature of the air change while the amount and pressure remain constant. Knowing three of the four variables, we can rearrange Charles's law to solve for the unknown.

BALLPARK ESTIMATE Charles's law predicts an increase in volume directly proportional to the increase in temperature from 273 K to 310 K. The increase of less than 20 K represents a relatively small change compared to the initial temperature of 273 K. A 10% increase, for example, would be equal to a temperature change of 27 K; so a 20-K change would be less than 10%. We would therefore expect the volume to increase by less than 10%, from 0.50 L to a little less than 0.55 L.

SOLUTION

STEP 1: Identify known information. Of the four variables in Charles's law, we know T_1, V_1, and T_2.

$T_1 = 293 \text{ K}$
$V_1 = 0.50 \text{ L}$
$T_2 = 310 \text{ K}$

STEP 2: Identify answer and units.

$V_2 = \text{?? L}$

STEP 3: Identify equation. Substitute the known variables into Charles's law and rearrange to isolate the unknown.

$$\frac{V_1}{T_1} = \frac{V_2}{T_2} \Rightarrow V_2 = \frac{V_1 T_2}{T_1}$$

STEP 4: Solve. Substitute the known information into Charles's law; check to make sure units cancel.

$$V_2 = \frac{V_1 T_2}{T_1} = \frac{(0.50 \text{ L})(310 \text{ K})}{293 \text{ K}} = 0.53 \text{ L}$$

BALLPARK CHECK This is consistent with our estimate!

PROBLEM 8.11
A sample of chlorine gas has a volume of 0.30 L at 273 K and 1 atm pressure. What temperature (in °C) would be required to increase the volume to 1.0 L? To decrease the volume to 0.20 L?

8.7 Gay-Lussac's Law: The Relation between Pressure and Temperature

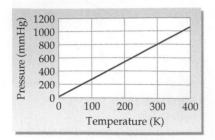

▲ **Figure 8.16**
Gay-Lussac's law.
Pressure is directly proportional to the temperature in kelvins for a fixed amount of gas at a constant volume. As the temperature goes up, the pressure also goes up.

Imagine next that you have a fixed amount of gas in a sealed container whose volume remains constant. What happens if you double the temperature (in kelvins)? The gas particles move with twice as much energy and collide with the walls of the container with twice as much force. Thus, the pressure in the container doubles. According to **Gay-Lussac's law**, the pressure of a fixed amount of gas at constant volume is directly proportional to its Kelvin temperature. As temperature goes up or down, pressure also goes up or down (Figure 8.16).

Gay-Lussac's law The pressure of a gas is directly proportional to its Kelvin temperature for a fixed amount of gas at a constant volume. That is, P divided by T is constant when n and V are held constant.

$$P \propto T \quad \text{(In kelvins)}$$

$$\text{or } \frac{P}{T} = k \quad \text{(A constant value)}$$

$$\text{or } \frac{P_1}{T_1} = \frac{P_2}{T_2}$$

According to the kinetic–molecular theory, the kinetic energy of molecules is directly proportional to absolute temperature. As the average kinetic energy of the molecules increases, the energy of collisions with the interior surface of the container increases, causing an increase in pressure. As an example of Gay-Lussac's law, think of what happens when an aerosol can is thrown into an incinerator. As the can gets hotter, pressure builds up inside and the can explodes (hence the warning statement on aerosol cans).

Worked Example 8.7 Using Gay-Lussac's Law: Finding Pressure at a Given Temperature

What does the inside pressure become if an aerosol can with an initial pressure of 4.5 atm is heated in a fire from room temperature (20 °C) to 600 °C?

ANALYSIS This is a Gay-Lussac's law problem because the pressure and temperature of the gas inside the can change while its amount and volume remain constant. We know three of the four variables in the equation for Gay-Lussac's law, and can find the unknown by substitution and rearrangement.

BALLPARK ESTIMATE Gay-Lussac's law states that pressure is directly proportional to temperature. Since the Kelvin temperature increases approximately threefold (from about 300 K to about 900 K), we expect the pressure to also increase by approximately threefold, from 4.5 atm to about 14 atm.

SOLUTION

STEP 1: Identify known information. Of the four variables in Gay-Lussac's law, we know P_1, T_1 and T_2. (Note that T must be in kelvins.)

$P_1 = 4.5 \text{ atm}$
$T_1 = 20 \,°\text{C} = 293 \text{ K}$
$T_2 = 600 \,°\text{C} = 873 \text{ K}$

STEP 2: Identify answer and units.

$P_2 = \text{?? atm}$

STEP 3: Identify equation. Substituting the known variables into Gay-Lussac's law, we rearrange to isolate the unknown.

$$\frac{P_1}{T_1} = \frac{P_2}{T_2} \implies P_2 = \frac{P_1 T_2}{T_1}$$

STEP 4: Solve. Substitute the known information into Gay-Lussac's law; check to make sure units cancel.

$$P_2 = \frac{P_1 T_2}{T_1} = \frac{(4.5 \text{ atm})(873 \text{ K})}{293 \text{ K}} = 13 \text{ atm}$$

BALLPARK CHECK Our estimate was 14 atm.

PROBLEM 8.12
Driving on a hot day causes tire temperature to rise. What is the pressure inside an automobile tire at 45 °C if the tire has a pressure of 30 psi at 15 °C? Assume that the volume and amount of air in the tire remain constant.

8.8 The Combined Gas Law

Since PV, V/T, and P/T all have constant values for a fixed amount of gas, these relationships can be merged into a **combined gas law**, which holds true whenever the amount of gas is fixed.

Combined gas law $\dfrac{PV}{T} = k$ (A constant value)

or $\dfrac{P_1 V_1}{T_1} = \dfrac{P_2 V_2}{T_2}$

If any five of the six quantities in this equation are known, the sixth quantity can be calculated. Furthermore, if any of the three variables T, P, or V is constant, that variable drops out of the equation, leaving behind Boyle's law, Charles's law, or Gay-Lussac's law. As a result, *the combined gas law is the only equation you need to remember for a fixed amount of gas.* Worked Example 8.8 gives a sample calculation.

Since $\quad \dfrac{P_1 V_1}{T_1} = \dfrac{P_2 V_2}{T_2}$

At constant T: $\quad \dfrac{P_1 V_1}{T} = \dfrac{P_2 V_2}{T}$ gives $\quad P_1 V_1 = P_2 V_2$ (Boyle's law)

At constant P: $\quad \dfrac{P V_1}{T_1} = \dfrac{P V_2}{T_2}$ gives $\quad \dfrac{V_1}{T_1} = \dfrac{V_2}{T_2}$ (Charles's law)

At constant V: $\quad \dfrac{P_1 V}{T_1} = \dfrac{P_2 V}{T_2}$ gives $\quad \dfrac{P_1}{T_1} = \dfrac{P_2}{T_2}$ (Gay-Lussac's law)

Worked Example 8.8 Using the Combined Gas Law: Finding Temperature

A 6.3 L sample of helium gas stored at 25 °C and 1.0 atm pressure is transferred to a 2.0 L tank and maintained at a pressure of 2.8 atm. What temperature is needed to maintain this pressure?

ANALYSIS This is a combined gas law problem because pressure, volume, and temperature change while the amount of helium remains constant. Of the six variables in this equation, we know P_1, V_1, T_1, P_2, and V_2, and we need to find T_2.

BALLPARK ESTIMATE Since the volume goes down by a little more than a factor of about 3 (from 6.3 L to 2.0 L) and the pressure goes up by a little less than a factor of about 3 (from 1.0 atm to 2.8 atm), the two changes roughly offset each other, and so the temperature should not change much. Since the volume-decrease factor (3.2) is slightly greater than the pressure-increase factor (2.8), the temperature will drop slightly ($T \propto V$).

SOLUTION

STEP 1: Identify known information. Of the six variables in combined gas law we know P_1, V_1, T_1, P_2, and V_2. (As always, T must be converted from Celsius degrees to kelvins.)

$P_1 = 1.0$ atm, $P_2 = 2.8$ atm
$V_1 = 6.3$ L, $V_2 = 2.0$ L
$T_1 = 25\,°\text{C} = 298$ K

STEP 2: Identify answer and units.

$T_2 = $?? kelvin

STEP 3: Identify the equation. Substitute the known variables into the equation for the combined gas law and rearrange to isolate the unknown.

$\dfrac{P_1 V_1}{T_1} = \dfrac{P_2 V_2}{T_2} \implies T_2 = \dfrac{P_2 V_2 T_1}{P_1 V_1}$

STEP 4: Solve. Solve the combined gas law equation for T_2; check to make sure units cancel.

$T_2 = \dfrac{P_2 V_2 T_1}{P_1 V_1} = \dfrac{(2.8\ \text{atm})(2.0\ \cancel{L})(298\ \text{K})}{(1.0\ \cancel{\text{atm}})(6.3\ \cancel{L})} = 260\ \text{K}\,(\Delta T = 2.38\,°\text{C})$

BALLPARK CHECK The relatively small decrease in temperature (38 °C, or 13% compared to the original temperature) is consistent with our prediction.

PROBLEM 8.13

A weather balloon is filled with helium to a volume of 275 L at 22 °C and 752 mmHg. The balloon ascends to an altitude where the pressure is 480 mmHg, and the temperature is −32 °C. What is the volume of the balloon at this altitude?

🗝 **KEY CONCEPT PROBLEM 8.14**

A balloon is filled under the initial conditions indicated below. If the pressure is then increased to 2 atm while the temperature is increased to 50 °C, which balloon on the right, (a) or (b), represents the new volume of the balloon?

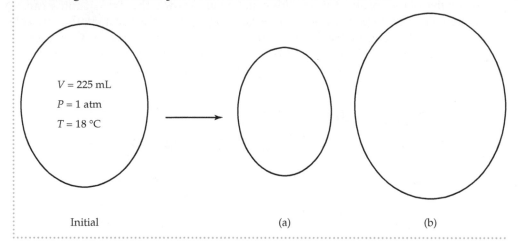

$V = 225$ mL

$P = 1$ atm

$T = 18$ °C

Initial   (a)   (b)

8.9 Avogadro's Law: The Relation between Volume and Molar Amount

Here we look at one final gas law, which takes changes in amount of gas into account. Imagine that you have two different volumes of a gas at the same temperature and pressure. How many moles does each sample contain? According to **Avogadro's law**, the volume of a gas is directly proportional to its molar amount at a constant pressure and temperature (Figure 8.17). A sample that contains twice the molar amount has twice the volume.

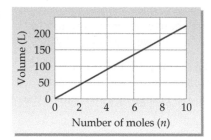

▲ **Figure 8.17**

Avogadro's law.
Volume is directly proportional to the molar amount, n, at a constant temperature and pressure. As the number of moles goes up, the volume also goes up.

Avogadro's law The volume of a gas is directly proportional to its molar amount at a constant pressure and temperature. That is, V divided by n is constant when P and T are held constant.

Volume $(V) \propto$ Number of moles (n)

or $\dfrac{V}{n} = k$ (A constant value; the same for all gases)

or $\dfrac{V_1}{n_1} = \dfrac{V_2}{n_2}$

Because the particles in a gas are so tiny compared to the empty space surrounding them, there is no interaction among gas particles as proposed by the kinetic–molecular theory. As a result, the chemical identity of the particles does not matter and the value of the constant k in the equation $V/n = k$ is the same for all gases. It is therefore possible to compare the molar amounts of *any* two gases simply by comparing their volumes at the same temperature and pressure.

Notice that the *values* of temperature and pressure do not matter; it is only necessary that T and P be the same for both gases. To simplify comparisons of gas samples, however, it is convenient to define a set of conditions called **standard temperature and pressure (STP)**, which specifies a temperature of 0 °C (273 K) and a pressure of 1 atm (760 mmHg).

At standard temperature and pressure, 1 mol of any gas (6.02×10^{23} particles) has a volume of 22.4 L, a quantity called the **standard molar volume** (Figure 8.18).

Standard temperature and pressure (STP) 0 °C (273.15 K); 1 atm (760 mmHg)

Standard molar volume of any ideal gas at STP 22.4 L/mol

◀ **Figure 8.18**
Avogadro's law.
Each of these 22.4 L bulbs contains 1.00 mol of gas at 0 °C and 1 atm pressure. Note that the volume occupied by 1 mol of gas is the same even though the mass (in grams) of 1 mol of each gas is different.

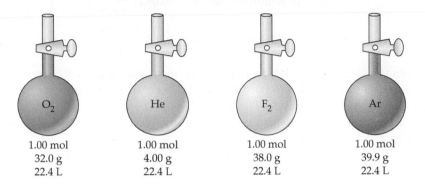

O_2	He	F_2	Ar
1.00 mol	1.00 mol	1.00 mol	1.00 mol
32.0 g	4.00 g	38.0 g	39.9 g
22.4 L	22.4 L	22.4 L	22.4 L

Worked Example 8.9 Using Avogadro's Law: Finding Moles in a Given Volume at STP

Use the standard molar volume of a gas at STP (22.4 L) to find how many moles of air at STP are in a room measuring 4.11 m wide by 5.36 m long by 2.58 m high.

ANALYSIS We first find the volume of the room and then use standard molar volume as a conversion factor to find the number of moles.

SOLUTION

STEP 1: Identify known information. We are given the room dimensions.

$\text{Length} = 5.36 \text{ m}$
$\text{Width} = 4.11 \text{ m}$
$\text{Height} = 2.58 \text{ m}$

STEP 2: Identify answer and units.

$\text{Moles of air} = \text{?? mol}$

STEP 3: Identify the equation. The volume of the room is the product of its three dimensions. Once we have the volume (in m³), we can convert to liters and use the molar volume at STP as a conversion factor to obtain moles of air.

$\text{Volume} = (4.11 \text{ m})(5.36 \text{ m})(2.58 \text{ m}) = 56.8 \text{ m}^3$

$= 56.8 \text{ m}^3 \times \dfrac{1000 \text{ L}}{1 \text{ m}^3} = 5.68 \times 10^4 \text{ L}$

$1 \text{ mol} = 22.4 \text{ L} \longrightarrow \dfrac{1 \text{ mol}}{22.4 \text{ L}}$

STEP 4: Solve. Use the room volume and the molar volume at STP to set up an equation, making sure unwanted units cancel.

$5.68 \times 10^4 \text{ L} \times \dfrac{1 \text{ mol}}{22.4 \text{ L}} = 2.54 \times 10^3 \text{ mol}$

PROBLEM 8.15
How many moles of methane gas, CH_4, are in a 1.00×10^5 L storage tank at STP? How many grams of methane is this? How many grams of carbon dioxide gas could the same tank hold?

8.10 The Ideal Gas Law

The relationships among the four variables *P*, *V*, *T*, and *n* for gases can be combined into a single expression called the **ideal gas law**. If you know the values of any three of the four quantities, you can calculate the value of the fourth.

Ideal gas law $\dfrac{PV}{nT} = R$ (A constant value)

or $PV = nRT$

Gas constant (R) The constant R in the ideal gas law, $PV = nRT$.

The constant R in the ideal gas law (instead of the usual k) is called the **gas constant**. Its value depends on the units chosen for pressure, with the two most common values being

$$\text{For } P \text{ in atmospheres: } \quad R = 0.0821 \frac{\text{L} \cdot \text{atm}}{\text{mol} \cdot \text{K}}$$

$$\text{For } P \text{ in millimeters Hg: } \quad R = 62.4 \frac{\text{L} \cdot \text{mmHg}}{\text{mol} \cdot \text{K}}$$

In using the ideal gas law, it is important to choose the value of R having pressure units that are consistent with the problem and, if necessary, to convert volume into liters and temperature into kelvins.

Table 8.3 summarizes the various gas laws, and Worked Examples 8.10 and 8.11 show how to use the ideal gas law.

TABLE 8.3 A Summary of the Gas Laws

	Gas Law	Variables	Constant
Boyle's law	$P_1V_1 = P_2V_2$	P, V	n, T
Charles's law	$V_1/T_1 = V_2/T_2$	V, T	n, P
Gay-Lussac's law	$P_1/T_1 = P_2/T_2$	P, T	n, V
Combined gas law	$P_1V_1/T_1 = P_2V_2/T_2$	P, V, T	n
Avogadro's law	$V_1/n_1 = V_2/n_2$	V, n	P, T
Ideal gas law	$PV = nRT$	P, V, T, n	R

Worked Example 8.10 Using the Ideal Gas Law: Finding Moles

How many moles of air are in the lungs of an average person with a total lung capacity of 3.8 L? Assume that the person is at 1.0 atm pressure and has a normal body temperature of 37 °C.

ANALYSIS This is an ideal gas law problem because it asks for a value of n when P, V, and T are known: $n = PV/RT$. The volume is given in the correct unit of liters, but temperature must be converted to kelvins.

SOLUTION

STEP 1: **Identify known information.** We know three of the four variables in the ideal gas law.

$P = 1.0 \text{ atm}$
$V = 3.8 \text{ L}$
$T = 37 °C = 310 \text{ K}$

STEP 2: **Identify answer and units.**

Moles of air, $n = ?? \text{ mol}$

STEP 3: **Identify the equation.** Knowing three of the four variables in the ideal gas law, we can rearrange and solve for the unknown variable, n. Note: because pressure is given in atm, we use the value of R that is expressed in atm:

$$PV = nRT \quad \Rightarrow \quad n = \frac{PV}{RT}$$

$$R = 0.0821 \frac{\text{L} \cdot \text{atm}}{\text{mol} \cdot \text{K}}$$

STEP 4: **Solve.** Substitute the known information and the appropriate value of R into the ideal gas law equation and solve for n.

$$n = \frac{PV}{RT} = \frac{(1.0 \text{ atm})(3.8 \text{ L})}{\left(0.0821 \dfrac{\text{L} \cdot \text{atm}}{\text{mol} \cdot \text{K}}\right)(310 \text{ K})} = 0.15 \text{ mol}$$

Worked Example 8.11 Using the Ideal Gas Law: Finding Pressure

Methane gas is sold in steel cylinders with a volume of 43.8 L containing 5.54 kg. What is the pressure in atmospheres inside the cylinder at a temperature of 20.0 °C (293.15 K)? The molar mass of methane (CH_4) is 16.0 g/mol.

ANALYSIS This is an ideal gas law problem because it asks for a value of P when V, T, and n are given. Although not provided directly, enough information is given so that we can calculate the value of n ($n = g/MW$).

SOLUTION

STEP 1: Identify known information. We know two of the four variables in the ideal gas law; V, T, and can calculate the third, n, from the information provided.

$V = 43.8$ L
$T = 37$ °C $= 310$ K

STEP 2: Identify answer and units.

Pressure, $P = ??$ atm

STEP 3: Identify equation. First, calculate the number of moles, n, of methane in the cylinder by using molar mass (16.0 g/mol) as a conversion factor. Then use the ideal gas law to calculate the pressure.

$$n = (5.54 \text{ kg methane})\left(\frac{1000 \text{ g}}{1 \text{ kg}}\right)\left(\frac{1 \text{ mol}}{16.0 \text{ g}}\right) = 346 \text{ mol methane}$$

$$PV = nRT \implies P = \frac{nRT}{V}$$

STEP 4: Solve. Substitute the known information and the appropriate value of R into the ideal gas law equation and solve for P.

$$P = \frac{nRT}{V} = \frac{(346 \text{ mol})\left(0.0821 \dfrac{\text{L} \cdot \text{atm}}{\text{mol} \cdot \text{K}}\right)(293 \text{ K})}{43.8 \text{ L}} = 190 \text{ atm}$$

PROBLEM 8.16

An aerosol spray can of deodorant with a volume of 350 mL contains 3.2 g of propane gas (C_3H_8) as propellant. What is the pressure in the can at 20 °C?

PROBLEM 8.17

A helium gas cylinder of the sort used to fill balloons has a volume of 180 L and a pressure of 2200 psi (150 atm) at 25 °C. How many moles of helium are in the tank? How many grams?

🔑 **KEY CONCEPT PROBLEM 8.18**

Show the approximate level of the movable piston in drawings (a) and (b) after the indicated changes have been made to the initial gas sample (assume a constant pressure of 1 atm).

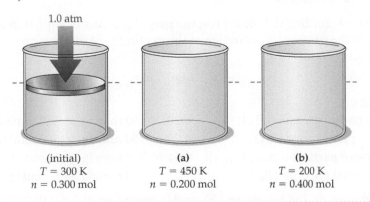

1.0 atm

(initial)	(a)	(b)
$T = 300$ K	$T = 450$ K	$T = 200$ K
$n = 0.300$ mol	$n = 0.200$ mol	$n = 0.400$ mol

8.11 Partial Pressure and Dalton's Law

According to the kinetic–molecular theory, each particle in a gas acts independently of all others because there are no attractive forces between them and they are so far apart. To any individual particle, the chemical identity of its neighbors is irrelevant. Thus, *mixtures* of gases behave the same as pure gases and obey the same laws.

Dry air, for example, is a mixture of about 21% oxygen, 78% nitrogen, and 1% argon by volume, which means that 21% of atmospheric air pressure is caused by O_2 molecules, 78% by N_2 molecules, and 1% by Ar atoms. The contribution of each gas in a mixture to the total pressure of the mixture is called the **partial pressure** of that gas. According to **Dalton's law**, the total pressure exerted by a gas mixture (P_{total}) is the sum of the partial pressures of the components in the mixture:

Partial pressure The contribution of a given gas in a mixture to the total pressure.

Dalton's law $P_{total} = P_{gas\ 1} + P_{gas\ 2} + g$

In dry air at a total air pressure of 760 mmHg, the partial pressure caused by the contribution of O_2 is 0.21×760 mmHg = 160 mmHg, the partial pressure of N_2 is 0.78×760 mmHg = 593 mmHg, and that of argon is 7 mmHg. *The partial pressure exerted by each gas in a mixture is the same pressure that the gas would exert if it were alone.* Put another way, the pressure exerted by each gas depends on the frequency of collisions of its molecules with the walls of the container. However, this frequency does not change when other gases are present, because the different molecules have no influence on one another.

To represent the partial pressure of a specific gas, we add the formula of the gas as a subscript to P, the symbol for pressure. You might see the partial pressure of oxygen represented as P_{O_2}, for instance. Moist air inside the lungs at 37 °C and atmospheric pressure has the following average composition at sea level. Note that P_{total} is equal to atmospheric pressure, 760 mmHg.

$$P_{total} = P_{N_2} \quad + \quad P_{O_2} \quad + \quad P_{CO_2} \quad + \quad P_{H_2O}$$
$$= 573\ \text{mmHg} + 100\ \text{mmHg} + 40\ \text{mmHg} + 47\ \text{mmHg}$$
$$= 760\ \text{mmHg}$$

The composition of air does not change appreciably with altitude, but the total pressure decreases rapidly. The partial pressure of oxygen in air therefore decreases with increasing altitude, and it is this change that leads to difficulty in breathing at high elevations.

Worked Example 8.12 Using Dalton's Law: Finding Partial Pressures

Humid air on a warm summer day is approximately 20% oxygen, 75% nitrogen, 4% water vapor, and 1% argon. What is the partial pressure of each component if the atmospheric pressure is 750 mmHg?

ANALYSIS According to Dalton's law, the partial pressure of any gas in a mixture is equal to the percent concentration of the gas times the total gas pressure (750 mmHg). In this case,

$$P_{total} = P_{O_2} + P_{N_2} + P_{H_2O} + P_{Ar}$$

SOLUTION

Oxygen partial pressure (P_{O_2}): 0.20×750 mmHg = 150 mmHg
Nitrogen partial pressure (P_{N_2}): 0.75×750 mmHg = 560 mmHg
Water vapor partial pressure (P_{H_2O}): 0.04×750 mmHg = 30 mmHg
Argon partial pressure (P_{Ar}): 0.01×750 mmHg = 8 mmHg

Total pressure = 748 mmHg → 750 mmHg (rounding to 2 significant figures!)

Note that the sum of the partial pressures must equal the total pressure (within rounding error).

PROBLEM 8.19

Assuming a total pressure of 9.5 atm, what is the partial pressure of each component in the mixture of 98% helium and 2.0% oxygen breathed by deep-sea divers? How does the partial pressure of oxygen in diving gas compare with its partial pressure in normal air?

PROBLEM 8.20

Determine the percent composition of air in the lungs from the following composition in partial pressures: $P_{N_2} = 573$ mmHg, $P_{O_2} = 100$ mmHg, $P_{CO_2} = 40$ mmHg, $P_{H_2O} = 47$ mmHg; all at 37 °C and 1 atm pressure.

PROBLEM 8.21

The atmospheric pressure on the top of Mt. Everest, an altitude of 29,035 ft, is only 265 mmHg. What is the partial pressure of oxygen in the lungs at this altitude (assuming that the % O_2 is the same as in dry air)?

🔑 KEY CONCEPT PROBLEM 8.22

Assume that you have a mixture of He (MW = 4 amu) and Xe (MW = 131 amu) at 300 K. The total pressure of the mixture is 750 mmHg. What are the partial pressures of each of the gases? (blue = He; green = Xe)?

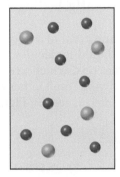

8.12 Liquids

Molecules are in constant motion in the liquid state, just as they are in gases. If a molecule happens to be near the surface of a liquid, and if it has enough energy, it can break free of the liquid and escape into the gas state, called **vapor**. In an open container, the now gaseous molecule will wander away from the liquid, and the process will continue until all the molecules escape from the container (Figure 8.19a). This, of course, is what happens during *evaporation*. We are all familiar with puddles of water evaporating after a rainstorm.

Vapor The gas molecules are in equilibrium with a liquid.

If the liquid is in a closed container, the situation is different because the gaseous molecules cannot escape. Thus, the random motion of the molecules occasionally brings them back into the liquid. After the concentration of molecules in the gas state has increased sufficiently, the number of molecules reentering the liquid becomes equal to the number escaping from the liquid (Figure 8.19b). At this point, a dynamic equilibrium exists, exactly as in a chemical reaction at equilibrium. Evaporation and condensation take place at the same rate, and the concentration of vapor in the container is constant as long as the temperature does not change.

Once molecules have escaped from the liquid into the gas state, they are subject to all the gas laws previously discussed. In a closed container at equilibrium, for example, the vapor molecules will make their own contribution to the total pressure of gases above the liquid according to Dalton's Law (Section 8.11). We call this contribution the **vapor pressure** of the liquid.

Vapor pressure The partial pressure of vapor molecules in equilibrium with a liquid.

▶ **Figure 8.19**
The transfer of molecules between liquid and gas states.
(a) Molecules escape from an open container and drift away until the liquid has entirely evaporated.
(b) Molecules in a closed container cannot escape. Instead, they reach an equilibrium in which the rates of molecules leaving the liquid and returning to the liquid are equal, and the concentration of molecules in the gas state is constant.

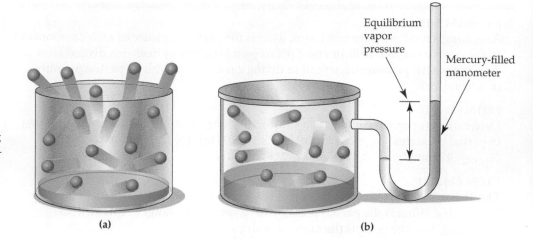

(a)   (b)

▲ Because bromine is colored, it is possible to see its gaseous reddish vapor above the liquid.

Normal boiling point The boiling point at a pressure of exactly 1 atmosphere.

Vapor pressure depends on both temperature and the chemical identity of a liquid. As the temperature rises, molecules become more energetic and more likely to escape into the gas state. Thus, vapor pressure rises with increasing temperature until ultimately it becomes equal to the pressure of the atmosphere. At this point, bubbles of vapor form under the surface and force their way to the top, giving rise to the violent action observed during a vigorous boil. At an atmospheric pressure of exactly 760 mmHg, boiling occurs at what is called the **normal boiling point**.

The vapor pressure and boiling point of a liquid will also depend on the intermolecular forces at work between liquid molecules. Ether molecules, for example, can engage in dipole–dipole interactions, which are weaker than the hydrogen bonds formed between water molecules. As a result, ether exhibits both lower vapor pressures and a lower boiling point than water, as seen in Figure 8.20.

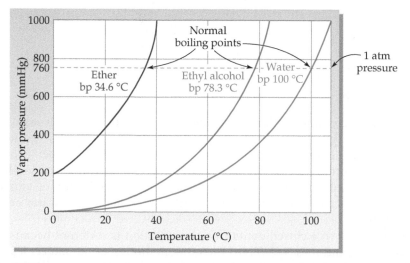

▲ **Figure 8.20**
A plot of the change of vapor pressure with temperature for ethyl ether, ethyl alcohol, and water. At a liquid's boiling point, its vapor pressure is equal to atmospheric pressure. Commonly reported boiling points are those at 760 mmHg.

If atmospheric pressure is higher or lower than normal, the boiling point of a liquid changes accordingly. At high altitudes, for example, atmospheric pressure is lower than at sea level, and boiling points are also lower. On top of Mt. Everest (29,035 ft; 8850 m), atmospheric pressure is about 245 mmHg and the boiling temperature of water is only 71 °C. If the atmospheric pressure is higher than normal, the boiling point is also higher. This principle is used in strong vessels known as *autoclaves*, in which water at high pressure is heated to the temperatures needed for sterilizing medical and dental instruments (170 °C).

Many familiar properties of liquids can be explained by the intermolecular forces just discussed. We all know, for instance, that some liquids, such as water or gasoline, flow easily when poured, whereas others, such as motor oil or maple syrup, flow sluggishly.

The measure of a liquid's resistance to flow is called its *viscosity*. Not surprisingly, viscosity is related to the ease with which individual molecules move around in the liquid and thus to the intermolecular forces present. Substances such as gasoline, which have small, nonpolar molecules, experience only weak intermolecular forces and have relatively low viscosities, whereas more polar substances such as glycerin $[C_3H_5(OH)_3]$ experience stronger intermolecular forces and so have higher viscosities.

Another familiar property of liquids is *surface tension*, the resistance of a liquid to spreading out and increasing its surface area. The beading-up of water on a newly waxed car and the ability of a water strider to walk on water are both due to surface tension.

Surface tension is caused by the difference between the intermolecular forces experienced by molecules at the surface of the liquid and those experienced by molecules in the interior. Molecules in the interior of a liquid are surrounded and experience maximum intermolecular forces, whereas molecules at the surface have fewer neighbors and feel weaker forces. Surface molecules are therefore less stable, and the liquid acts to minimize their number by minimizing the surface area (Figure 8.21).

▲ Surface tension allows a water strider to walk on water without penetrating the surface.

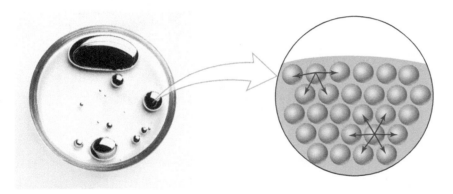

◄ **Figure 8.21**
Surface tension.
Surface tension is caused by the different forces experienced by molecules in the interior of a liquid and those on the surface. Molecules on the surface are less stable because they feel fewer attractive forces, so the liquid acts to minimize their number by minimizing surface area.

▶▶ Recall from Section 1.13 that specific heat is the amount of heat required to raise the temperature of 1g of a substance by 1 °C.

8.13 Water: A Unique Liquid

Ours is a world based on water. Water covers nearly 71% of the earth's surface, it accounts for 66% of the mass of an adult human body, and it is needed by all living things. The water in our blood forms the transport system that circulates substances throughout our body, and water is the medium in which all biochemical reactions are carried out. Largely because of its strong hydrogen bonding, water has many properties that are quite different from those of other compounds.

Water has the highest specific heat of any liquid, giving it the capacity to absorb a large quantity of heat while changing only slightly in temperature. As a result, large lakes and other bodies of water tend to moderate the air temperature and climate of surrounding areas. Another consequence of the high specific heat of water is that the human body is better able to maintain a steady internal temperature under changing outside conditions.

In addition to a high specific heat, water has an unusually high *heat of vaporization* (540 cal/g or 2.3 k J/g), meaning that it carries away a large amount of heat when it evaporates. You can feel the effect of water evaporation on your wet skin when the wind blows. Even when comfortable, your body is still relying for cooling on the heat carried away from the skin and lungs by evaporating water. The heat generated by the

▲ The moderate year-round temperatures in San Francisco are due to the large heat capacity of the surrounding waters.

chemical reactions of metabolism is carried by blood to the skin, where water moves through cell walls to the surface and evaporates. When metabolism, and therefore heat generation, speeds up, blood flow increases and capillaries dilate so that heat is brought to the surface faster.

Water is also unique in what happens as it changes from a liquid to a solid. Most substances are more dense as solids than as liquids because molecules are more closely packed in the solid than in the liquid. Water, however, is different. Liquid water has a maximum density of 1.000 g/mL at 3.98 °C but then becomes *less* dense as it cools. When it freezes, its density decreases still further to 0.917 g/mL.

As water freezes, each molecule is locked into position by hydrogen bonding to four other water molecules (Figure 8.22). The resulting structure has more open space than does liquid water, accounting for its lower density. As a result, ice floats on liquid water, and lakes and rivers freeze from the top down. If the reverse were true, fish would be killed in winter as they became trapped in ice at the bottom.

► **Figure 8.22**
Ice.
Ice consists of individual H_2O molecules held rigidly together in an ordered manner by hydrogen bonds. The open, cage-like crystal structure shows why ice is less dense than liquid water.

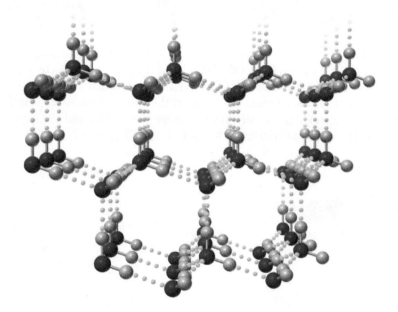

8.14 Solids

A brief look around us reveals that most substances are solids rather than liquids or gases. It is also obvious that there are many different kinds of solids. Some, such as iron and aluminum, are hard and metallic; others, such as sugar and table salt, are crystalline and easily broken; and still others, such as rubber and many plastics, are soft and amorphous.

▲ **Crystalline solids, such as pyrite (left) and fluorite (right) have flat faces and distinct angles. The octahedral shape of pyrite and the cubic shape of fluorite reflect similarly ordered arrangements of particles at the atomic level.**

The most fundamental distinction between solids is that some are crystalline and some are amorphous. A **crystalline solid** is one whose particles—whether atoms, ions, or molecules—have an ordered arrangement extending over a long range. This order on the atomic level is also seen on the visible level, because crystalline solids usually have flat faces and distinct angles.

Crystalline solids can be further categorized as ionic, molecular, covalent network, or metallic. *Ionic solids* are those like sodium chloride, whose constituent particles are ions. A crystal of sodium chloride is composed of alternating Na^+ and Cl^- ions ordered in a regular three-dimensional arrangement and held together by ionic bonds (see Figure 3.3). *Molecular solids* are those like sucrose or ice, whose constituent particles are molecules held together by the intermolecular forces discussed in Section 8.2. *Covalent network solids* are those like diamond (Figure 8.23) or quartz (SiO_2), whose atoms are linked together by covalent bonds into a giant three-dimensional array. In effect, a covalent network solid is one *very* large molecule.

Crystalline solid A solid whose atoms, molecules, or ions are rigidly held in an ordered arrangement.

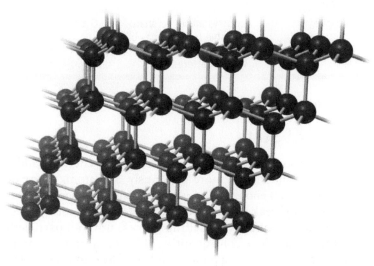

▲ **Figure 8.23**
Diamond. Diamond is a covalent network solid—one very large molecule of carbon atoms linked by covalent bonds.

Metallic solids, such as silver or iron, can be viewed as vast three-dimensional arrays of metal cations immersed in a sea of electrons that are free to move about. This continuous electron sea acts both as a glue to hold the cations together and as a mobile carrier of charge to conduct electricity. Furthermore, the fact that bonding attractions extend uniformly in all directions explains why metals are malleable rather than brittle. When a metal crystal receives a sharp blow, no spatially oriented bonds are broken; instead, the electron sea simply adjusts to the new distribution of cations.

An **amorphous solid**, by contrast with a crystalline solid, is one whose constituent particles are randomly arranged and have no ordered long-range structure. Amorphous solids often result when liquids cool before they can achieve internal order, or when their molecules are large and tangled together, as happens in many polymers. Glass is an amorphous solid, as are tar, the gemstone opal, and some hard candies. Amorphous solids differ from crystalline solids by softening over a wide temperature range rather than having sharp melting points and by shattering to give pieces with curved rather than planar faces.

Amorphous solid A solid whose particles do not have an orderly arrangement.

A summary of the different types of solids and their characteristics is given in Table 8.4.

TABLE 8.4 Types of Solids

Substance	Smallest Unit	Interparticle Forces	Properties	Examples
Ionic solid	Ions	Attraction between positive and negative ions	Brittle and hard; high mp; crystalline	$NaCl$, KI, $Ca_3(PO_4)_2$
Molecular solid	Molecules	Intermolecular forces	Soft; low to moderate mp; crystalline	Ice, wax, frozen CO_2, all solid organic compounds
Covalent network	Atoms	Covalent bonds	Very hard; very high mp; crystalline	Diamond, quartz (SiO_2), tungsten carbide (WC)
Metal or alloy	Metal atoms	Metallic bonding (attraction between metal ions and surrounding mobile electrons)	Lustrous; soft (Na) to hard (Ti); high melting; crystalline	Elements (Fe, Cu, Sn, . . .), bronze (CuSn alloy), amalgams (Hg+ other metals)
Amorphous solid	Atoms, ions, or molecules (including polymer molecules)	Any of the above	Noncrystalline; no sharp mp; able to flow (may be very slow); curved edges when shattered	Glasses, tar, some plastics

8.15 Changes of State

What happens when a solid is heated? As more and more energy is added, molecules begin to stretch, bend, and vibrate more vigorously, and atoms or ions wiggle about with more energy. Finally, if enough energy is added and the motions become vigorous enough, particles start to break free from one another and the substance starts to melt. Addition of more heat continues the melting process until all particles have broken free and are in the liquid phase. The quantity of heat required to completely melt a substance once it reaches its melting point is called its **heat of fusion**. After melting is complete, further addition of heat causes the temperature of the liquid to rise.

The change of a liquid into a vapor proceeds in the same way as the change of a solid into a liquid. When you first put a pan of water on the stove, all the added heat goes into raising the temperature of the water. Once the boiling point is reached, further absorbed heat goes into freeing molecules from their neighbors as they escape into the gas state. The quantity of heat needed to completely vaporize a liquid once it reaches its boiling point is called its **heat of vaporization**. A liquid with a low heat of vaporization, like rubbing alcohol (isopropyl alcohol), evaporates rapidly and is said to be *volatile*. If you spill a volatile liquid on your skin, you will feel a cooling effect as it evaporates because it is absorbing heat from your body.

It is important to know the difference between heat that is added or removed to change the *temperature* of a substance and heat that is added or removed to change the *phase* of a substance. Remember that temperature is a measure of the kinetic energy in a substance (see Section 7.1). When a substance is above or below its phase-change temperature (i.e., melting point or boiling point), adding or removing heat will simply change the kinetic energy and, hence, the temperature of the substance. The amount of heat needed to produce a given temperature change was presented previously (Section 1.13), but is worth presenting again here:

$$\text{Heat (cal or J)} = \text{Mass (g)} \times \text{Temperature change (°C)} \times \text{Specific heat} \left(\frac{\text{cal or J}}{\text{g} \times \text{°C}} \right)$$

In contrast, when a substance is at its phase-change temperature, heat that is added is being used to overcome the intermolecular forces holding particles in that phase. The temperature remains constant until *all* particles have been converted to the next phase. The energy needed to complete the phase change depends only on the amount

Heat of fusion The quantity of heat required to completely melt one gram of a substance once it has reached its melting point.

Heat of vaporization The quantity of heat needed to completely vaporize one gram of a liquid once it has reached its boiling point.

of the substance and the heat of fusion (for melting) or the heat of vaporization (for boiling).

$$\text{Heat (cal or J)} = \text{Mass (g)} \times \text{Heat of fusion} \left(\frac{\text{cal or J}}{g} \right)$$

$$\text{Heat (cal or J)} = \text{Mass (g)} \times \text{Heat of vaporization} \left(\frac{\text{cal or J}}{g} \right)$$

If the intermolecular forces are strong then large amounts of heat must be added to overcome these forces, and the heats of fusion and vaporization will be large. A list of heats of fusion and heats of vaporization for some common substances is given in Table 8.5. Butane, for example, has a small heat of vaporization since the predominant intermolecular forces in butane (dispersion) are relatively weak. Water, on the other hand, has a particularly high heat of vaporization because of its unusually strong hydrogen bonding interactions. Thus, water evaporates more slowly than many other liquids, takes a long time to boil away, and absorbs more heat in the process. A so-called *heating curve*, which indicates the temperature and state changes as heat is added, is shown in Figure 8.24.

TABLE 8.5 Melting Points, Boiling Points, Heats of Fusion, and Heats of Vaporization of Some Common Substances

Substance	Melting Point (°C)	Boiling Point (°C)	Heat of Fusion (cal/g; J/g)	Heat of Vaporization (cal/g; J/g)
Ammonia	−77.7	−33.4	84.0; 351	327; 1370
Butane	−138.4	−0.5	19.2; 80.3	92.5; 387
Ether	−116	34.6	23.5; 98.3	85.6; 358
Ethyl alcohol	−117.3	78.5	26.1; 109	200; 837
Isopropyl alcohol	−89.5	82.4	21.4; 89.5	159; 665
Sodium	97.8	883	14.3; 59.8	492; 2060
Water	0.0	100.0	79.7; 333	540; 2260

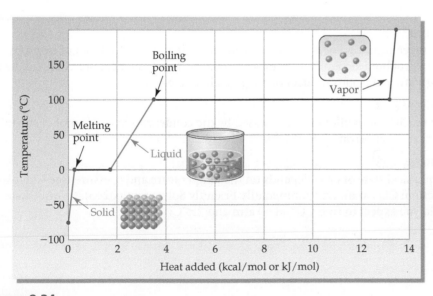

▲ **Figure 8.24**
A heating curve for water, showing the temperature and state changes that occur when heat is added.
The horizontal lines at 0 °C and 100 °C represent the heat of fusion and heat of vaporization, respectively.

Worked Example 8.13 Heat of Fusion: Calculating Total Heat of Melting

Naphthalene, an organic substance often used in mothballs, has a heat of fusion of 35.7 cal/g (149 J/g) and a molar mass of 128.0 g/mol. How much heat in kilocalories is required to melt 0.300 mol of naphthalene?

ANALYSIS The heat of fusion tells how much heat is required to melt 1 g. To find the amount of heat needed to melt 0.300 mol, we need a mole-to-mass conversion.

BALLPARK ESTIMATE Naphthalene has a molar mass of 128.0 g/mol, so 0.300 mol has a mass of about one-third this amount, or about 40 g. Approximately 35 cal or 150 J is required to melt 1 g, so we need about 40 times this amount of heat, or $(35 \times 40 = 1400 \text{ cal} = 1.4 \text{ kcal}, \text{ or } 150 \times 40 = 6000 \text{ J} = 6.0 \text{ kJ})$.

SOLUTION

STEP 1: Identify known information. We know heat of fusion (cal/g), and the number of moles of naphthalene.

Heat of fusion = 35.7 cal/g, or 149 J/g
Moles of naphthalene = 0.300 mol

STEP 2: Identify answer and units.

Heat = ?? cal or J

STEP 3: Identify conversion factors. First convert moles of naphthalene to grams using the molar mass (128 g/mol) as a conversion factor. Then use the heat of fusion as a conversion factor to calculate the total heat necessary to melt the mass of naphthalene.

$$(0.300 \text{ mol naphthalene})\left(\frac{128.0 \text{ g}}{1 \text{ mol}}\right) = 38.4 \text{ g naphthalene}$$

Heat of fusion = 35.7 cal/g or 149 J/g

STEP 4: Solve. Multiplying the mass of naphthalene by the heat of fusion then gives the answer.

$$(38.4 \text{ g naphthalene})\left(\frac{35.7 \text{ cal}}{1 \text{ g naphthalene}}\right) = 1370 \text{ cal} = 1.37 \text{ kcal, or}$$

$$(38.4 \text{ g naphthalene})\left(\frac{149 \text{ J}}{1 \text{ g naphthalene}}\right) = 5720 \text{ J} = 5.72 \text{ kJ}$$

BALLPARK CHECK The calculated result agrees with our estimate (1.4 kcal or 6.0 kJ)

PROBLEM 8.23
How much heat in kilocalories is required to melt and boil 1.50 mol of isopropyl alcohol (rubbing alcohol; molar mass = 60.0 g/mol)? The heat of fusion and heat of vaporization of isopropyl alcohol are given in Table 8.5.

PROBLEM 8.24
How much heat in kilojoules is released by the condensation of 2.5 mol of steam? The heat of vaporization is given in Table 8.5.

PROBLEM 8.25
The physical state of CO_2 depends on the temperature and pressure (see Chemistry in Action: CO_2 as an Environmentally Friendly Solvent on p. 245). In what state would you expect to find CO_2 at 50 atm and 25 °C?

CHEMISTRY IN ACTION

CO₂ as an Environmentally Friendly Solvent

When you think of CO_2 you most likely think of the gas that is absorbed by plants for photosynthesis or exhaled by animals during respiration. You have also probably seen CO_2 in the form of dry ice, that very cold solid that sublimes to a gas. But how can CO_2 be a solvent? After all, carbon dioxide is a gas, not a liquid, at room temperature. Furthermore, CO_2 at atmospheric pressure does not become liquid even when cooled. When the temperature drops to $-78\,°C$ at 1 atm pressure, CO_2 goes directly from gas to solid (dry ice) without first becoming liquid. Only when the pressure is raised does liquid CO_2 exist. At a room temperature of $22.4\,°C$, a pressure of 60 atm is needed to force gaseous CO_2 molecules close enough together so they condense to a liquid. Even as a liquid, though, CO_2 is not a particularly good solvent. Only when it enters an unusual and rarely seen state of matter called the *supercritical state* does CO_2 become a remarkable solvent.

To understand the supercritical state of matter, consider the two factors that determine the physical state of a substance: temperature and pressure. In the solid state, molecules are packed closely together and do not have enough kinetic energy to overcome the intermolecular forces. If we increase the temperature, however, we can increase the kinetic energy so that the molecules can move apart and produce a phase change to either a liquid or a gas. In the gas state, molecules are too far apart to interact, but increasing the pressure will force molecules closer together, and, eventually, intermolecular attractions between molecules will cause them to condense into a liquid or solid state. This dependence of the physical state on temperature and pressure is represented by a *phase diagram*, such as the one shown here for CO_2.

The supercritical state represents a situation that is intermediate between liquid and gas. There is *some* space between molecules, but not much. The molecules are too far apart to be truly a liquid, yet they are too close together to be truly a gas. Supercritical CO_2 exists above the *critical point*, when the pressure is above 72.8 atm and the temperature is above $31.2\,°C$.

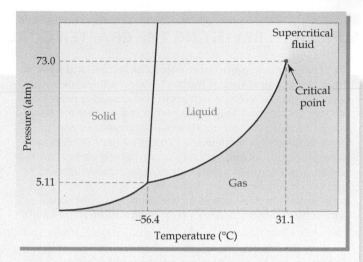

This pressure is high enough to force molecules close together and prevent them from expanding into the gas state. Above this temperature, however, the molecules have too much kinetic energy to condense into the liquid state.

Because open spaces already exist between CO_2 molecules, it is energetically easy for dissolved molecules to slip in, and supercritical CO_2 is therefore an extraordinarily good solvent. Among its many applications, supercritical CO_2 is used in the beverage and food-processing industries to decaffeinate coffee beans and to obtain spice extracts from vanilla, pepper, cloves, nutmeg, and other seeds. In the cosmetics and perfume industry, fragrant oils are extracted from flowers using supercritical CO_2. Perhaps the most important future application is the use of carbon dioxide for dry-cleaning clothes, thereby replacing environmentally harmful chlorinated solvents.

The use of supercritical CO_2 as a solvent has many benefits, including the fact that it is nontoxic and nonflammable. Most important, though, is that the technology is environmentally friendly. Industrial processes using CO_2 are designed as closed systems so that the CO_2 is recaptured after use and continually recycled. No organic solvent vapors are released into the atmosphere and no toxic liquids seep into groundwater supplies, as can occur with current procedures using chlorinated organic solvents. The future looks bright for this new technology.

See Chemistry in Action Problems 8.104 and 8.105 at the end of the chapter.

SUMMARY: REVISITING THE CHAPTER GOALS

1. What are the major intermolecular forces, and how do they affect the states of matter? There are three major types of *intermolecular forces*, which act to hold molecules near one another in solids and liquids. *Dipole–dipole forces* are the electrical attractions that occur between polar molecules. *London dispersion forces* occur between all molecules as a result of temporary molecular polarities due to unsymmetrical electron distribution. These forces increase in strength with molecular weight and with the surface area of molecules. *Hydrogen bonding*, the strongest of the three intermolecular forces, occurs between a hydrogen atom bonded to O, N, or F and a nearby O, N, or F atom (*see Problems 34–37, 116*).

2. How do scientists explain the behavior of gases? According to the *kinetic-molecular theory of gases*, the physical behavior of gases can be explained by assuming that they consist of particles moving rapidly at random, separated from other particles by great distances, and colliding without loss of energy. Gas pressure is the result of molecular collisions with a surface (*see Problems 29, 30, 40, 41, 53, 59, 68, 102, 103, 106*).

3. How do gases respond to changes in temperature, pressure, and volume? *Boyle's law* says that the volume of a fixed amount of gas at constant temperature is inversely proportional to its pressure ($P_1V_1 = P_2V_2$). *Charles's law* says that the volume of a fixed amount of gas at constant pressure is directly proportional to its Kelvin temperature ($V_1/T_1 = V_2/T_2$). *Gay-Lussac's law* says that the pressure of a fixed amount of gas at constant volume is directly proportional to its Kelvin temperature ($P_1/T_1 = P_2/T_2$). Boyle's law, Charles's law, and Gay-Lussac's law together give the *combined gas law* ($P_1V_1/T_1 = P_2V_2/T_2$), which applies to changing conditions for a fixed quantity of gas. *Avogadro's law* says that equal volumes of gases at the same temperature and pressure contain the same number of moles ($V_1/n_1 = V_2/n_2$) (*see Problems 26, 27, 32, 38–75, 107, 111, 112, 115*).

4. What is the ideal gas law? The four gas laws together give the *ideal gas law*, $PV = nRT$, which relates the effects of temperature, pressure, volume, and molar amount. At 0 °C and 1 atm pressure, called *standard temperature and pressure (STP)*, 1 mol of any gas (6.02×10^{23} molecules) occupies a volume of 22.4 L (*see Problems 76–85, 108–110, 113–115, 118, 119*).

5. What is partial pressure? The amount of pressure exerted by an individual gas in a mixture is called the *partial pressure* of the gas. According to *Dalton's law*, the total pressure exerted by the mixture is equal to the sum of the partial pressures of the individual gases (*see Problems 33, 86–89, 117*).

6. What are the various kinds of solids, and how do they differ? Solids are either crystalline or amorphous. *Crystalline solids* are those whose constituent particles have an ordered arrangement; *amorphous solids* lack internal order and do not have sharp melting points. There are several kinds of crystalline solids: *Ionic solids* are those such as sodium chloride, whose constituent particles are ions. *Molecular solids* are those such as ice, whose constituent particles are molecules held together by intermolecular forces. *Covalent network solids* are those such as diamond, whose atoms are linked together by covalent bonds into a giant three-dimensional array. *Metallic solids*, such as silver or iron, also consist of large arrays of atoms, but their crystals have metallic properties such as electrical conductivity (*see Problems 96–99*).

7. What factors affect a change of state? When a solid is heated, particles begin to move around freely at the *melting point*, and the substance becomes liquid. The amount of heat necessary to melt a given amount of solid at its melting point is its *heat of fusion*. As a liquid is heated, molecules escape from the surface of a liquid until an equilibrium is reached between liquid and gas, resulting in a *vapor pressure* of the liquid. At a liquid's *boiling point*, its vapor pressure equals atmospheric pressure, and the entire liquid is converted into gas. The amount of heat necessary to vaporize a given amount of liquid at its boiling point is called its *heat of vaporization* (*see Problems 27, 28, 31, 90–95, 98, 99, 104*).

KEY WORDS

Amorphous solid, *p. 241*

Avogadro's law, *p. 232*

Boiling point (bp), *p. 215*

Boyle's law, *p. 226*

Change of state, *p. 214*

Charles's law, *p. 229*

Combined gas law, *p. 231*

Crystalline solid, *p. 241*

Dalton's law, *p. 236*

Dipole–dipole force, *p. 216*

Gas constant (R), *p. 234*

Gas laws, *p. 225*

Gay-Lussac's law, *p. 230*

Heat of fusion, *p. 242*

Heat of vaporization, *p. 242*

Hydrogen bond, *p. 217*

Ideal gas, *p. 221*

Ideal gas law, *p. 233*

Intermolecular force, *p. 216*

Kinetic–molecular theory of gases, *p. 220*

London dispersion force, *p. 217*

Melting point (mp), *p. 215*

Normal boiling point, *p. 238*

Partial pressure, *p. 236*

Pressure (P), *p. 221*

Standard temperature and pressure (STP), *p. 233*

Standard molar volume, *p. 233*

Vapor, *p. 237*

Vapor pressure, *p. 237*

CONCEPT MAP: GASES, LIQUIDS, AND SOLIDS

Concept Map. The physical state of matter (solid, liquid, gas) depends on the strength of the intermolecular forces between molecules compared to the kinetic energy of the molecules. When the kinetic energy (i.e, temperature) is greater than the forces holding molecules in a given state, then a phase change occurs. Thus, the physical properties of matter (melting and boiling points, etc.) depend on the strength of the intermolecular forces between molecules, which depend on chemical structure and molecular shape. These relationships are reflected here in Figure 8.25.

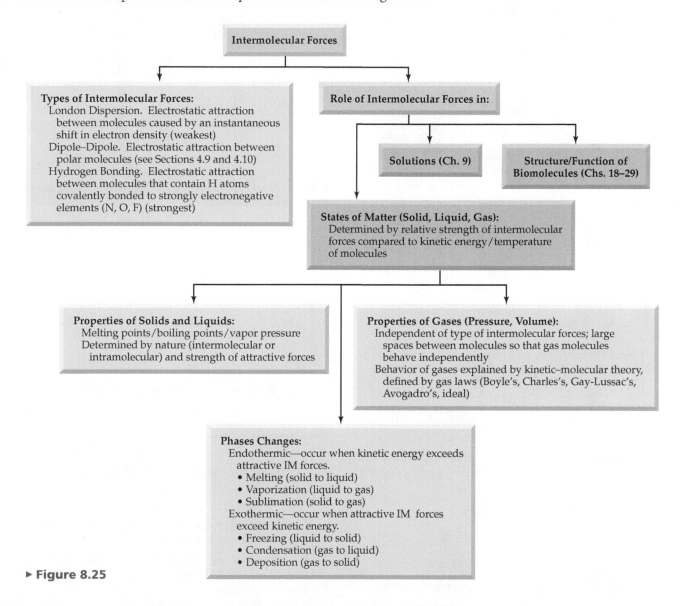

▶ **Figure 8.25**

UNDERSTANDING KEY CONCEPTS

8.26   Assume that you have a sample of gas in a cylinder with a movable piston, as shown in the following drawing:

Redraw the apparatus to show what the sample will look like after the following changes:

(a) The temperature is increased from 300 K to 450 K at constant pressure.

(b) The pressure is increased from 1 atm to 2 atm at constant temperature.

(c) The temperature is decreased from 300 K to 200 K and the pressure is decreased from 3 atm to 2 atm.

8.27   Assume that you have a sample of gas at 350 K in a sealed container, as represented in part (a). Which of the drawings (b)–(d) represents the gas after the temperature is lowered from 350 K to 150 K if the gas has a boiling point of 200 K? Which drawing represents the gas at 150 K if the gas has a boiling point of 100 K?

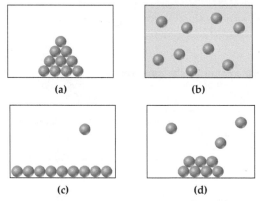

8.28   Assume that drawing (a) represents a sample of H_2O at 200 K. Which of the drawings (b)–(d) represents what the sample will look like when the temperature is raised to 300 K?

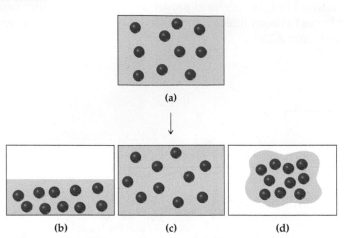

8.29   Three bulbs, two of which contain different gases and one of which is empty, are connected as shown in the following drawing:

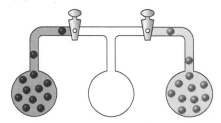

Redraw the apparatus to represent the gases after the stopcocks are opened and the system is allowed to come to equilibrium.

8.30   Redraw the following open-ended manometer to show what it would look like when stopcock A is opened.

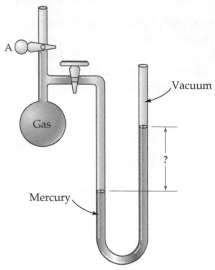

8.31   The following graph represents the heating curve of a hypothetical substance:

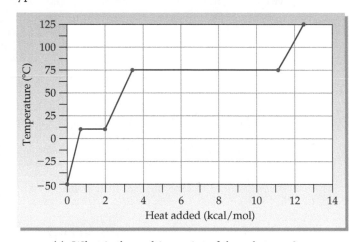

(a) What is the melting point of the substance?

(b) What is the boiling point of the substance?

(c) Approximately what is the heat of fusion for the substance in kcal/mol?

(d) Approximately what is the heat of vaporization for the substance in kcal/mol?

8.32   Show the approximate level of the movable piston in drawings (a)–(c) after the indicated changes have been made to the gas.

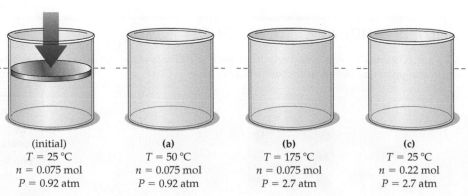

(initial)	(a)	(b)	(c)
T = 25 °C	T = 50 °C	T = 175 °C	T = 25 °C
n = 0.075 mol	n = 0.075 mol	n = 0.075 mol	n = 0.22 mol
P = 0.92 atm	P = 0.92 atm	P = 2.7 atm	P = 2.7 atm

8.33   The partial pressure of the blue gas in the container represented in the picture is 240 mmHg. What are the partial pressures of the yellow and red gases? What is the total pressure inside the container?

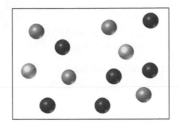

ADDITIONAL PROBLEMS

INTERMOLECULAR FORCES

8.34   What characteristic must a compound have to experience the following intermolecular forces?

(a) London dispersion forces   (b) Dipole–dipole forces

(c) Hydrogen bonding

8.35   Identify the predominant intermolecular force in each of the following substances.

(a) N_2 (b) HCN   (c) CCl_4

(d) NH_3 (e) CH_3Cl (f) CH_3COOH

8.36   Dimethyl ether (CH_3OCH_3) and ethanol (C_2H_5OH) have the same formula (C_2H_6O), but the boiling point of dimethyl ether is $-25\,^\circ C$, while that of ethanol is $78\,^\circ C$. Explain this difference in boiling points.

8.37   Iodine is a solid at room temperature $(mp = 113.5\,^\circ C)$ while bromine is a liquid $(mp = -7\,^\circ C)$. Explain this difference in terms of intermolecular forces.

GASES AND PRESSURE

8.38   How is 1 atm of pressure defined?

8.39   List four common units for measuring pressure.

8.40   What are the four assumptions of the kinetic–molecular theory of gases?

8.41   How does the kinetic–molecular theory of gases explain gas pressure?

8.42   Convert the following values into mmHg:

(a) Standard pressure   (b) 25.3 psi   (c) 7.5 atm

(d) 28.0 in. Hg   (e) 41.8 Pa

8.43   Atmospheric pressure at the top of Mt. Whitney in California is 440 mmHg.

(a) How many atmospheres is this?

(b) How many pascals is this?

8.44   What is the pressure (in mmHg) inside a container of gas connected to a mercury-filled, open-ended manometer of the sort shown in Figure 8.10 when the level in the arm connected to the container is 17.6 cm lower than the level in the arm open to the atmosphere and the atmospheric pressure reading outside the apparatus is 754.3 mmHg? What is the pressure inside the container in atm?

8.45   What is the pressure (in atmospheres) inside a container of gas connected to a mercury-filled, open-ended manometer of the sort shown in Figure 8.10 when the level in the arm connected to the container is 28.3 cm higher than the level in the arm open to the atmosphere, and the atmospheric pressure reading outside the apparatus is 1.021 atm? What is the pressure in mmHg?

BOYLE'S LAW

8.46   What is Boyle's law, and what variables must be kept constant for the law to hold?

8.47   Which assumption(s) of the kinetic–molecular theory explain the behavior of gases described by Boyle's Law? Explain your answer.

8.48   The pressure of gas in a 600.0 mL cylinder is 65.0 mmHg. What is the new volume when the pressure is increased to 385 mmHg?

8.49   The volume of a balloon is 2.85 L at 1.00 atm. What pressure is required to compress the balloon to a volume of 1.70 L?

8.50   The use of chlorofluorocarbons (CFCs) as refrigerants and propellants in aerosol cans has been discontinued as a result of concerns about the ozone layer. If an aerosol can contained 350 mL of CFC gas at a pressure of 5.0 atm, what volume would this gas occupy at 1.0 atm?

8.51   A balloon occupies a volume of 1.25 L at sea level where the ambient pressure is 1 atm. What volume would the balloon occupy at an altitude of 35,000 ft, where the air pressure is only 220 mmHg?

CHARLES'S LAW

8.52   What is Charles's law, and what variables must be kept constant for the law to hold?

8.53   Which assumption(s) of the kinetic–molecular theory explain the behavior of gases described by Charles's Law? Explain your answer.

8.54   A hot-air balloon has a volume of 960 L at 291 K. To what temperature (in $^\circ C$) must it be heated to raise its volume to 1200 L, assuming the pressure remains constant?

8.55   A hot-air balloon has a volume of 875 L. What is the original temperature of the balloon if its volume changes to 955 L when heated to $56\,^\circ C$?

8.56   A gas sample has a volume of 185 mL at $38\,^\circ C$. What is its volume at $97\,^\circ C$?

8.57   A balloon has a volume of 43.0 L at $25\,^\circ C$. What is its volume at $2.8\,^\circ C$?

GAY-LUSSAC'S LAW

8.58 What is Gay-Lussac's law, and what variables must be kept constant for the law to hold?

8.59 Which assumption(s) of the kinetic–molecular theory explain the behavior of gases described by Gay-Lussac's Law? Explain your answer.

8.60 A glass laboratory flask is filled with gas at 25 °C and 0.95 atm pressure, sealed, and then heated to 117 °C. What is the pressure inside the flask?

8.61 An aerosol can has an internal pressure of 3.85 atm at 25 °C. What temperature is required to raise the pressure to 18.0 atm?

COMBINED GAS LAW

8.62 A gas has a volume of 2.84 L at 1.00 atm and 0 °C. At what temperature does it have a volume of 7.50 L at 520 mmHg?

8.63 A compressed-air tank carried by scuba divers has a volume of 6.80 L and a pressure of 120 atm at 20 °C. What is the volume of air in the tank at 0 °C and 1.00 atm pressure (STP)?

8.64 When H_2 gas was released by the reaction of HCl with Zn, the volume of H_2 collected was 75.4 mL at 23 °C and 748 mmHg. What is the volume of the H_2 at 0 °C and 1.00 atm pressure (STP)?

8.65 What is the effect on the volume of a gas if you simultaneously:

(a) Halve its pressure and double its Kelvin temperature?

(b) Double its pressure and double its Kelvin temperature?

8.66 What is the effect on the pressure of a gas if you simultaneously:

(a) Halve its volume and double its Kelvin temperature?

(b) Double its volume and halve its Kelvin temperature?

8.67 A small cylinder of helium gas used for filling balloons has a volume of 2.30 L and a pressure of 1850 atm at 25 °C. How many balloons can you fill if each one has a volume of 1.5 L and a pressure of 1.25 atm at 25 °C?

AVOGADRO'S LAW AND STANDARD MOLAR VOLUME

8.68 Explain Avogadro's law using the kinetic–molecular theory of gases.

8.69 What conditions are defined as standard temperature and pressure (STP)?

8.70 How many molecules are in 1.0 L of O_2 at STP or 1.0 L? How may grams of O_2?

8.71 How many moles of gas are in a volume of 48.6 L at STP?

8.72 What is the mass of CH_4 in a sample that occupies a volume of 16.5 L at STP?

8.73 Assume that you have 1.75 g of the deadly gas hydrogen cyanide, HCN. What is the volume of the gas at STP?

8.74 A typical room is 4.0 m long, 5.0 m wide, and 2.5 m high. What is the total mass of the oxygen in the room assuming that the gas in the room is at STP and that air contains 21% oxygen and 79% nitrogen?

8.75 What is the total volume and number of moles of nitrogen in the room described in Problem 8.74?

IDEAL GAS LAW

8.76 What is the ideal gas law?

8.77 How does the ideal gas law differ from the combined gas law?

8.78 Which sample contains more molecules: 2.0 L of Cl_2 at STP, or 3.0 L of CH_4 at 300 K and 1150 mmHg? Which sample weighs more?

8.79 Which sample contains more molecules: 2.0 L of CO_2 at 300 K and 500 mmHg, or 1.5 L of N_2 at 57 °C and 760 mmHg? Which sample weighs more?

8.80 If 2.3 mol of He has a volume of 0.15 L at 294 K, what is the pressure in atm? In psi?

8.81 If 3.5 mol of O_2 has a volume of 27.0 L at a pressure of 1.6 atm, what is its temperature in °C?

8.82 If 15.0 g of CO_2 gas has a volume of 0.30 L at 310 K, what is its pressure in mmHg?

8.83 If 20.0 g of N_2 gas has a volume of 4.00 L and a pressure of 6.0 atm, what is its temperature in degrees celsius?

8.84 If 18.0 g of O_2 gas has a temperature of 350 K and a pressure of 550 mmHg, what is its volume?

8.85 How many moles of a gas will occupy a volume of 0.55 L at a temperature of 347 K and a pressure of 2.5 atm?

DALTON'S LAW AND PARTIAL PRESSURE

8.86 What is meant by *partial pressure*?

8.87 What is Dalton's law?

8.88 If the partial pressure of oxygen in air at 1.0 atm is 160 mmHg, what is its partial pressure on the summit of Mt. Whitney, where atmospheric pressure is 440 mmHg? Assume that the percent oxygen is the same.

8.89 Scuba divers who suffer from decompression sickness are treated in hyperbaric chambers using heliox (21% oxygen, 79% helium), at pressures up to 120 psi. Calculate the partial pressure of O_2 (in mmHg) in a hyperbaric chamber under these conditions.

LIQUIDS

8.90 What is the vapor pressure of a liquid?

8.91 What is a liquid's heat of vaporization?

8.92 What is the effect of pressure on a liquid's boiling point?

8.93 Which of the following substances would you expect to have the higher vapor pressure: CH_3OH or CH_3Cl? Explain

8.94 The heat of vaporization of water is 9.72 kcal/mol.

(a) How much heat (in kilocalories) is required to vaporize 3.00 mol of H_2O?

(b) How much heat (in kilocalories) is released when 320 g of steam condenses?

8.95 Patients with a high body temperature are often given "alcohol baths." The heat of vaporization of isopropyl alcohol (rubbing alcohol) is 159 cal/g. How much heat is removed from the skin by the evaporation of 190 g (about 1/2 a cup) of isopropyl alcohol?

SOLIDS

8.96 What is the difference between an amorphous and a crystalline solid?

8.97 List three kinds of crystalline solids, and give an example of each.

8.98 The heat of fusion of acetic acid, the principal organic component of vinegar, is 45.9 cal/g. How much heat (in kilocalories) is required to melt 1.75 mol of solid acetic acid?

8.99 The heat of fusion of sodium metal is 630 cal/mol. How much heat (in kilocalories) is required to melt 262 g of sodium?

CHEMISTRY IN ACTION

8.100 What evidence is there that global warming is occurring? [*Greenhouse Gases and Global Warming, p. 224*]

8.101 What are the three most important greenhouse gases? [*Greenhouse Gases and Global Warming, p. 224*]

8.102 What is the difference between a systolic and a diastolic pressure reading? Is a blood pressure of 180/110 within the normal range? [*Blood Pressure, p. 228*]

8.103 Convert the blood pressure reading in Problem 8.102 to atm. [*Blood Pressure, p. 228*]

8.104 What is a supercritical fluid? [*CO_2 as an Environmentally Friendly Solvent, p. 245*]

8.105 What are the environmental advantages of using supercritical CO_2 in place of chlorinated organic solvents? [*CO_2 as an Environmentally Friendly Solvent, p. 245*]

GENERAL QUESTIONS AND PROBLEMS

8.106 Use the kinetic–molecular theory to explain why gas pressure increases if the temperature is raised and the volume is kept constant.

8.107 Hydrogen and oxygen react according to the equation $2 H_2(g) + O_2(g) \longrightarrow 2 H_2O(g)$. According to Avogadro's law, how many liters of hydrogen are required to react with 2.5 L of oxygen at STP?

8.108 If 3.0 L of hydrogen and 1.5 L of oxygen at STP react to yield water, how many moles of water are formed? What gas volume does the water have at a temperature of 100 °C and 1 atm pressure?

8.109 Approximately 240 mL/min of CO_2 is exhaled by an average adult at rest. Assuming a temperature of 37 °C and 1 atm pressure, how many moles of CO_2 is this?

8.110 How many grams of CO_2 are exhaled by an average resting adult in 24 hours? (See Problem 8.109.)

8.111 Imagine that you have two identical containers, one containing hydrogen at STP and the other containing oxygen at STP. How can you tell which is which without opening them?

8.112 When fully inflated, a hot-air balloon has a volume of 1.6×10^5 L at an average temperature of 375 K and 0.975 atm. Assuming that air has an average molar mass of 29 g/mol, what is the density of the air in the hot-air balloon? How does this compare with the density of air at STP?

8.113 A 10.0 g sample of an unknown gas occupies 14.7 L at a temperature of 25 °C and a pressure of 745 mmHg. How many moles of gas are in the sample? What is the molar mass of the gas?

8.114 One mole of any gas has a volume of 22.4 L at STP. What are the molecular weights of the following gases, and what are their densities in grams per liter at STP?

(a) CH_4 (b) CO_2 (c) O_2

8.115 Gas pressure outside the space shuttle is approximately 1×10^{-14} mm Hg at a temperature of approximately 1 K. If the gas is almost entirely hydrogen atoms (H, not H_2), what volume of space is occupied by 1 mol of atoms? What is the density of H gas in atoms per liter?

8.116 Ethylene glycol, $C_2H_6O_2$, has one OH bonded to each carbon.

(a) Draw the Lewis dot structure of ethylene glycol.

(b) Draw the Lewis dot structure of chloroethane, C_2H_5Cl.

(c) Chloroethane has a slightly higher molar mass than ethylene glycol, but a much lower boiling point (3 °C versus 198 °C). Explain.

8.117 A rule of thumb for scuba diving is that the external pressure increases by 1 atm for every 10 m of depth. A diver using a compressed air tank is planning to descend to a depth of 25 m.

(a) What is the external pressure at this depth? (Remember that the pressure at sea level is 1 atm.)

(b) Assuming that the tank contains 20% oxygen and 80% nitrogen, what is the partial pressure of each gas in the diver's lungs at this depth?

8.118 The *Rankine* temperature scale used in engineering is to the Fahrenheit scale as the Kelvin scale is to the Celsius scale. That is, 1 Rankine degree is the same size as 1 Fahrenheit degree, and 0 °R = absolute zero.

(a) What temperature corresponds to the freezing point of water on the Rankine scale?

(b) What is the value of the gas constant R on the Rankine scale in $(L \cdot atm)/(°R \cdot mol)$?

8.119 Isooctane, C_8H_{18}, is the component of gasoline from which the term *octane rating* derives.

(a) Write a balanced equation for the combustion of isooctane to yield CO_2 and H_2O.

(b) Assuming that gasoline is 100% isooctane and that the density of isooctane is 0.792 g/mL, what mass of CO_2 (in kilograms) is produced each year by the annual U.S. gasoline consumption of 4.6×10^{10} L?

(c) What is the volume (in liters) of this CO_2 at STP?

CHAPTER 9

Solutions

◄ The giant sequoia relies on osmotic pressure—a colligative property of solutions—to transport water and nutrients from the roots to the treetops 300 ft up.

1. **What are solutions, and what factors affect solubility?**
   THE GOAL: Be able to define the different kinds of mixtures and explain the influence on solubility of solvent and solute structure, temperature, and pressure. (◀◀ B., E.)

2. **How is the concentration of a solution expressed?**
   THE GOAL: Be able to define, use, and convert between the most common ways of expressing solution concentrations.

3. **How are dilutions carried out?**
   THE GOAL: Be able to calculate the concentration of a solution prepared by dilution and explain how to make a desired dilution.

4. **What is an electrolyte?**
   THE GOAL: Be able to recognize strong and weak electrolytes and nonelectrolytes, and express electrolyte concentrations. (◀◀ A.)

5. **How do solutions differ from pure solvents in their behavior?**
   THE GOAL: Be able to explain vapor-pressure lowering, boiling-point elevation, and freezing-point depression for solutions. (◀◀ F., G.)

6. **What is osmosis?**
   THE GOAL: Be able to describe osmosis and some of its applications.

U p to this point, we have been concerned primarily with pure substances, both elements and compounds. In day-to-day life, however, most of the materials we come in contact with are mixtures. Air, for example, is a gaseous mixture of primarily oxygen and nitrogen; blood is a liquid mixture of many different components; and many rocks are solid mixtures of different minerals. In this chapter, we look closely at the characteristics and properties of mixtures, with particular attention to the uniform mixtures we call *solutions*.

9.1 Mixtures and Solutions

As we saw in Section 1.3, a *mixture* is an intimate combination of two or more substances, both of which retain their chemical identities. Mixtures can be classified as either *heterogeneous* or *homogeneous*, as indicated in Figure 9.1, depending on their appearance. **Heterogeneous mixtures** are those in which the mixing is not uniform and which therefore have regions of different composition. Rocky Road ice cream, for example, is a heterogeneous mixture, with something different in every spoonful. Granite and many other rocks are also heterogeneous, having a grainy character due to the heterogeneous mixing of different minerals. **Homogeneous mixtures** are those in which the mixing *is* uniform and that therefore have the same composition throughout. Seawater, a homogeneous mixture of soluble ionic compounds in water, is an example.

Homogeneous mixtures can be further classified as either *solutions* or *colloids*, according to the size of their particles. **Solutions**, the most important class of homogeneous mixtures, contain particles the size of a typical ion or small molecule—roughly 0.1–2 nm in diameter. **Colloids**, such as milk and fog, are also homogeneous in appearance but contain larger particles than solutions—in the range 2–500 nm diameter.

Liquid solutions, colloids, and heterogeneous mixtures can be distinguished in several ways. For example, liquid solutions are transparent (although they may be colored). Colloids may appear transparent if the particle size is small, but they have a murky or opaque appearance if the particle size is larger. Neither solutions nor small-particle colloids separate on standing, and the particles in both are too small to be removed by filtration. Heterogeneous mixtures and large-particle colloids, also known as "suspensions," are murky or opaque and their particles will slowly settle on prolonged standing. House paint is an example.

Heterogeneous mixture A nonuniform mixture that has regions of different composition.

Homogeneous mixture A uniform mixture that has the same composition throughout.

Solution A homogeneous mixture that contains particles the size of a typical ion or small molecule.

Colloid A homogeneous mixture that contains particles that range in diameter from 2 to 500 nm.

▶**Figure 9.1**
Classification of mixtures.
The components in heterogeneous mixtures are not uniformly mixed, and the composition varies with location within the mixture. In homogeneous mixtures, the components are uniformly mixed at the molecular level.

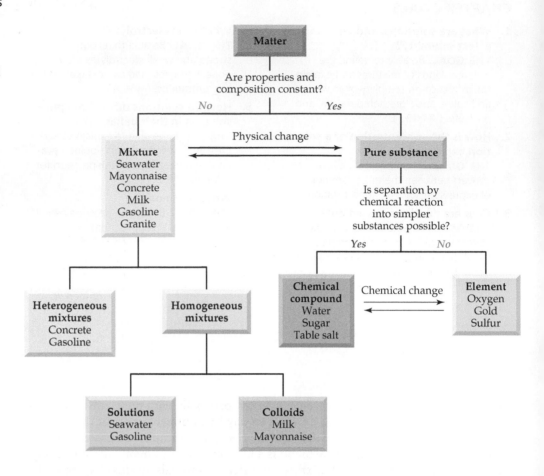

Table 9.1 gives some examples of solutions, colloids, and heterogeneous mixtures. It is interesting to note that blood has characteristics of all three. About 45% by volume of blood consists of suspended red and white cells, which settle slowly on standing; the remaining 55% is *plasma*, which contains ions in solution and colloidal protein molecules.

TABLE 9.1 Some Characteristics of Solutions, Colloids, and Heterogeneous Mixtures

Type of Mixture	Particle Size	Examples	Characteristics
Solution	<2.0 nm	Air, seawater, gasoline, wine	Transparent to light; does not separate on standing; nonfilterable
Colloid	2.0–500 nm	Butter, milk, fog, pearl	Often murky or opaque to light; does not separate on standing; nonfilterable
Heterogeneous	>500 nm	Blood, paint, aerosol sprays	Murky or opaque to light; separates on standing; filterable

Although we usually think of solids dissolved in liquids when we talk about solutions, solutions actually occur in all three phases of matter (Table 9.2). Metal alloys like 14-karat gold (58% gold with silver and copper) and brass (10–40% zinc with copper), for instance, are solutions of one solid with another. For solutions in which a gas or solid is dissolved in a liquid, the dissolved substance is called the **solute** and the liquid is called the **solvent**. In seawater, for example, the dissolved salts would be the solutes and water would be the solvent. When one liquid is dissolved in another, the minor component is usually considered the solute and the major component is the solvent.

Solute A substance that is dissolved in a solvent.

Solvent The substance in which another substance (the solute) is dissolved.

TABLE **9.2**   **Some Different Types of Solutions**

Type of Solution	Example
Gas in gas	Air (O_2, N_2, Ar, and other gases)
Gas in liquid	Seltzer water (CO_2 in water)
Gas in solid	H_2 in palladium metal
Liquid in liquid	Gasoline (mixture of hydrocarbons)
Liquid in solid	Dental amalgam (mercury in silver)
Solid in liquid	Seawater (NaCl and other salts in water)
Solid in solid	Metal alloys such as 14-karat gold (Au, Ag, and Cu)

PROBLEM 9.1

Classify the following liquid mixtures as heterogeneous or homogeneous. Further classify each homogeneous mixture as a solution or colloid.

(a) Orange juice   (b) Apple juice
(c) Hand lotion   (d) Tea

9.2 The Solution Process

What determines whether a substance is soluble in a given liquid? Solubility depends primarily on the strength of the attractions between solute and solvent particles relative to the strengths of the attractions within the pure substances. Ethyl alcohol is soluble in water, for example, because hydrogen bonding (Section 8.2) is nearly as strong between water and ethyl alcohol molecules as it is between water molecules alone or ethyl alcohol molecules alone.

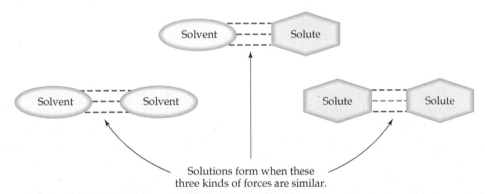

Solutions form when these
three kinds of forces are similar.

A good rule of thumb for predicting solubility is that "like dissolves like," meaning that substances with similar intermolecular forces form solutions with one another, whereas substances with different intermolecular forces do not (Section 8.2).

Polar solvents dissolve polar and ionic solutes; nonpolar solvents dissolve nonpolar solutes. Thus, a polar, hydrogen-bonding compound like water dissolves ethyl alcohol and sodium chloride, whereas a nonpolar organic compound like hexane (C_6H_{14}) dissolves other nonpolar organic compounds like fats and oils. Water and oil, however, do not dissolve one another, as summed up by the old saying, "Oil and water don't mix." The intermolecular forces between water molecules are so strong that after an oil–water mixture is shaken, the water layer re-forms, squeezing out the oil molecules.

Water solubility is not limited to ionic compounds and ethyl alcohol. Many polar organic substances, such as sugars, amino acids, and even some proteins, dissolve in water. In addition, small, moderately polar organic molecules such as chloroform ($CHCl_3$) are soluble in water to a limited extent. When mixed with water, a small amount of the organic compound dissolves, but the remainder forms a separate liquid layer. As the number of carbon atoms in organic molecules increases, though, water solubility decreases.

The process of dissolving an ionic solid in a polar liquid can be visualized as shown in Figure 9.2 for sodium chloride. When NaCl crystals are put in water, ions at the crystal surface come into contact with polar water molecules. Positively charged Na^+ ions are attracted to the negatively polarized oxygen of water, and negatively charged Cl^- ions are attracted to the positively polarized hydrogens. The combined forces of attraction between an ion and several water molecules pull the ion away from the crystal, exposing a fresh surface, until ultimately the crystal dissolves. Once in solution, Na^+ and Cl^- ions are completely surrounded by solvent molecules, a phenomenon called **solvation** (or, specifically for water, *hydration*). The water molecules form a loose shell around the ions, stabilizing them by electrical attraction.

Solvation The clustering of solvent molecules around a dissolved solute molecule or ion.

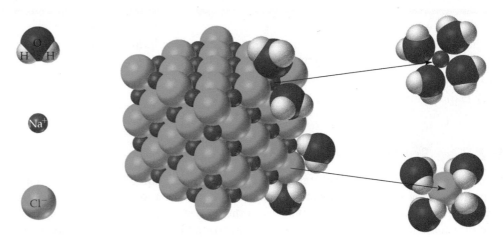

▲ **Figure 9.2**
Dissolution of an NaCl crystal in water.
Polar water molecules surround the individual Na^+ and Cl^- ions at an exposed edge or corner, pulling them from the crystal surface into solution and surrounding them. Note how the negatively polarized oxygens of water molecules cluster around Na^+ ions and the positively polarized hydrogens cluster around Cl^- ions.

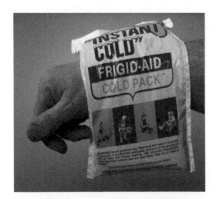

▲ Instant cold packs used to treat muscle strains and sprains often take advantage of the endothermic enthalpy of a solution of salts such as ammonium nitrate.

The dissolution of a solute in a solvent is a physical change, because the solution components retain their chemical identities. When sugar dissolves in water, for example, the individual sugar and water molecules still have the same chemical formulas as in the pure or undissolved state. Like all chemical and physical changes, the dissolution of a substance in a solvent has associated with it a heat change, or *enthalpy* change (Section 7.2). Some substances dissolve exothermically, releasing heat and warming the resultant solution, whereas other substances dissolve endothermically, absorbing heat and cooling the resultant solution. Calcium chloride, for example, *releases* 19.4 kcal/mol (81.2 kJ/mol) of heat energy when it dissolves in water, but ammonium nitrate (NH_4NO_3) *absorbs* 6.1 kcal/mol (25.5 kJ/mol) of heat energy. Athletes and others take advantage of both situations when they use instant hot packs or cold packs to treat injuries. Both hot and cold packs consist of a pouch of water and a dry chemical, such as $CaCl_2$ or $MgSO_4$ for hot packs, and NH_4NO_3 for cold packs. Squeezing the pack breaks the pouch and the solid dissolves, either raising or lowering the temperature.

Worked Example **9.1** Formation of Solutions

Which of the following pairs of substances would you expect to form solutions?
(a) Carbon tetrachloride (CCl_4) and hexane (C_6H_{14}).
(b) Octane (C_8H_{18}) and methyl alcohol (CH_3OH).

ANALYSIS Identify the kinds of intermolecular forces in each substance (Section 8.2). Substances with similar intermolecular forces tend to form solutions.

SOLUTION

(a) Hexane contains only C—H and C—C bonds, which are nonpolar. Carbon tetrachloride contains polar C—Cl bonds, but they are distributed symmetrically in the tetrahedral molecule so that it too is nonpolar. The major intermolecular force for both compounds is London dispersion forces, so they will form a solution.

(b) Octane contains only C—H and C—C bonds and so is nonpolar; the major intermolecular force is dispersion. Methyl alcohol contains polar C—O and O—H bonds; it is polar and forms hydrogen bonds. The intermolecular forces for the two substances are so dissimilar that they do not form a solution.

PROBLEM 9.2

Which of the following pairs of substances would you expect to form solutions?

(a) CCl_4 and water

(b) Benzene (C_6H_6) and $MgSO_4$

(c) Hexane (C_6H_{14}) and heptane (C_7H_{16})

(d) Ethyl alcohol (C_2H_5OH) and heptanol $(C_7H_{15}OH)$

9.3 Solid Hydrates

Some ionic compounds attract water strongly enough to hold on to water molecules even when crystalline, forming what are called *solid hydrates*. For example, the plaster of Paris used to make decorative objects and casts for broken limbs is calcium sulfate hemihydrate, $CaSO_4 \cdot \frac{1}{2}H_2O$. The dot between $CaSO_4$ and $\frac{1}{2}H_2O$ in the formula indicates that for every two $CaSO_4$ formula units in the crystal there is also one water molecule present.

$$CaSO_4 \cdot \tfrac{1}{2}H_2O \quad \text{A solid hydrate}$$

After being ground up and mixed with water to make plaster, $CaSO_4 \cdot \frac{1}{2}H_2O$ gradually changes into the crystalline dihydrate $CaSO_4 \cdot 2\,H_2O$, known as *gypsum*. During the change, the plaster hardens and expands in volume, causing it to fill a mold or shape itself closely around a broken limb. Table 9.3 lists some other ionic compounds that are handled primarily as hydrates.

TABLE 9.3 Some Common Solid Hydrates

Formula	Name	Uses
$AlCl_3 \cdot 6\,H_2O$	Aluminum chloride hexahydrate	Antiperspirant
$CaSO_4 \cdot 2\,H_2O$	Calcium sulfate dihydrate (gypsum)	Cements, wallboard molds
$CaSO_4 \cdot \frac{1}{2}H_2O$	Calcium sulfate hemihydrate (plaster of Paris)	Casts, molds
$CuSO_4 \cdot 5\,H_2O$	Copper(II) sulfate pentahydrate (blue vitriol)	Pesticide, germicide, topical fungicide
$MgSO_4 \cdot 7\,H_2O$	Magnesium sulfate heptahydrate (epsom salts)	Laxative, anticonvulsant
$Na_2B_4O_7 \cdot 10\,H_2O$	Sodium tetraborate decahydrate (borax)	Cleaning compounds, fireproofing agent
$Na_2S_2O_3 \cdot 5\,H_2O$	Sodium thiosulfate pentahydrate (hypo)	Photographic fixer

Hygroscopic Having the ability to pull water molecules from the surrounding atmosphere.

Still other ionic compounds attract water so strongly that they pull water vapor from humid air to become hydrated. Compounds that show this behavior, such as calcium chloride ($CaCl_2$), are called **hygroscopic** and are often used as drying agents. You might have noticed a small bag of a hygroscopic compound (probably silica gel, SiO_2) included in the packing material of a new MP3 player, camera, or other electronic device to keep humidity low during shipping.

PROBLEM 9.3
Write the formula of sodium sulfate decahydrate, known as Glauber's salt and used as a laxative.

PROBLEM 9.4
What mass of Glauber's salt must be used to provide 1.00 mol of sodium sulfate?

9.4 Solubility

We saw in Section 9.2 that ethyl alcohol is soluble in water because hydrogen bonding is nearly as strong between water and ethyl alcohol molecules as it is between water molecules alone or ethyl alcohol molecules alone. So similar are the forces in this particular case, in fact, that the two liquids are **miscible**, or mutually soluble in all proportions. Ethyl alcohol will continue to dissolve in water no matter how much is added.

Miscible Mutually soluble in all proportions.

Most substances, however, reach a solubility limit beyond which no more will dissolve in solution. Imagine, for instance that you are asked to prepare a saline solution (aqueous NaCl). You might measure out some water, add solid NaCl, and stir the mixture. Dissolution occurs rapidly at first but then slows down as more and more NaCl is added. Eventually the dissolution stops because an equilibrium is reached when the numbers of Na^+ and Cl^- ions leaving a crystal and going into solution are equal to the numbers of ions returning from solution to the crystal. At this point, the solution is said to be **saturated**. A maximum of 35.8 g of NaCl will dissolve in 100 mL of water at 20 °C. Any amount above this limit simply sinks to the bottom of the container and sits there.

Saturated solution A solution that contains the maximum amount of dissolved solute at equilibrium.

The equilibrium reached by a saturated solution is like the equilibrium reached by a reversible reaction (Section 7.7). Both are dynamic situations in which no *apparent* change occurs because the rates of forward and backward processes are equal. Solute particles leave the solid surface and reenter the solid from solution at the same rate.

$$\text{Solid solute} \underset{\text{Crystallize}}{\overset{\text{Dissolve}}{\rightleftharpoons}} \text{Solution}$$

Solubility The maximum amount of a substance that will dissolve in a given amount of solvent at a specified temperature.

The maximum amount of a substance that will dissolve in a given amount of a solvent at a given temperature, usually expressed in grams per 100 mL (g/100 mL), is called the substance's **solubility**. Solubility is a characteristic property of a specific solute–solvent combination, and different substances have greatly differing solubilities. Only 9.6 g of sodium hydrogen carbonate will dissolve in 100 mL of water at 20 °C, for instance, but 204 g of sucrose will dissolve under the same conditions.

9.5 The Effect of Temperature on Solubility

As anyone who has ever made tea or coffee knows, temperature often has a dramatic effect on solubility. The compounds in tea leaves or coffee beans, for instance, dissolve easily in hot water but not in cold water. The effect of temperature is different for every substance, however, and is usually unpredictable. As shown in Figure 9.3(a), the solubilities of most molecular and ionic solids increase with increasing temperature, but the solubilities of others (NaCl) are almost unchanged, and the solubilities of still others [$Ce_2(SO_4)_3$] decrease with increasing temperature.

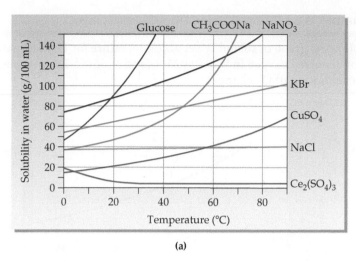

(a)

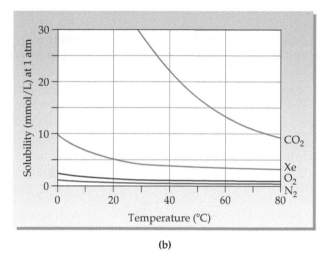

(b)

▲ **Figure 9.3**
Solubilities of some (a) solids and (b) gases, in water as a function of temperature.
Most solid substances become more soluble as temperature rises (although the exact relationship is usually complex), while the solubility of gases decreases.

Solids that are more soluble at high temperature than at low temperature can sometimes form what are called **supersaturated solutions**, which contain even more solute than a saturated solution. Suppose, for instance, that a large amount of a substance is dissolved at a high temperature. As the solution cools, the solubility decreases and the excess solute should precipitate to maintain equilibrium. But if the cooling is done very slowly, and if the container stands quietly, crystallization might not occur immediately and a supersaturated solution might result. Such a solution is unstable, however, and precipitation can occur dramatically when a tiny seed crystal is added or container disturbed to initiate crystallization (Figure 9.4).

Unlike solids, the influence of temperature on the solubility of gases *is* predictable: Addition of heat decreases the solubility of most gases, as seen in Figure 9.3(b) (helium is the only common exception). One result of this temperature-dependent decrease in gas solubility can sometimes be noted in a stream or lake near the outflow of warm water from an industrial operation. As water temperature increases, the concentration of dissolved oxygen in the water decreases, killing fish that cannot tolerate the lower oxygen levels.

Supersaturated solution A solution that contains more than the maximum amount of dissolved solute; a nonequilibrium situation.

▲ **Figure 9.4**
A supersaturated solution of sodium acetate in water.
When a tiny seed crystal is added, larger crystals rapidly grow and precipitate from the solution until equilibrium is reached.

Worked Example 9.2 Solubility of Gases: Effect of Temperature

From the following graph of solubility versus temperature for O_2, estimate the concentration of dissolved oxygen in water at 25 °C and at 35 °C. By what percentage does the concentration of O_2 change?

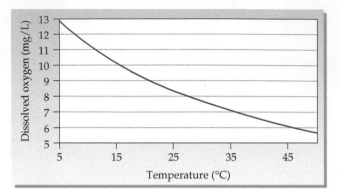

ANALYSIS The solubility of O_2 (on the *y*-axis) can be determined by finding the appropriate temperature (on the *x*-axis) and extrapolating. The percent change is calculated as

$$\frac{(\text{Solubility at 25 °C}) - (\text{Solubility at 35 °C})}{(\text{Solubility at 25 °C})} \times 100$$

SOLUTION
From the graph we estimate that the solubility of O_2 at 25 °C is approximately 8.3 mg/L and at 35 °C is 7.0 mg/L. The percent change in solubility is

$$\frac{8.3 - 7.0}{8.3} \times 100 = 16\%$$

PROBLEM 9.5
A solution is prepared by dissolving 12.5 g of KBr in 20 mL of water at 60 °C (see Figure 9.3). Is this solution saturated, unsaturated, or supersaturated? What will happen if the solution is cooled to 10 °C?

9.6 The Effect of Pressure on Solubility: Henry's Law

Pressure has virtually no effect on the solubility of a solid or liquid, but it has a strong effect on the solubility of a gas. According to **Henry's law**, the solubility (or concentration) of a gas in a liquid is directly proportional to the partial pressure of the gas over the liquid. If the partial pressure of the gas doubles, solubility doubles; if the gas pressure is halved, solubility is halved (Figure 9.5).

▶▶▶ Recall from Section 8.11 that each gas in a mixture exerts a partial pressure independent of other gases present (Dalton's law of partial pressures).

▶ **Figure 9.5**
Henry's law.
The solubility of a gas is directly proportional to its partial pressure. An increase in pressure causes more gas molecules to enter solution until equilibrium is restored between the dissolved and undissolved gas.

(a) Equilibrium   (b) Pressure increase   (c) Equilibrium restored

Henry's law   The solubility (or concentration) of a gas is directly proportional to the partial pressure of the gas if the temperature is constant. That is, concentration (C) divided by pressure (P) is constant when T is constant,

or $\dfrac{C}{P_{gas}} = k$ (At a constant temperature)

Henry's law can be explained using Le Châtelier's principle. In the case of a saturated solution of a gas in a liquid, an equilibrium exists whereby gas molecules enter and leave the solution at the same rate. When the system is stressed by increasing the pressure of the gas, more gas molecules go into solution to relieve that increase. Conversely, when the pressure of the gas is decreased, more gas molecules come out of solution to relieve the decrease.

▶▶▶ Le Châtelier's principle states that when a system at equilibrium is placed under stress, the equilibrium shifts to relieve that stress (Section 7.9).

$$\text{[Pressure increases} \longrightarrow]$$
$$\text{Gas + Solvent} \rightleftharpoons \text{Solution}$$

As an example of Henry's law in action, think about the fizzing that occurs when you open a bottle of soft drink or champagne. The bottle is sealed under greater than 1 atm of CO_2 pressure, causing some of the CO_2 to dissolve. When the bottle is opened, however, CO_2 pressure drops and gas comes fizzing out of solution.

Writing Henry's law in the form $P_{gas} = C/k$ shows that partial pressure can be used to express the concentration of a gas in a solution, a practice especially common in health-related sciences. Table 9.4 gives some typical values and illustrates the convenience of having the same unit for concentration of a gas in both air and blood. Compare the oxygen partial pressures in saturated alveolar air (air in the lungs) and in arterial blood, for instance. The values are almost the same because the gases dissolved in blood come to equilibrium with the same gases in the lungs.

TABLE 9.4   Partial Pressures and Normal Gas Concentrations in Body Fluids

Sample	Partial Pressure (mmHg)			
	P_{N_2}	P_{O_2}	P_{CO_2}	P_{H_2O}
Inspired air (dry)	597	159	0.3	3.7
Alveolar air (saturated)	573	100	40	47
Expired air (saturated)	569	116	28	47
Arterial blood	573	95	40	
Venous blood	573	40	45	
Peripheral tissues	573	40	45	

If the partial pressure of a gas over a solution changes while the temperature is constant, the new solubility of the gas can be found easily. Because C/P is a constant value at constant temperature, Henry's law can be restated to show how one variable changes if the other changes:

$$\frac{C_1}{P_1} = \frac{C_2}{P_2} = k \quad \text{(Where } k \text{ is constant at a fixed temperature)}$$

Worked Example 9.3 gives an illustration of how to use this equation.

Worked Example **9.3** Solubility of Gases: Henry's Law

At a partial pressure of oxygen in the atmosphere of 159 mmHg, the solubility of oxygen in blood is 0.44 g/100 mL. What is the solubility of oxygen in blood at 11,000 ft, where the partial pressure of O_2 is 56 mmHg?

ANALYSIS According to Henry's law, the solubility of the gas divided by its pressure is constant:

$$\frac{C_1}{P_1} = \frac{C_2}{P_2}$$

Of the four variables in this equation, we know P_1, C_1, and P_2, and we need to find C_2.

BALLPARK ESTIMATE The pressure drops by a factor of about 3 (from 159 mmHg to 56 mmHg). Since the ratio of solubility to pressure is constant, the solubility must also drop by a factor of 3 (from 0.44 g/100 mL to about 0.15 g/100 mL).

SOLUTION

STEP 1: Identify known information. We have values for P_1, C_1, and P_2.

$$P_1 = 159 \text{ mmHg}$$
$$C_1 = 0.44 \text{ g}/100 \text{ mL}$$
$$P_2 = 56 \text{ mmHg}$$

STEP 2: Identify answer and units. We are looking for the solubility of O_2 (C_2) at a partial pressure P_2.

Solubility of O_2, $C_2 = $?? g/100 mL

STEP 3: Identify conversion factors or equations. In this case, we restate Henry's law to solve for C_2.

$$\frac{C_1}{P_1} = \frac{C_2}{P_2} \Rightarrow C_2 = \frac{C_1 P_2}{P_1}$$

STEP 4: Solve. Substitute the known values into the equation and calculate C_2.

$$C_2 = \frac{C_1 P_2}{P_1} = \frac{(0.44 \text{ g}/100 \text{ mL})(56 \text{ mmHg})}{159 \text{ mmHg}} = 0.15 \text{ g}/100 \text{ mL}$$

BALLPARK CHECK The calculated answer matches our estimate.

PROBLEM 9.6

At 20 °C and a partial pressure of 760 mmHg, the solubility of CO_2 in water is 0.169 g/100 mL at this temperature. What is the solubility of CO_2 at 2.5×10^4 mmHg?

PROBLEM 9.7

At a total atmospheric pressure of 1.00 atm, the partial pressure of CO_2 in air is approximately 4.0×10^{-4} atm. Using the data in Problem 9.6, what is the solubility of CO_2 in an open bottle of seltzer water at 20 °C?

PROBLEM 9.8

The atmospheric pressure at the top of Mt. Everest is only 265 mmHg. If the atmospheric composition is 21% oxygen, calculate the partial pressure of O_2 at this altitude and determine the percent saturation of hemoglobin under these conditions (see Chemistry in Action: Breathing and Oxygen Transport on p. 263).

9.7 Units of Concentration

Although we speak casually of a solution of, say, orange juice as either "dilute" or "concentrated," laboratory work usually requires an exact knowledge of a solution's concentration. As indicated in Table 9.5 on page 264, there are several common methods for expressing concentration. The units differ, but all the methods describe how much solute is present in a given quantity of solution.

CHEMISTRY IN ACTION

Breathing and Oxygen Transport

Like all other animals, humans need oxygen. When we breathe, the freshly inspired air travels through the bronchial passages and into the lungs. The oxygen then diffuses through the delicate walls of the approximately 150 million alveolar sacs of the lungs and into arterial blood, which transports it to all body tissues.

Only about 3% of the oxygen in blood is dissolved; the rest is chemically bound to *hemoglobin* molecules, large proteins with *heme* groups embedded in them. Each hemoglobin molecule contains four heme groups, and each heme group contains an iron atom that is able to bind 1 O_2 molecule. Thus, a single hemoglobin molecule can bind up to 4 molecules of oxygen. The entire system of oxygen transport and delivery in the body depends on the pickup and release of O_2 by hemoglobin (Hb) according to the following series of equilibria:

$$O_2(\text{lungs}) \rightleftharpoons O_2(\text{blood}) \quad (\text{Henry's law})$$
$$Hb + 4 O_2(\text{blood}) \rightleftharpoons Hb(O_2)_4$$
$$Hb(O_2)_4 \rightleftharpoons Hb + 4 O_2 \text{ (cell)}$$

The delivery of oxygen depends on the concentration of O_2 in the various tissues, as measured by partial pressure (P_{O_2}, Table 9.4). The amount of oxygen carried by hemoglobin at any given value of P_{O_2} is usually expressed as a percent saturation and can be found from the curve shown in the accompanying figure. When $P_{O_2} = 100$ mmHg, the saturation in the lungs is 97.5%, meaning that each hemoglobin is carrying close to its maximum of 4 O_2 molecules. When $P_{O_2} = 26$ mmHg, however, the saturation drops to 50%.

So, how does the body ensure that enough oxygen is available to the various tissues? When large amounts of oxygen are needed—during a strenuous workout, for example—oxygen is released from hemoglobin to the hardworking, oxygen-starved muscle cells, where P_{O_2} is low. Increasing the supply of oxygen to the blood (by breathing harder and faster) shifts all the equilibria toward the right, according to Le Châtelier's principle (Section 7.9), to supply the additional O_2 needed by the muscles.

What about people living at high altitudes? In Leadville, CO, for example, where the altitude is 10,156 ft, the P_{O_2} in the lungs is only about 68 mmHg. Hemoglobin is only 90% saturated with O_2 at this pressure, meaning that less oxygen is available for delivery to the tissues. The body responds by producing erythropoietin (EPO), a hormone that stimulates the bone marrow to produce more red blood cells and hemoglobin molecules. The increase in Hb provides more capacity for O_2 transport and drives the Hb + O_2 equilibria to the right.

▲ **At high altitudes, the partial pressure of oxygen in the air is too low to saturate hemoglobin sufficiently. Additional oxygen is therefore needed.**

World-class athletes use the mechanisms of increased oxygen transport associated with higher levels of hemoglobin to enhance their performance. High-altitude training centers have sprung up, with living and training regimens designed to increase blood EPO levels. Unfortunately, some athletes have also tried to "cheat" by using injections of EPO and synthetic analogs, and "blood doping" to boost performance. This has led the governing bodies of many sports federations, including the Olympic Committee, to start testing for such abuse.

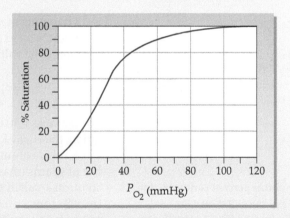

▲ **An oxygen-carrying curve for hemoglobin. The percent saturation of the oxygen binding sites on hemoglobin depends on the partial pressure of oxygen P_{O_2}.**

See Chemistry in Action Problem 9.90 at the end of the chapter.

TABLE **9.5** Some Units for Expressing Concentration		
Concentration Measure	**Solute Measure**	**Solution Measure**
Percent		
Mass/mass percent, (m/m)%	Mass (g)	Mass (g)
Volume/volume percent, (v/v)%	Volume*	Volume*
Mass/volume percent, (m/v)%	Mass (g)	Volume (mL)
Parts per million, ppm	Parts*	10^6 parts*
Parts per billion, ppb	Parts*	10^9 parts*
Molarity, M	Moles	Volume (L)

*Any units can be used as long as they are the same for both solute and solution.

Let us look at each of the concentration measures listed in Table 9.5 individually, beginning with *percent concentrations.*

Percent Concentrations

Percent concentrations express the amount of solute in one hundred units of solution. The amount of solute and the amount of solution can be represented in units of mass or volume. For solid solutions, such as a metal alloy, concentrations are typically expressed as **mass/mass percent concentration, (m/m)%**:

$$(m/m)\% \text{ concentration} = \frac{\text{Mass of solute (g)}}{\text{Mass of solution (g)}} \times 100\%$$

mass/mass percent concentration, (m/m)% Concentration expressed as the number of grams of solute per 100 grams of solution.

For example, the mass percent of copper in a red-gold ring that contains 19.20 g of gold and 4.80 g of copper would be calculated as:

$$(m/m)\% \text{ Cu} = \frac{\text{mass of Cu (g)}}{\text{mass of Cu (g)} + \text{mass of Au (g)}} \times 100\%$$

$$= \frac{4.80\,g}{4.80\,g + 19.20\,g} \times 100\% = 20.0\%$$

The concentration of a solution made by dissolving one liquid in another is often given by expressing the volume of solute as a percentage of the volume of final solution—the **volume/volume percent concentration, (v/v)%**.

$$(v/v)\% \text{ concentration} = \frac{\text{Volume of solute (mL)}}{\text{Volume of solution (mL)}} \times 100\%$$

volume/volume percent concentration, (v/v)% Concentration expressed as the number of milliliters of solute dissolved in 100 mL of solution.

For example, if 10.0 mL of ethyl alcohol is dissolved in enough water to give 100.0 mL of solution, the ethyl alcohol concentration is $(10.0\text{ mL}/100.0\text{ mL}) \times 100\% = 10.0\%\ (v/v)$.

A third common method for expressing percent concentration is to give the number of grams (mass) as a percentage of the number of milliliters (volume) of the final solution—called the **mass/volume percent concentration, (m/v)%**. Mathematically, (m/v)% concentration is found by taking the number of grams of solute per milliliter of solution and multiplying by 100%:

$$(m/v)\% \text{ concentration} = \frac{\text{Mass of solute (g)}}{\text{Volume of solution (mL)}} \times 100\%$$

mass/volume percent concentration, (m/v)% Concentration expressed as the number of grams of solute per 100 mL of solution.

For example, if 15 g of glucose is dissolved in enough water to give 100 mL of solution, the glucose concentration is 15 g/100 mL or 15% (m/v):

$$\frac{15\text{ g glucose}}{100\text{ mL solution}} \times 100\% = 15\%\ (m/v)$$

To prepare 100 mL of a specific mass/volume solution, the weighed solute is dissolved in just enough solvent to give a final volume of 100 mL, not in an initial volume of 100 mL solvent. (If the solute is dissolved in 100 mL of solvent, the final volume of the solution will likely be a bit larger than 100 mL, since the volume of the solute is included.) In practice, the appropriate amount of solute is weighed and placed in a *volumetric flask*, as shown in Figure 9.6. Enough solvent is then added to dissolve the solute, and further solvent is added until an accurately calibrated final volume is reached. The solution is then shaken until it is uniformly mixed. Worked Examples 9.4–9.7 illustrate how percent concentrations can be calculated for a solution, or how the percent concentration can be used as a conversion factor to determine the amount of solute in a given amount of solution.

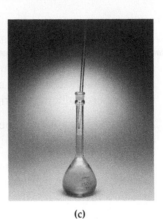

(a)   (b)   (c)

◄ **Figure 9.6**
Preparing a solution of known mass/volume percent concentration, (m/v)%.
(a) A measured number of grams of solute is placed in a volumetric flask. (b) Enough solvent is added to dissolve the solute by swirling. (c) Further solvent is carefully added until the calibration mark on the neck of the flask is reached, and the solution is shaken until uniform.

Worked Example 9.4 Mass Percent as Conversion Factor: Mass of Solution to Mass of Solute

The percentage of gold in jewelry is typically reported in carats, with 24 carats representing 100% gold. A sample of 18-carat gold would contain 18 grams of gold in 24 grams of metal, which would equal a (m/m)% of 75%. Calculate the mass of gold in a 5.05 g ring that is 18-carat gold.

ANALYSIS We are given a concentration and the total mass of the sample solution (the gold alloy in the ring), and we need to find the mass of gold by rearranging the equation for (m/m)% concentration.

BALLPARK ESTIMATE A 75% (m/m) solution contains 75 g for every 100 g of solution, so 10 g contains 7.5 g. The mass of the ring is a little more than 5 g (or half of 10 g) so the amount of gold in the ring will be slightly more than half of 7.5 g, or ~3.8 g gold.

SOLUTION

$$(5.05 \text{ g})\left(\frac{75 \text{ g Au}}{100 \text{ g solution}}\right) = 3.79 \text{ g Au}$$

BALLPARK CHECK The calculated answer is consistent with our estimate of 3.8 g gold.

Worked Example 9.5 Volume Percent as Conversion Factor: Volume of Solution to Volume of Solute

How many milliliters of methyl alcohol are needed to prepare 75 mL of a 5.0% (v/v) solution?

ANALYSIS We are given a solution volume (75 mL) and a concentration [5.0% (v/v), meaning 5.0 mL solute/100 mL solution]. The concentration acts as a conversion factor for finding the amount of methyl alcohol needed.

BALLPARK ESTIMATE A 5% (v/v) solution contains 5 mL of solute in 100 mL of solution, so the amount of solute in 75 mL of solution must be about three-fourths of 5 mL, which means between 3 and 4 mL.

SOLUTION

$$(75 \text{ mL solution})\left(\frac{5.0 \text{ mL methyl alcohol}}{100 \text{ mL solution}}\right) = 3.8 \text{ mL methyl alcohol}$$

BALLPARK CHECK The calculated answer is consistent with our estimate of between 3 and 4 mL.

Worked Example 9.6 Solution Concentration: Mass/Volume Percent

A solution of heparin sodium, an anticoagulant for blood, contains 1.8 g of heparin sodium dissolved to make a final volume of 15 mL of solution. What is the mass/volume percent concentration of this solution?

ANALYSIS Mass/volume percent concentration is defined as the mass of the solute in grams divided by the volume of solution in milliliters and multiplied by 100%.

BALLPARK ESTIMATE The mass of solute (1.8 g) is smaller than the volume of solvent (15 mL) by a little less than a factor of 10. The weight/volume percent should thus be a little greater than 10%.

SOLUTION

$$(\text{m/v})\% \text{ concentration} = \frac{1.8 \text{ g heparin sodium}}{15 \text{ mL}} \times 100\% = 12\% \, (\text{m/v})$$

BALLPARK CHECK The calculated (m/v)% is reasonably close to our original estimate of 10%.

Worked Example 9.7 Mass/Volume Percent as Conversion Factor: Volume to Mass

How many grams of NaCl are needed to prepare 250 mL of a 1.5% (m/v) saline solution?

ANALYSIS We are given a concentration and a volume, and we need to find the mass of solute by rearranging the equation for (m/v)% concentration.

BALLPARK ESTIMATE The desired (m/v)% value, 1.5%, is between 1 and 2%. For a volume of 250 mL, we would need 2.5 g of solute for a 1% (m/v) solution and 5.0 g of solute for a 2% solution. Thus, for our 1.5% solution, we need a mass midway between 2.5 and 5.0 g, or about 3.8 g.

SOLUTION

$$\text{Since} \quad (\text{m/v})\% = \frac{\text{Mass of solute in g}}{\text{Volume of solution in mL}} \times 100\%$$

$$\text{then} \quad \text{Mass of solute in g} = \frac{(\text{Volume of solution in mL})[(\text{m/v})]\%}{100\%}$$

$$= \frac{(250)(1.5\%)}{100\%} = 3.75 \text{ g} = 3.8 \text{ g NaCl}$$

$$(2 \text{ significant figures})$$

BALLPARK CHECK The calculated answer matches our estimate.

PROBLEM 9.9

A metal alloy contains 15.8% nickel (m/m)%. What mass of the metal alloy would contain 36.5 g of nickel?

PROBLEM 9.10

How would you use a 500.0 mL volumetric flask to prepare a 7.5% (v/v) solution of acetic acid in water?

PROBLEM 9.11

In clinical lab reports, some concentrations are given in mg/dL. Convert a Ca^{2+} concentration of 8.6 mg/dL to mass/volume percent.

PROBLEM 9.12

What amounts of solute or solvent are needed to prepare the following solutions?

(a) Mass of glucose needed to prepare 125.0 mL of 16% (m/v) glucose $(C_6H_{12}O_6)$

(b) Volume of water needed to prepare a 2.0% (m/v) KCl solution using 1.20 g KCl

Parts per Million (ppm) or Parts per Billion (ppb)

The concentration units mass/mass percent (m/m)%, volume/volume percent (v/v)%, and mass/volume percent (w/v)% can also be defined as *parts per hundred* (pph) since 1% means one item per 100 items. When concentrations are very small, as often occurs in dealing with trace amounts of pollutants or contaminants, it is more convenient to use **parts per million (ppm)** or **parts per billion (ppb)**. The "parts" can be in any unit of either mass or volume as long as the units of both solute and solvent are the same:

Parts per million (ppm) Number of parts per one million (10^6) parts.

Parts per billion (ppb) Number of parts per one billion (10^9) parts.

$$\text{ppm} = \frac{\text{Mass of solute (g)}}{\text{Mass of solution (g)}} \times 10^6 \quad \text{or} \quad \frac{\text{Volume of solute (mL)}}{\text{Volume of solution (mL)}} \times 10^6$$

$$\text{ppb} = \frac{\text{Mass of solute (g)}}{\text{Mass of solution (g)}} \times 10^9 \quad \text{or} \quad \frac{\text{Volume of solute (mL)}}{\text{Volume of solution (mL)}} \times 10^9$$

To take an example, the maximum allowable concentration in air of the organic solvent benzene (C_6H_6) is currently set by government regulation at 1 ppm. A concentration of 1 ppm means that if you take a million "parts" of air in any unit—say, mL—then 1 of those parts is benzene vapor and the other 999,999 parts are other gases:

$$1 \text{ ppm} = \frac{1 \text{ mL}}{1,000,000 \text{ mL}} \times 10^6$$

Because the density of water is approximately 1.0 g/mL at room temperature, 1.0 L (or 1000 mL) of an aqueous solution weighs 1000 g. Therefore, when dealing with very dilute concentrations of solutes dissolved in water, ppm is equivalent to mg solute/L solution, and ppb is equivalent to μg solute/L solution. To demonstrate that these units are equivalent, the conversion from ppm to mg/L is as follows:

$$1 \text{ ppm} = \left(\frac{1 \text{ g solute}}{10^6 \text{ g solution}}\right)\left(\frac{1 \text{ mg solute}}{10^{-3} \text{ g solute}}\right)\left(\frac{10^3 \text{ g solution}}{1 \text{ L solution}}\right) = \frac{1 \text{ mg solute}}{1 \text{ L solution}}$$

Worked Example 9.8 ppm as Conversion Factor: Mass of Solution to Mass of Solute

The maximum allowable concentration of chloroform, $CHCl_3$, in drinking water is 100 ppb. What is the maximum amount (in grams) of chloroform allowed in a glass containing 400 g (400 mL) of water?

ANALYSIS We are given a solution amount (400 g) and a concentration (100 ppb). This concentration of 100 ppb means

$$100 \text{ ppb} = \frac{\text{Mass of solute (g)}}{\text{Mass of solution (g)}} \times 10^9$$

This equation can be rearranged to find the mass of solute.

BALLPARK ESTIMATE A concentration of 100 ppb means there are $100 \times 10^{-9}\,\text{g}\,(1 \times 10^{-7}\,\text{g})$ of solute in 1 g of solution. In 400 g of solution, we should have 400 times this amount, or $400 \times 10^{-7} = 4 \times 10^{-5}\,\text{g}$.

SOLUTION

$$\text{Mass of solute (g)} = \frac{\text{Mass of solution (g)}}{10^9} \times 100\,\text{ppb}$$

$$= \frac{400\,\text{g}}{10^9} \times 100\,\text{ppb} = 4 \times 10^{-5}\,\text{g (or 0.04 mg)}$$

BALLPARK CHECK The calculated answer matches our estimate.

PROBLEM 9.13

What is the concentration in ppm of sodium fluoride in tap water that has been fluoridated by the addition of 32 mg of NaF for every 20 kg of solution?

PROBLEM 9.14

The maximum amounts of lead and copper allowed in drinking water are 0.015 mg/kg for lead and 1.3 mg/kg for copper. Express these values in parts per million, and tell the maximum amount of each (in grams) allowed in 100 g of water.

Mole/Volume Concentration: Molarity

We saw in Chapter 6 that the various relationships between amounts of reactants and products in chemical reactions are calculated in *moles* (Sections 6.1–6.3). Thus, the most generally useful means of expressing concentration in the laboratory is **molarity (M)**, the number of moles of solute dissolved per liter of solution. For example, a solution made by dissolving 1.00 mol (58.5 g) of NaCl in enough water to give 1.00 L of solution has a concentration of 1.00 mol/L, or 1.00 M. The molarity of any solution is found by dividing the number of moles of solute by the number of liters of solution (solute + solvent):

Molarity (M) Concentration expressed as the number of moles of solute per liter of solution.

$$\text{Molarity (M)} = \frac{\text{Moles of solute}}{\text{Liters of solution}}$$

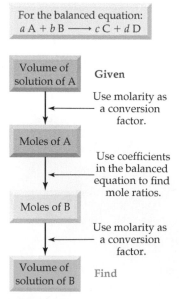

For the balanced equation:
$a\,\text{A} + b\,\text{B} \longrightarrow c\,\text{C} + d\,\text{D}$

Volume of solution of A — **Given**

Use molarity as a conversion factor.

Moles of A

Use coefficients in the balanced equation to find mole ratios.

Moles of B

Use molarity as a conversion factor.

Volume of solution of B — **Find**

▲ **Figure 9.7**
Molarity and conversions.
A flow diagram summarizing the use of molarity for conversions between solution volume and moles to find quantities of reactants and products for chemical reactions in solution.

Note that a solution of a given molarity is prepared by dissolving the solute in enough solvent to give a *final* solution volume of 1.00 L, not by dissolving it in an *initial* volume of 1.00 L. If an initial volume of 1.00 L was used, the final solution volume might be a bit larger than 1.00 L because of the additional volume of the solute. In practice, solutions are prepared using a volumetric flask, as shown previously in Figure 9.6.

Molarity can be used as a conversion factor to relate the volume of a solution to the number of moles of solute it contains. If we know the molarity and volume of a solution, we can calculate the number of moles of solute. If we know the number of moles of solute and the molarity of the solution, we can find the solution's volume.

$$\text{Molarity} = \frac{\text{Moles of solute}}{\text{Volume of solution (L)}}$$

$$\text{Moles of solute} = \text{Molarity} \times \text{Volume of solution}$$

$$\text{Volume of solution} = \frac{\text{Moles of solute}}{\text{Molarity}}$$

The flow diagram in Figure 9.7 shows how molarity is used in calculating the quantities of reactants or products in a chemical reaction, and Worked Examples 9.10 and 9.11 show how the calculations are done. Note that Problem 9.17 employs *millimolar* (mM) concentrations, which are useful in healthcare fields for expressing low concentrations such as are often found in body fluids (1 mM = 0.001 M).

Worked Example 9.9 Solution Concentration: Molarity

What is the molarity of a solution made by dissolving 2.355 g of sulfuric acid (H_2SO_4) in water and diluting to a final volume of 50.0 mL? The molar mass of H_2SO_4 is 98.1 g/mol.

ANALYSIS Molarity is defined as moles of solute per liter of solution: $M = mol/L$. Thus, we must first find the number of moles of sulfuric acid by doing a mass to mole conversion, and then divide the number of moles by the volume of the solution.

BALLPARK ESTIMATE The molar mass of sulfuric acid is about 100 g/mol, so 2.355 g is roughly 0.025 mol. The volume of the solution is 50.0 mL, or 0.05 L, so we have about 0.025 mol of acid in 0.05 L of solution, which is a concentration of about 0.5 M.

SOLUTION

STEP 1: **Identify known information.** We know the mass of sulfuric acid and the final volume of solution.

Mass of H_2SO_4 = 2.355 g
Volume of solution = 50.0 mL

STEP 2: **Identify answer including units.** We need to find the molarity (M) in units of moles per liter.

$$\text{Molarity} = \frac{\text{Moles } H_2SO_4}{\text{Liters of solution}}$$

STEP 3: **Identify conversion factors and equations.** We know both the amount of solute and the volume of solution, but first we must make two conversions: convert mass of H_2SO_4 to moles of H_2SO_4, using molar mass as a conversion factor, and convert volume from milliliters to liters.

$$(2.355 \text{ g } H_2SO_4)\left(\frac{1 \text{ mol } H_2SO_4}{98.1 \text{ g } H_2SO_4}\right) = 0.0240 \text{ mol } H_2SO_4$$

$$(50.0 \text{ mL})\left(\frac{1 \text{ L}}{1000 \text{ mL}}\right) = 0.0500 \text{ L}$$

STEP 4: **Solve.** Substitute the moles of solute and volume of solution into the molarity expression.

$$\text{Molarity} = \frac{0.0240 \text{ mol } H_2SO_4}{0.0500 \text{ L}} = 0.480 \text{ M}$$

BALLPARK CHECK The calculated answer is close to our estimate, which was 0.5 M.

Worked Example 9.10 Molarity as Conversion Factor: Molarity to Mass

A blood concentration of 0.065 M ethyl alcohol (EtOH) is sufficient to induce a coma. At this concentration, what is the total mass of alcohol (in grams) in an adult male whose total blood volume is 5.6 L? The molar mass of ethyl alcohol is 46.0 g/mol. (Refer to the flow diagram in Figure 9.7 to identify which conversions are needed.)

ANALYSIS We are given a molarity (0.065 M) and a volume (5.6 L), which allows us to calculate the number of moles of alcohol in the blood. A mole to mass conversion then gives the mass of alcohol.

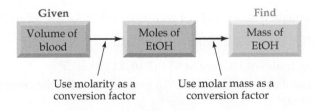

SOLUTION

$$(5.6 \text{ L blood})\left(\frac{0.065 \text{ mol EtOH}}{1 \text{ L blood}}\right) = 0.36 \text{ mol EtOH}$$

$$(0.36 \text{ mol EtOH})\left(\frac{46.0 \text{ g EtOH}}{1 \text{ mol EtOH}}\right) = 17 \text{ g EtOH}$$

Worked Example 9.11 Molarity as Conversion Factor: Molarity to Volume

In our stomachs, gastric juice that is about 0.1 M in HCl aids in digestion. How many milliliters of gastric juice will react completely with an antacid tablet that contains 500 mg of magnesium hydroxide? The molar mass of $Mg(OH)_2$ is 58.3 g/mol, and the balanced equation is

$$2\,HCl(aq) + Mg(OH)_2(aq) \longrightarrow MgCl_2(aq) + 2\,H_2O(l)$$

ANALYSIS We are given the molarity of HCl and need to find the volume. We first convert the mass of $Mg(OH)_2$ to moles and then use the coefficients in the balanced equation to find the moles of HCl that will react. Once we have the moles of HCl and the molarity in moles per liter, we can find the volume.

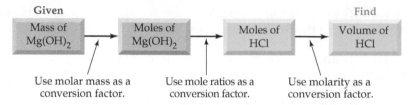

Given			Find
Mass of $Mg(OH)_2$	Moles of $Mg(OH)_2$	Moles of HCl	Volume of HCl

Use molar mass as a conversion factor.   Use mole ratios as a conversion factor.   Use molarity as a conversion factor.

SOLUTION

$$[500 \text{ mg } Mg(OH)_2]\left(\frac{1\text{ g}}{1000\text{ mg}}\right)\left[\frac{1\text{ mol } Mg(OH)_2}{58.3\text{ g } Mg(OH)_2}\right] = 0.008\,58 \text{ mol } Mg(OH)_2$$

$$[0.008\,58 \text{ mol } Mg(OH)_2]\left[\frac{2\text{ mol HCl}}{1\text{ mol } Mg(OH)_2}\right]\left(\frac{1\text{ L HCl}}{0.1\text{ mol HCl}}\right) = 0.2 \text{ L } (200 \text{ mL})$$

PROBLEM 9.15
What is the molarity of a solution that contains 50.0 g of vitamin B_1 hydrochloride (molar mass = 337 g/mol) in 160 mL of solution?

PROBLEM 9.16
How many moles of solute are present in the following solutions?
(a) 175 mL of 0.35 M $NaNO_3$
(b) 480 mL of 1.4 M HNO_3

PROBLEM 9.17
The concentration of cholesterol $(C_{27}H_{46}O)$ in blood is approximately 5.0 mM. How many grams of cholesterol are in 250 mL of blood?

PROBLEM 9.18
Calcium carbonate reacts with HCl according to the following equation:

$$2\,HCl(aq) + CaCO_3(aq) \longrightarrow CaCl_2(aq) + H_2O(l) + CO_2(g)$$

(a) How many moles of HCl are in 65 mL of 0.12 M HCl?
(b) What mass of calcium carbonate (in grams) is needed for complete reaction with the HCl in (a)?

9.8 Dilution

Many solutions, from orange juice to chemical reagents, are stored in high concentrations and then prepared for use by *dilution*—that is, by adding additional solvent to lower the concentration. For example, you might make up 1/2 gal of orange juice by adding water to a canned concentrate. In the same way, you might buy a medicine or chemical reagent as a concentrated solution and dilute it before use.

The key fact to remember about dilution is that the amount of *solute* remains constant; only the *volume* is changed by adding more solvent. If, for example, the initial and final concentrations are given in molarity, then we know that the number of moles of solute is the same both before and after dilution and can be determined by multiplying molarity times volume:

$$\text{Number of moles} = \text{Molarity (mol/L)} \times \text{Volume (L)}$$
$$M = \text{moles/volume}$$

Because the number of moles remains constant, we can set up the following equation, where M_c and V_c refer to the concentrated solution (before dilution), and M_d and V_d refer to the solution after dilution:

$$\text{Moles of solute} = M_c V_c = M_d V_d$$

This equation can be rewritten to solve for M_d, the concentration of the solution after dilution:

$$M_d = M_c \times \frac{V_c}{V_d} \quad \text{where} \quad \frac{V_c}{V_d} \quad \text{is a } \textit{dilution factor}$$

The equation shows that the concentration after dilution (M_d) can be found by multiplying the initial concentration (M_c) by a **dilution factor**, which is simply the ratio of the initial and final solution volumes (V_c/V_d). If, for example, the solution volume *increases* by a factor of 5, from 10 mL to 50 mL, then the concentration must *decrease* to one-fifth of its initial value because the dilution factor is 10 mL/50 mL, or 1/5. Worked Example 9.12 shows how to use this relationship for calculating dilutions.

Dilution factor The ratio of the initial and final solution volumes (V_c/V_d).

The relationship between concentration and volume can also be used to find what volume of initial solution to start with to achieve a given dilution:

$$\text{Since} \quad M_c V_c = M_d V_d$$
$$\text{then} \quad V_c = V_d \times \frac{M_d}{M_c}$$

In this case, V_c is the initial volume that must be diluted to prepare a less concentrated solution with volume V_d. The initial volume is found by multiplying the final volume (V_d) by the ratio of the final and initial concentrations (M_d/M_c). For example, to decrease the concentration of a solution to 1/5 its initial value, the initial volume must be 1/5 the desired final volume. Worked Example 9.13 gives a sample calculation.

Although the preceding discussion, and the following Worked Examples, use concentration units of molarity, the dilution equation can be generalized to allow for the use of other concentration units. A more general equation would be $C_c V_c = C_d V_d$, where *C* refers to other concentration units, such as ppm, or m/v%.

Worked Example 9.12 Dilution of Solutions: Concentration

What is the final concentration if 75 mL of a 3.5 M glucose solution is diluted to a volume of 450 mL?

ANALYSIS The number of moles of solute is constant, so

$$M_c V_c = M_d V_d$$

Of the four variables in this equation, we know the initial concentration M_c (3.5 M), the initial volume V_c (75 mL), and the final volume V_d (450 mL), and we need to find the final concentration M_d.

BALLPARK ESTIMATE The volume increases by a factor of 6, from 75 mL to 450 mL, so the concentration must decrease by a factor of 6, from 3.5 M to about 0.6 M.

SOLUTION

Solving the above equation for M_d and substituting in the known values gives

$$M_d = \frac{M_c V_c}{V_d} = \frac{(3.5 \text{ M glucose})(75 \text{ mL})}{450 \text{ mL}} = 0.58 \text{ M glucose}$$

BALLPARK CHECK The calculated answer is close to our estimate of 0.6 M.

Worked Example 9.13 Dilution of Solutions: Volume

Aqueous NaOH can be purchased at a concentration of 1.0 M. How would you use this concentrated solution to prepare 750 mL of 0.32 M NaOH?

ANALYSIS The number of moles of solute is constant, so

$$M_c V_c = M_d V_d$$

Of the four variables in this equation, we know the initial concentration M_c (1.0 M), the final volume V_d (750 mL), and the final concentration M_d (0.32 M), and we need to find the initial volume V_c.

BALLPARK ESTIMATE We want the solution concentration to decrease by a factor of about 3, from 1.0 M to 0.32 M, which means we need to dilute the 1.0 M solution by a factor of 3. This means the final volume must be about three times greater than the initial volume. Because our final volume is to be 750 mL, we must start with an initial volume of about 250 mL.

SOLUTION

Solving the above equation for V_1 and substituting in the known values gives

$$V_c = \frac{V_d M_d}{M_c} = \frac{(750 \text{ mL})(0.32 \text{ M})}{1.0 \text{ M}} = 240 \text{ mL}$$

To prepare the desired solution, dilute 240 mL of 1.0 M NaOH with water to make a final volume of 750 mL.

BALLPARK CHECK The calculated answer (240 mL) is reasonably close to our estimate of 250 mL.

PROBLEM 9.19

Aqueous ammonia is commercially available at a concentration of 16.0 M. How much of the concentrated solution would you use to prepare 500.0 mL of a 1.25 M solution?

PROBLEM 9.20

The Environmental Protection Agency has set the limit for arsenic in drinking water at 0.010 ppm. To what volume would you need to dilute 1.5 L of water containing 5.0 ppm arsenic to reach the acceptable limit?

9.9 Ions in Solution: Electrolytes

▶▶▶ As we learned in Section 3.1, electricity can only flow through a medium containing charged particles that are free to move.

Look at Figure 9.8, which shows a light bulb connected to a power source through a circuit that is interrupted by two metal strips dipped into a beaker of liquid. When the strips are dipped into pure water, the bulb remains dark, but when they are dipped into an aqueous NaCl solution, the circuit is closed and the bulb lights. This simple demonstration shows that ionic compounds in aqueous solution can conduct electricity.

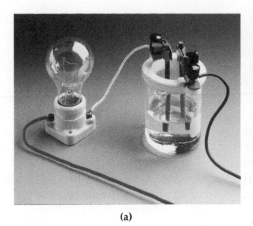
(a)

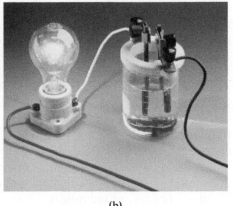
(b)

◄Figure 9.8
A simple demonstration shows that electricity can flow through a solution of ions.
(a) With pure water in the beaker, the circuit is incomplete, no electricity flows, and the bulb does not light. (b) With a concentrated NaCl solution in the beaker, the circuit is complete, electricity flows, and the light bulb glows.

Substances like NaCl that conduct an electric current when dissolved in water are called **electrolytes**. Conduction occurs because negatively charged Cl^- anions migrate through the solution toward the metal strip connected to the positive terminal of the power source, whereas positively charged Na^+ cations migrate toward the strip connected to the negative terminal. As you might expect, the ability of a solution to conduct electricity depends on the concentration of ions in solution. Distilled water contains virtually no ions and is nonconducting; ordinary tap water contains low concentrations of dissolved ions (mostly Na^+, K^+, Mg^{2+}, Ca^{2+}, and Cl^-) and is weakly conducting; and a concentrated solution of NaCl is strongly conducting.

Ionic substances like NaCl that ionize completely when dissolved in water are called **strong electrolytes**, and molecular substances like acetic acid (CH_3CO_2H) that are only partially ionized are **weak electrolytes**. Molecular substances like glucose that do not produce ions when dissolved in water are **nonelectrolytes**.

Electrolyte A substance that produces ions and therefore conducts electricity when dissolved in water.

Strong electrolyte; completely ionized
$$NaCl(s) \xrightarrow[\text{in water}]{\text{Dissolve}} Na^+(aq) + Cl^-(aq)$$

Weak electrolyte; partly ionized
$$CH_3CO_2H(l) \xrightleftharpoons[\text{in water}]{\text{Dissolve}} CH_3CO_2^-(aq) + H^+(aq)$$

Nonelectrolyte; not ionized
$$Glucose(s) \xrightleftharpoons[\text{in water}]{\text{Dissolve}} Glucose(aq)$$

Strong electrolyte A substance that ionizes completely when dissolved in water.

Weak electrolyte A substance that is only partly ionized in water.

Nonelectrolyte A substance that does not produce ions when dissolved in water.

9.10 Electrolytes in Body Fluids: Equivalents and Milliequivalents

What happens if NaCl and KBr are dissolved in the same solution? Because the cations (K^+ and Na^+) and anions (Cl^- and Br^-) are all mixed together and no reactions occur between them, an identical solution could just as well be made from KCl and NaBr. Thus, we can no longer speak of having a NaCl + KBr solution; we can only speak of having a solution with four different ions in it.

A similar situation exists for blood and other body fluids, which contain many different anions and cations. Since they are all mixed together, it is difficult to "assign" specific cations to specific anions or to talk about specific ionic compounds. Instead, we are interested only in individual ions and in the total numbers of positive and negative charges. To discuss such mixtures, we use a new term—*equivalents* of ions.

For ions, one **equivalent (Eq)** is equal to the number of ions that carry 1 mol of charge. Of more practical use is the unit **gram-equivalent (g-Eq)**, which is the amount of ion (in grams) that contains one mole of charge. It can be calculated simply as the molar mass of the ion divided by the absolute value of its charge.

Equivalent For ions, the amount equal to 1 mol of charge.

Gram-equivalent For ions, the molar mass of the ion divided by the ionic charge.

$$\text{One gram-equivalent of ion} = \frac{\text{Molar mass of ion (g)}}{\text{Charge on ion}}$$

If the ion has a charge of $+1$ or -1, 1 gram-equivalent of the ion is simply the molar mass of the ion in grams. Thus, 1 gram-equivalent of Na^+ is 23 g, and 1 gram-equivalent of Cl^- is 35.5 g. If the ion has a charge of $+2$ or -2, however, 1 gram-equivalent is equal to the ion's formula weight in grams divided by 2. Thus, 1 gram-equivalent of Mg^{2+} is $(24.3 \text{ g})/2 = 12.2$ g, and 1 gram-equivalent of CO_3^{2-} is $[12.0 \text{ g} + (3 \times 16.0 \text{ g})]/2 = 30.0$ g. The gram-equivalent is a useful conversion factor when converting from volume of solution to mass of ions, as seen in Worked Example 9.14.

The number of equivalents of a given ion per liter of solution can be found by multiplying the molarity of the ion (moles per liter) by the charge on the ion. Because ion concentrations in body fluids are often low, clinical chemists find it more convenient to talk about *milliequivalents* of ions rather than equivalents. One milliequivalent (mEq) of an ion is 1/1000 of an equivalent. For example, the normal concentration of Na^+ in blood is 0.14 Eq/L, or 140 mEq/L.

$$1 \text{ mEq} = 0.001 \text{ Eq} \qquad 1 \text{ Eq} = 1000 \text{ mEq}$$

Note that the gram-equivalent for an ion can now be expressed as grams per equivalent or as mg per mEq.

Average concentrations of the major electrolytes in blood plasma are given in Table 9.6. As you might expect, the total milliequivalents of positively and negatively charged electrolytes must be equal to maintain electrical neutrality. Adding the milliequivalents of positive and negative ions in Table 9.6, however, shows a higher concentration of positive ions than negative ions. The difference, called the *anion gap*, is made up by the presence of negatively charged proteins and the anions of organic acids.

TABLE 9.6 Concentrations of Major Electrolytes in Blood Plasma	
Cation	**Concentration (mEq/L)**
Na^+	136–145
Ca^{2+}	4.5–6.0
K^+	3.6–5.0
Mg^{2+}	3
Anion	**Concentration (mEq/L)**
Cl^-	98–106
HCO_3^-	25–29
SO_4^{2-} and HPO_4^{2-}	2

Worked Example 9.14 Equivalents as Conversion Factors: Volume to Mass

The normal concentration of Ca^{2+} in blood is 5.0 mEq/L. How many milligrams of Ca^{2+} are in 1.00 L of blood?

ANALYSIS We are given a volume and a concentration in milliequivalents per liter, and we need to find an amount in milligrams. Thus, we need to calculate the gram-equivalent for Ca^{2+} and then use concentration as a conversion factor between volume and mass, as indicated in the following flow diagram:

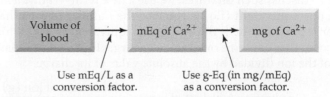

BALLPARK ESTIMATE   The molar mass of calcium is 40.08 g/mol, and the calcium ion carries a charge of 2+. Thus, 1 g-Eq of Ca^{2+} equals about 20 g/Eq or 20 mg/mEq. This means that the 5.0 mEq of Ca^{2+} ions in 1.00 L of blood corresponds to a mass of 5.0 mEq Ca^{2+} × 20 mg/mEq = 100 mg Ca^{2+}.

SOLUTION

$$(1.00 \text{ L blood})\left(\frac{5.0 \text{ mEq } Ca^{2+}}{1.0 \text{ L blood}}\right)\left(\frac{20.04 \text{ mg } Ca^{2+}}{1 \text{ mEq } Ca^{2+}}\right) = 100 \text{ mg } Ca^{2+}$$

BALLPARK CHECK   The calculated answer (100 mg of Ca^{2+} in 1.00 L of blood) matches our estimate.

PROBLEM 9.21
How many grams are in 1 Eq of the following ions? How many grams in 1 mEq?
(a) K^+ (b) Br^- (c) Mg^{2+} (d) SO_4^{2-} (e) Al^{3+} (f) PO_4^{3-}

PROBLEM 9.22
Look at the data in Table 9.6, and calculate how many milligrams of Mg^{2+} are in 250 mL of blood.

PROBLEM 9.23
A typical sports drink for electrolyte replacement contains 20 mEq/L of Na^+ and 10 mEq/L of K^+ ions (see Chemistry in Action: Electrolytes, Fluid Replacement, and Sports Drinks on p. 276). Convert these concentrations to m/v%.

9.11 Properties of Solutions

The properties of solutions are similar in many respects to those of pure solvents, but there are also some interesting and important differences. One such difference is that solutions have higher boiling points than the pure solvents; another is that solutions have lower freezing points. Pure water boils at 100.0 °C and freezes at 0.0 °C, for example, but a 1.0 M solution of NaCl in water boils at 101.0 °C and freezes at −3.7 °C.

The elevation of boiling point and the lowering of freezing point for a solution as compared with a pure solvent are examples of **colligative properties**—properties that depend on the *concentration* of a dissolved solute but not on its chemical identity. Other colligative properties are a lower vapor pressure for a solution compared with the pure solvent and *osmosis*, the migration of solvent molecules through a semipermeable membrane.

Colligative property A property of a solution that depends only on the number of dissolved particles, not on their chemical identity.

Colligative Properties

- Vapor pressure is lower for a solution than for a pure solvent.
- Boiling point is higher for a solution than for a pure solvent.
- Freezing point is lower for a solution than for a pure solvent.
- Osmosis occurs when a solution is separated from a pure solvent by a semipermeable membrane.

Vapor-Pressure Lowering in Solutions

We said in Section 8.13 that the vapor pressure of a liquid depends on the equilibrium between molecules entering and leaving the liquid surface. Only those molecules at the surface of the liquid that are sufficiently energetic will evaporate. If, however, some of the liquid (solvent) molecules at the surface are replaced by other (solute) particles that do not evaporate, then the rate of evaporation of solvent molecules decreases and the

CHEMISTRY IN ACTION

Electrolytes, Fluid Replacement, and Sports Drinks

Electrolytes are essential in many physiological processes, and significant changes in electrolyte levels can be potentially life-threatening if not addressed quickly. Heavy and continuous diarrhea from conditions such as cholera can result in dehydration and very low sodium levels in the body (hyponatremia). Restoration of electrolytes can be accomplished by oral rehydration therapy (ORT). The introduction of ORT in developing countries decreased infant mortality from diarrhea, which had previously been the leading cause of death in children under 5 years of age. A typical ORT solution contains sodium (75 mEq/L), potassium (75b mEq/L), chloride (65 mEq/L), citrate (10 mEq/L), and glucose (75 mmol/L). Heavy sweating during strenuous exercise can also lead to dehydration and loss of electrolytes.

The composition of sweat is highly variable, but the typical concentration for the Na^+ ion is about 30–40 mEq/L, and that of K^+ ion is about 5–10 mEq/L. In addition, there are small amounts of other metal ions, such as Mg^{2+}, and there are sufficient Cl^- ions (35–50 mEq/L) to balance the positive charge of all these cations. If water and electrolytes are not replaced, dehydration, hyperthermia and heat stroke, dizziness, nausea, muscle cramps, impaired kidney function, and other difficulties ensue. As a rule of thumb, a sweat loss equal to 5% of body weight—about 3.5 L for a 150 lb person—is the maximum amount that can be safely allowed for a well-conditioned athlete.

Plain water works perfectly well to replace sweat lost during short bouts of activity up to a few hours in length, but a carbohydrate–electrolyte beverage, or "sports drink," is much superior for rehydrating during and after longer activity in which substantial amounts of electrolytes have been lost. Some of the better known sports drinks are little more than overpriced sugar–water solutions, but others are carefully formulated and highly effective for fluid replacement. Nutritional research has shown that a serious sports drink should meet the following criteria. There are several dry-powder mixes on the market to choose from.

- The drink should contain 6–8% of soluble complex carbohydrates (about 15 g per 8 oz serving) and only a small amount of simple sugar for taste. The complex carbohydrates, which usually go by the name "maltodextrin," provide a slow release of glucose into the bloodstream. Not only does the glucose provide a steady source of energy, it also enhances the absorption of water from the stomach.

▲ Drinking water to replace fluids is adequate for short periods of activity, but extended exercise requires replacement of fluid and electrolytes, such as those found in sports drinks.

- The drink should contain electrolytes to replenish those lost in sweat. Concentrations of approximately 20 mEq/L for Na^+ ions, 10 mEq/L for K^+ ion, and 4 mEq/L for Mg^{2+} ions are recommended. These amounts correspond to about 100 mg sodium, 100 mg potassium, and 25 mg magnesium per 8 oz serving.
- The drink should be noncarbonated because carbonation can cause gastrointestinal upset during exercise, and it should not contain caffeine, which acts as a diuretic.
- The drink should taste good so the athlete will want to drink it. Thirst is a poor indicator of fluid requirements, and most people will drink less than needed unless a beverage is flavored.

In addition to complex carbohydrates, electrolytes, and flavorings, some sports drinks also contain vitamin A (as beta-carotene), vitamin C (ascorbic acid), and selenium, which act as antioxidants to protect cells from damage. Some drinks also contain the amino acid glutamine, which appears to lessen lactic acid buildup in muscles and thus helps muscles bounce back more quickly after an intense workout.

See Chemistry in Actions Problems 9.91 and 9.92 at the end of the chapter.

vapor pressure of a solution is lower than that of the pure solvent (Figure 9.9). Note that the *identity* of the solute particles is irrelevant; only their concentration matters.

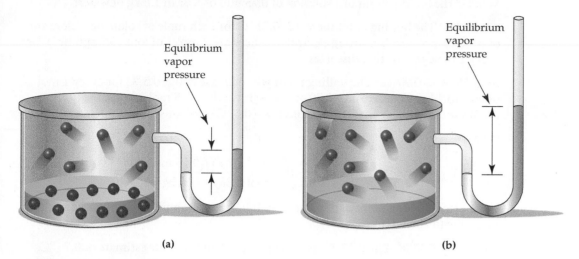

(a)   (b)

▲ **Figure 9.9**
Vapor-pressure lowering of solution.
(a) The vapor pressure of a solution is lower than (b) the vapor pressure of the pure solvent because fewer solvent molecules are able to escape from the surface of the solution.

Boiling Point Elevation of Solutions

One consequence of the vapor-pressure–lowering for a solution is that the boiling point of the solution is higher than that of the pure solvent. Recall from Section 8.13 that boiling occurs when the vapor pressure of a liquid reaches atmospheric pressure. But because the vapor pressure of a solution is lower than that of the pure solvent at a given temperature, the solution must be heated to a higher temperature for its vapor pressure to reach atmospheric pressure. Figure 9.10 shows a close-up plot of vapor pressure versus temperature for pure water and for a 1.0 M NaCl solution. The vapor pressure of pure water reaches atmospheric pressure (760 mmHg) at 100.0 °C, but the vapor pressure of the NaCl solution does not reach the same point until 101.0 °C.

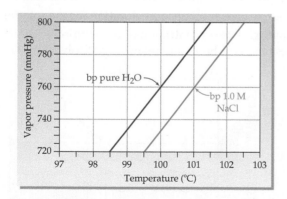

◄ **Figure 9.10**
Vapor pressure and temperature.
A close-up plot of vapor pressure versus temperature for pure water (red curve) and for a 1.0 M NaCl solution (blue curve). Pure water boils at 100.0 °C, but the solution does not boil until 101.0 °C.

For each mole of solute particles added, regardless of chemical identity, the boiling point of 1 kg of water is raised by 0.51 °C, or

$$\Delta T_{boiling} = \left(0.51\,°C\frac{kg\ water}{mol\ particles}\right)\left(\frac{mol\ particles}{kg\ water}\right)$$

The addition of 1 mol of a molecular substance like glucose to 1 kg of water therefore raises the boiling point from 100.0 °C to 100.51 °C. The addition of 1 mol of NaCl per kilogram of water, however, raises the boiling point by 2 × 0.51 °C = 1.02 °C because the solution contains 2 mol of solute particles—Na^+ and Cl^- ions.

Worked Example **9.15** Properties of Solutions: Boiling Point Elevation

What is the boiling point of a solution of 0.75 mol of KBr in 1.0 kg of water?

ANALYSIS The boiling point increases 0.51 °C for each mole of solute per kilogram of water. Since KBr is a strong electrolyte, there are 2 moles of ions (K^+ and Br^-) for every 1 mole of KBr that dissolves.

BALLPARK ESTIMATE The boiling point will increase about 0.5 °C for every 1 mol of ions in 1 kg of water. Since 0.75 mol of KBr produce 1.5 mol of ions, the boiling point should increase by (1.5 mol ions) $\times$ (0.5 °C/mol ions) = 0.75 °C.

SOLUTION

$$\Delta T_{boiling} = \left(0.51 \text{ °C}\frac{\text{kg water}}{\text{mol ions}}\right)\left(\frac{2 \text{ mol ions}}{1 \text{ mol KBr}}\right)\left(\frac{0.75 \text{ mol KBr}}{1.0 \text{ kg water}}\right) = 0.77 \text{ °C}$$

The normal boiling point of pure water is 100 °C, so the boiling point of the solution increases to 100.77 °C.

BALLPARK CHECK The 0.77 °C increase is consistent with our estimate of 0.75 °C.

PROBLEM 9.24
A solution is prepared by dissolving 0.67 mol of $MgCl_2$ in 0.50 kg of water.
(a) How many moles of ions are present in solution?
(b) What is the change in the boiling point of the aqueous solution?

PROBLEM 9.25
When 1.0 mol of HF is dissolved in 1.0 kg of water, the boiling point of the resulting solution is 100.5 °C. Is HF a strong or weak electrolyte? Explain.

KEY CONCEPT PROBLEM 9.26

The following diagram shows plots of vapor pressure versus temperature for a solvent and a solution.
(a) Which curve represents the pure solvent and which the solution?
(b) What is the approximate boiling point elevation for the solution?
(c) What is the approximate concentration of the solution in mol/kg, if 1 mol of solute particles raises the boiling point of 1 kg of solvent by 3.63 °C?

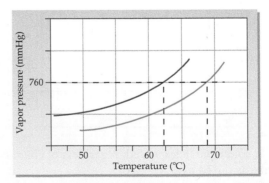

Freezing Point Depression of Solutions

Just as solutions have lower vapor pressure and consequently higher boiling points than pure solvents, they also have lower freezing points. Motorists in cold climates take advantage of this effect when they add "antifreeze" to the water in automobile cooling systems. Antifreeze is a nonvolatile solute, usually ethylene glycol ($HOCH_2CH_2OH$), that is added in sufficient concentration to lower the freezing point below the lowest expected outdoor temperature. In the same way, salt sprinkled on icy roads lowers the freezing point of ice below the road temperature and thus causes ice to melt.

Freezing point depression has much the same cause as vapor pressure lowering and boiling point elevation. Solute molecules are dispersed between solvent molecules throughout the solution, thereby making it more difficult for solvent molecules to come together and organize into ordered crystals.

For each mole of nonvolatile solute particles, the freezing point of 1 kg of water is lowered by 1.86 °C, or

$$\Delta T_{freezing} = \left(-1.86\,°C\,\frac{\text{kg water}}{\text{mol particles}}\right)\left(\frac{\text{mol particles}}{\text{kg water}}\right)$$

Thus, addition of 1 mol of antifreeze to 1 kg of water lowers the freezing point from 0.00 °C to −1.86 °C, and addition of 1 mol of NaCl (2 mol of particles) to 1 kg of water lowers the freezing point from 0.00 °C to −3.72 °C.

Worked Example 9.16 Properties of Solutions: Freezing Point Depression

The cells of a tomato contain mostly an aqueous solution of sugar and other substances. If a typical tomato freezes at −2.5 °C, what is the concentration of dissolved particles in the tomato cells (in moles of particles per kg of water)?

ANALYSIS The freezing point decreases by 1.86 °C for each mole of solute dissolved in 1 kg of water. We can use the decrease in freezing point (2.5 °C) to find the amount of solute per kg of water.

BALLPARK ESTIMATE The freezing point will decrease by about 1.9 °C for every 1 mol of solute particles in 1 kg of water. To lower the freezing point by 2.5 °C (about 30% more) will require about 30% more solute, or 1.3 mol.

SOLUTION

$$\Delta T_{freezing} = -2.5\,°C$$

$$= \left(-1.86\,°C\,\frac{\text{kg water}}{\text{mol solute particles}}\right)\left(\frac{??\ \text{mol solute particles}}{1.0\ \text{kg water}}\right)$$

We can rearrange this expression to

$$(-2.5\,°C)\left(\frac{1}{-1.86\,°C}\ \frac{\text{mol solute particles}}{\text{kg water}}\right) = 1.3\ \frac{\text{mol solute particles}}{\text{kg water}}$$

BALLPARK CHECK The calculated answer agrees with our estimate of 1.3 mol/kg.

PROBLEM 9.27
What is the freezing point of a solution of 1.0 mol of glucose in 1.0 kg of water?

PROBLEM 9.28
When 0.5 mol of a certain ionic substance is dissolved in 1.0 kg of water, the freezing point of the resulting solution is −2.8 °C. How many ions does the substance give when it dissolves?

9.12 Osmosis and Osmotic Pressure

Certain materials, including those that make up the membranes around living cells, are *semipermeable*. They allow water and other small molecules to pass through, but they block the passage of large solute molecules or ions. When a solution and a pure solvent, or two solutions of different concentration, are separated

Osmosis The passage of solvent through a semipermeable membrane separating two solutions of different concentration.

by a semipermeable membrane, solvent molecules pass through the membrane in a process called **osmosis**. Although the passage of solvent through the membrane takes place in both directions, passage from the pure solvent side to the solution side is favored and occurs more often. As a result, the amount of liquid on the pure solvent side decreases, the amount of liquid on the solution side increases, and the concentration of the solution decreases.

For the simplest explanation of osmosis, let us look at what happens on the molecular level. As shown in Figure 9.11, a solution inside a bulb is separated by a semipermeable membrane from pure solvent in the outer container. Solvent molecules in the outer container, because of their somewhat higher concentration, approach the membrane more frequently than do molecules in the bulb, thereby passing through more often and causing the liquid level in the attached tube to rise.

▶ **Figure 9.11**
The phenomenon of osmosis.
A solution inside the bulb is separated from pure solvent in the outer container by a semipermeable membrane. Solvent molecules in the outer container have a higher concentration than molecules in the bulb and therefore pass through the membrane more frequently. The liquid in the tube therefore rises until an equilibrium is reached. At equilibrium, the osmotic pressure exerted by the column of liquid in the tube is sufficient to prevent further net passage of solvent.

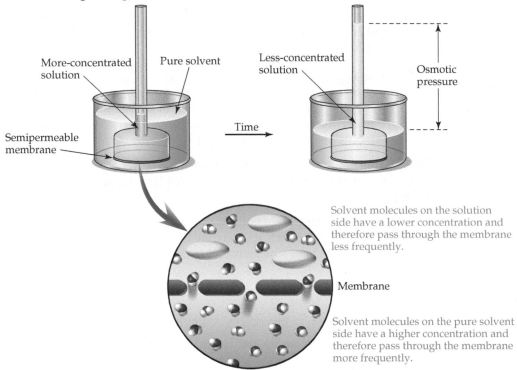

More-concentrated solution · Pure solvent · Less-concentrated solution · Osmotic pressure · Semipermeable membrane · Time

Solvent molecules on the solution side have a lower concentration and therefore pass through the membrane less frequently.

Membrane

Solvent molecules on the pure solvent side have a higher concentration and therefore pass through the membrane more frequently.

As the liquid in the tube rises, its increased weight creates an increased pressure that pushes solvent back through the membrane until the rates of forward and reverse passage become equal and the liquid level stops rising. The amount of pressure necessary to achieve this equilibrium is called the **osmotic pressure** (π) of the solution and can be determined from the expression

Osmotic pressure The amount of external pressure that must be applied to a solution to prevent the net movement of solvent molecules across a semipermeable membrane.

$$\pi = \left(\frac{n}{V}\right)RT$$

where n is the number of moles of particles in the solution, V is the solution volume, R is the gas constant (Section 8.10), and T is the absolute temperature of the solution. Note the similarity between this equation for the osmotic pressure of a solution and the equation for the pressure of an ideal gas, $P = (n/V)RT$. In both cases, the pressure has units of atmospheres.

Osmotic pressures can be extremely high, even for relatively dilute solutions. The osmotic pressure of a 0.15 M NaCl solution at 25 °C, for example, is 7.3 atm, a value that supports a difference in water level of approximately 250 ft!

As with other colligative properties, the amount of osmotic pressure depends only on the concentration of solute particles, not on their identity. Thus, it is convenient to use a new unit, *osmolarity* (osmol), to describe the concentration of particles in solution. The **osmolarity** of a solution is equal to the number of moles of dissolved particles (ions or molecules) per liter of solution. A 0.2 M glucose solution, for instance, has

Osmolarity (osmol) The sum of the molarities of all dissolved particles in a solution.

an osmolarity of 0.2 osmol, but a 0.2 M solution of NaCl has an osmolarity of 0.4 osmol because it contains 0.2 mol of Na^+ ions and 0.2 mol of Cl^- ions.

Osmosis is particularly important in living organisms because the membranes around cells are semipermeable. The fluids both inside and outside cells must therefore have the same osmolarity to prevent buildup of osmotic pressure and consequent rupture of the cell membrane.

In blood, the plasma surrounding red blood cells has an osmolarity of approximately 0.30 osmol and is said to be **isotonic** with (that is, has the same osmolarity as) the cell contents. If the cells are removed from plasma and placed in 0.15 M NaCl (called *physiological saline solution*), they are unharmed because the osmolarity of the saline solution (0.30 osmol) is the same as that of plasma. If, however, red blood cells are placed in pure water or in any solution with an osmolarity much lower than 0.30 osmol (a **hypotonic** solution), water passes through the membrane into the cell, causing the cell to swell up and burst, a process called *hemolysis*.

Finally, if red blood cells are placed in a solution having an osmolarity greater than the cell contents (a **hypertonic** solution), water passes out of the cells into the surrounding solution, causing the cells to shrivel, a process called *crenation*. Figure 9.12 shows red blood cells under all three conditions: isotonic, hypotonic, and hypertonic. Therefore, it is critical that any solution used intravenously be isotonic to prevent red blood cells from being destroyed.

Isotonic Having the same osmolarity.

Hypotonic Having an osmolarity *less than* the surrounding blood plasma or cells.

Hypertonic Having an osmolarity *greater than* the surrounding blood plasma or cells.

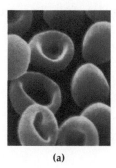 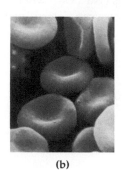 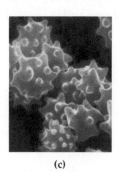

(a) (b) (c)

◀**Figure 9.12**
Red blood cells.
In an isotonic solution the blood cells are normal in appearance (a), but the cells in a hypotonic solution (b) are swollen because of water gain, and those in a hypertonic solution (c) are shriveled because of water loss.

Worked Example 9.17 Properties of Solutions: Osmolarity

The solution of glucose commonly used intravenously has a concentration of 5.0% (m/v) glucose. What is the osmolarity of this solution? The molar mass of glucose is 180 g/mol.

ANALYSIS Since glucose is a molecular substance that does not give ions in solution, the osmolarity of the solution is the same as the molarity. Recall from Section 9.7 that a solution of 5.0% (m/v) glucose has a concentration of 5.0 g glucose per 100 mL of solution, which is equivalent to 50 g per liter of solution. Thus, finding the molar concentration of glucose requires a mass to mole conversion.

BALLPARK ESTIMATE One liter of solution contains 50 g of glucose (MW = 180 g/mol). Thus, 50 g of glucose is equal to a little more than 0.25 mol, so a solution concentration of 50 g/L is equal to about 0.25 osmol, or 0.25 M.

SOLUTION

STEP 1: **Identify known information.** We know the (m/v)% concentration of the glucose solution.

$$5.0\% \ (m/v) = \frac{5.0 \ g \ glucose}{100 \ mL \ solution} \times 100\%$$

STEP 2: **Identify answer and units.** We are looking for osmolarity, which in this case is equal to the molarity of the solution because glucose is a molecular substance and does not dissociate into ions.

$$Osmolarity = Molarity = ?? \ mol/liter$$

STEP 3: Identify conversion factors. The (m/v)% concentration is defined as grams of solute per 100 mL of solution, and molarity is defined as moles of solute per liter of solution. We will need to convert from milliliters to liters and then use molar mass to convert grams of glucose to moles of glucose.

$$\frac{\text{g glucose}}{100\ \cancel{mL}} \times \frac{1000\ \cancel{mL}}{L} \longrightarrow \frac{\text{g glucose}}{L}$$

$$\frac{\cancel{\text{g glucose}}}{L} \times \frac{1\ \text{mol glucose}}{180\ \cancel{\text{g glucose}}} \longrightarrow \frac{\text{moles glucose}}{L}$$

STEP 4: Solve. Starting with the (m/v)% glucose concentration, we first find the number of grams of glucose in 1 L of solution and then convert to moles of glucose per liter.

$$\left(\frac{5.0\ \text{g glucose}}{100\ \cancel{mL}\ \text{solution}}\right)\left(\frac{1000\ \cancel{mL}}{1\ L}\right) = \frac{50\ \text{g glucose}}{L\ \text{solution}}$$

$$\left(\frac{50\ \cancel{g}\ \text{glucose}}{1\ L}\right)\left(\frac{1\ \text{mol}}{180\ \cancel{g}}\right) = 0.28\ \text{M glucose} = 0.28\ \text{osmol}$$

BALLPARK CHECK The calculated osmolarity is reasonably close to our estimate of 0.25 osmol.

Worked Example 9.18 Properties of Solutions: Osmolarity

What mass of NaCl is needed to make 1.50 L of a 0.300 osmol solution? The molar mass of NaCl is 58.44 g/mol.

ANALYSIS Since NaCl is an ionic substance that produces 2 mol of ions (Na^+, Cl^-) when it dissociates, the osmolarity of the solution is twice the molarity. From the volume and the osmolarity we can determine the moles of NaCl needed and then perform a mole to mass conversion.

SOLUTION

STEP 1: Identify known information. We know the volume and the osmolarity of the final NaCl solution.

$$V = 1.50\ L$$

$$0.300\ \text{osmol} = \left(\frac{0.300\ \text{mol ions}}{L}\right)$$

STEP 2: Identify answer and units. We are looking for the mass of NaCl.

$$\text{Mass of NaCl} = ??\ g$$

STEP 3: Identify conversion factors. Starting with osmolarity in the form (moles NaCl/L), we can use volume to determine the number of moles of solute. We can then use molar mass for the mole to mass conversion.

$$\left(\frac{\text{moles NaCl}}{\cancel{L}}\right) \times (\cancel{L}) = \text{moles NaCl}$$

$$(\cancel{\text{moles NaCl}}) \times \left(\frac{\text{g NaCl}}{\cancel{\text{mole NaCl}}}\right) = \text{g NaCl}$$

STEP 4: Solve. Use the appropriate conversions, remembering that NaCl produces two ions per formula unit, to find the mass of NaCl.

$$\left(\frac{0.300\ \cancel{\text{mol ions}}}{\cancel{L}}\right)\left(\frac{1\ \text{mol NaCl}}{2\ \cancel{\text{mol ions}}}\right)(1.50\ \cancel{L}) = 0.225\ \text{mol NaCl}$$

$$(0.225\ \cancel{\text{mol NaCl}})\left(\frac{58.44\ \text{g NaCl}}{\cancel{\text{mol NaCl}}}\right) = 13.1\ \text{g NaCl}$$

PROBLEM 9.29
What is the osmolarity of the following solutions?
(a) 0.35 M KBr
(b) 0.15 M glucose + 0.05 M K_2SO_4

PROBLEM 9.30
A typical oral rehydration solution (ORS) for infants contains 90 mEq/L Na^+, 20 mEq/L K^+, 110 mEq/L Cl^-, and 2.0% (m/v) glucose (MW = 180 g/mol).
(a) Calculate the concentration of each ORS component in units of molarity.
(b) What is the osmolarity of the solution, and how does it compare with the osmolarity of blood plasma?

9.13 Dialysis

Dialysis is similar to osmosis, except that the pores in a dialysis membrane are larger than those in an osmotic membrane so that both solvent molecules and small solute particles can pass through, but large colloidal particles such as proteins cannot pass. (The exact dividing line between a "small" molecule and a "large" one is imprecise, and dialysis membranes with a variety of pore sizes are available.) Dialysis membranes include animal bladders, parchment, and cellophane.

Perhaps the most important medical use of dialysis is in artificial kidney machines, where *hemodialysis* is used to cleanse the blood of patients whose kidneys malfunction (Figure 9.13). Blood is diverted from the body and pumped through a long cellophane dialysis tube suspended in an isotonic solution formulated to contain many of the same components as blood plasma. These substances—glucose, NaCl, $NaHCO_3$, and KCl— have the same concentrations in the dialysis solution as they do in blood so that they have no net passage through the membrane.

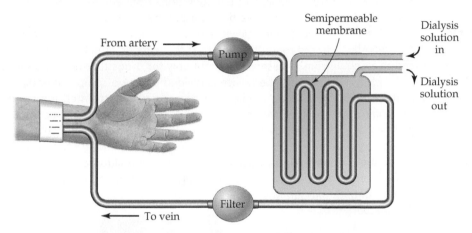

◄ **Figure 9.13**
Operation of a hemodialysis unit used for purifying blood.
Blood is pumped from an artery through a coiled semipermeable membrane of cellophane. Small waste products pass through the membrane and are washed away by an isotonic dialysis solution.

Small waste materials such as urea pass through the dialysis membrane from the blood to the solution side where they are washed away, but cells, proteins, and other important blood components are prevented from passing through the membrane because of their larger size. In addition, the dialysis fluid concentration can be controlled so that imbalances in electrolytes are corrected. The wash solution is changed every 2 h, and a typical hemodialysis procedure lasts for 4–7 h.

As noted above, colloidal particles are too large to pass through a semipermeable membreane. Protein molecules, in particular, do not cross semipermeable membranes and thus play an essential role in determining the osmolarity of body fluids. The distribution of water and solutes across the capillary walls that separate blood plasma from the fluid

◄ **The delivery of oxygen and nutrients to the cells and the removal of waste products are regulated by osmosis.**

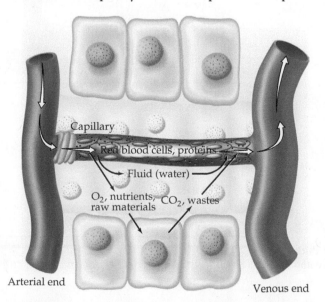

surrounding cells is controlled by the balance between blood pressure and osmotic pressure. The pressure of blood inside the capillary tends to push water out of the plasma (filtration), but the osmotic pressure of colloidal protein molecules tends to draw water into the plasma (reabsorption). The balance between the two processes varies with location in the body. At the arterial end of a capillary, where blood pumped from the heart has a higher pressure, filtration is favored, At the venous end, where blood pressure is lower, reabsorption is favored, causing waste products from metabolism to enter the bloodstream, to be removed by the kidneys.

CHEMISTRY IN ACTION

Timed-Release Medications

There is much more in most medications than medicine. Even something as simple as a generic aspirin tablet contains a binder to keep it from crumbling, a filler to bring it to the right size and help it disintegrate in the stomach, and a lubricant to keep it from sticking to the manufacturing equipment. Timed-release medications are more complex still.

The widespread use of timed-release medication dates from the introduction of Contac decongestant in 1961. The original idea was simple: tiny beads of medicine were encapsulated by coating them with varying thicknesses of a slow-dissolving polymer. Those beads with a thinner coat dissolve and release their medicine more rapidly; those with a thicker coat dissolve more slowly. Combining the right number of beads with the right thicknesses into a single capsule makes possible the gradual release of medication over a predictable time.

The technology of timed-release medications has become much more sophisticated in recent years, and the kinds of medications that can be delivered have become more numerous. Some medicines, for instance, either damage the stomach lining or are destroyed by the highly acidic environment in the stomach but can be delivered safely if given an *enteric coating*. The enteric coating is a polymeric material formulated so that it is stable in acid but reacts and is destroyed when it passes into the more basic environment of the intestines.

More recently, dermal patches have been developed to deliver drugs directly by diffusion through the skin. Patches are available to treat conditions from angina to motion sickness, as well as nicotine patches to help reduce cigarette cravings. One clever new device for timed release of medication through the skin uses the osmotic effect to force a drug from its reservoir. Useful only for drugs that do not dissolve in water, the device is divided into two compartments, one containing medication covered by a perforated membrane and the other containing a hygroscopic material (Section 9.3) covered by a semipermeable membrane. As moisture from the air diffuses through the membrane into the compartment with the hygroscopic material, the buildup of osmotic pressure squeezes the medication out of the other compartment through tiny holes.

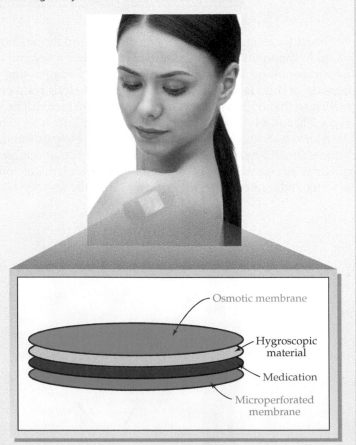

▲ The small beads of medicine are coated with different thicknesses of a slow-dissolving polymer so that they dissolve and release medicine at different times.

See Chemistry in Action Problem 9.93 at the end of the chapter.

SUMMARY: REVISITING THE CHAPTER GOALS

1. What are solutions, and what factors affect solubility? Mixtures are classified as either *heterogeneous*, if the mixing is nonuniform, or *homogeneous*, if the mixing is uniform. *Solutions* are homogeneous mixtures that contain particles the size of ions and molecules (<2.0 nm diameter), whereas larger particles (2.0–500 nm diameter) are present in *colloids*.

The maximum amount of one substance (the *solute*) that can be dissolved in another (the *solvent*) is called the substance's *solubility*. Substances tend to be mutually soluble when their intermolecular forces are similar. The solubility in water of a solid often increases with temperature, but the solubility of a gas always decreases with temperature. Pressure significantly affects gas solubilities, which are directly proportional to their partial pressure over the solution (*Henry's law*) (*see Problems 36–43, 94, 105*).

2. How is the concentration of a solution expressed? The concentration of a solution can be expressed in several ways, including molarity, weight/weight percent composition, weight/volume percent composition, and parts per million (or billion). Osmolarity is used to express the total concentration of dissolved particles (ions and molecules). Molarity, which expresses concentration as the number of moles of solute per liter of solution, is the most useful method when calculating quantities of reactants or products for reactions in aqueous solution (*see Problems 44–65, 86, 88, 89, 91, 94–105, 107, 108*).

3. How are dilutions carried out? A dilution is carried out by adding more solvent to an existing solution. Only the amount of solvent changes; the amount of solute remains the same. Thus, the molarity times the volume of the dilute solution is equal to the molarity times the volume of the concentrated solution: $M_c V_c = M_d V_d$ (*see Problems 35, 66–71, 98*).

4. What is an electrolyte? Substances that form ions when dissolved in water and whose water solutions therefore conduct an electric current are called *electrolytes*. Substances that ionize completely in water are *strong electrolytes*, those that ionize partially are *weak electrolytes*, and those that do not ionize are *nonelectrolytes*. Body fluids contain small amounts of many different electrolytes, whose concentrations are expressed as moles of ionic charge, or equivalents, per liter (*see Problems 32,33, 72–79, 97, 108*).

5. How do solutions differ from pure solvents in their behavior? In comparing a solution to a pure solvent, the solution has a lower vapor pressure at a given temperature, a higher boiling point, and a lower melting point. Called *colligative properties*, these effects depend only on the number of dissolved particles, not on their chemical identity (*see Problems 32, 33, 43, 80–83, 108*).

6. What is osmosis? *Osmosis* occurs when solutions of different concentration are separated by a semipermeable membrane that allows solvent molecules to pass but blocks the passage of solute ions and molecules. Solvent flows from the more dilute side to the more concentrated side until sufficient *osmotic pressure* builds up and stops the flow. An effect similar to osmosis occurs when membranes of larger pore size are used. In *dialysis*, the membrane allows the passage of solvent and small dissolved molecules but prevents passage of proteins and larger particles (*see Problems 31, 84, 85, 87*).

KEY WORDS

Colligative property, *p. 275*

Colloid, *p. 253*

Dilution factor, *p. 271*

Electrolyte, *p. 273*

Equivalent (Eq), *p. 273*

Gram-equivalent (g-Eq), *p. 273*

Henry's law, *p. 261*

Heterogeneous mixture, *p. 253*

Homogeneous mixture, *p. 253*

Hygroscopic, *p. 258*

Hypertonic, *p. 281*

Hypotonic, *p. 281*

Isotonic, *p. 281*

Mass/mass percent concentration, (m/m)%, *p. 264*

mass/volume percent concentration, (m/v)%, *p. 264*

Miscible, *p. 258*

Molarity (M), *p. 268*

Nonelectrolyte, *p. 273*

Osmolarity (osmol), *p. 280*

Osmosis, *p. 280*

Osmotic pressure, *p. 280*

Parts per billion (ppb), *p. 267*

Parts per million (ppm), *p. 267*

Saturated solution, *p. 258*

Solubility, *p. 258*

Solute, *p. 254*

Solution, *p. 253*

Solvation, *p. 256*

Solvent, *p. 254*

Strong electrolyte, *p. 273*

Supersaturated solution, *p. 259*

Volume/volume percent concentration, (v/v)%, *p. 264*

Weak electrolyte, *p. 273*

CONCEPT MAP: SOLUTIONS

Formation of a solution depends on many factors, including the attractive forces between solute and solvent particles, temperature, and pressure (gases). The extent to which a solute dissolves in solution can be expressed either qualitatively or using quantitative concentration units. The most common concentration unit in chemical applications is molarity (moles of solute/L solution), which is also useful in quantitative relationships involving reactions that take place in solution. Colligative properties of solution, including boiling and freezing points, will vary with the amount of solute dissolved in solution. These relationships are illustrated in the concept map in Figure 9.14.

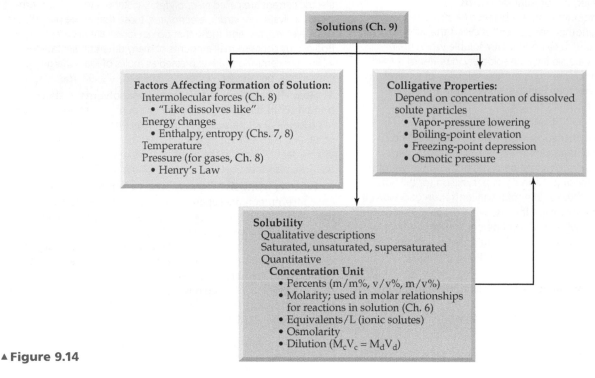

▲ **Figure 9.14**

UNDERSTANDING KEY CONCEPTS

9.31 Assume that two liquids are separated by a semipermeable membrane, with pure solvent on the right side, and a solution of a solute on the left side. Make a drawing that shows the situation after equilibrium is reached.

Before equilibrium

9.32 When 1 mol of HCl is added to 1 kg of water, the boiling point increases by 1.0 °C, but when 1 mol of acetic acid, CH_3CO_2H, is added to 1 kg of water, the boiling point increases by only 0.5 °C. Explain.

9.33 HF is a weak electrolyte and HBr is a strong electrolyte. Which of the curves in the figure represents the change in the boiling point of an aqueous solution when 1 mole of HF is added to 1 kg of water, and which represents the change when 1 mol of HBr is added?

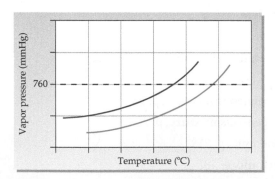

9.34 Assume that you have two full beakers, one containing pure water (blue) and the other containing an equal volume of a 10% (w/v) solution of glucose (green). Which of the drawings (a)–(c) best represents the two beakers after they have stood uncovered for several days and partial evaporation has occurred? Explain.

(a)   (b)   (c)

9.35   A beaker containing 150.0 mL of 0.1 M glucose is represented by (a). Which of the drawings (b)–(d) represents the

solution that results when 50.0 mL is withdrawn from (a) and then diluted by a factor of 4?

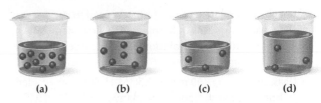

(a)   (b)   (c)   (d)

ADDITIONAL PROBLEMS

SOLUTIONS AND SOLUBILITY

9.36   What is the difference between a homogeneous mixture and a heterogeneous one?

9.37   How can you tell a solution from a colloid?

9.38   What characteristic of water allows it to dissolve ionic solids?

9.39   Why does water not dissolve motor oil?

9.40   Which of the following are solutions?

(a) Italian salad dressing   (b) Rubbing alcohol

(c) Algae in pond water   (d) Black coffee

9.41   Based on the predominant intermolecular forces, which of the following pairs of liquids are likely to be miscible?

(a) H_2SO_4 and H_2O (b) C_8H_{18} and C_6H_6

(c) CH_2Cl_2, and H_2O (d) CS_2 and CCl_4

9.42   The solubility of NH_3 gas in water at an NH_3 pressure of 760.0 mmHg is 51.8 g/100 mL. What is the solubility of NH_3 if its partial pressure is reduced to 225.0 mmHg?

9.43   The solubility of CO_2 gas in water is 0.15 g/100 mL at a CO_2 pressure of 760 mmHg. What is the solubility of CO_2 in a soft drink (which is mainly water) that was bottled under a CO_2 pressure of 4.5 atm?

CONCENTRATION AND DILUTION OF SOLUTIONS

9.44   Is a solution highly concentrated if it is saturated? Is a solution saturated if it is highly concentrated?

9.45   How is mass/volume percent concentration defined and for what types of solutions is it typically used?

9.46   How is molarity defined?

9.47   How is volume/volume percent concentration defined and for what types of solutions is it typically used?

9.48   How would you prepare 750.0 mL of a 6.0% (v/v) ethyl alcohol solution?

9.49   A dilute aqueous solution of boric acid, H_3BO_3 is often used as an eyewash. How would you prepare 500.0 mL of a 0.50% (m/v) boric acid solution?

9.50   Describe how you would prepare 250 mL of a 0.10 M NaCl solution.

9.51   Describe how you would prepare 1.50 L of a 7.50% (m/v) $Mg(NO_3)_2$ solution.

9.52   What is the mass/volume percent concentration of the following solutions?

(a) 0.078 mol KCl in 75 mL of solution

(b) 0.044 mol sucrose $(C_{12}H_{22}O_{11})$ in 380 mL of solution

9.53   The concentration of glucose in blood is approximately 90 mg/100 mL. What is the mass/volume percent concentration of glucose? What is the molarity of glucose?

9.54   How many moles of each substance are needed to prepare the following solutions?

(a) 50.0 mL of 8.0% (m/v) KCl (MW = 74.55 g/mol)

(b) 200.0 mL of 7.5% (m/v) acetic acid (MW = 60.05 g/mol)

9.55   Which of the following solutions is more concentrated?

(a) 0.50 M KCl or 5.0% (m/v) KCl

(b) 2.5% (m/v) $NaHSO_4$ or 0.025 M $NaHSO_4$

9.56   If you had only 23 g of KOH remaining in a bottle, how many milliliters of 10.0% (m/v) solution could you prepare? How many milliliters of 0.25 M solution?

9.57   Over-the-counter hydrogen peroxide (H_2O_2) solutions are 3% (m/v). What is this concentration in moles per liter?

9.58   The lethal dosage of potassium cyanide (KCN) in rats is 10 mg KCN per kilogram of body weight. What is this concentration in parts per million?

9.59   The maximum concentration set by the U.S. Environmental Protection Agency for lead in drinking water is 15 ppb. (*Hint*: 1 ppb = $1\,\mu g/L$)

(a) What is this concentration in milligrams per liter?

(b) How many liters of water contaminated at this maximum level must you drink to consume $1.0\,\mu g$ of lead?

9.60   What is the molarity of the following solutions?

(a) 12.5 g $NaHCO_3$ in 350.0 mL solution

(b) 45.0 g H_2SO_4 in 300.0 mL solution

(c) 30.0 g NaCl dissolved to make 500.0 mL solution

9.61   How many grams of solute are in the following solutions?

(a) 200 mL of 0.30 M acetic acid, CH_3CO_2H

(b) 1.50 L of 0.25 M NaOH

(c) 750 mL of 2.5 M nitric acid, HNO_3

9.62 How many milliliters of a 0.75 M HCl solution do you need to obtain 0.0040 mol of HCl?

9.63 Nalorphine, a relative of morphine, is used to combat withdrawal symptoms in heroin users. How many milliliters of a 0.40% (m/v) solution of nalorphine must be injected to obtain a dose of 1.5 mg?

9.64 A flask containing 450 mL of 0.50 M H_2SO_4 was accidentally knocked to the floor. How many grams of $NaHCO_3$ do you need to put on the spill to neutralize the acid according to the following equation?

$$H_2SO_4(aq) + 2\,NaHCO_3(aq) \longrightarrow$$
$$Na_2SO_4(aq) + 2\,H_2O(l) + 2\,CO_2(g)$$

9.65 Sodium thiosulfate $(Na_2S_2O_3)$, the major component in photographic fixer solution, reacts with silver bromide to dissolve it according to the following reaction:

$$AgBr(s) + 2\,Na_2S_2O_3(aq) \longrightarrow$$
$$Na_3Ag(S_2O_3)_2(aq) + NaBr(aq)$$

(a) How many moles of $Na_2S_2O_3$ would be required to react completely with 0.450 g of AgBr?

(b) How many mL of 0.02 M $Na_2S_2O_3$ contain this number of moles?

9.66 What is the final volume of an orange juice prepared from 100.0 mL of orange juice concentrate if the final juice is to be 20.0% of the strength of the original?

9.67 What is the final volume of NaOH solution prepared from 100.0 mL of 0.500 M NaOH if you wanted the final concentration to be 0.150 M?

9.68 An aqueous solution that contains 285 ppm of potassium nitrate (KNO_3) is being used to feed plants in a garden. What volume of this solution is needed to prepare 2.0 L of a solution that is 75 ppm in KNO_3?

9.69 What is the concentration of a NaCl solution, in (m/v)%, prepared by diluting 65 mL of a saturated solution, which has a concentration of 37 (m/v)%, to 480 mL?

9.70 Concentrated (12.0 M) hydrochloric acid is sold for household and industrial purposes under the name "muriatic acid." How many milliliters of 0.500 M HCl solution can be made from 25.0 mL of 12.0 M HCl solution?

9.71 Dilute solutions of $NaHCO_3$ are sometimes used in treating acid burns. How many milliliters of 0.100 M $NaHCO_3$ solution are needed to prepare 750.0 mL of 0.0500 M $NaHCO_3$ solution?

ELECTROLYTES

9.72 What is an electrolyte?

9.73 Give an example of a strong electrolyte and a nonelectrolyte.

9.74 What does it mean when we say that the concentration of Ca^{2+} in blood is 3.0 mEq/L?

9.75 What is the total anion concentration (in mEq/L) of a solution that contains 5.0 mEq/L Na^+, 12.0 mEq/L Ca^{2+}, and 2.0 mEq/L Li^+?

9.76 Kaochlor, a 10% (m/v) KCl solution, is an oral electrolyte supplement administered for potassium deficiency. How many milliequivalents of K^+ are in a 30 mL dose?

9.77 Calculate the gram-equivalent for each of the following ions:

(a) Ca^{2+} **(b)** K^+

(c) SO_4^{2-} **(d)** PO_4^{3-}

9.78 Look up the concentration of Cl^- ion in blood in Table 9.6. How many milliliters of blood would be needed to obtain 1.0 g of Cl^- ions?

9.79 Normal blood contains 3 mEq/L of Mg^{2+}. How many milligrams of Mg^{2+} are present in 150.0 mL of blood?

PROPERTIES OF SOLUTIONS

9.80 Which lowers the freezing point of 2.0 kg of water more, 0.20 mol NaOH or 0.20 mol $Ba(OH)_2$? Both compounds are strong electrolytes. Explain.

9.81 Which solution has the higher boiling point, 0.500 M glucose or 0.300 M KCl? Explain.

9.82 Methanol, CH_3OH, is sometimes used as an antifreeze for the water in automobile windshield washer fluids. How many moles of methanol must be added to 5.00 kg of water to lower its freezing point to $-10.0\,°C$? (For each mole of solute, the freezing point of 1 kg of water is lowered $1.86\,°C$.)

9.83 Hard candy is prepared by dissolving pure sugar and flavoring in water and heating the solution to boiling. What is the boiling point of a solution produced by adding 650 g of cane sugar (molar mass 342.3 g/mol) to 1.5 kg of water? (For each mole of nonvolatile solute, the boiling point of 1 kg of water is raised $0.51\,°C$.)

OSMOSIS

9.84 Why do red blood cells swell up and burst when placed in pure water?

9.85 What does it mean when we say that a 0.15 M NaCl solution is isotonic with blood, whereas distilled water is hypotonic?

9.86 Which of the following solutions has the higher osmolarity?

(a) 0.25 M KBr or 0.20 M Na_2SO_4

(b) 0.30 M NaOH or 3.0% (m/v) NaOH

9.87 Which of the following solutions will give rise to a greater osmotic pressure at equilibrium: 5.00 g of NaCl in 350.0 mL water or 35.0 g of glucose in 400.0 mL water? For NaCl, MW = 58.5 amu; for glucose, MW = 180 amu.

9.88 A pickling solution for preserving food is prepared by dissolving 270 g of NaCl in 3.8 L of water. Calculate the osmolarity of the solution.

9.89 An isotonic solution must be approximately 0.30 osmol. How much KCl is needed to prepare 175 mL of an isotonic solution?

CHEMISTRY IN ACTION

9.90 How does the body increase oxygen availability at high altitude? [*Breathing and Oxygen Transport, p. 263*]

9.91 What are the major electrolytes in sweat, and what are their approximate concentrations in mEq/L? [*Electrolytes, Fluid Replacement, and Sports Drinks, p. 276*]

9.92 Why is a sports drink more effective than plain water for rehydration after extended exercise? [*Electrolytes, Fluid Replacement, and Sports Drinks, p. 276*]

9.93 How does an enteric coating on a medication work? [*Timed-Release Medications, p. 284*]

GENERAL QUESTIONS AND PROBLEMS

9.94 Hyperbaric chambers, which provide high pressures (up to 6 atm) of either air or pure oxygen, are used to treat a variety of conditions, ranging from decompression sickness in deep-sea divers to carbon monoxide poisoning.

  (a) What is the partial pressure of O_2 (in millimeters of Hg) in a hyperbaric chamber pressurized to 5 atm with air that is 18% in O_2?

  (b) What is the solubility of O_2 (in grams per 100 mL) in the blood at this partial pressure? The solubility of O_2 is 2.1 g/100 mL for $P_{O_2} = 1$ atm.

9.95 Express the solubility of O_2 in Problem 9.94(b) in units of molarity.

9.96 Uric acid, the principal constituent of some kidney stones, has the formula $C_5H_4N_4O_3$. In aqueous solution, the solubility of uric acid is only 0.067 g/L. Express this concentration in (m/v)%, in parts per million, and in molarity.

9.97 Emergency treatment of cardiac arrest victims sometimes involves injection of a calcium chloride solution directly into the heart muscle. How many grams of $CaCl_2$ are administered in an injection of 5.0 mL of a 5.0% (m/v) solution? How many milliequivalents of Ca^{2+}?

9.98 Nitric acid, HNO_3, is available commercially at a concentration of 16 M.

  (a) What volume would you need to obtain 0.150 mol HNO_3?

  (b) To what volume must you dilute this volume of HNO_3 from part (a) to prepare a 0.20 M solution?

9.99 One test for vitamin C (ascorbic acid, $C_6H_8O_6$) is based on the reaction of the vitamin with iodine:

$$C_6H_8O_6(aq) + I_2(aq) \longrightarrow C_6H_6O_6(aq) + 2\,HI(aq)$$

  (a) A 25.0 mL sample of a fruit juice requires 13.0 mL of 0.0100 M I_2 solution for reaction. How many moles of ascorbic acid are in the sample?

  (b) What is the molarity of ascorbic acid in the fruit juice?

  (c) The Food and Drug Administration recommends that 60 mg of ascorbic acid be consumed per day. How many milliliters of the fruit juice in part (a) must a person drink to obtain the recommended dosage?

9.100 *Ringer's solution*, used in the treatment of burns and wounds, is prepared by dissolving 8.6 g of NaCl, 0.30 g of KCl, and 0.33 g of $CaCl_2$ in water and diluting to a volume of 1.00 L. What is the molarity of each component?

9.101 What is the osmolarity of Ringer's solution (see Problem 9.100)? Is it hypotonic, isotonic, or hypertonic with blood plasma (0.30 osmol)?

9.102 The typical dosage of statin drugs for the treatment of high cholesterol is 10 mg. Assuming a total blood volume of 5.0 L, calculate the (m/v)% concentration of drug in the blood in units of g/100 mL.

9.103 Assuming the density of blood in healthy individuals is approximately 1.05 g/mL, report the concentration of drug in Problem 9.102 in units of ppm.

9.104 In all 50 states, a person with a blood alcohol concentration of 0.080% (v/v) is considered legally drunk. What volume of total alcohol does this concentration represent, assuming a blood volume of 5.0 L?

9.105 Ammonia, NH_3, is very soluble in water (51.8 g/L at 20 °C and 760 mmHg).

  (a) Show how NH_3 can hydrogen bond to water.

  (b) What is the solubility of ammonia in water in moles per liter?

9.106 Cobalt(II) chloride, a blue solid, can absorb water from the air to form cobalt(II) chloride hexahydrate, a pink solid. The equilibrium is so sensitive to moisture in the air that $CoCl_2$ is used as a humidity indicator.

  (a) Write a balanced equation for the equilibrium. Be sure to include water as a reactant to produce the hexahydrate.

  (b) How many grams of water are released by the decomposition of 2.50 g of cobalt(II) chloride hexahydrate?

9.107 How many milliliters of 0.150 M $BaCl_2$ are needed to react completely with 35.0 mL of 0.200 M Na_2SO_4? How many grams of $BaSO_4$ will be formed?

9.108 Many compounds are only partially dissociated into ions in aqueous solution. Trichloroacetic acid (CCl_3CO_2H), for instance, is partially dissociated in water according to the equation

$$CCl_3CO_2H(aq) \rightleftharpoons H^+(aq) + CCl_3CO_2^-(aq)$$

For a solution prepared by dissolving 1.00 mol of trichloroacetic acid in 1.00 kg of water, 36.0% of the trichloroacetic acid dissociates to form H^+ and $CCl_3CO_2^-$ ions.

  (a) What is the total concentration of dissolved ions and molecules in 1 kg of water?

  (b) What is the freezing point of this solution? (The freezing point of 1 kg of water is lowered 1.86 °C for each mole of solute particles.)

CHAPTER 10

Acids and Bases

CONTENTS

◄ Acids are found in many of the foods we eat, including tomatoes, peppers, and these citrus fruits.

A cids! The word evokes images of dangerous, corrosive liquids that eat away everything they touch. Although a few well-known substances such as sulfuric acid (H_2SO_4) do indeed fit this description, most acids are relatively harmless. In fact, many acids, such as ascorbic acid (vitamin C), are necessary for life. We have already touched on the subject of acids and bases on several occasions, but the time has come for a more detailed study.

10.1 Acids and Bases in Aqueous Solution

Let us take a moment to review what we said about acids and bases in Sections 3.11 and 5.10 before going on to a more systematic study:

- An acid is a substance that produces hydrogen ions, H^+, when dissolved in water.
- A base is a substance that produces hydroxide ions, OH^-, when dissolved in water.
- The neutralization reaction of an acid with a base yields water plus a *salt*, an ionic compound composed of the cation from the base and the anion from the acid.

The above definitions of acids and bases were proposed in 1887 by the Swedish chemist Svante Arrhenius and are useful for many purposes. The definitions are limited, however, because they refer only to reactions that take place in aqueous solutions. (We will see shortly how the definitions can be broadened.) Another issue is that the H^+ ion is so reactive it does not exist in water. Instead, H^+ reacts with H_2O to give the **hydronium ion**, H_3O^+, as mentioned in Section 3.11. When gaseous HCl dissolves in water, for instance, H_3O^+ and Cl^- are formed. As described in Section 4.9 , electrostatic potential maps show that the hydrogen of HCl is positively polarized and electron-poor (blue), whereas the oxygen of water is negatively polarized and electron-rich (red):

Hydronium ion The H_3O^+ ion, formed when an acid reacts with water.

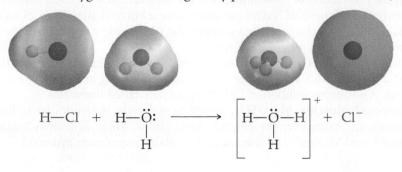

Thus, the Arrhenius definition is updated to acknowledge that an acid yields H_3O^+ in water rather than H^+. In practice, however, the notations H_3O^+ and $H^+(aq)$ are often used interchangeably.

The Arrhenius definition of a base is correct as far as it goes, but it is important to realize that the OH^- ions "produced" by the base can come from either of two sources. Metal hydroxides, such as NaOH, KOH, and $Ba(OH)_2$, are ionic compounds that already contain OH^- ions and merely release those ions when they dissolve in water. Some molecular compounds such as ammonia, however, are not ionic and contain no OH^- ions in their structure. Nonetheless, they can act as bases to produce OH^- ions in reactions with water, as will be seen in Section 10.3.

10.2 Some Common Acids and Bases

Acids and bases are present in a variety of foods and consumer products. Acids generally have a sour taste, and nearly every sour food contains an acid: Lemons, oranges, and grapefruit contain citric acid, for instance, and sour milk contains lactic acid. Bases are not so obvious in foods, but most of us have them stored under the kitchen or bathroom sink. Bases are present in many household cleaning agents, from perfumed bar soap, to ammonia-based window cleaners, to the substance you put down the drain to dissolve hair, grease, and other materials that clog it.

Some of the most common acids and bases are listed below. It is a good idea at this point to learn their names and formulas, because we will refer to them often.

▲ Common household cleaners typically contain bases (NaOH, NH_3). Soap is manufactured by the reaction of vegetable oils and animal fats with the bases NaOH and KOH.

- **Sulfuric acid, H_2SO_4,** is probably the most important raw material in the chemical and pharmaceutical industries, and it is manufactured in greater quantity worldwide than any other industrial chemical. Over 45 million tons are prepared in the United States annually for use in many hundreds of industrial processes, including the preparation of phosphate fertilizers. Its most common consumer use is as the acid found in automobile batteries. As anyone who has splashed battery acid on his or her skin or clothing knows, sulfuric acid is highly corrosive and can cause painful burns.

- **Hydrochloric acid, HCl,** or *muriatic acid*, as it was historically known, has many industrial applications, including its use in metal cleaning and in the manufacture of high-fructose corn syrup. Aqueous HCl is also present as "stomach acid" in the digestive systems of most mammals.

- **Phosphoric acid, H_3PO_4,** is used in vast quantities in the manufacture of phosphate fertilizers. In addition, it is also used as an additive in foods and toothpastes. The tart taste of many soft drinks is due to the presence of phosphoric acid.

- **Nitric acid, HNO_3,** is a strong oxidizing agent that is used for many purposes, including the manufacture of ammonium nitrate fertilizer and military explosives. When spilled on the skin, it leaves a characteristic yellow coloration because of its reaction with skin proteins.

- **Acetic acid, CH_3CO_2H,** is the primary organic constituent of vinegar. It also occurs in all living cells and is used in many industrial processes such as the preparation of solvents, lacquers, and coatings.

- **Sodium hydroxide, NaOH,** also called *caustic soda* or *lye*, is the most commonly used of all bases. Industrially, it is used in the production of aluminum from its ore, in the production of glass, and in the manufacture of soap from animal fat. Concentrated solutions of NaOH can cause severe burns if allowed to sit on the skin for long. Drain cleaners often contain NaOH because it reacts with the fats and proteins found in grease and hair.

- **Calcium hydroxide, $Ca(OH)_2$,** or *slaked lime*, is made industrially by treating lime (CaO) with water. It has many applications, including its use in mortars and cements. An aqueous solution of $Ca(OH)_2$ is often called *limewater*.

- **Magnesium hydroxide, $Mg(OH)_2$,** or *milk of magnesia*, is an additive in foods, toothpaste, and many over-the-counter medications. Antacids such as Rolaids™, Mylanta™, and Maalox™, for instance, all contain magnesium hydroxide.

- **Ammonia, NH₃,** is used primarily as a fertilizer, but it also has many other industrial applications, including the manufacture of pharmaceuticals and explosives. A dilute solution of ammonia is frequently used around the house as a glass cleaner.

10.3 The Brønsted–Lowry Definition of Acids and Bases

The Arrhenius definition of acids and bases discussed in Section 10.1 applies only to processes that take place in an aqueous solution. A far more general definition was proposed in 1923 by the Danish chemist Johannes Brønsted and the English chemist Thomas Lowry. A **Brønsted–Lowry acid** is any substance that is able to give a hydrogen ion, H^+, to another molecule or ion. A hydrogen *atom* consists of a proton and an electron, so a hydrogen *ion*, H^+, is simply a proton. Thus, we often refer to acids as *proton donors*. The reaction need not occur in water, and a Brønsted–Lowry acid need not give appreciable concentrations of H_3O^+ ions in water.

> **Brønsted–Lowry acid** A substance that can donate a hydrogen ion, H^+, to another molecule or ion.

Different acids can supply different numbers of H^+ ions, as we saw in Section 3.11. Acids with one proton to donate, such as HCl or HNO_3, are called *monoprotic acids*; H_2SO_4 is a *diprotic acid* because it has two protons to donate, and H_3PO_4 is a *triprotic acid* because it has three protons to donate. Notice that the acidic H atoms (that is, the H atoms that are donated as protons) are bonded to electronegative atoms, such as chlorine or oxygen.

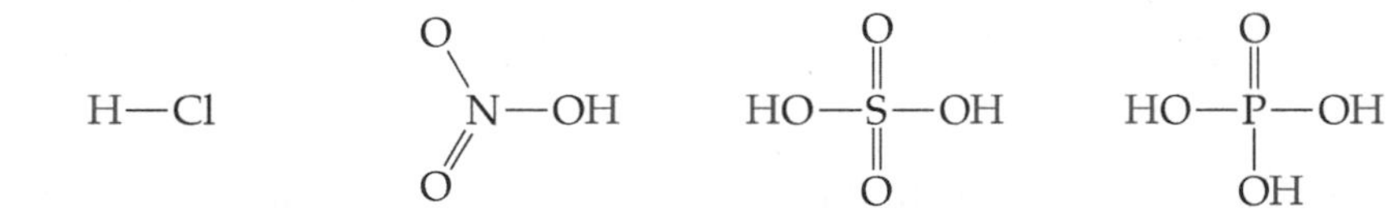

| Hydrochloric acid (monoprotic) | Nitric acid (monoprotic) | Sulfuric acid (diprotic) | Phosphoric acid (triprotic) |

Acetic acid (CH_3CO_2H), an example of an organic acid, actually has a total of 4 hydrogens, but only the one bonded to the electronegative oxygen is positively polarized and therefore acidic. The 3 hydrogens bonded to carbon are not acidic. Most organic acids are similar in that they contain many hydrogen atoms, but only the one in the $-CO_2H$ group (blue in the electrostatic potential map) is acidic:

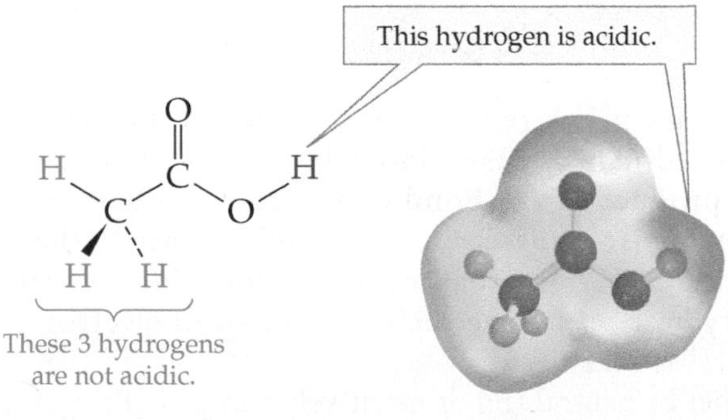

This hydrogen is acidic.

These 3 hydrogens are not acidic.

Acetic acid will react with water to produce H_3O^+ ions (Arrhenius acid definition) by donating a proton (Brønsted–Lowry acid definition) to water, as shown:

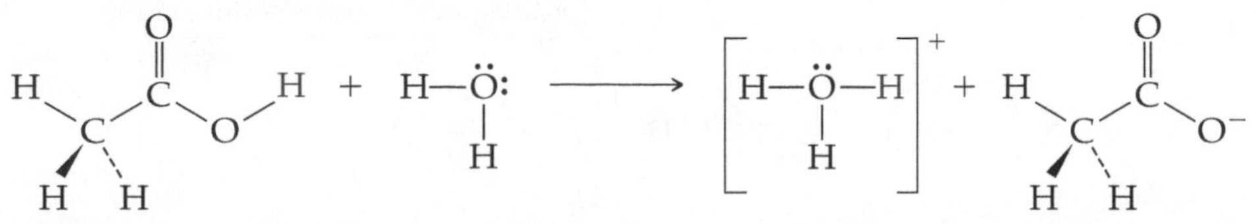

Whereas a Brønsted–Lowry acid is a substance that *donates* H^+ ions, a **Brønsted–Lowry base** is a substance that *accepts* H^+ ions from an acid. Ammonia will react

> **Brønsted–Lowry base** A substance that can accept H^+ ions from an acid.

with water to produce OH^- ions (Arrhenius base definition) by accepting a proton (Brønsted–Lowry base definition), as shown:

$$H-\overset{\cdot\cdot}{\underset{\overset{|}{H}}{N}}-H(g) + H_2O(l) \rightleftharpoons H-\overset{+}{\underset{\overset{|}{H}}{N}}-H(aq) + OH^-(aq)$$

> This OH^- ion comes from H_2O.

As with the acids, reactions involving Brønsted–Lowry bases need not occur in water, and the Brønsted–Lowry base need not give appreciable concentrations of OH^- ions in water. Gaseous NH_3, for example, acts as a base to accept H^+ from gaseous HCl and yield the ionic solid $NH_4^+ Cl^-$:

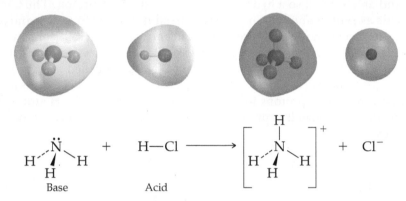

$$H\overset{\overset{\cdot\cdot}{N}}{\underset{\underset{H}{|}}{\diagup\diagdown}}H + H-Cl \longrightarrow \left[H\overset{\overset{\overset{|}{H}}{N}}{\underset{\underset{H}{|}}{\diagup\diagdown}}H\right]^+ + Cl^-$$

Base   Acid

Putting the acid and base definitions together, *an acid–base reaction is one in which a proton is transferred.* The general reaction between proton-donor acids and proton-acceptor bases can be represented as

> Electrons on base form bond with H^+ from acid.

$$B\!:\; + \; H-A \rightleftharpoons B\overset{+}{-}H + A^-$$

$$B\!:^- + \; H-A \rightleftharpoons B-H + A^-$$

where the abbreviation HA represents a Brønsted–Lowry acid and B: or B:$^-$ represents a Brønsted–Lowry base. Notice in these acid–base reactions that both electrons in the product B—H bond come from the base, as indicated by the curved arrow flowing from the electron pair of the base to the hydrogen atom of the acid. Thus, the B—H bond that forms is a coordinate covalent bond. In fact, a Brønsted–Lowry base *must* have such a lone pair of electrons; without them, it could not accept H^+ from an acid.

A base can either be neutral (B:) or negatively charged (B:$^-$). If the base is neutral, then the product has a positive charge (BH^+) after H^+ has been added. Ammonia is an example:

▶▶▶ Recall from Section 4.4 that a coordinate covalent bond is one where both electrons are donated by the same atom.

> Adding an H^+ creates positive charge.

$$H-\overset{\underset{\overset{|}{H}}{|}}{N}\!: + H-A \rightleftharpoons H-\overset{+}{\underset{\overset{|}{H}}{N}}-H + :A^-$$

Ammonia   Ammonium ion
(a neutral base, B:)

If the base is negatively charged, then the product is neutral (BH). Hydroxide ion is an example:

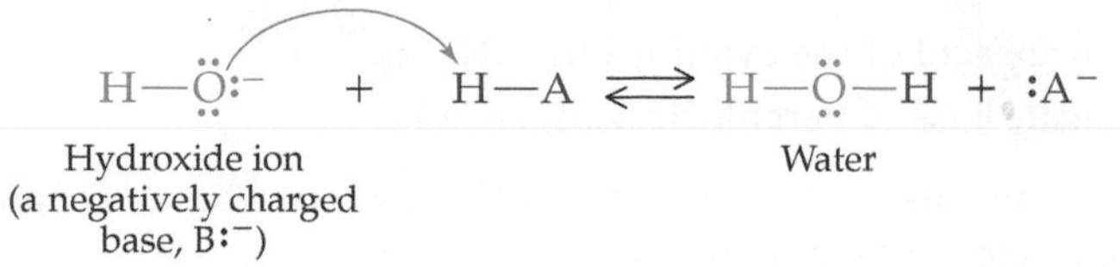

$$H-\ddot{\text{O}}\text{:}^- \quad + \quad H-A \rightleftharpoons H-\ddot{\text{O}}-H + \text{:}A^-$$

Hydroxide ion
(a negatively charged
base, B:⁻)   Water

An important consequence of the Brønsted–Lowry definitions is that the *products* of an acid–base reaction can also behave as acids and bases. Many acid–base reactions are reversible, although in some cases the equilibrium constant for the reaction is quite large. For example, suppose we have as a forward reaction an acid HA donating a proton to a base B to produce A^-. This product A^- is a base because it can act as a proton acceptor in the reverse reaction. At the same time, the product BH^+ acts as an acid because it may donate a proton in the reverse reaction:

▶▶▶ When the equilibrium constant for a reaction is greater than 1, the forward reaction is favored. When the equilibrium constant is less than 1, the reverse reaction is favored (Section 7.8).

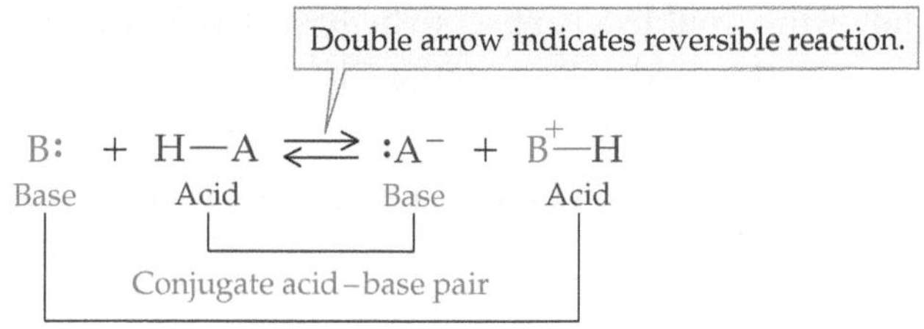

| Double arrow indicates reversible reaction. |

$$\text{B:} \quad + \quad H-A \rightleftharpoons \text{:}A^- \quad + \quad \overset{+}{B}-H$$

Base   Acid   Base   Acid

Conjugate acid–base pair

Pairs of chemical species such as B, BH^+ and HA, A^- are called **conjugate acid–base pairs**. They are species that are found on opposite sides of a chemical reaction whose formulas differ by only one H^+. Thus, the product anion A^- is the **conjugate base** of the reactant acid HA, and HA is the **conjugate acid** of the base A^-. Similarly, the reactant B is the conjugate base of the product acid BH^+, and BH^+ is the conjugate acid of the base B. The number of protons in a conjugate acid–base pair is always one greater than the number of protons in the base of the pair. To give some examples, acetic acid and acetate ion, the hydronium ion and water, and the ammonium ion and ammonia all make conjugate acid–base pairs:

Conjugate acid–base pair Two substances whose formulas differ by only a hydrogen ion, H^+.

Conjugate base The substance formed by loss of H^+ from an acid.

Conjugate acid The substance formed by addition of H^+ to a base.

Conjugate
acids
$$\left\{\begin{array}{l} CH_3\overset{O}{\overset{\|}{C}}OH \rightleftharpoons H^+ + CH_3\overset{O}{\overset{\|}{C}}O^- \\ H_3O^+ \rightleftharpoons H^+ + H_2O \\ NH_4^+ \rightleftharpoons H^+ + NH_3 \end{array}\right\}$$
Conjugate
bases

Worked Example 10.1 Acids and Bases: Identifying Brønsted–Lowry Acids and Bases

Identify each of the following as a Brønsted–Lowry acid or base:

(a) $PO_4{}^{3-}$ **(b)** $HClO_4$ **(c)** CN^-

ANALYSIS A Brønsted–Lowry acid must have a hydrogen that it can donate as H^+, and a Brønsted–Lowry base must have an atom with a lone pair of electrons that can bond to H^+. Typically, a Brønsted–Lowry base is an anion derived by loss of H^+ from an acid.

SOLUTION

(a) The phosphate anion $\left(PO_4{}^{3-}\right)$ has no proton to donate, so it must be a Brønsted–Lowry base. It is derived by loss of 3 H^+ ions from phosphoric acid, H_3PO_4.

(b) Perchloric acid $\left(HClO_4\right)$ is a Brønsted–Lowry acid because it can donate an H^+ ion.

(c) The cyanide ion $\left(CN^-\right)$ has no proton to donate, so it must be a Brønsted-Lowry base. It is derived by loss removal of an H^+ ion from hydrogen cyanide, HCN.

Worked Example 10.2 Acids and Bases: Identifying Conjugate Acid–Base Pairs

Write formulas for

(a) The conjugate acid of the cyanide ion, CN^-
(b) The conjugate base of perchloric acid, $HClO_4$

ANALYSIS A conjugate acid is formed by adding H^+ to a base; a conjugate base is formed by removing H^+ from an acid.

SOLUTION
(a) HCN is the conjugate acid of CN^-
(b) ClO_4^- is the conjugate base of $HClO_4$.

PROBLEM 10.1
Which of the following would you expect to be Brønsted–Lowry acids?
(a) HCO_2H (b) H_2S (c) $SnCl_2$

PROBLEM 10.2
Which of the following would you expect to be Brønsted–Lowry bases?
(a) SO_3^{2-} (b) Ag^+ (c) F^-

PROBLEM 10.3
Write formulas for:
(a) The conjugate acid of HS^- (b) The conjugate acid of PO_4^{3-}
(c) The conjugate base of H_2CO_3 (d) The conjugate base of NH_4^+

KEY CONCEPT PROBLEM 10.4

For the reaction shown here, identify the Brønsted–Lowry acids, bases, and conjugate acid–base pairs.

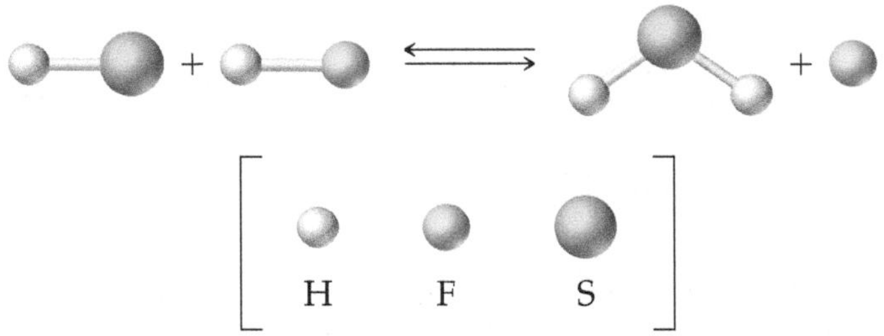

10.4 Acid and Base Strength

Some acids and bases, such as sulfuric acid (H_2SO_4), hydrochloric acid (HCl), or sodium hydroxide (NaOH), are highly corrosive. They react readily and, in contact with skin, can cause serious burns. Other acids and bases are not nearly as reactive. Acetic acid (CH_3COOH, the major component in vinegar) and phosphoric acid (H_3PO_4) are found in many food products. Why are some acids and bases relatively "safe," while others must be handled with extreme caution? The answer lies in how easily they produce the active ions for an acid (H^+) or a base (OH^-).

As indicated in Table 10.1, acids differ in their ability to give up a proton. The six acids at the top of the table are **strong acids**, meaning that they give up a proton easily and are essentially 100% **dissociated**, or split apart into ions, in water. Those remaining are **weak acids**, meaning that they give up a proton with difficulty and are substantially less than 100% dissociated in water. In a similar way, the conjugate bases at the

Strong acid An acid that gives up H^+ easily and is essentially 100% dissociated in water.

Dissociation The splitting apart of an acid in water to give H^+ and an anion.

Weak acid An acid that gives up H^+ with difficulty and is less than 100% dissociated in water.

TABLE 10.1 Relative Strengths of Acids and Conjugate Bases

		ACID		CONJUGATE BASE		
Increasing acid strength ↑	**Strong acids: 100% dissociated**	Perchloric acid	$HClO_4$	ClO_4^-	Perchlorate ion	**Increasing base strength**
		Sulfuric acid	H_2SO_4	HSO_4^-	Hydrogen sulfate ion	Little or no reaction as bases
		Hydriodic acid	HI	I^-	Iodide ion	
		Hydrobromic acid	HBr	Br^-	Bromide ion	
		Hydrochloric acid	HCl	Cl^-	Chloride ion	
		Nitric acid	HNO_3	NO_3^-	Nitrate ion	
		Hydronium ion	$\mathbf{H_3O^+}$	$\mathbf{H_2O}$	**Water**	
	Weak acids	Hydrogen sulfate ion	HSO_4^-	SO_4^{2-}	Sulfate ion	Very weak bases
		Phosphoric acid	H_3PO_4	$H_2PO_4^-$	Dihydrogen phosphate ion	
		Nitrous acid	HNO_2	NO_2^-	Nitrite ion	
		Hydrofluoric acid	HF	F^-	Fluoride ion	
		Acetic acid	CH_3COOH	CH_3COO^-	Acetate ion	
	Very weak acids	Carbonic acid	H_2CO_3	HCO_3^-	Bicarbonate ion	Weak bases
		Dihydrogen phosphate ion	$H_2PO_4^-$	HPO_4^{2-}	Hydrogen phosphate ion	
		Ammonium ion	NH_4^+	NH_3	Ammonia	
		Hydrocyanic acid	HCN	CN^-	Cyanide ion	
		Bicarbonate ion	HCO_3^-	CO_3^{2-}	Carbonate ion	
		Hydrogen phosphate ion	HPO_4^{2-}	PO_4^{3-}	Phosphate ion	
		Water	$\mathbf{H_2O}$	$\mathbf{OH^-}$	**Hydroxide ion**	Strong base

top of the table are **weak bases** because they have little affinity for a proton, and the conjugate bases at the bottom of the table are **strong bases** because they grab and hold a proton tightly.

Weak base A base that has only a slight affinity for H^+ and holds it weakly.

Note that diprotic acids, such as sulfuric acid H_2SO_4, undergo two stepwise dissociations in water. The first dissociation yields HSO_4^- and occurs to the extent of nearly 100%, so H_2SO_4 is a strong acid. The second dissociation yields SO_4^{2-} and takes place to a much lesser extent because separation of a positively charged H^+ from the negatively charged HSO_4^- anion is difficult. Thus, HSO_4^- is a weak acid:

Strong base A base that has a high affinity for H^+ and holds it tightly.

$$H_2SO_4(l) + H_2O(l) \longrightarrow H_3O^+(aq) + HSO_4^-(aq)$$
$$HSO_4^-(aq) + H_2O(l) \rightleftharpoons H_3O^+(aq) + SO_4^{2-}(aq)$$

Perhaps the most striking feature of Table 10.1 is the inverse relationship between acid strength and base strength. **The stronger the acid, the weaker its conjugate base; the weaker the acid, the stronger its conjugate base.** HCl, for example, is a strong acid, so Cl^- is a very weak base. H_2O, however, is a very weak acid, so OH^- is a strong base.

Why is there an inverse relationship between acid strength and base strength? To answer this question, think about what it means for an acid or base to be strong or weak. A strong acid H—A is one that readily gives up a proton, meaning that its conjugate base A^- has little affinity for the proton. But this is exactly the definition of a weak base—a substance that has little affinity for a proton. As a result, the reverse reaction occurs to a lesser extent, as indicated by the size of the forward and reverse arrows in the reaction:

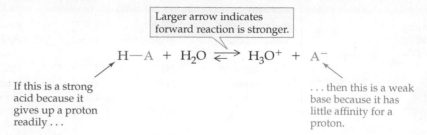

Larger arrow indicates forward reaction is stronger.

$$H{-}A + H_2O \rightleftharpoons H_3O^+ + A^-$$

If this is a strong acid because it gives up a proton readily . . .

. . . then this is a weak base because it has little affinity for a proton.

In the same way, a weak acid is one that gives up a proton with difficulty, meaning that its conjugate base has a high affinity for the proton. But this is just the definition of a strong base—a substance that has a high affinity for the proton. The reverse reaction now occurs more readily.

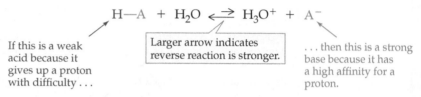

$$H{-}A + H_2O \rightleftharpoons H_3O^+ + A^-$$

If this is a weak acid because it gives up a proton with difficulty . . .

Larger arrow indicates reverse reaction is stronger.

. . . then this is a strong base because it has a high affinity for a proton.

Knowing the relative strengths of different acids as shown in Table 10.1 makes it possible to predict the direction of proton-transfer reactions. *An acid–base proton-transfer equilibrium always favors reaction of the stronger acid with the stronger base and formation of the weaker acid and base.* That is, the proton always leaves the stronger acid (whose weaker conjugate base cannot hold the proton) and always ends up in the weaker acid (whose stronger conjugate base holds the proton tightly). Put another way, in a contest for the proton, the stronger base always wins.

$$\text{Stronger acid} + \text{Stronger base} \rightleftharpoons \text{Weaker base} + \text{Weaker acid}$$

To try out this rule, compare the reactions of acetic acid with water and with hydroxide ion. The idea is to write the equation, identify the acid on each side of the arrow, and then decide which acid is stronger and which is weaker. For example, the reaction of acetic acid with water to give acetate ion and hydronium ion is favored in the reverse direction, because acetic acid is a weaker acid than H_3O^+:

$$\underset{\text{Weaker acid}}{CH_3\overset{O}{\overset{\|}{C}}OH} + H_2O \rightleftharpoons CH_3\overset{O}{\overset{\|}{C}}O^- + \underset{\text{Stronger acid}}{H_3O^+}$$

Reverse reaction is favored.

This base holds the proton less tightly . . .   . . . than this base does.

On the other hand, the reaction of acetic acid with hydroxide ion to give acetate ion and water is favored in the forward direction, because acetic acid is a stronger acid than H_2O :

$$\underset{\text{Stronger acid}}{CH_3\overset{O}{\overset{\|}{C}}OH} + OH^- \rightleftharpoons CH_3\overset{O}{\overset{\|}{C}}O^- + \underset{\text{Weaker acid}}{H_2O}$$

Forward reaction is favored.

This base holds the proton more tightly . . .   . . . than this base does.

CHEMISTRY IN ACTION

GERD—Too Much Acid or Not Enough?

Strong acids are very caustic substances that can dissolve even metals, and no one would think of ingesting them. However, the major component of the gastric juices secreted in the stomach is hydrochloric acid—a strong acid—and the acidic environment in the stomach is vital to good health and nutrition.

Stomach acid is essential for the digestion of proteins and for the absorption of certain micronutrients, such as calcium, magnesium, iron, and vitamin B_{12}. It also creates a sterile environment in the gut by killing yeast and bacteria that may be ingested. If these gastric juices leak up into the esophagus, the tube through which food and drink enter the stomach, they can cause the burning sensation in the chest or throat known as either heartburn or acid indigestion. Persistent irritation of the esophagus is known as gastro-esophageal reflux disease (GERD) and, if untreated, can lead to more serious health problems.

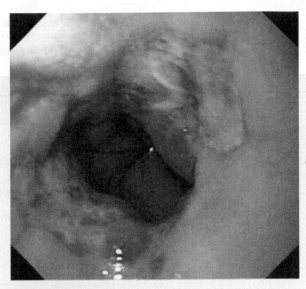

▲ **If not treated, GERD can cause ulcers and scarring of esophageal tissue.**

Hydrogen ions and chloride ions are secreted separately from the cytoplasm of parietal cells lining the stomach and then combine to form HCl that is usually close to 0.10 M. The HCl is then released into the stomach cavity, where the concentration is diluted to about 0.01–0.001 M. Unlike the esophagus, the stomach is coated by a thick mucus layer that protects the stomach wall from damage by this caustic solution.

Those who suffer from acid indigestion can obtain relief by using over-the-counter antacids, such as TUMS™ or Rolaids™ (see Section 10.12, p. 316). Chronic conditions such as GERD, however, are often treated with prescription medications. GERD can be treated by two classes of drugs. Proton-pump inhibitors (PPI), such as Prevacid™ and Prilosec™, prevent the production of the H^+ ions in the parietal cells, while H_2-receptor blockers (Tagamet™, Zantac™, and Pepcid™) prevent the release of stomach acid into the lumen. Both drugs effectively decrease the production of stomach acid to ease the symptoms of GERD.

Ironically, GERD can also be caused by not having enough stomach acid—a condition known as *hypochlorhydria*. The valve that controls the release of stomach contents to the small intestine is triggered by acidity. If this valve fails to open because the stomach is not acidic enough, the contents of the stomach can be churned back up into the esophagus.

See Chemistry in Action Problems 10.94 and 10.95 at the end of the chapter.

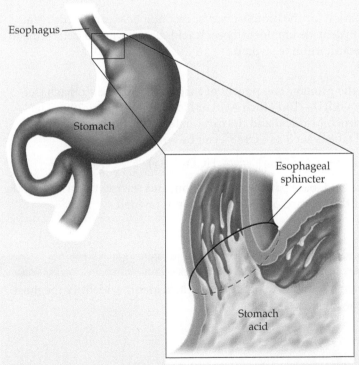

▲ **The burning sensation and other symptoms associated with GERD are caused by the reflux of the acidic contents of the stomach into the esophagus.**

Worked Example **10.3** Acid/Base Strength: Predicting Direction of H-transfer Reactions

Write a balanced equation for the proton-transfer reaction between phosphate ion (PO_4^{3-}) and water, and determine in which direction the equilibrium is favored.

ANALYSIS Look in Table 10.1 to see the relative acid and base strengths of the species involved in the reaction. The acid–base proton-transfer equilibrium will favor reaction of the stronger acid and formation of the weaker acid.

SOLUTION
Phosphate ion is the conjugate base of a weak acid (HPO_4^{2-}) and is therefore a relatively strong base. Table 10.1 shows that HPO_4^{2-} is a stronger acid than H_2O, and OH^- is a stronger base than PO_4^{3-}, so the reaction is favored in the reverse direction:

$$PO_4^{3-}(aq) \ + \ H_2O(l) \ \rightleftharpoons \ HPO_4^{3-}(aq) \ + \ OH^-(aq)$$
Weaker base   Weaker acid   Stronger acid   Stronger base

PROBLEM 10.5
Use Table 10.1 to identify the stronger acid in the following pairs:
(a) H_2O or NH_4^+ **(b)** H_2SO_4 or CH_3CO_2H **(c)** HCN or H_2CO_3

PROBLEM 10.6
Use Table 10.1 to identify the stronger base in the following pairs:
(a) F^- or Br^- **(b)** OH^- or HCO_3^-

PROBLEM 10.7
Write a balanced equation for the proton-transfer reaction between a hydrogen phosphate ion and a hydroxide ion. Identify each acid–base pair, and determine in which direction the equilibrium is favored.

PROBLEM 10.8
Hydrochloric acid is the primary component of gastric juice in the stomach (see Chemistry in Action: GERD—Too Much Acid or Not Enough? on p. 299). The reaction between hydrochloric acid and the carbonate ion, the primary active ingredient in antacid tablets such as TUMS®, can be written as

$$HCl(aq) + CO_3^{2-}(aq) \rightleftharpoons HCO_3^-(aq) + Cl^-(aq)$$

Identify the conjugate acid–base pairs in the reaction, and rewrite the arrows in the reaction to indicate if the forward or reverse reaction is favored.

🔑 **KEY CONCEPT PROBLEM 10.9**

From this electrostatic potential map of the amino acid alanine, identify the most acidic hydrogens in the molecule:

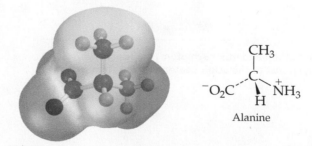

Alanine

10.5 Acid Dissociation Constants

The reaction of a weak acid with water, like any chemical equilibrium, can be described by an equilibrium equation (Section 7.8), where square brackets indicate the concentrations of the enclosed species in molarity (moles per liter).

For the reaction $HA(aq) + H_2O(l) \rightleftharpoons H_3O^+(aq) + A^-(aq)$

We have $K = \dfrac{[H_3O^+][A^-]}{[HA][H_2O]}$

Because water is a solvent as well as a participant for the reaction, its concentration is essentially constant and has no effect on the equilibrium. Therefore, we usually put the equilibrium constant K and the water concentration $[H_2O]$ together to make a new constant called the **acid dissociation constant, (K_a)**. The acid dissociation constant is simply the hydronium ion concentration $[H_3O^+]$ times the conjugate base concentration $[A^-]$ divided by the undissociated acid concentration $[HA]$:

$$Acid\ dissociation\ constant \quad K_a = K[H_2O] = \dfrac{[H_3O^+][A^-]}{[HA]}$$

Acid dissociation constant, (K_a) The equilibrium constant for the dissociation of an acid (HA), equal to $[H^+][A^-]/[HA]$.

For a strong acid, the H_3O^+ and A^- concentrations are much larger than the HA concentration, so K_a is very large. In fact, the K_a values for strong acids such as HCl are so large that it is difficult and not very useful to measure them. For a weak acid, however, the H_3O^+ and A^- concentrations are smaller than the HA concentration, so K_a is small. Table 10.2 gives K_a values for some common acids and illustrates several important points:

- Strong acids have K_a values much greater than 1 because dissociation is favored.
- Weak acids have K_a values much less than 1 because dissociation is not favored.
- Donation of each successive H^+ from a polyprotic acid is more difficult than the one before it, so K_a values become successively lower.
- Most organic acids, which contain the $-CO_2H$ group, have K_a values near 10^{-5}.

TABLE 10.2 Some Acid Dissociation Constants, K_a, at 25 °C

Acid	K_a	Acid	K_a
Hydrofluoric acid (HF)	3.5×10^{-4}	*Polyprotic acids*	
Hydrocyanic acid (HCN)	4.9×10^{-10}	Sulfuric acid	
Ammonium ion (NH_4^+)	5.6×10^{-10}	H_2SO_4	Large
		HSO_4^-	1.2×10^{-2}
Organic acids		Phosphoric acid	
Formic acid (HCOOH)	1.8×10^{-4}	H_3PO_4	7.5×10^{-3}
Acetic acid (CH_3COOH)	1.8×10^{-5}	$H_2PO_4^-$	6.2×10^{-8}
Propanoic acid (CH_3CH_2COOH)	1.3×10^{-5}	HPO_4^{2-}	2.2×10^{-13}
		Carbonic acid	
Ascorbic acid (vitamin C)	7.9×10^{-5}	H_2CO_3	4.3×10^{-7}
		HCO_3^-	5.6×10^{-11}

PROBLEM 10.10
Benzoic acid ($C_7H_5CO_2H$) has $K_a = 6.5 \times 10^{-5}$ and citric acid ($C_6H_8O_7$) has $K_a = 7.2 \times 10^{-4}$. Which is the stronger conjugate base, benzoate ($C_7H_5CO_2^-$) or citrate ($C_6H_7O_7^-$)?

10.6 Water as Both an Acid and a Base

Water is neither an acid nor a base in the Arrhenius sense because it does not contain appreciable concentrations of either H_3O^+ or OH^-. In the Brønsted–Lowry sense, however, water can act as *both* an acid and a base. When in contact with a base, water reacts as a Brønsted–Lowry acid and *donates* a proton to the base. In its reaction with ammonia, for example, water donates H^+ to ammonia to form the ammonium ion:

$$NH_3 \; + \; H_2O \; \longrightarrow \; NH_4{}^+ \; + \; OH^-$$

Ammonia	Water	Ammonium ion	Hydroxide ion
(base)	(acid)	(acid)	(base)

When in contact with an acid, water reacts as a Brønsted–Lowry base and *accepts* H^+ from the acid. This, of course, is exactly what happens when an acid such as HCl dissolves in water, as discussed in Section 10.1.

Water uses two electrons to form a bond to H^+.

$$H-\overset{..}{\underset{|}{\overset{}{O}}}: \; + \; H-Cl \; \longrightarrow \; H-\overset{..}{\underset{|}{\overset{+}{O}}}-H \; + \; Cl^-$$

Water	(An acid)	Hydronium ion
(A base)		

Amphoteric A substance that can react as either an acid or a base.

Substances like water, which can react as either an acid or a base depending on the circumstances, are said to be **amphoteric** (am-pho-**tare**-ic). When water acts as an acid, it donates H^+ and becomes OH^-; when it acts as a base, it accepts H^+ and becomes H_3O^+. (*Note:* $HCO_3{}^-$, $H_2PO_4{}^-$ and $HPO_4{}^{2-}$ are also amphoteric.)

Dissociation of Water

We have seen how water can act as an acid when a base is present and as a base when an acid is present. But what about when no other acids or bases are present? In this case, one water molecule acts as an acid while another water molecule acts as a base, reacting to form the hydronium and hydroxide ions:

$$H_2O(l) \; + \; H_2O(l) \; \rightleftharpoons \; H_3O^+(aq) \; + \; OH^-(aq)$$

Because each dissociation reaction yields 1 H_3O^+ ion and 1 OH^- ion, the concentrations of the 2 ions are identical. Also, the equilibrium arrows indicate that this reaction favors reactants, so that not many H_3O^+ and OH^- ions are present at equilibrium. At 25 °C, the concentration of each is 1.00×10^{-7} M. We can write the equilibrium constant expression for the dissociation of water as

$$K = \frac{[H_3O^+][OH^-]}{[H_2O][H_2O]}$$

where $[H_3O^+] = [OH^-] = 1.00 \times 10^{-7}$ M (at 25 °C)

▶▶▶ Refer to discussion of equilibria involving pure liquids and solids in Section 7.8.

Ion-product constant for water (K_w) The product of the H_3O^+ and OH^- molar concentrations in water or any aqueous solution ($K_w = [H_3O^+][OH^-] = 1.00 \times 10^{-14}$).

As a pure substance the concentration of water is essentially constant. We can therefore put the water concentrations $[H_2O]$ together to make a new constant called the **ion-product constant for water (K_w)**, which is simply the H_3O^+ concentration times the OH^- concentration. At 25 °C, $K_w = 1.00 \times 10^{-14}$.

$$\begin{aligned} \textit{Ion-product constant for water} \quad K_w &= K[H_2O][H_2O] \\ &= [H_3O^+][OH^-] \\ &= 1.0 \times 10^{-14} \quad (\text{at } 25\,°C) \end{aligned}$$

The importance of the equation $K_w = [H_3O^+][OH^-]$ is that it applies to all aqueous solutions, not just to pure water. Since the product of $[H_3O^+]$ times $[OH^-]$ is always constant for any solution, we can determine the concentration of one species if we know the concentration of the other. If an acid is present in solution, for instance, so that $[H_3O^+]$ is large, then $[OH^-]$ must be small. If a base is present in solution so that $[OH^-]$ is large, then $[H_3O^+]$ must be small. For example, for a 0.10 M HCl solution, we know that $[H_3O^+] = 0.10$ M because HCl is 100% dissociated. Thus, we can calculate that $[OH^-] = 1.0 \times 10^{-13}$ M:

$$\text{Since } K_w \times [H_3O^+][OH^-] = 1.00 \times 10^{-14}$$

$$\text{we have } [OH^-] = \frac{K_w}{[H_3O^+]} = \frac{1.00 \times 10^{-14}}{0.10} = 1.0 \times 10^{-13} \text{ M}$$

Similarly, for a 0.10 M NaOH solution, we know that $[OH^-] = 0.10$ M, so $[H_3O^+] = 1.0 \times 10^{-13}$ M:

$$[H_3O^+] = \frac{K_w}{[OH^-]} = \frac{1.00 \times 10^{-14}}{0.10} = 1.0 \times 10^{-13} \text{ M}$$

Solutions are identified as acidic, neutral, or basic (*alkaline*) according to the value of their H_3O^+ and OH^- concentrations:

Acidic solution: $[H_3O^+] > 10^{-7}$ M and $[OH^-] < 10^{-7}$ M
Neutral solution: $[H_3O^+] = 10^{-7}$ M and $[OH^-] = 10^{-7}$ M
Basic solution: $[H_3O^+] < 10^{-7}$ M and $[OH^-] > 10^{-7}$ M

Worked Example 10.4 Water Dissociation Constant: Using K_w to Calculate $[OH^-]$

Milk has an H_3O^+ concentration of 4.5×10^{-7} M. What is the value of $[OH^-]$? Is milk acidic, neutral, or basic?

ANALYSIS The OH^- concentration can be found by dividing K_w by $[H_3O^+]$. An acidic solution has $[H_3O^+] > 10^{-7}$ M, a neutral solution has $[H_3O^+] = 10^{-7}$ M, and a basic solution has $[H_3O^+] < 10^{-7}$ M.

BALLPARK ESTIMATE Since the H_3O^+ concentration is slightly *greater* than 10^{-7} M, the OH^- concentration must be slightly *less* than 10^{-7} M, on the order of 10^{-8}.

SOLUTION

$$[OH^-] = \frac{K_w}{[H_3O^+]} = \frac{1.00 \times 10^{-14}}{4.5 \times 10^{-7}} = 2.2 \times 10^{-8} \text{ M}$$

Milk is slightly acidic because its H_3O^+ concentration is slightly larger than 1×10^{-7} M.

BALLPARK CHECK The OH^- concentration is of the same order of magnitude as our estimate.

PROBLEM 10.11
Identify the following solutions as either acidic or basic. What is the value of $[OH^-]$ in each?
(a) Household ammonia, $[H_3O^+] = 3.1 \times 10^{-12}$ M
(b) Vinegar, $[H_3O^+] = 4.0 \times 10^{-3}$ M

10.7 Measuring Acidity in Aqueous Solution: pH

In many fields, from medicine to chemistry to winemaking, it is necessary to know the exact concentration of H_3O^+ or OH^- in a solution. If, for example, the H_3O^+ concentration in blood varies only slightly from a value of 4.0×10^{-8} M, death can result.

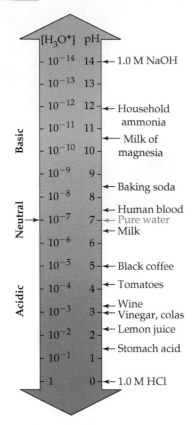

▲ Figure 10.1

The pH scale and the pH values of some common substances.

A low pH corresponds to a strongly acidic solution, a high pH corresponds to a strongly basic solution, and a pH of 7 corresponds to a neutral solution.

p function The negative common logarithm of some variable, $pX = -\log(X)$.

pH A measure of the acid strength of a solution; the negative common logarithm of the H_3O^+ concentration.

Although correct, it is nevertheless awkward or, in some instances inconvenient, to refer to low concentrations of H_3O^+ using molarity. Fortunately, there is an easier way to express and compare H_3O^+ concentrations—the *pH scale*.

The pH of an aqueous solution is a number, usually between 0 and 14, that indicates the H_3O^+ concentration of the solution. A pH smaller than 7 corresponds to an acidic solution, a pH larger than 7 corresponds to a basic solution, and a pH of exactly 7 corresponds to a neutral solution. The pH scale and pH values of some common substances are shown in Figure 10.1.

Mathematically, a **p function** is defined as the negative common logarithm of some variable. The **pH** of a solution, therefore, is the negative common logarithm of the H_3O^+ concentration:

$$pH = -\log[H^+] \ (or[H_3O^+])$$

If you have studied logarithms, you may remember that the common logarithm of a number is the power to which 10 must be raised to equal the number. The pH definition can therefore be restated as

$$[H_3O^+] = 10^{-pH}$$

For example, in neutral water at 25 °C, where $[H_3O^+] = 1 \times 10^{-7}$ M, the pH is 7; in a strong acid solution where $[H_3O^+] = 1 \times 10^{-1}$ M, the pH is 1; and in a strong base solution where $[H_3O^+] = 1 \times 10^{-14}$ M, the pH is 14:

Acidic solution: pH < 7, $[H_3O^+] > 1 \times 10^{-7}$ M

Neutral solution: pH = 7, $[H_3O^+] = 1 \times 10^{-7}$ M

Basic solution: pH > 7, $[H_3O^+] < 1 \times 10^{-7}$ M

Keep in mind that the pH scale covers an enormous range of acidities because it is a *logarithmic* scale, which involves powers of 10 (Figure 10.2). A change of only 1 pH unit means a 10-fold change in $[H_3O^+]$, a change of 2 pH units means a 100-fold change in $[H_3O^+]$, and a change of 12 pH units means a change of 10^{12} (a trillion) in $[H_3O^+]$.

To get a feel for the size of the quantities involved, think of a typical backyard swimming pool, which contains about 100,000 L of water. You would have to add only 0.10 mol of HCl (3.7 g) to lower the pH of the pool from 7.0 (neutral) to 6.0, but you would have to add 10,000 mol of HCl (370 kg!) to lower the pH of the pool from 7.0 to 1.0.

The logarithmic pH scale is a convenient way of reporting the relative acidity of solutions, but using logarithms can also be useful when calculating H_3O^+ and OH^- concentrations. Remember that the equilibrium between H_3O^+ and OH^- in aqueous solutions is expressed by K_w, where

$$K_w = [H_3O^+][OH^-] = 1 \times 10^{-14} \quad (\text{at } 25 \,°C)$$

If we convert this equation to its negative logarithmic form, we obtain

$$-\log(K_w) = -\log[H_3O^+] - \log[OH^-]$$
$$-\log(1 \times 10^{-14}) = -\log[H_3O^+] - \log[OH^-]$$
$$or \quad 14.00 = pH + pOH$$

The logarithmic form of the K_w equation can simplify the calculation of solution pH from OH^- concentration, as demonstrated in Worked Example 10.7.

Worked Example 10.5 Measuring Acidity: Calculating pH from $[H_3O^+]$

The H_3O^+ concentration in coffee is about 1×10^{-5} M. What pH is this?

ANALYSIS The pH is the negative common logarithm of the H_3O^+ concentration: $pH = -\log[H_3O^+]$.

SOLUTION

Since the common logarithm of 1×10^{-5} M is -5.0, the pH is 5.0.

Worked Example 10.6 Measuring Acidity: Calculating $[H_3O^+]$ from pH

Lemon juice has a pH of about 2. What $[H_3O^+]$ is this?

ANALYSIS In this case, we are looking for the $[H_3O^+]$, where $[H_3O^+] = 10^{-pH}$.

SOLUTION
Since pH = 2.0, $[H_3O^+] = 10^{-2} = 1 \times 10^{-2}\,M$.

Worked Example 10.7 Measuring Acidity: Using K_w to Calculate $[H_3O^+]$ and pH

A cleaning solution is found to have $[OH^-] = 1 \times 10^{-3}\,M$. What is the pH?

ANALYSIS To find pH, we must first find the value of $[H_3O^+]$ by using the equation $[H_3O^+] = K_w/[OH^-]$. Alternatively, we can calculate the pOH of the solution and then use the logarithmic form of the K_w equation: pH = 14.00 − pOH.

SOLUTION
Rearranging the K_w equation, we have

$$[H_3O^+] = \frac{K_w}{[OH^-]} = \frac{1.00 \times 10^{-14}}{1 \times 10^{-3}} = 1 \times 10^{-11}\,M$$

$$pH = -\log(1 \times 10^{-11}) = 11.0$$

Using the logarithmic form of the K_w equation, we have

$$pH = 14.0 - pOH = 14.0 - (-\log[OH^-])$$
$$pH = 14.0 - (-\log(1 \times 10^{-3}))$$
$$pH = 14.0 - 3.0 = 11.0$$

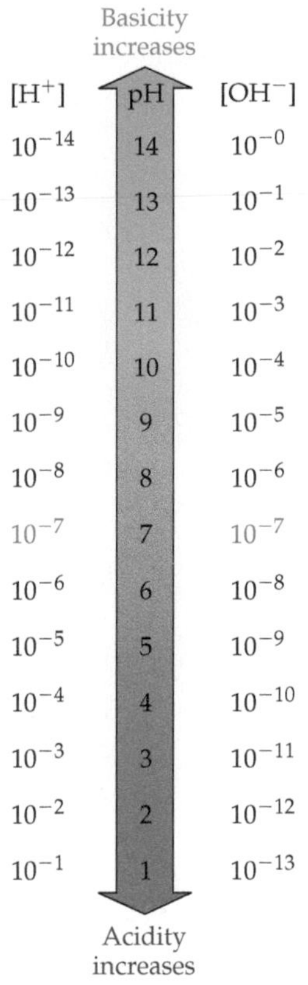

Basicity increases

$[H^+]$	pH	$[OH^-]$
10^{-14}	14	10^{-0}
10^{-13}	13	10^{-1}
10^{-12}	12	10^{-2}
10^{-11}	11	10^{-3}
10^{-10}	10	10^{-4}
10^{-9}	9	10^{-5}
10^{-8}	8	10^{-6}
10^{-7}	7	10^{-7}
10^{-6}	6	10^{-8}
10^{-5}	5	10^{-9}
10^{-4}	4	10^{-10}
10^{-3}	3	10^{-11}
10^{-2}	2	10^{-12}
10^{-1}	1	10^{-13}

Acidity increases

▲ **Figure 10.2**
The relationship of the pH scale to H^+ and OH^- concentrations.

Worked Example 10.8 Measuring Acidity: Calculating pH of Strong Acid Solutions

What is the pH of a 0.01 M solution of HCl?

ANALYSIS To find pH, we must first find the value of $[H_3O^+]$.

SOLUTION
Since HCl is a strong acid (Table 10.1), it is 100% dissociated, and the H_3O^+ concentration is the same as the HCl concentration: $[H_3O^+] = 0.01\,M$, or $1 \times 10^{-2}\,M$, and pH = 2.0.

PROBLEM 10.12
Calculate the pH of the solutions in Problem 10.11.

PROBLEM 10.13
Give the hydronium ion and hydroxide ion concentrations of solutions with the following values of pH. Which of the solutions is most acidic? Which is most basic?
(a) pH 13.0   **(b)** pH 3.0   **(c)** pH 8.0

PROBLEM 10.14
Which solution would have the higher pH: 0.010 M HNO_2 or 0.010 M HNO_3? Explain.

10.8 Working with pH

Converting between pH and H_3O^+ concentration is easy when the pH is a whole number, but how do you find the H_3O^+ concentration of blood, which has a pH of 7.4, or the pH of a solution with $[H_3O^+] = 4.6 \times 10^{-3}$ M? Sometimes it is sufficient to make an estimate. The pH of blood (7.4) is between 7 and 8, so the H_3O^+ concentration of blood must be between 1×10^{-7} and 1×10^{-8} M. To be exact about finding pH values, though, requires a calculator.

Converting from pH to $[H_3O^+]$ requires finding the *antilogarithm* of the negative pH, which is done on many calculators with an "INV" key and a "log" key. Converting from $[H_3O^+]$ to pH requires finding the logarithm, which is commonly done with a "log" key and an "expo" or "EE" key for entering exponents of 10. Consult your calculator instructions if you are not sure how to use these keys. Remember that the sign of the number given by the calculator must be changed from minus to plus to get the pH.

The H_3O^+ concentration in blood with pH = 7.4 is

$$[H_3O^+] = \text{antilog}(-7.4) = 4 \times 10^{-8} \text{ M}$$

The pH of a solution with $[H_3O^+] = 4.6 \times 10^{-3}$ M is

$$pH = -\log(4.6 \times 10^{-3}) = -(-2.34) = 2.34$$

A note about significant figures: an antilogarithm contains the same number of significant figures as the original number has to the right of the decimal point. A logarithm contains the same number of digits to the right of the decimal point as the number of significant figures in the original number.

$$\text{antilog}(-7.4) = 4 \times 10^{-8} \qquad \log(4.6 \times 10^{-3}) = -2.34$$

| 1 digit after decimal point | 1 digit | 2 digits | 2 digits after decimal point |

Worked Example 10.9 Working with pH: Converting a pH to $[H_3O^+]$

Soft drinks usually have a pH of approximately 3.1. What is the $[H_3O^+]$ concentration in a soft drink?

ANALYSIS To convert from a pH value to an $[H_3O^+]$ concentration requires using the equation $[H_3O^+] = 10^{-pH}$, which requires finding an antilogarithm on a calculator.

BALLPARK ESTIMATE Because the pH is between 3.0 and 4.0, the $[H_3O^+]$ must be between 1×10^{-3} and 1×10^{-4}. A pH of 3.1 is very close to 3.0, so the $[H_3O^+]$ must be just slightly below 1×10^{-3} M.

SOLUTION
Entering the negative pH on a calculator (-3.1) and pressing the "INV" and "log" keys gives the answer 7.943×10^{-4}, which must be rounded off to 8×10^{-4} because the pH has only one digit to the right of the decimal point.

BALLPARK CHECK The calculated $[H_3O^+]$ of 8×10^{-4} M is between 1×10^{-3} M and 1×10^{-4} M and, as we estimated, just slightly below 1×10^{-3} M. (Remember, 8×10^{-4} is 0.8×10^{-3}.)

Worked Example 10.10 Working with pH: Calculating pH for Strong Acid Solutions

What is the pH of a 0.0045 M solution of $HClO_4$?

ANALYSIS Finding pH requires first finding $[H_3O^+]$ and then using the equation $pH = -\log[H_3O^+]$. Since $HClO_4$ is a strong acid (see Table 10.1), it is 100% dissociated, and so the H_3O^+ concentration is the same as the $HClO_4$ concentration.

BALLPARK ESTIMATE Because $[H_3O^+] = 4.5 \times 10^{-3}$ M is close to midway between 1×10^{-2} M and 1×10^{-3} M, the pH must be close to the midway point between 2.0 and 3.0. (Unfortunately, because the logarithm scale is not linear, trying to estimate the midway point is not a simple process.)

SOLUTION
$[H_3O^+] = 0.0045$ M $= 4.5 \times 10^{-3}$ M. Taking the negative logarithm gives pH = 2.35.

BALLPARK CHECK The calculated pH is consistent with our estimate.

Worked Example 10.11 Working with pH: Calculating pH for Strong Base Solutions

What is the pH of a 0.0032 M solution of NaOH?

ANALYSIS Since NaOH is a strong base, the OH^- concentration is the same as the NaOH concentration. Starting with the OH^- concentration, finding pH requires either using the K_w equation to find $[H_3O^+]$ or calculating pOH and then using the logarithmic form of the K_w equation.

BALLPARK ESTIMATE Because $[OH^-] = 3.2 \times 10^{-3}$ M is close to midway between 1×10^{-2} M and 1×10^{-3} M, the pOH must be close to the midway point between 2.0 and 3.0. Subtracting the pOH from 14 would therefore yield a pH between 11 and 12.

SOLUTION
$$[OH^-] = 0.0032 \text{ M} = 3.2 \times 10^{-3} \text{ M}$$
$$[H_3O^+] = \frac{K_w}{(3.2 \times 10^{-3})} = 3.1 \times 10^{-12} \text{ M}$$

Taking the negative logarithm gives pH $= -\log(3.1 \times 10^{-12}) = 11.51$. Alternatively, we can calculate pOH and subtract from 14.00 using the logarithmic form of the K_w equation. For $[OH^-] = 0.0032$ M,
$$\text{pOH} = -\log(3.2 \times 10^{-3}) = 2.49$$
$$\text{pH} = 14.00 - 2.49 = 11.51$$

Since the given OH^- concentration included two significant figures, the final pH includes two significant figures beyond the decimal point.

BALLPARK CHECK The calculated pH is consistent with our estimate.

PROBLEM 10.15
Identify the following solutions as acidic or basic, estimate $[H_3O^+]$ and $[OH^-]$ values for each, and rank them in order of increasing acidity:
(a) Saliva, pH = 6.5
(b) Pancreatic juice, pH = 7.9
(c) Orange juice, pH = 3.7
(d) Wine, pH = 3.5

PROBLEM 10.16
Calculate the pH of the following solutions and report it to the correct number of significant figures:
(a) Seawater with $[H_3O^+] = 5.3 \times 10^{-9}$ M
(b) A urine sample with $[H_3O^+] = 8.9 \times 10^{-6}$ M

PROBLEM 10.17
What is the pH of a 0.0025 M solution of HCl?

10.9 Laboratory Determination of Acidity

Acid–base indicator A dye that changes color depending on the pH of a solution.

The pH of water is an important indicator of water quality in applications ranging from swimming pool and spa maintenance to municipal water treatment. There are several ways to measure the pH of a solution. The simplest but least accurate method is to use an **acid–base indicator**, a dye that changes color depending on the pH of the solution. For example, the well-known dye *litmus* is red below pH 4.8 but blue above pH 7.8 and the indicator *phenolphthalein* (fee-nol-**thay**-lean) is colorless below pH 8.2 but red above pH 10. To make pH determination particularly easy, test kits are available that contain a mixture of indicators known as *universal indicator* to give approximate pH measurements in the range 2–10 (Figure 10.3a). Also available are rolls of "pH paper," which make it possible to determine pH simply by putting a drop of solution on the paper and comparing the color that appears to the color on a calibration chart (Figure 10.3b).

▶ **Figure 10.3**
Finding pH.
(a) The color of universal indicator in solutions of known pH from 1 to 12. (b) Testing pH with a paper strip. Comparing the color of the strip with the code on the package gives the approximate pH.

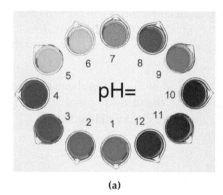

(a)

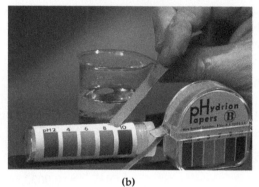

(b)

A much more accurate way to determine pH uses an electronic pH meter like the one shown in Figure 10.4. Electrodes are dipped into the solution, and the pH is read from the meter.

▲ **Figure 10.4**
Using a pH meter to obtain an accurate reading of pH.
Is milk of magnesia acidic or basic?

Buffer A combination of substances that act together to prevent a drastic change in pH; usually a weak acid and its conjugate base.

10.10 Buffer Solutions

Much of the body's chemistry depends on maintaining the pH of blood and other fluids within narrow limits. This is accomplished through the use of **buffers**—combinations of substances that act together to prevent a drastic change in pH.

Most buffers are mixtures of a weak acid and a roughly equal concentration of its conjugate base—for example, a solution that contains 0.10 M acetic acid and 0.10 M acetate ion. If a small amount of OH^- is added to a buffer solution, the pH increases, but not by much because the acid component of the buffer neutralizes the added OH^-. If a small amount of H_3O^+ is added to a buffer solution, the pH decreases, but again not by much because the base component of the buffer neutralizes the added H_3O^+.

To see why buffer solutions work, look at the equation for the acid dissociation constant of an acid HA.

For the reaction: $HA(aq) + H_2O(l) \rightleftharpoons A^-(aq) + H_3O^+(aq)$

we have $K_a = \dfrac{[H_3O^+][A^-]}{[HA]}$

Rearranging this equation shows that the value of $[H_3O^+]$, and thus the pH, depends on the ratio of the undissociated acid concentration to the conjugate base concentration, $[HA]/[A^-]$:

$$[H_3O^+] = K_a \frac{[HA]}{[A^-]}$$

In the case of the acetic acid–acetate ion buffer, for instance, we have

$$CH_3CO_2H(aq) + H_2O(l) \rightleftharpoons H_3O^+(aq) + CH_3CO_2^-(aq)$$
$$\text{(0.10 M)} \qquad\qquad\qquad\qquad \text{(0.10 M)}$$

$$\text{and} \quad [H_3O^+] = K_a\frac{[CH_3CO_2H]}{[CH_3CO_2^-]}$$

Initially, the pH of the 0.10 M acetic acid–0.10 M acetate ion buffer solution is 4.74. When acid is added, most will be removed by reaction with $CH_3CO_2^-$. The equilibrium reaction shifts to the left, and as a result the concentration of CH_3CO_2H increases and the concentration of $CH_3CO_2^-$ decreases. As long as the changes in $[CH_3CO_2H]$ and $[CH_3CO_2^-]$ are relatively small, however, the ratio of $[CH_3CO_2H]$ to $[CH_3CO_2^-]$ changes only slightly, and there is little change in the pH.

When base is added to the buffer, most will be removed by reaction with CH_3CO_2H. The equilibrium shifts to the right, and so the concentration of CH_3CO_2H decreases and the concentration of $CH_3CO_2^-$ increases. Here too, though, as long as the concentration changes are relatively small, there is little change in the pH.

The ability of a buffer solution to resist changes in pH when acid or base is added is illustrated in Figure 10.5. Addition of 0.010 mol of H_3O^+ to 1.0 L of pure water changes the pH from 7 to 2, and addition of 0.010 mol of OH^- changes the pH from 7 to 12. A similar addition of acid to 1.0 L of a 0.10 M acetic acid–0.10 M acetate ion buffer, however, changes the pH from only 4.74 to 4.68, and addition of base changes the pH from only 4.74 to 4.85.

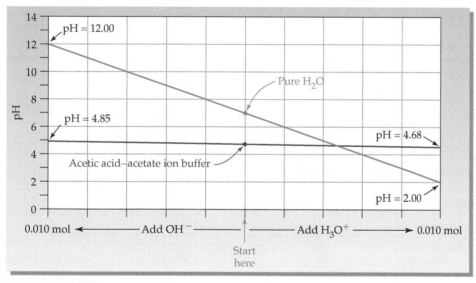

▲ **Figure 10.5**
A comparison of the change in pH.
When 0.010 mol of acid or 0.010 mol of base are added to 1.0 L of pure water and to 1.0 L of a 0.10 M acetic acid–0.10 M acetate ion buffer, the pH of the water varies between 12 and 2, while the pH of the buffer varies only between 4.85 and 4.68.

As we did with K_w, we can convert the rearranged K_a equation to its logarithmic form to obtain

$$pH = pK_a - \log\left(\frac{[HA]}{[A^-]}\right)$$

$$\text{or} \quad pH = pK_a + \log\left(\frac{[A^-]}{[HA]}\right)$$

This expression is known as the **Henderson–Hasselbalch equation** and is very useful in buffer applications, particularly in biology and biochemistry. Examination of the Henderson–Hasselbalch equation provides useful insights into how to prepare a buffer and into the factors that affect the pH of a buffer solution.

Henderson–Hasselbalch equation
The logarithmic form of the K_a equation for a weak acid, used in applications involving buffer solutions.

The effective pH range of a buffer will depend on the pK_a of the acid HA and on the relative concentrations of HA and conjugate base A^-. In general, the most effective buffers meet the following conditions:

- The pK_a for the weak acid should be close to the desired pH of the buffer solution.
- The ratio of $[HA]$ to $[A^-]$ should be close to 1, so that neither additional acid nor additional base changes the pH of the solution dramatically.
- The molar amounts of HA and A^- in the buffer should be approximately 10 times greater than the molar amounts of either acid or base you expect to add so that the ratio $[A^-]/[HA]$ does not undergo a large change.

The pH of body fluids is maintained by three major buffer systems. Two of these buffers, the carbonic acid–bicarbonate ($H_2CO_3 - HCO_3^-$) system and the dihydrogen phosphate–hydrogen phosphate ($H_2PO_4 - HPO_4^{2-}$) system, depend on weak acid–conjugate base interactions exactly like those of the acetate buffer system described previously:

$$H_2CO_3(aq) + H_2O(l) \rightleftharpoons HCO_3^-(aq) + H_3O^+(aq) \qquad pK_a = 6.37$$
$$H_2PO_4^-(aq) + H_2O(l) \rightleftharpoons HPO_4^{2-}(aq) + H_3O^+(aq) \qquad pK_a = 7.21$$

The third buffer system depends on the ability of proteins to act as either proton acceptors or proton donors at different pH values.

LOOKING AHEAD ▶▶▶ In Chapter 29, we will see how the regulation of blood pH by the bicarbonate buffer system is particularly important in preventing *acidosis* and *alkalosis*.

Worked Example 10.12 Buffers: Selecting a Weak Acid for a Buffer Solution

Which of the organic acids in Table 10.2 would be the most appropriate for preparing a pH 4.15 buffer solution?

ANALYSIS The pH of the buffer solution depends on the pK_a of the weak acid. Remember that $pK_a = -\log(K_a)$.

SOLUTION
The K_a and pK_a values for the four organic acids in Table 10.2 are tabulated below. The ascorbic acid ($pK_a = 4.10$) will produce a buffer solution closest to the desired pH of 4.15.

Organic Acid	K_a	pK_a
Formic acid (HCOOH)	1.8×10^{-4}	3.74
Acetic acid (CH_3COOH)	1.8×10^{-5}	4.74
Propanoic acid (CH_3CH_2COOH)	1.3×10^{-5}	4.89
Ascorbic acid (vitamin C)	7.9×10^{-5}	4.10

Worked Example 10.13 Buffers: Calculating the pH of a Buffer Solution

What is the pH of a buffer solution that contains 0.100 M HF and 0.120 M NaF? The K_a of HF is 3.5×10^{-4}, and so $pK_a = 3.46$.

ANALYSIS The Henderson–Hasselbalch equation can be used to calculate the pH of a buffer solution: $pH = pK_a + \log\left(\dfrac{[F^-]}{[HF]}\right)$.

BALLPARK ESTIMATE If the concentrations of F^- and HF were equal, the log term in our equation would be zero, and the pH of the solution would be equal to the pK_a for HF, which means pH = 3.46. However, since the concentration of the conjugate base ($[F^-] = 0.120$ M) is slightly higher than the concentration of the conjugate acid ($[HF] = 0.100$ M), then the pH of the buffer solution will be slightly higher (more basic) than the pK_a.

SOLUTION

$$pH = pK_a + \log\left(\frac{[F^-]}{[HF]}\right)$$

$$pH = 3.46 + \log\left(\frac{0.120}{0.100}\right) = 3.46 + 0.08 = 3.54$$

BALLPARK CHECK The calculated pH of 3.54 is consistent with the prediction that the final pH will be slightly higher than the pK_a of 3.46.

Worked Example 10.14 Buffers: Measuring the Effect of Added Base on pH

What is the pH of 1.00 L of the 0.100 M hydrofluoric acid–0.120 M fluoride ion buffer system described in Worked Example 10.13 after 0.020 mol of NaOH is added?

ANALYSIS Initially, the 0.100 M HF–0.120 M NaF buffer has pH $= 3.54$, as calculated in Worked Example 10.13. The added base will react with the acid as indicated in the neutralization reaction,

$$HF(aq) + OH^-(aq) \longrightarrow H_2O(l) + F^-(aq)$$

which means $[HF]$ decreases and $[F^-]$ increases. With the pK_a and the concentrations of HF and F^- known, pH can be calculated using the Henderson–Hasselbalch equation.

BALLPARK ESTIMATE After the neutralization reaction, there is more conjugate base (F^-) and less conjugate acid (HF), and so we expect the pH to increase slightly from the initial value of 3.54.

SOLUTION

When 0.020 mol of NaOH is added to 1.00 L of the buffer, the HF concentration *decreases* from 0.100 M to 0.080 M as a result of an acid–base reaction. At the same time, the F^- concentration *increases* from 0.120 M to 0.140 M because additional F^- is produced by the neutralization. Using these new values gives

$$pH = 3.46 + \log\left(\frac{0.140}{0.080}\right) = 3.46 + 0.24 = 3.70$$

The addition of 0.020 mol of base causes the pH of the buffer to rise only from 3.54 to 3.70.

BALLPARK CHECK The final pH, 3.70, is slightly more basic than the initial pH of 3.54, consistent with our prediction.

PROBLEM 10.18
What is the pH of 1.00 L of the 0.100 M hydrofluoric acid–0.120 M fluoride ion buffer system described in Worked Example 10.13 after 0.020 mol of HNO_3 is added?

PROBLEM 10.19
The ammonia/ammonium buffer system is sometimes used to optimize polymerase chain reactions (PCR) used in DNA studies. The equilibrium for this buffer can be written as

$$NH_4^+(aq) + H_2O(l) \rightleftharpoons H_3O^+(aq) + NH_3(aq)$$

Calculate the pH of a buffer that contains 0.050 M ammonium chloride and 0.080 M ammonia. The K_a of ammonium is 5.6×10^{-10}.

PROBLEM 10.20
What is the ratio of bicarbonate ion to carbonic acid $([HCO_3^-]/[H_2CO_3])$ in blood serum that has a pH of 7.40? (see Chemistry in Action: Buffers in the Body: Acidosis and Alkalosis on p. 312).

CHEMISTRY IN ACTION

Buffers in the Body: Acidosis and Alkalosis

A group of teenagers at a rock concert experience a collective fainting spell. A person taking high doses of aspirin for chronic pain appears disoriented and is having trouble breathing. A person with type 1 diabetes complains of tiredness and stomach pains. An athlete who recently completed a highly strenuous workout suffers from muscle cramps and nausea. A patient on an HIV drug regimen experiences increasing weakness and numbness in the hands and feet. What do all these individuals have in common? They are all suffering from abnormal fluctuations in blood pH, resulting in conditions known as *acidosis* (pH < 7.35) or *alkalosis* (pH > 7.45).

Each of the fluids in our bodies has a pH range suited to its function, as shown in the accompanying table. The stability of cell membranes, the shapes of huge protein molecules that must be folded in certain ways to function, and the activities of enzymes are all dependent on appropriate H_3O^+ concentrations. Blood plasma and the interstitial fluid surrounding cells, which together compose one-third of body fluids, have a slightly basic pH with a normal range of 7.35–7.45. The highly complex series of reactions and equilibria that take place throughout the body are very sensitive to pH—variations of even a few tenths of a pH unit can produce severe physiological symptoms.

pH of Body Fluids

Fluid	pH
Blood plasma	7.4
Interstitial fluid	7.4
Cytosol	7.0
Saliva	5.8–7.1
Gastric juice	1.6–1.8
Pancreatic juice	7.5–8.8
Intestinal juice	6.3–8.0
Urine	4.6–8.0
Sweat	4.0–6.8

Maintaining the pH of blood serum in its optimal range is accomplished by the carbonic acid–bicarbonate buffer system (Section 10.10), which depends on the relative amounts of CO_2 and bicarbonate dissolved in the blood. Because carbonic acid is unstable and therefore in equilibrium with CO_2 and water, there is an extra step in the bicarbonate buffer mechanism:

$$CO_2(aq) + H_2O(l) \rightleftharpoons$$
$$H_2CO_3(aq) \rightleftharpoons HCO_3^-(aq) + H_3O^+(aq)$$

As a result, the bicarbonate buffer system is intimately related to the elimination of CO_2, which is continuously produced in cells and transported to the lungs to be exhaled. Anything that significantly shifts the balance between dissolved CO_2 and HCO_3^- can upset these equilibria and raise or lower the pH. How does this happen, and how does the body compensate?

▲ **Hyperventilation, the rapid breathing due to excitement or stress, removes CO_2 and increases blood pH resulting in respiratory alkalosis.**

The relationships between the bicarbonate buffer system, the lungs, and the kidneys are shown in the figure on the next page. Under normal circumstances, the reactions shown in the figure are in equilibrium. Addition of excess acid (red arrows) causes formation of H_2CO_3 and results in lowering of H_3O^+ concentration. Removal of acid (blue arrows) causes formation of more H_3O^+ by dissociation of H_2CO_3. The maintenance of pH by this mechanism is supported by a reserve of bicarbonate ions in body fluids. Such a buffer can accommodate large additions of H_3O^+ before there is a significant change in the pH.

Additional backup to the bicarbonate buffer system is provided by the kidneys. Each day a quantity of acid equal to that produced in the body is excreted in the urine. In the process, the kidney returns HCO_3^- to the extracellular fluids, where it becomes part of the bicarbonate reserve.

Respiratory acidosis can be caused by a decrease in respiration, which leads to a buildup of excess CO_2 in the blood and a corresponding decrease in pH. This could be caused by a blocked air passage due to inhaled food—removal of the blockage restores normal breathing and a return to the optimal pH. *Metabolic acidosis* results from an excess of other acids in the blood that reduce the bicarbonate concentration. High doses of aspirin (acetylsalicylic acid, Section 17.5), for example, increase the hydronium ion concentration and decrease the pH. Strenuous exercise generates excess lactate in the muscles, which is released into the bloodstream (Section 23.11). The liver converts lactate into glucose, which is the body's major source of energy; this process consumes bicarbonate ions, which decreases the pH. Some HIV drug therapies can damage cellular mitochondria (Section 21.3), resulting in a buildup of lactic acid in the cells and bloodstream. In the case of a person with diabetes, lack of insulin causes the body to start burning fat, which generates ketones and keto acids (Chapter 16), organic compounds that lower the blood pH.

The body attempts to correct acidosis by increasing the rate and depth of respiration—breathing faster "blows off" CO_2, shifting the CO_2–bicarbonate equilibrium to the left and raising the pH. The net effect is rapid reversal of the acidosis.

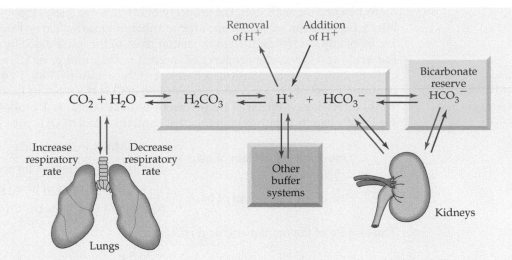

Although this may be sufficient for cases of respiratory acidosis, it provides only temporary relief for metabolic acidosis. A long-term solution depends on removal of excess acid by the kidneys, which can take several hours.

What about our teenage fans? In their excitement they have hyperventilated—their increased breathing rate has removed too much CO_2 from their blood and they are suffer-

ing from *respiratory alkalosis*. The body responds by "fainting" to decrease respiration and restore the CO_2 levels in the blood. When they regain consciousness, they will be ready to rock once again.

See Chemistry in Action Problems 10.96 and 10.97 at the end of the chapter.

🔑 **KEY CONCEPT PROBLEM 10.21**

A buffer solution is prepared using CN^- (from NaCN salt) and HCN in the amounts indicated. The K_a for HCN is 4.9×10^{-10}. Calculate the pH of the buffer solution.

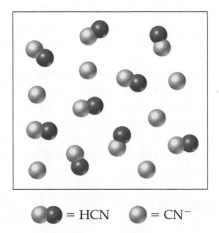

⬤⬤ = HCN   ⬤ = CN^-

10.11 Acid and Base Equivalents

We said in Section 9.10 that it is sometimes useful to think in terms of ion *equivalents* (Eq) and *gram-equivalents* (g-Eq) when we are primarily interested in an ion itself rather than the compound that produced the ion. For similar reasons, it can also be useful to consider acid or base equivalents and gram-equivalents.

Equivalent of acid Amount of an acid that contains 1 mole of H^+ ions.

Equivalent of base Amount of base that contains 1 mole of OH^- ions.

When dealing with ions, the property of interest was the charge on the ion. Therefore, 1 Eq of an ion was defined as the number of ions that carry 1 mol of charge, and 1 g-Eq of any ion was defined as the molar mass of the ion divided by the ionic charge. For acids and bases, the property of interest is the number of H^+ ions (for an acid) or the number of OH^- ions (for a base) per formula unit. Thus, 1 **equivalent of acid** contains 1 mol of H^+ ions, and 1 g-Eq of an acid is the mass in grams that contains 1 mol of H^+ ions. Similarly, 1 **equivalent of base** contains 1 mol of OH^- ions, and 1 g-Eq of a base is the mass in grams that contains 1 mol of OH^- ions:

$$\text{One gram-equivalent of acid} = \frac{\text{Molar mass of acid (g)}}{\text{Number of } H^+ \text{ ions per formula unit}}$$

$$\text{One gram-equivalent of base} = \frac{\text{Molar mass of base (g)}}{\text{Number of } OH^- \text{ ions per formula unit}}$$

Thus 1 g-Eq of the monoprotic acid HCl is

$$1 \text{ g-Eq HCl} = \frac{36.5 \text{ g}}{1 \text{ } H^+ \text{ per HCl}} = 36.5 \text{ g}$$

which is equal to molar mass of the acid, but one gram-equivalent of the diprotic acid H_2SO_4 is

$$1 \text{ g-Eq } H_2SO_4 = \frac{98.0 \text{ g}}{2 \text{ } H^+ \text{ per } H_2SO_4} = 49.0 \text{ g}$$

which is the molar mass divided by 2, because 1 mol of H_2SO_4 contains 2 mol of H^+.

$$\text{One equivalent of } H_2SO_4 = \frac{\text{Molar mass of } H_2SO_4}{2} = \frac{98.0 \text{ g}}{2} = 49.0 \text{ g}$$

Divide by 2 because H_2SO_4 is diprotic.

Using acid–base equivalents has two practical advantages: First, they are convenient when only the acidity or basicity of a solution is of interest rather than the identity of the acid or base. Second, they show quantities that are chemically equivalent in their properties; 36.5 g of HCl and 49.0 g of H_2SO_4 are chemically equivalent quantities because each reacts with 1 Eq of base. *One equivalent of any acid neutralizes one equivalent of any base.*

Normality (N) A measure of acid (or base) concentration expressed as the number of acid (or base) equivalents per liter of solution.

Because acid–base equivalents are so useful, clinical chemists sometimes express acid and base concentrations in *normality* rather than molarity. The **normality (N)** of an acid or base solution is defined as the number of equivalents (or milliequivalents) of acid or base per liter of solution. For example, a solution made by dissolving 1.0 g-Eq (49.0 g) of H_2SO_4 in water to give 1.0 L of solution has a concentration of 1.0 Eq/L, which is 1.0 N. Similarly, a solution that contains 0.010 Eq/L of acid is 0.010 N and has an acid concentration of 10 mEq/L:

$$\text{Normality (N)} = \frac{\text{Equivalents of acid or base}}{\text{Liters of solution}}$$

The values of molarity (M) and normality (N) are the same for monoprotic acids, such as HCl, but are not the same for diprotic or triprotic acids. A solution made by diluting 1.0 g-Eq (49.0 g = 0.50 mol) of the diprotic acid H_2SO_4 to a volume of 1.0 L has a *normality* of 1.0 N but a *molarity* of 0.50 M. For any acid or base, normality is always equal to molarity times the number of H^+ or OH^- ions produced per formula unit:

Normality of acid = (Molarity of acid) × (Number of H^+ ions produced per formula unit)

Normality of base = (Molarity of base) × (Number of OH^- ions produced per formula unit)

Worked Example 10.15 Equivalents: Mass to Equivalent Conversion for Diprotic Acid

How many equivalents are in 3.1 g of the diprotic acid H_2S? The molar mass of H_2S is 34.0 g.

ANALYSIS The number of acid or base equivalents is calculated by doing a gram to mole conversion using molar mass as the conversion factor and then multiplying by the number of H^+ ions produced.

BALLPARK ESTIMATE The 3.1 g is a little less than 0.10 mol of H_2S. Since it is a diprotic acid, (two H^+ per mole), this represents a little less than 0.2 Eq of H_2S.

SOLUTION

$$(3.1 \text{ g } H_2S)\left(\frac{1 \text{ mol } H_2S}{34.0 \text{ g } H_2S}\right)\left(\frac{2 \text{ Eq } H_2S}{1 \text{ mol } H_2S}\right) = 0.18 \text{ Eq } H_2S$$

BALLPARK CHECK The calculated value of 0.18 is consistent with our prediction of a little less than 0.2 Eq of H_2S.

Worked Example 10.16 Equivalents: Calculating Equivalent Concentrations

What is the normality of a solution made by diluting 6.5 g of H_2SO_4 to a volume of 200 mL? What is the concentration of this solution in milliequivalents per liter? The molar mass of H_2SO_4 is 98.0 g.

ANALYSIS Calculate how many equivalents of H_2SO_4 are in 6.5 g by using the molar mass of the acid as a conversion factor and then determine the normality of the acid.

SOLUTION

STEP 1: Identify known information. We know the molar mass of H_2SO_4, the mass of H_2SO_4 to be dissolved, and the final volume of solution.

MW of H_2SO_4 = 98.0 g/mol
Mass of H_2SO_4 = 6.5 g
Volume of solution = 200 mL

STEP 2: Identify answer including units. We need to calculate the normality of the final solution.

Normality = ?? (equiv./L)

STEP 3: Identify conversion factors. We will need to convert the mass of H_2SO_4 to moles, and then to equivalents of H_2SO_4. We will then need to convert volume from mL to L.

$$(6.5 \text{ g } H_2SO_4)\left(\frac{1 \text{ mol } H_2SO_4}{98.0 \text{ g } H_2SO_4}\right)\left(\frac{2 \text{ Eq } H_2SO_4}{1 \text{ mol } H_2SO_4}\right)$$
$$= 0.132 \text{ Eq } H_2SO_4 \text{ (don't round yet!)}$$
$$(200 \text{ mL})\left(\frac{1 \text{ L}}{1000 \text{ mL}}\right) = 0.200 \text{ L}$$

STEP 4: Solve. Dividing the number of equivalents by the volume yields the Normality.

$$\frac{0.132 \text{ Eq } H_2SO_4}{0.200 \text{ L}} = 0.66 \text{ N}$$

The concentration of the sulfuric acid solution is 0.66 N, or 660 mEq/L.

PROBLEM 10.22
How many equivalents are in the following?
(a) 5.0 g HNO_3
(b) 12.5 g $Ca(OH)_2$
(c) 4.5 g H_3PO_4

PROBLEM 10.23
What are the normalities of the solutions if each sample in Problem 10.22 is dissolved in water and diluted to a volume of 300.0 mL?

10.12 Some Common Acid–Base Reactions

Among the most common of the many kinds of Brønsted–Lowry acid–base reactions are those of an acid with hydroxide ion, an acid with bicarbonate or carbonate ion, and an acid with ammonia or a related nitrogen-containing compound. Let us look briefly at each of the three types.

Reaction of Acids with Hydroxide Ion

One equivalent of an acid reacts with 1 Eq of a metal hydroxide to yield water and a salt in a neutralization reaction:

$$HCl(aq) + KOH(aq) \longrightarrow H_2O(l) + KCl(aq)$$

(An acid)   (A base)   (Water)   (A salt)

Such reactions are usually written with a single arrow because their equilibria lie far to the right and they have very large equilibrium constants ($K = 5 \times 10^{15}$; Section 7.8). The net ionic equation (Section 5.8) for all such reactions makes clear why acid–base equivalents are useful and why the properties of the acid and base disappear in neutralization reactions: The equivalent ions for the acid (H^+) and the base (OH^-) are used up in the formation of water.

$$H^+(aq) + OH^-(aq) \longrightarrow H_2O(l)$$

PROBLEM 10.24

Maalox, an over-the-counter antacid, contains aluminum hydroxide, $Al(OH)_3$, and magnesium hydroxide, $Mg(OH)_2$. Write balanced equations for the reaction of both with stomach acid (HCl).

Reaction of Acids with Bicarbonate and Carbonate Ion

Bicarbonate ion reacts with acid by accepting H^+ to yield carbonic acid, H_2CO_3. Similarly, carbonate ion accepts 2 protons in its reaction with acid. Carbonic acid is unstable, however, rapidly decomposing to carbon dioxide gas and water:

$$H^+(aq) + HCO_3^-(aq) \longrightarrow [H_2CO_3(aq)] \longrightarrow H_2O(l) + CO_2(g)$$
$$2\,H^+(aq) + CO_3^{2-}(aq) \longrightarrow [H_2CO_3(aq)] \longrightarrow H_2O(l) + CO_2(g)$$

Most metal carbonates are insoluble in water—marble, for example, is almost pure calcium carbonate, $CaCO_3$—but they nevertheless react easily with aqueous acid. In fact, geologists often test for carbonate-bearing rocks by putting a few drops of aqueous HCl on the rock and watching to see if bubbles of CO_2 form (Figure 10.6). This reaction is also responsible for the damage to marble and limestone artwork caused by acid rain (See Chemistry in Action: Acid Rain on p. 320). The most common application involving carbonates and acid, however, is the use of antacids that contain carbonates, such as TUMS™ or Rolaids™, to neutralize excess stomach acid.

▲ **Figure 10.6**
Marble.
Marble, which is primarily $CaCO_3$, releases bubbles of CO_2 when treated with hydrochloric acid.

PROBLEM 10.25

Write a balanced equation for each of the following reactions:
(a) $HCO_3^-(aq) + H_2SO_4(aq) \longrightarrow$?
(b) $CO_3^{2-}(aq) + HNO_3(aq) \longrightarrow$?

Reaction of Acids with Ammonia

Acids react with ammonia to yield ammonium salts, such as ammonium chloride, NH_4Cl, most of which are water-soluble:

$$NH_3(aq) + HCl(aq) \rightarrow NH_4Cl(aq)$$

Living organisms contain a group of compounds called *amines*, which contain nitrogen atoms bonded to carbon. Amines react with acids just as ammonia does, yielding water-soluble salts. Methylamine, for example, an organic compound found in rotting fish, reacts with HCl:

Methylamine   Methylammonium chloride

LOOKING AHEAD ▶▶▶ In Chapter 15, we will see that amines occur in all living organisms, both plant and animal, as well as in many pharmaceutical agents. Amines called amino acids form the building blocks from which proteins are made, as we will see in Chapter 18.

PROBLEM 10.26

What products would you expect from the reaction of ammonia and sulfuric acid in aqueous solution?

$$2\,NH_3(aq) + H_2SO_4(aq) \longrightarrow ?$$

PROBLEM 10.27

Show how ethylamine $(C_2H_5NH_2)$ reacts with hydrochloric acid to form an ethylammonium salt.

10.13 Titration

Determining the pH of a solution gives the solution's H_3O^+ concentration but not necessarily its total acid concentration. That is because the two are not the same thing. The H_3O^+ concentration gives only the amount of acid that has dissociated into ions, whereas total acid concentration gives the sum of dissociated plus undissociated acid. In a 0.10 M solution of acetic acid, for instance, the total acid concentration is 0.10 M, yet the H_3O^+ concentration is only 0.0013 M (pH = 2.89) because acetic acid is a weak acid that is only about 1% dissociated.

The total acid or base concentration of a solution can be found by carrying out a **titration** procedure, as shown in Figure 10.7. Let us assume, for instance, that we want to find the acid concentration of an HCl solution. (Likewise, we might need to find the base concentration of an NaOH solution.) We begin by measuring out a known volume of the HCl solution and adding an acid–base indicator. Next, we fill a calibrated glass tube called a *buret* with an NaOH solution of known concentration, and we slowly add the NaOH to the HCl until neutralization is complete (the *end point*), identified by a color change in the indicator.

Reading from the buret gives the volume of the NaOH solution that has reacted with the known volume of HCl. Knowing both the concentration and volume of the NaOH solution then allows us to calculate the molar amount of NaOH, and the coefficients in the balanced equation allow us to find the molar amount of HCl that has been neutralized. Dividing the molar amount of HCl by the volume of the HCl solution

Titration A procedure for determining the total acid or base concentration of a solution.

▶ **Figure 10.7**
Titration of an acid solution of unknown concentration with a base solution of known concentration.
(a) A measured volume of the acid solution is placed in the flask along with an indicator. (b) The base of known concentration is then added from a buret until the color change of the indicator shows that neutralization is complete (the *end point*).

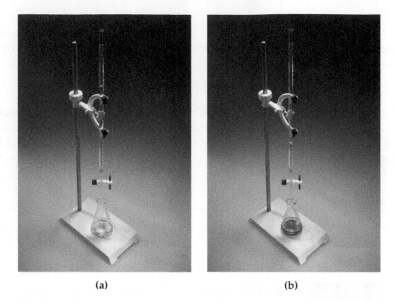

(a)   (b)

gives the concentration. The calculation thus involves mole–volume conversions just like those done in Section 9.7. Figure 10.8 shows a flow diagram of the strategy, and Worked Example 10.17 shows how to calculate total acid concentration.

When the titration involves a neutralization reaction in which one mole of acid reacts with one mole of base, such as that shown in Figure 10.8, then the moles of acid and base needed for complete reaction can be represented as

$$M_{acid} \times V_{acid} = M_{base} \times V_{base}$$

When the coefficients for the acid and base in the balanced neutralization reaction are not the same, such as in the reaction of a diprotic acid (H_2SO_4) with a monoprotic base (NaOH), then we can use equivalents of acid and base instead of moles, and Normality instead of Molarity:

$$(Eq)_{acid} = (Eq)_{base}$$
$$N_{acid} \times V_{acid} = N_{base} \times V_{base}.$$

We can convert between Normality and Molarity as described in Section 10.11.

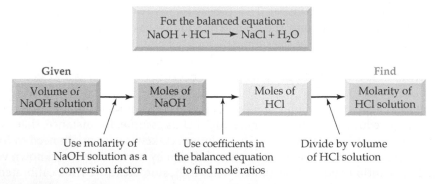

▲ **Figure 10.8**
A flow diagram for an acid–base titration.
This diagram summarizes the calculations needed to determine the concentration of an HCl solution by titration with an NaOH solution of known concentration. The steps are similar to those shown in Figure 9.7.

Worked Example 10.17 Titrations: Calculating Total Acid Concentration

When a 5.00 mL sample of household vinegar (dilute aqueous acetic acid) is titrated, 44.5 mL of 0.100 M NaOH solution is required to reach the end point. What is the acid concentration of the vinegar in moles per liter, equivalents per liter, and milliequivalents per liter? The neutralization reaction is

$$CH_3CO_2H(aq) + NaOH(aq) \longrightarrow CH_3CO_2{}^-Na^+(aq) + H_2O(l)$$

ANALYSIS To find the molarity of the vinegar, we need to know the number of moles of acetic acid dissolved in the 5.00 mL sample. Following a flow diagram similar to Figure 10.8, we use the volume and molarity of NaOH to find the number of moles. From the chemical equation, we use the mole ratio to find the number of moles of acid, and then divide by the volume of the acid solution. Because acetic acid is a monoprotic acid, the normality of the solution is numerically the same as its molarity.

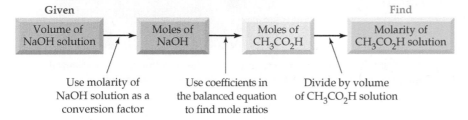

BALLPARK ESTIMATE The 5.00 mL of vinegar required nearly nine times as much NaOH solution (44.5 mL) for complete reaction. Since the neutralization stoichiometry is 1:1, the molarity of the acetic acid in the vinegar must be nine times greater than the molarity of NaOH, or approximately 0.90 M.

SOLUTION
Substitute the known information and appropriate conversion factors into the flow diagram, and solve for the molarity of the acetic acid:

$$(44.5 \text{ mL NaOH})\left(\frac{0.100 \text{ mol NaOH}}{1000 \text{ mL}}\right)\left(\frac{1 \text{ mol CH}_3\text{CO}_2\text{H}}{1 \text{ mol NaOH}}\right)$$

$$\times \left(\frac{1}{0.005\ 00 \text{ L}}\right) = 0.890 \text{ M CH}_3\text{CO}_2\text{H}$$

$$= 0.890 \text{ N CH}_3\text{CO}_2\text{H}$$

Expressed in milliequivalents, this concentration is

$$\frac{0.890 \text{ Eq}}{\text{L}} \times \frac{1000 \text{ mEq}}{1 \text{ Eq}} = 890 \text{ mEq/L}$$

BALLPARK CHECK The calculated result (0.890 M) is very close to our estimate of 0.90 M.

PROBLEM 10.28
A titration is carried out to determine the concentration of the acid in an old bottle of aqueous HCl whose label has become unreadable. What is the HCl concentration if 58.4 mL of 0.250 M NaOH is required to titrate a 20.0 mL sample of the acid?

CHEMISTRY IN ACTION

Acid Rain

As the water that evaporates from oceans and lakes condenses into raindrops, it dissolves small quantities of gases from the atmosphere. Under normal conditions, rain is slightly acidic, with a pH close to 5.6, because of atmospheric CO_2 that dissolves to form carbonic acid:

$$CO_2(aq) + H_2O(l) \rightleftharpoons$$
$$H_2CO_3(aq) \rightleftharpoons HCO_3^-(aq) + H_3O^+(aq)$$

In recent decades, however, the acidity of rainwater in many industrialized areas of the world has increased by a factor of over 100, to a pH between 3 and 3.5.

The primary cause of this so-called *acid rain* is industrial and automotive pollution. Each year, large power plants and smelters pour millions of tons of sulfur dioxide (SO_2) gas into the atmosphere, where some is oxidized by air to produce sulfur trioxide (SO_3). Sulfur oxides then dissolve in rain to form dilute sulfurous acid (H_2SO_3) and sulfuric acid (H_2SO_4):

$$SO_2(g) + H_2O(l) \longrightarrow H_2SO_3(aq)$$
$$SO_3(g) + H_2O(l) \longrightarrow H_2SO_4(aq)$$

Nitrogen oxides produced by the high-temperature reaction of N_2 with O_2 in coal-burning plants and in automobile engines further contribute to the problem. Nitrogen dioxide (NO_2) dissolves in water to form dilute nitric acid (HNO_3) and nitric oxide (NO):

$$3 NO_2(g) + H_2O(l) \longrightarrow 2 HNO_3(aq) + NO(g)$$

Oxides of both sulfur and nitrogen have always been present in the atmosphere, produced by such natural sources as volcanoes and lightning bolts, but their amounts have increased dramatically over the last century because of industrialization. The result is a notable decrease in the pH of rainwater in more densely populated regions, including Europe and the eastern United States.

Many processes in nature require such a fine pH balance that they are dramatically upset by the shift that has occurred in the pH of rain. Some watersheds contain soils that have high "buffering capacity" and so are able to neutralize acidic compounds in acid rain. Other areas, such as the northeastern United States and eastern Canada, where soil-buffering capacity is poor, have experienced negative ecological effects. Acid rain releases aluminum salts from soil, and the ions then wash into streams. The low pH and increased aluminum levels are so toxic to fish and other organisms that many lakes and streams in these areas are devoid of aquatic life. Massive tree die-offs have occurred throughout central and eastern Europe as acid rain has lowered the pH of the soil and has leached nutrients from leaves.

Fortunately, acidic emissions in the United States have been greatly reduced in recent years as a result of the Clean Air Act

▲ This limestone statue adorning the Rheims Cathedral in France has been severely eroded by acid rain.

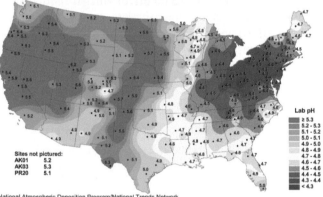

Hydrogen ion concentration as pH from measurements made at the Central Analytical Laboratory, 1996

National Atmospheric Deposition Program/National Trends Network
http://nadp.sws.uiuc.edu

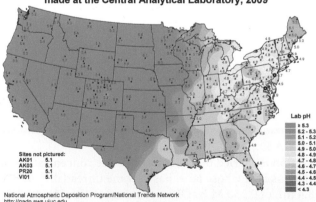

Hydrogen ion concentration as pH from measurements made at the Central Analytical Laboratory, 2009

National Atmospheric Deposition Program/National Trends Network
http://nadp.sws.uiuc.edu

▲ These maps compare the average pH of precipitation in the United States in 1996 and in 2009. During this period, total acid deposition in much of the eastern United States decreased substantially.

Amendments of 1990. Industrial emissions of SO_2 and nitrogen oxides decreased by over 40% from 1990 to 2007, resulting in a decrease in acid rain depositions, particularly in the eastern United States and Canada (see accompanying figure). While significant reductions have been realized, most environmental scientists agree that additional reductions in these pollutant emissions are necessary to ensure the recovery of affected lakes and streams.

See Chemistry in Action Problems 10.98 and 10.99 at the end of the chapter.

PROBLEM 10.29

How many milliliters of 0.150 M NaOH are required to neutralize 50.0 mL of 0.200 M H_2SO_4? The balanced neutralization reaction is:

$$H_2SO_4(aq) + 2\,NaOH(aq) \longrightarrow Na_2SO_4(aq) + 2\,H_2O(l).$$

PROBLEM 10.30

A 21.5 mL sample of a KOH solution of unknown concentration requires 16.1 mL of 0.150 M H_2SO_4 solution to reach the end point in a titration.

(a) How many moles of H_2SO_4 were necessary to reach the end point? How many equivalents?

(b) What is the molarity of the KOH solution?

PROBLEM 10.31

Titration of a 50.00 ml sample of acid rain required 9.30 mL of 0.0012 M NaOH to reach the end point. What was the total $[H_3O^+]$ in the rain sample? What was the pH? (see Chemistry in Action: Acid Rain on p. 320).

10.14 Acidity and Basicity of Salt Solutions

It is tempting to think of all salt solutions as neutral; after all, they come from the neutralization reaction between an acid and a base. In fact, salt solutions can be neutral, acidic, or basic, depending on the ions present, because some ions react with water to produce H_3O^+ and some ions react with water to produce OH^-. To predict the acidity of a salt solution, it is convenient to classify salts according to the acid and base from which they are formed in a neutralization reaction. The classification and some examples are given in Table 10.3.

TABLE 10.3 Acidity and Basicity of Salt Solutions

Anion Derived from Acid That Is:	Cation Derived from Base That Is:	Solution	Example
Strong	Weak	Acidic	NH_4Cl, NH_4NO_3
Weak	Strong	Basic	$NaHCO_3$, KCH_3CO_2
Strong	Strong	Neutral	$NaCl$, KBr, $Ca(NO_3)_2$
Weak	Weak	More information needed	

The general rule for predicting the acidity or basicity of a salt solution is that the stronger partner from which the salt is formed dominates. That is, a salt formed from a strong acid and a weak base yields an acidic solution because the strong acid dominates; a salt formed from a weak acid and a strong base yields a basic solution because the base dominates; and a salt formed from a strong acid and a strong base yields a neutral solution because neither acid nor base dominates. Here are some examples.

Salt of Strong Acid + Weak Base ⟶ Acidic Solution

A salt such as NH_4Cl, which can be formed by reaction of a strong acid (HCl) with a weak base (NH_3), yields an acidic solution. The Cl^- ion does not react with water, but the NH_4^+ ion is a weak acid that gives H_3O^+ ions:

$$NH_4^+(aq) + H_2O(l) \rightleftharpoons NH_3(aq) + H_3O^+(aq)$$

Salt of Weak Acid + Strong Base ⟶ Basic Solution

A salt such as sodium bicarbonate, which can be formed by reaction of a weak acid (H_2CO_3) with a strong base (NaOH), yields a basic solution. The Na^+ ion does not react with water, but the HCO_3^- ion is a weak base that gives OH^- ions:

$$HCO_3^-(aq) + H_2O(l) \rightleftharpoons H_2CO_3(aq) + OH^-(aq)$$

Salt of Strong Acid + Strong Base ⟶ Neutral Solution

A salt such as NaCl, which can be formed by reaction of a strong acid (HCl) with a strong base (NaOH), yields a neutral solution. Neither the Cl^- ion nor the Na^+ ion reacts with water.

Salt of Weak Acid + Weak Base

Both cation and anion in this type of salt react with water, so we cannot predict whether the resulting solution will be acidic or basic without quantitative information. The ion that reacts to the greater extent with water will govern the pH—it may be either the cation or the anion.

Worked Example 10.18 Acidity and Basicity of Salt Solutions

Predict whether the following salts produce an acidic, basic, or neutral solution:

(a) $BaCl_2$ **(b)** NaCN   **(c)** NH_4NO_3

ANALYSIS Look in Table 10.1 to see the classification of acids and bases as strong or weak.

SOLUTION

(a) $BaCl_2$ gives a neutral solution because it is formed from a strong acid (HCl) and a strong base $[Ba(OH)_2]$.

(b) NaCN gives a basic solution because it is formed from a weak acid (HCN) and a strong base (NaOH).

(c) NH_4NO_3 gives an acidic solution because it is formed from a strong acid (HNO_3) and a weak base (NH_3).

PROBLEM 10.32
Predict whether the following salts produce an acidic, basic, or neutral solution:
(a) K_2SO_4 **(b)** Na_2HPO_4 **(c)** MgF_2 **(d)** NH_4Br

SUMMARY: REVISITING THE CHAPTER GOALS

1. What are acids and bases? According to the *Brønsted–Lowry definition*, an acid is a substance that donates a hydrogen ion (a proton, H^+) and a base is a substance that accepts a hydrogen ion. Thus, the generalized reaction of an acid with a base involves the reversible transfer of a proton:

$$B: + H{-}A \rightleftharpoons A:^- + H{-}B^+$$

In aqueous solution, water acts as a base and accepts a proton from an acid to yield a *hydronium ion*, H_3O^+. Reaction of an acid with a metal hydroxide, such as KOH, yields water and a salt; reaction with bicarbonate ion (HCO_3^-) or carbonate ion (CO_3^{2-}) yields water, a salt, and CO_2 gas; and reaction with ammonia yields an ammonium salt (*see Problems 33, 37, 38, 42, 43, 60, 94, 100, 102*).

2. What effect does the strength of acids and bases have on their reactions? Different acids and bases differ in their ability to give up or accept a proton. A *strong acid* gives up a proton easily and is 100% *dissociated* in aqueous solution; a *weak acid* gives up a proton with difficulty, is only slightly dissociated in water, and establishes an equilibrium between dissociated and undissociated forms. Similarly, a *strong base* accepts and holds a proton readily, whereas a *weak base* has a low affinity for a proton and establishes an equilibrium in aqueous solution. The two substances that are related by the gain or loss of a proton are called a *conjugate acid–base pair*. The exact strength of an acid is defined by an *acid dissociation constant*, K_a:

For the reaction $HA + H_2O \rightleftharpoons H_3O^+ + A^-$

we have $K_a = \dfrac{[H_3O^+][A^-]}{[HA]}$

A proton-transfer reaction always takes place in the direction that favors formation of the weaker acid (*see Problems 34–36, 38–41, 44–55, 58–65, 99, 104, 108*).

3. What is the ion-product constant for water? Water is *amphoteric*; that is, it can act as either an acid or a base. Water also dissociates slightly into H_3O^+ ions and OH^- ions; the product of whose concentrations in any aqueous solution is the *ion-product constant for water*, $K_w = [H_3O^+][OH^-] = 1.00 \times 10^{-14}$ at 25 °C (*see Problems 56, 69–71, 101*).

4. What is the pH scale for measuring acidity? The acidity or basicity of an aqueous solution is given by its *pH*, defined as the negative logarithm of the hydronium ion concentration, $[H_3O^+]$. A pH below 7 means an acidic solution; a pH equal to 7 means a neutral solution; and a pH above 7 means a basic solution (*see Problems 57, 61–71, 76, 78, 94, 96–101, 104, 110*).

5. What is a buffer? The pH of a solution can be controlled through the use of a *buffer* that acts to remove either added H_3O^+ ions or added OH^- ions. Most buffer solutions consist of roughly equal amounts of a weak acid and its conjugate base. The bicarbonate buffer present in blood and the hydrogen phosphate buffer present in cells are particularly important examples (*see Problems 72–79, 105, 107*).

6. How is the acid or base concentration of a solution determined? Acid (or base) concentrations are determined in the laboratory by *titration* of a solution of unknown concentration with a base (or acid) solution of known strength until an indicator signals that neutralization is complete (*see Problems 80–93, 103, 106, 109, 110*).

CONCEPT MAP: ACIDS AND BASES

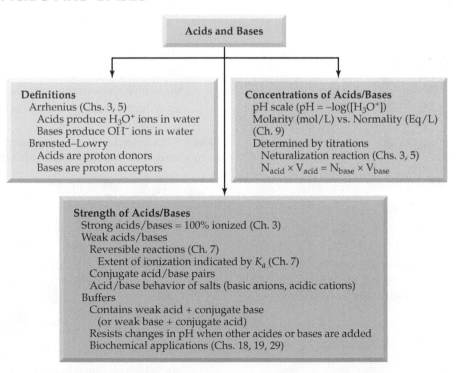

▲ **Figure 10.9**

Acids and bases play important roles in many chemical and biochemical processes, and many common substances are classified as acids or bases. Acid and base behavior is related to the ability to exchange protons, or to form H_3O^+ or OH^- ions, respectively, in water. Strong acids and bases ionize completely in aqueous solution, while weak acids/bases ionize only partially and establish an equilibrium with their conjugates. The relationship between these concepts and some of their practical and/or quantitative applications are illustrated in Figure 10.9.

KEY WORDS

Acid dissociation constant (K_a), *p. 301*

Acid–base indicator, *p. 308*

Amphoteric, *p. 302*

Brønsted–Lowry acid, *p. 293*

Brønsted–Lowry base, *p. 293*

Buffer, *p. 308*

Conjugate acid, *p. 295*

Conjugate acid–base pair, *p. 295*

Conjugate base, *p. 295*

Dissociation, *p. 296*

Equivalent of acid, *p. 314*

Equivalent of base, *p. 314*

Gram-equivalent of acid, *p. 314*

Gram-equivalent of base, *p. 314*

Henderson–Hasselbalch equation, *p. 309*

Hydronium ion, *p. 291*

Ion-product constant
for water (K_w), *p. 302*

Normality (N), *p. 314*

p function, *p. 304*

pH, *p. 304*

Strong acid, *p. 296*

Strong base, *p. 297*

Titration, *p. 317*

Weak acid, *p. 296*

Weak base, *p. 297*

UNDERSTANDING KEY CONCEPTS

10.33 An aqueous solution of OH^-, represented as a blue sphere, is allowed to mix with a solution of an acid H_nA, represented as a red sphere. Three possible outcomes are depicted by boxes (1)–(3), where the green spheres represent A^{n-}, the anion of the acid:

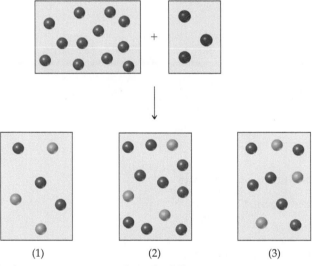

Which outcome corresponds to the following reactions?

    (a) $HF + OH^- \longrightarrow H_2O + F^-$

    (b) $H_2SO_3 + 2\,OH^- \longrightarrow 2\,H_2O + SO_3^{2-}$

    (c) $H_3PO_4 + 3\,OH^- \longrightarrow 3\,H_2O + PO_4^{3-}$

10.34 Electrostatic potential maps of acetic acid (CH_3CO_2H) and ethyl alcohol (CH_3CH_2OH) are shown. Identify the most acidic hydrogen in each, and tell which of the two is likely to be the stronger acid.

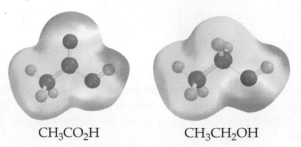

CH_3CO_2H CH_3CH_2OH

10.35 The following pictures represent aqueous acid solutions. Water molecules are not shown.

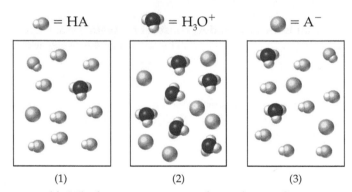

  (1)   (2)   (3)

    (a) Which picture represents the weakest acid?

    (b) Which picture represents the strongest acid?

    (c) Which picture represents the acid with the smallest value of K_a?

10.36 The following pictures represent aqueous solutions of a diprotic acid H_2A. Water molecules are not shown.

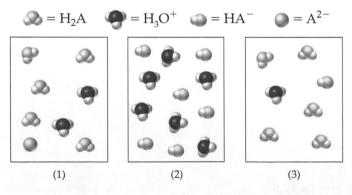

  (1)   (2)   (3)

    (a) Which picture represents a solution of a weak diprotic acid?

    (b) Which picture represents an impossible situation?

10.37 Assume that the red spheres in the buret represent H_3O^+ ions, the blue spheres in the flask represent OH^- ions, and you are carrying out a titration of the base with the acid. If the volumes in the buret and the flask are identical and the concentration of the acid in the buret is 1.00 M, what is the concentration of the base in the flask?

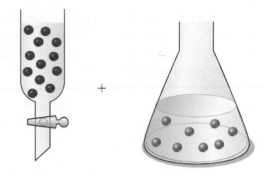

+

ADDITIONAL PROBLEMS

ACIDS AND BASES

10.38 What happens when a strong acid such as HBr is dissolved in water?

10.39 What happens when a weak acid such as CH_3CO_2H is dissolved in water?

10.40 What happens when a strong base such as KOH is dissolved in water?

10.41 What happens when a weak base such as NH_3 is dissolved in water?

10.42 What is the difference between a monoprotic acid and a diprotic acid? Give an example of each.

10.43 What is the difference between H^+ and H_3O^+?

10.44 Which of the following are strong acids? Look at Table 10.1 if necessary.

(a) $HClO_4$ (b) H_2CO_3 (c) H_3PO_4
(d) NH_4^+ (e) HI   (f) $H_2PO_4^-$

10.45 Which of the following are weak bases? Look at Table 10.1 if necessary.

(a) NH_3 (b) $Ca(OH)_2$ (c) HPO_4^{2-}
(d) LiOH   (e) CN^- (f) NH_2^-

BRØNSTED–LOWRY ACIDS AND BASES

10.46 Identify the following substances as a Brønsted–Lowry base, a Brønsted–Lowry acid, or neither:

(a) HCN   (b) $CH_3CO_2^-$ (c) $AlCl_3$
(d) H_2CO_3 (e) Mg^{2+} (f) $CH_3NH_3^+$

10.47 Label the Brønsted–Lowry acids and bases in the following equations, and tell which substances are conjugate acid–base pairs.

(a) $CO_3^{2-}(aq) + HCl(aq) \longrightarrow$
    $HCO_3^-(aq) + Cl^-(aq)$
(b) $H_3PO_4(aq) + NH_3(aq) \longrightarrow$
    $H_2PO_4^-(aq) + NH_4^+(aq)$
(c) $NH_4^+(aq) + CN^-(aq) \rightleftharpoons NH_3(aq) + HCN(aq)$
(d) $HBr(aq) + OH^-(aq) \longrightarrow H_2O(l) + Br^-(aq)$
(e) $H_2PO_4^-(aq) + N_2H_4(aq) \rightleftharpoons$
    $HPO_4^{2-}(aq) + N_2H_5^+(aq)$

10.48 Write the formulas of the conjugate acids of the following Brønsted–Lowry bases:

(a) $ClCH_2CO_2^-$ (b) C_5H_5N
(c) SeO_4^{2-} (d) $(CH_3)_3N$

10.49 Write the formulas of the conjugate bases of the following Brønsted–Lowry acids:

(a) HCN   (b) $(CH_3)_2NH_2^+$
(c) H_3PO_4 (d) $HSeO_3^-$

10.50 The hydrogen-containing anions of many polyprotic acids are amphoteric. Write equations for HCO_3^- and $H_2PO_4^-$ acting as bases with the strong acid HCl and as acids with the strong base NaOH.

10.51 Write balanced equations for proton-transfer reactions between the listed pairs. Indicate the conjugate pairs, and determine the favored direction for each equilibrium.

(a) HCl and PO_4^{3-} (b) HCN and SO_4^{2-}
(c) $HClO_4$ and NO_2^- (d) CH_3O^- and HF

10.52 Sodium bicarbonate ($NaHCO_3$), also known as baking soda, is a common home remedy for acid indigestion and is also used to neutralize acid spills in the laboratory. Write a balanced chemical equation for the reaction of sodium bicarbonate with

(a) Gastric juice (HCl)   (b) Sulfuric acid (H_2SO_4)

10.53 Refer to Section 10.12 to write balanced equations for the following acid–base reactions:

(a) $LiOH + HNO_3 \longrightarrow$ (b) $BaCO_3 + HI \longrightarrow$
(c) $H_3PO_4 + KOH \longrightarrow$ (d) $Ca(HCO_3)_2 + HCl \longrightarrow$
(e) $Ba(OH)_2 + H_2SO_4 \longrightarrow$

ACID AND BASE STRENGTH: K_a AND pH

10.54 How is K_a defined? Write the equation for K_a for the generalized acid HA.

10.55 Rearrange the equation you wrote in Problem 10.54 to solve for $[H_3O^+]$ in terms of K_a.

10.56 How is K_w defined, and what is its numerical value at 25 °C?

10.57 How is pH defined?

10.58 A solution of 0.10 M HCl has a pH = 1.00, whereas a solution of 0.10 M CH_3COOH has a pH = 2.88. Explain.

10.59   Calculate $[H_3O^+]$ for the 0.10 M CH_3COOH solution in Problem 10.58. What percent of the weak acid is dissociated?

10.60   Write the expressions for the acid dissociation constants for the three successive dissociations of phosphoric acid, H_3PO_4, in water.

10.61   Based on the K_a values in Table 10.1, rank the following solutions in order of increasing pH: 0.10 M HCOOH, 0.10 M HF, 0.10 M H_2CO_3, 0.10 M HSO_4^-, 0.10 M NH_4^+.

10.62   The electrode of a pH meter is placed in a sample of urine, and a reading of 7.9 is obtained. Is the sample acidic, basic, or neutral? What is the concentration of H_3O^+ in the urine sample?

10.63   A 0.10 M solution of the deadly poison hydrogen cyanide, HCN, has a pH of 5.2. Calculate the $[H_3O^+]$ of the solution. Is HCN a strong or a weak acid?

10.64   Human sweat can have a pH ranging from 4.0–6.8. Calculate the range of $[H_3O^+]$ in normal human sweat. How many orders of magnitude does this range represent?

10.65   Saliva has a pH range of 5.8–7.1. Approximately what is the H_3O^+ concentration range of saliva?

10.66   What is the approximate pH of a 0.02 M solution of a strong monoprotic acid? Of a 0.02 M solution of a strong base, such as KOH?

10.67   Calculate the pOH of each solution in Problems 10.62–10.65.

10.68   Without using a calculator, match the H_3O^+ concentrations of the following solutions, (a)–(d), to the corresponding pH, i–iv:

(a) Fresh egg white: $[H_3O^+] = 2.5 \times 10^{-8}$ M
(b) Apple cider: $[H_3O^+] = 5.0 \times 10^{-4}$ M
(c) Household ammonia: $[H_3O^+] = 2.3 \times 10^{-12}$ M
(d) Vinegar (acetic acid): $[H_3O^+] = 4.0 \times 10^{-3}$ M

i. pH = 3.30   ii. pH = 2.40   iii. pH = 11.64   iv. pH = 7.60

10.69   What are the OH^- concentration and pOH for each solution in Problem 10.68? Rank the solutions according to increasing acidity.

10.70   What are the H_3O^+ and OH^- concentrations of solutions that have the following pH values?

(a) pH 4   (b) pH 11   (c) pH 0
(d) pH 1.38   (e) pH 7.96

10.71   About 12% of the acid in a 0.10 M solution of a weak acid dissociates to form ions. What are the H_3O^+ and OH^- concentrations? What is the pH of the solution?

BUFFERS

10.72   What are the two components of a buffer system? How does a buffer work to hold pH nearly constant?

10.73   Which system would you expect to be a better buffer: $HNO_3 + Na^+NO_3^-$, or $CH_3CO_2H + CH_3CO_2^-Na^+$? Explain.

10.74   The pH of a buffer solution containing 0.10 M acetic acid and 0.10 M sodium acetate is 4.74.

(a) Write the Henderson–Hasselbalch equation for this buffer.
(b) Write the equations for reaction of this buffer with a small amount of HNO_3 and with a small amount of NaOH.

10.75   Which of the following buffer systems would you use if you wanted to prepare a solution having a pH of approximately 9.5?

(a) 0.08 M $H_2PO_4^-$ / 0.12 M HPO_4^{2-}
(b) 0.08 M NH_4^+ / 0.12 M NH_3

10.76   What is the pH of a buffer system that contains 0.200 M hydrocyanic acid (HCN) and 0.150 M sodium cyanide (NaCN)? The pK_a of hydrocyanic acid is 9.31.

10.77   Consider 1.00 L of the buffer system described in Problem 10.76.

(a) What are the $[HCN]$ and $[CN^-]$ after 0.020 mol of HCl is added? What is the pH?
(b) What are the $[HCN]$ and $[CN^-]$ after 0.020 mol of NaOH is added? What is the pH?

10.78   What is the pH of a buffer system that contains 0.15 M NH_4^+ and 0.10 M NH_3? The pK_a of NH_4^+ is 9.25.

10.79   How many moles of NaOH must be added to 1.00 L of the solution described in Problem 10.78 to increase the pH to 9.25? (Hint: What is the $[NH_3]/[NH_4^+]$ when the pH = pK_a?)

CONCENTRATIONS OF ACID AND BASE SOLUTIONS

10.80   What does it mean when we talk about acid *equivalents* and base *equivalents*?

10.81   How does normality compare to molarity for monoprotic and polyprotic acids??

10.82   Calculate the gram-equivalent for each of the following acids and bases.

(a) HNO_3 (b) H_3PO_4 (c) KOH   (d) $Mg(OH)_2$

10.83   What mass of each of the acids and bases in Problem 10.82 is needed to prepare 500 mL of 0.15 N solution?

10.84   How many milliliters of 0.0050 N KOH are required to neutralize 25 mL of 0.0050 N H_2SO_4? To neutralize 25 mL of 0.0050 M H_2SO_4?

10.85   How many equivalents are in 75.0 mL of 0.12 M H_2SO_4 solution? In 75.0 mL of a 0.12 M H_3PO_4 solution?

10.86   How many equivalents of an acid or base are in the following?

(a) 0.25 mol $Mg(OH)_2$
(b) 2.5 g $Mg(OH)_2$
(c) 15 g CH_3CO_2H

10.87   What mass of citric acid (triprotic, $C_6H_5O_7H_3$) contains 152 mEq of citric acid?

10.88   What are the molarity and the normality of a solution made by dissolving 5.0 g of $Ca(OH)_2$ in enough water to make 500.0 mL of solution?

10.89   What are the molarity and the normality of a solution made by dissolving 25 g of citric acid (triprotic, $C_6H_5O_7H_3$) in enough water to make 800 mL of solution?

10.90 Titration of a 12.0 mL solution of HCl requires 22.4 mL of 0.12 M NaOH. What is the molarity of the HCl solution?

10.91 How many equivalents are in 15.0 mL of 0.12 M $Ba(OH)_2$ solution? What volume of 0.085 M HNO_3 is required to reach the end point when titrating 15.0 mL of this solution?

10.92 Titration of a 10.0 mL solution of KOH requires 15.0 mL of 0.0250 M H_2SO_4 solution. What is the molarity of the KOH solution?

10.93 If 35.0 mL of a 0.100 N acid solution is needed to reach the end point in titration of 21.5 mL of a base solution, what is the normality of the base solution?

CHEMISTRY IN ACTION

10.94 The concentration of HCl when released to the stomach cavity is diluted to between 0.01 and 0.001 M [*GERD—Too Much Acid or Not Enough? p. 299*]

  (a) What is the pH range in the stomach cavity?

  (b) Write a balanced equation for the neutralization of stomach acid by $NaHCO_3$.

  (c) How many grams of $NaHCO_3$ are required to neutralize 15.0 mL of a solution having a pH of 1.8?

10.95 What are the functions of the acidic gastric juices in the stomach? [*GERD—Too Much Acid or Not Enough? p. 299*]

10.96 Metabolic acidosis is often treated by administering bicarbonate intravenously. Explain how this treatment can increase blood serum pH. [*Buffers in the Body: Acidosis and Alkalosis, p. 312*]

10.97 Which body fluid is most acidic? Which is most basic? [*Buffers in the Body: Acidosis and Alkalosis, p. 312*]

10.98 Rain typically has a pH of about 5.6. What is the H_3O^+ concentration in rain? [*Acid Rain, p. 320*]

10.99 Acid rain with a pH as low as 1.5 has been recorded in West Virginia. [*Acid Rain, p. 320*]

  (a) What is the H_3O^+ concentration in this acid rain?

  (b) How many grams of HNO_3 must be dissolved to make 25 L of solution that has a pH of 1.5?

GENERAL QUESTIONS AND PROBLEMS

10.100 A solution is prepared by bubbling 15.0 L of $HCl(g)$ at 25 °C and 1 atm into 250.0 mL of water.

  (a) Assuming all the HCl dissolves in the water, how many moles of HCl are in solution?

  (b) What is the pH of the solution?

10.101 The dissociation of water into H_3O^+ and OH^- ions depends on temperature. At 0 °C the $[H_3O^+] = 3.38 \times 10^{-8}$ M, at 25 °C the $[H_3O^+] = 1.00 \times 10^{-7}$ M, and at 50 °C the $[H_3O^+] = 2.34 \times 10^{-7}$ M.

  (a) Calculate the pH of water at 0 °C and 50 °C.

  (b) What is the value of K_w at 0 °C and 50 °C?

  (c) Is the dissociation of water endothermic or exothermic?

10.102 Alka-Seltzer™, a drugstore antacid, contains a mixture of $NaHCO_3$, aspirin, and citric acid, $C_6H_5O_7H_3$. Why does Alka-Seltzer™ foam and bubble when dissolved in water? Which ingredient is the antacid?

10.103 How many milliliters of 0.50 M NaOH solution are required to titrate 40.0 mL of a 0.10 M H_2SO_4 solution to an end point?

10.104 Which solution contains more acid, 50 mL of a 0.20 N HCl solution or 50 mL of a 0.20 N acetic acid solution? Which has a higher hydronium ion concentration? Which has a lower pH?

10.105 One of the buffer systems used to control the pH of blood involves the equilibrium between $H_2PO_4^-$ and HPO_4^{2-}. The pK_a for $H_2PO_4^-$ is 7.21.

  (a) Write the Henderson–Hasselbalch equation for this buffer system.

  (b) What HPO_4^{2-} to $H_2PO_4^-$ ratio is needed to maintain the optimum blood pH of 7.40?

10.106 A 0.15 N solution of HCl is used to titrate 30.0 mL of a $Ca(OH)_2$ solution of unknown concentration. If 140.0 mL of HCl is required, what is the normality of the $Ca(OH)_2$ solution? What is the molarity?

10.107 Which of the following combinations produces an effective buffer solution? Assuming equal concentrations of each acid and its conjugate base, calculate the pH of each buffer solution.

  (a) NaF and HF   (b) $HClO_4$ and $NaClO_4$

  (c) NH_4Cl and NH_3 (d) KBr and HBr

10.108 One method of analyzing ammonium salts is to treat them with NaOH and then heat the solution to remove the NH_3 gas formed.

$$NH_4^+(aq) + OH^-(aq) \longrightarrow NH_3(g) + H_2O(l)$$

  (a) Label the Brønsted–Lowry acid–base pairs.

  (b) If 2.86 L of NH_3 at 60 °C and 755 mmHg is produced by the reaction of NH_4Cl, how many grams of NH_4Cl were in the original sample?

10.109 One method of reducing acid rain is "scrubbing" the combustion products before they are emitted from power plant smoke stacks. The process involves addition of an aqueous suspension of lime (CaO) to the combustion chamber and stack, where the lime reacts with SO_2 to give calcium sulfite ($CaSO_3$):

$$CaO(aq) + SO_2(g) \longrightarrow CaSO_3(aq)$$

  (a) How much lime (in g) is needed to remove 1 mol of SO_2?

  (b) How much lime (in kg) is needed to remove 1 kg of SO_2?

10.110 Sodium oxide, Na_2O, reacts with water to give NaOH.

  (a) Write a balanced equation for the reaction.

  (b) What is the pH of the solution prepared by allowing 1.55 g of Na_2O to react with 500.0 mL of water? Assume that there is no volume change.

  (c) How many milliliters of 0.0100 M HCl are needed to neutralize the NaOH solution prepared in (b)?

Nuclear Chemistry

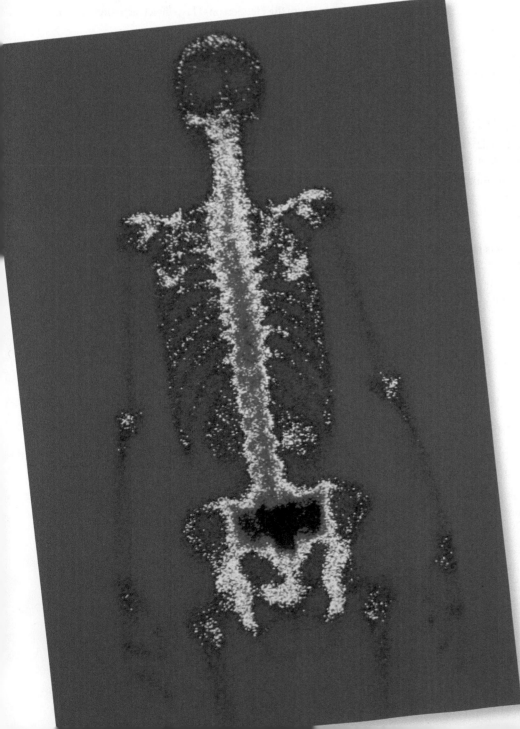

CONTENTS

◄ Many medical diagnostic techniques, including this total body bone scan, take advantage of the properties of radioactive isotopes.

1. **What is a nuclear reaction, and how are equations for nuclear reactions balanced?**
    THE GOAL: Be able to write and balance equations for nuclear reactions. (◀◀ A, B, C.)

2. **What are the different kinds of radioactivity?**
    THE GOAL: Be able to list the characteristics of three common kinds of radiation—α, β, and γ (alpha, beta, and gamma).

3. **How are the rates of nuclear reactions expressed?**
    THE GOAL: Be able to explain half-life and calculate the quantity of a radioisotope remaining after a given number of half-lives.

4. **What is ionizing radiation?**
    THE GOAL: Be able to describe the properties of the different types of ionizing radiation and their potential for harm to living tissue.

5. **How is radioactivity measured?**
    THE GOAL: Be able to describe the common units for measuring radiation.

6. **What is transmutation?**
    THE GOAL: Be able to explain nuclear bombardment and balance equations for nuclear bombardment reactions. (◀◀ A, B, and C.)

7. **What are nuclear fission and nuclear fusion?**
    THE GOAL: Be able to explain nuclear fission and nuclear fusion.

In all of the reactions we have discussed thus far, only the *bonds* between atoms have changed; the chemical identities of atoms themselves have remained unchanged. Anyone who reads the paper or watches television knows, however, that atoms *can* change, often resulting in the conversion of one element into another. Atomic weapons, nuclear energy, and radioactive radon gas in our homes are all topics of societal importance, and all involve *nuclear chemistry*—the study of the properties and reactions of atomic nuclei.

11.1 Nuclear Reactions

Recall from Section 2.2 that an atom is characterized by its *atomic number, Z*, and its *mass number, A*. The atomic number, written below and to the left of the element symbol, gives the number of protons in the nucleus and identifies the element. The mass number, written above and to the left of the element symbol, gives the total number of **nucleons**, a general term for both protons (p) and neutrons (n). The most common isotope of carbon, for example, has 12 nucleons: 6 protons and 6 neutrons: $^{12}_{6}C$.

Nucleon A general term for both protons and neutrons.

Mass number $\longrightarrow$ $^{12}_{6}C$ $\longleftarrow$ Atomic number
Carbon-12

6 protons
6 neutrons
12 nucleons

Atoms with identical atomic numbers but different mass numbers are called *isotopes*, and the nucleus of a specific isotope is called a **nuclide**. Thirteen isotopes of carbon are known—two occur commonly (^{12}C and ^{13}C) and one (^{14}C) is produced in small amounts in the upper atmosphere by the action of neutrons from cosmic rays on ^{14}N. The remaining 10 carbon isotopes have been produced artificially. Only the two commonly occurring isotopes are stable indefinitely; the others undergo spontaneous **nuclear reactions**, which change their nuclei. Carbon-14, for example, is an unstable isotope that slowly decomposes and is converted to nitrogen-14 plus an electron, a process we can write as

$$^{14}_{6}C \longrightarrow ^{14}_{7}N + ^{0}_{-1}e$$

▶▶ The different isotopes of an atom each have the same number of protons and only differ in their number of neutrons (Section 2.3).

Nuclide The nucleus of a specific isotope of an element.

Nuclear reaction A reaction that changes an atomic nucleus, usually causing the change of one element into another.

The electron is often written as $^{0}_{-1}e$, where the superscript 0 indicates that the mass of an electron is essentially zero when compared with that of a proton or neutron, and the subscript −1 indicates that the charge is −1. (The subscript in this instance is not a true atomic number; in Section 11.4 the purpose of representing the electron this way will become clear.)

Nuclear reactions, such as the spontaneous decay of ^{14}C, are distinguished from chemical reactions in several ways:

- A *nuclear* reaction involves a change in an atom's nucleus, usually producing a different element. A *chemical* reaction, by contrast, involves only a change in distribution of the outer-shell electrons around the atom and never changes the nucleus itself or produces a different element.
- Different isotopes of an element have essentially the same behavior in chemical reactions but often have completely different behavior in nuclear reactions.
- The rate of a nuclear reaction is unaffected by a change in temperature or pressure or by the addition of a catalyst.
- The nuclear reaction of an atom is essentially the same whether it is in a chemical compound or in an uncombined, elemental form.
- The energy change accompanying a nuclear reaction can be up to several million times greater than that accompanying a chemical reaction. The nuclear transformation of 1.0 g of uranium-235 releases 3.4×10^8 kcal (1.4×10^9 kJ), for example, whereas the chemical combustion of 1.0 g of methane releases only 12 kcal (50 kJ).

11.2 The Discovery and Nature of Radioactivity

The discovery of *radioactivity* dates to the year 1896 when the French physicist Henri Becquerel made a remarkable observation. While investigating the nature of phosphorescence—the luminous glow of some minerals and other substances that remains when the light is suddenly turned off—Becquerel happened to place a sample of a uranium-containing mineral on top of a photographic plate that had been wrapped in black paper and put in a drawer to protect it from sunlight. On developing the plate, Becquerel was surprised to find a silhouette of the mineral. He concluded that the mineral was producing some kind of unknown radiation, which passed through the paper and exposed the photographic plate.

Radioactivity The spontaneous emission of radiation from a nucleus.

Marie Sklodowska Curie and her husband, Pierre, took up the challenge and began a series of investigations into this new phenomenon, which they termed **radioactivity**. They found that the source of the radioactivity was the element uranium (U) and that two previously unknown elements, which they named polonium (Po) and radium (Ra), were also radioactive. For these achievements, Becquerel and the Curies shared the 1903 Nobel Prize in physics.

Further work on radioactivity by the English scientist Ernest Rutherford established that there were at least two types of radiation, which he named *alpha* (α) and *beta* (β) after the first two letters of the Greek alphabet. Shortly thereafter, a third type of radiation was found and named for the third Greek letter, *gamma* (γ).

Subsequent studies showed that when the three kinds of radiation are passed between two plates with opposite electrical charges, each is affected differently. Alpha radiation bends toward the negative plate and must therefore have a positive charge. Beta radiation, by contrast, bends toward the positive plate and must have a negative charge, whereas gamma radiation does not bend toward either plate and has no charge (Figure 11.1).

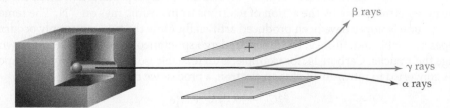

▲ **Figure 11.1**
The effect of an electric field on α, β, and γ, radiation.
The radioactive source in the shielded box emits radiation, which passes between the two electrically charged plates. Alpha radiation is deflected toward the negative plate, β radiation is deflected toward the positive plate, and γ radiation is not deflected.

Another difference among the three kinds of radiation soon became apparent when it was discovered that alpha and beta radiations are composed of small particles with a measurable mass, whereas **gamma (γ) radiation** consists of high-energy electromagnetic waves and has no mass. Rutherford was able to show that a **beta (β) particle** is an electron (e^-) and that an **alpha (α) particle** is actually a helium nucleus, He^{2+}. (Recall that a helium *atom* consists of two protons, two neutrons, and two electrons. When the two electrons are removed, the remaining helium nucleus, or α particle, has only the two protons and two neutrons.)

Yet a third difference among the three kinds of radiation is their penetrating power. Because of their relatively large mass, α particles move slowly (up to about $1/10$ the speed of light) and can be stopped by a few sheets of paper or by the top layer of skin. Beta particles, because they are much lighter, move at up to $9/10$ the speed of light and have about 100 times the penetrating power of α particles. A block of wood or heavy protective clothing is necessary to stop β radiation, which can otherwise penetrate the skin and cause burns and other damage. Gamma rays move at the speed of light (3.00×10^8 m/s) and have about 1000 times the penetrating power of α particles. A lead block several inches thick is needed to stop γ radiation, which can otherwise penetrate and damage the body's internal organs.

The characteristics of the three kinds of radiation are summarized in Table 11.1. Note that an α particle, even though it is an ion with a $+2$ charge, is usually written using the symbol ^4_2He without the charge. A β particle is usually written $^0_{-1}e$, as noted previously.

Gamma (γ) radiation Radioactivity consisting of high-energy light waves.

▶▶▶ See Chemistry in Action: Atoms and Light on p. 66 in Chapter 2 for a discussion of gamma rays and the rest of the electromagnetic spectrum.

Beta (β) particle An electron (e^-), emitted as radiation.

Alpha (α) particle A helium nucleus (He^{2+}), emitted as α radiation.

TABLE 11.1 Characteristics of α, β, and γ Radiation

Type of Radiation	Symbol	Charge	Composition	Mass (AMU)	Velocity	Relative Penetrating Power
Alpha	α, ^4_2He	$+2$	Helium nucleus	4	Up to 10% speed of light	Low (1)
Beta	β, $^0_{-1}e$	-1	Electron	1/1823	Up to 90% speed of light	Medium (100)
Gamma	γ, $^0_0\gamma$	0	High-energy radiation	0	Speed of light (3.00×10^8 m/s)	High (1000)

11.3 Stable and Unstable Isotopes

Every element in the periodic table has at least one radioactive isotope, or **radioisotope**, and more than 3300 radioisotopes are known. Their radioactivity is the result of having unstable nuclei, although the exact causes of this instability are not fully understood. Radiation is emitted when an unstable radioactive nucleus, or **radionuclide**, spontaneously changes into a more stable one.

For elements in the first few rows of the periodic table, stability is associated with a roughly equal number of neutrons and protons (Figure 11.2). Hydrogen, for example, has stable ^1_1H (protium) and ^2_1H (deuterium) isotopes, but its ^3_1H isotope (tritium) is radioactive. As elements get heavier, the number of neutrons relative to protons in stable nuclei increases. Lead-208 ($^{208}_{82}Pb$), for example, the most abundant stable isotope of lead, has 126 neutrons and 82 protons in its nuclei. Nevertheless, of the 35 known isotopes of lead, only 3 are stable whereas 32 are radioactive. In fact, there are only 264 stable isotopes among all the elements. All isotopes of elements with atomic numbers higher than that of bismuth (83) are radioactive.

Most of the more than 3300 known radioisotopes have been made in high-energy particle accelerators by reactions that will be described in Section 11.10. Such isotopes are called *artificial radioisotopes* because they are not found in nature. All isotopes of the transuranium elements (those heavier than uranium) are artificial. The much smaller number of radioactive isotopes found in Earth's crust, such as $^{238}_{92}U$, are called *natural radioisotopes*.

Radioisotope A radioactive isotope.

Radionuclide The nucleus of a radioactive isotope.

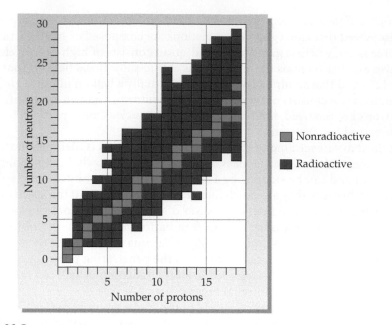

▲ **Figure 11.2**
A plot of the numbers of neutrons and protons for known isotopes of the first 18 elements.
Stable (nonradioactive) isotopes of these elements have equal or nearly equal numbers of neutrons and protons.

Aside from their radioactivity, different radioisotopes of the same element have the same chemical properties as stable isotopes, which accounts for their great usefulness as *tracers*. A chemical compound tagged with a radioactive atom undergoes exactly the same reactions as its nonradioactive counterpart. The difference is that the tagged compound can be located with a radiation detector and its location determined, as discussed in Chemistry in Action: Body Imaging on page 348.

11.4 Nuclear Decay

Think for a minute about the consequences of α and β radiation. If radioactivity involves the spontaneous emission of a small particle from an unstable atomic nucleus, then the nucleus itself must undergo a change. With that understanding of radioactivity came the startling discovery that atoms of one element can change into atoms of another element, something that had previously been thought impossible. The spontaneous emission of a particle from an unstable nucleus is called **nuclear decay**, or *radioactive decay*, and the resulting change of one element into another is called **transmutation**.

> **Nuclear decay:** Radioactive element $\longrightarrow$ New element $+$ Emitted particle

We now look at what happens to a nucleus when nuclear decay occurs.

Alpha Emission

When an atom of uranium-238 ($^{238}_{92}$U) emits an α particle, the nucleus loses 2 protons and 2 neutrons. Because the number of protons in the nucleus has now changed from 92 to 90, the *identity* of the atom has changed from uranium to thorium. Furthermore, since the total number of nucleons has decreased by 4, uranium-238 has become thorium-234 ($^{234}_{90}$Th) (Figure 11.3).

Note that the equation for a nuclear reaction is not balanced in the usual chemical sense because the kinds of atoms are not the same on both sides of the arrow. Instead, we say that a nuclear equation is balanced when the number of nucleons on both sides of the equation is the same and when the sums of the charges on the nuclei plus any ejected subatomic particles (protons or electrons) are the same on both sides of the

Nuclear decay The spontaneous emission of a particle from an unstable nucleus.

Transmutation The change of one element into another.

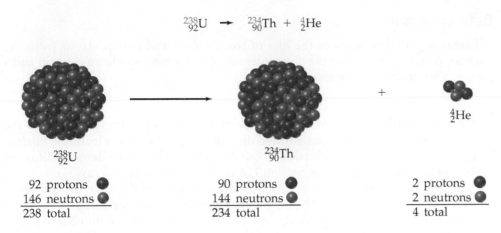

$$^{238}_{92}U \longrightarrow {}^{234}_{90}Th + {}^{4}_{2}He$$

$^{238}_{92}U$	$^{234}_{90}Th$	$^{4}_{2}He$
92 protons	90 protons	2 protons
146 neutrons	144 neutrons	2 neutrons
238 total	234 total	4 total

◀ **Figure 11.3**
Alpha emission.
Emission of an α particle from an atom of uranium-238 produces an atom of thorium-234.

equation. In the decay of $^{238}_{92}U$ to give $^{4}_{2}He$ and $^{234}_{90}Th$, for example, there are 238 nucleons and 92 nuclear charges on both sides of the nuclear equation.

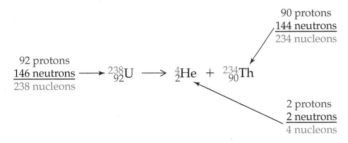

Worked Example 11.1 Balancing Nuclear Reactions: Alpha Emission

Polonium-208 is one of the α emitters studied by Marie Curie. Write the equation for the α decay of polonium-208, and identify the element formed.

ANALYSIS Look up the atomic number of polonium (84) in the periodic table, and write the known part of the nuclear equation, using the standard symbol for polonium-208:

$$^{208}_{84}Po \longrightarrow {}^{4}_{2}He + ?$$

Then, calculate the mass number and atomic number of the product element, and write the final equation.

SOLUTION
The mass number of the product is $208 - 4 = 204$, and the atomic number is $84 - 2 = 82$. A look at the periodic table identifies the element with atomic number 82 as lead (Pb).

$$^{208}_{84}Po \longrightarrow {}^{4}_{2}He + {}^{204}_{82}Pb$$

Check your answer by making sure that the mass numbers and atomic numbers on the two sides of the equation are balanced:

Mass numbers: $208 = 4 + 204$ Atomic numbers: $84 = 2 + 82$

PROBLEM 11.1
High levels of radioactive radon-222 $\left({}^{222}_{86}Rn\right)$ have been found in many homes built on radium-containing rock, leading to the possibility of health hazards. What product results from α emission by radon-222?

PROBLEM 11.2
What isotope of radium (Ra) is converted into radon-222 by α emission?

Beta Emission

Whereas α emission leads to the loss of two protons and two neutrons from the nucleus, β emission involves the *decomposition* of a neutron to yield an electron and a proton. This process can be represented as

$$\,^1_0\text{n} \longrightarrow \,^1_1\text{p} + \,^{\ 0}_{-1}\text{e}$$

where the electron ($\,^{\ 0}_{-1}\text{e}$) is ejected as a β particle, and the proton is retained by the nucleus. Note that the electrons emitted during β radiation come from the *nucleus* and not from the occupied orbitals surrounding the nucleus. The decomposition of carbon-14 to form nitrogen-14 in Section 11.1 is an example of beta decay.

The net result of β emission is that the atomic number of the atom *increases* by 1 because there is a new proton. The mass number of the atom remains the same, however, because a neutron has changed into a proton, leaving the total number of nucleons unchanged. For example, iodine-131 ($\,^{131}_{53}\text{I}$), a radioisotope used in detecting thyroid problems, undergoes nuclear decay by β emission to yield xenon-131 ($\,^{131}_{54}\text{Xe}$):

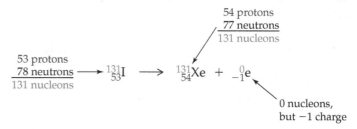

Note that the superscripts (mass numbers) are balanced in this equation because a β particle has a mass near zero, and the subscripts are balanced because a β particle has a charge of -1.

Worked Example 11.2 Balancing Nuclear Reactions: Beta Emission

Write a balanced nuclear equation for the β decay of chromium-55.

ANALYSIS Write the known part of the nuclear equation:

$$\,^{55}_{24}\text{Cr} \longrightarrow \,^{\ 0}_{-1}\text{e} + \,?$$

Then calculate the mass number and atomic number of the product element, and write the final equation.

SOLUTION
The mass number of the product stays at 55, and the atomic number increases by 1, $24 + 1 = 25$, so the product is manganese-55.

$$\,^{55}_{24}\text{Cr} \longrightarrow \,^{\ 0}_{-1}\text{e} + \,^{55}_{25}\text{Mn}$$

Check your answer by making sure that the mass numbers and atomic numbers on the two sides of the equation are balanced:

Mass numbers: $55 = 0 + 55$ Atomic numbers: $24 = -1 + 25$

PROBLEM 11.3
Strontium-89 is a short-lived β emitter often used in the treatment of bone tumors. Write a nuclear equation for the decay of strontium-89.

PROBLEM 11.4
Write nuclear equations for the formation of each of the following nuclides by β emission.

(a) $\,^3_2\text{He}$ (b) $\,^{210}_{83}\text{Bi}$ (c) $\,^{20}_{10}\text{Ne}$

Gamma Emission

Emission of γ rays, unlike the emission of α and β particles, causes no change in mass or atomic number because γ rays are simply high-energy electromagnetic waves. Although γ emission can occur alone, it usually accompanies α or β emission as a mechanism for the new nucleus that results from a transmutation to release some extra energy.

Since γ emission affects neither mass number nor atomic number, it is often omitted from nuclear equations. Nevertheless, γ rays are of great importance. Their penetrating power makes them by far the most dangerous kind of external radiation for humans and also makes them useful in numerous medical applications. Cobalt-60, for example, is used in cancer therapy as a source of penetrating γ rays that kill cancerous tissue.

$$^{60}_{27}\text{Co} \longrightarrow \, ^{60}_{28}\text{Ni} + \, ^{0}_{-1}\text{e} + \, ^{0}_{0}\gamma$$

Positron Emission

In addition to α, β, and γ radiation, there is another common type of radioactive decay process called *positron emission*, which involves the conversion of a proton in the nucleus into a neutron plus an ejected **positron**, $^{0}_{1}\text{e}$ or β^{+}. A positron, which can be thought of as a "positive electron," has the same mass as an electron but a positive charge. This process can be represented as

Positron A "positive electron," which has the same mass as an electron but a positive charge.

$$^{1}_{1}\text{p} \longrightarrow \, ^{1}_{0}\text{n} + \, ^{0}_{1}\text{e}$$

The result of positron emission is a decrease in the atomic number of the product nucleus because a proton has changed into a neutron, but no change in the mass number. Potassium-40, for example, undergoes positron emission to yield argon-40, a nuclear reaction important in geology for dating rocks. Note once again that the sum of the two subscripts on the right of the nuclear equation $(18 + 1 = 19)$ is equal to the subscript in the $^{40}_{19}\text{K}$ nucleus on the left.

19 protons
21 neutrons
40 nucleons

$$^{40}_{19}\text{K} \longrightarrow \, ^{40}_{18}\text{Ar} + \, ^{0}_{1}\text{e}$$

0 nucleons
but 1 charge

18 protons
22 neutrons
40 nucleons

Electron Capture

Electron capture, symbolized E.C., is a process in which the nucleus captures an inner-shell electron from the surrounding electron cloud, thereby converting a proton into a neutron, and energy is released in the form of gamma rays. The mass number of the product nucleus is unchanged, but the atomic number decreases by 1, just as in positron emission. The conversion of mercury-197 into gold-197 is an example:

Electron capture (E.C.) A process in which the nucleus captures an inner-shell electron from the surrounding electron cloud, thereby converting a proton into a neutron.

80 protons
117 neutrons
197 nucleons

Inner-shell
electron

79 protons
118 neutrons
197 nucleons

$$^{197}_{80}\text{Hg} + \, ^{0}_{-1}\text{e} \longrightarrow \, ^{197}_{79}\text{Au}$$

Do not plan on using this reaction to get rich, however. Mercury-197 is not one of the naturally occurring isotopes of Hg and is typically produced by transmutation reactions as discussed in Section 11.10.

In Figure 11.2 we see that most of the stable isotopes of the lighter elements have nearly the same number of neutrons and protons. With this fact in mind, we can often predict the most likely decay mode: unstable isotopes that have more protons than neutrons are more likely to undergo β decay to convert a proton to a neutron, while unstable isotopes having more neutrons than protons are more likely to undergo either positron emission or electron capture to convert a neutron to a proton. Also, the very heavy isotopes ($Z > 83$) will most likely undergo α-decay to lose both neutrons and protons to decrease the atomic number. Characteristics of the five kinds of radioactive decay processes are summarized in Table 11.2.

TABLE 11.2 A Summary of Radioactive Decay Processes

Process	Symbol	Change in Atomic Number	Change in Mass Number	Change in Number of Neutrons
α emission	^4_2He or α	-2	-4	-2
β emission	$^0_{-1}\text{e}$ or β^{-*}	$+1$	0	-1
γ emission	$^0_0\gamma$ or γ	0	0	0
Positron emission	^0_1e or β^{+*}	-1	0	$+1$
Electron capture	E.C.	-1	0	$+1$

*Superscripts are used to indicate the charge associated with the two forms of beta decay; β^-, or a beta particle, carries a -1 charge, while β^+, or a positron, carries a $+1$ charge.

Worked Example 11.3 Balancing Nuclear Reactions: Electron Capture, Positron Emission

Write balanced nuclear equations for the following processes:

(a) Electron capture by polonium-204: $^{204}_{84}\text{Po} + ^0_{-1}\text{e} \longrightarrow$?

(b) Positron emission from xenon-118: $^{118}_{54}\text{Xe} \longrightarrow ^0_1\text{e} +$?

ANALYSIS The key to writing nuclear equations is to make sure that the number of nucleons is the same on both sides of the equation and that the number of charges is the same.

SOLUTION

(a) In electron capture, the mass number is unchanged and the atomic number decreases by 1, giving bismuth-204: $^{204}_{84}\text{Po} + ^0_{-1}\text{e} \longrightarrow ^{204}_{83}\text{Bi}$.

Check your answer by making sure that the number of nucleons and the number of charges are the same on both sides of the equation:

Mass number: $204 + 0 = 204$ Atomic number: $84 + (-1) = 83$

(b) In positron emission, the mass number is unchanged and the atomic number decreases by 1, giving iodine-118: $^{118}_{54}\text{Xe} \longrightarrow ^0_1\text{e} + ^{118}_{53}\text{I}$.

CHECK! Mass number: $118 = 0 + 118$ Atomic number: $54 = 1 + 53$

PROBLEM 11.5

Write nuclear equations for positron emission from the following radioisotopes:

(a) $^{38}_{20}\text{Ca}$ (b) $^{118}_{54}\text{Xe}$ (c) $^{79}_{37}\text{Rb}$

PROBLEM 11.6

Write nuclear equations for the formation of the following radioisotopes by electron capture:

(a) $^{62}_{29}\text{Cu}$ (b) $^{110}_{49}\text{In}$ (c) $^{81}_{35}\text{Br}$

KEY CONCEPT PROBLEM 11.7

The red arrow in this graph indicates the changes that occur in the nucleus of an atom during a nuclear reaction. Identify the isotopes involved as product and reactant, and name the type of decay process.

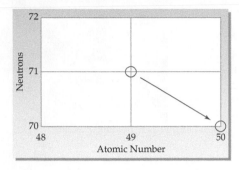

11.5 Radioactive Half-Life

The rate of radioactive decay varies greatly from one radioisotope to another. Some radioisotopes, such as uranium-238, decay at a barely perceptible rate over billions of years, but others, such as carbon-17, decay within thousandths of a second.

Rates of nuclear decay are measured in units of **half-life ($t_{1/2}$)**, defined as the amount of time required for one-half of a radioactive sample to decay. For example, the half-life of iodine-131 is 8.021 days. If today you have 1.000 g of $^{131}_{53}I$, then 8.021 days from now you will have only 50% of that amount (0.500 g) because one-half of the sample will have decayed into $^{131}_{54}Xe$. After 8.021 more days (16.063 days total), you will have only 25% (0.250 g) of your original $^{131}_{53}I$ sample; after another 8.021 days (24.084 days total), you will have only 12.5% (0.125 g); and so on. Each passage of a half-life causes the decay of one-half of whatever sample remains. The half-life of any particular isotope is the same no matter what the size of the sample, the temperature, or any other external conditions. There is no known way to slow down, speed up, or otherwise change the characteristics of radioactive decay.

Half-life ($t_{1/2}$) The amount of time required for one-half of a radioactive sample to decay.

$$1.000 \text{ g } ^{131}_{53}I \xrightarrow[\text{days}]{8} 0.500 \text{ g } ^{131}_{53}I \xrightarrow[\text{days}]{8} 0.250 \text{ g } ^{131}_{53}I \xrightarrow[\text{days}]{8} 0.125 \text{ g } ^{131}_{53}I \longrightarrow$$

	One half-life	Two half-lives (16 days total)	Three half-lives (24 days total)
100%	50% remaining	25% remaining	12.5% remaining

The fraction of radioisotope remaining after the passage of each half-life is represented by the curve in Figure 11.4 and can be calculated as

$$\text{fraction remaining} = (0.5)^n$$

where n is the number of half-lives that have elapsed.

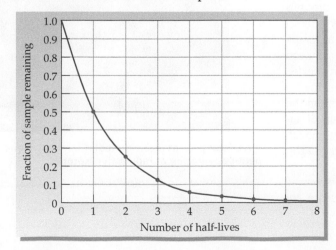

◄ **Figure 11.4**
The decay of a radioactive nucleus over time.
All nuclear decays follow this curve, whether the half-lives are measured in years, days, minutes, or seconds. That is, the fraction of sample remaining after one half-life is 0.50, the fraction remaining after two half-lives is 0.25, the fraction remaining after three half-lives is 0.125, and so on.

CHEMISTRY IN ACTION

Medical Uses of Radioactivity

The origins of nuclear medicine date from 1901, when the French physician Henri Danlos first used radium in the treatment of a tubercular skin lesion. Since that time, the use of radioactivity has become a crucial part of modern medical care, both diagnostic and therapeutic. Current nuclear techniques can be grouped into three classes: (1) *in vivo* procedures, (2) radiation therapy, and (3) imaging procedures. The first two are described here, and the third one is described on page 348 in the Chemistry in Action: Body Imaging.

In Vivo Procedures

In vivo studies—those that take place inside the body—are carried out to assess the functioning of a particular organ or body system. A *radiopharmaceutical* agent is administered, and its path in the body—whether absorbed, excreted, diluted, or concentrated—is determined by analysis of blood or urine samples.

Among the many *in vivo* procedures utilizing radioactive agents is a simple method for the determination of whole-blood volume, a common indicator used in the diagnosis of congestive heart failure, hypertension, and renal failure. A known quantity of red blood cells labeled with radioactive chromium-51 is injected into the patient and allowed to circulate to be distributed evenly throughout the body. After a suitable interval, a blood sample is taken and blood volume is calculated by comparing the concentration of labeled cells in the blood with the quantity of labeled cells injected. This and similar procedures are known as *isotope dilution* and are described by

$$R_{sample} = R_{tracer}\left(\frac{W_{sample}}{W_{system} + W_{tracer}}\right)$$

where R_{sample} is the counting rate (a measure of radioactivity) of the analyzed sample, R_{tracer} is the counting rate of the tracer added to the system, and W refers to either the mass or volume of the analyzed sample, added tracer, or total system as indicated.

Therapeutic Procedures

Therapeutic procedures—those in which radiation is purposely used as a weapon to kill diseased tissue—involve either external or internal sources of radiation. External radiation therapy for the treatment of cancer is often carried out with γ rays emanating from a cobalt-60 source. The highly radioactive source is shielded by a thick lead container and has a small opening directed toward the site of the tumor. By focusing the radiation beam on the tumor, the tumor receives the full exposure while exposure of surrounding parts of the body is minimized. Nevertheless, enough healthy tissue is affected so that most patients treated in this manner suffer the effects of radiation sickness.

Internal radiation therapy is a much more selective technique than external therapy. In the treatment of thyroid disease, for

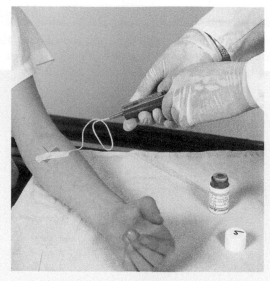

▲ **A person's blood volume can be found by injecting a small amount of radioactive chromium-51 and measuring the dilution factor.**

example, a radioactive substance such as iodine-131 is administered. This powerful β emitter is incorporated into the iodine-containing hormone thyroxine, which concentrates in the thyroid gland. Because β particles penetrate no farther than several millimeters, the localized ^{131}I produces a high radiation dose that destroys only the surrounding diseased tissue. To treat some tumors, such as those in the female reproductive system, a radioactive source is placed physically close to the tumor for a specific amount of time.

Boron neutron-capture therapy (BNCT) is a relatively new technique in which boron-containing drugs are administered to a patient and concentrate in the tumor site. The tumor is then irradiated with a neutron beam from a nuclear reactor. The boron absorbs a neutron and undergoes transmutation to produce an alpha particle and a lithium nucleus. These highly energetic particles have very low penetrating power and can kill nearby tumor tissue while sparing the healthy surrounding tissue. Because one disadvantage of BNCT is the need for access to a nuclear reactor, this treatment is available only in limited locations.

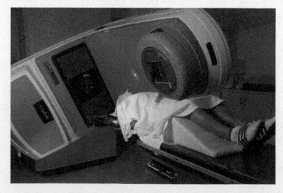

▲ **A cancer patient receiving radiotherapy treatments, a therapeutic application of radioactive isotopes.**

See Chemistry in Action Problems 11.70 and 11.71 at the end of the chapter.

One of the better known half-life applications is radiocarbon dating to determine the age of archaeological artifacts. The method is based on the slow and constant production of radioactive carbon-14 atoms in the upper atmosphere by bombardment of nitrogen atoms with neutrons from cosmic rays. Carbon-14 atoms combine with oxygen to yield $^{14}CO_2$, which slowly mixes with ordinary $^{12}CO_2$ and is then taken up by plants during photosynthesis. When these plants are eaten by animals, carbon-14 enters the food chain and is distributed evenly throughout all living organisms.

As long as a plant or animal is living, a dynamic equilibrium is established in which the organism excretes or exhales the same amount of ^{14}C that it takes in. As a result, the ratio of ^{14}C to ^{12}C in the living organism is the same as that in the atmosphere—about 1 part in 10^{12}. When the plant or animal dies, however, it no longer takes in more ^{14}C. Thus, the $^{14}C/^{12}C$ ratio in the organism slowly decreases as ^{14}C undergoes radioactive decay. At 5730 years (one ^{14}C half-life) after the death of the organism, the $^{14}C/^{12}C$ ratio has decreased by a factor of 2; at 11,460 years after death, the $^{14}C/^{12}C$ ratio has decreased by a factor of 4; and so on. By measuring the amount of ^{14}C remaining in the traces of any once-living organism, archaeologists can determine how long ago the organism died. The accuracy of the technique lessens as a sample gets older, but artifacts with an age of 1000–20,000 years can be dated with reasonable accuracy.

The half-lives of some useful radioisotopes are given in Table 11.3. As you might expect, radioisotopes that are used internally for medical applications have fairly short half-lives so that they decay rapidly and do not remain in the body for prolonged periods.

TABLE 11.3 Half-Lives of Some Useful Radioisotopes

Radioisotope	Symbol	Radiation	Half-Life	Use
Tritium	^3_1H	β	12.33 years	Biochemical tracer
Carbon-14	$^{14}_6C$	β	5730 years	Archaeological dating
Sodium-24	$^{24}_{11}Na$	β	14.959 hours	Examining circulation
Phosphorus-32	$^{32}_{15}P$	β	14.262 days	Leukemia therapy
Potassium-40	$^{40}_{19}K$	β, β^+	1.277×10^9 years	Geological dating
Cobalt-60	$^{60}_{27}Co$	β, γ	5.271 years	Cancer therapy
Arsenic-74	$^{74}_{33}As$	β^+	17.77 days	Locating brain tumors
Technetium-99m*	$^{99m}_{43}Tc$	γ	6.01 hours	Brain scans
Iodine 131	$^{131}_{53}I$	β	8.021 days	Thyroid therapy
Uranium-235	$^{235}_{92}U$	α, γ	7.038×10^8 years	Nuclear reactors

*The *m* in technetium-99m stands for *metastable*, meaning that the nucleus undergoes γ emission but does not change its mass number or atomic number.

Worked Example 11.4 Nuclear Reactions: Half-Life

Phosphorus-32, a radioisotope used in leukemia therapy, has a half-life of about 14 days. Approximately what percentage of a sample remains after 8 weeks?

ANALYSIS Determine how many half-lives have elapsed. For an integral number of half-lives, we can multiply the starting amount (100%) by 1/2 for each half-life that has elapsed.

SOLUTION
Since one half-life of $^{32}_{15}P$ is 14 days (2 weeks), 8 weeks represents four half-lives. The fraction that remains after 8 weeks is thus

Four half-lives

$$\text{Final Percentage} = 100\% \times (0.5)^4 = 100\% \times \left(\tfrac{1}{2} \times \tfrac{1}{2} \times \tfrac{1}{2} \times \tfrac{1}{2}\right)$$
$$= 100\% \times \tfrac{1}{16} = 6.25\%$$

Worked Example 11.5 Nuclear Reactions: Half-Life

As noted in Table 11.3, iodine-131 has a half-life of about 8 days. Approximately what fraction of a sample remains after 20 days?

ANALYSIS Determine how many half-lives have elapsed. For a non-integral number (i.e., fraction) of half-lives, use the equation below to determine the fraction of radioisotope remaining.

$$\text{fraction remaining} = (0.5)^n$$

BALLPARK ESTIMATE Since the half-life of iodine-131 is 8 days, an elapsed time of 20 days is 2.5 half-lives. The fraction remaining should be between 0.25 (fraction remaining after two half-lives) and 0.125 (fraction remaining after three half-lives). Since the relationship between the number of half-lives and fraction remaining is not linear (see Figure 11.4), the fraction remaining will not be exactly halfway between these values but instead will be slightly closer to the lower fraction, say 0.17.

SOLUTION

$$\text{fraction remaining} = (0.5)^n = (0.5)^{2.5} = 0.177$$

BALLPARK CHECK The fraction remaining is close to our estimate of 0.17.

PROBLEM 11.8

The half-life of carbon-14, an isotope used in archaeological dating, is 5730 years. What percentage of $^{14}_{6}C$ remains in a sample estimated to be 17,000 years old?

PROBLEM 11.9

A 1.00 mL sample of red blood cells containing chromium-51 as a tracer was injected into a patient. After several hours a 5.00 mL sample of blood was drawn and its activity compared to the activity of the injected tracer sample. If the collected sample activity was 0.10% of the original tracer, calculate the total blood volume of the patient (see Chemistry in Action: Medical Uses of Radioactivity, p. 338).

KEY CONCEPT PROBLEM 11.10

What is the half-life of the radionuclide that shows the following decay curve?

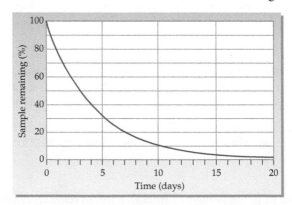

11.6 Radioactive Decay Series

When a radioactive isotope decays, nuclear change occurs and a different element is formed. Often, this newly formed nucleus is stable, but sometimes the product nucleus is itself radioactive and undergoes further decay. In fact, some radioactive nuclei undergo an extended **decay series** of nuclear disintegrations before they ultimately reach a nonradioactive product. This is particularly true for the isotopes of heavier elements. Uranium-238, for example, undergoes a series of 14 sequential nuclear reactions, ultimately stopping at lead-206 (Figure 11.5).

Decay series A sequential series of nuclear disintegrations leading from a heavy radioisotope to a non-radioactive product.

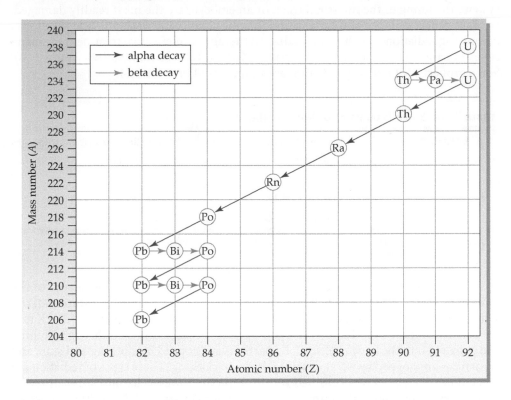

◄ **Figure 11.5**
The decay series from $^{238}_{92}U$ to $^{206}_{82}Pb$. Each isotope except for the last is radioactive and undergoes nuclear decay. The long slanted arrows represent α emissions, and the short horizontal arrows represent β emissions.

One of the intermediate radionuclides in the uranium-238 decay series is radium-226. Radium-226 has a half-life of 1600 years and undergoes α decay to produce radon-222, a gas. Rocks, soil, and building materials that contain radium are sources of radon-222, which can seep through cracks in basements and get into the air inside homes and other buildings. Radon itself is a gas that passes in and out of the lungs without being incorporated into body tissue. If, however, a radon-222 atom should happen to undergo alpha decay while in the lungs, the result is the solid decay product polonium-218. Further decay of the ^{218}Po emits α particles, which can damage lung tissue.

11.7 Ionizing Radiation

High-energy radiation of all kinds is often grouped together under the name **ionizing radiation**. This includes not only α particles, β particles, and γ rays but also *X rays* and *cosmic rays*. **X rays** are like γ rays; they have no mass and consist of high-energy electromagnetic radiation. The only difference between them is that the energy of X rays is somewhat less than that of γ rays (see Chemistry in Action: Atoms and Light in Chapter 2). **Cosmic rays** are not rays at all but are a mixture of high-energy particles that shower Earth from outer space. They consist primarily of protons, along with some α and β particles.

The interaction of any kind of ionizing radiation with a molecule knocks out an orbital electron, converting the atom or molecule into an extremely reactive ion:

$$\text{Molecule} \xrightarrow[\text{radiation}]{\text{ionizing}} \text{Ion} + e^-$$

This reactive ion can react with other molecules nearby, creating still other fragments that can in turn cause further reactions. In this manner, a large dose of ionizing radiation can destroy the delicate balance of chemical reactions in living cells, ultimately causing the death of an organism.

Ionizing radiation A general name for high-energy radiation of all kinds.

X rays Electromagnetic radiation with an energy somewhat less than that of γ rays.

Cosmic rays A mixture of high-energy particles—primarily of protons and various atomic nuclei—that shower Earth from outer space.

A small dose of ionizing radiation may not cause visible symptoms but can nevertheless be dangerous if it strikes a cell nucleus and damages the genetic machinery inside. The resultant changes might lead to a genetic mutation, to cancer, or to cell death. The nuclei of rapidly dividing cells, such as those in bone marrow, the lymph system, the lining of the intestinal tract, or an embryo, are the most readily damaged. Because cancer cells are also rapidly dividing they are highly susceptible to the effects of ionizing radiation, which is why radiation therapy is an effective treatment for many types of cancer (see Chemistry in Action: Medical Uses of Radioactivity on p. 338). Some properties of ionizing radiation are summarized in Table 11.4.

TABLE 11.4 Some Properties of Ionizing Radiation

Type of Radiation	Energy Range*	Penetrating Distance in Water**
α	3–9 MeV	0.02–0.04 mm
β	0–3 MeV	0–4 mm
X	100 eV–10 keV	0.01–1 cm
γ	10 keV–10 MeV	1–20 cm

* The energies of subatomic particles are often measured in electron volts (eV): 1 eV = 6.703×10^{-19} cal, or 2.805×10^{-18} J.
** Distance at which one-half of the radiation is stopped.

The effects of ionizing radiation on the human body vary with the energy of the radiation, its distance from the body, the length of exposure, and the location of the source outside or inside the body. When coming from outside the body, γ rays and X rays are potentially more harmful than α and β particles because they pass through clothing and skin and into the body's cells. Alpha particles are stopped by clothing and skin, and β particles are stopped by wood or several layers of clothing. These types of radiation are much more dangerous when emitted within the body, however, because all their radiation energy is given up to the immediately surrounding tissue. Alpha emitters are especially hazardous internally and are almost never used in medical applications.

Health professionals who work with X rays or other kinds of ionizing radiation protect themselves by surrounding the source with a thick layer of lead or other dense material. Protection from radiation is also afforded by controlling the distance between the worker and the radiation source because radiation intensity (I) decreases with the square of the distance from the source. The intensities of radiation at two different distances, 1 and 2, are given by the equation

$$\frac{I_1}{I_2} = \frac{d_2^{\,2}}{d_1^{\,2}}$$

For example, suppose a source delivers 16 units of radiation at a distance of 1.0 m. Doubling the distance to 2.0 m decreases the radiation intensity to one-fourth:

$$\frac{16 \text{ units}}{I_2} = \frac{(2\text{ m})^2}{(1\text{ m})^2}$$

$$I_2 = 16 \text{ units} \times \frac{1 \text{ m}^2}{4 \text{ m}^2} = 4 \text{ units}$$

Worked Example 11.6 Ionizing Radiation: Intensity versus Distance from the Source

If a radiation source gives 75 units of radiation at a distance of 2.4 m, at what distance does the source give 25 units of radiation?

ANALYSIS Radiation intensity (I) decreases with the square of the distance (d) from the source according to the equation

$$\frac{I_1}{I_2} = \frac{d_2^{\,2}}{d_1^{\,2}}$$

We know three of the four variables in this equation (I_1, I_2, and d_1), and we need to find d_2.

BALLPARK ESTIMATE In order to decrease the radiation intensity from 75 units to 25 units (a factor of 3), the distance must *increase* by a factor of $\sqrt{3} = 1.7$. Thus, the distance should increase from 2.4 m to about 4 m.

SOLUTION

STEP 1: **Identify known information.** We know three of the four variables.

STEP 2: **Identify answer and units.**

STEP 3: **Identify equation.** Rearrange the equation relating intensity and distance to solve for d_2.

STEP 4: **Solve.** Substitute in known values so that unwanted units cancel.

$I_1 = 75$ units

$I_2 = 25$ units

$d_1 = 2.4$ m

$d_2 = ???$ m

$$\frac{I_1}{I_2} = \frac{d_2^2}{d_1^2}$$

$$d_2^2 = \frac{I_1 d_1^2}{I_2} \quad \Rightarrow \quad d_2 = \sqrt{\frac{I_1 d_1^2}{I_2}}$$

$$d_2 = \sqrt{\frac{(75 \text{ units})(2.4 \text{ m})^2}{(25 \text{ units})}} = 4.2 \text{ m}$$

BALLPARK CHECK The calculated result is consistent with our estimate of about 4 m.

PROBLEM 11.11

A β-emitting radiation source gives 250 units of radiation at a distance of 4.0 m. At what distance does the radiation drop to one-tenth its original value?

11.8 Detecting Radiation

Small amounts of naturally occurring radiation have always been present, but people have been aware of it only within the past 100 years. The problem is that radiation is invisible. We cannot see, hear, smell, touch, or taste radiation, no matter how high the dose. We can, however, detect radiation by taking advantage of its ionizing properties.

The simplest device for detecting exposure to radiation is the photographic film badge worn by people who routinely work with radioactive materials. The film is protected from exposure to light, but any other radiation striking the badge causes the film to fog (remember Becquerel's discovery). At regular intervals, the film is developed and compared with a standard to indicate the radiation exposure.

The most versatile method for measuring radiation in the laboratory is the *scintillation counter*, a device in which a substance called a *phosphor* emits a flash of light when struck by radiation. The number of flashes are counted electronically and converted into an electrical signal.

Perhaps the best-known method for detecting and measuring radiation is the *Geiger counter*, an argon-filled tube containing two electrodes (Figure 11.6). The inner walls of the tube are coated with an electrically conducting material and given a negative charge, and a wire in the center of the tube is given a positive charge. As radiation enters the tube through a thin window, it strikes and ionizes argon atoms, which briefly conduct a tiny electric current between the walls and the center electrode. The passage of the current is detected, amplified, and used to produce a clicking sound or to register on a meter. The more radiation that enters the tube, the more frequent the clicks. Geiger counters are useful for seeking out a radiation source in a large area and for gauging the intensity of emitted radiation.

▲ This photographic film badge is a common device for monitoring radiation exposure.

▶ **Figure 11.6**
A Geiger counter for measuring radiation.
As radiation enters the tube through a thin window, it ionizes argon atoms and produces electrons that conduct a tiny electric current between the walls and the center electrode. The current flow then registers on the meter.

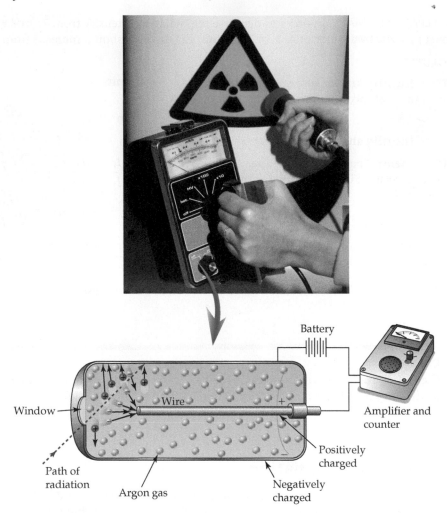

11.9 Measuring Radiation

Radiation intensity is expressed in different ways, depending on what characteristic of the radiation is measured (Table 11.5). Some units measure the number of nuclear decay events, while others measure exposure to radiation or the biological consequences of radiation.

TABLE **11.5** Common Units for Measuring Radiation		
Unit	**Quantity Measured**	**Description**
Curie (Ci)	Decay events	Amount of radiation equal to 3.7×10^{10} disintegrations per second
Roentgen (R)	Ionizing intensity	Amount of radiation producing 2.1×10^{9} charges per cubic centimeter of dry air
Rad	Energy absorbed per gram of tissue	1 rad = 1 R
Rem	Tissue damage	Amount of radiation producing the same damage as 1 R of X rays
Sievert (Sv)	Tissue damage	1 Sv = 100 rem

CHEMISTRY IN ACTION

Irradiated Food

The idea of irradiating food to kill harmful bacteria is not new; it goes back almost as far as the earliest studies on radiation. Not until the 1940s did serious work get under way, however, when U.S. Army scientists found that irradiation increased the shelf-life of ground beef. Nevertheless, widespread civilian use of the technique has been a long time in coming, spurred on in recent years by outbreaks of food poisoning that resulted in several deaths.

The principle of food irradiation is simple: exposure of contaminated food to ionizing radiation—usually γ rays produced by cobalt-60 or cesium-137—destroys the genetic material of any bacteria or other organisms present, thereby killing them. Irradiation will not, however, kill viruses or prions (see Chemistry in Action: Prions: Proteins That Cause Disease in Chapter 18), the cause of "mad-cow" disease. The amount of radiation depends on the desired effect. For example, to delay ripening of fruit may require a dose of 0.25 – 0.75 kGy, while sterilization of packaged meat requires a much higher dose of 25 – 70 kGy. The food itself undergoes little if any change when irradiated and does not itself become radioactive. The only real argument against food irradiation, in fact, is that it is *too* effective. Knowing that irradiation will kill nearly all harmful organisms, a food processor might be tempted to cut back on normal sanitary practices!

Food irradiation has been implemented to a much greater extent in Europe than in the United States. The largest marketers of irradiated food are Belgium, France, and the Netherlands, which irradiate between 10,000 and 20,000 tons of food per year. Currently, over 40 countries permit food irradiation and over 500,000 metric tons of food are treated annually worldwide.

▲ **Irradiating food kills bacteria and extends shelf life. Most irradiated food products are labeled with the Radura symbol (in green) to inform the public that the food product was exposed to radiation.**

One of the major concerns in the United States is the possible generation of *radiolytic products*, compounds formed in food by exposure to ionizing radiation. The U.S. Food and Drug Administration, after studying the matter extensively, has declared that food irradiation is safe and that it does not appreciably alter the vitamin or other nutritional content of food. Spices, fruits, pork, and vegetables were approved for irradiation in 1986, followed by poultry in 1990 and red meat, particularly ground beef, in 1997. In 2000, approval was extended to whole eggs and sprouting seeds. Should the food industry adopt irradiation of meat as its standard practice, occurrences of *E. coli* and *salmonella* contaminations, resulting in either massive product recalls or serious health concerns for consumers will become a thing of the past.

See Chemistry in Action Problems 11.72 and 11.73 at the end of the chapter.

- **Curie**   The *curie* (Ci), the *millicurie* (mCi), and the *microcurie* (μCi) measure the number of radioactive disintegrations occurring each second in a sample. One curie is the decay rate of 1 g of radium, equal to 3.7×10^{10} disintegrations per second; 1 mCi = 0.001 Ci = 3.7×10^7 disintegrations per second; and 1 μCi = 0.000 001 Ci = 3.7×10^4 disintegrations per second.

  The dosage of a radioactive substance administered orally or intravenously is usually given in millicuries. To calculate the size of a dose, it is necessary to determine the decay rate of the isotope solution per milliliter. Because the emitter concentration is constantly decreasing as it decays, the activity must be measured immediately before administration. Suppose, for example, that a solution containing iodine-131 for a thyroid-function study is found to have a decay rate of 0.020 mCi/mL and the dose administered is to be 0.050 mCi. The amount of the solution administered must be

$$\frac{0.05 \text{ mCi}}{\text{Dose}} \times \frac{1 \text{ mL } ^{131}\text{I solution}}{0.020 \text{ mCi}} = 2.5 \text{ mL } ^{131}\text{I solution/dose}$$

- **Roentgen**   The *roentgen* (R) is a unit for measuring the ionizing intensity of γ or X radiation. In other words, the roentgen measures the capacity of the radiation for affecting matter. One roentgen is the amount of radiation that produces 2.1×10^9 units of charge in 1 cm^3 of dry air at atmospheric pressure. Each collision of ionizing radiation with an atom produces one ion, or one unit of charge.

- **Rad** The *rad* (radiation absorbed dose) is a unit for measuring the energy absorbed per gram of material exposed to a radiation source and is defined as the absorption of 1×10^{-5} J of energy per gram. The energy absorbed varies with the type of material irradiated and the type of radiation. For most purposes, though, the roentgen and the rad are so close that they can be considered identical when used for X rays and γ rays: 1 R = 1 rad.

- **Rem** The *rem* (roentgen equivalent for man) measures the amount of tissue damage caused by radiation. One rem is the amount of radiation that produces the same effect as 1 R of X rays. Rems are the preferred units for medical purposes because they measure equivalent doses of different kinds of radiation. The rem is calculated as

$$\text{Rems} = \text{rads} \times \text{RBE}$$

where RBE is a *relative biological effectiveness* factor, which takes into account the differences in energy and of the different types of radiation. Although the actual biological effects of radiation depend greatly on both the source and the energy of the radiation, the RBE of X rays, γ rays, and β particles are essentially equivalent (RBE = 1), while the accepted RBE for α particles is 20. For example, 1 rad of α radiation causes 20 times more tissue damage than 1 rad of γ rays, but 1 rem of α radiation and 1 rem of γ rays cause the same amount of damage. Thus, the rem takes both ionizing intensity and biological effect into account, whereas the rad deals only with intensity.

- **SI Units** In the SI system, the *becquerel* (Bq) is defined as one disintegration per second. The SI unit for energy absorbed is the *gray* (Gy; 1 Gy = 100 rad). For radiation dose, the SI unit is the *sievert* (Sv), which is equal to 100 rem.

The biological consequences of different radiation doses are given in Table 11.6. Although the effects seem frightening, the average radiation dose received annually by most people is only about 0.27 rem. About 80% of this *background radiation* comes from natural sources (rocks and cosmic rays); the remaining 20% comes from consumer products and from medical procedures such as X rays. The amount due to emissions from nuclear power plants and to fallout from testing of nuclear weapons in the 1950s is barely detectable.

TABLE 11.6 Biological Effects of Short-Term Radiation on Humans

Dose (rem)	Biological Effects
0–25	No detectable effects
25–100	Temporary decrease in white blood cell count
100–200	Nausea, vomiting, longer-term decrease in white blood cells
200–300	Vomiting, diarrhea, loss of appetite, listlessness
300–600	Vomiting, diarrhea, hemorrhaging, eventual death in some cases
Above 600	Eventual death in nearly all cases

PROBLEM 11.12
Radiation released during the 1986 Chernobyl nuclear power plant disaster is expected to increase the background radiation level worldwide by about 5 mrem. By how much will this increase the annual dose of the average person? Express your answer as a percentage.

PROBLEM 11.13
A solution of selenium-75, a radioisotope used in the diagnosis of pancreatic disease, is found just prior to administration to have an activity of 44 μCi/mL. If 3.98 mL were delivered intravenously to the patient, what dose of Se-75 (in μCi) did the patient receive?

11.10 Artificial Transmutation

Very few of the approximately 3300 known radioisotopes occur naturally. Most are made from stable isotopes by **artificial transmutation**, the change of one atom into another brought about by nuclear bombardment reactions.

When an atom is bombarded with a high-energy particle, such as a proton, a neutron, an α particle, or even the nucleus of another element, an unstable nucleus is created in the collision. A nuclear change then occurs, and a different element is produced. For example, transmutation of ^{14}N to ^{14}C occurs in the upper atmosphere when neutrons produced by cosmic rays collide with atmospheric nitrogen. In the collision, a neutron dislodges a proton (^{1}H) from the nitrogen nucleus as the neutron and nucleus fuse together:

$$^{14}_{7}\text{N} + {}^{1}_{0}\text{n} \longrightarrow {}^{14}_{6}\text{C} + {}^{1}_{1}\text{H}$$

Artificial transmutation can lead to the synthesis of entirely new elements never before seen on Earth. In fact, all the *transuranium elements*—those elements with atomic numbers greater than 92—have been produced by bombardment reactions. For example, plutonium-241 (^{241}Pu) can be made by bombardment of uranium-238 with α particles:

$$^{238}_{92}\text{U} + {}^{4}_{2}\text{He} \longrightarrow {}^{241}_{94}\text{Pu} + {}^{1}_{0}\text{n}$$

Plutonium-241 is itself radioactive, with a half-life of 14.35 years, decaying by β emission to yield americium-241, which in turn decays by α emission with a half-life of 432.2 years. (If the name *americium* sounds vaguely familiar, it is because this radioisotope is used in smoke detectors.)

$$^{241}_{94}\text{Pu} \longrightarrow {}^{241}_{95}\text{Am} + {}^{0}_{-1}\text{e}$$

Note that all the equations just given for artificial transmutations are balanced. The sum of the mass numbers and the sum of the charges are the same on both sides of each equation.

Artificial transmutation The change of one atom into another brought about by a nuclear bombardment reaction.

▲ Smoke detectors contain a small amount of americium-241. The α particles emitted by this radioisotope ionize the air within the detector, causing it to conduct a tiny electric current. When smoke enters the chamber, conductivity drops and an alarm is triggered.

Worked Example 11.7 Balancing Nuclear Reactions: Transmutation

Californium-246 is formed by bombardment of uranium-238 atoms. If 4 neutrons are also formed, what particle is used for the bombardment?

ANALYSIS First write an incomplete nuclear equation incorporating the known information:

$$^{238}_{92}\text{U} + ? \longrightarrow {}^{246}_{98}\text{Cf} + 4{}^{1}_{0}\text{n}$$

Then find the numbers of nucleons and charges necessary to balance the equation. In this instance, there are 238 nucleons on the left and $246 + 4 = 250$ nucleons on the right, so the bombarding particle must have $250 - 238 = 12$ nucleons. Furthermore, there are 92 nuclear charges on the left and 98 on the right, so the bombarding particle must have $98 - 92 = 6$ protons.

SOLUTION
The missing particle is $^{12}_{6}\text{C}$.

$$^{238}_{92}\text{U} + {}^{12}_{6}\text{C} \longrightarrow {}^{246}_{98}\text{Cf} + 4{}^{1}_{0}\text{n}$$

CHEMISTRY IN ACTION

Body Imaging

We are all familiar with the appearance of a standard X-ray image, produced when X rays pass through the body and the intensity of the radiation that exits is recorded on film. X-ray imaging is, however, only one of a host of noninvasive imaging techniques that are now in common use.

Among the most widely used imaging techniques are those that give diagnostic information about the health of various parts of the body by analyzing the distribution pattern of a radioactively tagged substance in the body. A radiopharmaceutical agent that is known to concentrate in a specific organ or other body part is injected into the body, and its distribution pattern is monitored by an external radiation detector such as a γ ray camera. Depending on the medical condition, a diseased part might concentrate more of the radiopharmaceutical than normal and thus show up on the film as a radioactive hot spot against a cold background. Alternatively, the diseased part might concentrate less of the radiopharmaceutical than normal and thus show up as a cold spot on a hot background.

Among the radioisotopes most widely used for diagnostic imaging is technetium-99*m*, whose short half-life of only 6 hours minimizes the patient's exposure to radioactivity. Enhanced body images, such as the brain scan shown in the accompanying photograph, are an important tool in the diagnosis of cancer and many other medical conditions.

Several other techniques now used in medical diagnosis are made possible by *tomography*, a technique in which computer processing allows production of images through "slices" of the body. In X-ray tomography, commonly known as *CAT* or *CT* scanning (computerized tomography), the X-ray source and an array of detectors move rapidly in a circle around a patient's body, collecting up to 90,000 readings. CT scans can detect structural abnormalities such as tumors without the use of radioactive materials.

Combining tomography with radioisotope imaging gives cross-sectional views of regions that concentrate a radioactive substance.

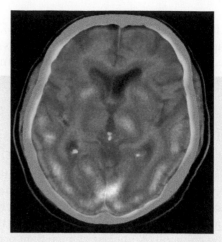

▲ **This enhanced image of the brain of a 72-year old male was obtained using PET following injection of 20 mCi of Tc-99m. The results can be used to distinguish between dementia and depression.**

One such technique, *positron emission tomography* (PET), utilizes radioisotopes that emit positrons and ultimately yield γ rays. Oxygen-15, nitrogen-13, carbon-11, and fluorine-18 are commonly used for PET because they can be readily incorporated into many physiologically active compounds. An ^{18}F-labeled glucose derivative, for instance, is useful for imaging brain regions that respond to various stimuli. The disadvantage of PET scans is that the necessary radioisotopes are so short-lived that they must be produced on-site immediately before use. The cost of PET is therefore high, because a hospital must install and maintain the necessary nuclear facility.

Magnetic resonance imaging (MRI) is a medical imaging technique that uses powerful magnetic and radio-frequency fields to interact with specific nuclei in the body (usually the nuclei of hydrogen atoms) to generate images in which the contrast between soft tissues is much better than that seen with CT. The original name for this technique was *nuclear* magnetic resonance imaging, but the *nuclear* was eliminated because in the public mind this word conjured up negative images of ionizing radiation. Ironically, MRI does not involve any nuclear radiation at all.

See Chemistry in Action Problems 11.74 and 11.75 at the end of the chapter.

PROBLEM 11.15

What isotope results from α decay of the americium-241 in smoke detectors?

PROBLEM 11.16

The element berkelium, first prepared at the University of California at Berkeley in 1949, is made by α bombardment of $^{241}_{95}Am$. Two neutrons are also produced during the reaction. What isotope of berkelium results from this transmutation? Write a balanced nuclear equation.

PROBLEM 11.17

Write a balanced nuclear equation for the reaction of argon-40 with a proton:

$$^{40}_{18}Ar + {}^{1}_{1}H \longrightarrow ? + {}^{1}_{0}n$$

PROBLEM 11.18

Technetium-99*m* (Tc-99*m*) is used extensively in diagnostic applications, including positron emission tomography (PET) scans (see Chemistry in Action: Body Imaging on p. 348). The half-life of Tc-99*m* is 6 hours. How long will it take for the Tc-99*m* activity to decrease to 0.1% of its original activity?

11.11 Nuclear Fission and Nuclear Fusion

In the preceding section, we saw that particle bombardment of various elements causes artificial transmutation and results in the formation of new, usually heavier elements. Under very special conditions with a very few isotopes, however, different kinds of nuclear events occur. Certain very heavy nuclei can split apart, and certain very light nuclei can fuse together. The two resultant processes—**nuclear fission** for the fragmenting of heavy nuclei and **nuclear fusion** for the joining together of light nuclei—have changed the world since their discovery in the late 1930s and early 1940s.

The huge amounts of energy that accompany these nuclear processes are the result of mass-to-energy conversions and are predicted by Einstein's equation

$$E = mc^2$$

where E = energy, m = mass change associated with the nuclear reaction, and c = the speed of light $(3.0 \times 10^8$ m/s$)$. Based on this relationship, a mass change as small as 1 µg results in a release of 2.15×10^4 kcal $(9.00 \times 104$ kJ$)$ of energy!

Nuclear fission The fragmenting of heavy nuclei.

Nuclear fusion The joining together of light nuclei.

Nuclear Fission

Uranium-235 is the only naturally occurring isotope that undergoes nuclear fission. When this isotope is bombarded by a stream of relatively slow-moving neutrons, its nucleus splits to give isotopes of other elements. The split can take place in more than 400 ways, and more than 800 different fission products have been identified. One of the more frequently occurring pathways generates barium-142 and krypton-91, along with 2 additional neutrons plus the 1 neutron that initiated the fission:

$$^{1}_{0}n + {}^{235}_{92}U \longrightarrow {}^{142}_{56}Ba + {}^{91}_{36}Kr + 3 \, {}^{1}_{0}n$$

As indicated by the balanced nuclear equation above, *one* neutron is used to initiate fission of a ^{235}U nucleus, but *three* neutrons are released. Thus, a nuclear **chain reaction** can be started: 1 neutron initiates one fission that releases 3 neutrons. Those 3 neutrons initiate three new fissions that release 9 neutrons. The 9 neutrons initiate nine fissions that release 27 neutrons, and so on at an ever-faster pace (Figure 11.7). It is worth noting that the neutrons produced by fission reactions are highly energetic. They possess penetrating power greater than α and β particles, but less than γ rays. In a nuclear fission reactor, the neutrons must first be slowed down to allow them to react. If the sample size is small, many of the neutrons escape before initiating additional fission events, and the chain reaction stops. If a sufficient amount of ^{235}U is present, however—an amount called the **critical mass**—then the chain reaction becomes self-sustaining. Under high-pressure conditions that confine the ^{235}U to a small volume, the chain reaction occurs so rapidly that a nuclear explosion results. For ^{235}U, the critical mass is about 56 kg, although the amount can be reduced to approximately 15 kg by placing a coating of ^{238}U around the ^{235}U to reflect back some of the escaping neutrons.

An enormous quantity of heat is released during nuclear fission—the fission of just 1.0 g of uranium-235 produces 3.4×10^8 kcal $(1.4 \times 109$ kJ$)$ for instance. This heat can be used to convert water to steam, which can be harnessed to turn huge generators and produce electric power. Although the United States, France, and Japan are responsible for nearly 50% of all nuclear power generated worldwide, only about 19% of the

Chain reaction A reaction that, once started, is self-sustaining.

Critical mass The minimum amount of radioactive material needed to sustain a nuclear chain reaction.

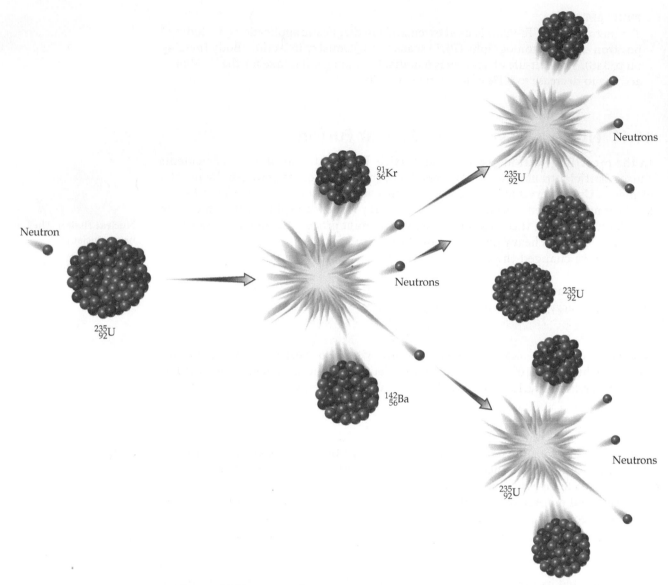

▲ **Figure 11.7**
A chain reaction.
Each fission event produces additional neutrons that induce more fissions. The rate of the process increases at each stage. Such chain reactions usually lead to the formation of many different fission products in addition to the two indicated.

electricity consumed in the United States is nuclear-generated. In France, nearly 80% of electricity is generated by nuclear power plants.

Two major objections that have caused much public debate about nuclear power plants are safety and waste disposal. Although a nuclear explosion is not possible under the conditions that typically exist in a power plant, there is a serious potential radiation hazard should an accident rupture the containment vessel holding the nuclear fuel and release radioactive substances to the environment. There have been several such instances in the last 35 years, most notably Three Mile Island in Pennsylvania (1979), Chernobyl in the Ukraine (1986), and the more recent Fukushima reactor damaged by the tsunami in Japan (2011). Perhaps even more important is the problem posed by disposal of radioactive wastes from nuclear plants. Many of these wastes have such long half-lives that hundreds or even thousands of years must elapse before they will be safe for humans to approach. How to dispose of such hazardous materials safely is an unsolved problem.

PROBLEM 11.19
What other isotope besides tellurium-137 is produced by nuclear fission of uranium-235?

$$^{235}_{92}U + ^{1}_{0}n \longrightarrow ^{137}_{52}Te + 2\,^{1}_{0}n + ?$$

Nuclear Fusion

Just as heavy nuclei such as ^{235}U release energy when they undergo *fission*, very light nuclei such as the isotopes of hydrogen release enormous amounts of energy when they undergo *fusion*. In fact, it is just such a fusion reaction of hydrogen nuclei to produce helium that powers our sun and other stars. Among the processes thought to occur in the sun are those in the following sequence leading to helium-4:

$$^{1}_{1}H + ^{2}_{1}H \longrightarrow ^{3}_{2}He$$
$$^{3}_{2}He + ^{3}_{2}He \longrightarrow ^{4}_{2}He + 2\,^{1}_{1}H$$
$$^{3}_{2}He + ^{1}_{1}H \longrightarrow ^{4}_{2}He + ^{0}_{1}e$$

Under the conditions found in stars, where the temperature is on the order of 2×10^7 K and pressures approach 10^5 atmospheres, nuclei are stripped of all their electrons and have enough kinetic energy that nuclear fusion readily occurs. The energy of our sun, and all the stars, comes from thermonuclear fusion reactions in their core that fuse hydrogen and other light elements, transmuting them into heavier elements. On Earth, however, the necessary conditions for nuclear fusion are not easily created. For more than 50 years scientists have been trying to create the necessary conditions for fusion in laboratory reactors, including the Tokamak Fusion Test Reactor (TFTR) at Princeton, New Jersey, and the Joint European Torus (JET) at Culham, England. Recent advances in reactor design have raised hopes that a commercial fusion reactor will be realized within the next 20 years.

If the dream becomes reality, controlled nuclear fusion can provide the ultimate cheap, clean power source. The fuel is deuterium (^2H), available in the oceans in limitless amounts, and there are few radioactive by-products.

PROBLEM 11.20
One of the possible reactions for nuclear fusion involves the collision of 2 deuterium nuclei. Complete the reaction by identifying the missing particle:

$$^{2}_{1}H + ^{2}_{1}H \longrightarrow ^{1}_{0}n + ?$$

SUMMARY: REVISITING THE CHAPTER GOALS

1. What is a nuclear reaction, and how are equations for nuclear reactions balanced? A *nuclear reaction* is one that changes an atomic nucleus, causing the change of one element into another. Loss of an α particle leads to a new atom whose atomic number is 2 less than that of the starting atom. Loss of a β particle leads to an atom whose atomic number is 1 greater than that of the starting atom:

α emission: $^{238}_{92}U \longrightarrow ^{234}_{90}Th + ^{4}_{2}He$
β emission: $^{131}_{53}I \longrightarrow ^{131}_{54}Xe + ^{0}_{-1}e$

A nuclear reaction is balanced when the sum of the *nucleons* (protons and neutrons) is the same on both sides of the reaction arrow and when the sum of the charges on the nuclei plus any ejected subatomic particles is the same (see *Problems 22, 24, 26, 38, 40, 41, 44–53, 81, 82, 84, 85, 90–95*).

2. What are the different kinds of radioactivity? *Radioactivity* is the spontaneous emission of radiation from the nucleus of an unstable atom. The three major kinds of radiation are called *alpha* (α), *beta* (β), and *gamma* (γ). Alpha radiation consists of helium nuclei, small particles containing 2 protons and

2 neutrons ($^4_2$He); β radiation consists of electrons ($^{\ 0}_{-1}$e); and γ radiation consists of high-energy light waves. Every element in the periodic table has at least one radioactive isotope, or *radio-isotope* (*see Problems 22, 25, 27, 29, 30–32, 40, 41, 44–47, 49, 81, 82, 93*).

3. How are the rates of nuclear reactions expressed? The rate of a nuclear reaction is expressed in units of *half-life* ($t_{1/2}$), where one half-life is the amount of time necessary for one half of the radioactive sample to decay (*see Problems 21, 23, 28, 29, 54–59, 77, 83, 85*).

4. What is ionizing radiation? High-energy radiation of all types—α particles, β particles, γ rays, and X rays—is called *ion-izing radiation*. When any of these kinds of radiation strikes an atom, it dislodges an orbital electron and gives a reactive ion that can be lethal to living cells. Gamma rays and X rays are the most penetrating and most harmful types of external radiation; α and β particles are the most dangerous types of internal radiation because of their high energy and the resulting damage to sur-rounding tissue (*see Problems 33–37, 63, 65, 72, 76, 84, 86, 87*).

5. How is radioactivity measured? Radiation intensity is expressed in different ways according to the property being measured. The *curie* (*Ci*) measures the number of radioactive

disintegrations per second in a sample; the *roentgen* (*R*) measures the ionizing ability of radiation. The *rad* measures the amount of radiation energy absorbed per gram of tissue; and the *rem* measures the amount of tissue damage caused by radiation. Radiation effects become noticeable with a human exposure of 25 rem and become lethal at an exposure above 600 rem (*see Problems 60–69, 79, 80*).

6. What is transmutation? *Transmutation* is the change of one element into another brought about by a nuclear reaction. Most known radioisotopes do not occur naturally but are made by bombardment of an atom with a high-energy particle. In the ensuing collision between particle and atom, a nuclear change occurs and a new element is produced by *artificial transmutation* (*see Problems 38, 39, 48, 50, 51, 53, 90, 94, 95*).

7. What are nuclear fission and nuclear fusion? With a very few isotopes, including $^{235}_{92}$U, the nucleus is split apart by neutron bombardment to give smaller fragments. A large amount of energy is released during this *nuclear fission*, lead-ing to use of the reaction for generating electric power. *Nuclear fusion* results when small nuclei such as those of tritium ($^3_1$H) and deuterium ($^2_1$H) combine to give a heavier nucleus (*see Problems 42, 43, 48, 88, 91, 92*).

KEY WORDS

Alpha (α) particle, *p. 331*

Artificial transmutation, *p. 347*

Beta (β) particle, *p. 331*

Chain reaction, *p. 349*

Cosmic rays, *p. 341*

Critical mass, *p. 349*

Decay series, *p. 341*

Electron capture (E.C.), *p. 335*

Gamma (γ) radiation, *p. 331*

Half-life ($t_{1/2}$) *p. 337*

Ionizing radiation, *p. 341*

Nuclear decay, *p. 332*

Nuclear fission, *p. 349*

Nuclear fusion, *p. 349*

Nuclear reaction, *p. 329*

Nucleon, *p. 329*

Nuclide, *p. 329*

Positron, *p. 335*

Radioactivity, *p. 330*

Radioisotope, *p. 331*

Radionuclide, *p. 331*

Transmutation, *p. 332*

X rays, *p. 341*

UNDERSTANDING KEY CONCEPTS

11.21 Magnesium-28 decays by β emission to give aluminum-28. If yellow spheres represent $^{28}_{12}$Mg atoms and blue spheres represent $^{28}_{13}$Al atoms, how many half-lives have passed in the following sample?

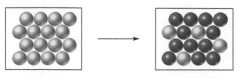

11.22 Write a balanced nuclear equation to represent the decay reaction described in Problem 11.21.

11.23 Refer to Figure 11.4 and then make a drawing similar to those in Problem 11.21 representing the decay of a sample of $^{28}_{12}$Mg after approximately four half-lives have passed.

11.24 Write the symbol of the isotope represented by the fol-lowing drawing. Blue spheres represent neutrons and red spheres represent protons.

11.25 Shown in the following graph is a portion of the decay series for plutonium-241 ($^{241}_{94}$Pu). The series has two kinds of arrows: shorter arrows pointing right and longer arrows pointing left. Which arrow corresponds to an α emission, and which to a β emission? Explain.

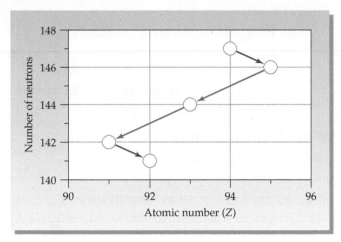

11.26 Identify and write the symbol for each of the five nuclides in the decay series shown in Problem 11.25.

11.27 Identify the isotopes involved, and tell the type of decay process occurring in the following nuclear reaction:

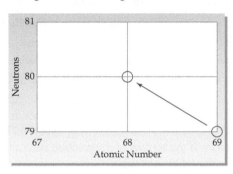

11.28 What is the half-life of the radionuclide that shows the following decay curve?

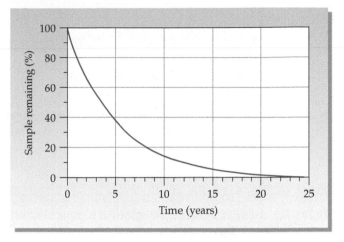

11.29 What is wrong with the following decay curve? Explain.

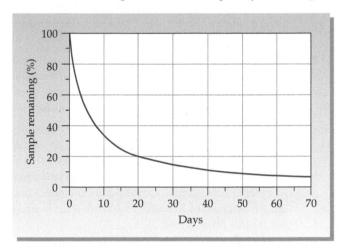

ADDITIONAL PROBLEMS

RADIOACTIVITY

11.30 What does it mean to say that a substance is radioactive?

11.31 Describe how α radiation, β radiation, γ radiation, positron emission, and electron capture differ.

11.32 List three of the five ways in which a nuclear reaction differs from a chemical reaction.

11.33 What happens when ionizing radiation strikes an atom in a chemical compound?

11.34 How does ionizing radiation lead to cell damage?

11.35 What are the main sources of background radiation?

11.36 How can a nucleus emit an electron during β decay when there are no electrons present in the nucleus to begin with?

11.37 What is the difference between an α particle and a helium atom?

NUCLEAR DECAY AND TRANSMUTATION

11.38 What does it mean to say that a nuclear equation is balanced?

11.39 What are transuranium elements, and how are they made?

11.40 What happens to the mass number and atomic number of an atom that emits an α particle? A β particle?

11.41 What happens to the mass number and atomic number of an atom that emits a γ ray? A positron?

11.42 How does nuclear fission differ from normal radioactive decay?

11.43 What characteristic of uranium-235 fission causes a chain reaction?

11.44 What products result from radioactive decay of the following β emitters?

(a) $^{35}_{16}S$ (b) $^{24}_{10}Ne$ (c) $^{90}_{38}Sr$

11.45 What radioactive nuclides will produce the following products following α decay?

(a) $^{186}_{76}Os$ (b) $^{204}_{85}At$ (c) $^{241}_{94}Pu$

11.46 Identify the starting radioisotopes needed to balance each of these nuclear reactions:

(a) $? + {}^4_2He \longrightarrow {}^{113}_{49}In$ (b) $? + {}^4_2He \longrightarrow {}^{13}_7N + {}^1_0n$

11.47 Identify the radioisotope product needed to balance each of these nuclear reactions:

(a) $^{26}_{11}\text{Na} \longrightarrow ? + ^{0}_{-1}\text{e}$ (b) $^{212}_{83}\text{Bi} \longrightarrow ? + ^{4}_{2}\text{He}$

11.48 Balance the following equations for the nuclear fission of $^{235}_{92}\text{U}$:

(a) $^{235}_{92}\text{U} + ^{1}_{0}\text{n} \longrightarrow ^{160}_{62}\text{Sm} + ^{72}_{30}\text{Zn} + ? \ ^{1}_{0}\text{n}$

(b) $^{235}_{92}\text{U} + ^{1}_{0}\text{n} \longrightarrow ^{87}_{35}\text{Br} + ? + 3\ ^{1}_{0}\text{n}$

11.49 Complete the following nuclear equations and identify each as α decay, β decay, positron emission, or electron capture:

(a) $^{126}_{50}\text{Sn} \longrightarrow ? + ^{126}_{51}\text{Sb}$

(b) $^{210}_{88}\text{Ra} \longrightarrow ? + ^{206}_{86}\text{Rn}$

(c) $^{76}_{36}\text{Kr} + ? \longrightarrow ^{76}_{35}\text{Br}$

11.50 For centuries, alchemists dreamed of turning base metals into gold. The dream finally became reality when it was shown that mercury-198 can be converted into gold-198 when bombarded by neutrons. What small particle is produced in addition to gold-198? Write a balanced nuclear equation for the reaction.

11.51 Cobalt-60 (half-life = 5.3 years) is used to irradiate food, to treat cancer, and to disinfect surgical equipment. It is produced by irradiation of cobalt-59 in a nuclear reactor. It decays to nickel-60. Write nuclear equations for the formation and decay reactions of cobalt-60.

11.52 Bismuth-212 attaches readily to monoclonal antibodies and is used in the treatment of various cancers. This bismiuth-212 is formed after the parent isotope undergoes a decay series consisting of four α decays and one β decay. (the decays could be in any order). What is the parent isotope for this decay series?

11.53 Meitnerium-266 ($^{266}_{109}\text{Mt}$) was prepared in 1982 by bombardment of bismuth-209 atoms with iron-58. What other product must also have been formed? Write a balanced nuclear equation for the transformation.

HALF-LIFE

11.54 What does it mean when we say that strontium-90, a waste product of nuclear power plants, has a half-life of 28.8 years?

11.55 How many half lives must pass for the mass of a radioactive sample to decrease to 35% of the original mass? To 10%?

11.56 Selenium-75, a β emitter with a half-life of 120 days, is used medically for pancreas scans.

(a) Approximately how long would it take for a 0.050 g sample of selenium-75 to decrease to 0.010 g?

(b) Approximately how much selenium-75 would remain from a 0.050 g sample that has been stored for one year? (*Hint:* How many half-lives are in one year?)

11.57 Approximately how long would it take a sample of selenium-75 to lose 75% of its radioactivity? To lose 99%? (See Problem 11.56.)

11.58 The half-life of mercury-197 is 64.1 hours. If a patient undergoing a kidney scan is given 5.0 ng of mercury-197, how much will remain after 7 days? After 30 days?

11.59 Gold-198, a β emitter used to treat leukemia, has a half-life of 2.695 days. The standard dosage is about 1.0 mCi/kg body weight.

(a) What is the product of the β emission of gold-198?

(b) How long does it take a 30.0 mCi sample of gold-198 to decay so that only 3.75 mCi remains?

(c) How many millicuries are required in a single dosage administered to a 70.0 kg adult?

MEASURING RADIOACTIVITY

11.60 Describe how a Geiger counter works.

11.61 Describe how a film badge works.

11.62 Describe how a scintillation counter works.

11.63 Why are rems the preferred units for measuring the health effects of radiation?

11.64 Approximately what amount (in rems) of short-term exposure to radiation produces noticeable effects in humans?

11.65 Match each unit in the left column with the property being measured in the right column:

1. curie   (a) Ionizing intensity of radiation
2. rem   (b) Amount of tissue damage
3. rad   (c) Number of disintegrations per second
4. roentgen   (d) Amount of radiation per gram of tissue

11.66 Technetium-99*m* is used for radioisotope-guided surgical biopsies of certain bone cancers. A patient must receive an injection of 28 mCi of technetium-99*m* 6–12 hours before surgery. If the activity of the solution is 15 mCi, what volume should be injected?

11.67 Sodium-24 is used to study the circulatory system and to treat chronic leukemia. It is administered in the form of saline (NaCl) solution, with a therapeutic dosage of 180 μCi/kg body weight.

(a) What dosage (in mCi) would be administered to a 68 kg adult patient?

(b) How many milliliters of a 6.5 mCi/mL solution are needed to treat a 68 kg adult?

11.68 A selenium-75 source is producing 300 rem at a distance of 2.0 m?

(a) What is its intensity at 16 m?

(b) What is its intensity at 25 m?

11.69 If a radiation source has an intensity of 650 rem at 1.0 m, what distance is needed to decrease the intensity of exposure to below 25 rem, the level at which no effects are detectable?

CHEMISTRY IN ACTION

11.70 What are the three main classes of techniques used in nuclear medicine? Give an example of each. [*Medical Uses of Radioactivity, p. 338*]

11.71 A 2 mL solution containing 1.25 μCi/mL is injected into the bloodstream of a patient. After dilution, a 1.00 mL sample is withdrawn and found to have an activity of

2.6×10^{-4} μCi. Calculate total blood volume. [*Medical Uses of Radioactivity, p. 338*]

11.72 What is the purpose of food irradiation, and how does it work? [*Irradiated Food, p. 345*]

11.73 What kind of radiation is used to treat food? [*Irradiated Food, p. 345*]

11.74 What are the advantages of CT and PET relative to conventional X rays? [*Body Imaging, p. 348*]

11.75 What advantages does MRI have over CT and PET imaging? [*Body Imaging, p. 348*]

GENERAL QUESTIONS AND PROBLEMS

11.76 Film badge dosimeters typically include filters to target specific types of radiation. A film badge is constructed that includes a region containing a tin foil filter, a region containing a plastic film filter, and a region with no filter. Which region monitors exposure to α-radiation? Which monitors exposure to β-radiation? Which monitors γ-radiation? Explain.

11.77 Some dried beans with a $^{14}C/^{12}C$ ratio one-eighth of the current value are found in an old cave. How old are the beans?

11.78 Harmful chemical spills can often be cleaned up by treatment with another chemical. For example, a spill of H_2SO_4 might be neutralized by addition of $NaHCO_3$. Why is it that the harmful radioactive wastes from nuclear power plants cannot be cleaned up as easily?

11.79 Why is a scintillation counter or Geiger counter more useful for determining the existence and source of a new radiation leak than a film badge?

11.80 A Geiger counter records an activity of 28 counts per minute (cpm) when located at a distance of 10 m. What will be the activity (in cpm) at a distance of 5 m?

11.81 Most of the stable isotopes for elements lighter than Ca-40 have equal numbers of protons and neutrons in the nucleus. What would be the most probable decay mode for an isotope that had more protons than neutrons? More neutrons than protons?

11.82 Technetium-99*m*, used for brain scans and to monitor heart function, is formed by decay of molybdenum-99.

 (a) By what type of decay does ^{99}Mo produce ^{99m}Tc?

 (b) Molybdenum-99 is formed by neutron bombardment of a natural isotope. If one neutron is absorbed and there are no other by-products of this process, from what isotope is ^{99}Mo formed?

11.83 The half-life of technetium-99*m* (Problem 11.82) is 6.01 hours. If a sample with an initial activity of 15 μCi is injected into a patient, what is the activity in 24 hours, assuming that none of the sample is excreted?

11.84 Plutonium-238 is an α emitter used to power batteries for heart pacemakers.

 (a) Write the balanced nuclear equation for this emission.

 (b) Why is a pacemaker battery enclosed in a metal case before being inserted into the chest cavity?

11.85 Sodium-24, a beta-emitter used in diagnosing circulation problems, has a half-life of 15 hours.

 (a) Write the balanced nuclear equation for this emission.

 (b) What fraction of sodium-24 remains after 50 hours?

11.86 High levels of radioactive fallout after the 1986 accident at the Chernobyl nuclear power plant in what is now Ukraine resulted in numerous miscarriages in humans and many instances of farm animals born with severe defects. Why are embryos and fetuses particularly susceptible to the effects of radiation?

11.87 One way to demonstrate the dose factor of ionizing radiation (penetrating distance $\times$ ionizing energy) is to think of radiation as cookies. Imagine that you have four cookies—an α cookie, a β cookie, a γ cookie, and a neutron cookie. Which one would you eat, which would you hold in your hand, which would you put in your pocket, and which would you throw away?

11.88 What are the main advantages of nuclear fission relative to nuclear fusion as an energy source? What are the drawbacks?

11.89 Although turning lead into gold in a nuclear reactor is technologically feasible (Problem 11.50), it is not economical. It is far easier to convert gold into lead. The process involves a series of neutron bombardments, and can be summarized as

$$^{197}_{79}\text{Au} + ?\,^{1}_{0}n \longrightarrow \,^{204}_{82}\text{Pb} + ?\,^{0}_{-1}e$$

How many neutrons and β particles are involved?

11.90 Balance the following transmutation reactions:

 (a) $^{253}_{99}\text{Es} + ? \longrightarrow \,^{256}_{101}\text{Md} + \,^{1}_{0}n$

 (b) $^{250}_{98}\text{Cf} + \,^{11}_{5}\text{B} \longrightarrow ? + 4\,^{1}_{0}n$

11.91 The most abundant isotope of uranium, ^{238}U, does not undergo fission. In a *breeder reactor*, however, a ^{238}U atom captures a neutron and emits 2 beta particles to make a fissionable isotope of plutonium, which can then be used as fuel in a nuclear reactor. Write the balanced nuclear equation.

11.92 Boron is used in *control rods* for nuclear reactors because it can absorb neutrons to keep a chain reaction from becoming supercritical, and decays by emitting alpha particles. Balance the equation:

$$^{10}_{5}\text{B} + \,^{1}_{0}n \longrightarrow ? + \,^{4}_{2}\text{He}$$

11.93 Thorium-232 decays by a 10-step series, ultimately yielding lead-208. How many α particles and how many β particles are emitted?

11.94 Californium-246 is formed by bombardment of uranium-238 atoms. If four neutrons are formed as by-products, what particle is used for the bombardment?

11.95 The most recently discovered element 117 (Ununseptium, Uus) was synthesized by nuclear transmutation reactions in which berkelium-249 was bombarded with calcium-48. Two isotopes of Uus were identified:

$$^{48}_{20}\text{Ca} + \,^{249}_{97}\text{Bk} \longrightarrow \,^{294}_{117}\text{Uus} + ?\,^{1}_{0}n$$

$$^{48}_{20}\text{Ca} + \,^{249}_{97}\text{Bk} \longrightarrow \,^{293}_{117}\text{Uus} + ?\,^{1}_{0}n$$

How many neutrons are produced in each reaction?

Chapters 12-24 were taken from

General, Organic, and Biological Chemistry: Structures of Life,
Fifth Edition

by Karen C. Timberlake

12

Introduction to Organic Chemistry: Hydrocarbons

AT 4:35 A.M., A RESCUE CREW RESPONDED TO A

call about a house fire. At the scene, Jack, a firefighter/emergency medical technician (EMT) found Diane, a 62-year old woman, lying in the front yard of her house. In his assessment, Jack, reported that Diane had second- and third-degree burns over 40% of her body as well as a broken leg. He placed an oxygen re-breather mask on Diane to provide a high concentration of oxygen. Another firefighter/EMT, Nancy, began dressing the burns with sterile water and cling film, a first aid material made of polyvinyl chloride, which does not stick to the skin and is protective. Jack and his crew transported Diane to the burn center for further treatment.

At the scene of the fire, arson investigators used trained dogs to find traces of accelerants and fuel. Gasoline, which is often found at arson scenes, is a mixture of organic molecules called alkanes. Alkanes or hydrocarbons are chains of carbon and hydrogen atoms. The alkanes present in gasoline consist of a mixture of 5 to 8 carbon atoms in a chain. Alkanes are extremely combustible; they react with oxygen to form carbon dioxide, water, and large amounts of heat. Because alkanes undergo combustion reactions, they can be used to start arson fires.

CAREER Firefighter/Emergency Medical Technician

Firefighters/emergency medical technicians are first responders to fires, accidents, and other emergency situations. They are required to have an emergency medical technician certification in order to be able to treat seriously injured people. By combining the skills of a firefighter and an emergency medical technician, they increase the survival rates of the injured. The physical demands of firefighters are extremely high as they fight, extinguish, and prevent fires while wearing heavy protective clothing and gear. They also train for and participate in firefighting drills, and maintain fire equipment so that it is always working and ready.

Firefighters must also be knowledgeable about fire codes, arson, and the handling and disposal of hazardous materials. Since firefighters also provide emergency care for sick and injured people, they need to be aware of emergency medical and rescue procedures, as well as the proper methods for controlling the spread of infectious disease.

At the beginning of the nineteenth century, scientists classified chemical compounds as inorganic and organic. An inorganic compound was a substance that was composed of minerals, and an organic compound was a substance that came from an organism, thus the use of the word *organic*. Early scientists thought that some type of "vital force," which could be found only in living cells, was required to synthesize an organic compound. This idea was shown to be incorrect in 1828 when the German chemist Friedrich Wöhler synthesized urea, a product of protein metabolism, by heating an inorganic compound, ammonium cyanate.

$$NH_4CNO \xrightarrow{\text{Heat}} H_2N-\overset{\overset{\displaystyle O}{\|}}{C}-NH_2$$

Ammonium cyanate (inorganic)   Urea (organic)

The simplest organic compounds are the hydrocarbons that contain only the elements carbon and hydrogen. All the carbon-to-carbon bonds in a hydrocarbon known as an alkane are single C—C bonds. Some common alkanes include methane (CH_4), propane (C_3H_8), and butane (C_4H_{10}).

Alkenes are hydrocarbons that contain one or more carbon-to-carbon double bonds (C=C). Because double bonds are very reactive, they easily add hydrogen atoms (hydrogenation) or water (hydration) to the carbon atoms in the double bond. One important compound containing a double bond is ethene (ethylene), which is used to ripen fruit when ready for market. A common compound with a triple bond is ethyne (acetylene), which burns at high temperatures and is used in welding metals.

Learning about the structures and reactions of organic molecules will provide you with a foundation for understanding the more complex molecules of biochemistry.

CHAPTER READINESS*

⚛ CORE CHEMISTRY SKILLS

- Drawing Lewis Structures (6.6)
- Predicting Shape (6.8)
- Balancing a Chemical Equation (7.1)

*These Core Chemistry Skills from previous chapters are listed here for your review as you proceed to the new material in this chapter.

LEARNING GOAL

Identify properties characteristic of organic or inorganic compounds.

12.1 Organic Compounds

Organic chemistry is the study of carbon compounds. The element carbon has a special role because many carbon atoms can bond together to give a vast array of molecular compounds. **Organic compounds** always contain carbon and hydrogen, and sometimes other nonmetals such as oxygen, sulfur, nitrogen, phosphorus, or a halogen. We find organic compounds in many common products we use every day, such as gasoline, medicines, shampoos, plastics, and perfumes. The food we eat is composed of organic compounds such as carbohydrates, fats, and proteins that supply us with fuel for energy and the carbon atoms needed to build and repair the cells of our bodies.

We organize organic compounds by their *functional groups*, which are groups of atoms bonded in a specific way. Compounds that contain the same functional group have similar physical and chemical properties. The identification of functional groups allows us to classify organic compounds according to their structure, to name compounds within each family, and to predict their chemical reactions.

The formulas of organic compounds are written with carbon first, followed by hydrogen, and then any other elements. Organic compounds typically have low melting and boiling points, are not soluble in water, and are less dense than water. For example, vegetable oil, which is a mixture of organic compounds, does not dissolve in water but floats on top. Many organic compounds undergo combustion and burn vigorously in air. By contrast, many inorganic compounds have high melting and boiling points. Inorganic compounds that are ionic are usually soluble in water, and most do not burn in air. Table 12.1 contrasts some of the properties associated with organic and inorganic compounds, such as propane, C_3H_8, and sodium chloride, NaCl (see Figure 12.1).

Vegetable oil, a mixture of organic compounds, is not soluble in water.

TABLE 12.1 Some Properties of Organic and Inorganic Compounds

Property	Organic	Example: C_3H_8	Inorganic	Example: NaCl
Elements Present	C and H, sometimes O, S, N, P, or Cl (F, Br, I)	C and H	Most metals and nonmetals	Na and Cl
Particles	Molecules	C_3H_8	Mostly ions	Na^+ and Cl^-
Bonding	Mostly covalent	Covalent	Many are ionic, some covalent	Ionic
Polarity of Bonds	Nonpolar, unless a strongly electronegative atom is present	Nonpolar	Most are ionic or polar covalent, a few are nonpolar covalent	Ionic
Melting Point	Usually low	$-188\,°C$	Usually high	$801\,°C$
Boiling Point	Usually low	$-42\,°C$	Usually high	$1413\,°C$
Flammability	High	Burns in air	Low	Does not burn
Solubility in Water	Not soluble, unless a polar group is present	No	Most are soluble, unless nonpolar	Yes

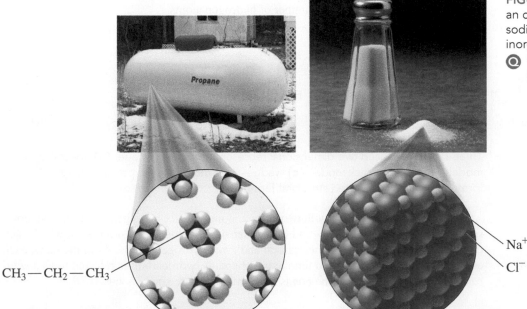

$CH_3—CH_2—CH_3$

FIGURE 12.1 ▶ Propane, C_3H_8, is an organic compound, whereas sodium chloride, NaCl, is an inorganic compound.

Q Why is propane used as a fuel?

Na^+
Cl^-

> **SAMPLE PROBLEM 12.1 Properties of Organic Compounds**
>
> Indicate whether the following properties are more typical of organic or inorganic compounds:
>
> **a.** is not soluble in water
> **b.** has a high melting point
> **c.** burns in air
>
> **SOLUTION**
>
> **a.** Many organic compounds are not soluble in water.
> **b.** Inorganic compounds are more likely to have high melting points.
> **c.** Organic compounds are more likely to be flammable.
>
> **STUDY CHECK 12.1**
>
> What elements are always found in organic compounds?
>
> **ANSWER**
>
> C and H

Representations of Carbon Compounds

Hydrocarbons are organic compounds that consist of only carbon and hydrogen. In organic molecules, every carbon atom has four bonds. In the simplest hydrocarbon, methane (CH_4), the carbon atom forms an octet by sharing its four valence electrons with four hydrogen atoms.

The most accurate representation of methane is the three-dimensional *space-filling model* **(a)** in which spheres show the relative size and shape of all the atoms. Another type of three-dimensional representation is the *ball-and-stick model* **(b)**, where the atoms are shown as balls and the bonds between them are shown as sticks. In the ball-and-stick model of methane, CH_4, the covalent bonds from the carbon atom to each hydrogen atom are directed to the corners of a tetrahedron with bond angles of 109°. In the *wedge–dash model* **(c)**, the three-dimensional shape is represented by symbols of the atoms with lines for bonds in the plane of the page, wedges for bonds that project out from the page, and dashes for bonds that are behind the page.

However, the three-dimensional models are awkward to draw and view for more complex molecules. Therefore, it is more practical to use their corresponding two-dimensional formulas. The **expanded structural formula (d)** shows all of the atoms and the bonds connected to each atom. A **condensed structural formula (e)** shows the carbon atoms each grouped with the attached number of hydrogen atoms.

 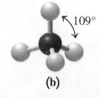

(a)	(b)	(c)	(d)	(e)

Three-dimensional and two-dimensional representations of methane: **(a)** space-filling model, **(b)** ball-and-stick model, **(c)** wedge–dash model, **(d)** expanded structural formula, and **(e)** condensed structural formula.

The hydrocarbon ethane with two carbon atoms and six hydrogen atoms can be represented by a similar set of three- and two-dimensional models and formulas in which each carbon atom is bonded to another carbon and three hydrogen atoms. As in methane, each carbon atom in ethane retains a tetrahedral shape. A hydrocarbon is referred to as a *saturated hydrocarbon* when all the bonds in the molecule are single bonds.

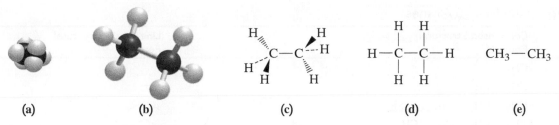

Three-dimensional and two-dimensional representations of ethane: **(a)** space-filling model, **(b)** ball-and-stick model, **(c)** wedge–dash model, **(d)** expanded structural formula, and **(e)** condensed structural formula.

QUESTIONS AND PROBLEMS

12.1 Organic Compounds

LEARNING GOAL Identify properties characteristic of organic or inorganic compounds.

12.1 Identify each of the following as a formula of an organic or inorganic compound:
  a. KCl   **b.** C_4H_{10}
  c. C_2H_6O **d.** H_2SO_4
  e. $CaCl_2$ **f.** C_3H_7Cl

12.2 Identify each of the following as a formula of an organic or inorganic compound:
  a. $C_6H_{12}O_6$ **b.** K_3PO_4
  c. I_2 **d.** C_2H_6S
  e. $C_{10}H_{22}$ **f.** C_4H_9Br

12.3 Identify each of the following properties as more typical of an organic or inorganic compound:
  a. is soluble in water
  b. has a low boiling point
  c. contains carbon and hydrogen
  d. contains ionic bonds

12.4 Identify each of the following properties as more typical of an organic or inorganic compound:
  a. contains Li and F   **b.** is a gas at room temperature
  c. contains covalent bonds   **d.** produces ions in water

12.5 Match each of the following physical and chemical properties with ethane, C_2H_6, or sodium bromide, NaBr:
  a. boils at $-89\,°C$ **b.** burns vigorously in air
  c. is a solid at $250\,°C$ **d.** dissolves in water

12.6 Match each of the following physical and chemical properties with cyclohexane, C_6H_{12}, or calcium nitrate, $Ca(NO_3)_2$:
  a. melts at $500\,°C$
  b. is insoluble in water
  c. does not burn in air
  d. is a liquid at room temperature

12.7 How are the hydrogen atoms of methane, CH_4, arranged in space?

12.8 In a propane molecule with three carbon atoms, what is the shape around each carbon atom?

Propane

12.2 Alkanes

More than 90% of the compounds in the world are organic compounds. The large number of carbon compounds is possible because the covalent bond between carbon atoms (C—C) is very strong, allowing carbon atoms to form long, stable chains.

The **alkanes** are a type of hydrocarbon in which the carbon atoms are connected only by single bonds. One of the most common uses of alkanes is as fuels. Methane, used in gas heaters and gas cooktops, is an alkane with one carbon atom. The alkanes ethane, propane, and butane contain two, three, and four carbon atoms, respectively, connected in a row or a *continuous chain*. As we can see, the names for alkanes end in *ane*. Such names are part of the **IUPAC** (International Union of Pure and Applied Chemistry) **system** used by chemists to name organic compounds. Alkanes with five or more carbon atoms in a chain are named using Greek prefixes: *pent* (5), *hex* (6), *hept* (7), *oct* (8), *non* (9), and *dec* (10) (see Table 12.2).

LEARNING GOAL

Write the IUPAC names and draw the condensed or line-angle structural formulas for alkanes and cycloalkanes.

TABLE 12.2 IUPAC Names of the First 10 Alkanes

Number of Carbon Atoms	Molecular Formula	Condensed Structural Formula	Line-Angle Structural Formula
1	CH_4	CH_4	
2	C_2H_6	CH_3-CH_3	
3	C_3H_8	$CH_3-CH_2-CH_3$	
4	C_4H_{10}	$CH_3-CH_2-CH_2-CH_3$	
5	C_5H_{12}	$CH_3-CH_2-CH_2-CH_2-CH_3$	
6	C_6H_{14}	$CH_3-CH_2-CH_2-CH_2-CH_2-CH_3$	
7	C_7H_{16}	$CH_3-CH_2-CH_2-CH_2-CH_2-CH_2-CH_3$	
8	C_8H_{18}	$CH_3-CH_2-CH_2-CH_2-CH_2-CH_2-CH_2-CH_3$	
9	C_9H_{20}	$CH_3-CH_2-CH_2-CH_2-CH_2-CH_2-CH_2-CH_2-CH_3$	
10	$C_{10}H_{22}$	$CH_3-CH_2-CH_2-CH_2-CH_2-CH_2-CH_2-CH_2-CH_2-CH_3$	

⚛ CORE CHEMISTRY SKILL

Naming and Drawing Alkanes

Condensed and Line-Angle Structural Formulas

In a condensed structural formula, each carbon atom and its attached hydrogen atoms are written as a group. A subscript indicates the number of hydrogen atoms bonded to each carbon atom.

$$H-\underset{\underset{H}{|}}{\overset{\overset{H}{|}}{C}}- \quad = \quad CH_3- \qquad\qquad -\underset{\underset{H}{|}}{\overset{\overset{H}{|}}{C}}- \quad = \quad -CH_2-$$

Expanded   Condensed   Expanded   Condensed

When an organic molecule consists of a chain of three or more carbon atoms, the carbon atoms do not lie in a straight line. Rather, they are arranged in a zigzag pattern.

A simplified structure called the **line-angle structural formula** shows a zigzag line in which carbon atoms are represented as the ends of each line and as corners. For example, in the line-angle structural formula of pentane, each line in the zigzag drawing represents a single bond. The carbon atoms on the ends are bonded to three hydrogen atoms. However, the carbon atoms in the middle of the carbon chain are each bonded to two carbons and two hydrogen atoms as shown in Sample Problem 12.2.

Guide to Drawing Structural Formulas for Alkanes

STEP 1
Draw the carbon chain.

STEP 2
Draw the expanded structural formula by adding the hydrogen atoms using single bonds to each of the carbon atoms.

STEP 3
Draw the condensed structural formula by combining the H atoms with each C atom.

STEP 4
Draw the line-angle structural formula as a zigzag line in which the ends and corners represent C atoms.

▶ SAMPLE PROBLEM 12.2 Drawing Expanded, Condensed, and Line-Angle Structural Formulas for an Alkane

Draw the expanded, condensed, and line-angle structural formulas for pentane.

SOLUTION

STEP 1 Draw the carbon chain. A molecule of pentane has five carbon atoms in a continuous chain.

$$C-C-C-C-C$$

STEP 2 Draw the expanded structural formula by adding the hydrogen atoms using single bonds to each of the carbon atoms.

$$H-\underset{\underset{H}{|}}{\overset{\overset{H}{|}}{C}}-\underset{\underset{H}{|}}{\overset{\overset{H}{|}}{C}}-\underset{\underset{H}{|}}{\overset{\overset{H}{|}}{C}}-\underset{\underset{H}{|}}{\overset{\overset{H}{|}}{C}}-\underset{\underset{H}{|}}{\overset{\overset{H}{|}}{C}}-H$$

STEP 3 Draw the condensed structural formula by combining the H atoms with each C atom.

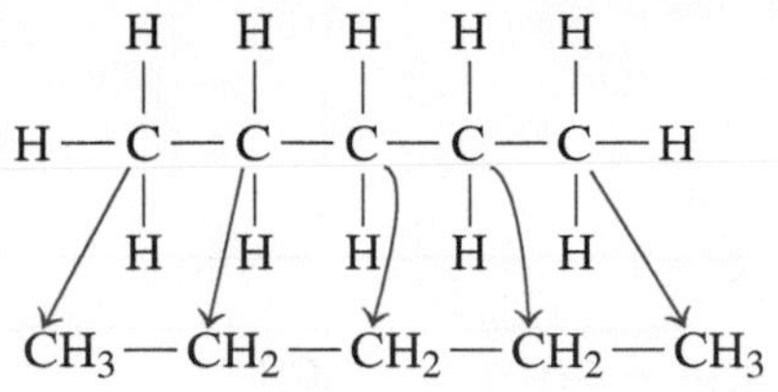

$$
\begin{array}{ccccc}
\text{H} & \text{H} & \text{H} & \text{H} & \text{H} \\
| & | & | & | & | \\
\text{H}-\text{C}-\text{C}-\text{C}-\text{C}-\text{C}-\text{H} \\
| & | & | & | & | \\
\text{H} & \text{H} & \text{H} & \text{H} & \text{H}
\end{array}
$$

Expanded structural formula

$CH_3-CH_2-CH_2-CH_2-CH_3$ Condensed structural formula

STEP 4 Draw the line-angle structural formula as a zigzag line in which the ends and corners represent C atoms.

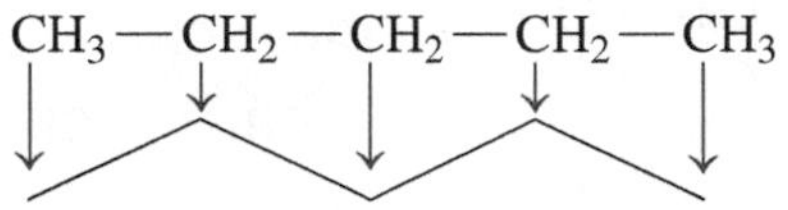

$CH_3-CH_2-CH_2-CH_2-CH_3$ Condensed structural formula

Line-angle structural formula

STUDY CHECK 12.2

Draw the condensed structural formula and give the name for the following line-angle structural formula:

ANSWER

$CH_3-CH_2-CH_2-CH_2-CH_2-CH_2-CH_3$ heptane

Conformations of Alkanes

Because an alkane has only single carbon–carbon bonds, the groups attached to each C are not in fixed positions. They can rotate freely about the bond connecting the carbon atoms. This motion is analogous to the independent rotation of the wheels of a toy car. Thus, different arrangements, known as *conformations*, occur during the rotation about a single bond.

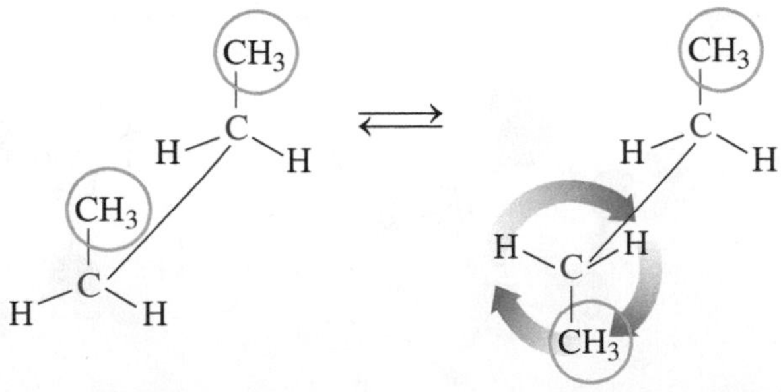

Suppose we could look at butane, C_4H_{10}, as it rotates. Sometimes the $-CH_3$ groups line up in front of each other, and at other times they are opposite each other. As the $-CH_3$ groups turn around the single bond, the carbon chain in the condensed structural formulas may appear at different angles. For example, butane can be drawn using a variety of two-dimensional condensed structural formulas as shown in Table 12.3. All these condensed structural formulas represent the same compound with four carbon atoms.

TABLE 12.3 Some Structural Formulas for Butane, C_4H_{10}

Expanded Structural Formula

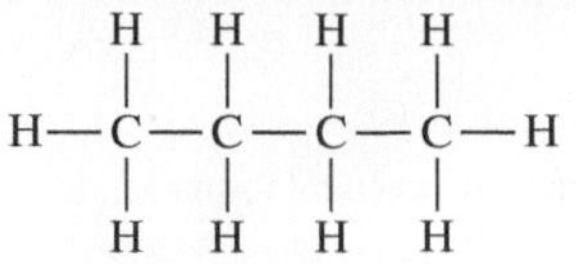

$$
\begin{array}{ccccc}
& H & H & H & H \\
& | & | & | & | \\
H- & C- & C- & C- & C-H \\
& | & | & | & | \\
& H & H & H & H
\end{array}
$$

Condensed Structural Formulas

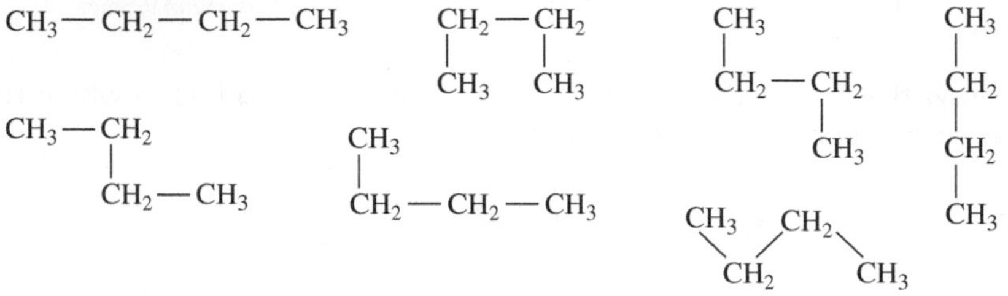

$CH_3-CH_2-CH_2-CH_3$

$\begin{array}{cc} CH_2-CH_2 \\ | \quad\quad | \\ CH_3 \quad CH_3 \end{array}$

$\begin{array}{c} CH_3 \\ | \\ CH_2-CH_2 \\ \quad\quad | \\ \quad\quad CH_3 \end{array}$

$\begin{array}{c} CH_3 \\ | \\ CH_2 \\ | \\ CH_2 \\ | \\ CH_3 \end{array}$

$\begin{array}{c} CH_3-CH_2 \\ \quad\quad | \\ \quad\quad CH_2-CH_3 \end{array}$

$\begin{array}{c} CH_3 \\ | \\ CH_2-CH_2-CH_3 \end{array}$

$CH_3 \quad CH_2$
$\quad\quad CH_2 \quad CH_3$

Line-Angle Structural Formulas

Cycloalkanes

Hydrocarbons can also form cyclic or ring structures called **cycloalkanes**, which have two fewer hydrogen atoms than the corresponding alkanes. The simplest cycloalkane, cyclopropane (C_3H_6), has a ring of three carbon atoms bonded to six hydrogen atoms. Most often cycloalkanes are drawn using their line-angle structural formulas, which appear as simple geometric figures. As seen for alkanes, each corner of the line-angle structural formula for a cycloalkane represents a carbon atom.

The ball-and-stick models, condensed structural formulas, and line-angle structural formulas for several cycloalkanes are shown in Table 12.4. A cycloalkane is named by adding the prefix *cyclo* to the name of the alkane with the same number of carbon atoms.

TABLE 12.4 Formulas of Some Common Cycloalkanes

Name			
Cyclopropane	Cyclobutane	Cyclopentane	Cyclohexane

Ball-and-Stick Model

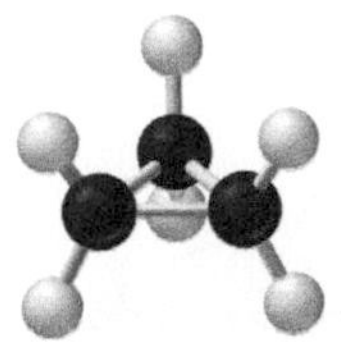

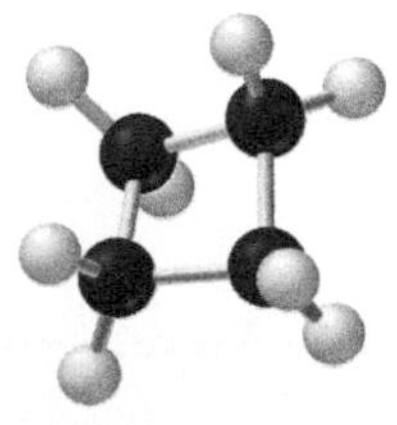

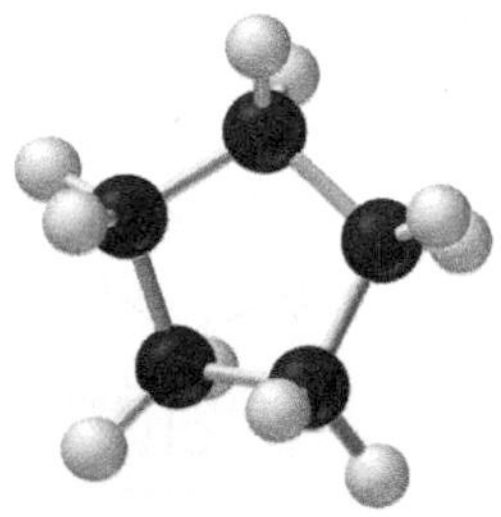

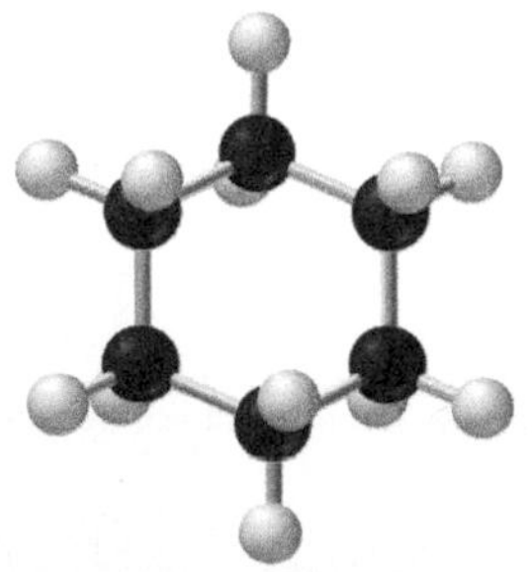

Condensed Structural Formula

$\begin{array}{c} CH_2 \\ H_2C-CH_2 \end{array}$

$\begin{array}{c} H_2C-CH_2 \\ H_2C-CH_2 \end{array}$

$\begin{array}{c} CH_2 \\ H_2C \quad CH_2 \\ H_2C-CH_2 \end{array}$

$\begin{array}{c} CH_2 \\ H_2C \quad CH_2 \\ H_2C \quad CH_2 \\ CH_2 \end{array}$

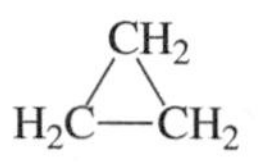

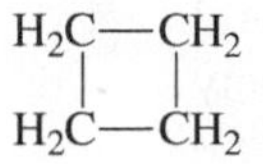

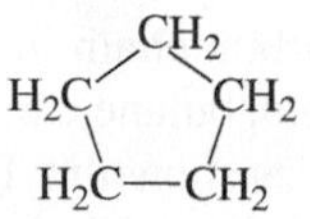

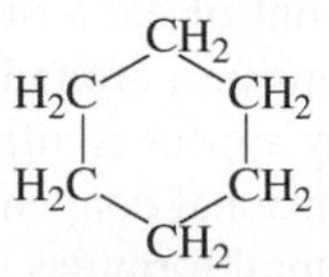

Line-Angle Structural Formula

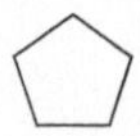

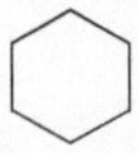

SAMPLE PROBLEM 12.3 Naming Alkanes and Cycloalkanes

Give the IUPAC name for each of the following:

a.    b.

SOLUTION

a. A chain with eight carbon atoms is octane.

b. The ring of six carbon atoms is named cyclohexane.

STUDY CHECK 12.3

What is the IUPAC name of the following compound?

ANSWER

cyclobutane

QUESTIONS AND PROBLEMS

12.2 Alkanes

LEARNING GOAL Write the IUPAC names and draw the condensed or line-angle structural formulas for alkanes and cycloalkanes.

12.9 Give the IUPAC name for each of the following alkanes and cycloalkanes:

a.   b. CH_3—CH_3

c.   d.

12.10 Give the IUPAC name for each of the following alkanes and cycloalkanes:

a. CH_4 b.

c.   d.

12.11 Draw the condensed structural formula for alkanes or the line-angle structural formula for cycloalkanes for each of the following:
   a. methane
   b. ethane
   c. pentane
   d. cyclopropane

12.12 Draw the condensed structural formula for alkanes or the line-angle structural formula for cycloalkanes for each of the following:
   a. propane
   b. hexane
   c. heptane
   d. cyclopentane

12.3 Alkanes with Substituents

When an alkane has four or more carbon atoms, the atoms can be arranged so that a side group called a *branch* or **substituent** is attached to a carbon chain. For example, there are different ball-and-stick models for two compounds that have the molecular formula C_4H_{10}. One model is shown as a chain of four carbon atoms. In the other model, a carbon atom is attached as a branch or substituent to a carbon in a chain of three atoms (see Figure 12.2). An alkane with at least one branch is called a *branched alkane*. When the two compounds have the same molecular formula but different arrangements of atoms, they are called **structural isomers**.

LEARNING GOAL

Write the IUPAC names for alkanes with substituents and draw their condensed and line-angle structural formulas.

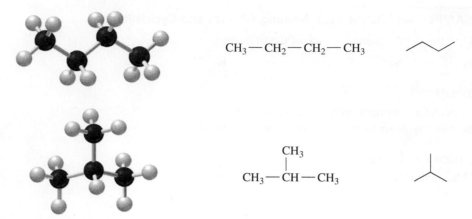

$$CH_3-CH_2-CH_2-CH_3$$

$$\begin{array}{c} CH_3 \\ | \\ CH_3-CH-CH_3 \end{array}$$

FIGURE 12.2 ▶ The structural isomers of C_4H_{10} have the same number and type of atoms but are bonded in a different order.

🅠 What makes these molecules structural isomers?

In another example, we can draw the condensed and line-angle structural formulas for three different structural isomers with the molecular formula C_5H_{12} as follows:

Structural Isomers of C_5H_{12}

Condensed	$CH_3-CH_2-CH_2-CH_2-CH_3$	$\begin{array}{c}CH_3\\|\\CH_3-CH-CH_2-CH_3\end{array}$	$\begin{array}{c}CH_3\\|\\CH_3-C-CH_3\\|\\CH_3\end{array}$
Line-Angle			

▶ **SAMPLE PROBLEM 12.4 Structural Isomers**

Identify each pair of formulas as structural isomers or the same molecule.

a. $\begin{array}{cc}CH_3 & CH_3\\|&|\\CH_2-CH_2\end{array}$ and $\begin{array}{c}CH_2-CH_2-CH_3\\|\\CH_3\end{array}$

b.   and

SOLUTION

a. When we add up the number of C atoms and H atoms, they give the same molecular formula C_4H_{10}. The condensed structural formula on the left has a chain of four C atoms. Even though the $-CH_3$ ends are drawn up, they are part of the four-carbon chain. The condensed structural formula on the right also has a four-carbon chain even though one $-CH_3$ end is drawn down. Thus both condensed structural formulas represent the same molecule and are not structural isomers.

b. When we add up the number of C atoms and H atoms, they give the same molecular formula C_6H_{14}. The line-angle structural formula on the left has a five-carbon chain with a $-CH_3$ substituent on the second carbon of the chain. The line-angle structural formula on the right has a four-carbon chain with two $-CH_3$ substituents, one bonded to the second carbon and one bonded to the third carbon. Thus there is a different order of bonding of atoms, which represents structural isomers.

STUDY CHECK 12.4

Why does the following formula represent a different structural isomer of the molecules in Sample Problem 12.4, part **b**?

ANSWER

This formula represents a different structural isomer because the —CH_3 substituent is on the third carbon of the chain.

Substituents in Alkanes

In the IUPAC names for alkanes, a carbon branch is named as an **alkyl group**, which is an alkane that is missing one hydrogen atom. The alkyl group is named by replacing the *ane* ending of the corresponding alkane name with *yl*. Alkyl groups cannot exist on their own: They must be attached to a carbon chain. When a halogen atom is attached to a carbon chain, it is named as a *halo* group: *fluoro, chloro, bromo,* or *iodo*. Some of the common groups attached to carbon chains are illustrated in Table 12.5.

TABLE 12.5 Formulas and Names of Some Common Substituents

Formula	CH_3-		CH_3-CH_2-		
Name	methyl		ethyl		

Formula	$CH_3-CH_2-CH_2-$		$CH_3-CH-CH_3$ (with CH on top)		
Name	propyl		isopropyl		

Formula	$CH_3-CH_2-CH_2-CH_2-$	$CH_3-CH-CH_2-$ (with CH_3 on top)	$CH_3-CH-CH_2-CH_3$ (with CH_3 on top, sec)	CH_3-C-CH_3 (with CH_3 top and bottom, tert)
Name	butyl	isobutyl	*sec*-butyl	*tert*-butyl

Formula	F—	Cl—	Br—	I—
Name	fluoro	chloro	bromo	iodo

Naming Alkanes with Substituents

In the IUPAC system of naming, a carbon chain is numbered to give the location of the substituents. Let's take a look at how we use the IUPAC system to name the alkane shown in Sample Problem 12.5.

Interactive Video

Naming Alkanes

▶ **SAMPLE PROBLEM 12.5 Writing IUPAC Names for Alkanes with Substituents**

Give the IUPAC name for the following alkane:

$$CH_3-CH-CH_2-C-CH_2-CH_3$$

(with CH_3 on the second carbon, Br and CH_3 on the fourth carbon)

SOLUTION

ANALYZE THE PROBLEM	Given	Need
	six carbon chain, two methyl groups, one bromo group	IUPAC name

STEP 1 Write the alkane name for the longest chain of carbon atoms.

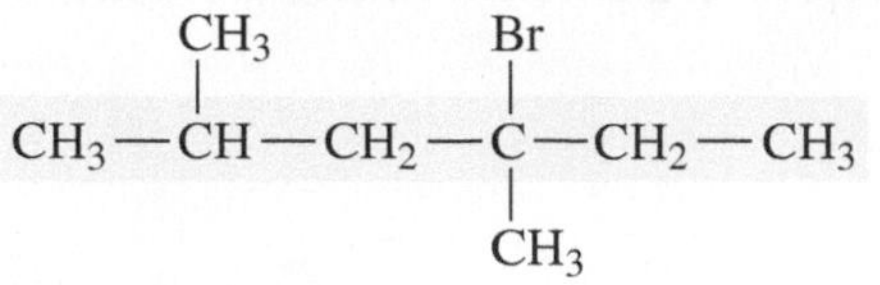

$$CH_3-CH-CH_2-C-CH_2-CH_3 \qquad \text{hexane}$$

with CH₃ above CH and Br above C, CH₃ below C.

STEP 2 Number the carbon atoms starting from the end nearer a substituent. Carbon 1 is the carbon atom nearer a methyl group, —CH₃, on the left.

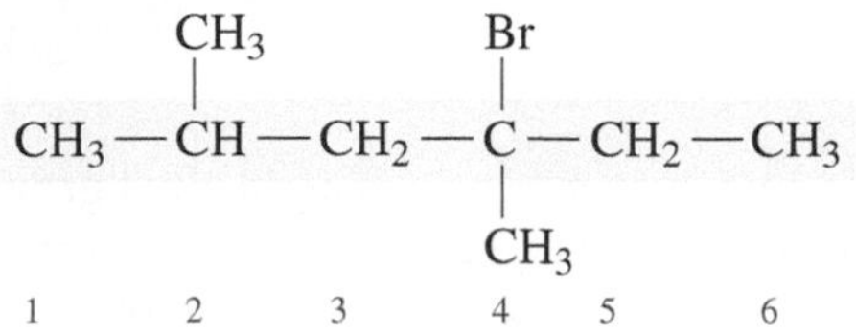

$$CH_3-CH-CH_2-C-CH_2-CH_3 \qquad \text{hexane}$$

1   2   3   4   5   6

with CH₃ above CH and Br above C, CH₃ below C.

STEP 3 Give the location and name for each substituent (alphabetical order) as a prefix to the name of the main chain. The substituents, which are bromo and methyl groups, are listed in alphabetical order (bromo first, then methyl). A hyphen is placed between the number on the carbon chain and the substituent name. When there are two or more of the same substituent, a prefix (*di*, *tri*, *tetra*) is used in front of the name. However, these prefixes are not used to determine the alphabetical order of the substituents. Then commas are used to separate the numbers for the locations of the substituents.

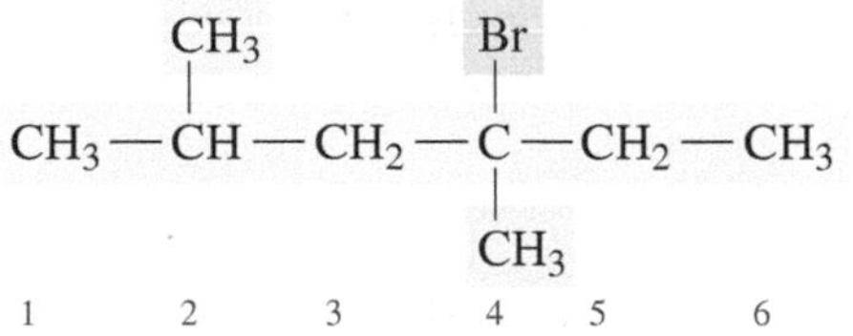

$$CH_3-CH-CH_2-C-CH_2-CH_3 \qquad \text{4-bromo-2,4-dimethylhexane}$$

1   2   3   4   5   6

with CH₃ above CH and Br above C, CH₃ below C.

STUDY CHECK 12.5

Give the IUPAC name for the following compound:

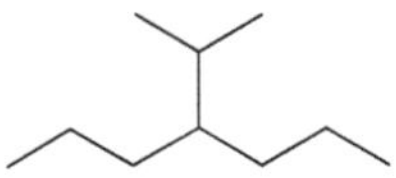

ANSWER

4-isopropylheptane

Naming Cycloalkanes with Substituents

When one substituent is attached to a carbon atom in a cycloalkane, the name of the substituent is placed in front of the cycloalkane name. No number is needed for a single alkyl group or halogen atom because the carbon atoms in the cycloalkane are equivalent. However, if two or more substituents are attached, the ring is numbered by assigning carbon 1 to the substituent that comes first alphabetically. Then we count the carbon atoms in the ring in the direction (clockwise or counterclockwise) that gives the lower numbers to the substituents.

Methylcyclopentane 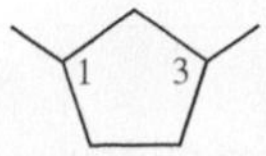   1,3-Dimethylcyclopentane 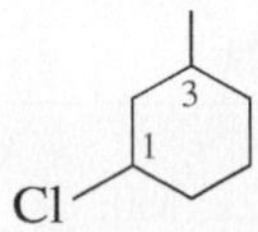   1-Chloro-3-methylcyclohexane

Haloalkanes

In a *haloalkane*, halogen atoms replace hydrogen atoms in an alkane. The halo substituents are numbered and arranged alphabetically, just as we did with the alkyl groups. Many times chemists use the common, traditional name for these compounds rather than the systematic IUPAC name. Simple haloalkanes are commonly named as alkyl halides; the carbon group is named as an alkyl group followed by the halide name.

Examples of Haloalkanes

Formula	CH_3-Cl	CH_3-CH_2-Br	$CH_3-\underset{\underset{F}{\vert}}{CH}-CH_3$	$CH_3-\underset{\underset{CH_3}{\vert}}{\overset{\overset{Cl}{\vert}}{C}}-CH_3$
IUPAC	Chloromethane	Bromoethane	2-Fluoropropane	2-Chloro-2-methylpropane
Common	Methyl chloride	Ethyl bromide	Isopropyl fluoride	*tert*-Butyl chloride

Drawing Condensed and Line-Angle Structural Formulas for Alkanes

The IUPAC name gives all the information needed to draw the condensed structural formula for an alkane. Suppose you are asked to draw the condensed structural formula for 2,3-dimethylbutane. The alkane name gives the number of carbon atoms in the longest chain. The names in the beginning indicate the substituents and where they are attached. We can break down the name in the following way:

2,3-Dimethylbutane

2,3-	Di	methyl	but	ane
Substituents on carbons 2 and 3	two identical groups	—CH₃ alkyl groups	four C atoms in the main chain	single (C—C) bonds

---

▶ **SAMPLE PROBLEM 12.6 Drawing Condensed Structures from IUPAC Names**

Draw the condensed and line-angle structural formulas for 2,3-dimethylbutane.

ANALYZE THE PROBLEM	Given	Need
	2,3-dimethylbutane	condensed and line-angle structural formulas

SOLUTION

STEP 1 Draw the main chain of carbon atoms. For butane, we draw a chain or a zigzag line of four carbon atoms.

$$C-C-C-C$$

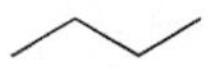

STEP 2 Number the chain and place the substituents on the carbons indicated by the numbers. The first part of the name indicates two methyl groups —CH₃: one on carbon 2 and one on carbon 3.

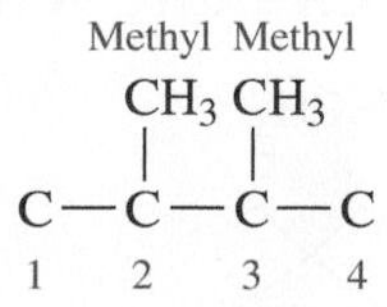

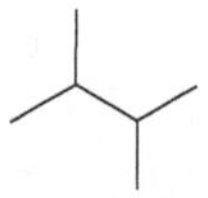

> **Guide to Drawing Structural Formulas for Alkanes with Substituents**
>
> **STEP 1**
> Draw the main chain of carbon atoms.
>
> **STEP 2**
> Number the chain and place the substituents on the carbons indicated by the numbers.
>
> **STEP 3**
> For the condensed structural formula, add the correct number of hydrogen atoms to give four bonds to each C atom.

STEP **3** For the condensed structural formula, add the correct number of hydrogen atoms to give four bonds to each C atom.

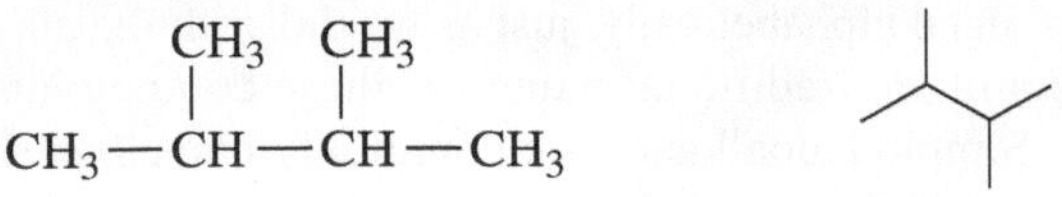

$$CH_3-CH-CH-CH_3$$

with CH₃ substituents on the two middle carbons

2,3-Dimethylbutane

STUDY CHECK 12.6

Draw the condensed and line-angle structural formulas for 2-bromo-3-ethyl-4-methylpentane.

ANSWER

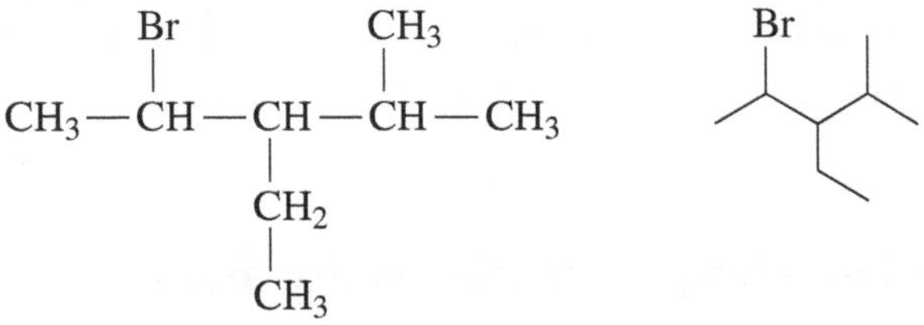

$$CH_3-CH-CH-CH-CH_3$$

with Br, CH₃, and CH₂—CH₃ substituents

QUESTIONS AND PROBLEMS

12.3 Alkanes with Substituents

LEARNING GOAL Write the IUPAC names for alkanes with substituents and draw their condensed and line-angle structural formulas.

12.13 Indicate whether each of the following pairs represent structural isomers or the same molecule:

a. 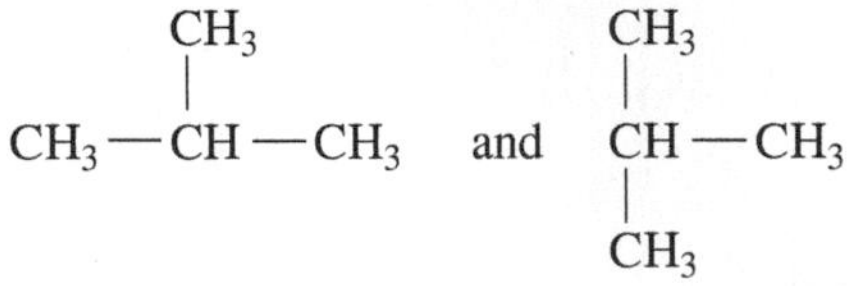 $CH_3-CH-CH_3$ and $CH-CH_3$
   (with CH₃ substituents)

b. 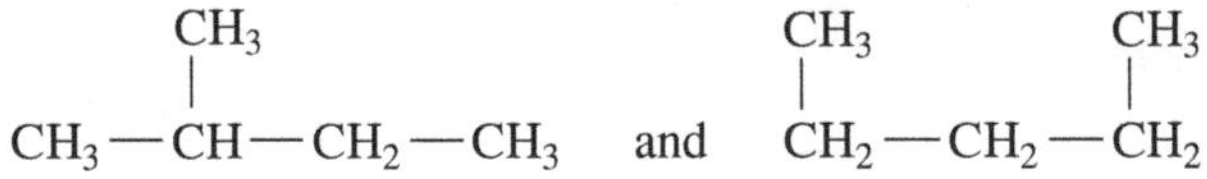 $CH_3-CH-CH_2-CH_3$ and $CH_2-CH_2-CH_2$
   (with CH₃ substituents)

c. 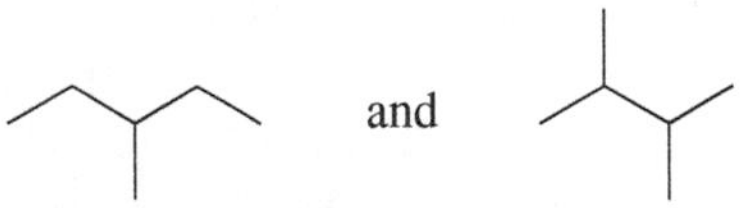 and

12.14 Indicate whether each of the following pairs represent structural isomers or the same molecule:

a. 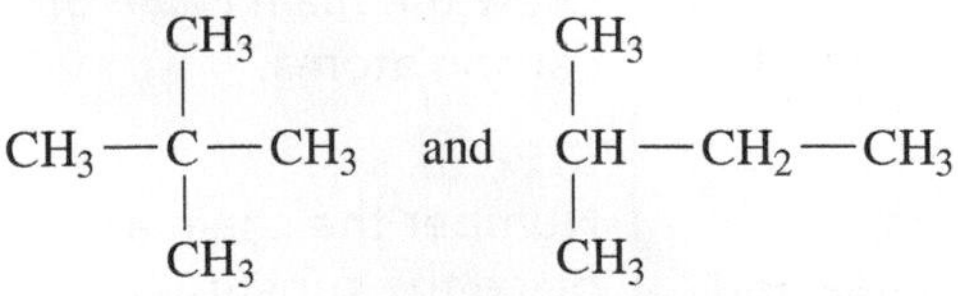 CH_3-C-CH_3 and $CH-CH_2-CH_3$
   (with CH₃ substituents)

b. $CH_3-CH-CH-CH_2$ and
   (with CH₃ CH₃ CH₃ substituents)
   $CH_3-CH-CH_2-CH-CH_3$
   (with CH₃ substituents)

c. and

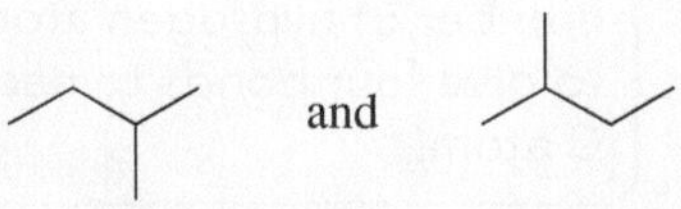

12.15 Give the IUPAC name for each of the following:

a. 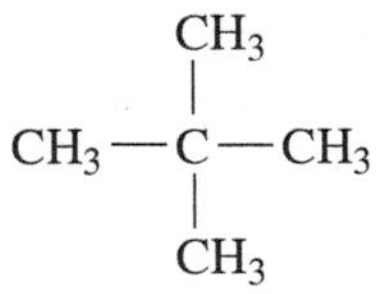 CH_3-C-CH_3
   (with CH₃ substituents)

b.

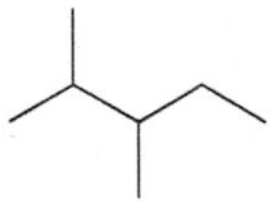

c. 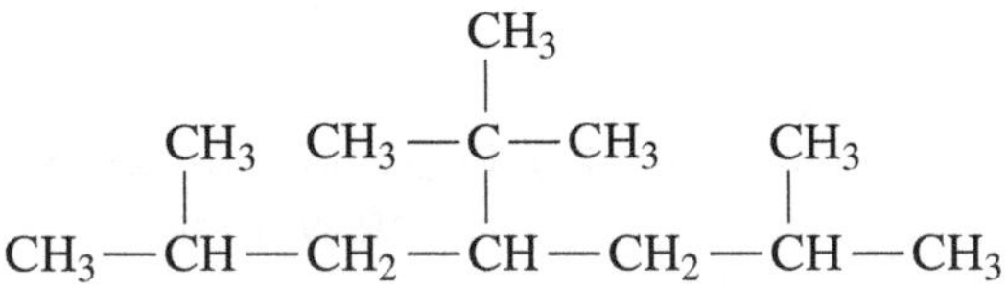 $CH_3-CH-CH_2-CH-CH_2-CH-CH_3$
   (with CH₃, CH₃—C—CH₃, CH₃ substituents)

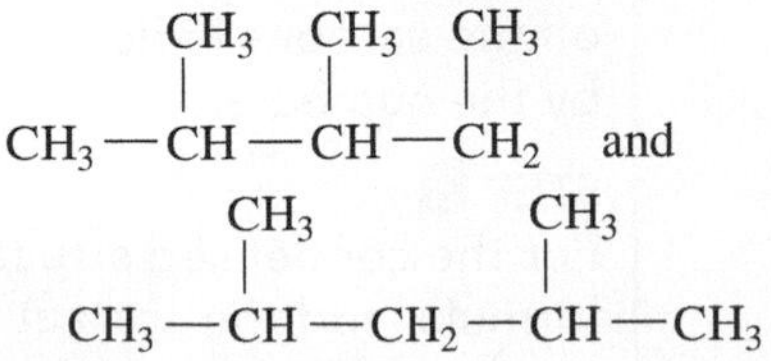

d.

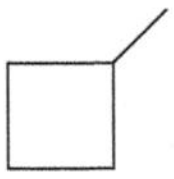

e.

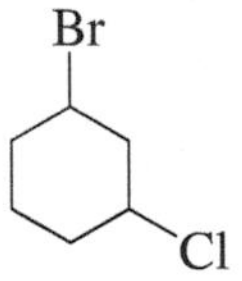

12.16 Give the IUPAC name for each of the following:

a. 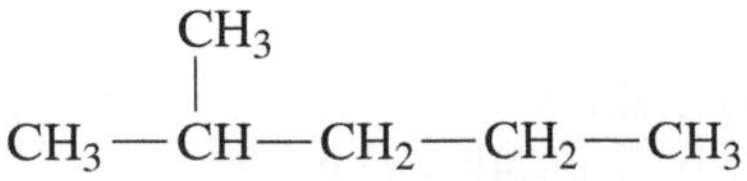 $CH_3-CH-CH_2-CH_2-CH_3$
   (with CH₃ substituent)

b.

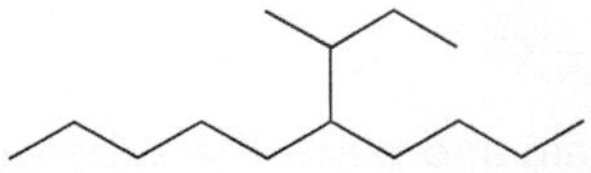

c. 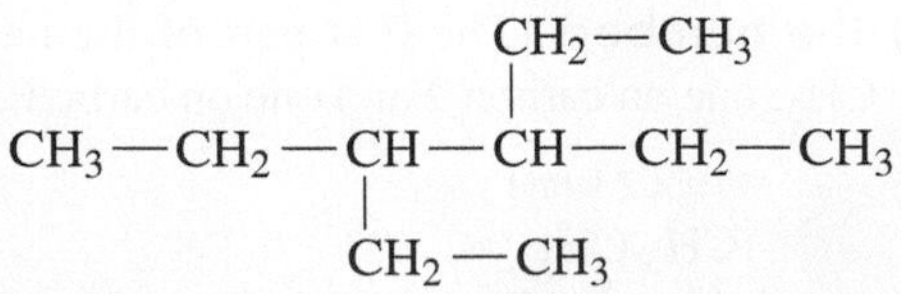 $CH_3-CH_2-CH-CH-CH_2-CH_3$
   (with CH₂—CH₃ and CH₂—CH₃ substituents)

d.

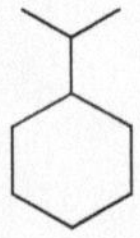

e.

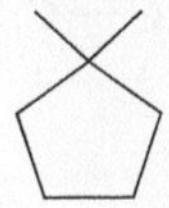

12.17 Draw the condensed structural formula for each of the following alkanes:
   a. 3,3-dimethylpentane
   b. 2,3,5-trimethylhexane
   c. 3-ethyl-5-isopropyloctane
   d. 1-bromo-2-chloroethane

12.18 Draw the condensed structural formula for each of the following alkanes:
   a. 3-ethylpentane
   b. 4-isopropyl-3-methylheptane
   c. 4-ethyl-2,2-dimethyloctane
   d. 2-bromopropane

12.19 Draw the line-angle structural formula for each of the following:
   a. 3-methylheptane
   b. 1-chloro-3-ethylcyclopentane
   c. bromocyclobutane
   d. 2,3-dichlorohexane

12.20 Draw the line-angle structural formula for each of the following:
   a. 1-bromo-2-methylpentane
   b. 1,2,3-trimethylcyclopropane
   c. ethylcyclohexane
   d. 4-chlorooctane

12.4 Properties of Alkanes

Many types of alkanes are the components of fuels that power our cars and oil that heats our homes. You may have used a mixture of hydrocarbons such as mineral oil as a laxative or petrolatum jelly to soften your skin. The differences in uses of many of the alkanes result from their physical properties, including solubility and density.

Some Uses of Alkanes

The first four alkanes—methane, ethane, propane, and butane—are gases at room temperature and are widely used as heating fuels.

Alkanes having five to eight carbon atoms (pentane, hexane, heptane, and octane) are liquids at room temperature. They are highly volatile, which makes them useful in fuels such as gasoline.

Liquid alkanes with 9 to 17 carbon atoms have higher boiling points and are found in kerosene, diesel, and jet fuels. Motor oil is a mixture of high-molecular-weight liquid hydrocarbons and is used to lubricate the internal components of engines. Mineral oil is a mixture of liquid hydrocarbons and is used as a laxative and a lubricant. Alkanes with 18 or more carbon atoms are waxy solids at room temperature. Known as paraffins, they are used in waxy coatings added to fruits and vegetables to retain moisture, inhibit mold, and enhance appearance. Petrolatum jelly, or Vaseline, is a semisolid mixture of hydrocarbons with more than 25 carbon atoms used in ointments and cosmetics and as a lubricant.

LEARNING GOAL

Identify the properties of alkanes and write a balanced chemical equation for combustion.

The solid alkanes that make up waxy coatings on fruits and vegetables help retain moisture, inhibit mold, and enhance appearance.

Melting and Boiling Points

Alkanes have the lowest melting and boiling points of all the organic compounds. This occurs because alkanes contain only the nonpolar bonds of $C—C$ and $C—H$. Therefore, the attractions that occur between alkane molecules in the solid and liquid states are because of the relatively weak dispersion forces. As the number of carbon atoms increases, there is also an increase in the number of electrons, which increases the attraction because of the dispersion forces. Thus, alkanes with higher masses have higher melting and boiling points.

CH_4	$CH_3—CH_3$	$CH_3—CH_2—CH_3$	$CH_3—CH_2—CH_2—CH_3$	$CH_3—CH_2—CH_2—CH_2—CH_3$
Methane	Ethane	Propane	Butane	Pentane
bp $= -164$ °C	bp $= -89$ °C	bp $= -42$ °C	bp $= 0.5$ °C	bp $= 36$ °C

Number of Carbon Atoms Increases
Boiling Point Increases

The boiling points of branched alkanes are generally lower than the straight-chain isomers. The branched-chain alkanes tend to be more compact, which reduces the points of contact between the molecules. In an analogy, we can think of the carbon chains of straight-chain alkanes as pieces of licorice in a package. Because they have linear shapes, they can line up very close to each other, which gives many points of contact between the surface of the molecules. In our analogy, we can also think of branched alkanes as tennis balls in a can that, because of their spherical shapes, have only a small area of contact. One tennis ball represents an entire molecule. Because branched alkanes have fewer attractions, they have lower melting and boiling points.

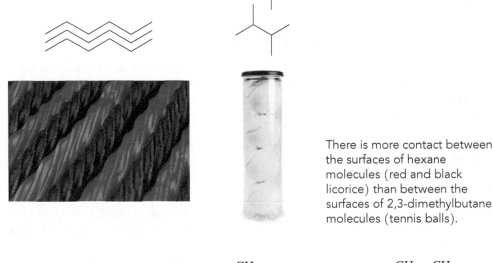

There is more contact between the surfaces of hexane molecules (red and black licorice) than between the surfaces of 2,3-dimethylbutane molecules (tennis balls).

$$CH_3-CH_2-CH_2-CH_2-CH_2-CH_3 \qquad CH_3-CH_2-\overset{\overset{\displaystyle CH_3}{|}}{CH}-CH_2-CH_3 \qquad CH_3-\overset{\overset{\displaystyle CH_3}{|}}{CH}-\overset{\overset{\displaystyle CH_3}{|}}{CH}-CH_3$$

Hexane
bp = 69 °C

3-Methylpentane
bp = 63 °C

2,3-Dimethylbutane
bp = 58 °C

Number of Branches Increases
Boiling Point Decreases

Cycloalkanes have higher boiling points than the straight-chain alkanes with the same number of carbon atoms. Because rotation of carbon bonds is restricted, cycloalkanes maintain a rigid structure. Cycloalkanes with their rigid structures can be stacked closely together, which gives them many points of contact and therefore many attractions to each other.

We can compare the boiling points of straight-chain alkanes, branched-chain alkanes, and cycloalkanes with five carbon atoms as shown in Table 12.6.

Combustion of Alkanes

The carbon–carbon single bonds in alkanes are difficult to break, which makes them the least reactive family of organic compounds. However, alkanes burn readily in oxygen to produce carbon dioxide, water, and energy.

$$\text{Alkane}(g) + O_2(g) \xrightarrow{\Delta} CO_2(g) + H_2O(g) + \text{energy}$$

For example, methane is the natural gas we use to cook our food and heat our homes. The equation for the combustion of methane (CH_4) is written:

$$CH_4(g) + 2O_2(g) \xrightarrow{\Delta} CO_2(g) + 2H_2O(g) + \text{energy}$$
Methane

TABLE 12.6 Comparison of Boiling Points of Alkanes and Cycloalkanes with Five Carbons

Formula	Name	Boiling Point (°C)
Straight-Chain Alkane		
$CH_3-CH_2-CH_2-CH_2-CH_3$	Pentane	36
Branched-Chain Alkanes		
$CH_3-\overset{\overset{CH_3}{\mid}}{CH}-CH_2-CH_3$	2-Methylbutane	28
$CH_3-\overset{\overset{CH_3}{\mid}}{\underset{\underset{CH_3}{\mid}}{C}}-CH_3$	Dimethylpropane	10
Cycloalkane		
⬠	Cyclopentane	49

In another example, propane is the gas used in portable heaters and gas barbecues (see Figure 12.3). The equation for the combustion of propane (C_3H_8) is written:

$$C_3H_8(g) + 5O_2(g) \xrightarrow{\Delta} 3CO_2(g) + 4H_2O(g) + \text{energy}$$
Propane

In the cells of our bodies, energy is produced by the combustion of glucose. Although a series of reactions is involved, we can write the overall combustion of glucose in our cells as follows:

$$C_6H_{12}O_6(aq) + 6O_2(g) \xrightarrow{\text{Enzymes}} 6CO_2(g) + 6H_2O(l) + \text{energy}$$
Glucose

FIGURE 12.3 ▶ The propane fuel in the tank undergoes combustion, which provides energy.

◉ What is the balanced equation for the combustion of propane?

Solubility and Density

Alkanes are nonpolar, which makes them insoluble in water. However, they are soluble in nonpolar solvents such as other alkanes. Alkanes have densities from 0.62 g/mL to about 0.79 g/mL, which is less than the density of water (1.0 g/mL).

If there is an oil spill in the ocean, the alkanes in the oil, which do not mix with water, form a thin layer on the surface that spreads over a large area. In April 2010, an explosion on an oil-drilling rig in the Gulf of Mexico caused the largest oil spill in U.S. history. At its maximum, an estimated 10 million liters of oil was leaked every day. Other major oil spills occurred in Queensland, Australia (2009), the coast of Wales (1996), the Shetland Islands (1993), and Alaska, from the *Exxon Valdez*, in 1989 (see Figure 12.4). If the crude oil reaches land, there can be considerable damage to beaches, shellfish, birds, and wildlife habitats. When animals such as birds are covered with oil, they must be cleaned quickly because ingestion of the hydrocarbons when they try to clean themselves is fatal.

Cleanup of oil spills includes mechanical, chemical, and microbiological methods. A boom may be placed around the leaking oil until it can be removed. Boats called skimmers then scoop up the oil and place it in tanks. In a chemical method, a substance that attracts oil is used to pick up oil, which is then scraped off into recovery tanks. Certain bacteria that ingest oil are also used to break oil down into less harmful products.

FIGURE 12.4 ▶ In oil spills, large quantities of oil spread out to form a thin layer on top of the ocean surface.

◉ What physical properties cause oil to remain on the surface of water?

QUESTIONS AND PROBLEMS

12.4 Properties of Alkanes

LEARNING GOAL Identify the properties of alkanes and write a balanced chemical equation for combustion.

12.21 Heptane, used as a solvent for rubber cement, has a density of 0.68 g/mL and boils at 98 °C.
   a. Draw the condensed and line-angle structural formulas for heptane.
   b. Is heptane a solid, liquid, or gas at room temperature?
   c. Is heptane soluble in water?
   d. Will heptane float on water or sink?
   e. Write the balanced chemical equation for the complete combustion of heptane.

12.22 Nonane has a density of 0.79 g/mL and boils at 151 °C.
   a. Draw the condensed and line-angle structural formulas for nonane.
   b. Is nonane a solid, liquid, or gas at room temperature?
   c. Is nonane soluble in water?
   d. Will nonane float on water or sink?
   e. Write the balanced chemical equation for the complete combustion of nonane.

12.23 Write the balanced chemical equation for the complete combustion of each of the following compounds:
   a. ethane
   b. cyclopropane
   c. octane

12.24 Write the balanced chemical equation for the complete combustion of each of the following compounds:
   a. hexane   **b.** cyclopentane   **c.** butane

Butane in a portable burner undergoes combustion.

12.25 In each of the following pairs of hydrocarbons, which one would you expect to have the higher boiling point?
   a. pentane or heptane
   b. propane or cyclopropane
   c. hexane or 2-methylpentane

12.26 In each of the following pairs of hydrocarbons, which one would you expect to have the higher boiling point?
   a. propane or butane
   b. hexane or cyclohexane
   c. 2,2-dimethylpentane or heptane

LEARNING GOAL

Identify structural formulas as alkenes, cycloalkenes, and alkynes, and write their IUPAC names.

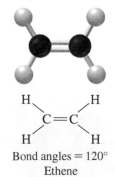

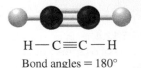

Bond angles = 120°
Ethene

H—C≡C—H

Bond angles = 180°
Ethyne

FIGURE 12.5 ▶ Ball-and-stick models of ethene and ethyne show the double or triple bonds and the bond angles.

◉ Why are these compounds called unsaturated hydrocarbons?

12.5 Alkenes and Alkynes

Alkenes and *alkynes* are families of hydrocarbons that contain double and triple bonds, respectively. They are called *unsaturated hydrocarbons* because they do not contain the maximum number of hydrogen atoms, as do alkanes. They react with hydrogen gas to increase the number of hydrogen atoms to become alkanes, which are *saturated hydrocarbons*.

Identifying Alkenes and Alkynes

Alkenes contain one or more carbon–carbon double bonds that form when adjacent carbon atoms share two pairs of valence electrons. Recall that *a carbon atom always forms four covalent bonds*. In the simplest alkene, ethene, C_2H_4, two carbon atoms are connected by a double bond and each is also attached to two H atoms. This gives each carbon atom in the double bond a trigonal planar arrangement with bond angles of 120°. As a result, the ethene molecule is flat because the carbon and hydrogen atoms all lie in the same plane (see Figure 12.5).

Ethene, more commonly called ethylene, is an important plant hormone involved in promoting the ripening of fruit. Commercially grown fruit, such as avocados, bananas, and tomatoes, are often picked before they are ripe. Before the fruit is brought to market, it is exposed to ethylene to accelerate the ripening process. Ethylene also accelerates the breakdown of cellulose in plants, which causes flowers to wilt and leaves to fall from trees.

In an **alkyne**, a triple bond forms when two carbon atoms share three pairs of valence electrons. In the simplest alkyne, ethyne (C_2H_2), the two carbon atoms of the triple bond are each attached to one hydrogen atom, which gives a triple bond a linear geometry. Ethyne, commonly called acetylene, is used in welding where it reacts with oxygen to produce flames with temperatures above 3300 °C.

Fruit is ripened with ethene, a plant hormone.

A mixture of acetylene and oxygen undergoes combustion during the welding of metals.

Naming Alkenes and Alkynes

The IUPAC names for alkenes and alkynes are similar to those of alkanes. Using the alkane name with the same number of carbon atoms, the *ane* ending is replaced with *ene* for an alkene and *yne* for an alkyne (see Table 12.7). Cyclic alkenes are named as *cycloalkenes*.

TABLE 12.7 Comparison of Names for Alkanes, Alkenes, and Alkynes

Alkane	Alkene	Alkyne
CH_3-CH_3	$H_2C=CH_2$	$HC\equiv CH$
Ethane	Ethene (ethylene)	Ethyne (acetylene)
$CH_3-CH_2-CH_3$	$CH_3-CH=CH_2$	$CH_3-C\equiv CH$
Propane	Propene	Propyne

Examples of naming an alkene and an alkyne are seen in Sample Problem 12.7.

▶**SAMPLE PROBLEM 12.7** Naming Alkenes and Alkynes

Write the IUPAC name for each of the following:

        CH_3
        |
a. $CH_3-CH-CH=CH-CH_3$ **b.** $CH_3-CH_2-C\equiv C-CH_2-CH_3$

SOLUTION

a.

	Given	Need
ANALYZE THE PROBLEM	five-carbon chain, double bond, methyl group	IUPAC name

STEP 1 Name the longest carbon chain that contains the double bond. There are five carbon atoms in the longest carbon chain containing the double bond. Replace the *ane* in the corresponding alkane name with *ene* to give pentene.

        CH_3
        |
   $CH_3-CH-CH=CH-CH_3$ pentene

Explore Your World
Ripening Fruit

Obtain two unripe green bananas. Place one in a plastic bag and seal the bag. Leave the banana and the bag with a banana on the counter. Check the bananas twice a day to observe any difference in the ripening process.

Questions

1. What compound is used to ripen the bananas?
2. What are some possible reasons for any difference in the ripening rate?
3. If you wish to ripen an avocado, what procedure might you use?

Guide to Naming Alkenes and Alkynes

STEP 1
Name the longest carbon chain that contains the double or triple bond.

STEP 2
Number the carbon chain starting from the end nearer the double or triple bond.

STEP 3
Give the location and name for each substituent (alphabetical order) as a prefix to the alkene or alkyne name.

STEP **2** Number the carbon chain starting from the end nearer the double bond. Place the number of the first carbon in the double bond in front of the alkene name.

$$CH_3-\underset{5}{CH}-\underset{4}{CH}=\underset{3}{CH}-\underset{2}{CH_3} \qquad \text{2-pentene}$$

with CH_3 group on carbon 4.

Alkenes or alkynes with two or three carbons do not need numbers. For example, the double bond in ethene or propene must be between carbon 1 and carbon 2.

STEP **3** Give the location and name for each substituent (alphabetical order) as a prefix to the alkene name. The methyl group is located on carbon 4.

$$CH_3-\underset{5}{CH}-\underset{4}{CH}=\underset{3}{CH}-\underset{2}{CH_3} \qquad \text{4-methyl-2-pentene}$$

b.

ANALYZE THE PROBLEM	Given	Need
	six carbon chain, triple bond	IUPAC name

STEP **1** Name the longest carbon chain that contains the triple bond. There are six carbon atoms in the longest chain containing the triple bond. Replace the *ane* in the corresponding alkane name with *yne* to give hexyne.

$$CH_3-CH_2-C\equiv C-CH_2-CH_3 \qquad \text{hexyne}$$

STEP **2** Number the carbon chain starting from the end nearer the triple bond. Place the number of the first carbon in the triple bond in front of the alkyne name.

$$\underset{1}{CH_3}-\underset{2}{CH_2}-\underset{3}{C}\equiv \underset{4}{C}-\underset{5}{CH_2}-\underset{6}{CH_3} \qquad \text{3-hexyne}$$

STEP **3** Give the location and name for each substituent (alphabetical order) as a prefix to the alkyne name. There are no substituents in this formula.

STUDY CHECK 12.7

Name each of the following:

a.

b.

ANSWER

a. 2-pentyne

b. 2-chloro-1-hexene

Naming Cycloalkenes

Some alkenes called *cycloalkenes* have a double bond within a ring structure. If there is no substituent, the double bond does not need a number. If there is a substituent, the carbons in the double bond are numbered as 1 and 2, and the ring is numbered in the direction that will give the lower number to the substituent.

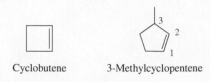

Cyclobutene   3-Methylcyclopentene

Chemistry Link to the Environment

Fragrant Alkenes

The odors you associate with lemons, oranges, roses, and lavender are because of volatile compounds that are synthesized by the plants. The pleasant flavors and fragrances of many fruits and flowers are often because of unsaturated compounds. They were some of the first kinds of compounds to be extracted from natural plant material. In ancient times, they were highly valued in their pure forms. Limonene and myrcene give the characteristic odors and flavors to lemons and bay leaves, respectively. Geraniol and citronellal give roses and lemongrass their distinct aromas. In the food and perfume industries, these compounds are extracted or synthesized and used as perfumes and flavorings.

The characteristic odor of a rose is because of geraniol, a 10-carbon alcohol with two double bonds.

$$CH_3-\overset{\overset{\displaystyle CH_3}{|}}{C}=CH-CH_2-CH_2-\overset{\overset{\displaystyle CH_3}{|}}{C}=CH-CH_2-OH$$

Geraniol, roses

$$CH_3-\overset{\overset{\displaystyle CH_3}{|}}{C}=CH-CH_2-CH_2-\overset{\overset{\displaystyle CH_2}{||}}{C}-CH=CH_2$$

Myrcene, bay leaves

$$CH_3-\overset{\overset{\displaystyle CH_3}{|}}{C}=CH-CH_2-CH_2-\overset{\overset{\displaystyle CH_3}{|}}{CH}-CH_2-\overset{\overset{\displaystyle O}{||}}{C}-H$$

Citronellal, lemongrass

Limonene, lemons and oranges

QUESTIONS AND PROBLEMS

12.5 Alkenes and Alkynes

LEARNING GOAL Identify structural formulas as alkenes, cycloalkenes, and alkynes, and write their IUPAC names.

12.27 Identify the following as alkanes, alkenes, cycloalkenes, or alkynes:

a. $$H-\overset{\overset{\displaystyle H}{|}}{\underset{\underset{\displaystyle H}{|}}{C}}-\overset{\overset{\displaystyle H}{|}}{C}=\overset{\overset{\displaystyle H}{|}}{C}-H$$ b. $CH_3-CH_2-C\equiv C-H$

c. (line-angle structure)   d. (line-angle structure)

12.28 Identify the following as alkanes, alkenes, cycloalkenes, or alkynes:

a. (triangle structure)   b. (line-angle structure)

c. $$CH_3-\overset{\overset{\displaystyle CH_3}{|}}{\underset{\underset{\displaystyle CH_3}{|}}{C}}=C-CH_3$$ d. (cyclopentane with $C\equiv CH$)

12.29 Give the IUPAC name for each of the following:

a. $$CH_3-\overset{\overset{\displaystyle CH_3}{|}}{C}=CH_2$$ b.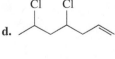

c. (cyclopentene structure)   d. (line-angle structure)

12.30 Give the IUPAC name for each of the following:

a. $H_2C=CH-CH_2-CH_2-CH_2-CH_3$

b. $$CH_3-C\equiv C-CH_2-CH_2-\overset{\overset{\displaystyle CH_3}{|}}{CH}-CH_3$$

c. (cyclohexene structure)   d.

12.31 Draw the condensed structural formulas for **a** and **b** and line-angle structural formulas for **c** and **d**:
a. 1-pentene
b. 2-methyl-1-butene
c. 3-methylcyclohexene
d. 1-chloro-3-hexyne

12.32 Draw the condensed structural formulas for **a** and **b** and line-angle structural formulas for **c** and **d**:
a. 3-methyl-1-butyne
b. 3,4-dimethyl-1-pentene
c. 1,2-dichlorocyclopentene
d. 2-methyl-2-hexene

LEARNING GOAL

Draw the condensed and line-angle structural formulas and give the names for the cis–trans isomers of alkenes.

12.6 Cis–Trans Isomers

In any alkene, the double bond is rigid, which means there is no rotation around the double bond (see Explore Your World "Modeling Cis–Trans Isomers"). As a result, the atoms or groups are attached to the carbon atoms in the double bond on one side or the other, which gives two different structures called *geometric isomers* or *cis–trans isomers*.

For example, the formula for 1,2-dichloroethene can be drawn as two different molecules, which are cis–trans isomers. In the expanded structural formulas, the atoms bonded to the carbon atoms in the double bond have bond angles of 120°. When we draw 1,2-dichloroethene, we add the prefix *cis* or *trans* to denote whether the atoms bonded to the carbon atoms are on the same side or opposite sides of the molecule. In the **cis isomer**, the chlorine atoms are on the same side of the double bond. In the **trans isomer**, the chlorine atoms are on opposite sides of the double bond. *Trans* means "across," as in transcontinental; *cis* means "on this side."

$$Cl—CH=CH—Cl$$
1,2-Dichloroethene

Chlorine atoms are on the same side of the double bond.

cis-1,2-Dichloroethene   *trans*-1,2-Dichloroethene

Chlorine atoms are on opposite sides of the double bond.

Another example of a cis–trans isomer is 2-butene. If we look closely at 2-butene, we find that each carbon in the double bond is bonded to a $—CH_3$ group and a hydrogen atom. We can draw cis–trans isomers for 2-butene. In the *cis*-2-butene isomer, the $—CH_3$ groups are attached on the same side of the double bond. In the *trans*-2-butene isomer, the $—CH_3$ groups are attached to the double bond on opposite sides, as shown in their ball-and-stick models (see Figure 12.6).

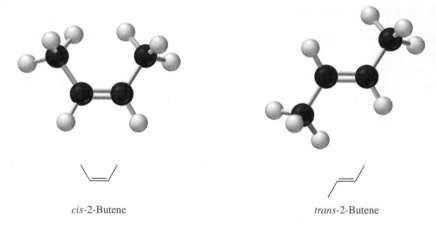

FIGURE 12.6 ▶ Ball-and-stick models and line-angle structural formulas of the cis and trans isomers of 2-butene.

◉ What feature in 2-butene accounts for the cis and trans isomers?

cis-2-Butene   *trans*-2-Butene

As with any pair of cis–trans isomers, *cis*-2-butene and *trans*-2-butene are different compounds with different physical properties and chemical properties. In general, trans isomers are more stable than their cis counterparts because the groups that are bigger than hydrogen atoms on the double bond are farther apart.

$$CH_3—CH=CH—CH_3$$
2-Butene

cis-2-Butene
(mp −139 °C; bp 3.7 °C)

trans-2-Butene
(mp −106 °C; bp 0.3 °C)

When the carbon atoms in the double bond are attached to two different atoms or groups of atoms, an alkene can have cis–trans isomers. For example, 3-hexene can be drawn with cis and trans isomers because there is one H atom and a $CH_3—CH_2—$ group attached to each carbon atom in the double bond. When you are asked to draw the formula for an alkene, it is important to consider the possibility of cis and trans isomers.

$$CH_3—CH_2—CH=CH—CH_2—CH_3$$

3-Hexene

Same side   Opposite sides

$$CH_3—CH_2 \diagdown \diagup CH_2—CH_3$$
$$C=C$$
$$H \diagup \diagdown H$$

cis-3-Hexene

$$CH_3—CH_2 \diagdown \diagup H$$
$$C=C$$
$$H \diagup \diagdown CH_2—CH_3$$

trans-3-Hexene

Same side   Opposite sides

When an alkene has identical groups on the same carbon atom of the double bond, cis and trans isomers cannot be drawn. For example, 1,1-dichloropropene has just one condensed structural formula and does not form cis–trans isomers.

$$Cl \diagdown \diagup CH_3$$
$$C=C$$
$$Cl \diagup \diagdown H$$

1,1-Dichloropropene

When identical groups are attached to carbon 1, there are no cis–trans isomers.

▶ SAMPLE PROBLEM 12.8 Identifying Cis–Trans Isomers

Identify each of the following as the cis or trans isomer and give its name:

a. Br   Cl

b.

SOLUTION

a. This is a cis isomer because the two halogen atoms attached to the carbon atoms of the double bond are on the same side. The name of the two-carbon alkene, starting with the bromo group on carbon 1, is *cis*-1-bromo-2-chloroethene.

b. This is a trans isomer because the two alkyl groups attached to the carbon atoms of the double bond are on opposite sides of the double bond. This isomer of the five-carbon alkene, 2-pentene, is named *trans*-2-pentene.

STUDY CHECK 12.8

Give the name for the following compound, including cis or trans:

ANSWER
trans-3-hexene

Explore Your World

Modeling Cis–Trans Isomers

Because cis–trans isomerism is not easy to visualize, here are some things you can do to understand the difference in rotation around a single bond compared to a double bond and how it affects groups that are attached to the carbon atoms in the double bond.

Put the tips of your index fingers together. This is a model of a single bond. Consider the index fingers as a pair of carbon atoms, and think of your thumbs and other fingers as other parts of a carbon chain. While your index fingers are touching, twist your hands and change the position of your thumbs relative to each other. Notice how the relationship of your other fingers changes.

Now place the tips of your index fingers and middle fingers together in a model of a double bond. As you did before, twist your hands to move your thumbs away from each other. What happens? Can you change the location of your thumbs relative to each other without breaking the double bond? The difficulty of moving your hands with two fingers touching represents the lack of rotation about a double bond. You have made a model of a cis isomer when both thumbs point in the same direction. If you turn one hand over so one thumb points down and the other thumb points up, you have made a model of a trans isomer.

Cis-hands (cis-thumbs/fingers)

Using Gumdrops and Toothpicks to Model Cis–Trans Isomers

Obtain some toothpicks and yellow, green, and black gumdrops. The black gumdrops represent C atoms, the yellow gumdrops represent H atoms, and the green gumdrops represent Cl atoms. Place a toothpick between two black gumdrops. Use three more toothpicks to attach two yellow gumdrops and one green gumdrop to each black gumdrop carbon atom. Rotate one of the gumdrop carbon atoms to show the conformations of the attached H and Cl atoms.

Remove a toothpick and yellow gumdrop from each black gumdrop. Place a second toothpick between the carbon atoms, which makes a double bond. Try to twist the double bond of toothpicks. Can you do it? When you observe the location of the green gumdrops, does the model you made represent a cis or trans isomer? Why? If

Trans-hands (trans-thumbs/fingers)

your model is a cis isomer, how would you change it to a trans isomer? If your model is a trans isomer, how would you change it to a cis isomer?

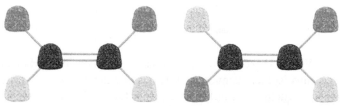

Models from gumdrops represent cis and trans isomers.

 # Chemistry Link to the Environment

Pheromones in Insect Communication

Many insects emit minute quantities of chemicals called *pheromones* to send messages to individuals of the same species. Some pheromones warn of danger, others call for defense, mark a trail, or attract the opposite sex. In the past 40 yr, the structures of many pheromones have been chemically determined. One of the most studied is bombykol, the sex pheromone produced by the female silkworm moth. The bombykol molecule contains one cis double bond and one trans double bond. Even a few nanograms of bombykol will attract male silkworm moths from distances of over 1 km. The effectiveness of many of these pheromones depends on the cis or trans configuration of the double bonds in the molecules. A certain species will respond to one isomer but not the other.

Scientists are interested in synthesizing pheromones to use as nontoxic alternatives to pesticides. When placed in a trap, bombykol can be used to capture male silkworm moths. When a synthetic pheromone is released in a field, the males cannot locate the females, which disrupts the reproductive cycle. This technique has been successful with controlling the oriental fruit moth, the grapevine moth, and the pink bollworm.

Pheromones allow insects to attract mates from a great distance.

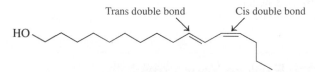

Bombykol, sex attractant for the silkworm moth

Chemistry Link to Health

Cis–Trans Isomers for Night Vision

The retinas of the eyes consist of two types of cells: rods and cones. The rods on the edge of the retina allow us to see in dim light, and the cones, in the center, produce our vision in bright light. In the rods, there is a substance called *rhodopsin* that absorbs light. Rhodopsin is composed of *cis*-11-retinal, an unsaturated compound, attached to a protein. When rhodopsin absorbs light, the *cis*-11-retinal isomer is converted to its trans isomer, which changes its shape. The trans form no longer fits the protein, and it separates from the protein. The change from the cis to trans isomer and its separation from the protein generate an electrical signal that the brain converts into an image.

An enzyme (isomerase) converts the trans isomer back to the *cis*-11-retinal isomer and the rhodopsin re-forms. If there is a deficiency of rhodopsin in the rods of the retina, *night blindness* may occur. One common cause is a lack of vitamin A in the diet. In our diet, we obtain vitamin A from plant pigments containing β-carotene, which is found in foods such as carrots, squash, and spinach. In the small intestine, the β-carotene is converted to vitamin A, which can be converted to *cis*-11-retinal or stored in the liver for future use. Without a sufficient quantity of retinal, not enough rhodopsin is produced to enable us to see adequately in dim light.

Cis–Trans Isomers of Retinal

cis-11-Retinal   *trans*-11-Retinal

QUESTIONS AND PROBLEMS

12.6 Cis–Trans Isomers

LEARNING GOAL Draw the condensed and line-angle structural formulas and give the names for the cis–trans isomers of alkenes.

12.33 Give the IUPAC name for each of the following, using cis or trans prefixes:

a.

$$CH_3 \quad CH_3$$
$$C=C$$
$$H \quad H$$

b.

$$CH_3-CH_2 \quad H$$
$$C=C$$
$$H \quad CH_2-CH_2-CH_2-CH_3$$

c.

12.34 Give the IUPAC name for each of the following, using cis or trans prefixes:

a.

$$CH_3 \quad CH_2-CH_3$$
$$C=C$$
$$H \quad H$$

b.

$$CH_3 \quad H$$
$$C=C$$
$$H \quad CH_2-CH_2-CH_2-CH_3$$

c.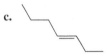

12.35 Draw the condensed structural formula for each of the following:
  a. *trans*-1-bromo-2-chloroethene
  b. *cis*-2-hexene
  c. *trans*-3-heptene

12.36 Draw the condensed structural formula for each of the following:
  a. *cis*-1,2-difluoroethene
  b. *trans*-2-pentene
  c. *cis*-4-octene

12.37 Which of the following cannot have cis–trans isomers? Explain.
  a. $H_2C=CH-CH_3$
  b. $CH_3-CH_2-CH=CH-CH_3$

  c.

12.38 Which of the following cannot have cis–trans isomers? Explain.

  a.

$$H \quad H$$
$$C=C$$
$$CH_3-CH_2 \quad CH_2-CH_3$$

  b. $CH_3-CH_2-CH_2-CH=CH_2$

  c.

12.7 Addition Reactions for Alkenes

The most characteristic reaction of alkenes is the **addition** of atoms or groups of atoms to the carbon atoms in a double bond. Addition occurs because double bonds are easily broken, providing electrons to form new single bonds.

The addition reactions have different names that depend on the type of reactant we add to the alkene, as Table 12.8 shows.

TABLE 12.8 Summary of Addition Reactions

Name of Addition Reaction	Reactants	Catalysts	Product
Hydrogenation	Alkene + H_2	Pt, Ni, or Pd	Alkane
Hydration	Alkene + H_2O	H^+ (strong acid)	Alcohol
Polymerization	Alkenes	High temperature, pressure	Polymer

Hydrogenation

In a reaction called **hydrogenation**, H atoms add to each of the carbon atoms in a double bond of an alkene. During hydrogenation, the double bonds are converted to single bonds in alkanes. A catalyst such as finely divided platinum (Pt), nickel (Ni), or palladium (Pd) is used to speed up the reaction.

Some examples of the hydrogenation of alkenes follow:

$$CH_3-CH=CH-CH_3 + H_2 \xrightarrow{Pt} CH_3-CH_2-CH_2-CH_3$$

2-Butene   Butane

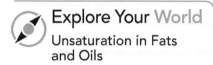

Cyclohexene   Cyclohexane

▶ **SAMPLE PROBLEM 12.9** Writing Equations for Hydrogenation

Draw the structural formula for the product of each of the following hydrogenation reactions:

a. $CH_3-CH=CH_2 + H_2 \xrightarrow{Pt}$?   b. ⬠ $+ H_2 \xrightarrow{Pt}$?

SOLUTION

In an addition reaction, hydrogen adds to the double bond to give an alkane.

ANALYZE THE PROBLEM	Given	Need
	alkene + H_2	structural formula of product

a. $CH_3-CH_2-CH_3$ b. ⬠

STUDY CHECK 12.9

Draw the condensed structural formula for the product of the hydrogenation of 2-methyl-1-butene, using a platinum catalyst.

ANSWER

$$\overset{\displaystyle CH_3}{\underset{\displaystyle }{CH_3-CH-CH_2-CH_3}}$$

Chemistry Link to **Health**

Hydrogenation of Unsaturated Fats

Vegetable oils such as corn oil or safflower oil are unsaturated fats composed of fatty acids that contain double bonds. The process of hydrogenation is used commercially to convert the double bonds in the unsaturated fats in vegetable oils to saturated fats such as margarine, which are more solid. Adjusting the amount of added hydrogen produces partially hydrogenated fats such as soft margarine, solid margarine in sticks, and shortenings, which are used in cooking. For example, oleic acid is a typical unsaturated fatty acid in olive oil and has a cis double bond at carbon 9. When oleic acid is hydrogenated, it is converted to stearic acid, a saturated fatty acid.

The unsaturated fats in vegetable oils are converted to saturated fats to make a more solid product.

Cis double bond

Oleic acid (found in olive oil and other unsaturated fats)

Single bond

Stearic acid (found in saturated fats)

Hydration

In **hydration**, an alkene reacts with water (H—OH). A hydrogen atom (H—) from water forms a bond with one carbon atom in the double bond, and the oxygen atom in —OH forms a bond with the other carbon. The reaction is catalyzed by a strong acid such as H_2SO_4, written as H^+. Hydration is used to prepare alcohols, which have the hydroxyl (—OH) functional group. When water (H—OH) adds to a symmetrical alkene, such as ethene, a single product is formed.

Interactive Video

Addition to an Asymmetric Bond

Ethene → Ethanol (ethyl alcohol)

Functional group of alcohols

However, when H_2O adds to a double bond in an asymmetrical alkene, two products are possible. We can determine the prevalent product that forms using **Markovnikov's Rule**, named after the Russian chemist Vladimir Markovnikov. The rule states that when water adds to a double bond in which the carbon atoms are attached to different numbers of H atoms (an asymmetrical double bond), the H— from H—OH attaches to the carbon that has the *greater* number of H atoms and the —OH adds to the other carbon atom from the double bond. In the following example, the H— from H—OH attaches to the end carbon of the double bond, which has more hydrogen atoms, and the —OH adds to the middle carbon atom:

This C in the C=C has more H atoms.

Propene → 2-Propanol

> **SAMPLE PROBLEM 12.10** Hydration

Draw the condensed structural formula for the product that forms in the following hydration reaction:

$$CH_3—CH_2—CH_2—CH{=}CH_2 \ + \ H_2O \ \xrightarrow{H^+}$$

SOLUTION

ANALYZE THE PROBLEM	Given	Need
	hydration, asymmetrical alkene	condensed structural formula for the product

For an asymmetrical alkene, the H— from water (H—OH) adds to the carbon with the *greater* number of hydrogen atoms, and the —OH bonds to the carbon with fewer H atoms.

$$CH_3—CH_2—CH_2—\overset{\overset{\text{OH}}{\downarrow}}{CH}{=}\overset{\overset{\text{H}}{\downarrow}}{CH_2} \ \xrightarrow{H^+} \ CH_3—CH_2—CH_2—\overset{\overset{\text{OH}}{|}}{CH}—CH_3$$

STUDY CHECK 12.10

Draw the condensed structural formula for the product obtained by the hydration of 2-methyl-2-butene.

ANSWER

$$CH_3—\overset{\overset{\text{OH}}{|}}{\underset{\underset{\text{CH}_3}{|}}{C}}—CH_2—CH_3$$

Addition of Alkenes: Polymerization

A **polymer** is a large molecule that consists of small repeating units called **monomers**. In the past hundred years, the plastics industry has made synthetic polymers that are in many of the materials we use every day, such as carpeting, plastic wrap, nonstick pans, plastic cups, and rain gear. In medicine, synthetic polymers are used to replace diseased or damaged body parts such as hip joints, pacemakers, teeth, heart valves, and blood vessels (see Figure 12.7). There are about 100 billion kg of plastics produced every year, which is about 15 kg for every person on Earth.

Many of the synthetic polymers are made by addition reactions of small alkene monomers. Many polymerization reactions require high temperature, a catalyst, and high pressure (over 1000 atm). In an addition reaction, a polymer grows longer as each monomer is added at the end of the chain. A polymer may contain as many as 1000 monomers. Polyethylene, a polymer made from ethylene monomers, is used in plastic bottles, film, and plastic dinnerware. More polyethylene is produced worldwide than any other polymer. Low-density polyethylene (LDPE) is flexible, breakable, less dense, and more branched than high-density polyethylene (HDPE). High-density polyethylene is stronger, more dense, and melts at a higher temperature than LDPE.

FIGURE 12.7 ▶ Synthetic polymers are used to replace diseased veins and arteries.

ⓠ Why are the substances in these plastic devices called polymers?

Monomer unit repeats

Ethene (ethylene) monomers   Polyethylene section

Table 12.9 lists several alkene monomers that are used to produce common synthetic polymers, and Figure 12.8 shows examples of each. The alkane-like nature of these plastic synthetic polymers makes them unreactive. Thus, they do not decompose easily (they are not biodegradable). As a result, they have become significant contributors to pollution, on land and in the oceans. Efforts are being made to make them more degradable.

TABLE 12.9 Some Alkenes and Their Polymers

Recycling Code	Monomer	Polymer Section	Common Uses
2 HDPE **4** LDPE	$H_2C{=}CH_2$ Ethene (ethylene)	Polyethylene (PE)	Plastic bottles, film, insulation materials, shopping bags
3 V	$H_2C{=}CH$ Chloroethene (vinyl chloride)	Polyvinyl chloride (PVC)	Plastic pipes and tubing, garden hoses, garbage bags, shower curtains, credit cards, medical containers
5 PP	$H_2C{=}CH$ Propene (propylene)	Polypropylene (PP)	Ski and hiking clothing, carpets, artificial joints, plastic bottles, food containers, medical face masks, tubing
	$F{-}C{=}C{-}F$ Tetrafluoroethene	Polytetrafluoroethylene (PTFE)	Nonstick coatings, Teflon
	$H_2C{=}C{-}Cl$ 1,1-Dichloroethene	Polydichloroethylene (Saran)	Plastic film and wrap, Gore-Tex rainwear, medical implants
6 PS	$H_2C{=}CH$ Phenylethene (styrene)	Polystyrene (PS)	Plastic coffee cups and cartons, insulation

You can identify the type of polymer used to manufacture a plastic item by looking for the recycling symbol (arrows in a triangle) found on the label or on the bottom of the plastic container. For example, the number 5 or the letters PP inside the triangle is the code for a polypropylene plastic. There are now many cities that maintain recycling programs that reduce the amount of plastic materials that are transported to landfills.

Today, products such as lumber, tables and benches, trash receptacles, and pipes used for irrigation systems are made from recycled plastics.

Tables, benches, and trash receptacles can be manufactured from recycled plastics.

Explore Your World
Polymers and Recycling Plastics

1. Make a list of the items you use or have in your room or home that are made of polymers.
2. Recycling information on the bottom or side of a plastic bottle includes a triangle with a code number that identifies the type of polymer used to make the plastic. Make a collection of several different kinds of plastic bottles. Try to find plastic items with each type of polymer.

Questions

1. What are the most common types of plastics among the plastic containers in your collection?
2. What are the monomers of some of the plastics you looked at?

Polyethylene

Polyvinyl chloride

Polypropylene

Polytetrafluoroethylene
(Teflon)

Polydichloroethylene
(Saran)

Polystyrene

FIGURE 12.8 ▶ Synthetic polymers provide a wide variety of items that we use every day.

❓ What are some alkenes used to make the polymers in these plastic items?

SAMPLE PROBLEM 12.11 Polymers

A firefighter/EMT arrives at a home where a premature baby has been delivered. To prevent hypothermia during transport to the neonatal facility, she wraps the baby in cling wrap. Draw and name the monomer unit and draw a portion of the polymer formed from three monomer units for cling wrap, which is polydichloroethylene (ethene).

SOLUTION

$$H_2C=C-Cl$$
1,1-Dichloroethene

$$-C-C-C-C-C-C-$$
(with H, Cl, H, Cl, H, Cl on top and H, Cl, H, Cl, H, Cl on bottom)

STUDY CHECK 12.11

Draw the condensed structural formula for the monomer used in the manufacturing of PVC.

ANSWER

$$H_2C=CH-Cl$$

QUESTIONS AND PROBLEMS

12.7 Addition Reactions for Alkenes

LEARNING GOAL Draw the condensed or line-angle structural formulas and give the names for the organic products of addition reactions of alkenes. Draw a condensed structural formula for a section of a polymer.

12.39 Draw the structural formula for the product in each of the following reactions using Markovnikov's rule when necessary:

a. $CH_3-CH_2-CH_2-CH=CH_2 + H_2 \xrightarrow{Pt}$

b. $H_2C=\overset{\overset{\displaystyle CH_3}{|}}{C}-CH_2-CH_3 + H_2O \xrightarrow{H^+}$

c. $\diagup\!\!\diagdown\!\!\diagup + H_2 \xrightarrow{Pt}$

d. ⬡ $+ H_2O \xrightarrow{H^+}$

12.40 Draw the structural formula for the product in each of the following reactions using Markovnikov's rule when necessary:

a. $CH_3-CH_2-CH=CH_2 + H_2O \xrightarrow{H^+}$

b. ⟍⟋⟍⟋ $+ H_2 \xrightarrow{Pt}$

c. ⬡ $+ H_2 \xrightarrow{Pt}$

d. ⟍⟋⟍⟋ $+ H_2O \xrightarrow{H^+}$

12.41 What is a polymer?

12.42 What is a monomer?

12.43 Write an equation that represents the formation of a portion of polypropylene from three of its monomers.

12.44 Write an equation that represents the formation of a portion of polystyrene from three of its monomers.

12.45 The plastic polyvinylidene difluoride, PVDF, is made from monomers of 1,1-difluoroethene. Draw the expanded structural formula for a portion of the polymer formed from three monomers of 1,1-difluoroethene.

12.46 The polymer polyacrylonitrile, PAN, used in the fabric material Orlon is made from monomers of acrylonitrile. Draw the expanded structural formula for a portion of the polymer formed from three monomers of acrylonitrile.

$$H_2C=\overset{\overset{\displaystyle CN}{|}}{CH}$$

Acrylonitrile

12.8 Aromatic Compounds

In 1825, Michael Faraday isolated a hydrocarbon called **benzene**, which consists of a ring of six carbon atoms with one hydrogen atom attached to each carbon. Because many compounds containing benzene had fragrant odors, the family of benzene compounds became known as **aromatic compounds**. Some common examples of aromatic compounds that we use for flavor are anisole from anise, estragole from tarragon, and thymol from thyme.

LEARNING GOAL

Describe the bonding in benzene; name aromatic compounds, and draw their line-angle structural formulas.

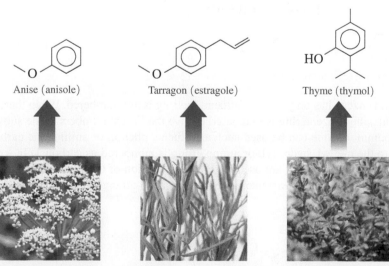

Anise (anisole)   Tarragon (estragole)   Thyme (thymol)

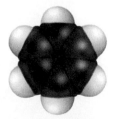

The space-filling model for benzene consists of a six-carbon ring with six hydrogen atoms.

The aroma and flavor of the herbs anise, tarragon, and thyme are because of aromatic compounds.

In benzene, each carbon atom uses three valence electrons to bond to the hydrogen atom and two adjacent carbons. That leaves one valence electron, which scientists first thought was shared in a double bond with an adjacent carbon. In 1865, August Kekulé proposed that the carbon atoms in benzene were arranged in a flat ring with alternating single and double bonds between the adjacent carbon atoms. There are two possible structural representations of benzene in which the double bonds can form between two different carbon atoms. If there were double bonds as in alkenes, then benzene should be much more reactive than it is.

However, unlike the alkenes and alkynes, aromatic hydrocarbons do not easily undergo addition reactions. If their reaction behavior is quite different, they must also differ in how the atoms are bonded in their structures. Today, we know that the six electrons are shared equally among the six carbon atoms. This unique feature of benzene makes it especially stable. Benzene is most often represented as a line-angle structural formula, which shows a hexagon with a circle in the center. Some of the ways to represent benzene are shown as follows:

Equivalent structures for benzene   Structural formulas for benzene

Naming Aromatic Compounds

Many compounds containing benzene have been important in chemistry for many years and still use their common names. Names such as toluene, aniline, and phenol are allowed by IUPAC rules.

Toluene	Aniline	Phenol
(methylbenzene)	(aminobenzene)	(hydroxybenzene)

When a benzene ring is a substituent, $-C_6H_5$, it is named as a phenyl group.

$$CH_3-CH-CH=CH_2$$

Phenyl group   3-Phenyl-1-butene

When benzene has only one substituent, the ring is not numbered. When there are two substituents, the benzene ring is numbered to give the lowest numbers to the substituents. When a common name can be used such as toluene, phenol, or aniline, the carbon atom attached to the methyl, hydroxyl, or amine group is numbered as carbon 1. In a common name, there are prefixes that are used to show the position of two substituents. The prefix **ortho** (*o*) indicates a 1,2-arrangement, **meta** (*m*) is a 1,3-arrangement, and **para** (*p*) is used for 1,4- arrangements.

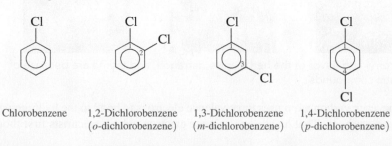

Chlorobenzene	1,2-Dichlorobenzene	1,3-Dichlorobenzene	1,4-Dichlorobenzene
	(*o*-dichlorobenzene)	(*m*-dichlorobenzene)	(*p*-dichlorobenzene)

The common name xylene is used for the isomers of dimethylbenzene.

1,2-Dimethylbenzene   1,3-Dimethylbenzene   1,4-Dimethylbenzene
  (*o*-xylene)   (*m*-xylene)   (*p*-xylene)

When there are three or more substituents attached to the benzene ring, they are numbered in the direction to give the lowest set of numbers and then named alphabetically.

SAMPLE PROBLEM 12.12 Naming Aromatic Compounds

Give the IUPAC name for the following:

SOLUTION

4-bromo-3-chlorotoluene

STUDY CHECK 12.12

Give the IUPAC and common name for the following compound:

CH_2-CH_3

CH_2-CH_3

ANSWER

1,3-diethylbenzene (*m*-diethylbenzene)

 Chemistry Link to **Health**

Some Common Aromatic Compounds in Nature and Medicine

Aromatic compounds are common in nature and in medicine. Toluene is used as a reactant to make drugs, dyes, and explosives such as TNT (trinitrotoluene). The benzene ring is found in some amino acids (the building blocks of proteins); in pain relievers such as aspirin, acetaminophen, and ibuprofen; and in flavorings such as vanillin.

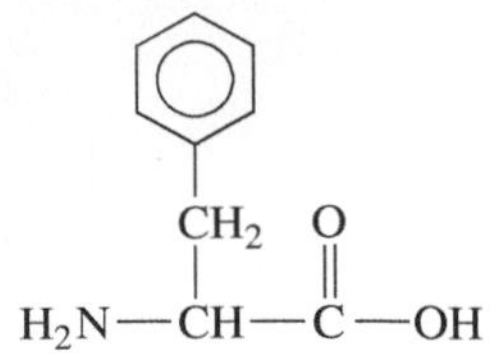

Phenylalanine
(amino acid)

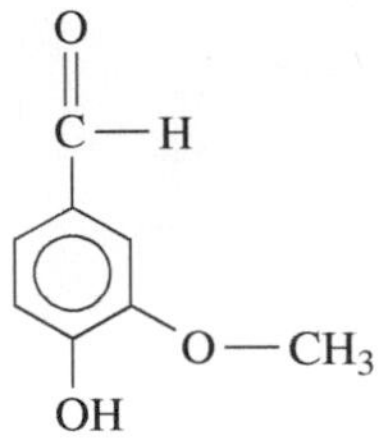

Vanillin

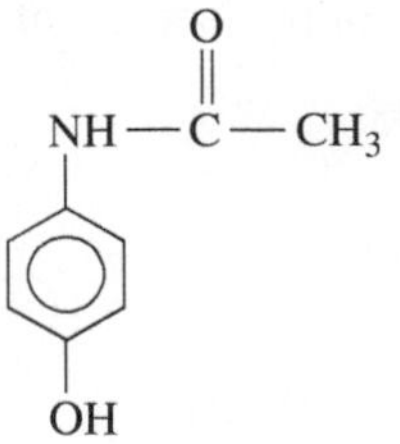

Acetaminophen

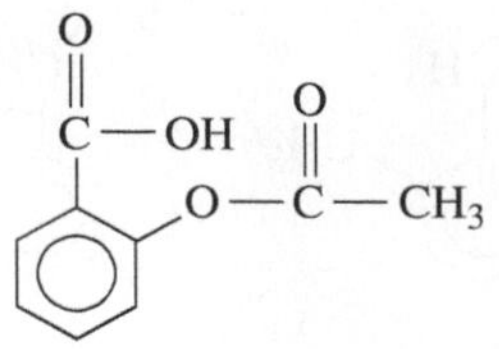

Aspirin

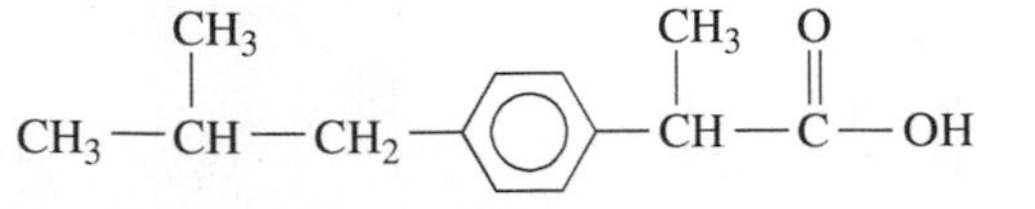

Ibuprofen

Properties of Aromatic Compounds

The flat symmetrical structure of benzene allows the individual cyclic structures to be very close together, which contributes to the higher melting points and boiling points of benzene and its derivatives. For example, hexane melts at $-95\,°C$, whereas benzene melts at $6\,°C$. Among the disubstituted benzene compounds, the *para* isomers are more symmetric and have higher melting points than the *ortho* and *meta* isomers: *o*-xylene melts at $-26\,°C$ and *m*-xylene melts at $-48\,°C$, whereas *p*-xylene melts at $13\,°C$.

Aromatic compounds are less dense than water, although they are somewhat denser than other hydrocarbons. Halogenated benzene compounds are denser than water. Aromatic hydrocarbons are insoluble in water and are used as solvents for other organic compounds. Only those aromatic compounds containing strongly polar functional groups such as —OH or —COOH will be somewhat soluble in water. Benzene and other aromatic compounds are resistant to reactions that break up the aromatic system, although they are flammable, as are other hydrocarbon compounds.

QUESTIONS AND PROBLEMS

12.8 Aromatic Compounds

LEARNING GOAL Describe the bonding in benzene; name aromatic compounds, and draw their line-angle structural formulas.

12.47 Give the IUPAC name and any common name for each of the following:

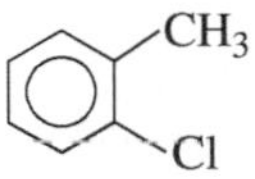

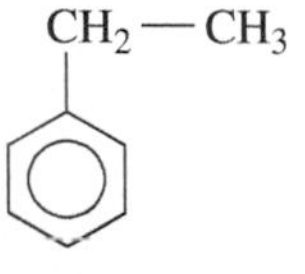

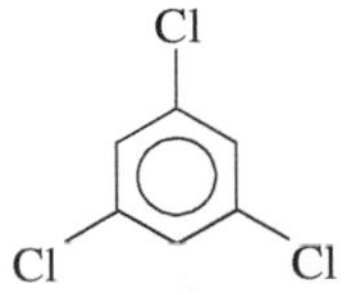

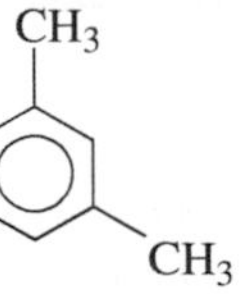

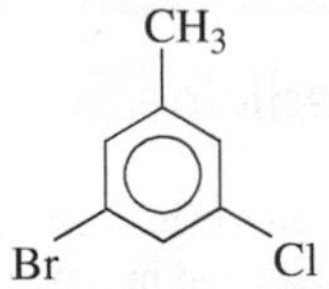

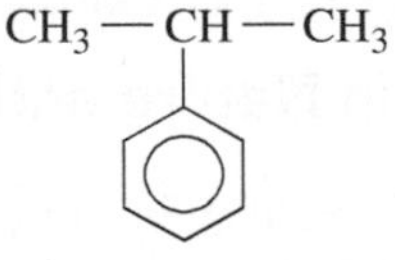

12.48 Give the IUPAC name and any common name for each of the following:

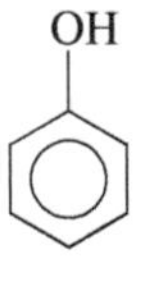

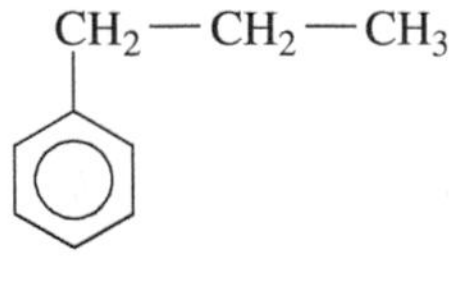

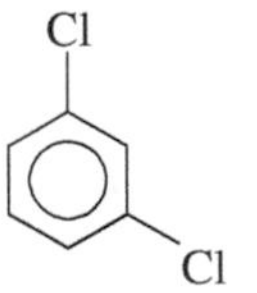

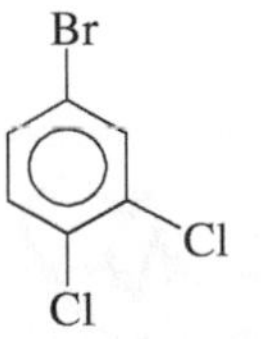

12.49 Draw the structural formula for each of the following:
   a. aniline
   b. 1-bromo-3-chlorobenzene
   c. 1-ethyl-4-methylbenzene
   d. *p*-chlorotoluene

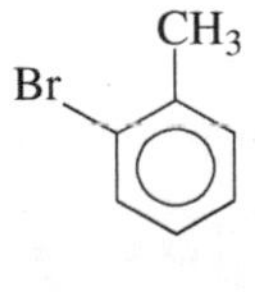

12.50 Draw the structural formula for each of the following:
   a. *m*-dibromobenzene
   b. *o*-chloroethylbenzene
   c. propylbenzene
   d. 1,2,4-trichlorobenzene

Chemistry Link to Health
Polycyclic Aromatic Hydrocarbons (PAHs)

Large aromatic compounds known as *polycyclic aromatic hydrocarbons* (PAHs) are formed by fusing together two or more benzene rings edge to edge. In a fused-ring compound, neighboring benzene rings share two carbon atoms. Naphthalene, with two benzene rings, is well known for its use in mothballs; anthracene, with three rings, is used in the manufacture of dyes.

the DNA in the cells, causing abnormal cell growth and cancer. Increased exposure to carcinogens increases the chance of DNA alterations in the cells. Benzo[*a*]pyrene, a product of combustion, has been identified in coal tar, tobacco smoke, barbecued meats, and automobile exhaust.

Naphthalene   Anthracene   Phenanthrene

Benzo[*a*]pyrene

When a polycyclic compound contains phenanthrene, it may act as a carcinogen, a substance known to cause cancer.

Compounds containing five or more fused benzene rings such as benzo[*a*]pyrene are potent carcinogens. The molecules interact with

Aromatic compounds such as benzo[a]pyrene are strongly associated with lung cancers.

Clinical Update
Diane's Treatment in the Burn Unit

When Diane arrived at the hospital, she was transferred to the ICU burn unit. She had second-degree burns that caused damage to the underlying layers of skin and third-degree burns that caused damage to all the layers of the skin. Because body fluids are lost when deep burns occur, a lactated Ringer's solution was administered. The most common complications of burns are

related to infection. To prevent infection, her skin was covered with a topical antibiotic. The next day Diane was placed in a tank to remove dressings, lotions, and damaged tissue. Dressings and ointments were changed every eight hours. Over a period of 3 months, grafts of Diane's unburned skin were used to cover burned areas. She remained in the burn unit for 3 months and then was discharged. However, Diane returned to the hospital for more skin grafts and plastic surgery.

The arson investigators determined that gasoline was the primary accelerant used to start the fire at Diane's house. Because there was a lot of paper and dry wood in the area, the fire spread quickly. Some of the hydrocarbons found in gasoline include hexane, heptane, octane, nonane, decane, and cyclohexane. Some other hydrocarbons in

gasoline are isooctane, butane, 3-ethyltoluene, isopentane, toluene, and 1,3-dimethylbenzene.

℞ Clinical Applications

12.51 The medications for Diane were contained in blister packs made of polychlorotrifluoroethylene (PCTFE). Draw the expanded structural formula for a portion of PCTFE polymer from three monomers of chlorotrifluoroethylene shown below:

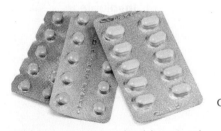

Tablets are contained in blister packs made from polychlorotrifluoroethylene (PCTFE).

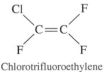

Chlorotrifluoroethylene

12.52 New polymers have been synthesized to replace PVC in IV bags and cling film. One of these is EVA, ethylene polyvinyl-acetate. Draw the expanded structural formula for a portion of EVA using an alternating sequence that has three of each monomer shown below:

Ethylene

Vinyl acetate

12.53 Write the balanced chemical equation for the complete combustion of each of the following hydrocarbons found in gasoline used to start a fire:
a. nonane
b. isopentane (2-methylbutane)
c. 3-ethyltoluene

12.54 Write the balanced chemical equation for the complete combustion of each of the following hydrocarbons found in gasoline used to start a fire:
a. isooctane (2,2,4-trimethylpentane)
b. cyclohexane
c. 1,3-dimethylbenzene

CONCEPT MAP

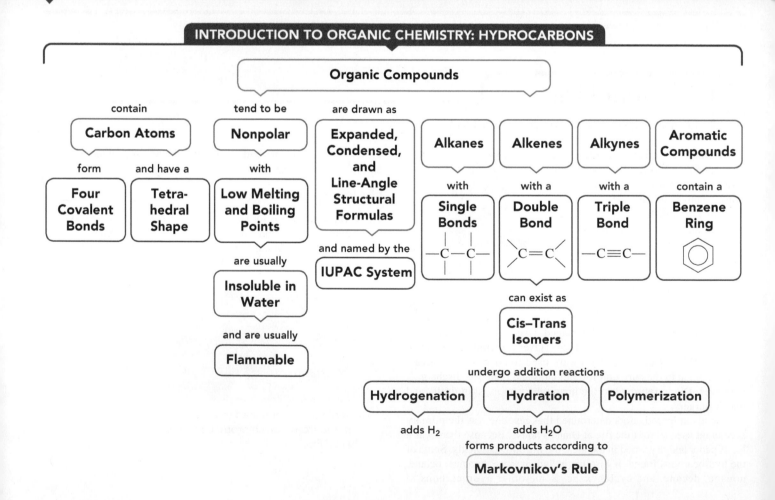

CHAPTER REVIEW

12.1 Organic Compounds
LEARNING GOAL Identify properties characteristic of organic or inorganic compounds.

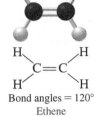

- Organic compounds have covalent bonds, most form nonpolar molecules, have low melting points and low boiling points, are not very soluble in water, dissolve as molecules in solutions, and burn vigorously in air.
- Inorganic compounds are often ionic or contain polar covalent bonds and form polar molecules, have high melting and boiling points, are usually soluble in water, produce ions in water, and do not burn in air.
- In the simplest organic molecule, methane, CH_4, the C—H bonds that attach four hydrogen atoms to the carbon atom are directed to the corners of a tetrahedron with bond angles of 109°.
- In the expanded structural formula, a separate line is drawn for every bond.

12.2 Alkanes
LEARNING GOAL Write the IUPAC names and draw the condensed or line-angle structural formulas for alkanes and cycloalkanes.

- Alkanes are hydrocarbons that have only C—C single bonds.
- A condensed structural formula depicts groups composed of each carbon atom and its attached hydrogen atoms.
- A line-angle structural formula represents the carbon skeleton as ends and corners of a zigzag line or geometric figure.
- The IUPAC system is used to name organic compounds by indicating the number of carbon atoms.
- The name of a cycloalkane is written by placing the prefix *cyclo* before the alkane name with the same number of carbon atoms.

12.3 Alkanes with Substituents
LEARNING GOAL Write the IUPAC names for alkanes with substituents and draw their condensed and line-angle structural formulas.

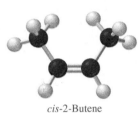

- Structural isomers are compounds with the same molecular formulas that differ in the order in which their atoms are bonded.
- Substituents, which are attached to an alkane chain, include alkyl groups and halogen atoms (F, Cl, Br, or I).
- In the IUPAC system, alkyl substituents have names such as methyl, propyl, and isopropyl; halogen atoms are named as fluoro, chloro, bromo, or iodo.

12.4 Properties of Alkanes
LEARNING GOAL Identify the properties of alkanes and write a balanced chemical equation for combustion.

- Alkanes, which are nonpolar molecules, are not soluble in water, and usually less dense than water.
- Alkanes undergo combustion in which they react with oxygen to produce carbon dioxide, water, and energy.

12.5 Alkenes and Alkynes
LEARNING GOAL Identify structural formulas as alkenes, cycloalkenes, and alkynes, and write their IUPAC names.

- Alkenes are unsaturated hydrocarbons that contain carbon–carbon double bonds.
- Alkynes contain a carbon–carbon triple bond.
- The IUPAC names of alkenes end with *ene*, while alkyne names end with *yne*. The main chain is numbered from the end nearer the double or triple bond.

H C=C H H Bond angles = 120°
Ethene

12.6 Cis–Trans Isomers
LEARNING GOAL Draw the condensed and line-angle structural formulas and give the names for the cis–trans isomers of alkenes.

- Geometric or cis–trans isomers of alkenes occur when the carbon atoms in the double bond are connected to different atoms or groups.
- In the cis isomer, the similar groups are on the same side of the double bond, whereas in the trans isomer they are connected on opposite sides of the double bond.

cis-2-Butene

12.7 Addition Reactions for Alkenes
LEARNING GOAL Draw the condensed or line-angle structural formulas and give the names for the organic products of addition reactions of alkenes. Draw a condensed structural formula for a section of a polymer.

- The addition of small molecules to the double bond is a characteristic reaction of alkenes.
- Hydrogenation adds hydrogen atoms to the double bond of an alkene to yield an alkane.
- Hydration adds water to a double bond of an alkene to form an alcohol.
- When a different number of hydrogen atoms are attached to the carbons in a double bond, the H— from water adds to the carbon with the greater number of H atoms (Markovnikov's rule).
- Polymers are long-chain molecules that consist of many repeating units of smaller carbon molecules called monomers.
- Many materials that we use every day are made from synthetic polymers, including carpeting, plastic wrap, nonstick pans, and nylon.
- Many synthetic materials are made using addition reactions in which a catalyst links the carbon atoms from various kinds of alkene molecules (monomers).
- Many materials used in medicine are made from synthetic polymers, including tubing, IV containers, and face masks.

12.8 Aromatic Compounds

LEARNING GOAL Describe the bonding in benzene; name aromatic compounds, and draw their line-angle structural formulas.

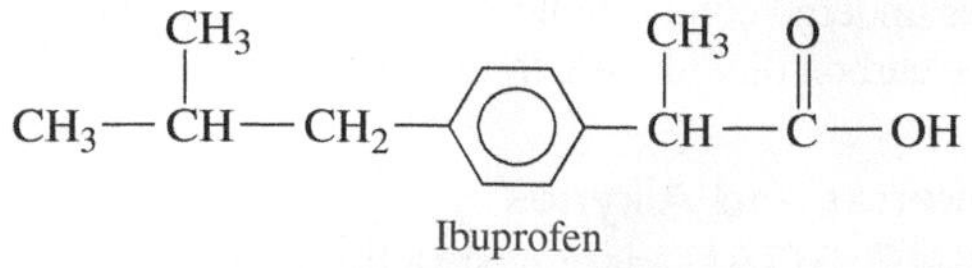

Ibuprofen

- Most aromatic compounds contain benzene, C_6H_6, a cyclic structure containing six carbon atoms and six hydrogen atoms.
- The structure of benzene is represented as a hexagon with a circle in the center.
- The IUPAC system uses the names of benzene, toluene, aniline, and phenol.
- In the IUPAC name, two or more substituents are numbered and listed in alphabetical order. In the common name, with two substituents, the positions are shown by the prefixes *ortho* (1,2-), *meta* (1,3-), and *para* (1,4-).

SUMMARY OF NAMING

Family	Structure	IUPAC Name	Common Name
Alkane	CH_3—CH_2—CH_3	Propane	
	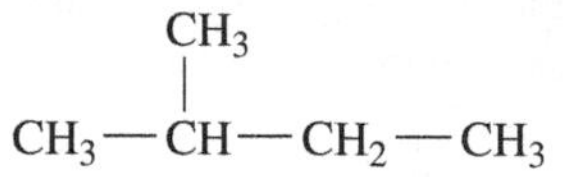 CH_3—CH—CH_2—CH_3 (with CH_3 branch)	2-Methylbutane	Isopentane
Haloalkane	CH_3—CH_2—CH_2—Cl	1-Chloropropane	Propyl chloride
Cycloalkane	 (hexagon)	Cyclohexane	
Alkene	CH_3—CH=CH_2	Propene	Propylene
	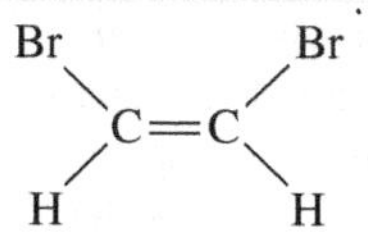 (C=C with Br, Br top; H, H bottom)	*cis*-1,2-Dibromoethene	
	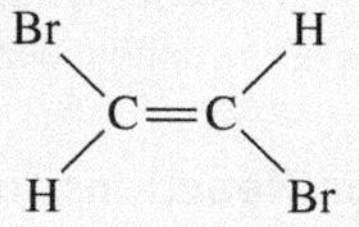 (C=C with Br, H top; H, Br bottom)	*trans*-1,2-Dibromoethene	
Cycloalkene	 (triangle)	Cyclopropene	
Alkyne	CH_3—C≡CH	Propyne	
Aromatic	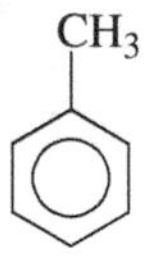 (benzene with CH_3)	Methylbenzene; toluene	
	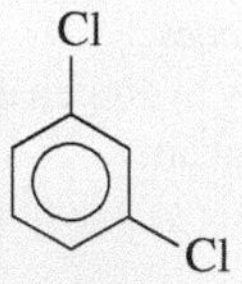 (benzene with Cl, Cl)	1,3-Dichlorobenzene	*m*-Dichlorobenzene

SUMMARY OF REACTIONS

The chapter sections to review are shown after the name of the reaction.

Combustion (12.4)

$$CH_3—CH_2—CH_3(g) + 5O_2(g) \xrightarrow{\Delta} 3CO_2(g) + 4H_2O(g) + \text{energy}$$

Propane

Hydrogenation (12.7)

$$H_2C=CH—CH_3 + H_2 \xrightarrow{Pt} CH_3—CH_2—CH_3$$

Propene   Propane

Hydration (12.7)

Markovnikov's Rule

$$H_2C = CH - CH_3 + H_2O \xrightarrow{H^+} CH_3 - \underset{\underset{\displaystyle OH}{|}}{CH} - CH_3$$

Propene   2-Propanol

Polymerization (12.7)

$$H_2C = CH_2 + H_2C = CH_2 + H_2C = CH_2 \xrightarrow[\text{catalyst}]{\text{Heat, pressure,}} -CH_2 - CH_2 - CH_2 - CH_2 - CH_2 - CH_2 -$$

Ethene   Polyethylene

KEY TERMS

addition A reaction in which atoms or groups of atoms bond to a carbon–carbon double bond. Addition reactions include the addition of hydrogen (hydrogenation), and water (hydration).

alkane A hydrocarbon that contains only single bonds between carbon atoms.

alkene A hydrocarbon that contains one or more carbon–carbon double bonds ($C=C$).

alkyl group An alkane minus one hydrogen atom. Alkyl groups are named like the alkanes except a *yl* ending replaces *ane*.

alkyne A hydrocarbon that contains one or more carbon–carbon triple bonds ($C\equiv C$).

aromatic compound A compound that contains the ring structure of benzene.

benzene A ring of six carbon atoms, each of which is attached to a hydrogen atom, C_6H_6.

cis isomer An isomer of an alkene in which similar groups in the double bond are on the same side.

condensed structural formula A structural formula that shows the arrangement of the carbon atoms in a molecule but groups each carbon atom with its bonded hydrogen atoms

$$-CH_3, \ -CH_2-, \ \text{or} \ -\underset{|}{CH}-.$$

cycloalkane An alkane that is a ring or cyclic structure.

expanded structural formula A type of structural formula that shows the arrangement of the atoms by drawing each bond in the hydrocarbon.

hydration An addition reaction in which the components of water, $H-$ and $-OH$, bond to the carbon–carbon double bond to form an alcohol.

hydrocarbon An organic compound that contains only carbon and hydrogen.

hydrogenation The addition of hydrogen (H_2) to the double bond of alkenes to yield alkanes.

IUPAC system A system for naming organic compounds devised by the International Union of Pure and Applied Chemistry.

line-angle structural formula A simplified structure that shows a zig-zag line in which carbon atoms are represented as the ends of each line and as corners.

Markovnikov's rule When adding water to alkenes with different numbers of groups attached to the double bonds, the $H-$ adds to the carbon that has the greater number of hydrogen atoms.

meta A method of naming that indicates substituents at carbons 1 and 3 of a benzene ring.

monomer The small organic molecule that is repeated many times in a polymer.

organic compound A compound made of carbon that typically has covalent bonds, is nonpolar, has low melting and boiling points, is insoluble in water, and is flammable.

ortho A method of naming that indicates substituents at carbons 1 and 2 of a benzene ring.

para A method of naming that indicates substituents at carbons 1 and 4 of a benzene ring.

polymer A very large molecule that is composed of many small, repeating monomer units.

structural isomers Organic compounds in which identical molecular formulas have different arrangements of atoms.

substituent Groups of atoms such as an alkyl group or a halogen bonded to the main carbon chain or ring of carbon atoms.

trans isomer An isomer of an alkene in which similar groups in the double bond are on opposite sides.

⚛ CORE CHEMISTRY SKILLS

The chapter section containing each Core Chemistry Skill is shown in parentheses at the end of each heading.

Naming and Drawing Alkanes (12.2)

- The alkanes ethane, propane, and butane contain two, three, and four carbon atoms, respectively, connected in a row or a *continuous* chain.
- Alkanes with five or more carbon atoms in a chain are named using the prefixes *pent* (5), *hex* (6), *hept* (7), *oct* (8), *non* (9), and *dec* (10).

- In the condensed structural formula, the carbon and hydrogen atoms on the ends are written as $-CH_3$ and the carbon and hydrogen atoms in the middle are written as $-CH_2-$.

Example: **a.** What is the name of $CH_3-CH_2-CH_2-CH_3$?
         b. Draw the condensed structural formula for pentane.

Answer: **a.** An alkane with a four-carbon chain is named with the prefix *but* followed by *ane*, which is butane.

         b. Pentane is an alkane with a five-carbon chain. The carbon atoms on the ends are attached to three H atoms each, and the carbon atoms in the middle are attached to two H each. $CH_3-CH_2-CH_2-CH_2-CH_3$

Writing Equations for Hydrogenation, Hydration, and Polymerization (12.7)

- The addition of small molecules to the double bond is a characteristic reaction of alkenes.
- Hydrogenation adds hydrogen atoms to the double bond of an alkene to form an alkane.
- Hydration adds water to a double bond of an alkene to form an alcohol.
- When a different number of hydrogen atoms are attached to the carbons in a double bond, the H— from water adds to the carbon atom with the greater number of H atoms, and the —OH adds to the other carbon atom from the double bond.

Example: **a.** Draw the condensed structural formula for 2-methyl-2-butene.
b. Draw the condensed structural formula for the product of the hydrogenation of 2-methyl-2-butene.
c. Draw the condensed structural formula for the product of the hydration of 2-methyl-2-butene.

Answer: **a.**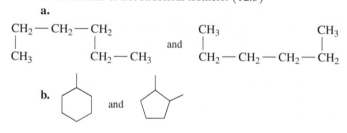

b. When H_2 adds to a double bond, the product is an alkane with the same number of carbon atoms.

$$CH_3—CH—CH_2—CH_3$$
with CH_3 attached to the second carbon

c. When water adds to a double bond, the product is an alcohol, which has an —OH group. The H— from water adds to the carbon atom in the double bond that has the greater number of H atoms.

$$CH_3—\underset{OH}{\overset{CH_3}{C}}—CH_2—CH_3$$

UNDERSTANDING THE CONCEPTS

The chapter sections to review are shown in parentheses at the end of each question.

12.55 Match the following physical and chemical properties with potassium chloride, KCl, used in salt substitutes, or butane, C_4H_{10}, used in lighters: (12.1)

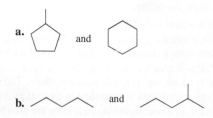

a. melts at $-138\,°C$
b. burns vigorously in air
c. melts at $770\,°C$
d. contains ionic bonds
e. is a gas at room temperature

12.56 Match the following physical and chemical properties with octane, C_8H_{18}, found in gasoline, or magnesium sulfate, $MgSO_4$, also called Epsom salts: (12.1)
a. contains only covalent bonds
b. melts at $1124\,°C$
c. is insoluble in water
d. is a liquid at room temperature
e. is a strong electrolyte

12.57 Identify the compounds in each of the following pairs as structural isomers or not structural isomers: (12.3)

12.58 Identify the compounds in each of the following pairs as structural isomers or not structural isomers: (12.3)

a.
$$\underset{CH_3}{\overset{|}{CH_2}}—CH_2—CH_2 \qquad \underset{CH_2—CH_3}{\overset{|}{CH_2}}$$ and $$\underset{CH_2—CH_2—CH_2—CH_2}{\overset{|}{CH_3}} \qquad \overset{CH_3}{\overset{|}{}}$$

b.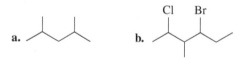

12.59 Convert each of the following line-angle structural formulas to a condensed structural formula and give its IUPAC name: (12.3)

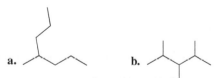

12.60 Convert each of the following line-angle structural formulas to a condensed structural formula and give its IUPAC name: (12.3)

12.61 Draw a portion of the polymer of Teflon, which is made from 1,1,2,2-tetrafluoroethene (use three monomers). (12.7)

Teflon is used as a nonstick coating on cooking pans.

12.62 A garden hose is made of polyvinyl chloride (PVC) from chloroethene (vinyl chloride). Draw a portion of the polymer (use three monomers) for PVC. (12.7)

A garden hose is made of polyvinyl chloride (PVC).

12.63 Give the number of carbon atoms and the types of carbon–carbon bonds for each of the following: (12.2, 12.3, 12.5)
a. propane   **b.** cyclopropane
c. propene   **d.** propyne

12.64 Give the number of carbon atoms and the types of carbon–carbon bonds for each of the following: (12.2, 12.3, 12.5)
a. butane   **b.** cyclobutane
c. cyclobutene   **d.** 2-butyne

ADDITIONAL QUESTIONS AND PROBLEMS

12.65 Give the IUPAC name for each of the following: (12.3)

a. $CH_3-CH_2-\underset{\underset{CH_3}{|}}{\overset{\overset{CH_3}{|}}{C}}-CH_3$

b. CH_3-CH_2-Cl

c. $CH_3-CH_2-\underset{\underset{CH_3-CH_2}{|}}{CH}-CH_2-\underset{\underset{Br}{|}}{CH}-CH_3$

d.

12.66 Give the IUPAC name for each of the following: (12.3)

a.

b. $Cl-CH_2-\underset{\underset{Br}{|}}{CH}-CH_2-Br$

c. $CH_3-\underset{\underset{CH_2}{|}}{\overset{\overset{CH_3}{|}}{CH}}-CH-CH_3$
    $\underset{\underset{CH_3}{|}}{\overset{}{CH_2}}$

d. $CH_3-CH_2-\underset{\underset{CH_2}{|}}{\overset{\overset{Cl}{|}}{C}}-CH_2-CH_3$
    $\underset{\underset{CH_3}{|}}{\overset{}{CH_2}}$

12.67 Draw the condensed structural formula for alkanes or the line-angle structural formula for cycloalkanes for each of the following: (12.3, 12.5, 12.6)
a. 1,2-dibromocyclopentene
b. 2-hexyne
c. *cis*-2-heptene

12.68 Draw the condensed structural formula for alkanes or the line-angle structural formula for cycloalkanes for each of the following: (12.3, 12.5, 12.6)
a. *trans*-3-hexene
b. 2-bromo-3-chlorocyclohexene
c. 3-chloro-1-butyne

12.69 Give the IUPAC name for each of the following: (12.5, 12.6)

a. $\underset{H}{\overset{CH_3}{C}}=\underset{CH_2-CH_3}{\overset{H}{C}}$

b.

c.

12.70 Give the IUPAC name for each of the following: (12.5, 12.6)

a. $H_2C=\underset{\underset{CH_3}{|}}{C}-CH_2-CH_2-CH_3$

b.

c.

12.71 Indicate if each of the following pairs represents structural isomers, cis–trans isomers, or identical compounds: (12.5, 12.6)

a. and

b. $\underset{H}{\overset{CH_3}{C}}=\underset{CH_3}{\overset{H}{C}}$ and $\underset{H}{\overset{CH_3}{C}}=\underset{H}{\overset{CH_3}{C}}$

12.72 Indicate if each of the following pairs represents structural isomers, cis–trans isomers, or identical compounds: (12.5, 12.6)

a. $H_2C=\underset{\underset{CH_2-CH_2}{|}}{\overset{}{CH}}$ and $CH_3-CH_2-CH_2-CH=CH_2$
    $\underset{\underset{CH_3}{|}}{\overset{}{}}$

b. and

12.73 Write the IUPAC name, including cis or trans, for each of the following: (12.5, 12.6)

a. $\underset{H}{\overset{CH_3-CH_2}{C}}=\underset{H}{\overset{CH_2-CH_2-CH_3}{C}}$

b. ∕∕═∕∖

CH₃   H
        ∖ ∕
c.   C═C
        ∕   ∖
   H   CH₂—CH₂—CH₂—CH₃

12.74 Write the IUPAC name, including cis or trans, for each of the following: (12.5, 12.6)

a.
          CH₃
          |
    H   CH₂—CH—CH₃
    ∖   ∕
     C═C
    ∕   ∖
CH₃—CH₂   H

b. ∕═∕∖∕

          CH₃
          |
   CH₃—CH   H
        ∖   ∕
c.   C═C
        ∕   ∖
   H   CH₂—CH₂—CH₂—CH₃

12.75 Draw the condensed structural formulas for the cis and trans isomers for each of the following: (12.5, 12.6)
  a. 2-pentene   **b.** 3-hexene

12.76 Draw the condensed structural formulas for the cis and trans isomers for each of the following: (12.5, 12.6)
  a. 2-butene   **b.** 2-hexene

12.77 Write a balanced chemical equation for the complete combustion of each of the following: (12.4, 12.5)
  a. dimethylpropane
  b. cyclobutane
  c. 2-heptene

12.78 Write a balanced chemical equation for the complete combustion of each of the following: (12.4, 12.5)
  a. cycloheptane
  b. 2-methyl-1-pentene
  c. 3,3-dimethylhexane

12.79 Give the name for the product from the hydrogenation of each of the following: (12.7)
  a. 3-methyl-2-pentene
  b. 3-methylcyclohexene
  c. 2-butene

12.80 Give the name for the product from the hydrogenation of each of the following: (12.7)
  a. 1-hexene
  b. 2-methyl-2-butene
  c. 1-ethylcyclopentene

12.81 Draw the structural formula for the product of each of the following: (12.7)

a. ⬠ + H₂ —Ni→

b. ∕∕∖∕∖ + H₂O —H⁺→

          CH₃
          |
c. CH₃—CH₂—C═CH₂ + H₂O —H⁺→

12.82 Draw the structural formula for the product of each of the following: (12.7)

a. ⬠ + H₂O —H⁺→

b. CH₃—CH₂—CH₂—CH═CH₂ + H₂ —Ni→

c. ∕∖═∕ + H₂O —H⁺→

12.83 Copolymers contain more than one type of monomer. One copolymer used in medicine is made of alternating units of styrene and acrylonitrile. Draw the expanded structural formula for a section of the copolymer that would have three each of these alternating units. (12.7)

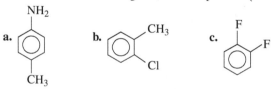

H₂C═CH   H₂C═CH
  Styrene   Acrylonitrile
          (CN)

12.84 Lucite, or Plexiglas, is a polymer of methyl methacrylate. Draw the expanded structural formula for a section of the polymer that is made from the addition of three of these monomers. (12.7)

          CH₃ O
           | ||
H₂C═C—C—O—CH₃
      Methyl methacrylate

12.85 Name each of the following aromatic compounds: (12.8)

         NH₂
          |
a. ⬡   **b.** ⬡—CH₃   **c.** ⬡—F
          | | F
         CH₃   Cl

12.86 Name each of the following aromatic compounds: (12.8)

         Cl   NH₂   CH₃
          | | |
a. ⬡   **b.** ⬡   **c.** ⬡
          | | |
         Cl   Br   CH₂—CH₃

12.87 Draw the structural formula for each of the following: (12.8)
  a. *p*-bromotoluene
  b. 2,6-dimethylaniline
  c. 1,4-dimethylbenzene

12.88 Draw the structural formula for each of the following: (12.8)
  a. ethylbenzene
  b. *m*-chloroaniline
  c. 1,2,4-trimethylbenzene

CHALLENGE QUESTIONS

12.89 If a female silkworm moth secretes 50 ng of bombykol, a sex attractant, how many molecules did she secrete? (See Chemistry Link to the Environment "Pheromones in Insect Communication.") (7.2, 12.6)

12.90 How many grams of hydrogen are needed to hydrogenate 30.0 g of 2-butene? (12.7)

12.91 Draw the condensed structural formula for and give the name of all the possible alkenes with molecular formula C_5H_{10} that have a five-carbon chain, including those with cis and trans isomers. (12.5, 12.6)

12.92 Draw the condensed structural formula for and give the name of all the possible alkenes with molecular formula C_6H_{12} that have a six-carbon chain, including those with cis and trans isomers. (12.5, 12.6)

12.93 Explosives used in mining contain TNT or 2,4,6-trinitrotoluene. (12.8)
  a. The functional group *nitro* is $-NO_2$. Draw the structural formula for 2,4,6-trinitrotoluene.
  b. TNT is actually a mixture of structural isomers of trinitrotoluene. Draw the structural formula for two other possible structural isomers.

Explosives containing TNT are used in mining.

12.94 Margarine is produced from the hydrogenation of vegetable oils, which contain unsaturated fatty acids. How many grams of hydrogen are required to completely saturate 75.0 g of oleic acid, $C_{18}H_{34}O_2$, which has one double bond? (12.7)

Margarines are produced by the hydrogenation of unsaturated fats.

ANSWERS

Answers to Selected Questions and Problems

12.1 a. inorganic   **b.** organic   **c.** organic
   d. inorganic   **e.** inorganic   **f.** organic

12.3 a. inorganic   **b.** organic
   c. organic   **d.** inorganic

12.5 a. ethane   **b.** cthanc
   c. NaBr   **d.** NaBr

12.7 In methane, the covalent bonds from the carbon atom to each hydrogen atom are directed to the corners of a tetrahedron with bond angles of 109°.

12.9 a. pentane   **b.** ethane
   c. hexane   **d.** cycloheptane

12.11 a. CH_4
   b. CH_3-CH_3
   c. $CH_3-CH_2-CH_2-CH_2-CH_3$
   d. △

12.13 a. same molecule
   b. structural isomers of C_5H_{12}
   c. structural isomers of C_6H_{14}

12.15 a. dimethylpropane
   b. 2,3-dimethylpentane
   c. 4-*tert*-butyl-2,6-dimethylheptane
   d. methylcyclobutane
   e. 1-bromo-3-chlorocyclohexane

12.17 a.
$$CH_3-CH_2-\overset{\overset{\displaystyle CH_3}{|}}{\underset{\underset{\displaystyle CH_3}{|}}{C}}-CH_2-CH_3$$

b.
$$CH_3-\overset{\overset{\displaystyle CH_3}{|}}{CH}-\overset{\overset{\displaystyle CH_3}{|}}{CH}-CH_2-\overset{\overset{\displaystyle CH_3}{|}}{CH}-CH_3$$

c.
$$CH_3-CH_2-\overset{\overset{\displaystyle CH_2-CH_3}{|}}{CH}-CH_2-\overset{\overset{\displaystyle CH_3 \quad CH_3}{\diagup}}{\underset{\underset{\displaystyle CH}{|}}{CH}}-CH_2-CH_2-CH_3$$

d. $Br-CH_2-CH_2-Cl$

12.19 a.

b.

c.

d.

12.21 a. $CH_3-CH_2-CH_2-CH_2-CH_2-CH_2-CH_3$

b. liquid
c. no
d. float
e. $C_7H_{16}(g) + 11O_2(g) \xrightarrow{\Delta} 7CO_2(g) + 8H_2O(g) + energy$

12.23 a. $2C_2H_6(g) + 7O_2(g) \xrightarrow{\Delta} 4CO_2(g) + 6H_2O(g) + energy$

b. $2C_3H_6(g) + 9O_2(g) \xrightarrow{\Delta} 6CO_2(g) + 6H_2O(g) + energy$

c. $2C_8H_{18}(g) + 25O_2(g) \xrightarrow{\Delta}$
$16CO_2(g) + 18H_2O(g) + energy$

12.25 a. heptane   **b.** cyclopropane   **c.** hexane

12.27 a. alkene   **b.** alkyne
      c. alkene   **d.** cycloalkene

12.29 a. 2-methylpropene   **b.** 4-bromo-2-pentyne
      c. 4-ethylcyclopentene   **d.** 4-ethyl-2-hexene

12.31 a. $H_2C{=}CH-CH_2-CH_2-CH_3$

b. $H_2C{=}\overset{\overset{\displaystyle CH_3}{|}}{C}-CH_2-CH_3$

c.

d. $Cl-$

12.33 a. *cis*-2-butene
b. *trans*-3-octene
c. *cis*-3-heptene

12.35 a.

$\overset{Br}{}\overset{}{\underset{H}{}}C{=}C\overset{H}{\underset{Cl}{}}$

b.

$\overset{CH_3}{\underset{H}{}}C{=}C\overset{CH_2-CH_2-CH_3}{\underset{H}{}}$

c.

$\overset{CH_3-CH_2}{\underset{H}{}}C{=}C\overset{H}{\underset{CH_2-CH_2-CH_3}{}}$

12.37 a and **c** cannot have cis–trans isomers because they each have two identical groups on at least one of the carbon atoms in the double bond.

12.39 a. $CH_3-CH_2-CH_2-CH_2-CH_3$

b. $CH_3-\overset{\overset{\displaystyle CH_3}{|}}{\underset{\underset{\displaystyle OH}{|}}{C}}-CH_2-CH_3$

c.

d.

12.41 A polymer is a very large molecule composed of small units (monomers) that are repeated many times.

12.43 $3\ H_2C{=}CH \longrightarrow -\overset{H}{\underset{H}{C}}-\overset{CH_3}{\underset{H}{C}}-\overset{H}{\underset{H}{C}}-\overset{CH_3}{\underset{H}{C}}-\overset{H}{\underset{H}{C}}-\overset{CH_3}{\underset{H}{C}}-$

12.45 $-\overset{F}{\underset{F}{C}}-\overset{H}{\underset{H}{C}}-\overset{F}{\underset{F}{C}}-\overset{H}{\underset{H}{C}}-\overset{F}{\underset{F}{C}}-\overset{H}{\underset{H}{C}}-$

12.47 a. 2-chlorotoluene
b. ethylbenzene
c. 1,3,5-trichlorobenzene
d. 1,3-dimethylbenzene (*m*-xylene)
e. 3-bromo-5-chlorotoluene
f. isopropylbenzene

12.49 a.
b.
c.
d.

12.51 $-\overset{Cl}{\underset{F}{C}}-\overset{F}{\underset{F}{C}}-\overset{Cl}{\underset{F}{C}}-\overset{F}{\underset{F}{C}}-\overset{Cl}{\underset{F}{C}}-\overset{F}{\underset{F}{C}}-$

12.53

a. $C_9H_{20}(l) + 14O_2(g) \xrightarrow{\Delta} 9CO_2(g) + 10H_2O(g) + energy$

b. $C_5H_{12}(l) + 8O_2(g) \xrightarrow{\Delta} 5CO_2(g) + 6H_2O(g) + energy$

c. $C_9H_{12}(l) + 12O_2(g) \xrightarrow{\Delta} 9CO_2(g) + 6H_2O(g) + energy$

12.55 a. butane
b. butane
c. potassium chloride
d. potassium chloride
e. butane

12.57 a. structural isomers
b. not structural isomers

12.59 a. $CH_3-\overset{\overset{\displaystyle CH_3}{|}}{CH}-CH_2-\overset{\overset{\displaystyle CH_3}{|}}{CH}-CH_3$
        2,4-Dimethylpentane

b. $CH_3-\overset{\overset{\displaystyle Cl}{|}}{CH}-\overset{\overset{\displaystyle CH_3}{|}}{CH}-\overset{\overset{\displaystyle Br}{|}}{CH}-CH_2-CH_3$
        4-Bromo-2-chloro-3-methylhexane

12.61 $-\overset{F}{\underset{F}{C}}-\overset{F}{\underset{F}{C}}-\overset{F}{\underset{F}{C}}-\overset{F}{\underset{F}{C}}-\overset{F}{\underset{F}{C}}-\overset{F}{\underset{F}{C}}-$

12.63 a. three carbon atoms; two carbon–carbon single bonds
b. three carbon atoms; three carbon–carbon single bonds in a ring
c. three carbon atoms; one carbon–carbon single bond; one carbon–carbon double bond
d. three carbon atoms; one carbon–carbon single bond; one carbon–carbon triple bond

12.65 a. 2,2-dimethylbutane
  b. chloroethane
  c. 2-bromo-4-ethylhexane
  d. methylcyclopentane

12.67 a.

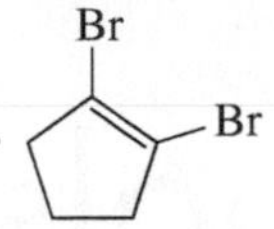

  b. $CH_3—C\equiv C—CH_2—CH_2—CH_3$

  c.

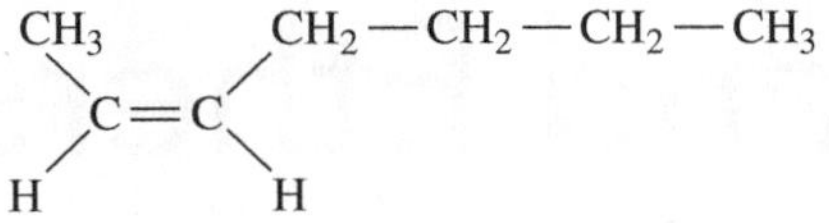

12.69 a. *trans*-2-pentene
  b. 4-bromo-5-methyl-1-hexene
  c. 1-methylcyclopentene

12.71 a. structural isomers
  b. cis–trans isomers

12.73 a. *cis*-3-heptene
  b. *trans*-2-methyl-3-hexene
  c. *trans*-2-heptene

12.75

  a.

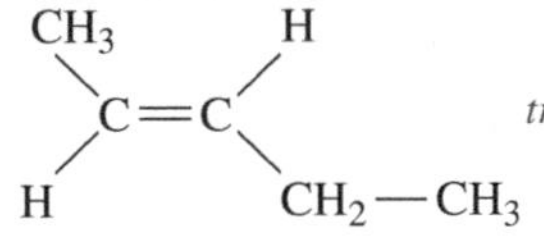

trans-2-Pentene

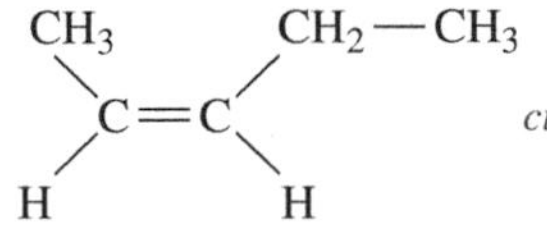

cis-2-Pentene

  b.

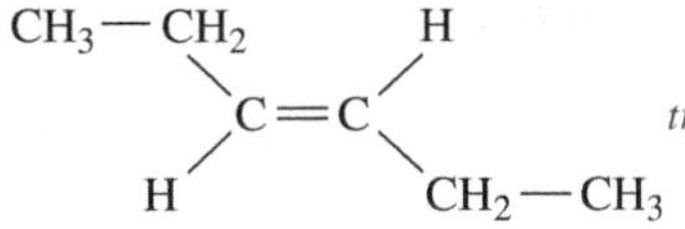

trans-3-Hexene

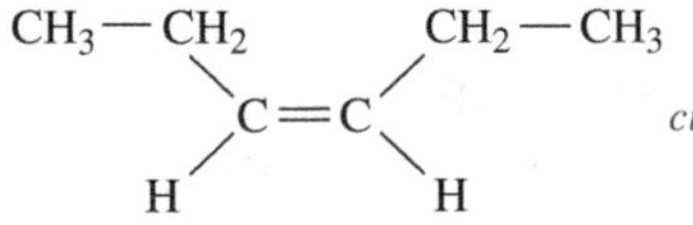

cis-3-Hexene

12.77 a. $C_5H_{12}(g) + 8O_2(g) \xrightarrow{\Delta} 5CO_2(g) + 6H_2O(g) + \text{energy}$

  b. $C_4H_8(g) + 6O_2(g) \xrightarrow{\Delta} 4CO_2(g) + 4H_2O(g) + \text{energy}$

  c. $2C_7H_{14}(l) + 21O_2(g) \xrightarrow{\Delta}$
$$14CO_2(g) + 14H_2O(g) + \text{energy}$$

12.79 a. 3-methylpentane   **b.** methylcyclohexane
  c. butane

12.81 a.

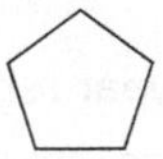

  b.

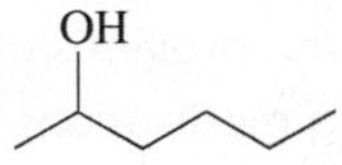

  c.

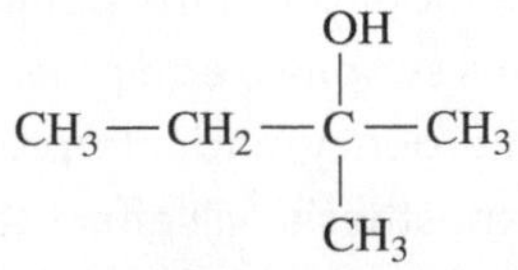

12.83

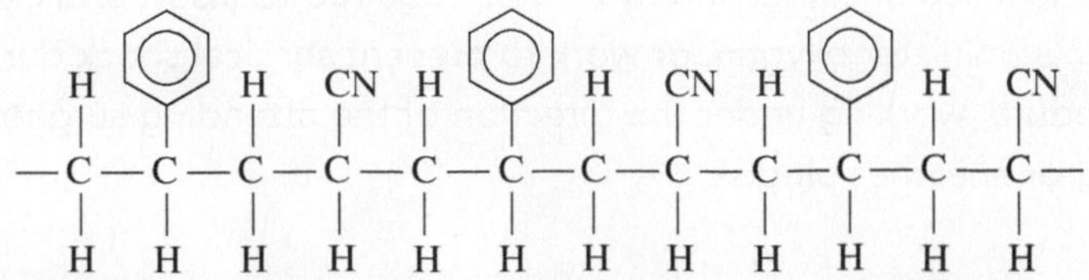

12.85 a. 3-methylaniline (*p*-methylaniline)
  b. 1-chloro-2-methylbenzene, 2-chlorotoluene
    (*o*-chlorotoluene)
  c. 1,2-difluorobenzene (*o*-difluorobenzene)

12.87 a.

  b.

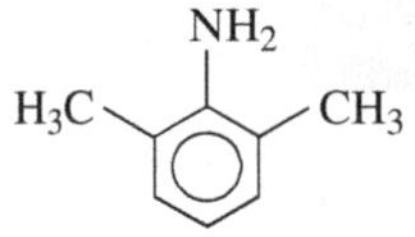

  c.

12.89 1×10^{14} molecules of bombykol

12.91 a. $H_2C=CH—CH_2—CH_2—CH_3$ 1-Pentene

  b.

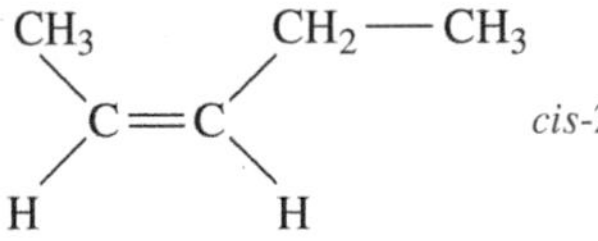

cis-2-Pentene

  c.

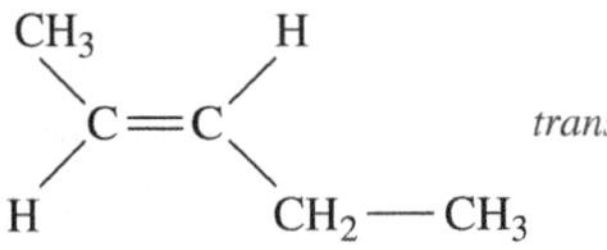

trans-2-Pentene

12.93 a.

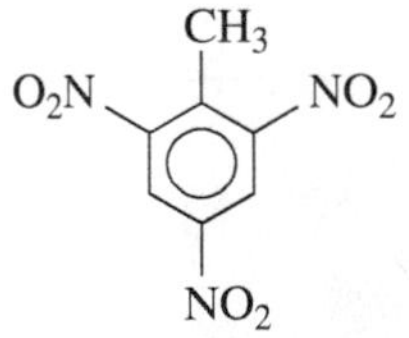

  b.

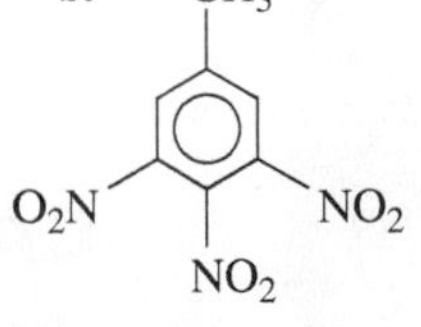

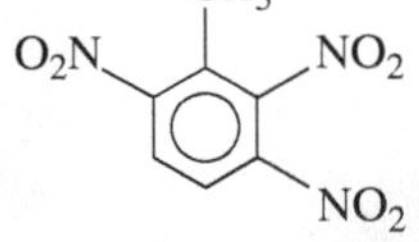

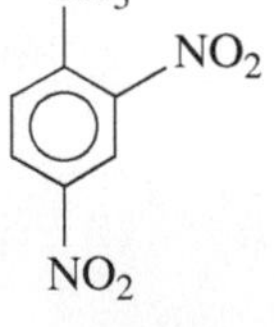

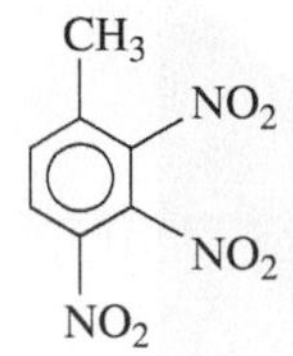

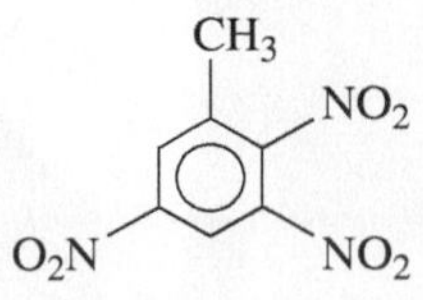

13

Alcohols, Phenols, Thiols, and Ethers

AN EPIDURAL IS A REGIONAL ANESTHESIA THAT

will provide pain relief for Janet during her labor and delivery by blocking pain in the lower half of her body. Tom, a nurse anesthetist, prepares the medication for the epidural injection, which consists of a local anesthetic, chloroprocaine, and a small amount of fentanyl, a common opioid. Tom administers the anesthetic through a catheter into Janet's lower spine and in a few minutes, her pain subsides.

One of the earliest anesthetics used in medicine was diethyl ether, more commonly referred to as ether. Diethyl ether contains an ether functional group, which is an oxygen atom bonded by single bonds to two carbon groups. Today, ether is rarely used because it is extremely flammable, and produces undesirable side effects such as postanesthetic nausea and vomiting. Sevoflurane, which also has an ether functional group, is a more modern anesthetic that does not cause nausea and vomiting.

Ethoxyethane
(diethyl ether)

Sevoflurane

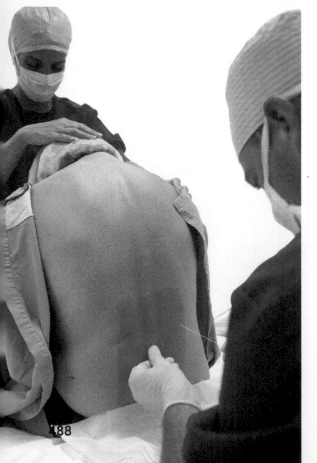

CAREER Nurse Anesthetist

More than 26 million people in the United States each year require anesthesia associated with a medical or dental procedure. Anesthesia is typically administered by a nurse anesthetist who provides care before, during, and after the procedure by giving medications to keep a patient asleep and pain-free while monitoring the patient's vital signs. A nurse anesthetist also obtains supplies, equipment, and an ample blood supply for a potential emergency, and interprets pre-surgical tests to determine how the anesthesia will affect the patient. A nurse anesthetist may also be required to insert artificial airways, administer oxygen, or work to prevent surgical shock during a procedure, working under the direction of the attending surgeon, dentist, or anesthesiologist.

In this chapter, we will look at organic compounds that contain functional groups with oxygen or sulfur atoms. Alcohols, which contain the hydroxyl group (—OH), are commonly found in nature and are used in industry and at home. For centuries, grains, vegetables, and fruits have been fermented to produce the ethanol present in alcoholic beverages. The hydroxyl group is important in biomolecules, such as sugars and starches, as well as in steroids, such as cholesterol and estradiol. Menthol is a cyclic alcohol with a minty odor and flavor that is used in cough drops, shaving creams, and ointments. The phenols contain the hydroxyl group attached to a benzene ring.

Ethers are compounds that contain an oxygen atom connected to two carbon atoms (—O—). Ethers are important solvents in chemistry and medical laboratories. Beginning in 1842, diethyl ether was used for about 100 years as a general anesthetic. Today, less flammable and more easily tolerated anesthetics are used. Thiols, which contain the —SH group, give the strong odors we associate with garlic and onions.

CHAPTER READINESS*

⚛ CORE CHEMISTRY SKILLS

- Naming and Drawing Alkanes (12.2)

*This Core Chemistry Skill from the previous chapter is listed here for your review as you proceed to the new material in this chapter.

13.1 Alcohols, Phenols, and Thiols

We can now classify and name alcohols, phenols, and thiols by their functional groups. In an **alcohol**, the functional group known as a hydroxyl group (—OH) replaces a hydrogen atom in a hydrocarbon. Oxygen (—O—) atoms are shown in red in the ball-and-stick models (see Figure 13.1). In a **phenol**, the hydroxyl group replaces a hydrogen atom attached to a benzene ring. A **thiol** contains a sulfur atom, shown in yellow-green in the ball-and-stick model, which makes a thiol similar to an alcohol except that —OH is replaced by a thiol group (—SH). Molecules of alcohols, phenols, and thiols have bent shapes around the oxygen or sulfur atom, similar to water.

LEARNING GOAL

Give the IUPAC and common names for alcohols, phenols, and thiols; draw their condensed and line-angle structural formulas.

⚛ CORE CHEMISTRY SKILL

Identifying Alcohols, Phenols, and Thiols

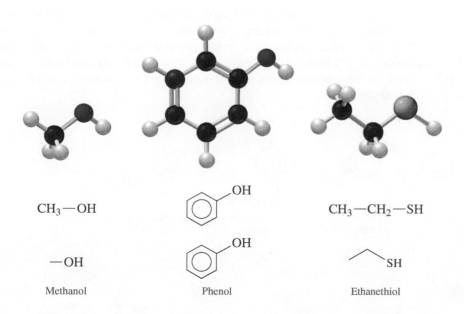

CH_3—OH

—OH

Methanol

OH

OH

Phenol

CH_3—CH_2—SH

SH

Ethanethiol

FIGURE 13.1 ▶ An alcohol has a hydroxyl group (—OH) attached to carbon, and a phenol has a hydroxyl group (—OH) attached to a benzene ring. A thiol has a thiol group (—SH) attached to carbon.

Q How is an alcohol different from a thiol?

Naming Alcohols

In the IUPAC system, an alcohol is named by replacing the *e* of the corresponding alkane name with *ol*. The common name of a simple alcohol uses the name of the alkyl group followed by *alcohol*.

CH$_3$—H   CH$_3$—OH   CH$_3$—CH$_2$—H   CH$_3$—CH$_2$—OH
Methane   Methanol   Ethane   Ethanol
              (methyl alcohol)   (ethyl alcohol)

Alcohols with one or two carbon atoms do not require a number for the hydroxyl group. When an alcohol consists of a chain with 3 or more carbon atoms, the chain is numbered to give the position of the —OH group and any substituents on the chain. An alcohol with two —OH groups is named as a *diol*, and an alcohol with three —OH groups is named as a *triol*.

CH$_3$—CH$_2$—CH$_2$—OH   CH$_3$—CH—CH$_3$ HO—CH$_2$—CH—CH$_2$—CH
  3   2   1 | 1   2   3   4
                                OH   OH
     1-Propanol   2-Propanol   1,2-Butanediol
   (propyl alcohol)   (isopropyl alcohol)

We can also draw the line-angle structural formulas for alcohols as shown for 2-propanol, 2-butanol, and 1,2-butanediol.

2-Propanol   2-Butanol   1,2-Butanediol

A cyclic alcohol is named as a *cycloalkanol*. If there are substituents, the ring is numbered from carbon 1, which is the carbon attached to the —OH group. Compounds with no substituents on the ring do not require a number for the hydroxyl group.

Cyclohexanol   2-Methylcyclopentanol

Naming Phenols

The term *phenol* is the IUPAC name when a hydroxyl group (—OH) is bonded to a benzene ring. When there is a second substituent, the benzene ring is numbered starting from carbon 1, which is the carbon bonded to the —OH group. As we have seen for other aromatic compounds with 2 substituents, the terms *ortho*, *meta*, and *para* (abbreviated *o*-, *m*-, and *p*-) are used for the common names of simple phenols. The common name *cresol* is also used for methylphenols.

Phenol   3-Chlorophenol   4-Ethylphenol   3-Methylphenol
           (*m*-chlorophenol)   (*p*-ethylphenol)   (*m*-cresol)

SAMPLE PROBLEM 13.1 Naming Alcohols

Give the IUPAC name for the following:

$$CH_3-\underset{\underset{CH_3}{|}}{CH}-CH_2-\underset{\underset{OH}{|}}{CH}-CH_3$$

SOLUTION

	Given	Need
ANALYZE THE PROBLEM	alcohol, five carbon chain, methyl substituent	IUPAC name

STEP 1 Name the longest carbon chain attached to the —OH group by replacing the *e* in the corresponding alkane name with *ol*. To name the alcohol, the *e* in alkane name pentane is replaced by *ol*.

$$CH_3-\underset{\underset{CH_3}{|}}{CH}-CH_2-\underset{\underset{OH}{|}}{CH}-CH_3 \qquad \text{pentanol}$$

STEP 2 Number the chain starting at the end nearer to the —OH group. This carbon chain is numbered from right to left to give the position of the —OH group as carbon 2, which is shown as a prefix in the name 2-pentanol.

$$\underset{5}{CH_3}-\underset{4}{\underset{\underset{CH_3}{|}}{CH}}-\underset{3}{CH_2}-\underset{2}{\underset{\underset{OH}{|}}{CH}}-\underset{1}{CH_3} \qquad \text{2-pentanol}$$

STEP 3 Give the location and name of each substituent relative to the —OH group.

$$\underset{5}{CH_3}-\underset{4}{\underset{\underset{CH_3}{|}}{CH}}-\underset{3}{CH_2}-\underset{2}{\underset{\underset{OH}{|}}{CH}}-\underset{1}{CH_3} \qquad \text{4-methyl-2-pentanol}$$

STUDY CHECK 13.1

Give the IUPAC name for the following:

ANSWER

3-chloro-1-butanol

SAMPLE PROBLEM 13.2 Naming Phenols

Give the IUPAC and common names for the following:

OH
⬡—Br

SOLUTION

	Given	Need
ANALYZE THE PROBLEM	phenol, bromo substituent	IUPAC and common names

Explore Your World

Alcohols in Household Products

Read the labels on household products such as sanitizers, mouthwashes, cold remedies, rubbing alcohol, and flavoring extracts. Look for names of alcohols, such as ethyl alcohol, isopropyl alcohol, thymol, and menthol.

Questions

1. What part of the name tells you that it is an alcohol?
2. What alcohol is usually meant by the term "alcohol"?
3. What is the percentage of alcohol in the products?
4. Draw the condensed structural formulas for the alcohols you find listed on the labels. You may need to use the Internet for some structures.

STEP 1 Name an aromatic alcohol as a *phenol*. The compound is a *phenol* because it contains an —OH group attached to a benzene ring.

OH
Br
phenol

STEP 2 Number the chain starting at the end nearer to the —OH group. For a phenol, the carbon atom attached to the —OH group is carbon 1.

OH
Br
phenol

STEP 3 Give the location and name for each substituent relative to the —OH group. For the common name, use the prefix *ortho* (*o-*).

OH
Br
2-bromophenol (*o*-bromophenol)

STUDY CHECK 13.2

Give the IUPAC and common names for the following:

OH
CH₃

ANSWER

4-methylphenol (*p*-methylphenol; *p*-cresol)

Chemistry Link to **Health**
Some Important Alcohols and Phenols

Methanol (*methyl alcohol*), the simplest alcohol, is found in many solvents and paint removers. If ingested, methanol is oxidized to formaldehyde, which can cause headaches, blindness, and death. Methanol is used to make plastics, medicines, and fuels. In car racing, it is used as a fuel because it is less flammable and has a higher octane rating than does gasoline.

Ethanol (*ethyl alcohol*) has been known since prehistoric times as an intoxicating product formed by the fermentation of grains, sugars, and starches.

$$C_6H_{12}O_6 \xrightarrow{\text{Fermentation}} 2CH_3-CH_2-OH + 2CO_2$$

Today, ethanol for commercial use is produced by reacting ethene and water at high temperatures and pressures. Ethanol is used as a solvent for perfumes, varnishes, and some medicines, such as tincture of iodine. Recent interest in alternative fuels has led to increased production of ethanol by the fermentation of sugars from grains such as corn, wheat, and rice. "Gasohol" is a mixture of ethanol and gasoline used as a fuel.

$$H_2C=CH_2 + H_2O \xrightarrow{\text{300 °C, 200 atm, H}^+} CH_3-CH_2-OH$$

1,2-Ethanediol (*ethylene glycol*) is used as an antifreeze in heating and cooling systems. It is also a solvent for paints, inks, and plastics, and it is used in the production of synthetic fibers such as Dacron. If ingested, it is extremely toxic. In the body, it is oxidized to oxalic acid, which forms insoluble salts in the kidneys that cause renal damage, convulsions, and death. Because its sweet taste is attractive to pets and children, ethylene glycol solutions must be carefully stored.

HO—CH$_2$—CH$_2$—OH $\xrightarrow{[O]}$ HO—C—C—OH

1,2-Ethanediol
(ethylene glycol)

Oxalic acid

Antifreeze (ethylene glycol) raises the boiling point and decreases the freezing point of water in a radiator.

Phenols are found in several of the essential oils of plants, which produce the odor or flavor of the plant. Eugenol is found in cloves, vanillin in vanilla bean, isoeugenol in nutmeg, and thymol in thyme and mint. Thymol has a pleasant, minty taste and is used in mouthwashes and by dentists to disinfect a cavity before adding a filling compound.

1,2,3-Propanetriol (*glycerol* or *glycerin*), a trihydroxy alcohol, is a viscous liquid obtained from oils and fats during the production of soaps. The presence of several polar —OH groups makes it strongly attracted to water, a feature that makes glycerol useful as a skin softener in products such as skin lotions, cosmetics, shaving creams, and liquid soaps.

HO—CH$_2$—CH—CH$_2$—OH

1,2,3-Propanetriol
(glycerol)

Bisphenol A (BPA) is used to make polycarbonate, a clear plastic that is used to manufacture beverage bottles, including baby bottles. Washing polycarbonate bottles with certain detergents or at high temperatures disrupts the polymer, causing small amounts of BPA to leach from the bottles. Because BPA is an estrogen mimic, there are concerns about the harmful effects from low levels of BPA. In 2008, Canada banned the use of polycarbonate baby bottles, which are now labeled "BPA free."

Bisphenol A (BPA)

Vanillin

Eugenol

Thymol

Isoeugenol

Derivatives of phenol are found in the oils of nutmeg, thyme, cloves, and vanilla.

Thiols

Thiols, also known as *mercaptans*, are a family of sulfur-containing organic compounds that have a *thiol* group (—SH). In the IUPAC system, thiols are named by adding *thiol* to the alkane name of the longest carbon chain and numbering the carbon chain from the end nearer the —SH group.

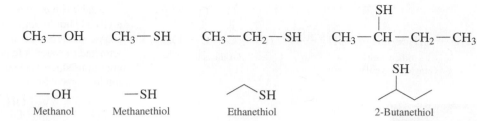

$$CH_3—OH \qquad CH_3—SH \qquad CH_3—CH_2—SH \qquad CH_3—\overset{\overset{\displaystyle SH}{|}}{CH}—CH_2—CH_3$$

—OH   —SH   ⌃⌄SH   (SH)

Methanol   Methanethiol   Ethanethiol   2-Butanethiol

An important property of thiols is a strong, sometimes disagreeable, odor. To help us detect natural gas (methane) leaks, a small amount of *tert*-butylthiol is added to the gas supply, which is normally odorless. There are thiols such as *trans*-2-butene-1-thiol in the spray emitted when a skunk senses danger.

$$\underset{\substack{H}}{\overset{\substack{CH_3}}{}} C=C \underset{\substack{CH_2—SH}}{\overset{\substack{H}}{}}$$

trans-2-Butene-1-thiol
(in skunk spray)

Methanethiol is the characteristic odor of oysters, cheddar cheese, and garlic. Garlic also contains 2-propene-1-thiol. The odor of onions is because of 1-propanethiol, which is also a lachrymator, a substance that makes eyes tear (see Figure 13.2).

The spray of a skunk contains a mixture of thiols.

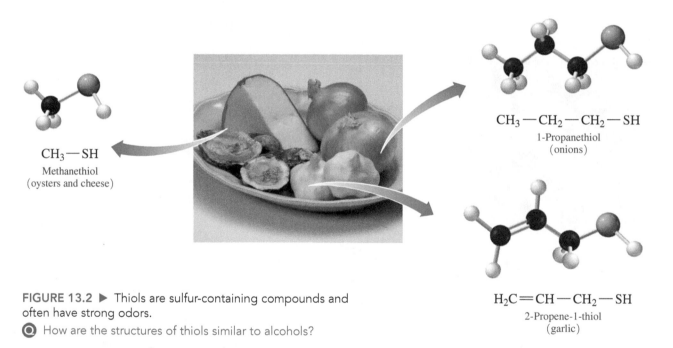

$CH_3—SH$
Methanethiol
(oysters and cheese)

$CH_3—CH_2—CH_2—SH$
1-Propanethiol
(onions)

$H_2C=CH—CH_2—SH$
2-Propene-1-thiol
(garlic)

FIGURE 13.2 ▶ Thiols are sulfur-containing compounds and often have strong odors.

Q How are the structures of thiols similar to alcohols?

QUESTIONS AND PROBLEMS

13.1 Alcohols, Phenols, and Thiols

LEARNING GOAL Give the IUPAC and common names for alcohols, phenols, and thiols; draw their condensed and line-angle structural formulas.

13.1 Give the IUPAC and common names for each of the following:

a. $CH_3—CH_2—OH$

b. $CH_3—CH_2—\overset{\overset{\displaystyle OH}{|}}{CH}—CH_3$

c. [line-angle structure with OH]

d. [cyclohexane ring with OH and CH₃]

e. [benzene ring with OH and F]

13.2 Give the IUPAC and common names for each of the following:

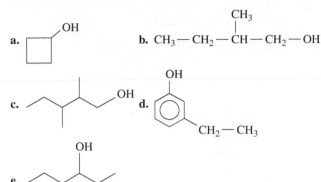

a.

b.
$$CH_3-CH_2-\overset{\overset{\displaystyle CH_3}{|}}{CH}-CH_2-OH$$

c.

d.

e.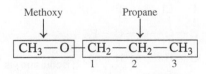

13.3 Draw the condensed or line-angle structural formula, if cyclic, for each of the following:
a. 1-propanol
b. 3-pentanol
c. 2-methyl-2-butanol
d. *p*-chlorophenol
e. 2-bromo-5-chlorophenol

13.4 Draw the condensed or line-angle structural formula, if cyclic, for each of the following:
a. 3-methyl-1-butanol
b. 2,4-dichlorocyclohexanol
c. 3-chloro-2-methyl-1-pentanol
d. *o*-bromophenol
e. 2,4-dimethylphenol

13.2 Ethers

An **ether** consists of an oxygen atom that is attached by single bonds to two carbon groups that are alkyl or aromatic groups.

LEARNING GOAL

Give the IUPAC and common names for ethers; draw their condensed or line-angle structural formulas.

$$CH_3-O-CH_3$$

Methoxymethane
(dimethyl ether)

$$CH_3-CH_2-O-CH_3$$

Methoxyethane
(ethyl methyl ether)

Methoxybenzene
(methyl phenyl ether)

Naming Ethers

In the common name of an ether, the names of the alkyl or aromatic groups attached to each side of the oxygen atom are written in alphabetical order, followed by the word *ether*.

Methyl ↓ Propyl ↓
$$\boxed{CH_3}-O-\boxed{CH_2-CH_2-CH_3}$$ Common name: Methyl propyl ether

In the IUPAC system, an ether is named with an *alkoxy* group made up of the smaller alkyl group and the oxygen atom, followed by the alkane name of the longer carbon chain.

Methoxy ↓ Propane ↓
$$\boxed{CH_3-O}-\boxed{CH_2-CH_2-CH_3}$$ IUPAC name: 1-Methoxypropane
$$\qquad\quad 1 \quad\; 2 \quad\;\; 3$$

Guide to Writing IUPAC Names for Ethers

STEP 1
Write the alkane name of the longer carbon chain.

STEP 2
Name the oxygen and smaller alkyl group as an alkoxy group.

STEP 3
Number the longer carbon chain from the end nearer the alkoxy group and give its location.

More examples of naming ethers with both IUPAC and common names follow:

$$CH_3-CH_2-O-CH_2-CH_3$$
Ethoxyethane
(diethyl ether)

$$CH_3-\underset{\underset{O-CH_3}{|}}{CH}-CH_2-CH_3$$
2-Methoxybutane

$$CH_3-CH_2-O-\bigcirc$$
Ethoxybenzene
(ethyl phenyl ether)

$$\bigcirc-O-\bigcirc$$
Phenoxybenzene
(diphenyl ether)

SAMPLE PROBLEM 13.3 Naming Ethers

Give the IUPAC name for the following:

$$CH_3-CH_2-O-CH_2-CH_2-CH_2-CH_3$$

SOLUTION

ANALYZE THE PROBLEM	Given	Need
	ether	IUPAC name

STEP 1 Write the alkane name of the longer carbon chain.

$$CH_3-CH_2-O-\underbrace{CH_2-CH_2-CH_2-CH_3}$$ butane
Longer carbon chain

STEP 2 Name the oxygen and smaller alkyl group as an alkoxy group.

$$CH_3-CH_2-\underset{\uparrow}{O}-CH_2-CH_2-CH_2-CH_3$$ ethoxybutane
Ethoxy group

STEP 3 Number the longer carbon chain from the end nearer the alkoxy group and give its location.

$$CH_3-CH_2-O-\underset{1}{CH_2}-\underset{2}{CH_2}-\underset{3}{CH_2}-\underset{4}{CH_3}$$ 1-ethoxybutane

STUDY CHECK 13.3

What is the IUPAC name of methyl phenyl ether?

ANSWER

methoxybenzene

Chemistry Link to Health
Ethers as Anesthetics

Anesthesia is the loss of sensation and consciousness. A general anesthetic is a substance that blocks signals to the awareness centers in the brain so the person has a loss of memory, a loss of feeling pain, and an artificial sleep. The term *ether* has been associated with anesthesia because diethyl ether was the most widely used anesthetic for more than a hundred years. Although it is easy to administer, ether is very volatile and highly flammable. A small spark in the operating room could cause an explosion. Since the 1950s, anesthetics such as Forane (isoflurane),

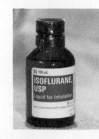

$$F-\underset{\underset{F}{|}}{\overset{\overset{F}{|}}{C}}-\underset{\underset{H}{|}}{\overset{\overset{Cl}{|}}{C}}-O-\underset{\underset{H}{|}}{\overset{\overset{F}{|}}{C}}-F$$
Forane
(isoflurane)

Forane (isoflurane) is an inhaled anesthetic.

Ethrane (enflurane), Suprane (desflurane), and Sevoflurane have been developed that are not as flammable. Most of these anesthetics retain the ether group, but the addition of halogen atoms reduces the volatility and flammability of the ethers.

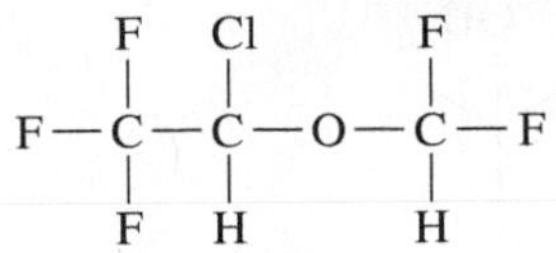

Forane
(isoflurane)

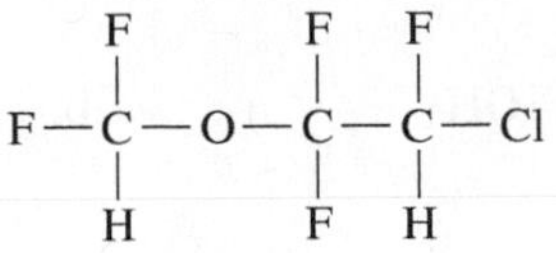

Ethrane
(enflurane)

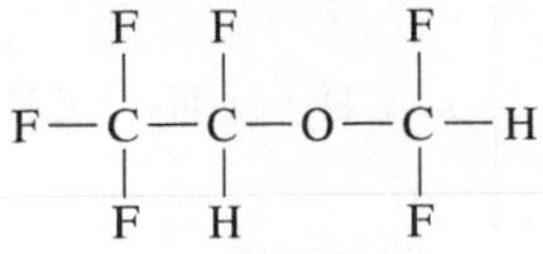

Suprane
(desflurane)

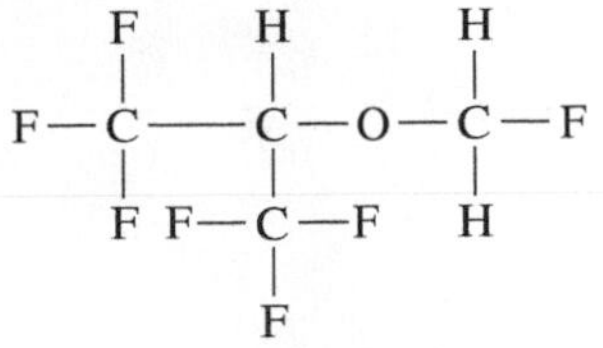

Sevoflurane

QUESTIONS AND PROBLEMS

13.2 Ethers

LEARNING GOAL Give the IUPAC and common names for ethers; draw their condensed or line-angle structural formulas.

13.5 Give the IUPAC name and any common name for each of the following ethers:

a. $CH_3-O-CH_2-CH_3$ b.

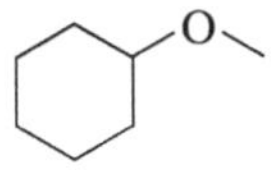

c.

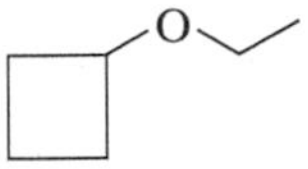

d. $CH_3-CH_2-CH_2-O-CH_3$

13.6 Give the IUPAC name and any common name for each of the following ethers:

a. $CH_3-CH_2-O-CH_2-CH_2-CH_3$

b.

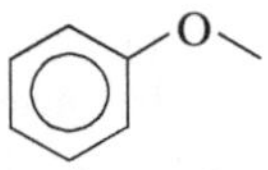

c.

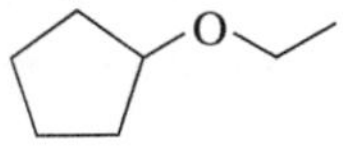

d. CH_3-O-CH_3

13.7 Draw the condensed or line-angle structural formula for each of the following:
a. ethyl propyl ether
b. cyclopropyl ethyl ether
c. methoxycyclopentane
d. 1-ethoxy-2-methylbutane
e. 2,3-dimethoxypentane

13.8 Draw the condensed or line-angle structural formula for each of the following:
a. diethyl ether
b. diphenyl ether
c. ethoxycyclohexane
d. 2-methoxy-2,3-dimethylbutane
e. 1,2-dimethoxybenzene

13.3 Physical Properties of Alcohols, Phenols, and Ethers

LEARNING GOAL

Describe the classification of alcohols; describe the boiling points and solubility of alcohols, phenols, and ethers.

Alcohols are classified by the number of alkyl groups attached to the carbon atom bonded to the hydroxyl group ($-OH$). A **primary (1°) alcohol** has one alkyl group attached to the carbon atom bonded to the $-OH$ group. The simplest alcohol, methanol (CH_3OH), which has a carbon attached to three H atoms but no alkyl group, is considered a primary alcohol; a **secondary (2°) alcohol** has two alkyl groups, and a **tertiary (3°) alcohol** has three alkyl groups.

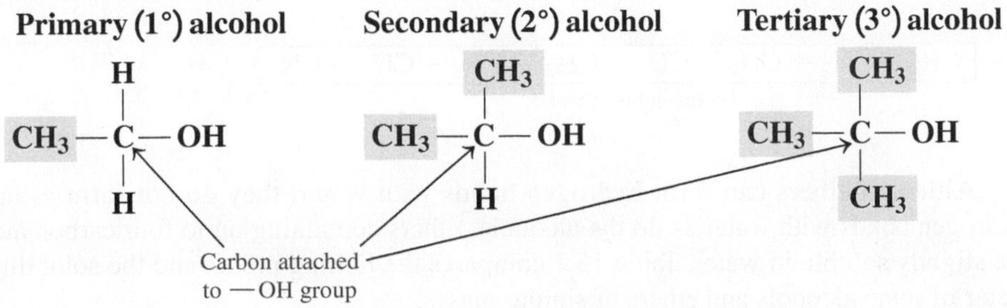

Primary (1°) alcohol

Secondary (2°) alcohol

Tertiary (3°) alcohol

Carbon attached to —OH group

▶**SAMPLE PROBLEM 13.4** Classifying Alcohols

Classify each of the following alcohols as primary (1°), secondary (2°), or tertiary (3°):

a. CH_3—CH_2—CH_2—OH **b.**

SOLUTION

a. The carbon atom bonded to the —OH group is attached to one alkyl group, which makes this a primary (1°) alcohol.
b. The carbon atom bonded to the —OH group is attached to three alkyl groups, which makes this a tertiary (3°) alcohol.

STUDY CHECK 13.4

Classify the following alcohol as primary (1°), secondary (2°), or tertiary (3°):

OH

ANSWER
secondary (2°)

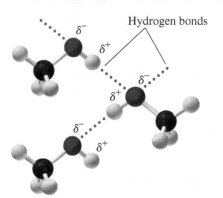

Methanol
(methyl alcohol)

Hydrogen bonds form between alcohol molecules but not between ether molecules.

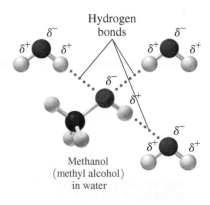

Methanol
(methyl alcohol)
in water

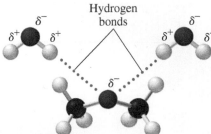

Dimethyl ether in water

Small alcohol and ether molecules are soluble in water because they form hydrogen bonds.

Boiling Points

Because there is a large electronegativity difference between the oxygen and hydrogen atoms in the —OH group, the oxygen has a partially negative charge, and the hydrogen has a partially positive charge. As a result, hydrogen bonds form between the oxygen of one alcohol and hydrogen in the —OH group of another alcohol. Hydrogen bonds cannot form between ether molecules because there are not any polar —OH groups.

Alcohols have higher boiling points than do ethers of the same mass because alcohols require higher temperatures to provide sufficient energy to break the many hydrogen bonds. The boiling points of ethers are similar to those of alkanes because neither can form hydrogen bonds.

Solubility of Alcohols and Ethers in Water

The electronegativity of the oxygen atom in both alcohols and ethers influences their solubility in water. In alcohols, the atoms in the —OH group can form hydrogen bonds with the H and O atoms of water. Alcohols with one to three carbon atoms are *miscible* in water, which means that any amount is completely soluble in water. However, the solubility provided by the polar —OH group decreases as the number of carbon atoms increases. Alcohols with four carbon atoms are slightly soluble, and alcohols with five or more carbon atoms are not soluble.

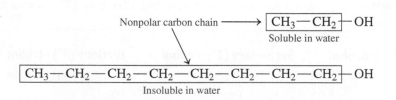

Although ethers can form hydrogen bonds with water, they do not form as many hydrogen bonds with water as do the alcohols. Ethers containing up to four carbon atoms are slightly soluble in water. Table 13.1 compares the boiling points and the solubility in water of some alcohols and ethers of similar mass.

TABLE 13.1 Boiling Points and Solubility of Some Alcohols and Ethers

Compound	Condensed Structural Formula	Number of Carbon Atoms	Boiling Point (°C)	Solubility in Water
Methanol	CH_3-OH	1	65	Soluble
Ethanol	CH_3-CH_2-OH	2	78	Soluble
1-Propanol	$CH_3-CH_2-CH_2-OH$	3	97	Soluble
1-Butanol	$CH_3-CH_2-CH_2-CH_2-OH$	4	118	Slightly soluble
1-Pentanol	$CH_3-CH_2-CH_2-CH_2-CH_2-OH$	5	138	Insoluble
Dimethyl ether	CH_3-O-CH_3	2	−23	Slightly soluble
Ethyl methyl ether	$CH_3-O-CH_2-CH_3$	3	8	Slightly soluble
Diethyl ether	$CH_3-CH_2-O-CH_2-CH_3$	4	35	Slightly soluble
Ethyl propyl ether	$CH_3-CH_2-O-CH_2-CH_2-CH_3$	5	64	Insoluble

Solubility and Boiling Point of Phenol

Phenol has a high boiling point (182 °C) because the —OH group allows phenol molecules to hydrogen bond with other phenol molecules. Phenol is slightly soluble in water because the —OH group can form hydrogen bonds with water molecules. In water, the —OH group of phenol ionizes slightly, which makes it a weak acid ($K_a = 1 \times 10^{-10}$). In fact, an early name for phenol was *carbolic acid*.

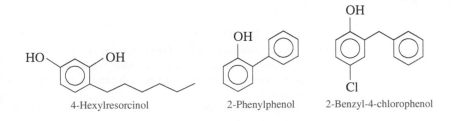

Phenol + H_2O ⇌ Phenoxide ion + H_3O^+

Phenol and Antiseptics

An *antiseptic* is a substance applied to the skin to kill microorganisms that cause infection. At one time, dilute solutions of phenol (carbolic acid) were used in hospitals as antiseptics. Joseph Lister (1827–1912) is considered a pioneer in antiseptic surgery and was the first to sterilize surgical instruments and dressings with phenol. Phenol was also used to disinfect wounds to prevent post-surgical infections such as gangrene. However, phenol is very corrosive and highly irritating to the skin; it can cause severe burns and ingestion can be fatal. Soon phenol solutions were replaced with other disinfectants. 4-Hexylresorcinol is a form of phenol used in topical antiseptics, throat lozenges, mouth washes, and throat sprays. Lysol, used to disinfect surfaces in a home or hospital, contains the antiseptics 2-phenylphenol and 2-benzyl-4-chlorophenol.

Joseph Lister was the first to use phenol to sterilize surgical instruments.

Lysol, used as a disinfectant, contains phenol compounds.

4-Hexylresorcinol   2-Phenylphenol   2-Benzyl-4-chlorophenol

Chemistry Link to **Health**
Hand Sanitizers and Ethanol

Hand sanitizers are used as an alternative to washing hands to kill most bacteria and viruses that spread colds and flu. As a gel or liquid solution, many hand sanitizers use ethanol as their active ingredient. Although safe for most adults, supervision is recommended when used by children because there is some concern about their risk to the health of children. After using an ethanol- or isopropyl alcohol-based hand sanitizer, children might ingest enough alcohol to make them sick.

In an alcohol-containing sanitizer, the amount of ethanol is typically 60% (v/v) but can be as high as 85% (v/v). This amount of

ethanol can make hand sanitizers a fire hazard in the home because ethanol is highly flammable. When ethanol undergoes combustion, it produces a transparent blue flame. When using an ethanol-containing sanitizer, it is important to rub hands until they are completely dry. It is also recommended that sanitizers containing ethanol be placed in storage areas that are away from heat sources in the home.

Some sanitizers are alcohol-free, but often the active ingredient is triclosan, which contains aromatic, ether, and phenol functional groups. The Food and Drug Administration is considering banning triclosan in personal-care products because when mixed with tap water for disposal, the triclosan that accumulates in the environment may promote the growth of antibiotic-resistant bacteria. Recent reports indicate that triclosan may disrupt the endocrine system and interfere with the function of estrogens, androgens, and thyroid hormones.

Hand sanitizers that contain ethanol are used to kill bacteria on the hands.

Triclosan is an antibacterial compound used in personal-care products.

QUESTIONS AND PROBLEMS

13.3 Physical Properties of Alcohols, Phenols, and Ethers

LEARNING GOAL Describe the classification of alcohols; describe the boiling points and solubility of alcohols, phenols, and ethers.

13.9 Classify each of the following alcohols as primary (1°), secondary (2°), or tertiary (3°):

a.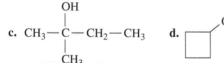

b. $CH_3-CH_2-CH_2-CH_2-OH$

c. $CH_3-\underset{\underset{CH_3}{|}}{\overset{\overset{OH}{|}}{C}}-CH_2-CH_3$ d. [structure: cyclobutanol with OH]

13.10 Classify each of the following alcohols as primary (1°), secondary (2°), or tertiary (3°):

a. [cyclopentane with CH₃ and OH]   b. [structure with OH]

c. [benzyl alcohol structure]

d. $CH_3-CH_2-CH_2-\underset{\underset{CH_3}{|}}{\overset{\overset{CH_3}{|}}{C}}-OH$

13.11 Predict the compound with the higher boiling point in each of the following pairs:
  a. ethane or methanol   b. diethyl ether or 1-butanol
  c. 1-butanol or pentane

13.12 Predict the compound with the higher boiling point in each of the following pairs:
  a. 2-propanol and 2-butanol   b. dimethyl ether or ethanol
  c. dimethyl ether or diethyl ether

13.13 Are each of the following soluble, slightly soluble, or insoluble in water? Explain.
  a. CH_3-CH_2-OH
  b. CH_3-O-CH_3
  c. $CH_3-CH_2-CH_2-CH_2-CH_2-CH_2-OH$

13.14 Are each of the following soluble, slightly soluble, or insoluble in water? Explain.
  a. $CH_3-CH_2-CH_2-OH$
  b. [phenol structure with OH]
  c. $CH_3-CH_2-O-CH_2-CH_3$

13.15 Give an explanation for each of the following observations:
  a. Methanol is soluble in water, but ethane is not.
  b. 2-Propanol is soluble in water, but 1-butanol is only slightly soluble.
  c. 1-Propanol is soluble in water, but ethyl methyl ether is only slightly soluble.

13.16 Give an explanation for each of the following observations:
  a. Ethanol is soluble in water, but propane is not.
  b. Dimethyl ether is slightly soluble in water, but pentane is not.
  c. 1-Propanol is soluble in water, but 1-hexanol is not.

13.4 Reactions of Alcohols and Thiols

LEARNING GOAL

Write equations for the combustion, dehydration, and oxidation of alcohols and thiols.

Alcohols, similar to hydrocarbons, undergo combustion in the presence of oxygen. For example, in a restaurant, a flaming dessert may be prepared by pouring a liquor on fruit or ice cream and lighting it (see Figure 13.3). The combustion of the ethanol in the liquor proceeds as follows:

$$CH_3-CH_2-OH(g) + 3O_2(g) \xrightarrow{\Delta} 2CO_2(g) + 3H_2O(g) + \text{energy}$$

Dehydration of Alcohols to Form Alkenes

In a **dehydration** reaction, alcohols lose a water molecule when they are heated at a high temperature ($180\,°C$) with an acid catalyst such as H_2SO_4. During the dehydration of an alcohol, $H-$ and $-OH$ are removed from *adjacent carbon atoms of the same alcohol* to produce a water molecule. A double bond forms between the same two carbon atoms to produce an alkene product.

FIGURE 13.3 ▶ A flaming dessert is prepared using an alcohol that undergoes combustion.

⊙ What is the equation for the complete combustion of the ethanol in the liquor?

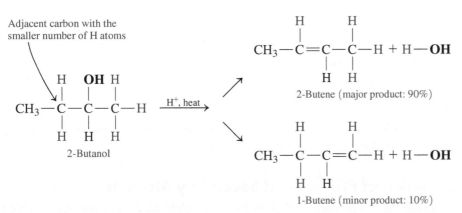

The dehydration of a secondary alcohol can result in the formation of two products. **Saytzeff's rule** states that the major product is the one that forms by removing the hydrogen from the carbon atom that has the smaller number of hydrogen atoms. A hydrogen atom is easier to remove from the carbon atom adjacent to the carbon atom attached to the $-OH$ group that has fewer hydrogen atoms.

⚛ CORE CHEMISTRY SKILL

Writing Equations for the Dehydration of Alcohols

Adjacent carbon with the smaller number of H atoms

CH₃—C—C—C—H $\xrightarrow{H^+, \text{heat}}$

H   OH H
(H   H   H)

2-Butanol

CH₃—C=C—C—H + H—OH
H H
2-Butene (major product: 90%)

CH₃—C—C=C—H + H—OH
H H
1-Butene (minor product: 10%)

▶**SAMPLE PROBLEM 13.5 Dehydration of Alcohols**

Draw the condensed structural formula for the major alkene produced by the dehydration of each of the following alcohols:

a. $CH_3-CH_2-CH_2-CH_2-OH \xrightarrow{H^+, \text{heat}}$

b. $CH_3-\overset{\displaystyle OH}{\underset{|}{CH}}-CH_2-CH_2-CH_3 \xrightarrow{H^+, \text{heat}}$

SOLUTION

a. The 1-butanol loses —OH from carbon 1 and H— from carbon 2 to form 1-butene. This is the only possible product.

$$CH_3 — CH_2 — CH = CH_2$$

b. For the dehydration of an asymmetrical alcohol, we use Saytzeff's rule to remove —OH from carbon 2 and H— from carbon 3, which has the smaller number of H atoms. The major product is 2-pentene.

$$CH_3 — CH = CH — CH_2 — CH_3$$

STUDY CHECK 13.5

What is the name of the alkene produced by the dehydration of cyclopentanol?

ANSWER

cyclopentene

Writing Equations for the Oxidation of Alcohols

The aldehyde functional group at the end of a chain has a C=O bonded to one carbon group and to H.

The ketone functional group in the middle of a chain has a C=O bonded to two carbon groups.

Oxidation of Alcohols

In organic chemistry, **oxidation** is a loss of hydrogen atoms or the addition of oxygen. When a compound is oxidized, there is an increase in the number of carbon–oxygen bonds. When a compound is reduced, there is a decrease in the number of carbon–oxygen bonds.

An aldehyde or ketone is more oxidized than an alcohol; a carboxylic acid is more oxidized than an aldehyde.

Oxidation of Primary and Secondary Alcohols

The oxidation of a primary alcohol produces an aldehyde, which contains a double bond between oxygen and the carbon atom at the end of the chain. For example, the oxidation of methanol and ethanol occurs by removing two hydrogen atoms, one from the —OH group and another from the carbon that is bonded to the —OH group. The oxidized product contains the same number of carbon atoms as the reactant. The reaction is written with the symbol [O] over the arrow to indicate that O is obtained from an oxidizing agent, such as $KMnO_4$ or $K_2Cr_2O_7$.

$$\underset{\substack{\text{Methanol}\\\text{(methyl alcohol)}}}{\overset{\overset{\displaystyle OH}{|}}{\underset{\underset{\displaystyle H}{|}}{H-C-H}}} \xrightarrow{\text{[O]}} \underset{\substack{\text{Methanal}\\\text{(formaldehyde)}}}{\overset{\overset{\displaystyle O}{\|}}{H-C-H}} + H_2O \qquad\qquad \underset{\substack{\text{Ethanol}\\\text{(ethyl alcohol)}}}{\overset{\overset{\displaystyle OH}{|}}{\underset{\underset{\displaystyle H}{|}}{CH_3-C-H}}} \xrightarrow{\text{[O]}} \underset{\substack{\text{Ethanal}\\\text{(acetaldehyde)}}}{\overset{\overset{\displaystyle O}{\|}}{CH_3-C-H}} + H_2O$$

Aldehydes oxidize further by the addition of oxygen to form carboxylic acids, which have three carbon–oxygen bonds. This step occurs so readily that it is often difficult to isolate the aldehyde product during oxidation.

$$\underset{\substack{\text{Ethanal}\\\text{(acetaldehyde)}}}{\overset{\overset{\displaystyle O}{\|}}{CH_3-C-H}} \xrightarrow{\text{[O]}} \underset{\substack{\text{Ethanoic acid}\\\text{(acetic acid)}}}{\overset{\overset{\displaystyle O}{\|}}{CH_3-C-OH}}$$

$$\overset{\overset{\displaystyle O}{\|}}{\underset{\quad\quad OH}{\diagup C}}$$

The carboxylic acid functional group at the end of a chain has a C=O bonded to one carbon group and to OH.

In the oxidation of secondary alcohols, the products are ketones. Two hydrogen atoms are removed, one from the —OH and the other from the carbon bonded to the —OH group. The result is a ketone that has the carbon–oxygen double bond attached to alkyl or aromatic groups on both sides. There is no further oxidation of a ketone because there are no hydrogen atoms attached to the carbon of the ketone group.

$$\underset{\substack{\text{2-Propanol}\\\text{(isopropyl alcohol)}}}{\overset{\overset{\displaystyle OH}{|}}{\underset{\underset{\displaystyle H}{|}}{CH_3-C-CH_3}}} \xrightarrow{\text{[O]}} \underset{\substack{\text{Propanone}\\\text{(dimethyl ketone; acetone)}}}{\overset{\overset{\displaystyle O}{\|}}{CH_3-C-CH_3}} + H_2O$$

Tertiary alcohols do not oxidize readily because there is no hydrogen atom on the carbon bonded to the —OH group. Because C—C bonds are usually too strong to oxidize, tertiary alcohols resist oxidation.

$$\underset{\substack{\text{Alcohol (3°)}}}{\overset{\overset{\displaystyle OH}{|}}{\underset{\underset{\displaystyle CH_3}{|}}{CH_3-C-CH_3}}} \xrightarrow{\text{[O]}} \text{No oxidation product readily forms}$$

No hydrogen on this carbon

No double bond forms

Chemistry Link to **Health**

Methanol Poisoning

Methanol, or "wood alcohol," is a highly toxic alcohol present in products such as windshield-washer fluid, Sterno, and paint strippers. Methanol is rapidly absorbed in the gastrointestinal tract. In the liver, it is metabolized to formaldehyde and then formic acid, a substance that causes nausea, severe abdominal pain, and blurred vision. Blindness can occur because the intermediate products destroy the retina of the eye. As little as 4 mL of methanol can produce blindness. The formic acid, which is not readily eliminated from the body, lowers blood

pH so severely that just 30 mL of methanol can lead to coma and death.

The treatment for methanol poisoning involves giving sodium bicarbonate to neutralize the formic acid in the blood. In some cases, ethanol is given intravenously to the patient. The enzymes in the liver pick up ethanol molecules to oxidize instead of methanol molecules. This process gives time for the methanol to be eliminated via the lungs without the formation of its dangerous oxidation products.

► **SAMPLE PROBLEM 13.6 Oxidation of Alcohols**

Draw the condensed or line-angle structural formula for the aldehyde or ketone formed by the oxidation of each of the following:

                             OH
                             |

a. $CH_3-CH_2-CH-CH_3$ **b.**

SOLUTION

a. This is a secondary (2°) alcohol, which oxidizes to a ketone.

$$CH_3-CH_2-\overset{\overset{\displaystyle O}{\|}}{C}-CH_3$$

b. This is a primary (1°) alcohol, which oxidizes to an aldehyde.

STUDY CHECK 13.6

Draw the condensed structural formula for the product formed by the oxidation of 2-pentanol.

ANSWER

$$CH_3-\overset{\overset{\displaystyle O}{\|}}{C}-CH_2-CH_2-CH_3$$

Interactive Video

Oxidation of Alcohols

During vigorous exercise, lactic acid accumulates in the muscles and causes fatigue. When the activity level is decreased, oxygen enters the muscles. The secondary —OH group in lactic acid is oxidized to a ketone group in pyruvic acid, which eventually is oxidized to CO_2 and H_2O. The muscles in highly trained athletes are capable of taking up greater quantities of oxygen so that vigorous exercise can be maintained for longer periods of time.

Secondary alcohol   Ketone group

$$CH_3-\overset{\overset{\displaystyle OH}{|}}{CH}-\overset{\overset{\displaystyle O}{\|}}{C}-OH \quad \xrightarrow[\text{dehydrogenase}]{\text{Lactic acid}} \quad CH_3-\overset{\overset{\displaystyle O}{\|}}{C}-\overset{\overset{\displaystyle O}{\|}}{C}-OH$$

Lactic acid   Pyruvic acid

Oxidation of Thiols

Thiols also undergo oxidation by a loss of hydrogen atoms from the —SH groups. The oxidized product is called a **disulfide**.

$$CH_3-S-H + H-S-CH_3 \xrightarrow{[O]} CH_3-S-S-CH_3 + H_2O$$
   Methanethiol   Dimethyl disulfide

Much of the protein in the hair is cross-linked by disulfide bonds, which occur between the thiol groups of the amino acid cysteine:

$$\text{Protein Chain}-CH_2-SH + HS-CH_2-\text{Protein Chain} \xrightarrow{[O]}$$
                           Cysteine side groups

$$\text{Protein Chain}-CH_2-S-S-CH_2-\text{Protein Chain} + H_2O$$
                                 Disulfide bond

Proteins in the hair take new shapes when disulfide bonds are reduced and oxidized.

When a person is given a "perm" ("permanent wave"), a reducing substance is used to break the disulfide bonds. While the hair is still wrapped around the curlers, an oxidizing substance is then applied that causes new disulfide bonds to form between different parts of the protein hair strands, which gives the hair a new shape.

Chemistry Link to **Health**

Oxidation of Alcohol in the Body

Ethanol is the most commonly abused drug in the United States. When ingested in small amounts, ethanol may produce a feeling of euphoria in the body despite the fact that it is a depressant. In the liver, enzymes such as alcohol dehydrogenase oxidize ethanol to acetaldehyde, a substance that impairs mental and physical coordination. If the blood alcohol concentration exceeds 0.4%, coma or death may occur. Table 13.2 gives some of the typical behaviors exhibited at various blood alcohol levels.

$$CH_3-CH_2-OH \xrightarrow{[O]} CH_3-\overset{\displaystyle O}{\overset{\displaystyle \|}{C}}-H \xrightarrow{[O]} 2CO_2 + H_2O$$

Ethanol (ethyl alcohol)   Ethanal (acetaldehyde)

calculate the blood alcohol concentration (BAC). Several devices are used to measure the BAC. When a Breathalyzer is used, a suspected drunk driver exhales through a mouthpiece into a solution containing the orange Cr^{6+} ion. Any alcohol present in the exhaled air is oxidized, which reduces the orange Cr^{6+} to a green Cr^{3+}.

$$CH_3-CH_2-OH + Cr^{6+} \xrightarrow{[O]} CH_3-\overset{\displaystyle O}{\overset{\displaystyle \|}{C}}-OH + Cr^{3+}$$

Ethanol   Orange   Ethanoic acid   Green

The Alcosensor uses the oxidation of alcohol in a fuel cell to generate an electric current that is measured. The Intoxilyzer measures the amount of light absorbed by the alcohol molecules.

TABLE 13.2 Typical Behaviors Exhibited by a 150-lb Person Consuming Alcohol

Number of Beers (12 oz) or Glasses of Wine (5 oz) in 1 h	Blood Alcohol Level (% m/v)	Typical Behavior
1	0.025	Slightly dizzy, talkative
2	0.050	Euphoria, loud talking and laughing
4	0.10	Loss of inhibition, loss of coordination, drowsiness, legally intoxicated in most states
8	0.20	Intoxicated, quick to anger, exaggerated emotions
12	0.30	Unconscious
16–20	0.40–0.50	Coma and death

The acetaldehyde produced from ethanol in the liver is further oxidized to acetic acid, which is converted to carbon dioxide and water in the citric acid cycle. Thus, the enzymes in the liver can eventually break down ethanol, but the aldehyde and carboxylic acid intermediates can cause considerable damage while they are present within the cells of the liver.

A person weighing 150 lb requires about one hour to metabolize the alcohol in 12 ounces of beer. However, the rate of metabolism of ethanol varies between nondrinkers and drinkers. Typically, nondrinkers and social drinkers can metabolize 12 to 15 mg of ethanol/dL of blood in one hour, but an alcoholic can metabolize as much as 30 mg of ethanol/dL in one hour. Some effects of alcohol metabolism include an increase in liver lipids (fatty liver), gastritis, pancreatitis, ketoacidosis, alcoholic hepatitis, and psychological disturbances.

When alcohol is present in the blood, it evaporates through the lungs. Thus, the percentage of alcohol in the lungs can be used to

Sometimes alcoholics are treated with a drug called Antabuse (disulfiram), which prevents the oxidation of acetaldehyde to acetic acid. As a result, acetaldehyde accumulates in the blood, which causes nausea, profuse sweating, headache, dizziness, vomiting, and respiratory difficulties. Because of these unpleasant side effects, the person is less likely to use alcohol.

A Breathalyzer test is used to determine blood alcohol level.

QUESTIONS AND PROBLEMS

13.4 Reactions of Alcohols and Thiols

LEARNING GOAL Write equations for the combustion, dehydration, and oxidation of alcohols and thiols.

13.17 Write the balanced chemical equation for the complete combustion of each of the following:
   a. methanol   **b.** 2-butanol

13.18 Write the balanced chemical equation for the complete combustion of each of the following:
   a. cyclopentanol   **b.** 3-hexanol

13.19 Draw the condensed or line-angle structural formula for the alkene that is the major product from each of the following dehydration reactions:

a. $CH_3-\underset{\underset{OH}{|}}{CH}-CH_2-CH_2-OH \xrightarrow{\ H^+,\ heat\ }$ (with CH_3 on the second carbon)

b. cyclopentanol $\xrightarrow{\ H^+,\ heat\ }$ **c.** cyclobutanol with OH $\xrightarrow{\ H^+,\ heat\ }$

d. $CH_3-\underset{\underset{CH_3}{|}}{CH}-CH_2-CH_2-\underset{\underset{OH}{|}}{CH}-CH_3 \xrightarrow{\ H^+,\ heat\ }$

13.20 Draw the condensed or line-angle structural formula for the alkene that is the major product from each of the following dehydration reactions:

a. $CH_3-\underset{\underset{CH_3}{|}}{CH}-CH_2-OH \xrightarrow{\ H^+,\ heat\ }$

b. $CH_3-\underset{\underset{OH}{|}}{CH}-\underset{\underset{CH_3}{|}}{CH}-CH_2-CH_3 \xrightarrow{\ H^+,\ heat\ }$

c. cyclohexanol with OH $\xrightarrow{\ H^+,\ heat\ }$

d. methylcyclopentanol with OH $\xrightarrow{\ H^+,\ heat\ }$

13.21 What alcohol(s) could be used to produce each of the following compounds?
   a. $CH_2{=}CH_2$ **b.** (line-angle alkene)   **c.** (cyclohexene)

13.22 What alcohol(s) could be used to produce each of the following compounds?
   a. (line-angle alkene)
   b. $CH_3-CH_2-\underset{\underset{CH_3}{|}}{C}{=}CH-CH_3$
   c. (methylcyclopentene)

13.23 Draw the condensed or line-angle structural formula for the aldehyde or ketone produced when each of the following alcohols is oxidized $[O]$ (if no reaction, write *none*):
   a. $CH_3-CH_2-CH_2-CH_2-CH_2-OH$

   b. $CH_3-CH_2-\underset{\underset{OH}{|}}{CH}-CH_3$

   c. (cyclohexanol with OH)

   d. (line-angle: 3,4-dimethyl-1-pentanol with OH)

   e. $CH_3-\underset{\underset{CH_3}{|}}{CH}-CH_2-CH_2-OH$

13.24 Draw the condensed or line-angle structural formula for the aldehyde or ketone produced when each of the following alcohols is oxidized $[O]$ (if no reaction, write *none*):
   a. (cyclobutylmethanol with OH)
   b. (line-angle secondary alcohol with OH)

   c. $CH_3-CH_2-\underset{\underset{CH_3}{\overset{OH}{|}}}{C}-CH_3$ **d.** (methylcyclohexanol with OH)

   e. (cyclobutanol with OH)

13.25 Draw the condensed or line-angle structural formula for the alcohol needed to give each of the following oxidation products:

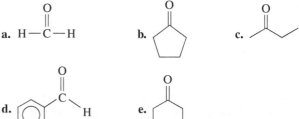

13.26 Draw the condensed or line-angle structural formula for the alcohol needed to give each of the following oxidation products:

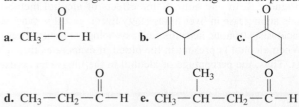

Clinical Update
Janet's New Diet Plan

At home, Janet decided to lose some weight after having her baby. For her new diet, she decided to eat more fruits and vegetables, including peppers and onions. Vegetables are low in calories, have no fat or cholesterol, contain fiber, vitamins, especially vitamin B_3 (niacin), and minerals. Peppers contain antioxidants, such as capsaicin, which gives hot peppers a burning taste. Onions contain fiber, folic acid, calcium, and antioxidants, which inhibit oxidation reactions in the body and act as protective agents. 2-Propene-1-thiol gives the taste and odor to garlic. Janet added ginger, which contains pungent compounds, such as gingerol and shogaol, which is a bioactive compound that has anti-nausea, anti-inflammatory, and anti-carcinogenic properties. Resveratrol, obtained from the skin of red grapes, may improve oxygenation of muscles.

Clinical Applications

13.27 a. Which of the functional groups alkene, alcohol, phenol, thiol, and ether are found in both gingerol and capsaicin?

b. Which of the functional groups alkene, alcohol, phenol, thiol, and ether are found in resveratrol from grapes?

c. What are the functional groups in 2-propene-1-thiol found in garlic?

13.28 a. Which of the functional groups alkene, alcohol, phenol, thiol, and ether are found in both gingerol and shogaol?

b. Which of the functional groups alkene, alcohol, phenol, thiol, and ether are found in capsaicin?

c. Write the balanced chemical equation for the reaction that would convert gingerol to shogaol.

Capsaicin

2-Propene-1-thiol

Gingerol

Shogaol

Resveratrol

CONCEPT MAP

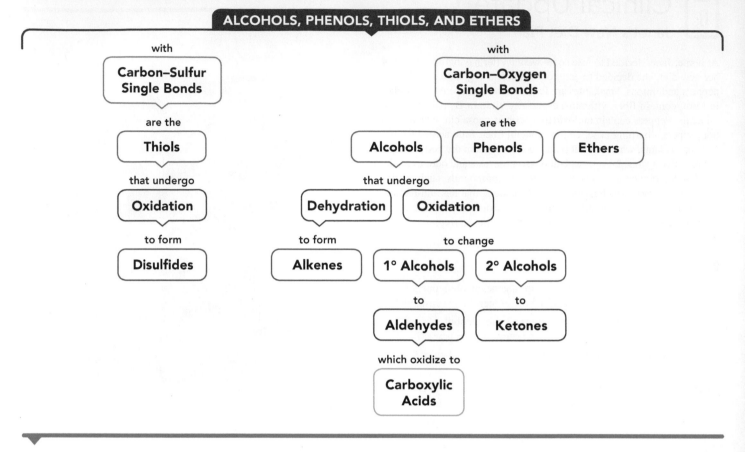

ALCOHOLS, PHENOLS, THIOLS, AND ETHERS

with Carbon–Sulfur Single Bonds

are the Thiols

that undergo Oxidation

to form Disulfides

with Carbon–Oxygen Single Bonds

are the Alcohols — Phenols — Ethers

that undergo Dehydration — Oxidation

to form Alkenes

to change 1° Alcohols — 2° Alcohols

to Aldehydes — **to** Ketones

which oxidize to Carboxylic Acids

CHAPTER REVIEW

13.1 Alcohols, Phenols, and Thiols

LEARNING GOAL Give the IUPAC and common names for alcohols, phenols, and thiols; draw their condensed and line-angle structural formulas.

$$CH_3-CH_2-CH_2-SH$$
1-Propanethiol
(onions)

- The functional group of an alcohol is the hydroxyl group (—OH) bonded to a carbon chain.
- In a phenol, the hydroxyl group is bonded to an aromatic ring.
- In thiols, the functional group is —SH, which is analogous to the —OH group of alcohols.
- In the IUPAC system, the names of alcohols have *ol* endings, and the location of the —OH group is given by numbering the carbon chain.
- A cyclic alcohol is named as a cycloalkanol.
- Simple alcohols are generally named by their common names, with the alkyl name preceding the term *alcohol*.
- An aromatic alcohol is named as a phenol.

13.2 Ethers

LEARNING GOAL Give the IUPAC and common names for ethers; draw their condensed or line-angle structural formulas.

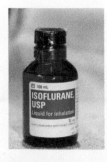

- In an ether, an oxygen atom is connected by single bonds to two alkyl or aromatic groups.

- In the common names of ethers, the alkyl groups are listed alphabetically, followed by the word *ether*.
- In the IUPAC name of an ether, the smaller alkyl group with the oxygen is named as an alkoxy group and is attached to the longer alkane chain, which is numbered to give the location of the alkoxy group.

13.3 Physical Properties of Alcohols, Phenols, and Ethers

LEARNING GOAL Describe the classification of alcohols; describe the boiling points and solubility of alcohols, phenols, and ethers.

Methanol (methyl alcohol)

- Alcohols are classified according to the number of alkyl groups bonded to the carbon that holds the —OH group.
- In a primary (1°) alcohol, one group is attached to the hydroxyl carbon.
- In a secondary (2°) alcohol, two groups are attached to the hydroxyl carbon.
- In a tertiary (3°) alcohol, there are three groups bonded to the hydroxyl carbon.
- The —OH group allows alcohols to hydrogen bond, which causes alcohols to have higher boiling points than alkanes and ethers of similar mass.
- Short-chain alcohols and ethers can hydrogen bond with water, which makes them soluble.

13.4 Reactions of Alcohols and Thiols
LEARNING GOAL Write equations for the combustion, dehydration, and oxidation of alcohols and thiols.

- Alcohols undergo combustion with O_2 to form CO_2, H_2O, and energy.
- At high temperatures, alcohols dehydrate in the presence of an acid to yield alkenes.

- Primary alcohols are oxidized to aldehydes, which can oxidize further to carboxylic acids.
- Secondary alcohols are oxidized to ketones.
- Tertiary alcohols do not oxidize.
- Thiols undergo oxidation to form disulfides.

SUMMARY OF NAMING

Family	Structure	IUPAC Name	Common Name
Alcohol	CH_3-OH	Methanol	Methyl alcohol
Phenol	⬡—OH	Phenol	Phenol
Thiol	CH_3-SH	Methanethiol	
Ether	CH_3-O-CH_3	Methoxymethane	Dimethyl ether

SUMMARY OF REACTIONS

The chapter sections to review are shown after the name of the reaction.

Combustion of Alcohols (13.4)

$$CH_3-CH_2-OH + 3O_2 \xrightarrow{\Delta} 2CO_2 + 3H_2O + energy$$
Ethanol   Oxygen   Carbon dioxide   Water

Dehydration of Alcohols to Form Alkenes (13.4)

$$CH_3-CH_2-CH_2-OH \xrightarrow{H^+, heat} CH_3-CH=CH_2 + H_2O$$
1-Propanol   Propene

Oxidation of Primary Alcohols to Form Aldehydes (13.4)

$$CH_3-\overset{OH}{\underset{}{CH_2}} \xrightarrow{[O]} CH_3-\overset{O}{\overset{\|}{C}}-H + H_2O$$
Ethanol   Ethanal

Oxidation of Secondary Alcohols to Form Ketones (13.4)

$$CH_3-\overset{OH}{\underset{}{CH}}-CH_3 \xrightarrow{[O]} CH_3-\overset{O}{\overset{\|}{C}}-CH_3 + H_2O$$
2-Propanol   Propanone

Oxidation of Aldehydes to Form Carboxylic Acids (13.4)

$$CH_3-\overset{O}{\overset{\|}{C}}-H \xrightarrow{[O]} CH_3-\overset{O}{\overset{\|}{C}}-OH$$
Ethanal   Ethanoic acid

KEY TERMS

alcohol An organic compound that contains the hydroxyl functional group (—OH) attached to a carbon chain.

dehydration A reaction that removes water from an alcohol in the presence of an acid to form alkenes at high temperatures.

disulfide A compound formed from thiols; disulfides contain the —S—S— functional group.

ether An organic compound in which an oxygen atom is bonded to two carbon groups that are alkyl or aromatic.

oxidation The loss of two hydrogen atoms from a reactant to give a more oxidized compound: primary alcohols oxidize to aldehydes, secondary alcohols oxidize to ketones. An oxidation can also be the addition of an oxygen atom, as in the oxidation of aldehydes to carboxylic acids.

phenol An organic compound that has a hydroxyl group (—OH) attached to a benzene ring.

primary (1°) alcohol An alcohol that has one alkyl group bonded to the alcohol's carbon atom.

Saytzeff's rule In the dehydration of an alcohol, hydrogen is removed from the carbon that already has the smaller number of hydrogen atoms to form an alkene.

secondary (2°) alcohol An alcohol that has two alkyl groups bonded to the carbon atom with the —OH group.

tertiary (3°) alcohol An alcohol that has three alkyl groups bonded to the carbon atom with the —OH group.

thiol An organic compound that contains a thiol group (—SH).

⚛ CORE CHEMISTRY SKILLS

The chapter section containing each Core Chemistry Skill is shown in parentheses at the end of each heading.

Identifying Alcohols, Phenols, and Thiols (13.1)

- Functional groups are specific groups of atoms in organic compounds, which undergo characteristic chemical reactions.
- Organic compounds with the same functional group have similar properties and reactions.

Example: Identify the functional group and classify the following molecule:

$$CH_3-CH_2-CH_2-CH_2-OH$$

Answer: The hydroxyl group (—OH) makes it an alcohol.

Naming Alcohols and Phenols (13.1)

- In the IUPAC system, an alcohol is named by replacing the *e* in the alkane name with *ol*.
- Simple alcohols are named with the alkyl name preceding the term *alcohol*.
- The carbon chain is numbered from the end nearer the —OH group and the location of the —OH is given in front of the name.
- A cyclic alcohol is named as a cycloalkanol.
- An aromatic alcohol is named as a phenol.

Example: Give the IUPAC name for the following:

$$CH_3-\overset{\overset{\displaystyle CH_3}{|}}{CH}-CH_2-OH$$

Answer: 2-methyl-1-propanol

Writing Equations for the Dehydration of Alcohols (13.4)

- At high temperatures, alcohols dehydrate in the presence of an acid to yield alkenes.
- Saytzeff's rule states that the major product from the dehydration of an asymmetrical alcohol is the one in which the —H atom is removed from the carbon atom that has the smaller number of H atoms.

Example: Draw the condensed structural formula for the organic product from the dehydration of 3-methyl-2-butanol.

Answer: $CH_3-\overset{\overset{\displaystyle CH_3}{|}}{C}=CH-CH_3$

Writing Equations for the Oxidation of Alcohols (13.4)

- Primary alcohols oxidize to aldehydes, which can oxidize further to carboxylic acids.
- Secondary alcohols oxidize to ketones.
- Tertiary alcohols do not oxidize.

Example: Draw the condensed structural formula for the product from the oxidation of 2-butanol.

Answer: $CH_3-\overset{\overset{\displaystyle O}{||}}{C}-CH_2-CH_3$

UNDERSTANDING THE CONCEPTS

The chapter sections to review are shown in parentheses at the end of each question.

13.29 Identify each of the following as an alcohol, a phenol, an ether, or a thiol: (13.1, 13.2)

a.

b.

c. $CH_3-\overset{\overset{\displaystyle SH}{|}}{CH}-CH_3$

d. $CH_3-\overset{\overset{\displaystyle OH}{|}}{\underset{\underset{\displaystyle CH_3}{|}}{C}}-CH_2-\overset{\overset{\displaystyle CH_3}{|}}{CH}-CH_3$

13.30 Identify each of the following as an alcohol, a phenol, an ether, or a thiol: (13.1, 13.2)

a.

b. $CH_3-CH_2-CH_2-SH$

c.

d.

13.31 Give the IUPAC and common names (if any) for each of the compounds in problem 13.29. (13.1, 13.2)

13.32 Give the IUPAC and common names (if any) for each of the compounds in problem 13.30. (13.1, 13.2)

13.33 Identify each of the following as an alcohol, a phenol, an ether, or a thiol: (13.1, 13.2)

a. $CH_3-CH_2-CH_2-O-CH_3$

b. $CH_3-CH_2-\overset{\overset{\displaystyle SH}{|}}{CH}-CH_3$

c. $CH_3-\overset{\overset{\displaystyle Br}{|}}{CH}-CH_2-\overset{\overset{\displaystyle OH}{|}}{CH}-CH_3$

d. (benzene ring with OH and CH₃ substituents)

13.34 Identify each of the following as an alcohol, a phenol, an ether, or a thiol: (13.1, 13.2)

a. $CH_3-CH_2-\overset{\overset{\displaystyle O-CH_3}{|}}{CH}-CH_2-CH_3$

b. (line structure with SH)

c. (cyclohexane ring with OH, Cl, and Cl substituents)

d. (benzene ring with OH and two CH₃ substituents)

13.35 Give the IUPAC and common names (if any) for each of the compounds in problem 13.33. (13.1, 13.2)

13.36 Give the IUPAC and common names (if any) for each of the compounds in problem 13.34. (13.1, 13.2)

ADDITIONAL QUESTIONS AND PROBLEMS

13.37 Draw the condensed or line-angle structural formula, if cyclic, for each of the following compounds: (13.1, 13.2)

a. 3-methylcyclopentanol
b. 4-chlorophenol
c. 2-methyl-3-pentanol
d. ethyl phenyl ether

13.38 Draw the condensed or line-angle structural formula, if cyclic, for each of the following compounds: (13.1, 13.2)

a. 3-methoxypentane
b. m-chlorophenol
c. 2,3-pentanediol
d. methyl propyl ether

13.39 Draw the condensed or line-angle structural formula, if cyclic, for each of the following compounds: (13.1, 13.2)

a. 3-pentanethiol
b. 2-methoxypentane
c. 2,4-dibromophenol
d. 2,3-dimethyl-2-butanol

13.40 Draw the condensed or line-angle structural formula, if cyclic, for each of the following compounds: (13.1, 13.2)

a. methanethiol
b. 3-methyl-2-butanol
c. 3,4-dichlorocyclohexanol
d. 1-ethoxypropane

13.41 Give the IUPAC name for each of the following alcohols, phenols, and ethers: (13.1, 13.2)

a. (branched structure with OH)

b. $CH_3-\overset{\overset{\displaystyle OH}{|}}{\underset{\underset{\displaystyle CH_3}{|}}{C}}-CH_2-\overset{\overset{\displaystyle CH_3}{|}}{CH}-CH_3$

c. (benzene ring with OH and Br)

d. $CH_3-\overset{\overset{\displaystyle O-CH_2-CH_3}{|}}{CH}-CH_2-CH_2-CH_3$

e. (cyclopentane ring with O—)

13.42 Give the IUPAC name for each of the following alcohols, phenols, and ethers: (13.1, 13.2)

a. (cyclopentane ring with HO)

b. (line structure with Br, Br, and OH)

c. (benzene ring with OH and CH₃)
d. (cyclopropane with O—)
e. $CH_3-\overset{\overset{\displaystyle O-CH_3}{|}}{CH}-CH_2-CH_3$

13.43 Draw the condensed structural formulas for all the alcohols with a molecular formula $C_4H_{10}O$. (13.1)

13.44 Draw the condensed structural formulas for all the ethers with a molecular formula $C_4H_{10}O$. (13.2)

13.45 Classify each of the following alcohols as primary (1°), secondary (2°), or tertiary (3°): (13.3)

a. (cyclohexane ring with OH)
b. (cyclohexane ring with CH₂OH)

c. $CH_3-\overset{\overset{\displaystyle CH_3}{|}}{CH}-CH_2-OH$

d. $CH_3-\overset{\overset{\displaystyle CH_3}{|}}{\underset{\underset{\displaystyle CH_3}{|}}{C}}-CH_2-\overset{\overset{\displaystyle OH}{|}}{CH}-CH_3$

e. $HO-CH_2-CH_2-CH_3$

f. (cyclopentane ring with OH)

13.46 Classify each of the following alcohols as primary (1°), secondary (2°), or tertiary (3°): (13.3)

a. (cyclopentane ring with HO)
b. (cyclohexane ring with OH)

c. $CH_3-\overset{\overset{\displaystyle CH_2-OH}{|}}{CH}-CH_2-CH_3$

d.
$$CH_3-\underset{\underset{CH_3}{|}}{\overset{\overset{OH}{|}}{C}}-CH_2-\underset{\underset{}{\overset{CH_3}{|}}}{CH}-CH_3$$

e. $CH_3-CH_2-CH_2-CH_2-OH$

f.

13.47 Which compound in each of the following pairs would you expect to have the higher boiling point? Explain. (13.3)
   a. butane or 1-propanol
   b. 1-propanol or ethyl methyl ether
   c. ethanol or 1-butanol

13.48 Which compound in each of the following pairs would you expect to have the higher boiling point? Explain. (13.3)
   a. propane or ethyl alcohol
   b. 2-propanol or 2-pentanol
   c. methyl propyl ether or 1-butanol

13.49 Explain why each of the following compounds would be soluble or insoluble in water: (13.3)
   a. 2-propanol
   b. dipropyl ether
   c. 1-hexanol

13.50 Explain why each of the following compounds would be soluble or insoluble in water: (13.3)
   a. glycerol
   b. butane
   c. 1,3-hexanediol

13.51 Which compound in each pair would be more soluble in water? Explain. (13.3)
   a. butane or 1-propanol
   b. 1-propanol or ethyl methyl ether
   c. ethanol or 1-hexanol

13.52 Which compound in each pair would be more soluble in water? Explain. (13.3)
   a. ethane or ethanol
   b. 2-propanol or 2-pentanol
   c. methyl propyl ether or 1-butanol

13.53 Write the balanced chemical equation for the complete combustion of each of the following: (13.4)
   a. $CH_3-CH_2-CH_2-CH_2-OH + O_2 \xrightarrow{\Delta}$
   b. $+ O_2 \xrightarrow{\Delta}$
   c. $+ O_2 \xrightarrow{\Delta}$

13.54 Write the balanced chemical equation for the complete combustion of each of the following: (13.4)
   a. $CH_3-CH_2-CH_2-CH_2-OH + O_2 \xrightarrow{\Delta}$
   b. $+ O_2 \xrightarrow{\Delta}$
   c. $+ O_2 \xrightarrow{\Delta}$

13.55 Draw the condensed or line-angle structural formula, if cyclic, for each of the following naturally occurring compounds: (13.1, 13.2)
   a. 2,5-dichlorophenol, a defense pheromone of a grasshopper
   b. 3-methyl-1-butanethiol and *trans*-2-butene-1-thiol, a mixture that gives skunk scent its odor
   c. pentachlorophenol, a wood preservative

13.56 Dimethyl ether and ethyl alcohol both have the molecular formula C_2H_6O. One has a boiling point of $-24\,°C$, and the other, $79\,°C$. (13.1, 13.2, 13.3)
   a. Draw the condensed structural formula for each compound.
   b. Decide which boiling point goes with which compound and explain.

13.57 Draw the condensed or line-angle structural formula for the alkene (major product), aldehyde, ketone, or *none* produced in each of the following: (13.4)
   a. $CH_3-CH_2-CH_2-OH \xrightarrow{H^+,\ heat}$
   b. $CH_3-CH_2-CH_2-OH \xrightarrow{[O]}$
   c. $\xrightarrow{H^+,\ heat}$
   d. $\xrightarrow{H^+,\ heat}$
   e. $\xrightarrow{[O]}$

13.58 Draw the condensed or line-angle structural formula for the alkene (major product), aldehyde, ketone, or *none* produced in each of the following: (13.4)
   a. $\xrightarrow{H^+,\ heat}$
   b.
$$CH_3-\underset{\underset{}{\overset{\overset{CH_3}{|}}{CH}}}{}-\underset{\underset{}{\overset{\overset{OH}{|}}{CH}}}{}-CH_3 \xrightarrow{H^+,\ heat}$$
   c. $\xrightarrow{[O]}$
   d. $\xrightarrow{[O]}$
   e.
$$CH_3-CH_2-CH_2-\underset{\underset{}{\overset{\overset{OH}{|}}{CH}}}{}-CH_3 \xrightarrow{H^+,\ heat}$$

Rx Clinical Applications

13.59 Hexylresorcinol, an antiseptic ingredient used in mouth washes and throat lozenges, has the IUPAC name of 4-hexyl-1,3-benzenediol. Draw its condensed structural formula. (13.1)

13.60 Menthol, which has a minty flavor, is used in throat sprays and lozenges. Thymol is used as a topical antiseptic to destroy mold. (13.1)
   a. Give the IUPAC name for each.
   b. What is similar and what is different about their structures?

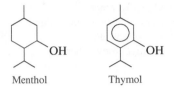

Menthol   Thymol

CHALLENGE QUESTIONS

The following groups of questions are related to the topics in this chapter. However, they do not all follow the chapter order, and they require you to combine concepts and skills from several sections. These questions will help you increase your critical thinking skills and prepare for your next exam.

13.61 A compound with the formula C_4H_8O is synthesized from 2-methyl-1-propanol and oxidizes easily to give a carboxylic acid. Draw the condensed structural formula for the compound. (13.4)

13.62 Methyl *tert*-butyl ether (MTBE), or 2-methoxy-2-methylpropane, has been used as a fuel additive for gasoline to boost the octane rating and to reduce CO emissions. (2.7, 7.5, 7.6, 7.7, 8.6, 13.4)
   a. If fuel mixtures are required to contain 2.7% oxygen by mass, how many grams of MTBE must be present in each 100. g of gasoline?
   b. How many liters of MTBE would be in 1.0 L of fuel if the density of both gasoline and MTBE is 0.740 g/mL?
   c. Write the balanced chemical equation for the complete combustion of MTBE.
   d. How many liters of air containing 21% (v/v) O_2 are required at STP to completely react (combust) 1.00 L of liquid MTBE?

Methyl *tert*-butyl ether (MTBE) is a gasoline additive.

13.63 Compound **A** is 1-propanol. When compound **A** is heated with strong acid, it dehydrates to form compound **B** (C_3H_6). When compound **A** is oxidized, compound **C** (C_3H_6O) forms. Draw the condensed structural formulas and give the IUPAC names for compounds **A**, **B**, and **C**. (13.4)

13.64 Compound **X** is 2-propanol. When compound **X** is heated with strong acid, it dehydrates to form compound **Y** (C_3H_6). When compound **X** is oxidized, compound **Z** (C_3H_6O) forms, which cannot be oxidized further. Draw the condensed structural formulas and give the IUPAC names for compounds **X**, **Y**, and **Z**. (13.4)

13.65 Sometimes several steps are needed to prepare a compound. Using a combination of the reactions we have studied, indicate how you might prepare the following from the starting substance given. For example, 2-propanol could be prepared from 1-propanol by first dehydrating the alcohol to give propene and then hydrating it again to give 2-propanol according to Markovnikov's rule, as follows: (13.4)

$$CH_3-CH_2-CH_2-OH \xrightarrow{H^+, \text{ heat}} CH_3-CH=CH_2 + H_2O$$
1-Propanol   Propene

$$\xrightarrow{H^+} CH_3-\overset{\overset{\displaystyle OH}{|}}{CH}-CH_3$$
2-Propanol

   a. prepare 2-methylpropane from 2-methyl-2-propanol
   b. prepare $CH_3-\overset{\overset{\displaystyle O}{||}}{C}-CH_3$ from 1-propanol

13.66 As in problem 13.65, indicate how you might prepare the following from the starting substance given: (13.4)
   a. prepare 1-pentene from 1-pentanol
   b. prepare cyclohexane from cyclohexanol

ANSWERS

Answers to Selected Questions and Problems

13.1 a. ethanol (ethyl alcohol)
   b. 2-butanol (*sec*-butyl alcohol)
   c. 2-pentanol
   d. 4-methylcyclohexanol
   e. 3-fluorophenol (*m*-fluorophenol)

13.3 a. $CH_3-CH_2-CH_2-OH$
   b. $CH_3-CH_2-\overset{\overset{\displaystyle OH}{|}}{CH}-CH_2-CH_3$
   c. $CH_3-\overset{\overset{\displaystyle OH}{|}}{\underset{\underset{\displaystyle CH_3}{|}}{C}}-CH_2-CH_3$

13.5 a. methoxyethane (ethyl methyl ether)
   b. methoxycyclohexane (cyclohexyl methyl ether)
   c. ethoxycyclobutane (cyclobutyl ethyl ether)
   d. 1-methoxypropane (methyl propyl ether)

13.7 a. $CH_3-CH_2-O-CH_2-CH_2-CH_3$
   b. [structure]
   c. [structure]
   d. $CH_3-CH_2-O-CH_2-\overset{\overset{\displaystyle CH_3}{|}}{CH}-CH_2-CH_3$
   e. $CH_3-\overset{\overset{\displaystyle O-CH_3}{|}}{CH}-CH-CH_2-CH_3$ with $O-CH_3$ below

13.9 a. 1°   **b.** 1°   **c.** 3°   **d.** 2°

13.11 a. methanol   **b.** 1-butanol   **c.** 1-butanol

13.13 a. Soluble; ethanol with a short carbon chain is soluble because the hydroxyl group forms hydrogen bonds with water.
   b. Slightly soluble; ethers with up to four carbon atoms are slightly soluble in water because they can form a few hydrogen bonds with water.
   c. Insoluble; an alcohol with a carbon chain of five or more carbon atoms is not soluble in water.

13.15 a. Methanol can form hydrogen bonds with water, but ethane cannot.
   b. 2-Propanol is more soluble because it has a shorter carbon chain.
   c. 1-Propanol is more soluble because it can form more hydrogen bonds.

13.17 a. $2CH_3-OH + 3O_2 \xrightarrow{\Delta} 2CO_2 + 4H_2O + energy$
   b. $CH_3-\overset{\overset{\displaystyle OH}{|}}{CH}-CH_2-CH_3 + 6O_2 \xrightarrow{\Delta}$
   $4CO_2 + 5H_2O + energy$

13.19 a. $CH_3-\overset{\overset{\displaystyle CH_3}{|}}{CH}-CH=CH_2$
   b. [structure]
   c. [structure]
   d. $CH_3-CH-CH_2-CH=CH-CH_3$

13.21 a. CH_3-CH_2-OH
   b. [structure]
   c. [structure]

13.23 a. $CH_3-CH_2-CH_2-CH_2-\overset{\overset{\displaystyle O}{||}}{C}-H$
   b. $CH_3-CH_2-\overset{\overset{\displaystyle O}{||}}{C}-CH_3$
   c. [structure]
   d. [structure]
   e. $CH_3-\overset{\overset{\displaystyle CH_3}{|}}{CH}-CH_2-\overset{\overset{\displaystyle O}{||}}{C}-H$

13.25 a. CH_3-OH
   b. [structure]
   c. [structure]
   d. [structure] CH_2-OH
   e. [structure]

13.27 a. Gingerol and capsaicin both have aromatic rings bonded to long hydrocarbon groups, with phenol and methoxy groups on the aromatic ring.
   b. Resveratrol contains phenol and alkene functional groups.
   c. 2-Propene-1-thiol contains alkene and thiol function groups.

13.29 a. alcohol   **b.** ether
   c. thiol   **d.** alcohol

13.31 a. 2-chloro-4-methylcyclohexanol
   b. methoxybenzene (methyl phenyl ether)
   c. 2-propanethiol
   d. 2,4-dimethyl-2-pentanol

13.33 a. ether   **b.** thiol
   c. alcohol   **d.** phenol

13.35 a. 1-methoxypropane (methyl propyl ether)
   b. 2-butanethiol
   c. 4-bromo-2-pentanol
   d. 3-methylphenol (*m*-methylphenol; *m*-cresol)

13.37 a. [structure]
   b. [structure]
   c. $CH_3-\overset{\overset{\displaystyle CH_3}{|}}{CH}-\overset{\overset{\displaystyle OH}{|}}{CH}-CH_2-CH_3$
   d.

13.39 a. 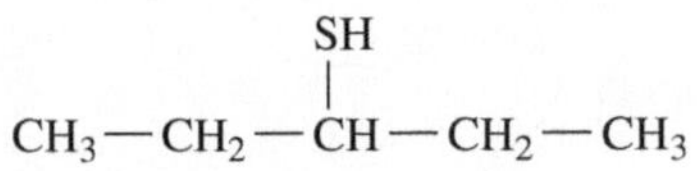 $CH_3-CH_2-\underset{\underset{SH}{|}}{CH}-CH_2-CH_3$

b. 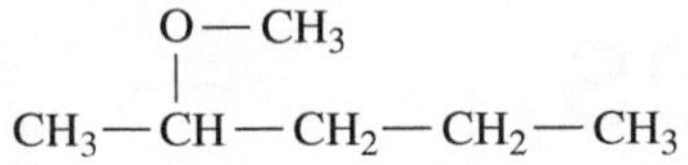 $CH_3-\underset{\underset{O-CH_3}{|}}{CH}-CH_2-CH_2-CH_3$

c.

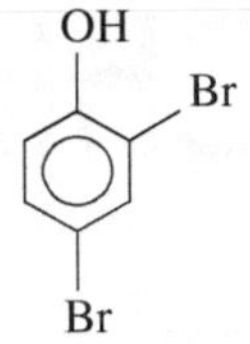

d. 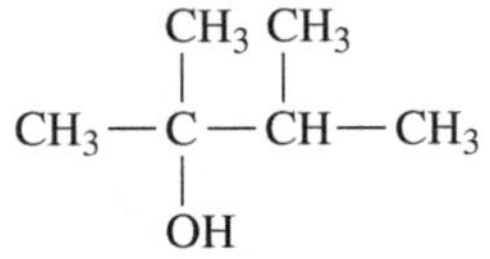 $CH_3-\underset{\underset{OH}{|}}{\overset{\overset{CH_3}{|}}{C}}-\underset{\overset{CH_3}{|}}{CH}-CH_3$

13.41 a. 2-methyl-2-propanol
b. 2,4-dimethyl-2-pentanol
c. 3-bromophenol
d. 2-ethoxypentane
e. methoxycyclopentane

13.43 $CH_3-CH_2-CH_2-CH_2-OH$

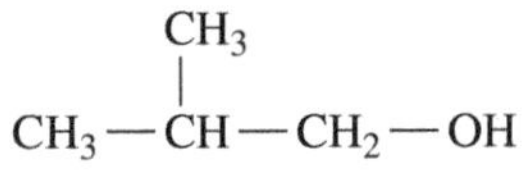

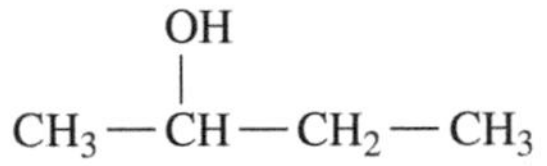

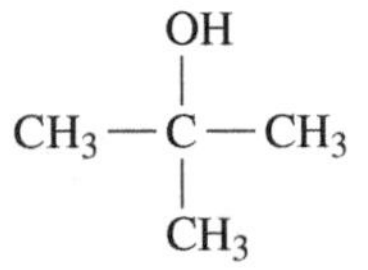

$CH_3-\underset{\overset{CH_3}{|}}{CH}-CH_2-OH$

$CH_3-\underset{\underset{OH}{|}}{CH}-CH_2-CH_3$

$CH_3-\underset{\underset{CH_3}{|}}{\overset{\overset{OH}{|}}{C}}-CH_3$

13.45 a. 2° **b.** 1° **c.** 1°
d. 2° **e.** 1° **f.** 3°

13.47 a. 1-propanol, hydrogen bonding
b. 1-propanol, hydrogen bonding
c. 1-butanol, greater molar mass

13.49 a. soluble, hydrogen bonding
b. insoluble, long carbon chain diminishes effect of hydrogen bonding of water to $-O-$
c. insoluble, long carbon chain diminishes effect of polar $-OH$ group on hydrogen bonding

13.51 a. 1-Propanol can form hydrogen bonds with its polar hydroxyl group.
b. An alcohol forms more hydrogen bonds than an ether.
c. Ethanol has a smaller number of carbon atoms.

13.53 a. $CH_3-CH_2-CH_2-CH_2-OH + 6O_2 \xrightarrow{\Delta}$
$4CO_2 + 5H_2O + $ energy

b. 2 $+ 15O_2 \xrightarrow{\Delta}$
$10CO_2 + 12H_2O + $ energy

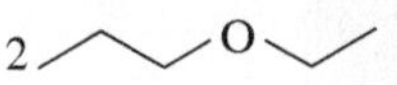

c. 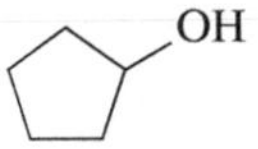 $+ 7O_2 \xrightarrow{\Delta} 5CO_2 + 5H_2O + $ energy

13.55 a.

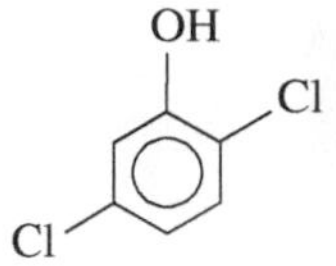

b. 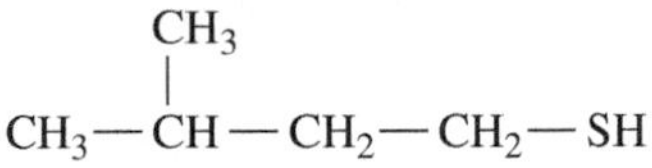 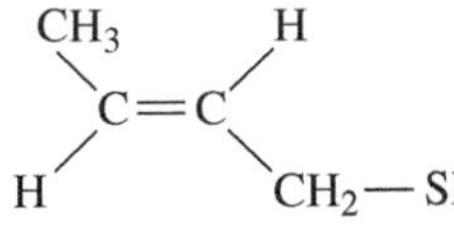 $CH_3-\underset{\overset{CH_3}{|}}{CH}-CH_2-CH_2-SH$

c.

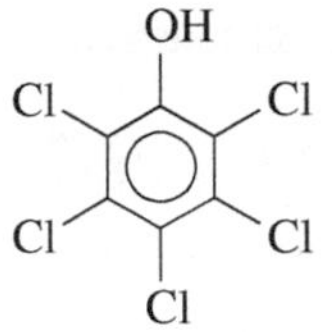

13.57 a. $CH_3-CH=CH_2$

b. 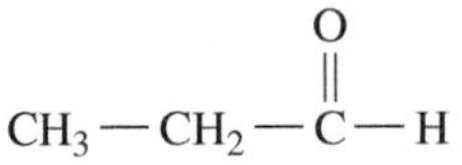 $CH_3-CH_2-\overset{\overset{O}{||}}{C}-H$

c.

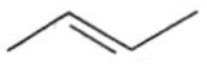

d.

e.

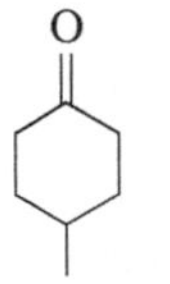

13.59

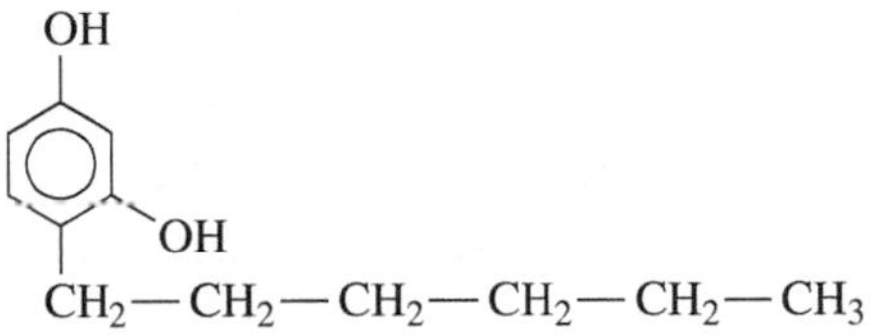

13.61 $CH_3-\underset{\overset{CH_3}{|}}{CH}-\overset{\overset{O}{||}}{C}-H$

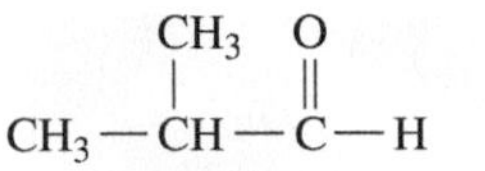

13.63 $CH_3-CH_2-CH_2-OH$ 1-Propanol
A

$CH_3-CH=CH_2$ Propene
B

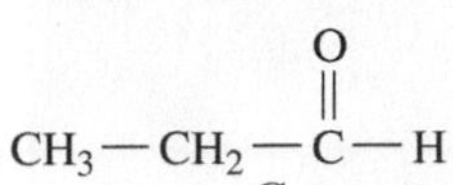

$CH_3-CH_2-\overset{\overset{O}{||}}{C}-H$ Propanal
C

13.65 a. 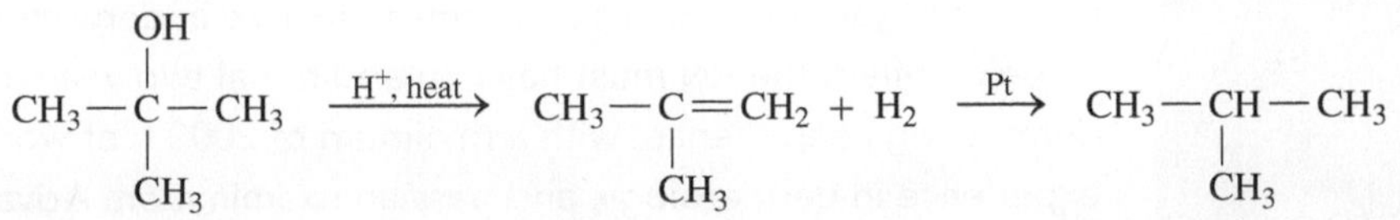 $CH_3-\underset{\underset{CH_3}{|}}{\overset{\overset{OH}{|}}{C}}-CH_3 \xrightarrow{H^+, heat} CH_3-\underset{\overset{CH_3}{|}}{C}=CH_2 + H_2 \xrightarrow{Pt} CH_3-\underset{\overset{CH_3}{|}}{CH}-CH_3$

b. 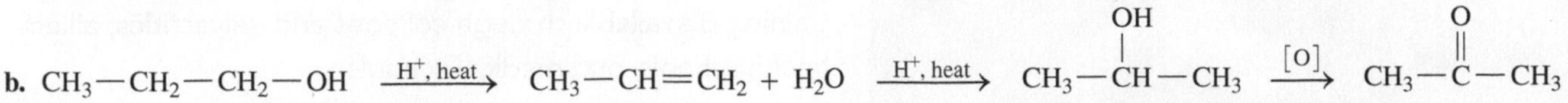 $CH_3-CH_2-CH_2-OH \xrightarrow{H^+, heat} CH_3-CH=CH_2 + H_2O \xrightarrow{H^+, heat} CH_3-\underset{\overset{OH}{|}}{CH}-CH_3 \xrightarrow{[O]} CH_3-\overset{\overset{O}{||}}{C}-CH_3$

14 Aldehydes, Ketones, and Chiral Molecules

RECENTLY, DIANA NOTICED THAT A BROWN MOLE

on her arm had changed appearance. For many years, it had been light brown in color, with a flat circular appearance. But over the last few weeks, Diana noticed that the mole had become raised, with irregular borders, and had darkened. She called her dermatologist for an appointment. Diana told Margaret, a dermatology nurse, that she had been going to tanning salons and had about 20 tanning sessions the previous year. She loved being outside but did not always apply sunscreen while in the sun or at the beach. Diana said she had no family history of malignant melanoma.

The risk factors for melanoma include frequent exposure to sun, severe sunburns at an early age, skin type, and family history. During Diana's skin exam, Margaret looked for other suspicious moles with nonuniform borders, changes in color, and changes in size. To treat the mole on Diana's arm, Margaret numbed the area, then removed a sample of skin tissue, which she sent to a lab for evaluation. Because the diagnosis indicated the presence of malignant melanoma cells, Margaret excised the entire mole including subcutaneous fat. Fortunately, the mole was not very large and no further treatment was needed. Margaret suggested that Diana return in six months for a follow-up skin check.

The number of cases of melanoma has been rising, unlike for many other types of cancer. Doctors think this change may be because of unprotected sun exposure, an increase in the use of tanning salons, and perhaps an increased awareness and detection of the disease.

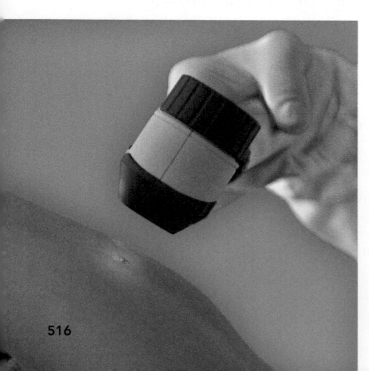

CAREER Dermatology Nurse

A dermatology nurse performs many of the duties of dermatologists, including treating skin conditions, assisting in surgeries, performing biopsies and excisions, writing prescriptions, freezing skin lesions, and screening patients for skin cancer. To become a dermatology nurse, you first become a nurse or physician assistant and then specialize in dermatology. To be certified, the RN must have an additional two years of dermatology experience, with a minimum of 2000 h of work experience in dermatology, and pass an examination. Advanced training is available through colleges and universities, allied health schools, and medical schools.

⚙ CORE CHEMISTRY SKILLS

- Naming and Drawing Alkanes (12.2)
- Naming Alcohols and Phenols (13.1)
- Writing Equations for the Oxidation of Alcohols (13.4)

*These Core Chemistry Skills from previous chapters are listed here for your review as you proceed to the new material in this chapter.

14.1 Aldehydes and Ketones

Aldehydes and ketones contain a **carbonyl group** that consists of a carbon–oxygen double bond with two groups of atoms attached to the carbon at angles of 120°. The oxygen atom with two lone pairs of electrons is much more electronegative than the carbon atom. Therefore, the carbonyl group has a strong dipole with a partial negative charge (δ^-) on the oxygen and a partial positive charge (δ^+) on the carbon. The polarity of the carbonyl group strongly influences the physical and chemical properties of aldehydes and ketones.

In an **aldehyde**, the carbon of the carbonyl group is bonded to at least one hydrogen atom. That carbon may also be bonded to another hydrogen atom, a carbon of an alkyl group, or an aromatic ring (see Figure 14.1). The aldehyde group may be written as separate atoms or as —CHO, with the double bond understood. In a **ketone**, the carbonyl group is bonded to two alkyl groups or aromatic rings. The keto group (C=O) can sometimes be written as CO. A line-angle structural formula may also be used to represent an aldehyde or ketone.

LEARNING GOAL

Identify compounds with carbonyl groups as aldehydes and ketones. Write the IUPAC and common names for aldehydes and ketones; draw their condensed or line-angle structural formulas.

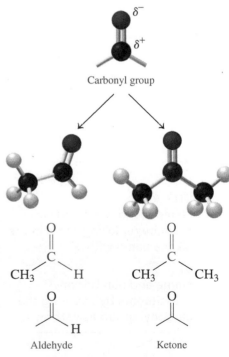

FIGURE 14.1 ▶ The carbonyl group is found in aldehydes and ketones.

◉ If aldehydes and ketones both contain a carbonyl group, how can you differentiate between compounds from each family?

Formulas for C₃H₆O

Aldehyde

$$CH_3-CH_2-\overset{\displaystyle O}{\overset{\|}{C}}-H = CH_3-CH_2-CHO = $$

Ketone

$$CH_3-\overset{\displaystyle O}{\overset{\|}{C}}-CH_3 = CH_3-CO-CH_3 = $$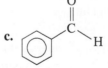

▶ **SAMPLE PROBLEM 14.1 Identifying Aldehydes and Ketones**

Identify each of the following compounds as an aldehyde or ketone:

a. **b.** **c.**

SOLUTION
a. aldehyde   **b.** ketone   **c.** aldehyde

STUDY CHECK 14.1

Identify the following compound as an aldehyde or ketone:

ANSWER
ketone

⚛️ **CORE CHEMISTRY SKILL**

Naming Aldehydes and Ketones

Naming Aldehydes

In the IUPAC system, an aldehyde is named by replacing the *e* of the corresponding alkane name with *al*. No number is needed for the aldehyde group because it always appears at the end of the chain. The aldehydes with carbon chains of one to four carbons are often referred to by their common names, which end in *aldehyde* (see Figure 14.2). The roots (*form, acet, propion,* and *butyr*) of these common names are derived from Latin or Greek words.

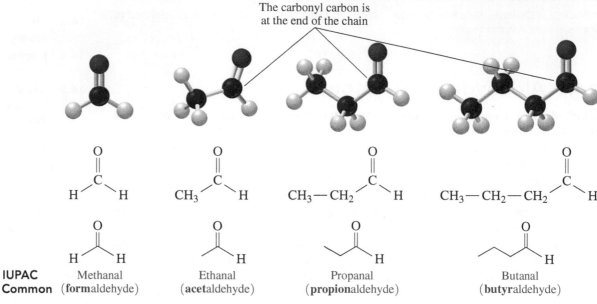

The carbonyl carbon is at the end of the chain

| IUPAC | Methanal | Ethanal | Propanal | Butanal |
| Common | (**form**aldehyde) | (**acet**aldehyde) | (**propion**aldehyde) | (**butyr**aldehyde) |

FIGURE 14.2 ▶ In the structures of aldehydes, the carbonyl group is always the end carbon.

❓ Why is the carbon in the carbonyl group in aldehydes always at the end of the chain?

The IUPAC system names the aldehyde of benzene as benzaldehyde.

Benzaldehyde

▶ **SAMPLE PROBLEM 14.2 Naming Aldehydes**

Give the IUPAC name for each of the following aldehydes:

a. $CH_3-CH_2-\underset{\underset{CH_3}{|}}{CH}-CH_2-\overset{\overset{O}{\|}}{C}-H$

b. $Cl-\bigcirc-\overset{\overset{O}{\|}}{C}-H$

SOLUTION

	Given	Need
ANALYZE THE PROBLEM	condensed structural formula of aldehyde	IUPAC name

Guide to Naming Aldehydes

STEP 1
Name the longest carbon chain by replacing the *e* in the alkane name with *al*.

STEP 2
Name and number any substituents by counting the carbonyl group as carbon 1.

a. **STEP 1** Name the longest carbon chain by replacing the *e* in the alkane name with *al*. The longest carbon chain containing the carbonyl group has five carbon atoms. It is named by replacing the *e* in the alkane name with *al* to give pentanal.

$CH_3-CH_2-\underset{\underset{CH_3}{|}}{CH}-CH_2-\overset{\overset{O}{\|}}{C}-H$　　pentanal

STEP 2 Name and number any substituents by counting the carbonyl group as carbon 1. The substituent, which is the —CH_3 group on carbon 3, is methyl. The IUPAC name for this compound is 3-methylpentanal.

$\underset{5}{CH_3}-\underset{4}{CH_2}-\underset{3}{\underset{\underset{CH_3}{|}}{CH}}-\underset{2}{CH_2}-\underset{1}{\overset{\overset{O}{\|}}{C}}-H$　　3-methylpentanal

b. STEP 1 Name the longest carbon chain by replacing the *e* in the alkane name with *al*. The longest carbon chain consists of a benzene ring attached to a carbonyl group, which is named benzaldehyde.

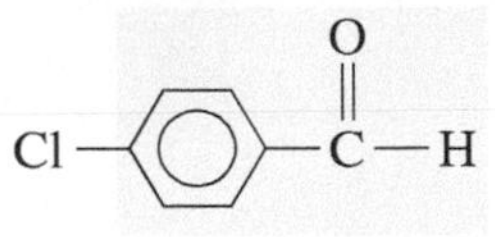

Cl—⟨benzene⟩—C—H   benzaldehyde

STEP 2 Name and number any substituents by counting the carbonyl group as carbon 1. Counting from carbon 1 of the ring where the carbonyl group is attached, the chloro group is attached to carbon 4.

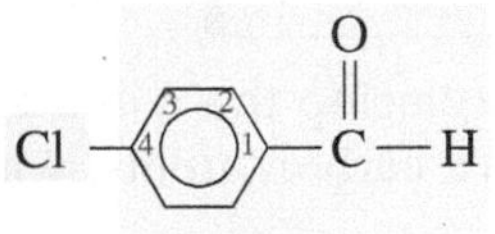

Cl—⟨benzene⟩—C—H   4-chlorobenzaldehyde

STUDY CHECK 14.2

What is the IUPAC name of the following compound?

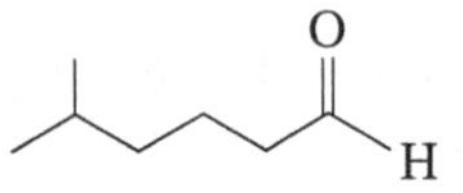

ANSWER

5-methylhexanal

Naming Ketones

Aldehydes and ketones are some of the most important classes of organic compounds. Because they have played a major role in organic chemistry for more than a century, the common names for unbranched ketones are still in use. In the common names, the alkyl groups bonded to the carbonyl group are named as substituents and are listed alphabetically, followed by *ketone*. Acetone, which is another name for propanone, has been retained by the IUPAC system.

In the IUPAC system, the name of a ketone is obtained by replacing the *e* in the corresponding alkane name with *one*. Carbon chains with five carbon atoms or more are numbered from the end nearer the carbonyl group.

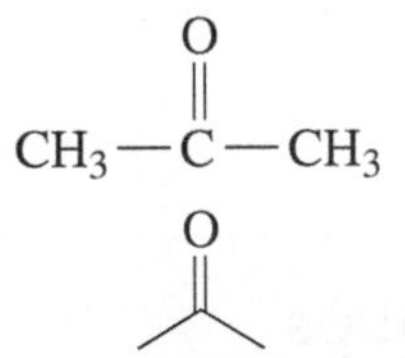

CH_3-C-CH_3 $CH_3-CH_2-C-CH_3$ $CH_3-CH_2-C-CH_2-CH_3$

Propanone
(dimethyl ketone; acetone)

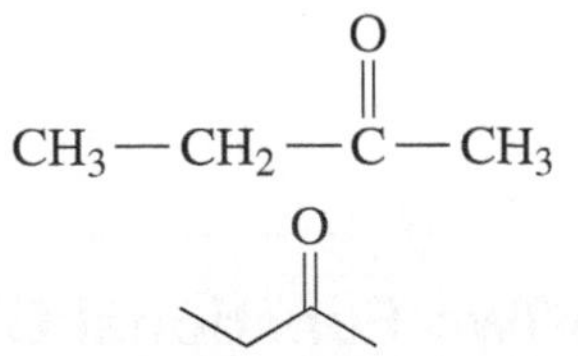

Butanone
(ethyl methyl ketone)

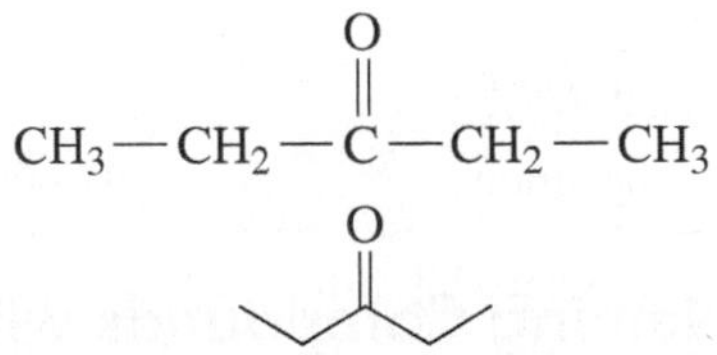

3-Pentanone
(diethyl ketone)

For cyclic ketones, the prefix *cyclo* is used in front of the ketone name. Any substituent is located by numbering the ring starting with the carbonyl carbon as carbon 1. The ring is numbered in the direction to give substituents the lowest possible numbers.

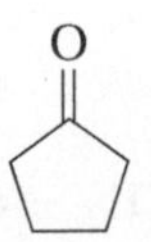

Cyclopentanone 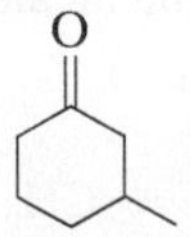   3-Methylcyclohexanone

Guide to Naming Ketones

STEP 1
Name the longest carbon chain by replacing the *e* in the alkane name with *one*.

STEP 2
Number the carbon chain starting from the end nearer the carbonyl group and indicate its location.

STEP 3
Name and number any substituents on the carbon chain.

▶ **SAMPLE PROBLEM 14.3 Naming Ketones**

Give the IUPAC name for the following ketone:

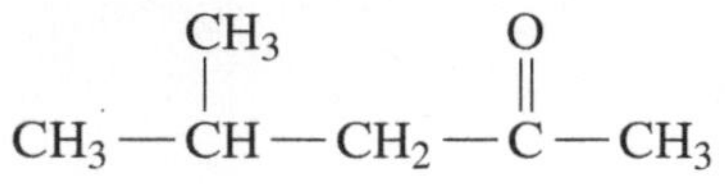

$$CH_3-CH-CH_2-C-CH_3$$

with CH_3 above CH and O above C.

SOLUTION

ANALYZE THE PROBLEM	Given	Need
	condensed structural formula of ketone	IUPAC name

STEP 1 Name the longest carbon chain by replacing the *e* in the alkane name with *one*. The longest chain has five carbon atoms, which is named pentanone.

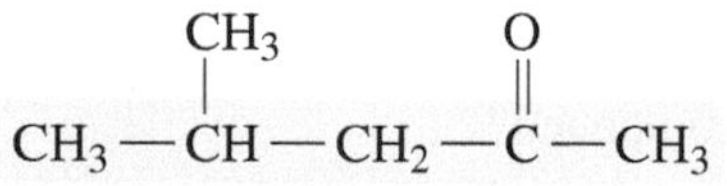

$$CH_3-CH-CH_2-C-CH_3 \qquad \text{pentanone}$$

STEP 2 Number the carbon chain starting from the end nearer the carbonyl group and indicate its location. Counting from the right, the carbonyl group is on carbon 2.

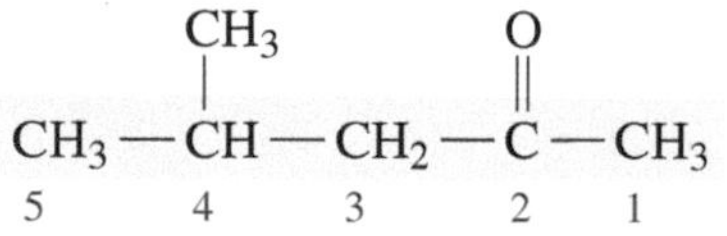

$$\underset{5}{CH_3}-\underset{4}{CH}-\underset{3}{CH_2}-\underset{2}{C}-\underset{1}{CH_3} \qquad \text{2-pentanone}$$

STEP 3 Name and number any substituents on the carbon chain. Counting from the right, the methyl group is on carbon 4. The IUPAC name is 4-methyl-2-pentanone.

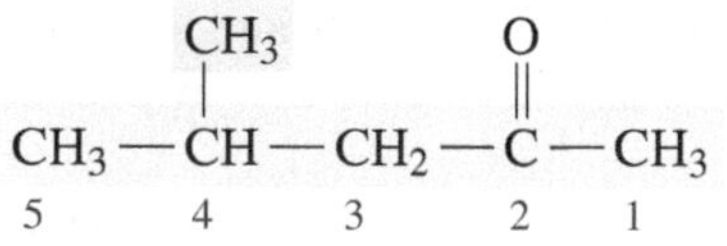

$$\underset{5}{CH_3}-\underset{4}{CH}-\underset{3}{CH_2}-\underset{2}{C}-\underset{1}{CH_3} \qquad \text{4-methyl-2-pentanone}$$

STUDY CHECK 14.3

What is the IUPAC name of ethyl propyl ketone?

ANSWER

3-hexanone

Naming Compounds with Two Functional Groups

When a compound contains more than one functional group, we need to identify which group is used as the name of the compound and which group is named as a substituent. According to IUPAC rules for nomenclature, the more oxidized group will take priority. Table 14.1 lists the priorities for the functional groups we have studied, and the names of the functional groups as substituents. The functional group that is highest on the list is named as the compound, and any group lower on the list is named as a substituent. Examples are given for naming an alcohol, a ketone, and an aldehyde.

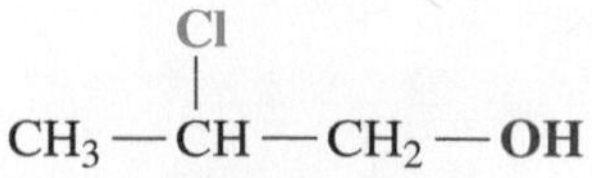

$$CH_3-CH-CH_2-OH$$
2-Chloro-1-propanol

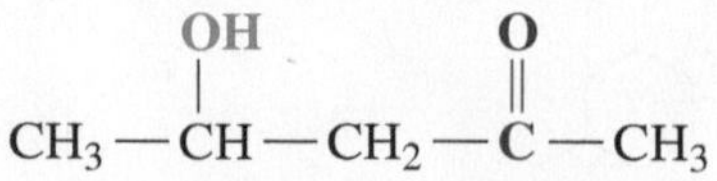

$$CH_3-CH-CH_2-C-CH_3$$
4-Hydroxy-2-pentanone

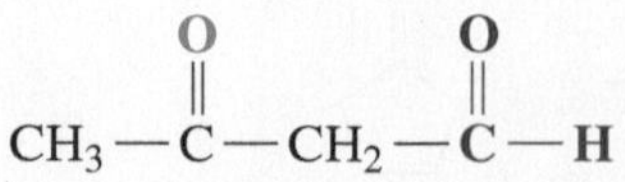

$$CH_3-C-CH_2-C-H$$
3-Oxobutanal

TABLE 14.1 Priority of Functional Groups in IUPAC Names

	Functional Group	Name as a Substituent
Highest Priority	aldehyde	formyl
	ketone	oxo
	alcohol	hydroxy
	alkane	alkyl
Lowest Priority	halogen	halo

 Chemistry Link to **Health**
Some Important Aldehydes and Ketones

Formaldehyde, the simplest aldehyde, is a colorless gas with a pungent odor. An aqueous solution called *formalin*, which contains 40% formaldehyde, is used as a germicide and to preserve biological specimens. Industrially, it is a reactant in the synthesis of polymers used to make fabrics, insulation materials, carpeting, pressed wood products such as plywood, and plastics for kitchen counters. Exposure to formaldehyde fumes can irritate the eyes, nose, and upper respiratory tract and cause skin rashes, headaches, dizziness, and general fatigue.

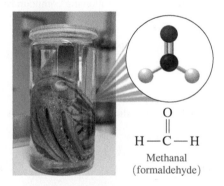

Methanal
(formaldehyde)

The simplest ketone, known as *acetone* or propanone (dimethyl ketone), is a colorless liquid with a mild odor that has wide use as a solvent in cleaning fluids, paint and nail polish removers, and rubber cement (see Figure 14.3). Acetone is extremely flammable, and care must be taken when using it. In the body, acetone may be produced in uncontrolled diabetes, fasting, and high-protein diets when large amounts of fats are metabolized for energy.

Muscone is a ketone used to make musk perfumes, and oil of spearmint contains carvone.

Several naturally occurring aromatic aldehydes are used to flavor food and as fragrances in perfumes. Benzaldehyde is found in almonds, vanillin in vanilla beans, and cinnamaldehyde in cinnamon.

Benzaldehyde
(almond)

Vanillin
(vanilla)

Cinnamaldehyde
(cinnamon)

FIGURE 14.3 ▶ Acetone is used as a solvent in paint and nail polish removers.

Q What is the IUPAC name for acetone?

Muscone
(musk)

Carvone
(spearmint oil)

QUESTIONS AND PROBLEMS

14.1 Aldehydes and Ketones

LEARNING GOAL Identify compounds with carbonyl groups as aldehydes and ketones. Write the IUPAC and common names for aldehydes and ketones; draw their condensed or line-angle structural formulas.

14.1 Identify each of the following compounds as an aldehyde or a ketone:

a. $CH_3-CH_2-\overset{\displaystyle O}{\overset{\displaystyle \|}{C}}-CH_3$ b.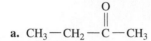

c.   d.

14.2 Identify each of the following compounds as an aldehyde or a ketone:

a.

b. $CH_3-\overset{\displaystyle CH_3}{\overset{\displaystyle |}{C}H}-\overset{\displaystyle O}{\overset{\displaystyle \|}{C}}-H$

c.

d.

14.3 Indicate if each of the following pairs represents structural isomers or not:

a. $CH_3-\overset{\displaystyle O}{\overset{\displaystyle \|}{C}}-CH_3$ and $CH_3-CH_2-\overset{\displaystyle O}{\overset{\displaystyle \|}{C}}-H$

b.   and

c. $CH_3-\overset{\displaystyle O}{\overset{\displaystyle \|}{C}}-CH_2-CH_3$ and

$CH_3-\overset{\displaystyle O}{\overset{\displaystyle \|}{C}}-CH_2-CH_2-CH_3$

14.4 Indicate if each of the following pairs represents structural isomers or not:

a. $CH_3-CH_2-CH_2-\overset{\displaystyle O}{\overset{\displaystyle \|}{C}}-H$ and

b.   and

c.   and

14.5 Give the IUPAC name for each of the following compounds:

a. $CH_3-\overset{\displaystyle Br}{\overset{\displaystyle |}{C}H}-CH_2-\overset{\displaystyle O}{\overset{\displaystyle \|}{C}}-H$ b.

c.   d.

14.6 Give the IUPAC name for each of the following compounds:

a.   b.

c.   d.

14.7 Give the common name for each of the following compounds:

a. $CH_3-\overset{\displaystyle O}{\overset{\displaystyle \|}{C}}-H$ b.

c. $H-\overset{\displaystyle O}{\overset{\displaystyle \|}{C}}-H$

14.8 Give the common name for each of the following compounds:

a.

b. $CH_3-CH_2-\overset{\displaystyle O}{\overset{\displaystyle \|}{C}}-CH_2-CH_3$

c. $CH_3-CH_2-\overset{\displaystyle O}{\overset{\displaystyle \|}{C}}-H$

14.9 Draw the condensed and line-angle structural formulas for each of the following compounds:
a. ethanal   b. 2-methyl-3-pentanone
c. butyl methyl ketone   d. 3-methylhexanal

14.10 Draw the condensed and line-angle structural formulas for each of the following compounds:
a. butyraldehyde   b. 3,4-dichloropentanal
c. 4-bromobutanone   d. acetone

℞ Clinical Applications

14.11 Anisaldehyde, from Korean mint or blue licorice, is a medicinal herb used in Chinese medicine. The IUPAC name of anisaldehyde is 4-methoxybenzaldehyde. Draw the line-angle structural formula for anisaldehyde.

14.12 The IUPAC name of ethyl vanillin, a synthetic compound used as a flavoring, is 3-ethoxy-4-hydroxybenzaldehyde. Draw the line-angle structural formula for ethyl vanillin.

14.2 Physical Properties of Aldehydes and Ketones

LEARNING GOAL

Describe the boiling points and solubilities of aldehydes and ketones.

At room temperature, methanal (formaldehyde) and ethanal (acetaldehyde) are gases. Aldehydes and ketones containing 3 to 10 carbon atoms are liquids. The polar carbonyl group with a partially negative oxygen atom and a partially positive carbon atom has an influence on the boiling points and the solubility of aldehydes and ketones in water.

Boiling Points of Aldehydes and Ketones

The polar carbonyl group in aldehydes and ketones provides dipole–dipole attractions, which alkanes do not have. Thus, aldehydes and ketones have higher boiling points than alkanes. However, aldehydes and ketones cannot form hydrogen bonds with each other as do alcohols. Thus, alcohols have higher boiling points than aldehydes and ketones of similar molar mass.

Dipole–dipole attractions in formaldehyde

	CH$_3$—CH$_2$—CH$_2$—CH$_3$	CH$_3$—CH$_2$—CHO	CH$_3$—CO—CH$_3$	CH$_3$—CH$_2$—CH$_2$—OH
Name	Butane	Propanal	Propanone	1-Propanol
Molar Mass	58	58	58	60
Family	Alkane	Aldehyde	Ketone	Alcohol
bp	0 °C	49 °C	56 °C	97 °C

Boiling Point Increases ⟶

For aldehydes and ketones, the boiling points increase as the number of carbon atoms in the chain increases. As the molecules become larger, there are more electrons and more temporary dipoles (dispersion forces), which give higher boiling points.

Table 14.2 gives the boiling points and solubility of selected aldehydes and ketones.

TABLE 14.2 Boiling Points and Solubility of Selected Aldehydes and Ketones

Compound	Condensed Structural Formula	Number of Carbon Atoms	Boiling Point (°C)	Solubility in Water
Methanal (formaldehyde)	H—CHO	1	−21	Soluble
Ethanal (acetaldehyde)	CH$_3$—CHO	2	21	Soluble
Propanal (propionaldehyde)	CH$_3$—CH$_2$—CHO	3	49	Soluble
Propanone (acetone)	CH$_3$—CO—CH$_3$	3	56	Soluble
Butanal (butyraldehyde)	CH$_3$—CH$_2$—CH$_2$—CHO	4	75	Soluble
Butanone	CH$_3$—CO—CH$_2$—CH$_3$	4	80	Soluble
Pentanal	CH$_3$—CH$_2$—CH$_2$—CH$_2$—CHO	5	103	Slightly soluble
2-Pentanone	CH$_3$—CO—CH$_2$—CH$_2$—CH$_3$	5	102	Slightly soluble
Hexanal	CH$_3$—CH$_2$—CH$_2$—CH$_2$—CH$_2$—CHO	6	129	Not soluble
2-Hexanone	CH$_3$—CO—CH$_2$—CH$_2$—CH$_2$—CH$_3$	6	127	Not soluble

Solubility of Aldehydes and Ketones in Water

Aldehydes and ketones contain a polar carbonyl group (carbon–oxygen double bond), which has a partially negative oxygen atom and a partially positive carbon atom. Because the electronegative oxygen atom forms hydrogen bonds with water molecules, aldehydes

Hydrogen bonds

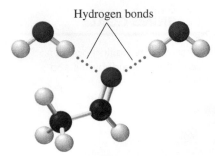

Acetaldehyde in water

Hydrogen bonds

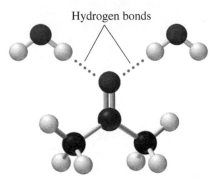

Acetone in water

FIGURE 14.4 ▶ Acetaldehyde and acetone form hydrogen bonds with water.

🅠 Would you expect propanal to be soluble in water?

and ketones with one to four carbons are very soluble (see Figure 14.4). However, aldehydes and ketones with five or more carbon atoms are not soluble because longer hydrocarbon chains, which are nonpolar, diminish the solubility effect of the polar carbonyl group. Table 14.2 compares the solubility of some aldehydes and ketones.

▶**SAMPLE PROBLEM 14.4 Boiling Point and Solubility**

a. Arrange pentane, 2-butanol, and butanone, which have similar molar masses, in order of increasing boiling points. Explain.
b. Why is butanone soluble in water, but 2-hexanone is not?

SOLUTION

a. The only attractions between molecules of alkanes such as pentane are dispersion forces. With no dipole–dipole attractions or hydrogen bonds, pentane has the lowest boiling point of the three compounds. With a polar carbonyl group, butanone molecules form dipole–dipole attractions, but no hydrogen bonds. Butanone has a higher boiling point than pentane. Because molecules of 2-butanol can form hydrogen bonds with other butanol molecules, it has the highest boiling point of the three compounds. The actual boiling points are pentane (36 °C), butanone (80 °C), and 2-butanol (100 °C).
b. Butanone contains a carbonyl group with an electronegative oxygen atom that forms hydrogen bonds with water. 2-Hexanone also contains a carbonyl group, but its longer hydrocarbon chain reduces the impact on the solubility of the polar carbonyl group.

STUDY CHECK 14.4

If acetone molecules cannot hydrogen bond with each other, why is acetone soluble in water?

ANSWER

The oxygen atom in the carbonyl group of acetone forms hydrogen bonds with water molecules.

QUESTIONS AND PROBLEMS

14.2 Physical Properties of Aldehydes and Ketones

LEARNING GOAL Describe the boiling points and solubilities of aldehydes and ketones.

14.13 Which compound in each of the following pairs would have the higher boiling point? Explain.

a. CH_3—CH_2—CH_3 or CH_3—$\overset{\overset{\displaystyle O}{\|}}{C}$—H
b. propanal or pentanal
c. butanal or 1-butanol

14.14 Which compound in each of the following pairs would have the higher boiling point? Explain.

a.

b. pentane or butanone
c. propanone or pentanone

14.15 Which compound in each of the following pairs would be more soluble in water? Explain.

a. CH_3—$\overset{\overset{\displaystyle O}{\|}}{C}$—$CH_2$—$CH_2$—$CH_3$ or

CH_3—$\overset{\overset{\displaystyle O}{\|}}{C}$—$\overset{\overset{\displaystyle O}{\|}}{C}$—$CH_2$—$CH_3$

b. propanal or pentanal
c. acetone or 2-pentanone

14.16 Which compound in each of the following pairs would be more soluble in water? Explain.
a. CH_3—CH_2—CH_3 or CH_3—CH_2—CHO
b. propanone or 3-hexanone
c. propane or propanone

14.17 Would you expect an aldehyde with a formula of $C_8H_{16}O$ to be soluble in water? Explain.

14.18 Would you expect an aldehyde with a formula of C_3H_6O to be soluble in water? Explain.

14.3 Oxidation and Reduction of Aldehydes and Ketones

Aldehydes oxidize readily to form carboxylic acids. In contrast, ketones do not undergo further oxidation.

LEARNING GOAL

Draw the condensed or line-angle structural formulas for the reactants and products in the oxidation or reduction of aldehydes and ketones.

$$CH_3-\overset{\displaystyle O}{\overset{\|}{C}}-H \xrightarrow[\text{oxidation}]{\text{Further}} CH_3-\overset{\displaystyle O}{\overset{\|}{C}}-OH$$

Ethanal   Ethanoic acid

$$CH_3-\overset{\displaystyle O}{\overset{\|}{C}}-CH_3 \xrightarrow[\text{oxidation}]{\text{Further}} \text{no reaction}$$

Propanone

Tollens' Test

The ease of oxidation of aldehydes allows certain mild oxidizing agents to oxidize the aldehyde functional group without oxidizing other functional groups. In the laboratory, **Tollens' test** may be used to distinguish between aldehydes and ketones. Tollens' reagent, which is a solution of Ag^+ ($AgNO_3$) and ammonia, oxidizes aldehydes, but not ketones. The silver ion is reduced and forms a layer called a "silver mirror" on the inside of the container.

$$CH_3-\overset{\displaystyle O}{\overset{\|}{C}}-H + 2Ag^+ \xrightarrow{[O]} 2Ag(s) + CH_3-\overset{\displaystyle O}{\overset{\|}{C}}-OH$$

Ethanal   Tollens'   Silver mirror   Ethanoic acid
(acetaldehyde)   reagent   (acetic acid)

Commercially, a similar process is used to make mirrors by applying a solution of $AgNO_3$ and ammonia on glass with a spray gun (see Figure 14.5).

Another test, called **Benedict's test**, gives a positive test with compounds that have an aldehyde functional group and an adjacent hydroxyl group. When Benedict's solution containing Cu^{2+} ($CuSO_4$) is added to this type of aldehyde and heated, a brick-red solid of Cu_2O forms (see Figure 14.6). The test is negative with simple aldehydes and ketones.

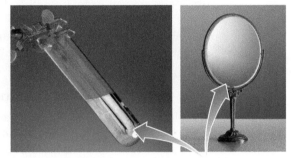

$$Ag^+ + 1\,e^- \longrightarrow Ag(s)$$

FIGURE 14.5 ▶ In Tollens' test, a "silver mirror" forms when the oxidation of an aldehyde reduces silver ions to metallic silver. The silvery surface of a mirror is formed in a similar way.

◉ What is the product of the oxidation of an aldehyde?

$$CH_3-\overset{OH}{\overset{|}{C}}H-\overset{\displaystyle O}{\overset{\|}{C}}-H + 2Cu^{2+} \longrightarrow Cu_2O(s) + CH_3-\overset{OH}{\overset{|}{C}}H-\overset{\displaystyle O}{\overset{\|}{C}}-OH$$

2-Hydroxypropanal   Benedict's   Brick-red   2-Hydroxypropanoic acid
                 reagent   solid

Because many sugars such as glucose contain this type of aldehyde grouping, Benedict's reagent can be used to determine the presence of glucose in blood or urine.

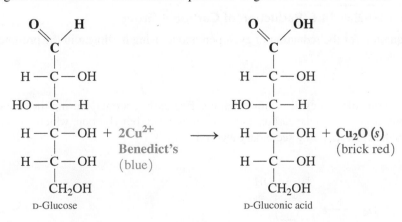

D-Glucose   D-Gluconic acid

Cu^{2+} $Cu_2O(s)$

FIGURE 14.6 ▶ The blue Cu^{2+} in Benedict's solution forms a brick-red solid of Cu_2O in a positive test for many sugars and aldehydes with adjacent hydroxyl groups.

◉ Which test tube indicates that glucose is present?

▶**SAMPLE PROBLEM 14.5** Tollens' Test

Draw the condensed structural formula for the product of oxidation, if any, when Tollens' reagent is added to each of the following compounds:

a. propanal **b.** propanone **c.** 2-methylbutanal

SOLUTION

Tollens' reagent will oxidize aldehydes but not ketones.

$$\textbf{a. } CH_3-CH_2-\overset{\displaystyle O}{\overset{\displaystyle \|}{C}}-OH \qquad \textbf{b. no reaction} \qquad \textbf{c. } CH_3-CH_2-\overset{\displaystyle CH_3}{\underset{}{\overset{|}{C}H}}-\overset{\displaystyle O}{\overset{\displaystyle \|}{C}}-OH$$

STUDY CHECK 14.5

Why does a silver mirror form when Tollens' reagent is added to a test tube containing benzaldehyde?

ANSWER

The oxidation of benzaldehyde reduces Ag^+ to metallic silver, which forms a silvery coating on the inside of the test tube.

Reduction of Aldehydes and Ketones

Aldehydes and ketones are reduced by hydrogen (H_2) or sodium borohydride ($NaBH_4$). In the **reduction** of organic compounds, there is a decrease in the number of carbon–oxygen bonds. Aldehydes are reduced to primary alcohols, and ketones are reduced to secondary alcohols. A catalyst such as nickel, platinum, or palladium is needed for the addition of hydrogen.

Aldehydes Reduce to Primary Alcohols

$$CH_3-CH_2-\overset{\displaystyle O}{\overset{\displaystyle \|}{C}}-H + \textbf{H}_2 \xrightarrow{Pt} CH_3-CH_2-\overset{\displaystyle OH}{\underset{\displaystyle H}{\overset{|}{\underset{|}{C}}}}-H$$

Propanal   1-Propanol (1° alcohol)
(propionaldehyde)   (propyl alcohol)

Ketones Reduce to Secondary Alcohols

$$CH_3-\overset{\displaystyle O}{\overset{\displaystyle \|}{C}}-CH_3 + \textbf{H}_2 \xrightarrow{Ni} CH_3-\overset{\displaystyle OH}{\underset{\displaystyle H}{\overset{|}{\underset{|}{C}}}}-CH_3$$

Propanone   2-Propanol (2° alcohol)
(dimethyl ketone)   (isopropyl alcohol)

▶**SAMPLE PROBLEM 14.6** Reduction of Carbonyl Groups

Write the equation for the reduction of cyclopentanone using hydrogen in the presence of a nickel catalyst.

SOLUTION

The reacting molecule is a cyclic ketone that has five carbon atoms. During the reduction, hydrogen atoms add to the carbon and oxygen in the carbonyl group, which reduces the ketone to the corresponding secondary alcohol.

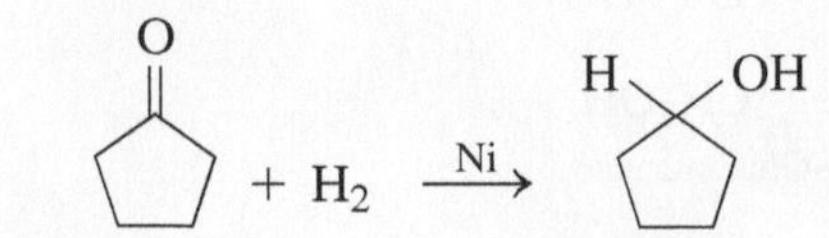

Cyclopentanone   Cyclopentanol

STUDY CHECK 14.6

What is the name of the product obtained from the hydrogenation of 2-methylbutanal?

ANSWER

2-methyl-1-butanol

QUESTIONS AND PROBLEMS

14.3 Oxidation and Reduction of Aldehydes and Ketones

LEARNING GOAL Draw the condensed or line-angle structural formulas for the reactants and products in the oxidation or reduction of aldehydes and ketones.

14.19 Draw the condensed or line-angle structural formula, if cyclic, for the product of oxidation (if any) for each of the following compounds:
  a. methanal
  b. butanone
  c. benzaldehyde
  d. 3-methylcyclohexanone

14.20 Draw the condensed or line-angle structural formula, if cyclic, for the product of oxidation (if any) for each of the following compounds:
  a. acetaldehyde
  b. 3-methylbutanone
  c. cyclohexanone
  d. 3-methylbutanal

14.21 Which of the following compounds would react with Tollens' reagent, Benedict's reagent, both, or neither?

$$\textbf{a.} \quad \underset{H}{\overset{O}{\underset{\|}{\diagdown}}} \qquad\qquad \textbf{b.} \quad CH_3 - \overset{O}{\overset{\|}{C}} - CH_3$$

$$\textbf{c.} \quad CH_3 - \overset{OH}{\underset{|}{CH}} - \overset{O}{\overset{\|}{C}} - H$$

14.22 Which of the following compounds would react with Tollens' reagent, Benedict's reagent, both, or neither?

$$\textbf{a.} \quad \overset{O}{\overset{\|}{\diagup\diagdown}} \qquad\qquad \textbf{b.} \quad CH_3 - CH_2 - \overset{OH}{\underset{|}{CH}} - \overset{O}{\overset{\|}{C}} - H$$

$$\textbf{c.} \quad CH_3 - \overset{O}{\overset{\|}{C}} - H$$

14.23 Draw the condensed structural formula for the product formed when each of the following is reduced by hydrogen in the presence of a nickel catalyst:
  a. butyraldehyde   **b.** acetone
  c. 3-bromohexanal   **d.** 2-methyl-3-pentanone

14.24 Draw the condensed structural formula for the product formed when each of the following is reduced by hydrogen in the presence of a nickel catalyst:
  a. ethyl propyl ketone   **b.** formaldehyde
  c. 3-chloropentanal   **d.** 2-pentanone

14.4 Hemiacetals and Acetals

We have seen that the carbonyl group (C=O) is polar, which makes aldehydes and ketones very reactive. One of the most common reactions of aldehydes and ketones is the addition of one or two molecules of an alcohol to the carbonyl group.

LEARNING GOAL

Draw the condensed or line-angle structural formulas for the products of the addition of alcohols to aldehydes and ketones.

Hemiacetal and Acetal Formation

When one alcohol adds to an aldehyde or ketone in the presence of an acid catalyst, the product is a **hemiacetal**, which contains two functional groups on the same C atom: a hydroxyl group (—OH) and an alkoxy group (—OR). However, hemiacetals are generally unstable and react with a second molecule of the alcohol to form a stable *acetal* and water. The **acetal** has two alkoxy groups (—OR) attached to the same carbon atom. Commercially, compounds that are acetals are used to produce vitamins, dyes, pharmaceuticals, and perfumes.

$$\underset{\substack{\text{Aldehyde} \\ \text{or ketone}}}{\overset{O^{\delta-}}{\underset{\|^{\delta+}}{\diagup}\underset{C}{\diagup}\diagdown}} + \underset{\text{Alcohol}}{HO-R} \;\overset{H^+}{\rightleftharpoons}\; \underset{\text{Hemiacetal}}{\overset{O-H}{\underset{|}{-C-OR}}} + \underset{\text{Alcohol}}{HO-R} \;\overset{H^+}{\rightleftharpoons}\; \underset{\text{Acetal}}{\overset{OR}{\underset{|}{-C-OR}}} + H-O-H$$

In general, aldehydes are more reactive than ketones because the carbonyl carbon is more positive in aldehydes. Also, the presence of two alkyl groups in ketones makes it more difficult for an alcohol to form a bond with the carbon in the carbonyl group.

▶**SAMPLE PROBLEM 14.7 Hemiacetals and Acetals**

Identify each of the following as a hemiacetal or acetal:

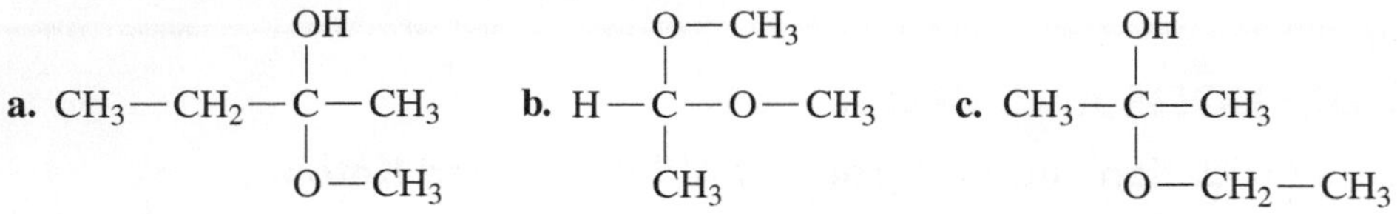

a. $CH_3-CH_2-\underset{\underset{\displaystyle O-CH_3}{|}}{\overset{\overset{\displaystyle OH}{|}}{C}}-CH_3$ b. $H-\underset{\underset{\displaystyle CH_3}{|}}{\overset{\overset{\displaystyle O-CH_3}{|}}{C}}-O-CH_3$ c. $CH_3-\underset{\underset{\displaystyle O-CH_2-CH_3}{|}}{\overset{\overset{\displaystyle OH}{|}}{C}}-CH_3$

SOLUTION

a. A hemiacetal has a carbon bonded to one alkoxy group and one hydroxyl group.
b. An acetal has a carbon bonded to two alkoxy groups.
c. A hemiacetal has a carbon bonded to one alkoxy group and one hydroxyl group.

STUDY CHECK 14.7

From the following descriptions, identify the compound as a hemiacetal or an acetal:

a. a molecule that contains a carbon atom attached to a hydroxyl group and an ethoxy group
b. a molecule that contains a carbon atom attached to two ethoxy groups

ANSWER

a. hemiacetal   b. acetal

Examples of the formation of a hemiacetal and acetal from an aldehyde and a ketone follow:

Hemiacetal and Acetal Formation from an Aldehyde

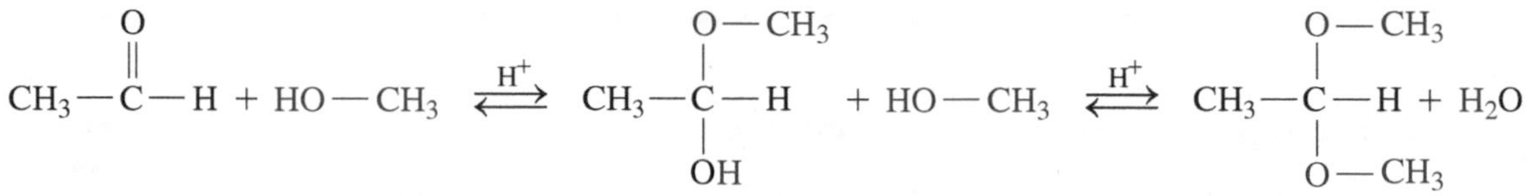

$$CH_3-\overset{\overset{\displaystyle O}{||}}{C}-H + HO-CH_3 \xrightleftharpoons{H^+} CH_3-\underset{\underset{\displaystyle OH}{|}}{\overset{\overset{\displaystyle O-CH_3}{|}}{C}}-H + HO-CH_3 \xrightleftharpoons{H^+} CH_3-\underset{\underset{\displaystyle O-CH_3}{|}}{\overset{\overset{\displaystyle O-CH_3}{|}}{C}}-H + H_2O$$

Ethanal   Methanol   Hemiacetal   Acetal

Hemiacetal and Acetal Formation from an Ketone

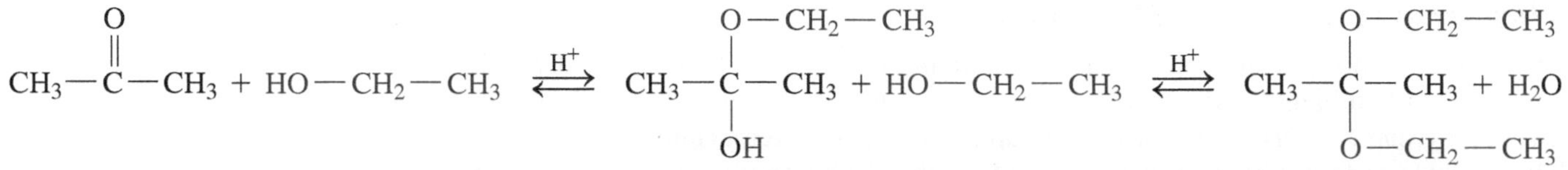

$$CH_3-\overset{\overset{\displaystyle O}{||}}{C}-CH_3 + HO-CH_2-CH_3 \xrightleftharpoons{H^+} CH_3-\underset{\underset{\displaystyle OH}{|}}{\overset{\overset{\displaystyle O-CH_2-CH_3}{|}}{C}}-CH_3 + HO-CH_2-CH_3 \xrightleftharpoons{H^+} CH_3-\underset{\underset{\displaystyle O-CH_2-CH_3}{|}}{\overset{\overset{\displaystyle O-CH_2-CH_3}{|}}{C}}-CH_3 + H_2O$$

Propanone   Ethanol   Hemiacetal   Acetal

The reactions in the formation of hemiacetals and acetals are reversible. As predicted by Le Châtelier's principle, the system shifts in the direction of the products by removing water from the reaction mixture. The system shifts in the direction of the ketone or aldehyde by adding water.

▶SAMPLE PROBLEM 14.8 **Hemiacetals and Acetals**

Draw the condensed structural formulas for the hemiacetal and acetal formed when methanol adds to propanal.

SOLUTION

To form the hemiacetal, the hydrogen from methanol adds to the oxygen of the carbonyl group to form a new hydroxyl group. The remaining part of the methanol adds to the carbon atom in the carbonyl group. The acetal forms when a second molecule of methanol adds to the carbonyl carbon atom.

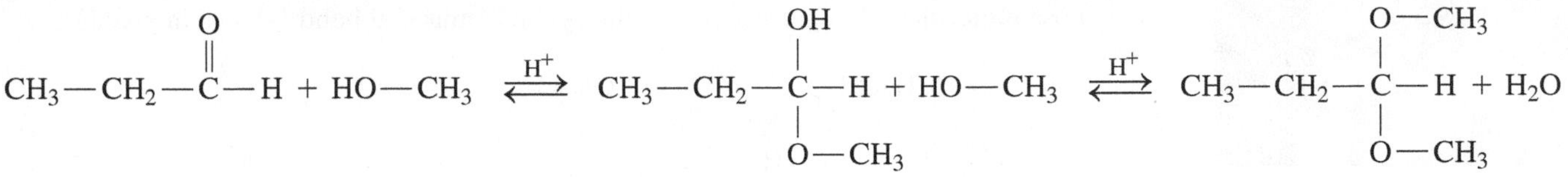

$$CH_3-CH_2-\overset{\overset{\displaystyle O}{\|}}{C}-H + HO-CH_3 \xrightleftharpoons{H^+} CH_3-CH_2-\underset{\underset{\displaystyle O-CH_3}{|}}{\overset{\overset{\displaystyle OH}{|}}{C}}-H + HO-CH_3 \xrightleftharpoons{H^+} CH_3-CH_2-\underset{\underset{\displaystyle O-CH_3}{|}}{\overset{\overset{\displaystyle O-CH_3}{|}}{C}}-H + H_2O$$

| Propanal | Methanol | Hemiacetal | Methanol | Acetal |

STUDY CHECK 14.8

Draw the condensed structural formula for the acetal formed when methanol adds to butanone.

ANSWER

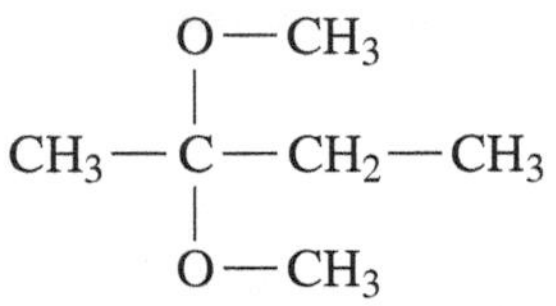

$$CH_3-\underset{\underset{\displaystyle O-CH_3}{|}}{\overset{\overset{\displaystyle O-CH_3}{|}}{C}}-CH_2-CH_3$$

Cyclic Hemiacetals

One very important type of hemiacetal that can be isolated is a *cyclic hemiacetal* that forms when the carbonyl group and the —OH group are in the *same* molecule.

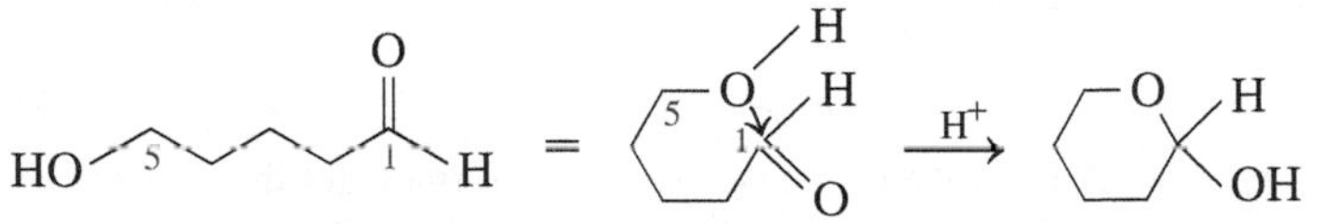

| Open chain | | Cyclic hemiacetal |

The five- and six-atom cyclic hemiacetals and acetals are more stable than their open-chain isomers. The importance of understanding acetals is shown for glucose, a carbohydrate, which has both carbonyl and hydroxyl groups that can form acetal bonds. Glucose forms a cyclic hemiacetal when the hydroxyl group on carbon 5 bonds with the carbonyl group on carbon 1. The hemiacetal of glucose is so stable that almost all the glucose (99%) exists as the cyclic hemiacetal in aqueous solution.

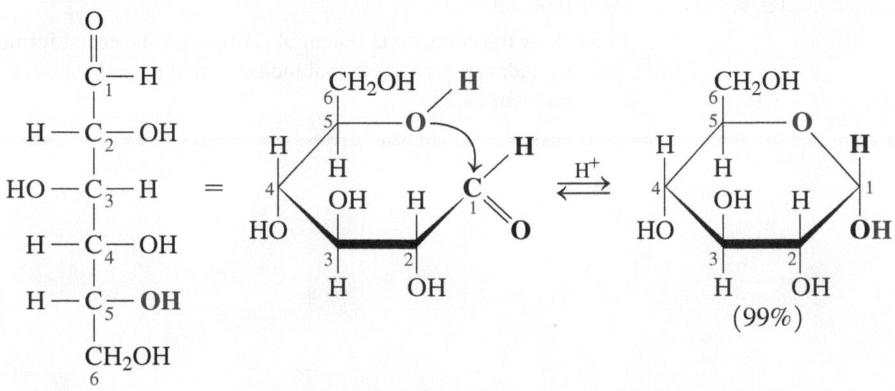

| Glucose | Formation of cyclic hemiacetal | Hemiacetal of glucose |

Maltose, a disaccharide, is produced from the hydrolysis of the starches in grains, such as barley.

An alcohol can add to the cyclic hemiacetal to form a cyclic acetal. This reaction is also very important in carbohydrate chemistry. It is the linkage that bonds glucose molecules to other glucose molecules in the formation of disaccharides and polysaccharides.

Cyclic hemiacetal + HO—CH₃ $\xrightarrow{H^+}$ Cyclic acetal + H₂O

Maltose is a disaccharide consisting of two glucose molecules, and is produced from the hydrolysis of starch from grains. In maltose, an acetal bond (shown in red) links two glucose molecules. One glucose retains the cyclic hemiacetal bond (shown in green).

α-Maltose

QUESTIONS AND PROBLEMS

14.4 Hemiacetals and Acetals

LEARNING GOAL Draw the condensed or line-angle structural formulas for the products of the addition of alcohols to aldehydes and ketones.

14.25 Indicate whether each of the following is a hemiacetal, acetal, or neither:

a. CH₃—CH₂—O—CH₂—OH

b. CH₃—CH₂—CH₂—C(—O—CH₃)(—OH)—H

c. CH₃—C(—O—CH₂—CH₃)(—O—CH₂—CH₃)—CH₂—CH₃

d. cyclohexane with OH and O—CH₂—CH₃

e. cyclopentane with CH₃—O and O—CH₃

14.26 Indicate whether each of the following is a hemiacetal, acetal, or neither:

a. CH₃—CH₂—O—CH₂—CH₃

b. HO—CH₂—CH₂—O—CH₂—CH₂—O—CH₃

c. CH₃—C(—O—CH₂—CH₃)(—OH)—CH₃

d. cyclohexane with two O—CH₃ groups

e. cyclopentane with O—CH₃ and O—CH₃

14.27 Draw the condensed structural formula for the hemiacetal formed by adding one methanol molecule to each of the following:

a. ethanal   b. propanone   c. butanal

14.28 Draw the condensed structural formula for the hemiacetal formed by adding one ethanol molecule to each of the following:

a. propanal   b. butanone   c. methanal

14.29 Draw the condensed structural formula for the acetal formed by adding a second methanol molecule to the compounds in problem 14.27.

14.30 Draw the condensed structural formula for the acetal formed by adding a second ethanol molecule to the compounds in problem 14.28.

14.5 Chiral Molecules

Molecules are structural isomers when they have the same molecular formula, but different bonding arrangements.

LEARNING GOAL

Identify chiral and achiral carbon atoms in an organic molecule.

Structural Isomers

C_2H_6O CH_3-CH_2-OH CH_3-O-CH_3
Ethanol   Dimethyl ether

C_3H_6O $CH_3-CH_2-\overset{\overset{O}{\|}}{C}-H$ $CH_3-\overset{\overset{O}{\|}}{C}-CH_3$
Propanal   Propanone

Another group of isomers called *stereoisomers* has identical molecular formulas, too, but they are not structural isomers. In **stereoisomers**, the atoms are bonded in the same sequence but differ in the way they are arranged in space.

Chirality

Everything has a mirror image. If you hold your right hand up to a mirror, you see its mirror image, which matches your left hand (see Figure 14.7). If you turn your palms toward each other, one hand is the mirror image of the other. If you look at the palms of your hands, your thumbs are on opposite sides. If you then place your right hand over your left hand, you cannot match up all the parts of the hands: palms, backs, thumbs, and little fingers.

Interactive Video

Chirality

Left hand   Mirror image of right hand   Right hand

FIGURE 14.7 ▶ The left and right hands are chiral because they have mirror images that cannot be superimposed on each other.

Q Why are your shoes chiral objects?

The thumbs and little fingers can be matched, but then the palms or backs of your hands are facing each other. Your hands are mirror images that cannot be superimposed on each other. When the mirror images cannot be completely matched, they are *nonsuperimposable*.

Objects such as hands that have nonsuperimposable mirror images are **chiral** (pronunciation *kai-ral*). Left and right shoes are chiral; left- and right-handed golf clubs are chiral. When we think of how difficult it is to put a left-hand glove on our right hand, put a right shoe on our left foot, or use left-handed scissors if we are right-handed, we begin to realize that certain properties of mirror images are very different.

When the mirror image of an object is identical and can be superimposed on the original, it is *achiral*. For example, the mirror image of a plain drinking glass is identical to the original glass, which means the mirror image can be superimposed on the glass (see Figure 14.8).

Chiral Carbon Atoms

A carbon compound is chiral if it has at least one carbon atom bonded to *four different atoms or groups*. This type of carbon atom is called a **chiral carbon** because there are two different ways that it can bond to four atoms or groups of atoms. The resulting structures

⚛ CORE CHEMISTRY SKILL

Identifying Chiral Molecules

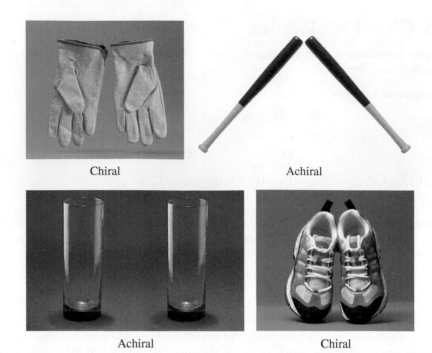

FIGURE 14.8 ▶ Everyday objects such as gloves and shoes are chiral, but an unmarked bat and a plain glass are achiral.

🄾 Why are some of the objects above chiral and others achiral?

are nonsuperimposable mirror images. Let's look at the mirror images of a carbon bonded to four different atoms (see Figure 14.9). If we line up the hydrogen and iodine atoms in the mirror images, the bromine and chlorine atoms appear on opposite sides. No matter how we turn the models, we cannot align all four atoms at the same time. When stereoisomers cannot be superimposed, they are called **enantiomers**.

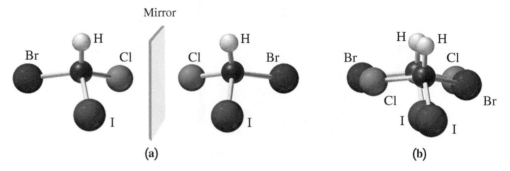

FIGURE 14.9 ▶ **(a)** The enantiomers of a chiral molecule are mirror images. **(b)** The enantiomers of a chiral molecule cannot be superimposed on each other.

🄾 Why is the carbon atom in this compound chiral?

If a molecule with two or more identical atoms bonded to the same atom is rotated, the atoms can be superimposed and the mirror images represent the same structure (see Figure 14.10).

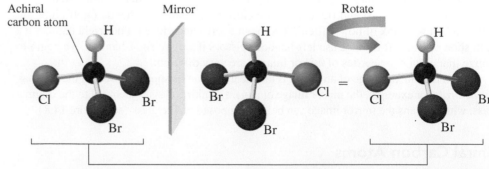

FIGURE 14.10 ▶ The mirror images of an achiral compound can be superimposed on each other.

🄾 Why can the mirror images of this compound be superimposed?

These are the same structures.

Explore Your World
Using Gumdrops and Toothpicks to Model Chiral Objects

Part 1: Achiral Objects

Obtain some toothpicks and orange, yellow, green, purple, and black gumdrops. Place four toothpicks into a black gumdrop making the ends of toothpicks the corners of a tetrahedron. Attach the gumdrops to the toothpicks: two orange, one green, and one yellow.

Using another black gumdrop, make a second model that is the mirror image of the original model. Now rotate one of the models and try to superimpose it on the other model. Are the models superimposable? If achiral objects have superimposable mirror images, are these models chiral or achiral?

Part 2: Chiral Objects

Using one of the original models, replace one orange gumdrop with a purple gumdrop. Now there are four different colors of gumdrops attached to the black gumdrop. Make its mirror image by replacing one orange gumdrop with a purple one on the second model. Now rotate one of the models, and try to superimpose it on the other model. Are the models superimposable? If chiral objects have nonsuperimposable mirror images, are these models chiral or achiral?

▶ SAMPLE PROBLEM 14.9 Chiral Carbons

For each of the following, indicate whether the carbon in red is chiral or achiral:

a. Glycerol, which is used to sweeten and preserve foods and as a lubricant in soaps, creams, and hair care products.

$$HO-\overset{\displaystyle H}{\underset{\displaystyle H}{C}}-\overset{\displaystyle OH}{\underset{\displaystyle H}{C}}-\overset{\displaystyle H}{\underset{\displaystyle H}{C}}-OH$$

Glycerol

b. Monosodium glutamate (MSG), which is the salt of the amino acid glutamic acid used as a flavor enhancer in foods.

$$Na^+ \ ^-O-\overset{\displaystyle O}{\overset{\|}{C}}-\overset{\displaystyle H}{\underset{\displaystyle H}{C}}-\overset{\displaystyle H}{\underset{\displaystyle H}{C}}-\overset{\displaystyle NH_2}{\underset{\displaystyle H}{C}}-\overset{\displaystyle O}{\overset{\|}{C}}-OH$$

Monosodium glutamate (MSG)

c. Ibuprofen, which is a nonsteroidal anti-inflammatory drug used to relieve fever and pain.

$$CH_3-\overset{\displaystyle H}{\underset{\displaystyle CH_3}{C}}-\overset{\displaystyle H}{\underset{\displaystyle H}{C}}-\bigcirc-\overset{\displaystyle \overset{O}{\overset{\|}{C}-OH}}{\underset{\displaystyle H}{C}}-CH_3$$

Ibuprofen

SOLUTION

a. Achiral. Two of the substituents on the carbon in red are the same:

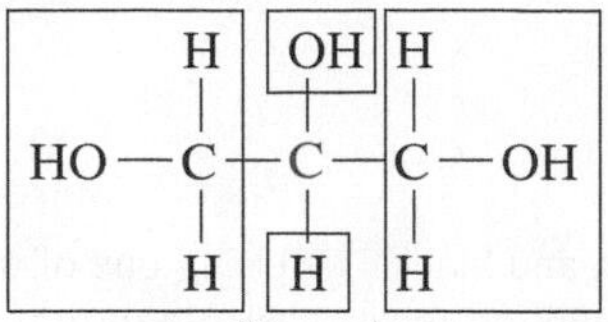

$$HO-\underset{\underset{H}{|}}{\overset{\overset{H}{|}}{C}}-\underset{\underset{\boxed{H}}{|}}{\overset{\overset{\boxed{OH}}{|}}{C}}-\underset{\underset{H}{|}}{\overset{\overset{H}{|}}{C}}-OH$$

Glycerol

b. Chiral. The carbon in red is bonded to four different groups:

$$Na^+\ {}^-O-\underset{}{\overset{\overset{O}{\|}}{C}}-\underset{\underset{H}{|}}{\overset{\overset{H}{|}}{C}}-\underset{\underset{H}{|}}{\overset{\overset{H}{|}}{C}}-\underset{\underset{\boxed{H}}{|}}{\overset{\overset{\boxed{NH_2}}{|}}{C}}-\underset{}{\overset{\overset{O}{\|}}{C}}-OH$$

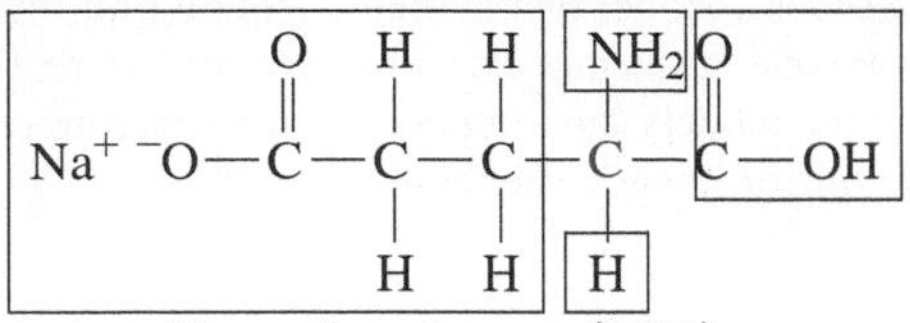

Monosodium glutamate (MSG)

c. Chiral. The carbon in red is bonded to four different groups:

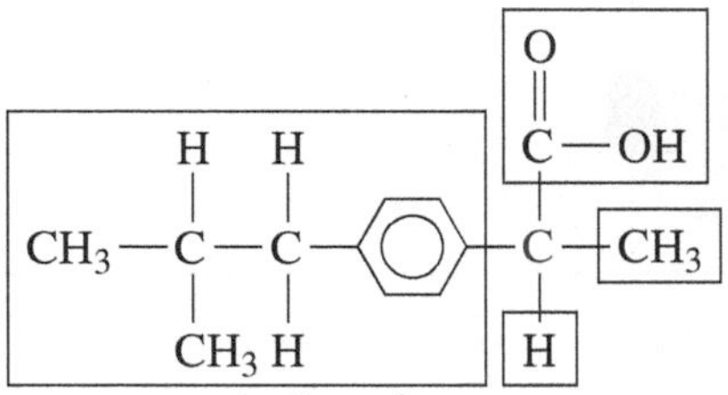

Ibuprofen

STUDY CHECK 14.9

Circle the chiral carbon of penicillamine, which is used in the treatment of rheumatoid arthritis.

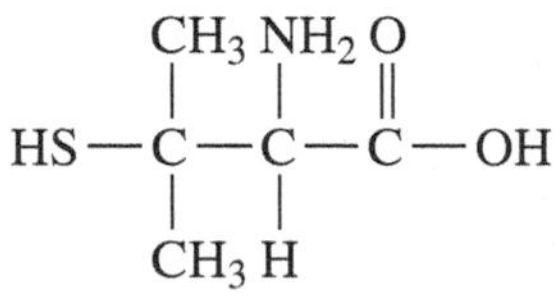

$$HS-\underset{\underset{CH_3}{|}}{\overset{\overset{CH_3}{|}}{C}}-\underset{\underset{H}{|}}{\overset{\overset{NH_2}{|}}{C}}-\underset{}{\overset{\overset{O}{\|}}{C}}-OH$$

ANSWER

$$HS-\underset{\underset{CH_3}{|}}{\overset{\overset{CH_3}{|}}{C}}-\underset{\underset{H}{|}}{\overset{\overset{NH_2}{|}}{Ⓒ}}-\underset{}{\overset{\overset{O}{\|}}{C}}-OH$$

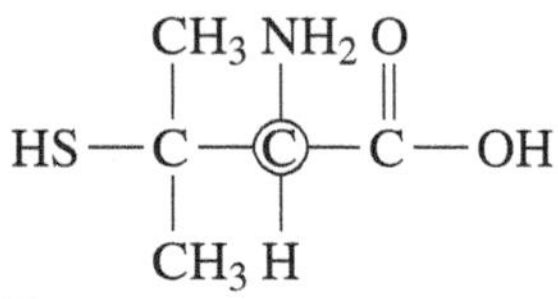

⚛ CORE CHEMISTRY SKILL

Identifying D- and L- Fischer Projections

Drawing Fischer Projections

Emil Fischer devised a simplified system for drawing stereoisomers that shows the arrangements of the atoms around the chiral carbons. Fischer received the Nobel Prize in Chemistry in 1902 for his contributions to carbohydrate and protein chemistry. Now we use his model, called a **Fischer projection**, to represent a three-dimensional structure of enantiomers. Vertical lines represent bonds that project backward from a carbon atom and horizontal lines represent bonds that project forward. In this model, the most highly oxidized carbon is placed at the top and the intersections of vertical and horizontal lines represent a carbon atom that is usually chiral.

For glyceraldehyde, the only chiral carbon is the middle carbon. In the Fischer projection, the carbonyl group, which is the most highly oxidized group, is drawn at the top above the chiral carbon and the —CH₂OH group is drawn at the bottom. The —H and —OH groups can be drawn at each end of a horizontal line, but in two different ways. The stereoisomer that has the —OH group drawn to the left of the chiral atom is designated as the L stereoisomer. The stereoisomer with the —OH group drawn to the right of the chiral carbon represents the D stereoisomer (see Figure 14.11).

Fischer projections can also be drawn for compounds that have two or more chiral carbons. For example, in the mirror images of erythrose, both of the carbon atoms at the

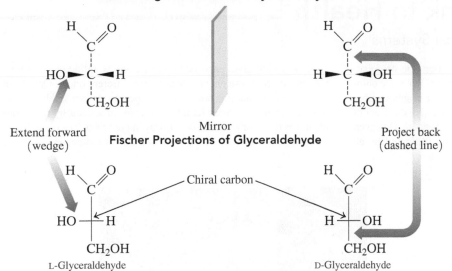

Dash–Wedge Structures of Glyceraldehyde

Extend forward (wedge)

Fischer Projections of Glyceraldehyde

Mirror

Project back (dashed line)

Chiral carbon

L-Glyceraldehyde

D-Glyceraldehyde

FIGURE 14.11 ▶ In a Fischer projection, the chiral carbon atom is at the center, with horizontal lines for bonds that project forward and vertical lines for bonds that point away.

◉ Why does glyceraldehyde have only one chiral carbon atom?

intersections are chiral. To draw the mirror image for L-erythrose, we need to reverse the positions of *all* the —H and the —OH groups on the horizontal lines. For compounds with two or more chiral carbons, the designation as a D or L stereoisomer is determined by the position of the —OH group attached to the chiral carbon *farthest from the carbonyl group*.

L Stereoisomer

L-Erythrose

D Stereoisomer

D-Erythrose

▶ **SAMPLE PROBLEM 14.10 Fischer Projections**

Identify each of the following as the D or L stereoisomer:

a. b. c.

SOLUTION

a. When the —OH group is drawn to the left of the chiral carbon, it is the L stereoisomer.
b. When the —OH group is drawn to the right of the chiral carbon, it is the D stereoisomer.
c. When the —OH group is drawn to the right of the chiral carbon farthest from the top of the Fischer projection, it is the D stereoisomer.

STUDY CHECK 14.10

Draw the Fischer projections for the D and L stereoisomers of 2-hydroxypropanal and label the D and L isomers.

ANSWER

D-2-Hydroxypropanal   L-2-Hydroxypropanal

Chemistry Link to **Health**

Enantiomers in Biological Systems

Molecules in nature also have mirror images, and often one stereoisomer has a different biological effect than the other one. For some compounds, one enantiomer has a certain odor, and the other enantiomer has a completely different odor. For example, the oils that give the scent of spearmint and caraway seeds are *both* composed of carvone. However, carvone has one chiral carbon in the carbon ring indicated by an asterisk, which gives carvone two enantiomers. Olfactory receptors in the nose detect these enantiomers as two different odors. One enantiomer of carvone that is produced by the spearmint plant smells and tastes like spearmint, whereas its mirror image, produced by the caraway plant, has the odor and taste of caraway in rye bread. Thus, our senses of smell and taste are responsive to the chirality of molecules.

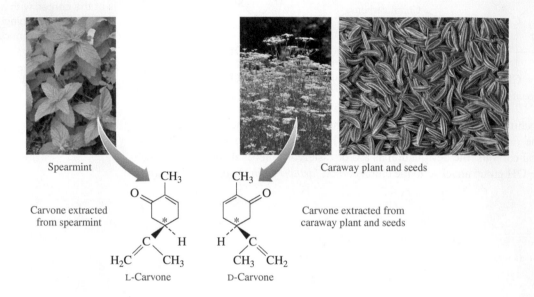

Spearmint

Carvone extracted from spearmint

Caraway plant and seeds

Carvone extracted from caraway plant and seeds

L-Carvone   D-Carvone

In the brain, one enantiomer of LSD affects the production of serotonin, which influences sensory perception and may lead to hallucinations. However, its enantiomer produces little effect in the brain. The behavior of nicotine and adrenaline (epinephrine) also depends upon only one of their enantiomers. For example, one enantiomer of nicotine is more toxic than the other. Only one enantiomer of epinephrine is responsible for the constriction of blood vessels.

Nicotine

Chiral carbon (shown with an asterisk *)

Adrenaline (epinephrine)

A substance used to treat Parkinson's disease is L-dopa, which is converted to dopamine in the brain, where it raises the serotonin level. However, the D-dopa enantiomer is not effective for the treatment of Parkinson's disease.

L-Dopa   D-Dopa

Many compounds in biological systems have only one enantiomer that is active. This happens because the enzymes and cell surface receptors on which metabolic reactions take place are themselves chiral. Thus, only one enantiomer interacts with its enzymes or receptors; the other is inactive. The chiral receptor fits the arrangement of the substituents in only one enantiomer; its mirror image does not fit properly (see Figure 14.12).

For many drugs, only one of the enantiomers is biologically active. However, for many years, drugs have been produced that were mixtures of their enantiomers. Today, drug researchers are using *chiral technology* to produce the active enantiomers of chiral drugs. Chiral catalysts are being designed that direct the formation of just one enantiomer rather than both. The active forms of several enantiomers are now being produced, such as L-dopa and naproxen. Naproxen is a nonsteroidal anti-inflammatory drug used to relieve pain, fever, and

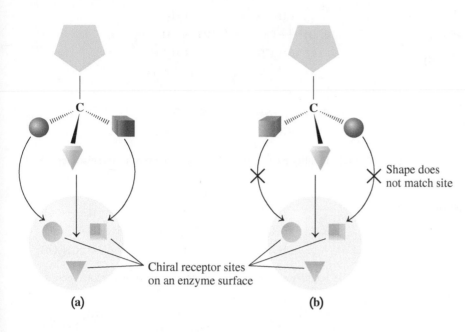

Shape does
not match site

Chiral receptor sites
on an enzyme surface

(a)　　　　　　　　(b)

FIGURE 14.12 ▶ **(a)** The substituents on the biologically active enantiomer bind to all the sites on a chiral receptor; **(b)** its enantiomer does not bind properly and is not active biologically.

◉ Why don't all the substituents of the mirror image of the active enantiomer fit into a chiral receptor site?

inflammation caused by osteoarthritis and tendinitis. The benefits of producing only the active enantiomer include using a lower dose, enhancing activity, reducing interactions with other drugs, and eliminating possible harmful side effects from the enantiomer.

The active enantiomer of the popular analgesic ibuprofen used in Advil, Motrin, and Nuprin has been produced. However, recent research shows that humans have an enzyme called *isomerase* that converts the inactive enantiomer of ibuprofen to its active form. Because of the lower cost of preparation, most manufacturers prepare ibuprofen as a mixture of inactive and active forms.

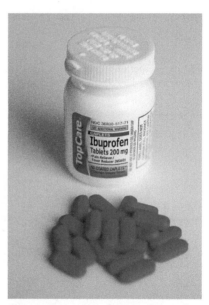

One enantiomer of ibuprofen is the active form, but its mirror image is inactive.

Active form of ibuprofen   Mirror image (inactive form)

QUESTIONS AND PROBLEMS

14.5 Chiral Molecules

LEARNING GOAL Identify chiral and achiral carbon atoms in an organic molecule.

14.31 Identify each of the following structures as chiral or achiral. If chiral, indicate the chiral carbon.

a. $CH_3-\overset{\underset{|}{OH}}{CH}-CH_3$　　b.

c. $CH_3-\overset{\underset{|}{Br}}{CH}-\overset{\overset{O}{\parallel}}{C}-H$

d. $CH_3-CH_2-\overset{\overset{\displaystyle OH}{|}}{\underset{\underset{\displaystyle CH_3}{|}}{C}}-CH_3$

14.32 Identify each of the following structures as chiral or achiral. If chiral, indicate the chiral carbon.

a. $CH_3-\overset{\overset{\displaystyle Cl}{|}}{\underset{\underset{\displaystyle CH_3}{|}}{C}}-CH_2-\overset{\overset{\displaystyle Cl}{|}}{CH}-CH_3$

b.
$$CH_3-\overset{\overset{\displaystyle Br}{|}}{C}=CH-CH_3$$

c.
$$\overset{\displaystyle OH}{\underset{\displaystyle OH}{\big|}}$$ (2-methylbutane-2,3-diol structure with OH groups)

d.
$$Br-CH_2-\overset{\overset{\displaystyle Cl}{|}}{CH}-CH_3$$

14.33 Draw the Fischer projection for each of the following dash–wedge structures:

a.
$$\underset{\displaystyle CH_3}{\overset{\displaystyle H\diagdown C=O}{HO\blacktriangleright C\blacktriangleleft Br}}$$

b.
$$\underset{\displaystyle OH}{\overset{\displaystyle H\diagdown C=O}{Cl\blacktriangleright C\blacktriangleleft Br}}$$

c.
$$\underset{\displaystyle CH_2CH_3}{\overset{\displaystyle H\diagdown C=O}{HO\blacktriangleright C\blacktriangleleft H}}$$

14.34 Draw the Fischer projection for each of the following dash–wedge structures:

a.
$$\underset{\displaystyle CH_2OH}{\overset{\displaystyle H\diagdown C=O}{HO\blacktriangleright C\blacktriangleleft Br}}$$

b.
$$\underset{\displaystyle CH_2OH}{\overset{\displaystyle H\diagdown C=O}{HO\blacktriangleright C\blacktriangleleft H}}$$

c.
$$\underset{\displaystyle CH_2OH}{\overset{\displaystyle H\diagdown C=O}{H\blacktriangleright C\blacktriangleleft OH}}$$

14.35 Indicate whether each pair of Fischer projections represents enantiomers or identical structures.

a.
$$\underset{\displaystyle CH_3}{\overset{\displaystyle CH_3}{Br-\!\!|\!\!-Cl}} \quad \text{and} \quad \underset{\displaystyle CH_3}{\overset{\displaystyle CH_3}{Cl-\!\!|\!\!-Br}}$$

b.
$$\underset{\displaystyle CH_3}{\overset{\displaystyle H\diagdown C=O}{HO-\!\!|\!\!-H}} \quad \text{and} \quad \underset{\displaystyle CH_3}{\overset{\displaystyle H\diagdown C=O}{H-\!\!|\!\!-OH}}$$

c.
$$\underset{\displaystyle H}{\overset{\displaystyle CH_3}{Cl-\!\!|\!\!-Br}} \quad \text{and} \quad \underset{\displaystyle H}{\overset{\displaystyle CH_3}{Br-\!\!|\!\!-Cl}}$$

d.
$$\underset{\displaystyle CH_3}{\overset{\displaystyle HO\diagdown C=O}{H-\!\!|\!\!-OH}} \quad \text{and} \quad \underset{\displaystyle CH_3}{\overset{\displaystyle HO\diagdown C=O}{HO-\!\!|\!\!-H}}$$

14.36 Indicate whether each pair of Fischer projections represents enantiomers or identical structures.

a.
$$\underset{\displaystyle CH_3}{\overset{\displaystyle CH_2OH}{Br-\!\!|\!\!-Cl}} \quad \text{and} \quad \underset{\displaystyle CH_3}{\overset{\displaystyle CH_2OH}{Cl-\!\!|\!\!-Br}}$$

b.
$$\underset{\displaystyle CH_3}{\overset{\displaystyle H\diagdown C=O}{H-\!\!|\!\!-H}} \quad \text{and} \quad \underset{\displaystyle CH_3}{\overset{\displaystyle H\diagdown C=O}{H-\!\!|\!\!-H}}$$

c.
$$\underset{\displaystyle CH_2CH_3}{\overset{\displaystyle CH_3}{H-\!\!|\!\!-OH}} \quad \text{and} \quad \underset{\displaystyle CH_2CH_3}{\overset{\displaystyle CH_3}{HO-\!\!|\!\!-H}}$$

d.
$$\underset{\displaystyle CH_3}{\overset{\displaystyle H\diagdown C=O}{H-\!\!|\!\!-NH_2}} \quad \text{and} \quad \underset{\displaystyle CH_3}{\overset{\displaystyle H\diagdown C=O}{H_2N-\!\!|\!\!-H}}$$

14.37 Identify each of the following as the D or L stereoisomer:

a.
$$\underset{\displaystyle CH_3}{\overset{\displaystyle CH_2OH}{H-\!\!|\!\!-OH}}$$

b.
$$\underset{\displaystyle CH_3}{\overset{\displaystyle H\diagdown C=O}{H-\!\!|\!\!-OH}}$$

c.
$$\underset{\displaystyle CH_2OH}{\overset{\displaystyle H\diagdown C=O}{HO-\!\!|\!\!-H}}$$

14.38 Identify each of the following as the D or L stereoisomer:

a.
$$\underset{\displaystyle CH_2OH}{\overset{\displaystyle H\diagdown C=O}{HO-\!\!|\!\!-H}}$$

b.
$$\underset{\displaystyle CH_2OH}{\overset{\displaystyle H\diagdown C=O}{\genfrac{}{}{0pt}{}{HO-\!\!|\!\!-H}{HO-\!\!|\!\!-H}}}$$

c.
$$\underset{\displaystyle CH_2OH}{\overset{\displaystyle HO\diagdown C=O}{H-\!\!|\!\!-OH}}$$

Rx Clinical Applications

14.39 Identify the chiral carbon in each of the following naturally occurring compounds:

a. citronellol; one enantiomer has the geranium odor

$$CH_3-\overset{\overset{\displaystyle CH_3}{|}}{C}=CH-CH_2-CH_2-\overset{\overset{\displaystyle CH_3}{|}}{CH}-CH_2-CH_2-OH$$

b. alanine, an amino acid

$$H_2N-\overset{\overset{\displaystyle CH_3}{|}}{CH}-\overset{\overset{\displaystyle O}{||}}{C}-OH$$

14.40 Identify the chiral carbon in each of the following naturally occurring compounds:

a. amphetamine (Benzedrine), stimulant, used in the treatment of hyperactivity

$$\text{(benzene ring)}-CH_2-\overset{\overset{\displaystyle CH_3}{|}}{CH}-NH_2$$

b. norepinephrine, increases blood pressure and nerve transmission

$$\underset{\displaystyle HO}{\overset{\displaystyle HO}{\text{(benzene ring)}}}-\overset{\overset{\displaystyle OH}{|}}{CH}-CH_2-NH_2$$

Clinical Update
Diana's Skin Protection Plan

After six months, Diana returns to the dermatology office for a follow-up skin check. There has been no change in the skin where the mole was excised and no other moles were found that were suspicious. Margaret reminded Diana to limit her exposure to the sun, especially between 10 A.M. and 3 P.M., and to wear protective clothing, including a hat, a long-sleeved shirt, and pants that cover her legs. On all exposed skin, Margaret tells Diana to use broad-spectrum sunscreen with an SPF of at least 15 every day. Sunscreen absorbs UV light radiation when the skin is exposed to sunlight and thus helps protect against sunburn. The SPF (sun protection factor) number, which ranges from 2 to 100, gives the amount of time for protected skin to sunburn compared to the time for unprotected skin to sunburn. The principal ingredients in sunscreens are usually aromatic molecules with carbonyl groups such as oxybenzone and avobenzone.

Sunscreen absorbs UV light, which protects against sunburn.

Clinical Applications

14.41 Oxybenzone is an effective sunscreen whose structural formula is shown.
   a. What functional groups are in oxybenzone?
   b. What is the molecular formula and molar mass of oxybenzone?
   c. If a bottle of sunscreen containing 178 mL has 6.0% (m/v) oxybenzone, how many grams of oxybenzone are present?

14.42 Avobenzone is a common ingredient in sunscreen. Its structural formula is shown.
   a. What functional groups are in avobenzone?
   b. What is the molecular formula and molar mass of avobenzone?
   c. If a bottle of sunscreen containing 236 mL has 3.0% (m/v) avobenzone, how many grams of avobenzone are present?

Oxybenzone

Avobenzone

CONCEPT MAP

ALDEHYDES, KETONES, AND CHIRAL MOLECULES

with

Carbon–Oxygen Double Bonds

can be

Chiral Compounds

are

Aldehydes

Ketones

with

Mirror Images

test positive with

react to form

react to form

drawn as

Tollens' Test

1° Alcohols

Hemiacetals

2° Alcohols

Fischer Projections

Benedict's Test

Carboxylic Acids

Acetals

CHAPTER REVIEW

14.1 Aldehydes and Ketones

LEARNING GOAL Identify compounds with carbonyl groups as aldehydes and ketones. Write the IUPAC and common names for aldehydes and ketones; draw their condensed or line-angle structural formulas.

Carbonyl group

- Aldehydes and ketones contain a carbonyl group (C=O), which is strongly polar.
- In aldehydes, the carbonyl group appears at the end of carbon chains attached to at least one hydrogen atom.
- In ketones, the carbonyl group occurs between two alkyl or aromatic groups.
- In the IUPAC system, the *e* in the corresponding alkane name is replaced with *al* for aldehydes and *one* for ketones. For ketones with more than four carbon atoms in the main chain, the carbonyl group is numbered to show its location.
- Many of the simple aldehydes and ketones use common names.
- Many aldehydes and ketones are found in biological systems, flavorings, and drugs.

14.2 Physical Properties of Aldehydes and Ketones

LEARNING GOAL Describe the boiling points and solubilites of aldehydes and ketones.

Hydrogen bonds

Acetone

- The polar carbonyl group in aldehydes and ketones gives higher boiling points than alkanes.
- The boiling points of aldehydes and ketones are lower than alcohols because aldehydes and ketones cannot hydrogen bond with each other.
- Aldehydes and ketones form hydrogen bonds with water molecules, which makes carbonyl compounds with one to four carbon atoms soluble in water.

14.3 Oxidation and Reduction of Aldehydes and Ketones

LEARNING GOAL Draw the condensed or line-angle structural formulas for the reactants and products in the oxidation or reduction of aldehydes and ketones.

- Primary alcohols can be oxidized to aldehydes, whereas secondary alcohols can oxidize to ketones.

- Aldehydes are easily oxidized to carboxylic acids, but ketones do not oxidize further.
- Aldehydes, but not ketones, react with Tollens' reagent to give "silver mirrors."
- In Benedict's test, aldehydes with adjacent hydroxyl groups reduce blue Cu^{2+} to give a brick-red Cu_2O solid.
- The reduction of aldehydes with hydrogen produces primary alcohols, whereas ketones are reduced to secondary alcohols.

14.4 Hemiacetals and Acetals

LEARNING GOAL Draw the condensed or line-angle structural formulas for the products of the addition of alcohols to aldehydes and ketones.

- Alcohols can add to the carbonyl group of aldehydes and ketones.
- The addition of one alcohol molecule forms a hemiacetal, whereas the addition of two alcohol molecules forms an acetal.
- Hemiacetals are not usually stable, except for cyclic hemiacetals, which are the most common form of simple sugars such as glucose.

14.5 Chiral Molecules

LEARNING GOAL Identify chiral and achiral carbon atoms in an organic molecule.

- Chiral molecules are molecules with mirror images that cannot be superimposed on each other. These types of stereoisomers are called enantiomers.
- A chiral molecule must have at least one chiral carbon, which is a carbon bonded to four different atoms or groups of atoms.
- The Fischer projection is a simplified way to draw the arrangements of atoms by placing the carbon atoms at the intersection of vertical and horizontal lines.
- The mirror images are labeled D or L to differentiate between enantiomers.

SUMMARY OF NAMING

Family	Structure	IUPAC Name	Common Name
Aldehyde	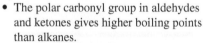	Methanal	Formaldehyde
Ketone	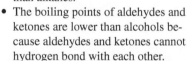	Propanone	Acetone; dimethyl ketone

SUMMARY OF REACTIONS

The chapter sections to review are shown after the name of the reaction.

Oxidation of Aldehydes to Form Carboxylic Acids (14.3)

$$CH_3-\underset{\underset{\text{Acetaldehyde}}{}}{\overset{\overset{O}{\|}}{C}}-H \xrightarrow{[O]} CH_3-\underset{\underset{\text{Acetic acid}}{}}{\overset{\overset{O}{\|}}{C}}-OH$$

Reduction of Aldehydes to Form Primary Alcohols (14.3)

$$CH_3-\underset{\underset{\text{Acetaldehyde}}{}}{\overset{\overset{O}{\|}}{C}}-H + H_2 \xrightarrow{Ni} CH_3-\underset{\underset{\text{Ethanol}}{}}{\overset{\overset{OH}{|}}{C}H_2}$$

Reduction of Ketones to Form Secondary Alcohols (14.3)

$$CH_3-\underset{\underset{\text{Acetone}}{}}{\overset{\overset{O}{\|}}{C}}-CH_3 + H_2 \xrightarrow{Ni} CH_3-\underset{\underset{\text{2-Propanol}}{}}{\overset{\overset{OH}{|}}{C}H}-CH_3$$

Addition of Alcohols to Form Hemiacetals and Acetals (14.4)

$$\underset{\text{Formaldehyde}}{H-\overset{\overset{O}{\|}}{C}-H} + \underset{\text{Methanol}}{HO-CH_3} \overset{H^+}{\rightleftharpoons} \underset{\text{Hemiacetal}}{H-\overset{\overset{O-CH_3}{|}}{\underset{\underset{OH}{|}}{C}}-H} + H_2O$$

$$\underset{\text{Hemiacetal}}{H-\overset{\overset{O-CH_3}{|}}{\underset{\underset{OH}{|}}{C}}-H} + HO-CH_3 \overset{H^+}{\rightleftharpoons} \underset{\text{Acetal}}{H-\overset{\overset{O-CH_3}{|}}{\underset{\underset{O-CH_3}{|}}{C}}-H} + H_2O$$

KEY TERMS

acetal The product of the addition of two alcohols to an aldehyde or ketone.

aldehyde An organic compound with a carbonyl functional group and at least one hydrogen attached to the carbon in the carbonyl group.

Benedict's test A test for aldehydes with adjacent hydroxyl groups in which Cu^{2+} $(CuSO_4)$ ions in Benedict's reagent are reduced to a brick-red solid of Cu_2O.

carbonyl group A group that has a carbon–oxygen double bond with two groups of atoms attached to the carbon at angles of 120°.

chiral Objects or molecules that have nonsuperimposable mirror images.

chiral carbon A carbon atom that is bonded to four different atoms or groups.

enantiomers Stereoisomers that are mirror images that cannot be superimposed.

Fischer projection A system for drawing stereoisomers; an intersection of a vertical and horizontal line represents a carbon atom. A vertical line represents bonds that project backwards from a carbon atom and a horizontal line represents bonds that project forward. The most highly oxidized carbon is at the top.

hemiacetal The product of the addition of one alcohol to the double bond of the carbonyl group in aldehydes and ketones.

ketone An organic compound in which the carbonyl functional group is bonded to two alkyl or aromatic groups.

reduction A decrease in the number of carbon–oxygen bonds by the addition of hydrogen to a carbonyl bond. Aldehydes are reduced to primary alcohols; ketones to secondary alcohols.

stereoisomers Isomers that have atoms bonded in the same order, but with different arrangements in space.

Tollens' test A test for aldehydes in which the Ag^+ in Tollens' reagent is reduced to metallic silver, which forms a "silver mirror" on the walls of the container.

⚛ CORE CHEMISTRY SKILLS

The chapter section containing each Core Chemistry Skill is shown in parentheses at the end of each heading.

Naming Aldehydes and Ketones (14.1)

- In the IUPAC system, an aldehyde is named by replacing the *e* in the alkane name with *al* and a ketone by replacing the *e* with *one*.
- The position of a substituent on an aldehyde is indicated by numbering the carbon chain from the carbonyl group and given in front of the name.
- For a ketone, the carbon chain is numbered from the end nearer the carbonyl group.

Example: Give the IUPAC name for the following:

$$CH_3-\overset{\overset{CH_3}{|}}{C}H-CH_2-\overset{\overset{O}{\|}}{C}-CH_3$$

Answer: 4-methyl-2-pentanone

Identifying Chiral Molecules (14.5)

- Chiral molecules are molecules with mirror images that cannot be superimposed on each other. These types of stereoisomers are called enantiomers.

- A chiral molecule must have at least one chiral carbon, which is a carbon bonded to four different atoms or groups of atoms.

Example: Identify each of the following as chiral or achiral:

a. $CH_3 - CH_2 - \overset{\overset{\displaystyle Br}{|}}{CH} - CH_3$

b. $CH_3 - CH_2 - CH_2 - Br$

c. $CH_3 - \overset{\overset{\displaystyle Br}{|}}{CH} - CH_3$

Answer: Molecule **a** is chiral; molecules **b** and **c** are achiral.

Identifying D- and L-Fischer Projections (14.5)

- The Fischer projection is a simplified way to draw the arrangements of atoms by placing the carbon atoms at the intersection of vertical and horizontal lines.

- The names of the mirror images are labeled D or L to differentiate between enantiomers of carbohydrates.

Example: Identify each of the following as the D or L stereoisomer:

a.
$$\begin{array}{c} H \diagdown O \\ C \\ HO - \!\!\!\mid\!\!\! - H \\ H - \!\!\!\mid\!\!\! - OH \\ CH_2OH \end{array}$$

b.
$$\begin{array}{c} CH_2OH \\ | \\ C = O \\ HO - \!\!\!\mid\!\!\! - H \\ HO - \!\!\!\mid\!\!\! - H \\ CH_2OH \end{array}$$

Answer: In **a**, the —OH group on the chiral carbon farthest from the carbonyl group is on the right; it is the D stereoisomer. In **b**, the —OH group on the chiral carbon farthest from the carbonyl group is on the left; it is the L stereoisomer.

UNDERSTANDING THE CONCEPTS

The chapter sections to review are shown in parentheses at the end of each question.

14.43 The compound cinnamaldehyde gives the flavor to cinnamon. Identify the functional groups in cinnamaldehyde. (14.1)

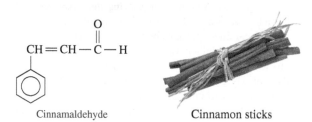

Cinnamaldehyde   Cinnamon sticks

14.44 The compound frambinone has the taste of raspberries and has been used in weight loss. Identify the functional groups in frambinone. (14.1)

$$HO - \!\!\!\!\bigcirc\!\!\!\! - CH_2 - CH_2 - \overset{\overset{\displaystyle O}{||}}{C} - CH_3$$

Frambinone

14.45 Draw the condensed and line-angle structural formulas for each of the following: (14.1)
a. *trans*-2-hexenal, alarm pheromone of ants
b. 2,6-dimethyl-5-heptenal, communication pheromone of ants

14.46 Draw the condensed structural and line-angle structural formulas for each of the following: (14.1)
a. 4-methyl-3-heptanone, ant trail pheromone
b. 2-nonanone, moth sex attractant pheromone

14.47 Why does the C=O double bond have a dipole, whereas the C=C double bond does not? (14.1)

14.48 Why are aldehydes and ketones with one to four carbon atoms soluble in water? (14.2)

14.49 Which of the following will give a positive Tollens' test? (14.3)

a. $CH_3 - CH_2 - \overset{\overset{\displaystyle O}{||}}{C} - H$ b. $CH_3 - \overset{\overset{\displaystyle CH_3}{|}}{CH} - \overset{\overset{\displaystyle O}{||}}{C} - H$

c. $CH_3 - O - CH_2 - CH_3$

14.50 Which of the following will give a positive Tollens' test? (14.3)

a. $CH_3 - CH_2 - CH_2 - OH$ b. $CH_3 - \overset{\overset{\displaystyle OH}{|}}{CH} - CH_3$

c. $\underset{\triangle}{\overset{\overset{\displaystyle O}{||}}{\underset{}{C} - H}}$

ADDITIONAL QUESTIONS AND PROBLEMS

14.51 Give the IUPAC name for each of the following compounds: (14.1)

a.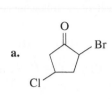

b.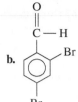

c. $Cl-CH_2-CH_2-\overset{\overset{\displaystyle O}{\|}}{C}-H$

d. (structure with Cl)

e. $CH_3-CH_2-\overset{\overset{\displaystyle O}{\|}}{C}-CH_2-\overset{\overset{\displaystyle Cl}{|}}{CH}-CH_3$

14.52 Give the IUPAC name for each of the following compounds: (14.1)

a. (structure)

b. (structure with Cl)

c.

d. $CH_3-\overset{\overset{\displaystyle CH_3}{|}}{CH}-\overset{\overset{\displaystyle CH_3}{|}}{CH}-CH_2-\overset{\overset{\displaystyle O}{\|}}{C}-H$

e. (structure)

14.53 Draw the condensed structural formula or line-angle structural formula, if cyclic, for each of the following: (14.1)
a. 3-methylcyclopentanone
b. pentanal
c. ethyl methyl ketone
d. 4-methylhexanal
e. 4-oxopentanal

14.54 Draw the condensed structural formula or line-angle structural formula, if cyclic, for each of the following: (14.1)
a. 2-chlorobutanal
b. 2-methylcyclohexanone
c. 3,5-dimethylhexanal
d. 3-bromocyclopentanone
e. 4-hydroxy-2-pentanone

14.55 Which of the following aldehydes or ketones are soluble in water? (14.2)

a. $CH_3-CH_2-\overset{\overset{\displaystyle O}{\|}}{C}-H$

b. $CH_3-\overset{\overset{\displaystyle O}{\|}}{C}-CH_3$

c. $CH_3-CH_2-\overset{\overset{\displaystyle O}{\|}}{C}-CH_2-CH_2-CH_3$

14.56 Which of the following aldehydes or ketones are soluble in water? (14.2)

a. $CH_3-CH_2-\overset{\overset{\displaystyle O}{\|}}{C}-CH_3$

b. $CH_3-\overset{\overset{\displaystyle O}{\|}}{C}-H$

c. $CH_3-CH_2-\overset{\overset{\displaystyle CH_3}{|}}{CH}-CH_2-\overset{\overset{\displaystyle O}{\|}}{C}-H$

14.57 In each of the following pairs of compounds, select the compound with the higher boiling point: (14.2)

a. $CH_3-CH_2-CH_2-OH$ or $CH_3-\overset{\overset{\displaystyle O}{\|}}{C}-CH_3$

b. $CH_3-CH_2-CH_2-CH_3$ or $CH_3-CH_2-\overset{\overset{\displaystyle O}{\|}}{C}-H$

c. CH_3-CH_2-OH or $CH_3-\overset{\overset{\displaystyle O}{\|}}{C}-H$

14.58 In each of the following pairs of compounds, select the compound with the higher boiling point: (14.2)

a. $CH_3-\overset{\overset{\displaystyle O}{\|}}{C}-H$ or $CH_3-CH_2-CH_2-CH_2-\overset{\overset{\displaystyle O}{\|}}{C}-H$

b. $CH_3-CH_2-\overset{\overset{\displaystyle O}{\|}}{C}-H$ or $CH_3-\overset{\overset{\displaystyle OH}{|}}{CH}-CH_3$

c. $CH_3-CH_2-CH_2-CH_3$ or $CH_3-\overset{\overset{\displaystyle O}{\|}}{C}-CH_3$

14.59 Draw the condensed structural formula for the product, if any, when each of the following is oxidized: (14.3)

a. $CH_3-CH_2-\overset{\overset{\displaystyle O}{\|}}{C}-H$ b. $CH_3-CH_2-CH_2-\overset{\overset{\displaystyle O}{\|}}{C}-H$

c.

14.60 Draw the condensed structural formula for the product, if any, when each of the following is oxidized: (14.3)

a. $CH_3-CH_2-\overset{\overset{\displaystyle O}{\|}}{C}-CH_3$

b. (structure)

c. $CH_3-\overset{\overset{\displaystyle CH_3}{|}}{CH}-CH_2-\overset{\overset{\displaystyle O}{\|}}{C}-H$

14.61 Draw the condensed structural formula for the product when hydrogen and a nickel catalyst reduce each of the following: (14.3)

a. $CH_3 - \overset{\overset{\displaystyle O}{\|}}{C} - CH_3$ b. $CH_2 - \overset{\overset{\displaystyle O}{\|}}{C} - H$

c. $CH_3 - \overset{\overset{\displaystyle CH_3}{|}}{CH} - CH_2 - \overset{\overset{\displaystyle O}{\|}}{C} - CH_3$

14.62 Draw the condensed structural formula for the product when $NaBH_4$ reduces each of the following: (14.3)

a. $CH_3 - \overset{\overset{\displaystyle O}{\|}}{C} - H$ b. (cyclopentanone with methyl group)

c. $H - \overset{\overset{\displaystyle O}{\|}}{C} - H$

14.63 Give the name of the alcohol, aldehyde, or ketone produced from each of the following reactions: (14.3)
  a. oxidation of 1-propanol
  b. oxidation of 2-pentanol
  c. reduction of butanone
  d. oxidation of cyclohexanol

14.64 Give the name of the alcohol, aldehyde, or ketone produced from each of the following reactions: (14.3)
  a. reduction of butyraldehyde
  b. oxidation of 3-methyl-2-pentanol
  c. reduction of 4-methyl-2-hexanone
  d. oxidation of 3-methylcyclopentanol

14.65 Identify the following as hemiacetals or acetals. Give the IUPAC names of the carbonyl compounds and alcohols used in their synthesis. (14.4)

a. $CH_3 - CH_2 - \overset{\overset{\displaystyle O-CH_3}{|}}{\underset{\underset{\displaystyle O-CH_3}{|}}{C}} - H$

b. $CH_3 - CH_2 - \overset{\overset{\displaystyle O-CH_2-CH_3}{|}}{\underset{\underset{\displaystyle OH}{|}}{C}} - CH_3$

c. $CH_3 - CH_2 - O \diagdown \diagup O - CH_2 - CH_3$ (cyclohexane ring)

14.66 Identify the following as hemiacetals or acetals. Give the IUPAC names of the carbonyl compounds and alcohols used in their synthesis. (14.4)

a. $CH_3 - CH_2 - \overset{\overset{\displaystyle O-CH_3}{|}}{\underset{\underset{\displaystyle OH}{|}}{C}} - H$ b. $HO \diagdown \diagup O - \overset{\overset{\displaystyle CH_3}{|}}{CH} - CH_3$ (cyclohexane ring)

c. $CH_3 - \overset{\overset{\displaystyle O-CH_2-CH_2-CH_3}{|}}{\underset{\underset{\displaystyle O-CH_2-CH_2-CH_3}{|}}{C}} - H$

14.67 Circle the chiral carbons, if any, in each of the following compounds: (14.5)

a. $H - \overset{\overset{\displaystyle Cl}{|}}{\underset{\underset{\displaystyle Cl}{|}}{C}} - \overset{\overset{\displaystyle Cl}{|}}{\underset{\underset{\displaystyle H}{|}}{C}} - OH$ b. $CH_3 - \overset{\overset{\displaystyle H}{|}}{C} = \overset{\overset{\displaystyle CH_3}{|}}{C} - CH_3$

c. $HO - CH_2 - \overset{\overset{\displaystyle OH}{|}}{CH} - CH_2 - OH$

d. $CH_3 - \overset{\overset{\displaystyle NH_2}{|}}{CH} - \overset{\overset{\displaystyle O}{\|}}{C} - H$

e. $CH_3 - CH_2 - \overset{\overset{\displaystyle Br}{|}}{CH} - CH_2 - CH_2 - CH_3$ f. (cyclohexane with OH)

14.68 Circle the chiral carbons, if any, in each of the following compounds: (14.5)

a. $CH_3 - \overset{\overset{\displaystyle O-CH_3}{|}}{CH} - CH_3$ b. $CH_3 - \overset{\overset{\displaystyle OH}{|}}{CH} - \overset{\overset{\displaystyle O}{\|}}{C} - CH_3$

c. $CH_3 - \overset{\overset{\displaystyle OH}{|}}{\underset{\underset{\displaystyle OH}{|}}{C}} - H$ d. $CH_3 - \overset{\overset{\displaystyle CH_3}{|}}{CH} - \overset{\overset{\displaystyle O}{\|}}{C} - CH_3$

e. $CH_3 - \overset{\overset{\displaystyle Br}{|}}{\underset{\underset{\displaystyle OH}{|}}{C}} - CH_2 - CH_3$ f. (cyclohexane with Cl at two positions)

14.69 Identify each of the following pairs of Fischer projections as enantiomers or identical compounds: (14.5)

a.
```
   CH2OH              CH2OH
H ─┼─ OH    and   HO ─┼─ H
   CH2OH              CH2OH
```

b.
```
  H   O              H   O
   \\ //              \\ //
    C                 C
H ─┼─ OH   and   HO ─┼─ H
   CH2OH             CH2OH
```

c.
```
   CH2OH              CH2OH
Cl ─┼─ H    and   H ─┼─ Cl
   CH3               CH3
```

d.
```
   OH                OH
H ─┼─ OH    and   HO ─┼─ H
   CH3               CH3
```

14.70 Identify each of the following pairs of Fischer projections as enantiomers or identical compounds: (14.5)

a.
$$CH_2OH$$
$$H \!-\!\!\mid\!\!-\! Cl$$
$$CH_2CH_3$$
and
$$CH_2OH$$
$$Cl \!-\!\!\mid\!\!-\! H$$
$$CH_2CH_3$$

c.
$$CH_2OH$$
$$H \!-\!\!\mid\!\!-\! Cl$$
$$CH_3$$
and
$$CH_2OH$$
$$H \!-\!\!\mid\!\!-\! Cl$$
$$CH_3$$

b.
$$CH_2OH$$
$$H \!-\!\!\mid\!\!-\! OH$$
$$CH_3$$
and
$$CH_2OH$$
$$HO \!-\!\!\mid\!\!-\! H$$
$$CH_3$$

d.
$$H{-}C{=}O$$
$$H \!-\!\!\mid\!\!-\! OH$$
$$CH_3$$
and
$$H{-}C{=}O$$
$$HO \!-\!\!\mid\!\!-\! H$$
$$CH_3$$

CHALLENGE QUESTIONS

The following groups of questions are related to the topics in this chapter. However, they do not all follow the chapter order, and they require you to combine concepts and skills from several sections. These questions will help you increase your critical thinking skills and prepare for your next exam.

Use the following condensed and line-angle structural formulas **A** to **F** to answer problems 14.71 and 14.72: (14.1, 14.5)

A $CH_3-CH_2-\overset{\displaystyle O}{\overset{\|}{C}}-CH_2-CH_3$

B $CH_3-CH_2-CH_2-\overset{\displaystyle O}{\overset{\|}{C}}-CH_3$

C $CH_3-\overset{\displaystyle O}{\overset{\|}{C}}-CH_2-CH_2-CH_3$

D $CH_3-CH_2-CH_2-CH_2-\overset{\displaystyle O}{\overset{\|}{C}}-H$

E (cyclopentanone, line-angle structure)

F (cyclobutane with $\overset{\displaystyle O}{\overset{\|}{C}}-H$ group)

14.71 True or False?
a. **A** and **B** are structural isomers.
b. **D** and **F** are aldehydes.
c. **B** and **C** are the same compound.
d. **C** and **D** are structural isomers.

14.72 True or False?
a. **E** and **F** are structural isomers.
b. **A** is chiral.
c. **A** and **C** are the same compound.
d. **B** and **E** are ketones.

14.73 A compound with the formula C_4H_8O is made by oxidation of 2-butanol and cannot be oxidized further. Draw the condensed structural formula and give the IUPAC name for the compound. (14.1, 14.3)

14.74 A compound with the formula C_4H_8O is made by oxidation of 2-methyl-1-propanol and oxidizes easily to give a carboxylic acid. Draw the condensed structural formula and give the IUPAC name for the compound. (14.1, 14.3)

14.75 Draw the condensed structural formulas and give the IUPAC names for all the aldehydes and ketones that have the molecular formula C_4H_8O. (14.1)

14.76 Draw the condensed structural formulas and give the IUPAC names for all the aldehydes and ketones that have the molecular formula $C_5H_{10}O$. (14.1)

14.77 The common name of compound **A** is propyl alcohol. When compound **A** is heated with a strong acid, it dehydrates to form compound **B** (C_3H_6). When compound **A** is oxidized, compound **C** (C_3H_6O) forms. Draw the condensed structural formulas and give the IUPAC names for compounds **A**, **B**, and **C**. (14.1, 14.3)

14.78 The common name of compound **X** is isopropyl alcohol. When compound **X** is heated with a strong acid, it dehydrates to form compound **Y** (C_3H_6). When compound **X** is oxidized, compound **Z** (C_3H_6O) forms, which cannot be oxidized further. Draw the condensed structural formulas and give the IUPAC names for compounds **X**, **Y**, and **Z**. (14.1, 14.3)

ANSWERS

Answers to Selected Questions and Problems

14.1 a. ketone
   c. ketone
   b. aldehyde
   d. aldehyde

14.3 a. structural isomers of C_3H_6O
   b. structural isomers of $C_5H_{10}O$
   c. not structural isomers

14.5 a. 3-bromobutanal
   c. 2-methylcyclopentanone
   b. 4-hydroxy-2-pentanone
   d. 3-bromobenzaldehyde

14.7 a. acetaldehyde
   c. formaldehyde
   b. methyl propyl ketone

14.9 a. $CH_3-\overset{\displaystyle O}{\overset{\|}{C}}-H$ (line-angle structure of acetaldehyde)

b. $CH_3-\overset{\displaystyle CH_3}{\overset{|}{C}H}-\overset{\displaystyle O}{\overset{\|}{C}}-CH_2-CH_3$ (line-angle structure)

c. $CH_3-\overset{\displaystyle O}{\overset{\|}{C}}-CH_2-CH_2-CH_2-CH_3$ (line-angle structure)

d. 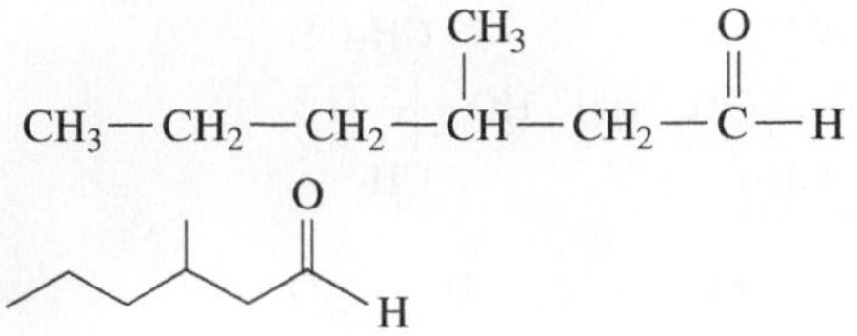 $CH_3-CH_2-CH_2-\overset{\overset{\displaystyle CH_3}{|}}{CH}-CH_2-\overset{\overset{\displaystyle O}{||}}{C}-H$

(structure: chain with O branch and H)

14.11

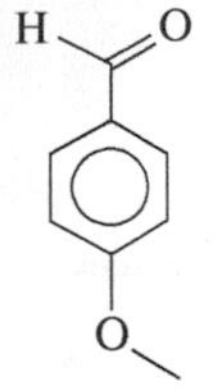

(structure: benzaldehyde with methoxy substituent, H—C=O on ring, O— substituent)

14.13 a. 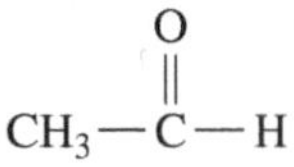 $CH_3-\overset{\overset{\displaystyle O}{||}}{C}-H$

Ethanal has a higher boiling point than propane because the polar carbonyl group in ethanal forms dipole–dipole attractions.
b. Pentanal has a longer carbon chain, more electrons, and more dispersion forces, which give it a higher boiling point.
c. 1-Butanol has a higher boiling point because it can hydrogen bond with other 1-butanol molecules.

14.15 a. 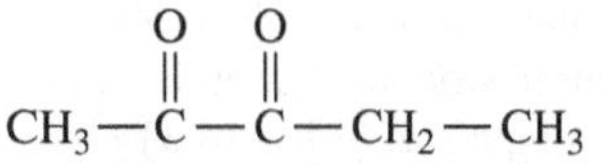 $CH_3-\overset{\overset{\displaystyle O}{||}}{C}-\overset{\overset{\displaystyle O}{||}}{C}-CH_2-CH_3$ has two polar carbonyl groups and can form more hydrogen bonds with water.
b. Propanal has a shorter carbon chain than pentanal, in which the larger hydrocarbon chain reduces the impact on solubility of the polar carbonyl group.
c. Acetone has a shorter carbon chain than 2-pentanone, in which the larger hydrocarbon chain reduces the impact on solubility of the polar carbonyl group.

14.17 No. A hydrocarbon chain of eight carbon atoms reduces the impact on solubility of the polar carbonyl group.

14.19 a. 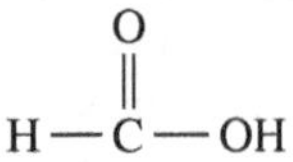 $H-\overset{\overset{\displaystyle O}{||}}{C}-OH$ **b.** none

c. 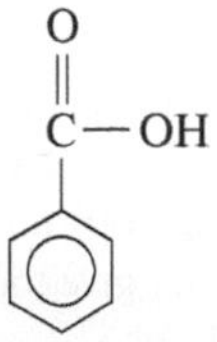 (benzoic acid: ring with $\overset{\overset{\displaystyle O}{||}}{C}-OH$)   **d.** none

14.21 a. Tollens' reagent   **b.** neither   **c.** both
14.23 a. $CH_3-CH_2-CH_2-CH_2-OH$
b. 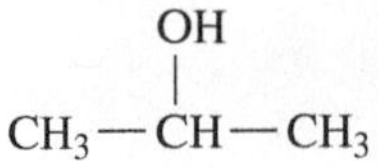 $CH_3-\overset{\overset{\displaystyle OH}{|}}{CH}-CH_3$
c. 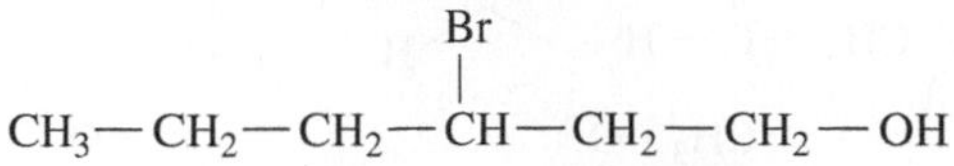 $CH_3-CH_2-CH_2-\overset{\overset{\displaystyle Br}{|}}{CH}-CH_2-CH_2-OH$
d. 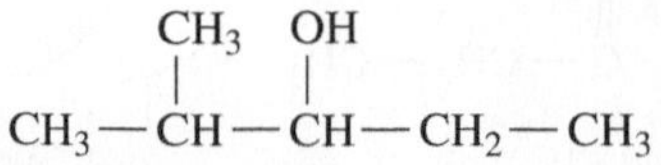 $CH_3-\overset{\overset{\displaystyle CH_3}{|}}{CH}-\overset{\overset{\displaystyle OH}{|}}{CH}-CH_2-CH_3$

14.25 a. hemiacetal   **b.** hemiacetal   **c.** acetal
d. hemiacetal
e. acetal

14.27 a. 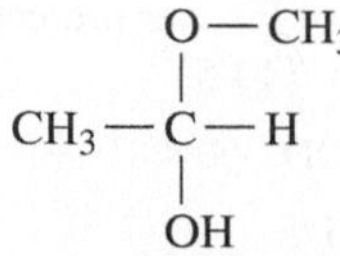 $CH_3-\overset{\overset{\displaystyle O-CH_3}{|}}{\underset{\underset{\displaystyle OH}{|}}{C}}-H$ **b.** $CH_3-\overset{\overset{\displaystyle O-CH_3}{|}}{\underset{\underset{\displaystyle OH}{|}}{C}}-CH_3$

c. $CH_3-CH_2-CH_2-\overset{\overset{\displaystyle O-CH_3}{|}}{\underset{\underset{\displaystyle OH}{|}}{C}}-H$

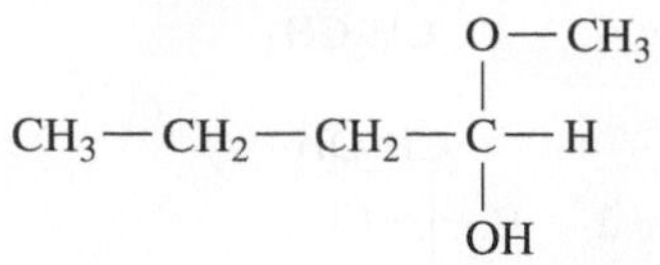

14.29 a. 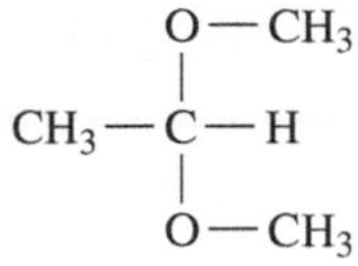 $CH_3-\overset{\overset{\displaystyle O-CH_3}{|}}{\underset{\underset{\displaystyle O-CH_3}{|}}{C}}-H$ **b.** $CH_3-\overset{\overset{\displaystyle O-CH_3}{|}}{\underset{\underset{\displaystyle O-CH_3}{|}}{C}}-CH_3$

c. $CH_3-CH_2-CH_2-\overset{\overset{\displaystyle O-CH_3}{|}}{\underset{\underset{\displaystyle O-CH_3}{|}}{C}}-H$

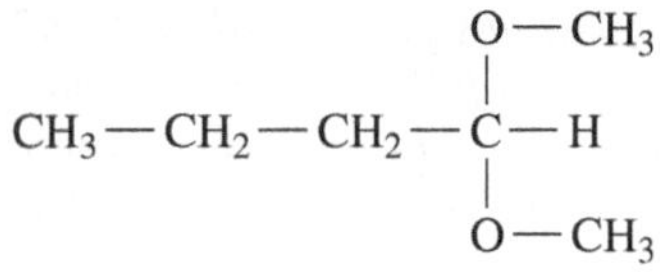

14.31 a. achiral
b. chiral

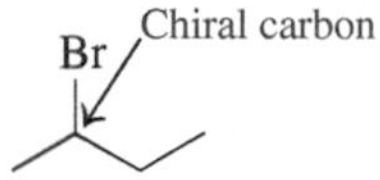

(structure with Br, labeled "Chiral carbon")

c. chiral

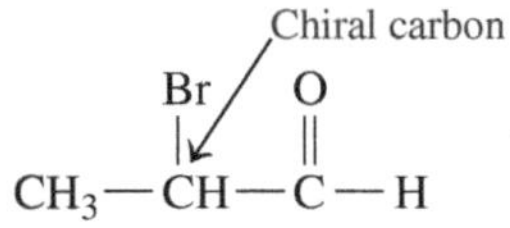

(structure $CH_3-CH-\overset{\overset{\displaystyle O}{||}}{C}-H$ with Br, labeled "Chiral carbon")

d. achiral

14.33 a. 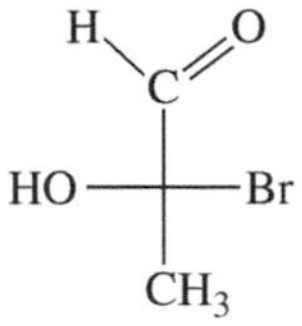 (Fischer projection: H—C=O top, HO—|—Br, CH_3 bottom)   **b.** (Fischer projection: H—C=O top, Cl—|—Br, OH bottom)

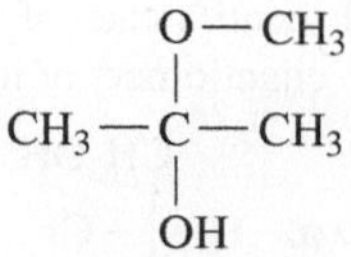

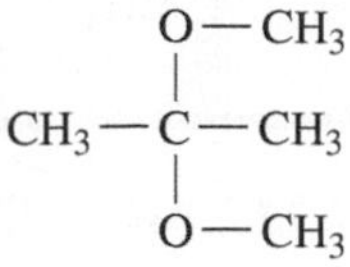

c. (Fischer projection: H—C=O top, HO—|—H, CH_2CH_3 bottom)

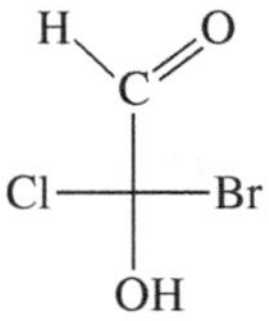

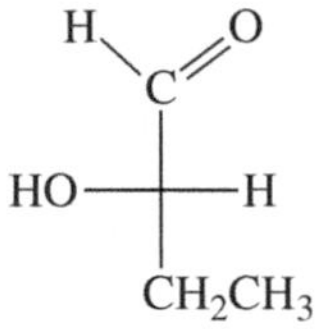

14.35 a. identical   **b.** enantiomers
c. enantiomers   **d.** enantiomers

14.37 a. D   **b.** D   **c.** L

14.39 a. 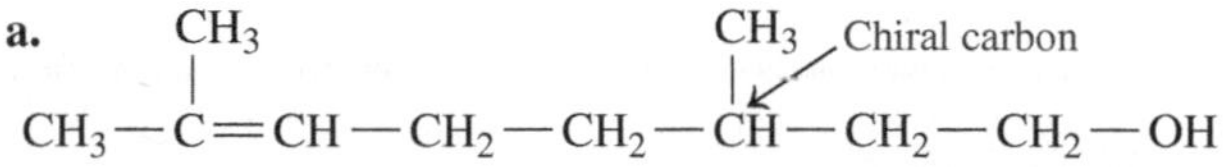 $CH_3-\overset{\overset{\displaystyle CH_3}{|}}{C}=CH-CH_2-CH_2-\overset{\overset{\displaystyle CH_3}{|}}{CH}-CH_2-CH_2-OH$ (labeled "Chiral carbon")

b. 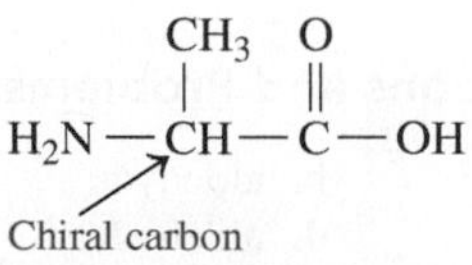 $H_2N-\overset{\overset{\displaystyle CH_3}{|}}{CH}-\overset{\overset{\displaystyle O}{||}}{C}-OH$ (labeled "Chiral carbon")

14.41 a. ether, phenol, ketone, aromatic
b. $C_{14}H_{12}O_3$, 228.2 g/mole
c. 10.7 g of oxybenzone

14.43 aromatic, alkene, aldehyde

14.45 a.

$$CH_3-CH_2-CH_2-\overset{\displaystyle H}{\underset{\displaystyle C=C}{}}-\overset{\displaystyle \overset{\text{O}}{\|}}{\underset{\displaystyle H}{C}}-H$$

b.

(structure: hexenal — carbon chain with C=C double bond and terminal CHO group)

$$CH_3-\overset{\displaystyle CH_3}{\underset{\displaystyle |}{C}}=CH-CH_2-CH_2-\overset{\displaystyle CH_3}{\underset{\displaystyle |}{CH}}-\overset{\displaystyle \overset{\text{O}}{\|}}{C}-H$$

(structure: branched chain with C=C double bond and terminal CHO group)

14.47 The C=O double bond has a dipole because the oxygen atom is highly electronegative compared to the carbon atom. In the C=C double bond, both atoms have the same electronegativity, and there is no dipole.

14.49 a and b

14.51 a. 2-bromo-4-chlorocyclopentanone
b. 2,4-dibromobenzaldehyde
c. 3-chloropropanal
d. 2-chloro-3-pentanone
e. 5-chloro-3-hexanone

14.53 a.

(structure: 3-methylcyclopentanone)

b. $CH_3-CH_2-CH_2-CH_2-\overset{\displaystyle \overset{\text{O}}{\|}}{C}-H$

c. $CH_3-CH_2-\overset{\displaystyle \overset{\text{O}}{\|}}{C}-CH_3$

d. $CH_3-CH_2-\overset{\displaystyle CH_3}{\underset{\displaystyle |}{CH}}-CH_2-CH_2-\overset{\displaystyle \overset{\text{O}}{\|}}{C}-H$

e. $CH_3-\overset{\displaystyle \overset{\text{O}}{\|}}{C}-CH_2-CH_2-\overset{\displaystyle \overset{\text{O}}{\|}}{C}-H$

14.55 a and b

14.57 a. $CH_3-CH_2-CH_2-OH$ **b.** $CH_3-CH_2-\overset{\displaystyle \overset{\text{O}}{\|}}{C}-H$
c. CH_3-CH_2-OH

14.59 a. $CH_3-CH_2-\overset{\displaystyle \overset{\text{O}}{\|}}{C}-OH$

b. $CH_3-CH_2-CH_2-\overset{\displaystyle \overset{\text{O}}{\|}}{C}-OH$

c. no reaction

14.61 a. $CH_3-\overset{\displaystyle OH}{\underset{\displaystyle |}{CH}}-CH_3$

b. (benzene ring)$-CH_2-CH_2-OH$

c. $CH_3-\overset{\displaystyle CH_3}{\underset{\displaystyle |}{CH}}-CH_2-\overset{\displaystyle OH}{\underset{\displaystyle |}{CH}}-CH_3$

14.63 a. propanal   **b.** 2-pentanone
c. 2-butanol   **d.** cyclohexanone

14.65 a. acetal; propanal and methanol
b. hemiacetal; butanone and ethanol
c. acetal; cyclohexanone and ethanol

14.67 a. $H-\overset{\displaystyle Cl}{\underset{\displaystyle Cl}{C}}-\overset{*}{\underset{\displaystyle H}{\underset{\displaystyle |}{\overset{\displaystyle Cl}{C}}}}-OH$ **b.** none

c. none   **d.** $CH_3-\overset{*}{CH}-\overset{\displaystyle \overset{\text{O}}{\|}}{C}-H$ (with NH_2 on the starred carbon)

e. $CH_3-CH_2-\overset{*}{\underset{\displaystyle Br}{CH}}-CH_2-CH_2-CH_3$
f. none

14.69 a. identical   **b.** enantiomers
c. enantiomers   **d.** identical

14.71 a. true   **b.** false   **c.** true   **d.** true

14.73 $CH_3-\overset{\displaystyle \overset{\text{O}}{\|}}{C}-CH_2-CH_3$ butanone

14.75 $CH_3-CH_2-CH_2-\overset{\displaystyle \overset{\text{O}}{\|}}{C}-H$ butanal

$CH_3-\overset{\displaystyle CH_3}{\underset{\displaystyle |}{CH}}-\overset{\displaystyle \overset{\text{O}}{\|}}{C}-H$ 2-methylpropanal

$CH_3-\overset{\displaystyle \overset{\text{O}}{\|}}{C}-CH_2-CH_3$ butanone

14.77 a. $CH_3-CH_2-CH_2-OH$ 1-propanol
b. $CH_3-CH=CH_2$ propene

c. $CH_3-CH_2-\overset{\displaystyle \overset{\text{O}}{\|}}{C}-H$ propanal

CI.27 A compound called butylated hydroxytoluene, or BHT, has been added to cereal and other foods since 1947 as an antioxidant. A common name for BHT is 2,6-di-*tert*-butyl-4-methylphenol. (2.6, 7.4, 7.5, 13.1)

a. Draw the line-angle structural formula for BHT.
b. BHT is produced from 4-methylphenol and 2-methylpropene. Draw the line-angle structural formulas for these reactants.
c. What are the molecular formula and molar mass of BHT?
d. The FDA (Food and Drug Administration) allows a maximum of 50. ppm of BHT added to cereal. How many milligrams of BHT could be added to a box of cereal that contains 15 oz of dry cereal?

CI.28 Used in sunless tanning lotions, the compound 1,3-dihydroxypropanone, or dihydroxyacetone (DHA), darkens the skin without exposure to sunlight. DHA reacts with amino acids in the outer surface of the skin. A typical drugstore lotion contains 4.0% (m/v) DHA. (2.6, 7.4, 7.5, 14.1)

A sunless tanning lotion contains DHA to darken the skin.

a. Draw the condensed structural formula for DHA.
b. What are the functional groups in DHA?
c. What are the molecular formula and molar mass of DHA?
d. A bottle of sunless tanning lotion contains 200 mL of lotion. How many milligrams of DHA are in a bottle?

CI.29 Acetone (propanone), a clear liquid solvent with an acrid odor, is used to remove nail polish, paints, and resins. It has a low boiling point and is highly flammable. (7.4, 7.5, 13.4, 14.1)

Acetone is a solvent used in polish remover.

a. Draw the condensed structural formula for propanone.
b. What are the molecular formula and molar mass of propanone?
c. Draw the condensed structural formula for the alcohol that can be oxidized to produce propanone.

CI.30 Acetone (propanone) has a density of 0.786 g/mL and a heat of combustion of 428 kcal/mole. Use your answers to problem CI.29 to solve the following: (7.1, 7.6, 7.9, 8.6, 14.1)
a. Write the equation for the complete combustion of propanone.
b. How much heat, in kilojoules, is released if 2.58 g of propanone reacts with oxygen?
c. How many grams of oxygen gas are needed to react with 15.0 mL of propanone?
d. How many liters of carbon dioxide gas are produced at STP in part c?

CI.31 One of the components of gasoline is octane, C_8H_{18}, which has a density of 0.803 g/mL. The combustion of 1 mole of octane provides 5510 kJ. A hybrid car has a fuel tank with a capacity of 11.9 gal and a gas mileage of 45 mi/gal. (2.6, 7.1, 7.5, 7.7, 7.9, 12.2)

Octane is one of the components of gasoline.

a. Write the balanced chemical equation for the combustion of octane.
b. Is the combustion of octane endothermic or exothermic?
c. How many moles of octane are in one tank of fuel, assuming it is all octane?
d. If the total mileage of this hybrid car for one year is 24 500 mi, how many kilograms of carbon dioxide would be produced from the combustion of the fuel, assuming it is all octane?

CI.32 Ionone is a compound that gives sweet violets their aroma. The small edible purple flowers of violets are used in salads and to make teas. An antioxidant called anthocyanin produces the blue and purple colors of violets. Liquid ionone has a density of 0.935 g/mL. (7.4, 7.7, 7.9, 8.6, 12.6, 13.1, 14.1)

Ionone

The aroma of violets is because of ionone.

a. What functional groups are present in ionone?
b. Is the double bond on the side chain cis or trans?
c. What are the molecular formula and molar mass of ionone?
d. How many moles are in 2.00 mL of ionone?
e. When ionone reacts with hydrogen in the presence of a platinum catalyst, hydrogen adds to the double bonds and converts the ketone group to an alcohol. What is the condensed structural formula and molecular formula for the product?
f. How many milliliters of hydrogen gas are needed at STP to completely react 5.0 mL of ionone?

CI.33 Butyraldehyde is a clear liquid solvent with an unpleasant odor. It has a low boiling point and is highly flammable. (14.1, 14.3)

The unpleasant odor of old gym socks is because of butyraldehyde.

a. Draw the condensed structural formula for butyraldehyde.
b. Draw the line-angle structural formula for butyraldehyde.
c. What is the IUPAC name of butyraldehyde?
d. Draw the condensed structural formula for the alcohol that is produced when butyraldehyde is reduced.

CI.34 Butyraldehyde has a density of 0.802 g/mL and a heat of combustion of 1520 kJ/mole. Use your answers to problem CI.33 to solve the following: (7.1, 7.7, 7.9, 8.6)
a. Write the balanced equation for the complete combustion of butyraldehyde.
b. How many grams of oxygen gas are needed to completely react 15.0 mL of butyraldehyde?
c. How many liters of carbon dioxide gas are produced at STP in part **b**?
d. Calculate the heat, in kilojoules, that is released from the combustion of butyraldehyde in part **b**.

ANSWERS

CI.27 a.

OH

b.

OH

4-Methylphenol

2-Methylpropene

c. $C_{15}H_{24}O$, 220.4 g/mole   **d.** 21 mg

CI.29 a. $CH_3 - \overset{\overset{\displaystyle O}{\|}}{C} - CH_3$

b. C_3H_6O, 58.08 g/mole

c. $CH_3 - \overset{\overset{\displaystyle OH}{|}}{CH} - CH_3$

CI.31 a. $2C_8H_{18}(l) + 25O_2(g) \overset{\Delta}{\longrightarrow}$
$16CO_2(g) + 18H_2O(g) + 11\ 020\ kJ$

b. exothermic
c. 317 moles of octane
d. 5.10×10^3 kg of CO_2

CI.33 a. $CH_3 - CH_2 - CH_2 - \overset{\overset{\displaystyle O}{\|}}{C} - H$

b.

c. butanal
d. $CH_3 - CH_2 - CH_2 - CH_2 - OH$

15

Carbohydrates

DURING HER ANNUAL PHYSICAL EXAMINATION,

Kate, a 64-year old woman, reported that she was bothered by blurry vision, frequent need to urinate, and in the past year she had gained 22 lb. She had tried to lose weight and increase her exercise for the past 6 months without success. Her diet was high in carbohydrates. For dinner, Kate typically ate two cups of pasta and three to four slices of bread with butter or olive oil. She also ate eight to ten pieces of fresh fruit per day at meals and as snacks. A physical examination showed that her fasting blood glucose level was 178 mg/dL, indicating type 2 diabetes. She was referred to the diabetes specialty clinic, where she met Paula, a diabetic nurse. Paula explained to Kate that complex carbohydrates are long chains of glucose molecules that we obtain from ingesting breads and grains. They are broken down in the body into glucose, which is a simple carbohydrate or a monosaccharide.

CAREER Diabetes Nurse

Diabetes nurses teach patients about diabetes, so they can self-manage and control their condition. This includes education on proper diets and nutrition for both diabetic and pre-diabetic patients. Diabetes nurses help patients learn to monitor their medication, blood sugar levels, and to look for symptoms like diabetic nerve damage and vision loss. Diabetes nurses may also work with patients who have been hospitalized because of complications from their disease. This requires a thorough knowledge of the endocrine system, as this system is often involved with obesity and other diseases, resulting in some overlap between diabetes and endocrinology nursing.

C arbohydrates are the most abundant of all the organic compounds in nature. In plants, energy from the Sun converts carbon dioxide and water into the carbohydrate glucose. Polysaccharides are made when many glucose molecules link to form long-chain polymers of starch that store energy or link in a different way to form cellulose to build the structure of the plant. About 65% of the foods in our diet consist of carbohydrates. Each day, we utilize carbohydrates in foods such as bread, pasta, potatoes, and rice. Other carbohydrates called disaccharides include sucrose (table sugar) and lactose in milk. During digestion and cellular metabolism, carbohydrates are converted into glucose, which is oxidized further in our cells to provide our bodies with energy and to provide the cells with carbon atoms for building molecules of proteins, lipids, and nucleic acids. In addition to providing the structural framework of plants, cellulose has other important uses too. The wood in our furniture, the pages in this book, and the cotton in our clothing are all made of cellulose.

Carbohydrates contained in foods such as pasta and bread provide energy for the body.

CHAPTER READINESS*

⚛ CORE CHEMISTRY SKILLS

- Naming Alcohols and Phenols (13.1)
- Writing Equations for the Oxidation of Alcohols (13.4)
- Naming Aldehydes and Ketones (14.1)

*These Core Chemistry Skills from previous chapters are listed here for your review as you proceed to the new material in this chapter.

15.1 Carbohydrates

Carbohydrates such as table sugar, lactose, and cellulose are all made of carbon, hydrogen, and oxygen. Simple sugars, which have formulas of $C_n(H_2O)_n$, were once thought to be hydrates of carbon, thus the name *carbohydrate*. In a series of reactions called *photosynthesis*, energy from the Sun is used to combine the carbon atoms from carbon dioxide (CO_2) and the hydrogen and oxygen atoms of water (H_2O) into the carbohydrate glucose.

$$6CO_2 + 6H_2O + \text{energy} \underset{\text{Respiration}}{\overset{\text{Photosynthesis}}{\rightleftarrows}} C_6H_{12}O_6 + 6O_2$$

Glucose

In the body, glucose is oxidized in a series of metabolic reactions known as *respiration*, which releases chemical energy to do work in the cells. Carbon dioxide and water are produced and returned to the atmosphere. The combination of photosynthesis and respiration is called the *carbon cycle*, in which energy from the Sun is stored in plants by photosynthesis and made available to us when the carbohydrates in our diets are metabolized (see Figure 15.1).

LEARNING GOAL

Classify a monosaccharide as an aldose or a ketose, and indicate the number of carbon atoms.

FIGURE 15.1 ▶ During photosynthesis, energy from the Sun combines CO_2 and H_2O to form glucose ($C_6H_{12}O_6$) and O_2. During respiration in the body, carbohydrates are oxidized to CO_2 and H_2O, while energy is produced.

🅠 What are the reactants and products of respiration?

Types of Carbohydrates

The simplest carbohydrates are the **monosaccharides**. A monosaccharide cannot be split or hydrolyzed into smaller carbohydrates. One of the most common carbohydrates, glucose, $C_6H_{12}O_6$, is a monosaccharide. A **disaccharide** consists of two monosaccharide units joined together, which can be split into two monosaccharide units. For example, ordinary table sugar, sucrose, $C_{12}H_{22}O_{11}$, is a disaccharide that can be split by water (hydrolysis) in the presence of an acid or an enzyme to give one molecule of glucose and one molecule of another monosaccharide, fructose.

$$C_{12}H_{22}O_{11} + H_2O \xrightarrow{\text{H}^+ \text{ or enzyme}} C_6H_{12}O_6 + C_6H_{12}O_6$$

Sucrose   Glucose   Fructose

A **polysaccharide** is a carbohydrate that contains many monosaccharide units, which is called a *polymer*. In the presence of an acid or an enzyme, a polysaccharide can be completely hydrolyzed to yield many monosaccharide molecules.

Example	Type of Carbohydrate	Products of Hydrolysis
Honey contains the monosaccharides fructose and glucose.	Monosaccharide + H_2O $\xrightarrow{\text{H}^+ \text{ or enzyme}}$	no hydrolysis
Milk contains lactose, which is a disaccharide.	Disaccharide + H_2O $\xrightarrow{\text{H}^+ \text{ or enzyme}}$	two monosaccharide molecules
Cotton consists of the polysaccharide cellulose.	Polysaccharide + many H_2O $\xrightarrow{\text{H}^+ \text{ or enzyme}}$	many monosaccharide molecules

Monosaccharides

A monosaccharide contains several hydroxyl groups attached to a chain of three to seven carbon atoms that also contains an aldehyde or a ketone group. Thus, a monosaccharide is known as a polyhydroxy aldehyde or polyhydroxy ketone. In an **aldose**, the first carbon in the chain is an aldehyde, whereas a **ketose** has a ketone as the second carbon atom.

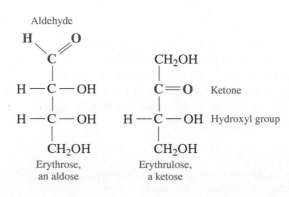

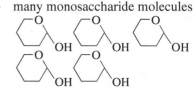
Erythrulose, used in sunless tanning lotions, reacts with amino acids or proteins in the skin to produce a bronze color.

Monosaccharides are also classified by the number of carbon atoms. A monosaccharide with three carbon atoms is a *triose*, one with four carbon atoms is a *tetrose*; a *pentose* has five carbons, and a *hexose* contains six carbons. We can use both classification systems to indicate the aldehyde or ketone group and the number of carbon atoms. An aldopentose is a five-carbon monosaccharide that is an aldehyde; a ketohexose is a six-carbon monosaccharide that is a ketone.

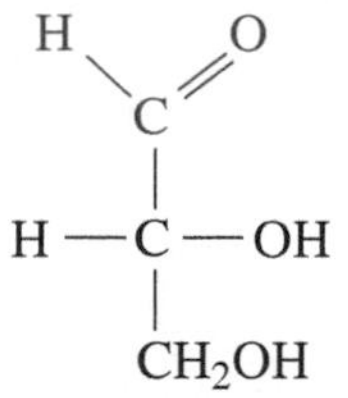

Glyceraldehyde (aldotriose) 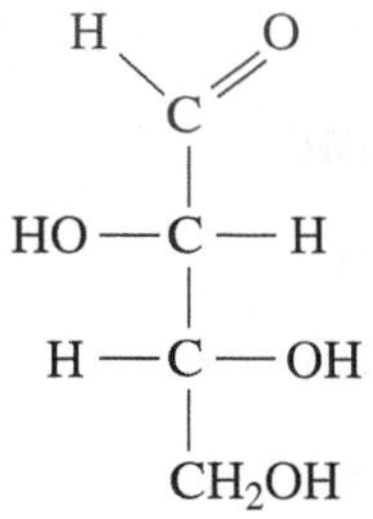   Threose (aldotetrose) 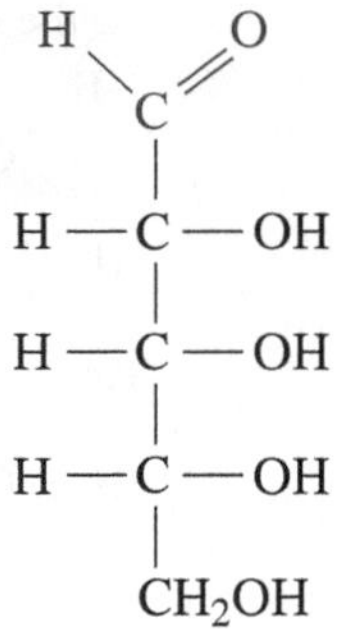   Ribose (aldopentose) 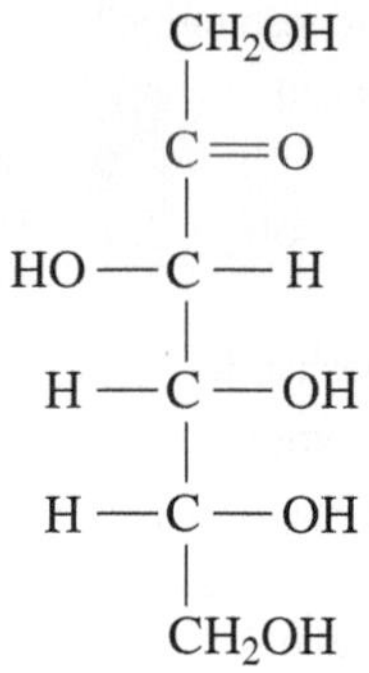   Fructose (ketohexose)

▶ **SAMPLE PROBLEM 15.1 Monosaccharides**

Classify each of the following monosaccharides as an aldopentose, ketopentose, aldohexose, or ketohexose:

a.

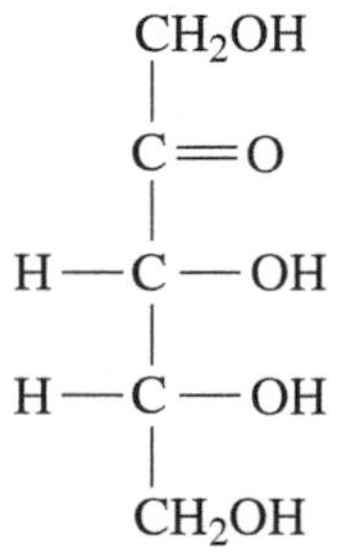

Ribulose

b.

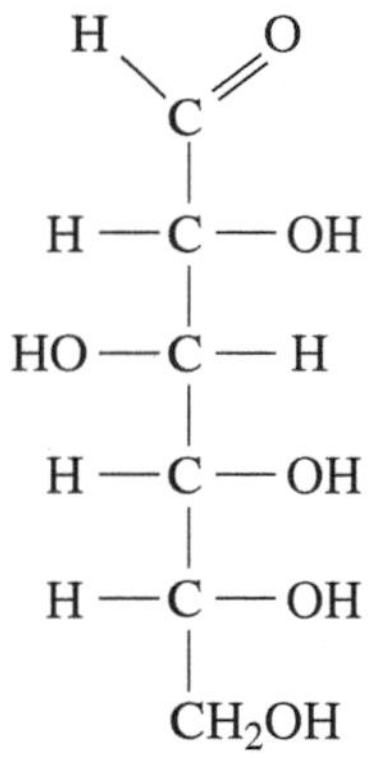

Glucose

SOLUTION

a. Ribulose has five carbon atoms (pentose) and is a ketone, which makes it a ketopentose.

b. Glucose has six carbon atoms (hexose) and is an aldehyde, which makes it an aldohexose.

STUDY CHECK 15.1

Classify the following monosaccharide, erythrose, as an aldotetrose, ketotetrose, aldopentose, or ketopentose:

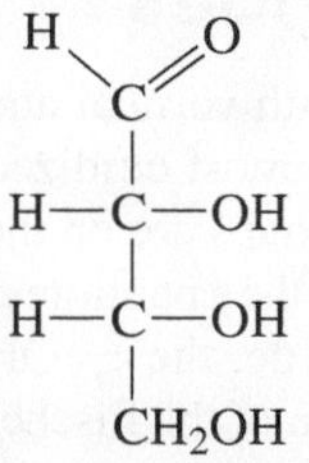

ANSWER

aldotetrose

QUESTIONS AND PROBLEMS

15.1 Carbohydrates

LEARNING GOAL Classify a monosaccharide as an aldose or a ketose, and indicate the number of carbon atoms.

15.1 What reactants are needed for photosynthesis and respiration?

15.2 What is the relationship between photosynthesis and respiration?

15.3 What is a monosaccharide? A disaccharide?

15.4 What is a polysaccharide?

15.5 What functional groups are found in all monosaccharides?

15.6 What is the difference between an aldose and a ketose?

15.7 What are the functional groups and number of carbons in a ketopentose?

15.8 What are the functional groups and number of carbons in an aldohexose?

℞ Clinical Applications

15.9 Classify each of the following monosaccharides as an aldopentose, ketopentose, aldohexose, or ketohexose:

a. Psicose is a carbohydrate present in low amounts in foods.

$$
\begin{array}{c}
CH_2OH \\
| \\
C=O \\
| \\
H-C-OH \\
| \\
H-C-OH \\
| \\
H-C-OH \\
| \\
CH_2OH
\end{array}
$$
Psicose

b. Lyxose is a component of bacterial glycolipids.

$$
\begin{array}{c}
H \quad O \\
\diagdown C \diagup \\
| \\
HO-C-H \\
| \\
HO-C-H \\
| \\
H-C-OH \\
| \\
CH_2OH
\end{array}
$$
Lyxose

15.10 Classify each of the following monosaccharides as an aldopentose, ketopentose, aldohexose, or ketohexose:

a. A solution of xylose is given to a patient to test its absorption by the intestines.

$$
\begin{array}{c}
H \quad O \\
\diagdown C \diagup \\
| \\
H-C-OH \\
| \\
HO-C-H \\
| \\
H-C-OH \\
| \\
CH_2OH
\end{array}
$$
Xylose

b. Tagatose is a carbohydrate found in fruit that is similar in sweetness to sugar.

$$
\begin{array}{c}
CH_2OH \\
| \\
C=O \\
| \\
HO-C-H \\
| \\
HO-C-H \\
| \\
H-C-OH \\
| \\
CH_2OH
\end{array}
$$
Tagatose

LEARNING GOAL

Identify and draw the D and L configurations of the Fischer projections for common monosaccharides.

$$
\begin{array}{cc}
H \quad O & H \quad O \\
\diagdown C \diagup & \diagdown C \diagup \\
\boxed{HO - \!\!\!- H} & \boxed{H - \!\!\!- OH} \\
CH_2OH & CH_2OH \\
\text{L-Glyceraldehyde} & \text{D-Glyceraldehyde}
\end{array}
$$

15.2 Fischer Projections of Monosaccharides

A Fischer projection for the simplest aldose, glyceraldehyde, is drawn with vertical and horizontal lines that represent the carbon chain. The aldehyde group (the most oxidized carbon) is placed at the top of the vertical line and the —H and —OH groups are on the horizontal intersecting line. In L-glyceraldehyde, the letter L is assigned to the enantiomer with the —OH group on the left of the chiral carbon. In D-glyceraldehyde, the —OH group is on the right. The carbon atom in the —CH₂OH group at the bottom of the Fischer projection is not chiral, because it does not have four different groups bonded to it.

The most common monosaccharides contain five or six carbon atoms with several chiral carbons. A chiral carbon atom is attached to four different atoms or groups. Each Fischer projection of a monosaccharide can be drawn as a mirror image, which gives a pair of enantiomers. By convention, the —OH group farthest from the aldehyde or ketone group is used to determine the D or L configuration of a monosaccharide. The following are the Fischer projections for the D and L enantiomers of ribose, a five-carbon monosaccharide, and the D and L enantiomers of glucose, a six-carbon monosaccharide. The vertical carbon chain is numbered starting from the top carbon.

In each pair of mirror images, it is important to see that all of the —OH groups on chiral carbon atoms are reversed so that they appear on the opposite sides of the molecule. For example, in L-ribose, all of the —OH groups drawn on the left side of the vertical line are drawn on the right side in the mirror image of D-ribose.

CORE CHEMISTRY SKILL

Identifying D- and L-Fischer Projections

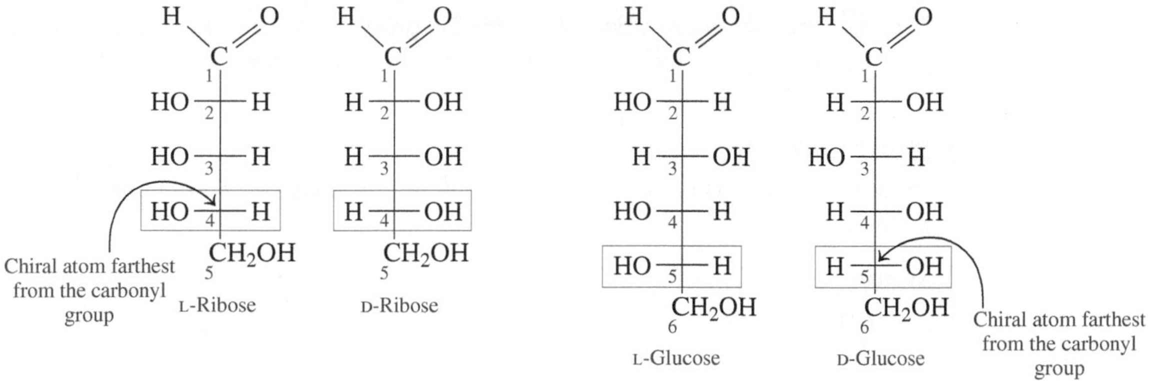

SAMPLE PROBLEM 15.2 Fischer Projections for Monosaccharides

Ribulose, which is used in various brands of artificial sweeteners, has the following Fischer projection:

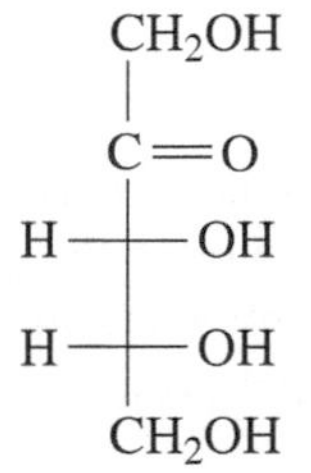

Identify the compound as D- or L-ribulose.

SOLUTION

	Given	Need
ANALYZE THE PROBLEM	Fischer projection of ribulose	identify as D- or L-ribulose

Guide to Identifying D- or L-Monosaccharides

STEP 1 Number the carbon chain starting at the top of the Fischer projection.

STEP 2 Locate the chiral carbon farthest from the top of the Fischer projection.

STEP 3 Identify the position of the —OH group as D- or L-.

STEP 1 Number the carbon chain starting at the top of the Fischer projection.

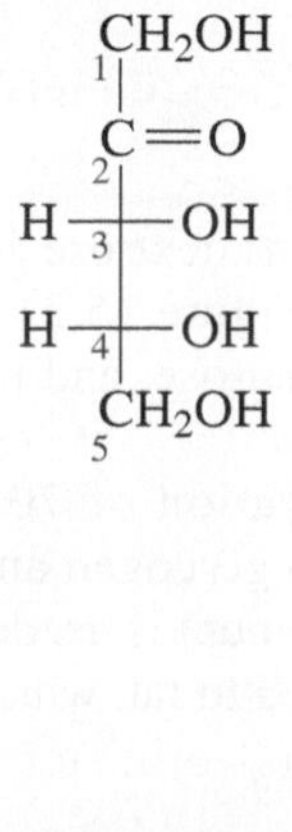

STEP **2**   Locate the chiral carbon farthest from the top of the Fischer projection. The chiral carbon farthest from the top is carbon 4.

$$
\begin{array}{c}
\underset{1}{CH_2OH} \\
\underset{2}{C}=O \\
H\underset{3}{\longrightarrow}OH \\
\boxed{H\underset{4}{\longrightarrow}OH} \\
\underset{5}{CH_2OH}
\end{array}
$$

STEP **3**   Identify the position of the —OH group as D- or L-. In this Fischer projection, the —OH group is drawn on the right of carbon 4, which makes it D-ribulose.

STUDY CHECK 15.2

Draw and name the Fischer projection for the mirror image of the ribulose in Sample Problem 15.2.

ANSWER

$$
\begin{array}{c}
CH_2OH \\
C=O \\
HO\longrightarrow H \\
HO\longrightarrow H \\
CH_2OH
\end{array}
$$

L-Ribulose

Some Important Monosaccharides

D-Glucose, D-galactose, and D-fructose are the most important monosaccharides. They are all hexoses with the molecular formula $C_6H_{12}O_6$ and are isomers of each other. Although we can draw Fischer projections for their D and L enantiomers, the D enantiomers are more commonly found in nature and used in the cells of the body. The Fischer projections for the D enantiomers are drawn as follows:

$$
\begin{array}{ccc}
\begin{array}{c}
H\diagdown\; _{C}\diagup O \\
H\underset{2}{\longrightarrow}OH \\
HO\underset{3}{\longrightarrow}H \\
H\underset{4}{\longrightarrow}OH \\
H\underset{5}{\longrightarrow}OH \\
\underset{6}{CH_2OH}
\end{array}
&
\begin{array}{c}
H\diagdown\; _{C}\diagup O \\
H\underset{2}{\longrightarrow}OH \\
HO\underset{3}{\longrightarrow}H \\
HO\underset{4}{\longrightarrow}H \\
H\underset{5}{\longrightarrow}OH \\
\underset{6}{CH_2OH}
\end{array}
&
\begin{array}{c}
\underset{1}{CH_2OH} \\
\underset{2}{C}=O \\
HO\underset{3}{\longrightarrow}H \\
H\underset{4}{\longrightarrow}OH \\
H\underset{5}{\longrightarrow}OH \\
\underset{6}{CH_2OH}
\end{array} \\
\text{D-Glucose} & \text{D-Galactose} & \text{D-Fructose}
\end{array}
$$

D-Glucose

The most common hexose, **D-glucose**, $C_6H_{12}O_6$, also known as dextrose and blood sugar, is found in fruits, vegetables, corn syrup, and honey (see Figure 15.2). D-glucose is a building block of the disaccharides sucrose, lactose, and maltose, and polysaccharides such as amylose, cellulose, and glycogen.

In the body, glucose normally occurs at a concentration of 70 to 90 mg/dL (1 dL = 100 mL) of blood. Excess glucose is converted to glycogen and stored in the liver and muscle. When the amount of glucose exceeds the amount is needed for energy in the body or stored as glycogen, the excess glucose is converted to fat, which can be stored in unlimited amounts.

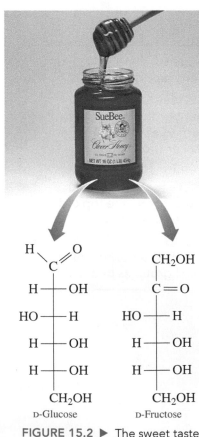

$$
\begin{array}{cc}
\begin{array}{c}
H\diagdown\; _{C}\diagup O \\
H\longrightarrow OH \\
HO\longrightarrow H \\
H\longrightarrow OH \\
H\longrightarrow OH \\
CH_2OH
\end{array}
&
\begin{array}{c}
CH_2OH \\
C=O \\
HO\longrightarrow H \\
H\longrightarrow OH \\
H\longrightarrow OH \\
CH_2OH
\end{array} \\
\text{D-Glucose} & \text{D-Fructose}
\end{array}
$$

FIGURE 15.2 ▶ The sweet taste of honey is because of the monosaccharides D-glucose and D-fructose.

🔍 What are some differences in the Fischer projections of D-glucose and D-fructose?

D-Galactose

D-Galactose, $C_6H_{12}O_6$, is an aldohexose that is obtained from the disaccharide lactose, which is found in milk and milk products. D-Galactose is important in the cellular membranes of the brain and nervous system. The only difference in the Fischer projections of D-glucose and D-galactose is the arrangement of the —OH group on carbon 4.

In a condition called *galactosemia*, an enzyme needed to convert D-galactose to D-glucose is missing. The accumulation of D-galactose in the blood and tissues can lead to cataracts, mental retardation, failure to thrive, and liver disease. The treatment for galactosemia is the removal of all foods containing D-galactose, mainly milk and milk products as well as breast milk, from the diet. However, soy milk does not contain lactose or D-galactose, and may be given to infants with galactosemia. If this is done for an infant immediately after birth, the damaging effects of D-galactose accumulation can be avoided.

D-Fructose

In contrast to D-glucose and D-galactose, **D-fructose**, $C_6H_{12}O_6$, is a ketohexose. The structure of D-fructose differs from glucose at carbons 1 and 2 by the location of the carbonyl group. D-Fructose is the sweetest of the carbohydrates, almost twice as sweet as sucrose (table sugar). This characteristic makes D-fructose popular with dieters because less fructose, and therefore fewer calories, is needed to provide a pleasant taste. D-Fructose, also called levulose and fruit sugar, is found in fruit juices and honey (see Figure 15.2).

D-Fructose is also obtained as one of the hydrolysis products of sucrose, the disaccharide known as table sugar. High-fructose corn syrup (HFCS) is a sweetener that is produced by using an enzyme to break down sucrose to D-glucose and D-fructose. An HFCS mixture containing about 50% D-fructose and 50% D-glucose is used in soft drinks and many foods, such as baked goods.

A food label shows that high fructose corn syrup is the sweetener in this product.

 ## Chemistry Link to **Health**

Hyperglycemia and Hypoglycemia

Kate's doctor ordered an oral glucose tolerance test (OGTT) to evaluate her body's ability to return to normal glucose concentrations (70 to 90 mg/dL) in response to the ingestion of a specified amount of glucose. After Kate fasted for 12 h, she drinks a solution containing 75 g of glucose. A blood sample is taken immediately, followed by more blood samples each half-hour for 2 h, and then every hour for a total of 5 h. After her test, Kate was told that her blood glucose was 178 mg/dL, which indicates hyperglycemia. The term *glyc* or *gluco* refers to "sugar." The prefix *hyper* means above or over; *hypo* means below or under. Thus, the blood sugar level in *hyperglycemia* is above normal and in *hypoglycemia* it is below normal.

An example of a disease that can cause hyperglycemia is *type 2 diabetes*, which occurs when the pancreas is unable to produce sufficient quantities of insulin. As a result, glucose levels in the body fluids can rise as high as 350 mg/dL. Kate's symptoms of type 2 diabetes include thirst, excessive urination, and increased appetite. In older adults, type 2 diabetes is sometimes a consequence of excessive weight gain.

When a person is hypoglycemic, the blood glucose level rises and then decreases rapidly to levels as low as 40 mg/dL. In some cases, hypoglycemia is caused by overproduction of insulin by the pancreas. Low blood glucose can cause dizziness, general weakness, and muscle tremors. A diet may be prescribed that consists of several small meals high in protein and low in carbohydrate. Some hypoglycemic patients are finding success with diets that include more complex carbohydrates rather than simple sugars.

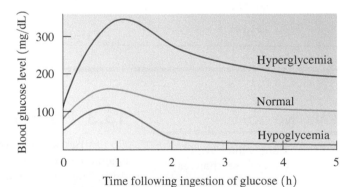

A glucose solution is given to determine blood glucose levels.

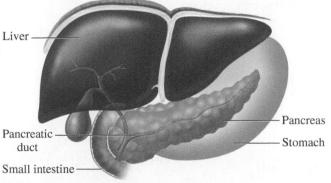

The insulin produced in the pancreas is needed in the digestive system for the metabolism of glucose.

QUESTIONS AND PROBLEMS

15.2 Fischer Projections of Monosaccharides

LEARNING GOAL Identify and draw the D and L configurations of the Fischer projections for common monosaccharides.

15.11 Identify each of the following as the D or L enantiomer:

a. 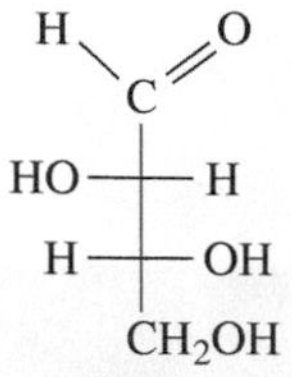
Threose

b. 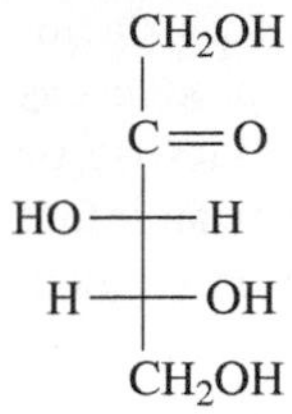
Xylulose

c. 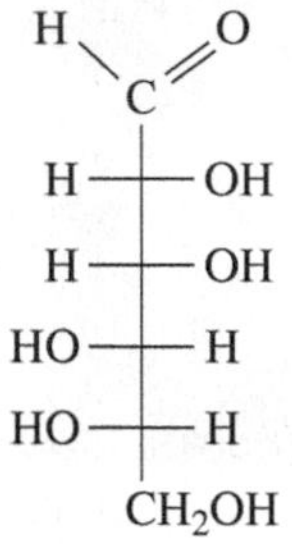
Mannose

d. 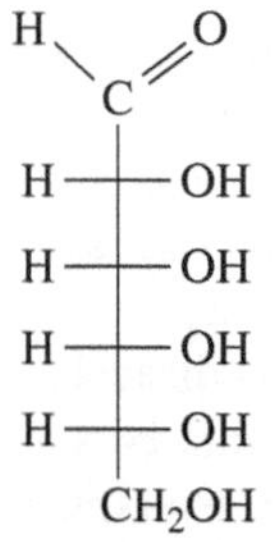
Allose

15.12 Identify each of the following as the D or L enantiomer:

a. 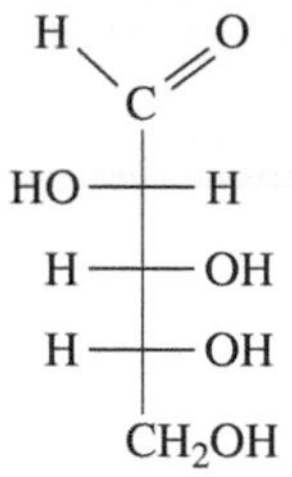
Arabinose

b. 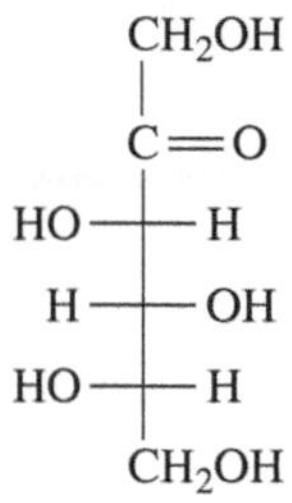
Sorbose

c. 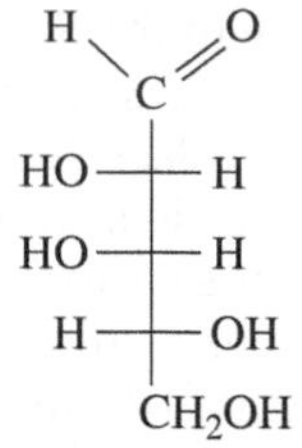
Lyxose

d. 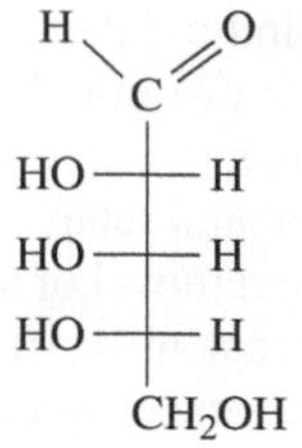
Ribose

15.13 Draw the Fischer projection for the other enantiomer of **a** to **d** in problem 15.11.

15.14 Draw the Fischer projection for the other enantiomer of **a** to **d** in problem 15.12.

15.15 Draw the Fischer projections for D-glucose and L-glucose.

15.16 Draw the Fischer projections for D-fructose and L-fructose.

℞ Clinical Applications

15.17 An infant with galactosemia can utilize D-glucose in milk but not D-galactose. How does the Fischer projection of D-galactose differ from that of D-glucose?

15.18 D-Fructose is the sweetest monosaccharide. How does the Fischer projection of D-fructose differ from that of D-glucose?

15.19 Identify the monosaccharide that fits each of the following descriptions:
   a. is also called blood sugar
   b. is not metabolized in a condition known as galactosemia

15.20 Identify a monosaccharide that fits each of the following descriptions:
   a. found in high blood levels in diabetes
   b. is also called fruit sugar

LEARNING GOAL

Draw and identify the Haworth structures for monosaccharides.

⚛ **CORE CHEMISTRY SKILL**

Drawing Haworth Structures

15.3 Haworth Structures of Monosaccharides

Up until now, we have drawn the Fischer projections for monosaccharides as open chains. However, the most stable form of pentoses and hexoses are five- or six-atom rings. These rings, known as **Haworth structures**, are the cyclic hemiacetals produced from the reaction of a carbonyl group and a hydroxyl group in the *same* molecule. We will now show how to draw the Haworth structure for D-glucose from its Fischer projection.

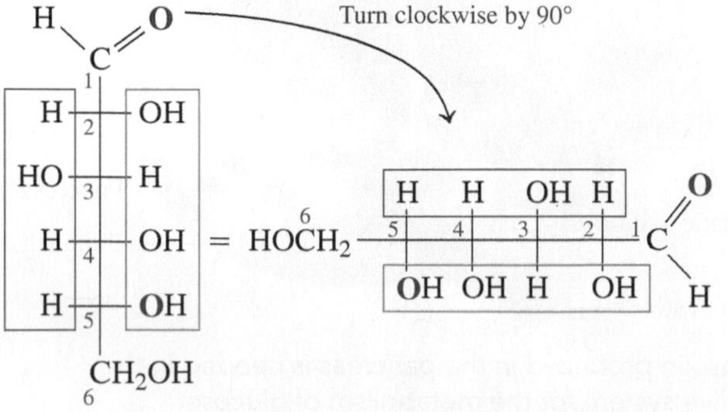

Drawing Haworth Structures

To convert a Fischer projection to a Haworth structure, turn the Fischer projection clockwise by 90°. The —H and —OH groups on the right of the vertical carbon chain are now below the horizontal carbon chain. Those on the left of the open chain are now above the horizontal carbon chain.

Fold the horizontal carbon chain into a hexagon, rotate the groups on carbon 5, and bond the O on carbon 5 to carbon 1. With carbons 2 and 3 as the base of a hexagon, move the remaining carbons upward. Rotate the groups on carbon 5 so that the —OH group

D-Glucose (open chain)

is close to carbon 1. To complete the Haworth structure, draw a bond between the oxygen of the —OH group on carbon 5 to carbon 1 to form a hemiacetal.

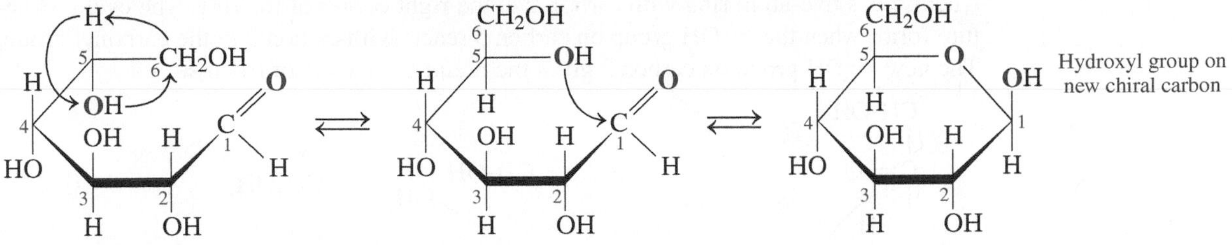

Rotation of groups on carbon 5   Carbon-5 oxygen bonds to carbon 1   Cyclic hemiacetal structure

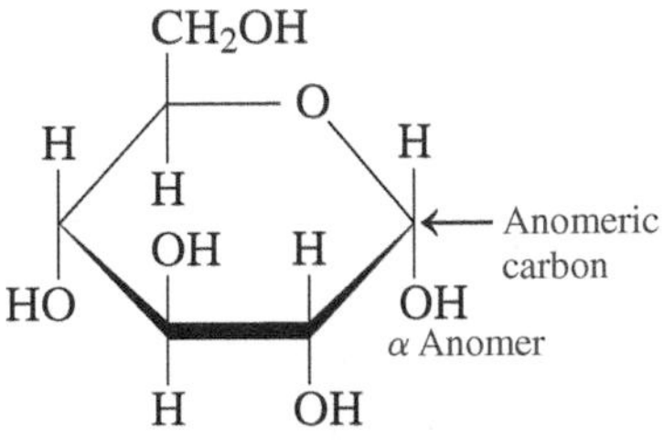

Because the new —OH group can be drawn above or below the plane of the Haworth structure, there are two forms of D-glucose. These different forms, called *anomers*, differ only by the position of the —OH group at carbon 1. In the α (alpha) anomer, the —OH group is drawn below the plane of the ring. In the β (beta) anomer, the —OH group is drawn above the plane of the ring. By convention, the carbon atoms in the ring are drawn as corners.

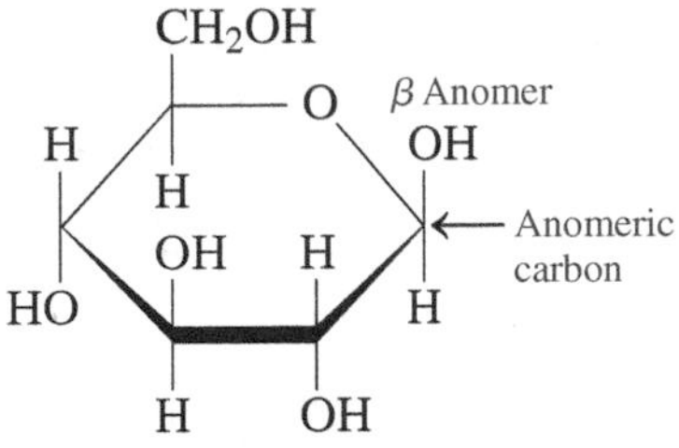

α-D-Glucose

Mutarotation of α- and β-D-Glucose

In an aqueous solution, the Haworth structure of α-D-glucose opens to give the open chain of D-glucose, which has an aldehyde group. At any given time, there is only a trace amount of the open chain because it closes quickly to form a stable cyclic structure. However, when the open chain closes again it can form β-D-glucose. In this process called *mutarotation*, each anomer converts to the open chain and back again. As the ring opens and closes, the —OH group on carbon 1 can form either the α or β anomer. An aqueous glucose solution contains a mixture of 36% α-D-glucose and 64% β-D-glucose.

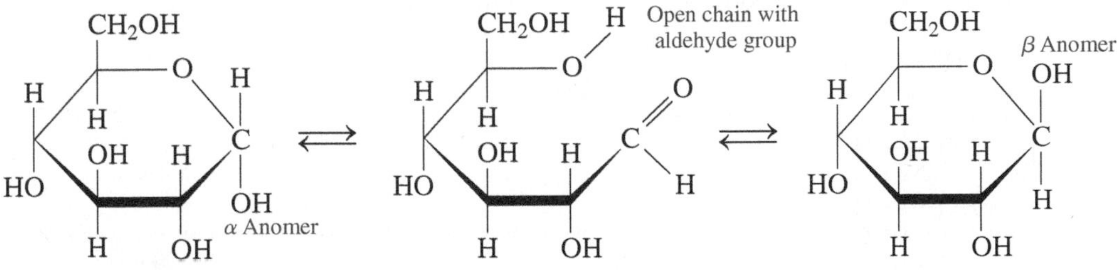

β-D-Glucose

α-D-Glucose (36%)   D-Glucose open chain (trace)   β-D-Glucose (64%)

Haworth Structures of Galactose

Galactose is an aldohexose that differs from glucose only in the arrangement of the —OH group on carbon 4. Thus, its Haworth structure is similar to glucose, except that the —OH group on carbon 4 is drawn above the ring. Galactose also exists as α and β anomers.

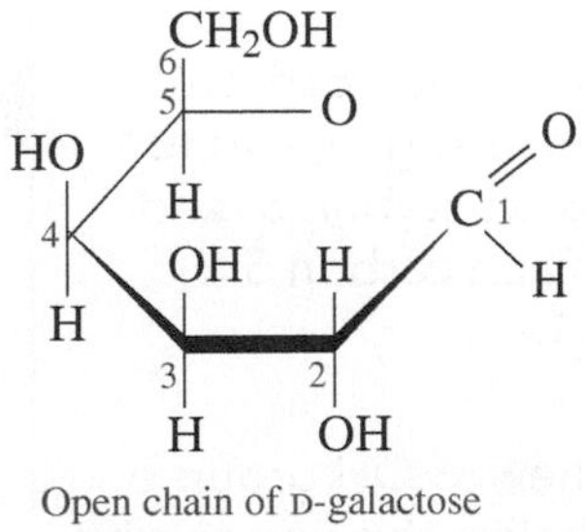

Open chain of D-galactose

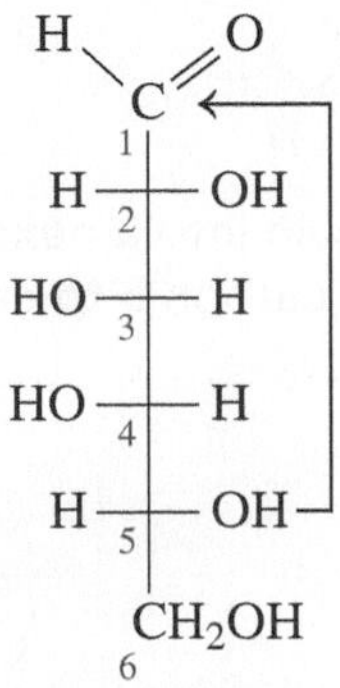

D-Galactose

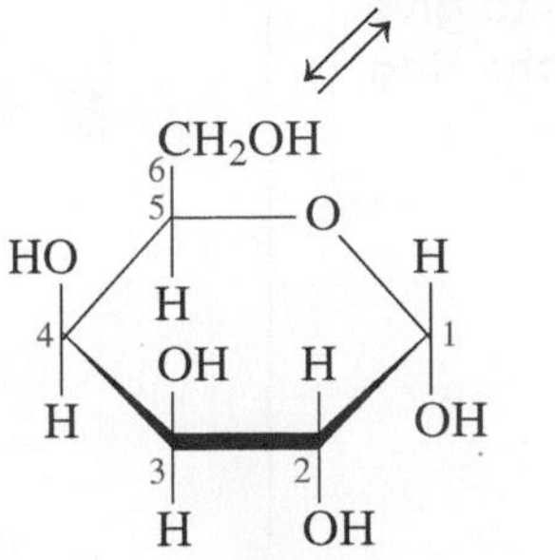

α-D-Galactose 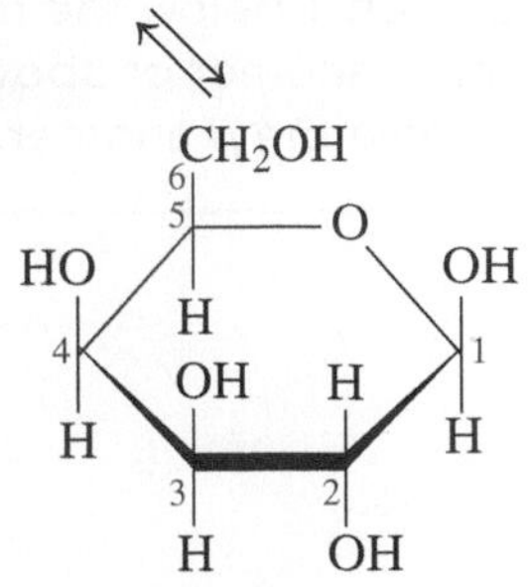   β-D-Galactose

Haworth Structures of Fructose

In contrast to glucose and galactose, fructose is a ketohexose. The Haworth structure for fructose is a five-atom ring with carbon 2 at the right corner of the ring. The cyclic structure forms when the —OH group on carbon 5 reacts with carbon 2 in the carbonyl group. The new —OH group on carbon 2 gives the α and β anomers of fructose.

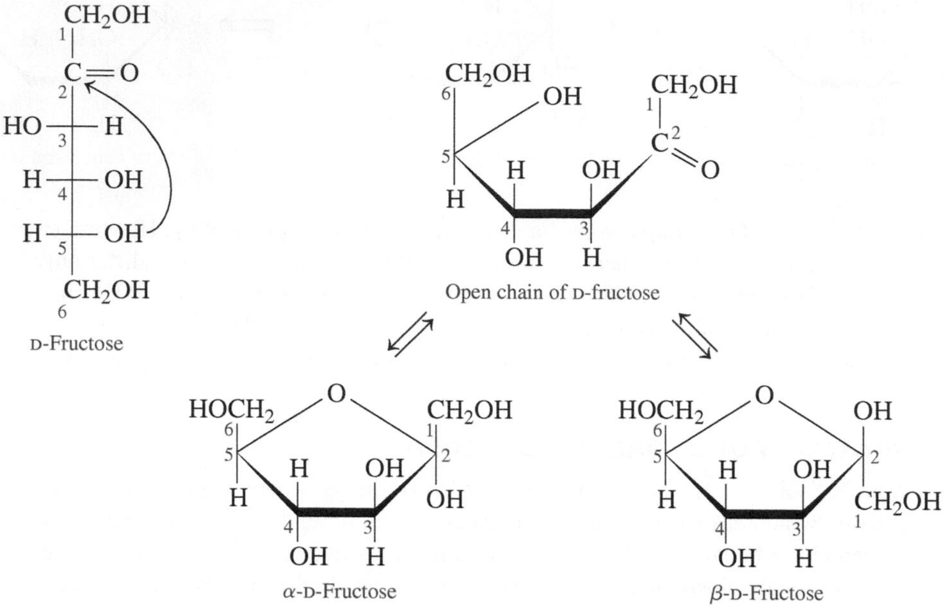

D-Fructose

Open chain of D-fructose

α-D-Fructose

β-D-Fructose

▶ **SAMPLE PROBLEM 15.3** **Drawing Haworth Structures for Sugars**

D-Mannose, a carbohydrate found in immunoglobulins, has the following Fischer projection. Draw the Haworth structure for β-D-mannose.

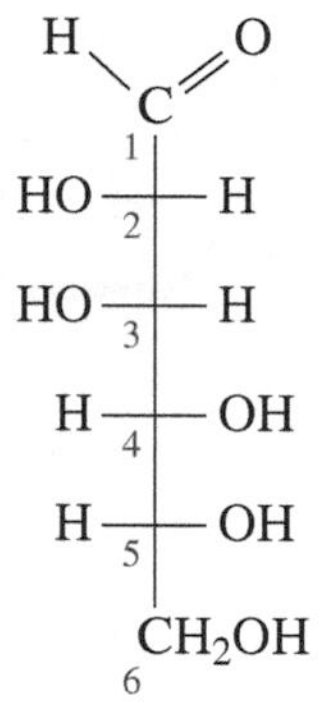

D-Mannose

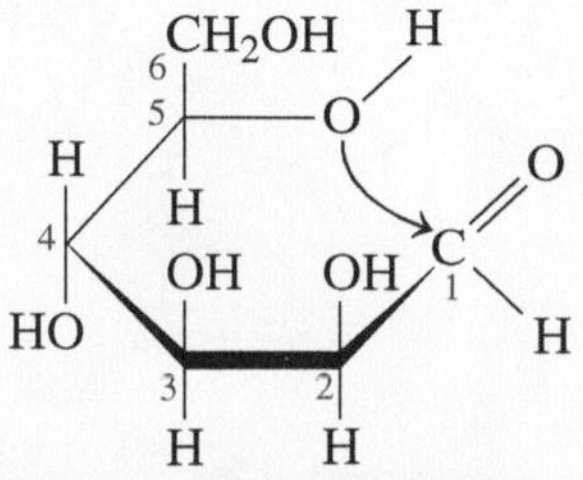

Guide to Drawing Haworth Structures

STEP 1
Turn the Fischer projection clockwise by 90°.

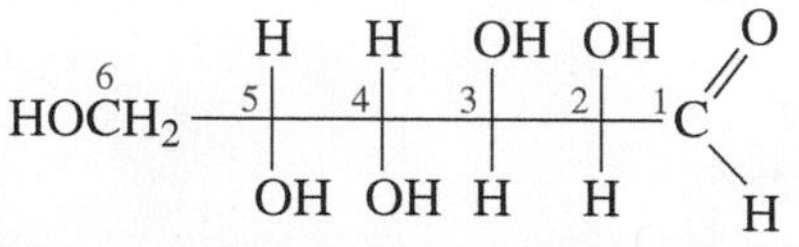

STEP 2
Fold the horizontal carbon chain into a hexagon, rotate the groups on carbon 5, and bond the O on carbon 5 to carbon 1.

STEP 3
Draw the new —OH group on carbon 1 below the ring to give the α anomer or above the ring to give the β anomer.

SOLUTION

STEP 1 Turn the Fischer projection clockwise by 90°.

STEP 2 Fold the horizontal carbon chain into a hexagon, rotate the groups on carbon 5, and bond the O on carbon 5 to carbon 1.

STEP 3 Draw the new —OH group on carbon 1 above the ring to give the β anomer.

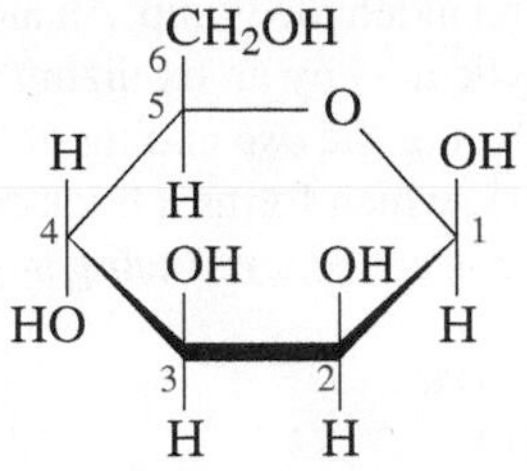

STUDY CHECK 15.3

Draw the Haworth structure for α-D-mannose.

ANSWER

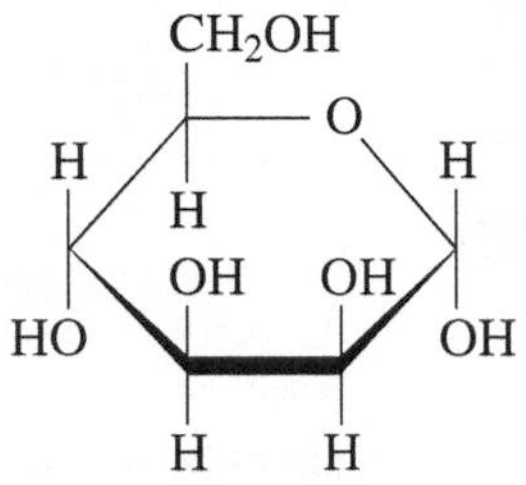

QUESTIONS AND PROBLEMS

15.3 Haworth Structures of Monosaccharides

LEARNING GOAL Draw and identify the Haworth structures for monosaccharides.

15.21 What are the kind and number of atoms in the ring portion of the Haworth structure of glucose?

15.22 What are the kind and number of atoms in the ring portion of the Haworth structure of fructose?

15.23 Draw the Haworth structures for α- and β-D-glucose.

15.24 Draw the Haworth structures for α- and β-D-fructose.

15.25 Identify each of the following as the α or β anomer:

a.

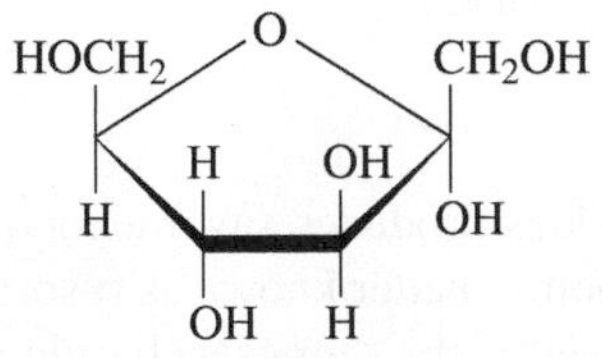

b.

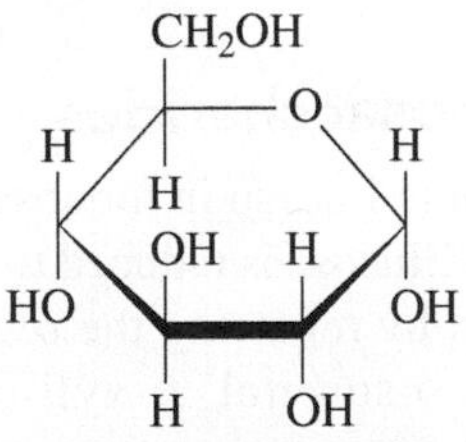

15.26 Identify each of the following as the α or β anomer:

a.

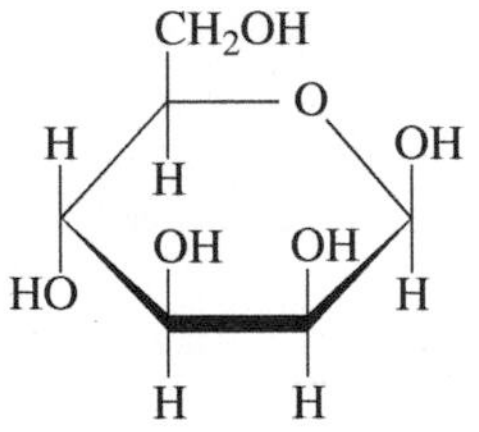

b.

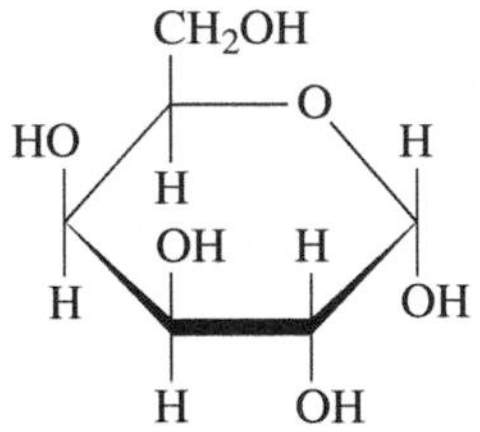

15.4 Chemical Properties of Monosaccharides

Monosaccharides contain functional groups that can undergo chemical reactions. In an aldose, the aldehyde group can be oxidized to a carboxylic acid. The carbonyl group in both an aldose and a ketose can be reduced to give a hydroxyl group. The hydroxyl groups can react with other compounds to form a variety of derivatives that are important in biological structures.

LEARNING GOAL

Identify the products of oxidation or reduction of monosaccharides; determine whether a carbohydrate is a reducing sugar.

Oxidation of Monosaccharides

Although monosaccharides exist mostly in cyclic forms, we have seen that a small amount of the open-chain form is always present, which provides an aldehyde group. An aldehyde group with an adjacent hydroxyl can be oxidized to a carboxylic acid by an oxidizing agent such as Benedict's reagent. The sugar acids are named by replacing the *ose* ending of the monosaccharide with *onic acid*. Then the Cu^{2+} is reduced to Cu^+, which forms a brick-red precipitate of Cu_2O. A carbohydrate that reduces another substance is called a **reducing sugar**.

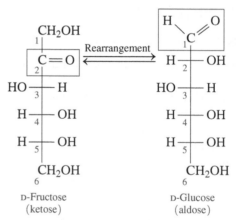

Open chain of D-glucose, a reducing sugar $+ 2Cu^{2+}$ (blue) $\xrightarrow{[O]}$ D-Gluconic acid (Oxidized) $+ Cu_2O(s)$ (Reduced, brick-red)

Fructose, a ketohexose, is also a reducing sugar. Usually a ketone cannot be oxidized. However, in a basic Benedict's solution, a rearrangement occurs between the ketone group on carbon 2 and the hydroxyl group on carbon 1. As a result, fructose is converted to glucose, which produces an aldehyde group with an adjacent hydroxyl that can be oxidized.

D-Fructose (ketose)   Rearrangement   D-Glucose (aldose)

Reduction of Monosaccharides

The reduction of the carbonyl group in monosaccharides produces sugar alcohols, which are also called *alditols*. D-Glucose is reduced to D-glucitol, better known as D-sorbitol. The sugar alcohols are named by replacing the *ose* ending of the monosaccharide with *itol*. Sugar alcohols such as D-sorbitol, D-xylitol from D-xylose, and D-mannitol from D-mannose are used as sweeteners in many sugar-free products such as diet drinks and sugarless gum as well as products for people with diabetes. However, there are some side effects of these sugar substitutes. Some people experience some discomfort such as gas and diarrhea from the ingestion of sugar alcohols. The development of cataracts in diabetics is attributed to the accumulation of D-sorbitol in the lens of the eye.

D-glucitol or D-sorbitol is used as a low-calorie sweetener in diet drinks and sugarless gum.

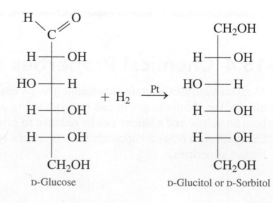

D-Glucose $+ H_2 \xrightarrow{Pt}$ D-Glucitol or D-Sorbitol

▶**SAMPLE PROBLEM 15.4 Reducing Sugars**

Why is D-glucose called a reducing sugar?

SOLUTION

The aldehyde group with an adjacent hydroxyl of D-glucose is easily oxidized by Benedict's reagent. A carbohydrate that reduces Cu^{2+} to Cu^+ is called a reducing sugar.

STUDY CHECK 15.4

A solution containing a tablet of Benedict's reagent turns brick red with a urine sample. According to Table 15.1, what might this result indicate?

ANSWER

The brick-red color of the Benedict's reagent shows a high level of reducing sugar (probably glucose) in the urine, which may indicate type 2 diabetes.

Benedict's solution gives a brick red precipitate with reducing sugars.

♥ Chemistry Link to **Health**
Testing for Glucose

Normally, blood glucose flows through the kidneys and is reabsorbed into the bloodstream. However, if the blood plasma level exceeds about 160 mg of glucose/dL the kidneys cannot reabsorb all of the glucose, and it spills over into the urine, a condition known as *glucosuria*. A symptom of diabetes is a high level of glucose in the urine.

Benedict's test can be used to determine the presence of glucose in urine. The amount of copper(I) oxide (Cu_2O) formed is proportional to the amount of reducing sugar present in the urine. Low to moderate levels of reducing sugar turn the solution green; solutions with high glucose levels turn Benedict's reagent yellow or brick red.

In another clinical test, the presence of glucose in the urine can be detected using a paper strip containing *o*-methylaniline and two enzymes glucose oxidase and peroxidase. When the paper strip comes in contact with any glucose in the urine, glucose and oxygen are converted by glucose oxidase to gluconic acid and hydrogen peroxide.

Then peroxidase converts the hydrogen peroxide into a compound that reacts with *o*-methylaniline in the test strip to form a color ranging from green to a dark brown. The intensity of the color depends on the amount of glucose present in the urine. Table 15.1 lists some colors associated with the concentration of glucose in the urine.

$$H_2O_2 + dye\ (\textit{o-methylaniline}) \xrightarrow{\text{Peroxidase}} \text{colored products}$$

o-Methylaniline

The color of the dye *o*-methylaniline on a test strip determines the glucose level in urine.

TABLE 15.1 Glucose Oxidase Test Results

	Glucose Present in Urine	
	% (m/v)	mg/dL
Blue	0	0
Blue-green	0.10	100
Green	0.25	250
Green-brown	0.50	500
Brown	1.00	1000
Dark-brown	2.00	2000

D-Glucose + O_2 $\xrightarrow{\text{Glucose oxidase}}$ D-Gluconic acid + H_2O_2 (Hydrogen peroxide)

Oxidized

QUESTIONS AND PROBLEMS

15.4 Chemical Properties of Monosaccharides

LEARNING GOAL Identify the products of oxidation or reduction of monosaccharides; determine whether a carbohydrate is a reducing sugar.

15.27 Draw the Fischer projection for D-xylitol produced when D-xylose is reduced.

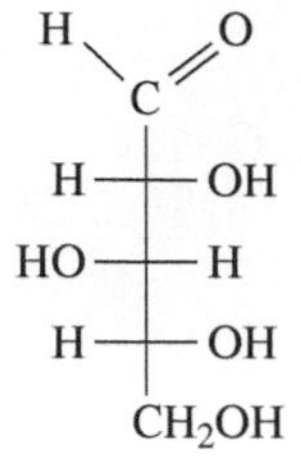

D-Xylose

15.28 Draw the Fischer projection for D-mannitol produced when D-mannose is reduced.

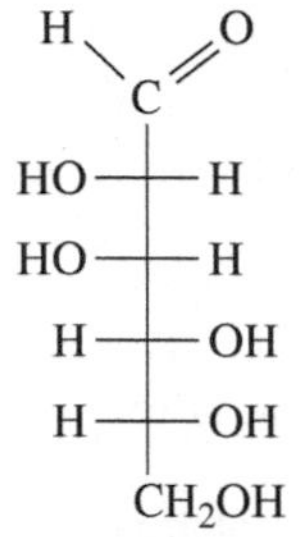

D-Mannose

15.29 Draw the Fischer projection for the oxidation and the reduction products of D-arabinose. What are the names of the sugar acid and the sugar alcohol produced?

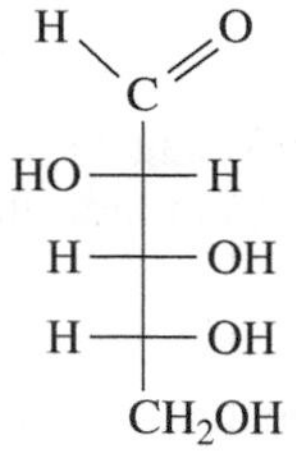

D-Arabinose

15.30 Draw the Fischer projection for the oxidation and the reduction products of D-ribose. What are the names of the sugar acid and sugar alcohol produced?

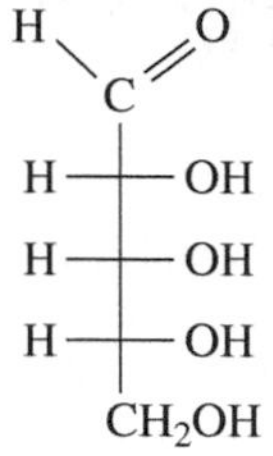

D-Ribose

LEARNING GOAL

Describe the monosaccharide units and linkages in disaccharides.

15.5 Disaccharides

A disaccharide is composed of two monosaccharides linked together. The most common disaccharides are maltose, lactose, and sucrose. When two monosaccharides combine in a dehydration reaction, the product is a disaccharide. The reaction occurs between the hydroxyl group on carbon 1 and one of the hydroxyl groups on a second monosaccharide.

$$\text{Glucose} + \text{glucose} \xrightarrow{\text{Maltose synthase}} \text{maltose} + H_2O$$

$$\text{Glucose} + \text{galactose} \xrightarrow{\text{Lactose synthase}} \text{lactose} + H_2O$$

$$\text{Glucose} + \text{fructose} \xrightarrow{\text{Sucrose synthase}} \text{sucrose} + H_2O$$

Maltose, or malt sugar, is obtained from starch and is found in germinating grains. When maltose in barley and other grains is hydrolyzed by yeast enzymes, glucose is obtained, which can undergo fermentation to give ethanol. Maltose is used in cereals, candies, and the brewing of beverages.

In the Haworth structure of a disaccharide, a **glycosidic bond** is a hemiacetal bond that connects two monosaccharides. In maltose, a glycosidic bond forms between the —OH groups of carbons 1 and 4 of two α-D-glucose molecules with a loss of a water molecule. The glycosidic bond in maltose is designated as an $\alpha(1 \rightarrow 4)$ linkage to show that an alpha —OH group on carbon 1 is joined to carbon 4 of the second glucose molecule. Because the second glucose molecule still has a free —OH group on carbon 1, it can form an open chain, which allows maltose to form both α and β anomers. The open chain provides an aldehyde group that can be oxidized, making maltose a reducing sugar.

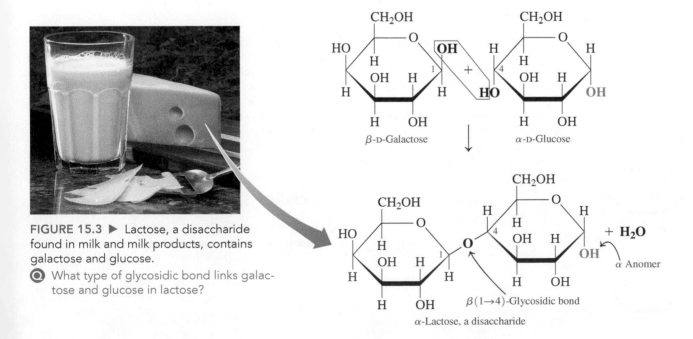

α-D-Glucose   +   α-D-Glucose

↓

α(1→4)-Glycosidic bond

α-Maltose, a disaccharide

+ H_2O

α Anomer

Lactose, milk sugar, is a disaccharide found in milk and milk products (see Figure 15.3). The bond in lactose is a β(1 → 4)-glycosidic bond because the —OH group on carbon 1 of β-D-galactose forms a glycosidic bond with the —OH group on carbon 4 of a D-glucose molecule. Because D-glucose still has a free —OH group on carbon 1, it can form an open chain, which allows lactose to form both α and β anomers. The open chain provides an aldehyde group that can be oxidized, making lactose a reducing sugar.

Lactose makes up 6 to 8% of human milk and about 4 to 5% of cow's milk, and it is used in products that attempt to duplicate mother's milk. When a person does not produce sufficient quantities of the enzyme lactase, which is needed to hydrolyze lactose, it remains undigested when it enters the colon. Then bacteria in the colon digest the lactose in a fermentation process that creates large amounts of gas including carbon dioxide and

FIGURE 15.3 ▶ Lactose, a disaccharide found in milk and milk products, contains galactose and glucose.

Q What type of glycosidic bond links galactose and glucose in lactose?

β-D-Galactose   +   α-D-Glucose

↓

β(1→4)-Glycosidic bond

+ H_2O

α Anomer

α-Lactose, a disaccharide

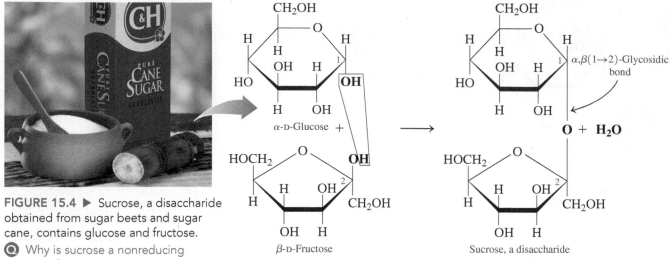

FIGURE 15.4 ▶ Sucrose, a disaccharide obtained from sugar beets and sugar cane, contains glucose and fructose.

Q Why is sucrose a nonreducing sugar?

methane, which cause bloating and abdominal cramps. In some commercial milk products, lactase has already been added to break down lactose.

Sucrose consists of an α-D-glucose and a β-D-fructose molecule joined by an α, β(1 → 2)-glycosidic bond (see Figure 15.4). Unlike maltose and lactose, the glycosidic bond in sucrose is between carbon 1 of glucose and carbon 2 of fructose. Thus, sucrose cannot form an open chain and cannot be oxidized. Sucrose cannot react with Benedict's reagent and is not a reducing sugar.

The sugar we use to sweeten our cereal, coffee, or tea is sucrose. Most of the sucrose for table sugar comes from sugar cane (20% by mass) or sugar beets (15% by mass). Both the raw and refined forms of sugar are sucrose. Some estimates indicate that each person in the United States consumes an average of 68 kg (150 lb) of sucrose every year, either by itself or in a variety of food products.

♡ Chemistry Link to **Health**

How Sweet Is My Sweetener?

Although many of the monosaccharides and disaccharides taste sweet, they differ considerably in their degree of sweetness. Dietetic foods contain sweeteners that are noncarbohydrate or carbohydrates that are sweeter than sucrose. Some examples of sweeteners compared with sucrose are shown in Table 15.2.

Sucralose, which is known as Splenda, is made from sucrose by replacing some of the hydroxyl groups with chlorine atoms.

Aspartame, which is marketed as NutraSweet or Equal, is used in a large number of sugar-free products. It is a noncarbohydrate sweetener made of aspartic acid and a methyl ester of phenylalanine. It does have some caloric value, but it is so sweet that a very small quantity is needed. However, phenylalanine, one of the breakdown products, poses a danger to anyone who cannot metabolize it properly, a condition called *phenylketonuria* (PKU).

Sucralose (Splenda)

Aspartame (NutraSweet)

Another artificial sweetener, Neotame, is a modification of the aspartame structure. The addition of a large alkyl group to the amine group prevents enzymes from breaking the amide bond between aspartic acid and phenylalanine. Thus, phenylalanine is not produced when Neotame is used as a sweetener. Very small amounts of Neotame are needed because it is about 10 000 times sweeter than sucrose.

TABLE 15.2 Relative Sweetness of Sugars and Artificial Sweeteners

	Sweetness Relative to Sucrose (=100)
Monosaccharides	
Galactose	30
Glucose	75
Fructose	175
Disaccharides	
Lactose	16
Maltose	33
Sucrose	100
Sugar Alcohols	
Sorbitol	60
Maltitol	80
Xylitol	100
Artificial Sweeteners (Noncarbohydrate)	
Aspartame	18 000
Saccharin	45 000
Sucralose	60 000
Neotame	1 000 000

Large alkyl group to modify Aspartame   Neotame

Saccharin, which is marketed as Sweet'N Low, has been used as a noncarbohydrate artificial sweetener for more than 60 yr. The use of saccharin has been banned in Canada because studies indicate that it may cause bladder tumors. However, it has still been approved by the FDA for use in the United States.

Saccharin (Sweet'N Low)

Artificial sweeteners may be used as sugar substitutes.

Chemistry Link to **Health**
Blood Types and Carbohydrates

Every individual's blood can be typed as one of four blood groups: A, B, AB, and O. Although there is some variation among ethnic groups in the United States, the incidence of blood types in the general population is about 43% O, 40% A, 12% B, and 5% AB.

The blood types A, B, and O are determined by terminal saccharides attached to the surface of red blood cells. Blood type O has three terminal monosaccharides: N-acetylglucosamine, galactose, and fucose. Blood type A contains the same three monosaccharides, but in addition, a molecule of N-acetylgalactosamine is attached to galactose in the saccharide chain. Blood type B also contains the same three monosaccharides, but in addition, a second molecule of galactose is attached to the saccharide chain. Blood type AB consists of the same monosaccharides found in blood types A and B. The structures of these monosaccharides are as follows:

N-Acetylglucosamine (N-AcGlu)   N-Acetylgalactosamine (N-AcGal)

← N-Acetyl →

L-Fucose (Fuc)   D-Galactose (Gal)

Because there is a different monosaccharide in type A blood than in type B blood, persons with type A blood produce antibodies against type B, and vice versa. For example, if a person with type A blood receives a transfusion of type B blood, the donor red blood cells are treated as if they are foreign invaders. An immune reaction occurs when the body sees the foreign saccharides on the red blood cells and makes antibodies against these donor red blood cells. The red blood cells will then clump together, or agglutinate, resulting in kidney failure, circulatory collapse, and death. The same thing will happen if a person with type B blood receives type A blood.

Because type O blood has only the three common terminal monosaccharides, a person with type O produces antibodies against blood types A, B, and AB. However, persons with blood types A, B, and AB can receive type O blood. Thus, persons with type O blood are *universal donors*. Because type AB blood contains all the terminal monosaccharides, a person with type AB blood produces no antibodies to type A, B, or O blood. Persons with type AB blood are *universal recipients*. Table 15.3 summarizes the compatibility of blood groups for transfusion.

Terminal Saccharides for Each Blood Type

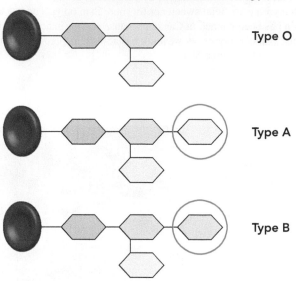

Blood from a donor is screened to make sure that there is an exact match with the blood type of the recipient.

TABLE 15.3 Compatibility of Blood Groups

Blood Type	Produces Antibodies Against	Can Receive
A	B, AB	A, O
B	A, AB	B, O
AB universal recipient	None	A, B, AB, O
O universal donor	A, B, AB	O

Red blood cell surface

N-Acetylglucosamine   N-Acetylgalactosamine

Fucose   Galactose

► **SAMPLE PROBLEM 15.5**
Glycosidic Bonds in Disaccharides

Melibiose is a disaccharide that is 30 times sweeter than sucrose.

a. What are the monosaccharide units in melibiose?
b. What type of glycosidic bond links the monosaccharides?
c. Identify the structure as α- or β-melibiose.

Melibiose

SOLUTION

a. First monosaccharide (left)

When the —OH group on carbon 4 is above the plane, it is D-galactose. When the —OH group on carbon 1 is below the plane, it is α-D-galactose.

Second monosaccharide (right)

When the —OH group on carbon 4 is below the plane, it is α-D-glucose.

b. Type of glycosidic bond

The —OH group at carbon 1 of α-D-galactose bonds with the —OH group on carbon 6 of glucose, which makes it an α(1 → 6)-glycosidic bond.

c. Name of disaccharide

The —OH group on carbon 1 of glucose is below the plane, which α-melibiose.

STUDY CHECK 15.5

Cellobiose is a disaccharide composed of two D-glucose molecules connected by a β(1 → 4)-glycosidic linkage. Draw the Haworth structure for β-cellobiose.

ANSWER

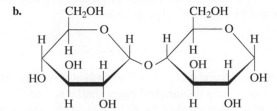

QUESTIONS AND PROBLEMS

15.5 Disaccharides

LEARNING GOAL Describe the monosaccharide units and linkages in disaccharides.

15.31 For each of the following, give the monosaccharide units produced by hydrolysis, the type of glycosidic bond, and the name of the disaccharide including α or β:

a.

b.

15.32 For each of the following, give the monosaccharide units produced by hydrolysis, the type of glycosidic bond, and the name of the disaccharide including α or β:

a.

b.

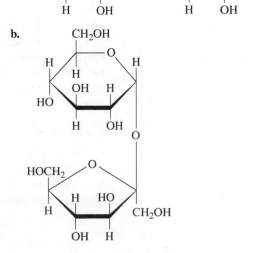

15.33 Indicate whether each disaccharide in problem 15.31 is a reducing sugar or not.

15.34 Indicate whether each disaccharide in problem 15.32 is a reducing sugar or not.

℞ Clinical Applications

15.35 Identify the disaccharide that fits each of the following descriptions:
  a. ordinary table sugar
  b. found in milk and milk products

  c. also called malt sugar
  d. hydrolysis gives galactose and glucose

15.36 Identify the disaccharide that fits each of the following descriptions:
  a. not a reducing sugar
  b. composed of two glucose units
  c. also called milk sugar
  d. hydrolysis gives glucose and fructose

Describe the structural features of amylose, amylopectin, glycogen, and cellulose.

15.6 Polysaccharides

A polysaccharide is a polymer of many monosaccharides joined together. Four important polysaccharides—*amylose, amylopectin, cellulose,* and *glycogen*—are all polymers of D-glucose that differ only in the type of glycosidic bonds and the amount of branching in the molecule.

Starch

Starch, a storage form of glucose in plants, is found as insoluble granules in rice, wheat, potatoes, beans, and cereals. Starch is composed of two kinds of polysaccharides, amylose and amylopectin. **Amylose**, which makes up about 20% of starch, consists of 250 to 4000 α-D-glucose molecules connected by $\alpha(1 \rightarrow 4)$-glycosidic bonds in a continuous chain. Sometimes called a straight-chain polymer, polymers of amylose are actually coiled in helical fashion (see Figure 15.5a).

Amylopectin, which makes up as much as 80% of starch, is a branched-chain polysaccharide. Like amylose, the glucose molecules are connected by $\alpha(1 \rightarrow 4)$-glycosidic bonds. However, at about every 25 glucose units, there is a branch of glucose molecules attached by an $\alpha(1 \rightarrow 6)$-glycosidic bond between carbon 1 of the branch and carbon 6 in the main chain (see Figure 15.5b).

Starches hydrolyze easily in water and acid to give smaller saccharides, called *dextrins*, which then hydrolyze to maltose and finally glucose. In our bodies, these complex carbohydrates are digested by the enzymes amylase (in saliva) and maltase (in the intestine). The glucose obtained provides about 50% of our nutritional calories.

$$\text{Amylose, amylopectin} \xrightarrow{\text{H}^+ \text{ or amylase}} \text{dextrins} \xrightarrow{\text{H}^+ \text{ or amylase}} \text{maltose} \xrightarrow{\text{H}^+ \text{ or maltase}} \text{many D-glucose units}$$

Glycogen

Glycogen, or animal starch, is a polymer of glucose that is stored in the liver and muscle of animals. It is hydrolyzed in our cells at a rate that maintains the blood level of glucose and provides energy between meals. The structure of glycogen is very similar to that of amylopectin found in plants, except that glycogen is more highly branched. In glycogen, the glucose units are joined by $\alpha(1 \rightarrow 4)$-glycosidic bonds, and branches occurring about every 10 to 15 glucose units are attached by $\alpha(1 \rightarrow 6)$-glycosidic bonds.

Cellulose

Cellulose is the major structural material of wood and plants. Cotton is almost pure cellulose. In cellulose, glucose molecules form a long unbranched chain similar to that of amylose. However, the glucose units in cellulose are linked by $\beta(1 \rightarrow 4)$-glycosidic bonds. The cellulose chains do not form coils like amylose but are aligned in parallel rows that

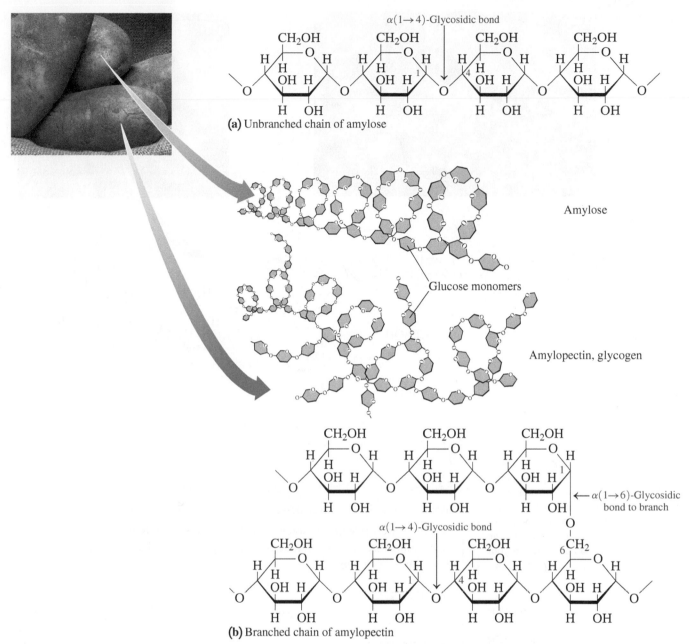

(a) Unbranched chain of amylose

Amylose

Glucose monomers

Amylopectin, glycogen

(b) Branched chain of amylopectin

FIGURE 15.5 ▶ The structure of amylose **(a)** is a straight-chain polysaccharide of glucose units, and the structure of amylopectin **(b)** is a branched chain of glucose.

What are the two types of glycosidic bonds that link glucose molecules in amylopectin?

are held in place by hydrogen bonds between hydroxyl groups in adjacent chains, making cellulose insoluble in water. This gives a rigid structure to the cell walls in wood and fiber that is more resistant to hydrolysis than are the starches (see Figure 15.6).

Humans have an enzyme called α-amylase in saliva and pancreatic juices that hydrolyze the $\alpha(1 \rightarrow 4)$-glycosidic bonds of starches, but not the $\beta(1 \rightarrow 4)$-glycosidic bonds of cellulose. Thus, humans cannot digest cellulose. Animals such as horses, cows, and goats can obtain glucose from cellulose because their digestive systems contain bacteria that provide enzymes such as cellulase to hydrolyze $\beta(1 \rightarrow 4)$-glycosidic bonds.

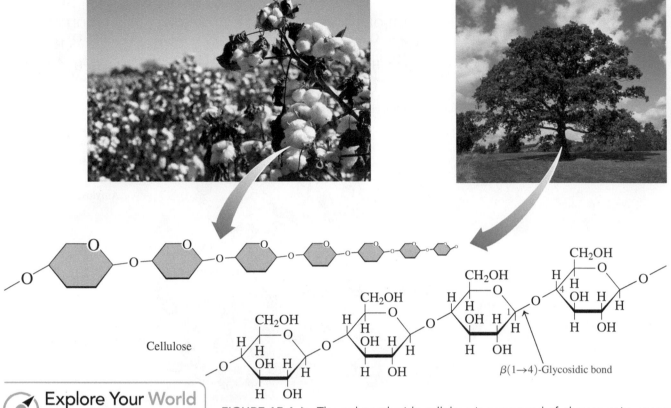

Cellulose

β(1→4)-Glycosidic bond

FIGURE 15.6 ▶ The polysaccharide cellulose is composed of glucose units connected by β(1 → 4)-glycosidic bonds.

🔍 Why are humans unable to digest cellulose?

Explore Your World
Polysaccharides

Read the nutrition label on a box of crackers, cereal, bread, chips, or pasta. The major ingredient in crackers is flour, which contains starch. Chew on a single cracker for 4 or 5 min. Note how the taste changes as you chew the cracker. An enzyme (amylase) in your saliva breaks apart the bonds in starch.

Questions

1. How are carbohydrates listed on the label?
2. What other carbohydrates are listed?
3. How did the taste of the cracker change during the time that you chewed it?
4. What happens to the starches in the cracker as the amylase enzyme in your saliva reacts with the amylose and amylopectin?

▶**SAMPLE PROBLEM 15.6 Structures of Polysaccharides**

Identify the polysaccharide described by each of the following:

a. a polysaccharide that is stored in the liver and muscle tissues
b. an unbranched polysaccharide containing β(1 → 4)-glycosidic bonds
c. a starch containing α(1 → 4)- and α(1 → 6)-glycosidic bonds

SOLUTION

a. glycogen   **b.** cellulose   **c.** amylopectin, glycogen

STUDY CHECK 15.6

Cellulose and amylose are both unbranched glucose polymers. How do they differ?

ANSWER

Cellulose contains glucose units connected by β(1 → 4)-glycosidic bonds, whereas the glucose units in amylose are connected by α(1 → 4)-glycosidic bonds.

QUESTIONS AND PROBLEMS

15.6 Polysaccharides

LEARNING GOAL Describe the structural features of amylose, amylopectin, glycogen, and cellulose.

15.37 Describe the similarities and differences in the following:
    a. amylose and amylopectin
    b. amylopectin and glycogen

15.38 Describe the similarities and differences in the following:
    a. amylose and cellulose
    b. cellulose and glycogen

℞ **Clinical Applications**

15.39 Give the name of one or more polysaccharides that matches each of the following descriptions:
    a. not digestible by humans
    b. the storage form of carbohydrates in plants
    c. contains only α(1 → 4)-glycosidic bonds
    d. the most highly branched polysaccharide

15.40 Give the name of one or more polysaccharides that matches each of the following descriptions:
  a. the storage form of carbohydrates in animals
  b. contains only $\beta(1 \rightarrow 4)$-glycosidic bonds
  c. contains both $\alpha(1 \rightarrow 4)$- and $\alpha(1 \rightarrow 6)$-glycosidic bonds
  d. produces maltose during digestion

Clinical Update
Kate's Program for Type 2 Diabetes

At Kate's next appointment, Paula showed Kate how to use a glucose meter. She instructed Kate to measure her blood glucose level twice a day before and after breakfast and dinner. Paula explains to Kate that her pre-meal blood glucose level should be 110 mg/dL or less, and if it increases by more than 50 mg/dL, she needs to lower the amount of carbohydrates she consumes.

Kate and Paula proceed to plan several meals. Because a meal should contain about 45 to 60 g of carbohydrates, they combined fruits and vegetables that have high and low levels of carbohydrates in the same meal to stay within the recommended range. Kate and Paula also discuss the fact that complex carbohydrates in the body take longer to break down into glucose, and therefore, raise the blood sugar level more gradually.

Kate increased her exercise to walking 30 minutes twice a day. She began to change her diet by eating 6 small meals a day consisting of more fruits and vegetables without starch such as green beans and broccoli, $\frac{1}{4}$ cup of whole grains, and $\frac{1}{4}$ cup of chicken or fish. Kate also decreased the amounts of breads and pasta because she knew carbohydrates would raise her blood sugar.

After three months, Kate reported that she had lost 10 lb and that her blood glucose had dropped to 146 mg/dL. Her blurry vision had improved and need to urinate had decreased.

℞ Clinical Applications

15.41 Kate's blood volume is 3.9 L. Before treatment, if her blood glucose was 178 mg/dL, how many grams of glucose were in her blood?

15.42 Kate's blood volume is 3.9 L. After three months of diet and exercise, if her blood glucose is 146 mg/dL, how many grams of glucose are in her blood?

15.43 For breakfast, Kate had 1 cup of orange juice (23 g carbohydrate), 2 slices of wheat toast (24 g carbohydrate), 2 tablespoons of grape jam (26 g carbohydrate), and coffee with sugar substitute (0 g carbohydrate).
  a. Has Kate remained within the limit of 45 to 60 g for carbohydrate?
  b. Using the energy value of 4 kcal/g for carbohydrate, calculate the total kilocalories from carbohydrates in Kate's breakfast, rounded to the tens place.

15.44 The next day, Kate had 1 cup of cereal (15 g carbohydrate) with skim milk (7 g carbohydrate), 1 banana (17 g carbohydrate), and 1/2 cup of orange juice (12 g carbohydrate) for breakfast.
  a. Has Kate remained within the limit of 45 to 60 g for carbohydrate?
  b. Using the energy value of 4 kcal/g for carbohydrate, calculate the total kilocalories from carbohydrates in Kate's breakfast, rounded to the tens place.

CONCEPT MAP

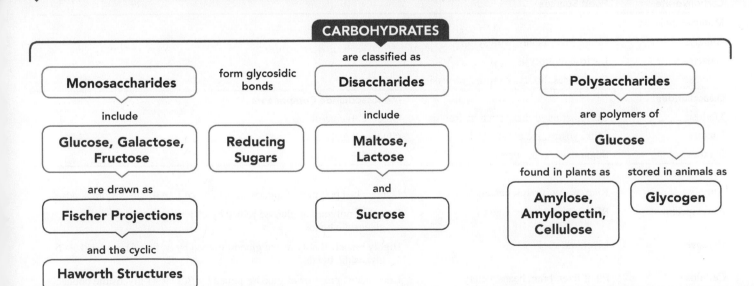

CARBOHYDRATES
are classified as

Monosaccharides — form glycosidic bonds — **Disaccharides** — **Polysaccharides**

include
Glucose, Galactose, Fructose

Reducing Sugars

include
Maltose, Lactose
and
Sucrose

are polymers of
Glucose

found in plants as
Amylose, Amylopectin, Cellulose

stored in animals as
Glycogen

are drawn as
Fischer Projections
and the cyclic
Haworth Structures

CHAPTER REVIEW

15.1 Carbohydrates
LEARNING GOAL Classify a monosaccharide as an aldose or a ketose, and indicate the number of carbon atoms.

- Carbohydrates are classified as monosaccharides (simple sugars), disaccharides (two monosaccharide units), or polysaccharides (many monosaccharide units).
- Monosaccharides are polyhydroxy aldehydes (aldoses) or ketones (ketoses).
- Monosaccharides are also classified by their number of carbon atoms: triose, tetrose, pentose, or hexose.

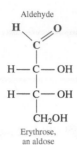
Aldehyde

Erythrose, an aldose

15.2 Fischer Projections of Monosaccharides
LEARNING GOAL Identify and draw the D and L configurations of the Fischer projections for common monosaccharides.

- In a D enantiomer, the —OH group is on the right of the chiral carbon farthest from the carbonyl group; the —OH group is on the left in the L enantiomer.
- Important monosaccharides are the aldohexoses, glucose and galactose, and the ketohexose, fructose.

L-Glucose   D-Glucose

15.3 Haworth Structures of Monosaccharides
LEARNING GOAL Draw and identify the Haworth structures for monosaccharides.

- The predominant form of a monosaccharide is a ring of five or six atoms.
- The cyclic structure forms when an —OH group (usually the one on carbon 5 in hexoses) reacts with the carbonyl group of the same molecule.
- The formation of a new hydroxyl group on carbon 1 gives α and β anomers of the cyclic monosaccharide.

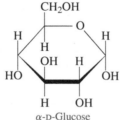
α-D-Glucose

15.4 Chemical Properties of Monosaccharides
LEARNING GOAL Identify the products of oxidation or reduction of monosaccharides; determine whether a carbohydrate is a reducing sugar.

- The aldehyde group in an aldose can be oxidized to a carboxylic acid, while the carbonyl group in an aldose or a ketose can be reduced to give a hydroxyl group.
- Monosaccharides that are reducing sugars have an aldehyde group in the open chain that can be oxidized.

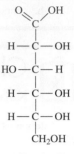
D-Gluconic acid

15.5 Disaccharides
LEARNING GOAL Describe the monosaccharide units and linkages in disaccharides.

- Disaccharides are two monosaccharide units joined together by a glycosidic bond.
- In the common disaccharides maltose, lactose, and sucrose, there is at least one glucose unit.
- Maltose and lactose form α and β anomers, which makes them reducing sugars.
- Sucrose does not have α and β anomers and is not a reducing sugar.

15.6 Polysaccharides
LEARNING GOAL Describe the structural features of amylose, amylopectin, glycogen, and cellulose.

- Polysaccharides are polymers of monosaccharide units.
- Amylose is an unbranched chain of glucose with α(1 → 4)-glycosidic bonds, and amylopectin is a branched polymer of glucose with α(1 → 4)- and α(1 → 6)-glycosidic bonds.
- Glycogen is similar to amylopectin with more branching.
- Cellulose is also a polymer of glucose, but in cellulose, the glycosidic bonds are β(1 → 4)-bonds.

SUMMARY OF CARBOHYDRATES

Carbohydrate	Food Sources	Monosaccharide Components
Monosaccharides		
Glucose	Fruit juices, honey, corn syrup	
Galactose	Lactose hydrolysis	
Fructose	Fruit juices, honey, sucrose hydrolysis	
Disaccharides		**Monosaccharide Components**
Maltose	Germinating grains, starch hydrolysis	Glucose + glucose
Lactose	Milk, yogurt, ice cream	Glucose + galactose
Sucrose	Sugar cane, sugar beets	Glucose + fructose
Polysaccharides		
Amylose	Rice, wheat, grains, cereals	Unbranched polymer of glucose joined by α(1 → 4)-glycosidic bonds
Amylopectin	Rice, wheat, grains, cereals	Branched polymer of glucose joined by α(1 → 4)- and α(1 → 6)-glycosidic bonds
Glycogen	Liver, muscles	Highly branched polymer of glucose joined by α(1 → 4)- and α(1 → 6)-glycosidic bonds
Cellulose	Plant fiber, bran, beans, celery	Unbranched polymer of glucose joined by β(1 → 4)-glycosidic bonds

SUMMARY OF REACTIONS

The chapter sections to review are shown after the name of the reaction.

Oxidation and Reduction of Monosaccharides (15.4)

D-Glucitol   D-Glucose   D-Gluconic acid

Formation of Disaccharides (15.5)

Monosaccharide   Monosaccharide   Disaccharide

Hydrolysis of Polysaccharides (15.6)

Amylose, amylopectin $\xrightarrow{\text{H}^+ \text{ or enzymes}}$ many D-glucose units

KEY TERMS

aldose A monosaccharide that contains an aldehyde group.

amylopectin A branched-chain polymer of starch composed of glucose units joined by $\alpha(1 \rightarrow 4)$- and $\alpha(1 \rightarrow 6)$-glycosidic bonds.

amylose An unbranched polymer of starch composed of glucose units joined by $\alpha(1 \rightarrow 4)$-glycosidic bonds.

carbohydrate A simple or complex sugar composed of carbon, hydrogen, and oxygen.

cellulose An unbranched polysaccharide composed of glucose units linked by $\beta(1 \rightarrow 4)$-glycosidic bonds that cannot be hydrolyzed by the human digestive system.

disaccharide A carbohydrate composed of two monosaccharides joined by a glycosidic bond.

fructose A monosaccharide that is also called levulose and fruit sugar and is found in honey and fruit juices; it is combined with glucose in sucrose.

galactose A monosaccharide that occurs combined with glucose in lactose.

glucose An aldohexose found in fruits, vegetables, corn syrup, and honey that is also known as blood sugar and dextrose. The most prevalent monosaccharide in the diet. Most polysaccharides are polymers of glucose.

glycogen A polysaccharide formed in the liver and muscles for the storage of glucose as an energy reserve. It is composed of

glucose in a highly branched polymer joined by $\alpha(1 \rightarrow 4)$- and $\alpha(1 \rightarrow 6)$-glycosidic bonds.

glycosidic bond The bond that forms when the hydroxyl group of one monosaccharide reacts with the hydroxyl group of another monosaccharide. It is the type of bond that links monosaccharide units in di- or polysaccharides.

Haworth structure The ring structure of a monosaccharide.

ketose A monosaccharide that contains a ketone group.

lactose A disaccharide consisting of glucose and galactose found in milk and milk products.

maltose A disaccharide consisting of two glucose units; it is obtained from the hydrolysis of starch and is found in germinating grains.

monosaccharide A polyhydroxy compound that contains an aldehyde or ketone group.

polysaccharide A polymer of many monosaccharide units, usually glucose. Polysaccharides differ in the types of glycosidic bonds and the amount of branching in the polymer.

reducing sugar A carbohydrate with an aldehyde group capable of reducing the Cu^{2+} in Benedict's reagent.

sucrose A disaccharide composed of glucose and fructose; a nonreducing sugar, commonly called table sugar or "sugar."

⚛ CORE CHEMISTRY SKILLS

Identifying D- and L-Fischer Projections (15.2)

- The Fischer projection is a simplified way to draw the arrangements of atoms by placing the carbon atoms at the intersection of vertical and horizontal lines.
- The names of the mirror images are labeled D or L to differentiate between enantiomers of carbohydrates.

Example: Identify each of the following as the D or L enantiomer:

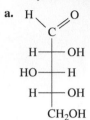

Answer: In **a**, the —OH group on the chiral carbon farthest from the carbonyl group is on the right; it is the D enantiomer.

In **b**, the —OH group on the chiral carbon farthest from the carbonyl group is on the left; it is the L enantiomer.

Drawing Haworth Structures (15.3)

- The Haworth structure shows the ring structure of a monosaccharide.
- Groups on the right side of the Fischer projection of the monosaccharide are below the plane of the ring, those on the left are above the plane.

- The new hemiacetal —OH group that forms is the α anomer if it is below the plane of the ring, or the β anomer if it is above the plane.

Example: Draw the Haworth structure for β-D-idose.

Answer: In the β-anomer, the new —OH group is above the plane of the ring.

UNDERSTANDING THE CONCEPTS

The chapter sections to review are shown in parentheses at the end of each question.

15.45 Isomaltose, obtained from the breakdown of starch, has the following Haworth structure: (15.3, 15.4, 15.5)

Isomaltose

a. Is isomaltose a mono-, di-, or polysaccharide?
b. What are the monosaccharides in isomaltose?
c. What is the glycosidic link in isomaltose?
d. Is this the α or β anomer of isomaltose?
e. Is isomaltose a reducing sugar?

15.46 Sophorose, a carbohydrate found in certain types of beans, has the following Haworth structure: (15.3, 15.4, 15.5)

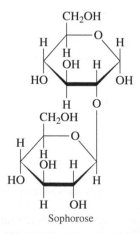

Sophorose

a. Is sophorose a mono-, di-, or polysaccharide?
b. What are the monosaccharides in sophorose?
c. What is the glycosidic link in sophorose?
d. Is this the α or β anomer of sophorose?
e. Is sophorose a reducing sugar?

15.47 Melezitose, a carbohydrate secreted by insects, has the following Haworth structure: (15.3, 15.4, 15.5)

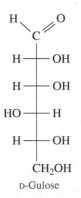

Melezitose

a. Is melezitose a mono-, di-, or trisaccharide?
b. What ketohexose and aldohexose are present in melezitose?
c. Is melezitose a reducing sugar?

15.48 What are the disaccharides and polysaccharides present in each of the following? (15.5, 15.6)

(a)   (b)

(c)   (d)

ADDITIONAL QUESTIONS AND PROBLEMS

15.49 What are the differences in the Fischer projections of D-fructose and D-galactose? (15.2)

15.50 What are the differences in the Fischer projections of D-glucose and D-fructose? (15.2)

15.51 What are the differences in the Fischer projections of D-galactose and L-galactose? (15.2)

15.52 What are the differences in the Haworth structures of α-D-glucose and β-D-glucose? (15.3)

15.53 The sugar D-gulose is a sweet-tasting syrup. (15.2, 15.3)

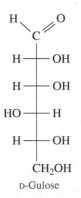

D-Gulose

a. Draw the Fischer projection for L-gulose.
b. Draw the Haworth structures for α- and β-D-gulose.

15.54 Use the Fischer projection for D-gulose in problem 15.53 to answer each of the following: (15.2, 15.4)
a. Draw the Fischer projection and name the product formed by the reduction of D-gulose.
b. Draw the Fischer projection and name the product formed by the oxidation of D-gulose.

15.55 D-Sorbitol, a sweetener found in seaweed and berries, contains only hydroxyl functional groups. When D-sorbitol is oxidized, it forms D-glucose. Draw the Fischer projection for D-sorbitol. (15.2, 15.4)

15.56 Raffinose is a trisaccharide found in Australian manna and in cottonseed meal. It is composed of three different monosaccharides. Identify the monosaccharides in raffinose. (15.3)

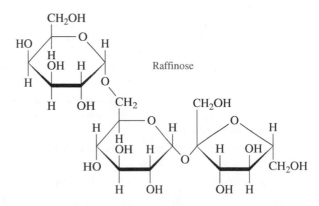

Raffinose

15.57 If α-galactose is dissolved in water, β-galactose is eventually present. Explain how this occurs. (15.4)

15.58 Why are lactose and maltose reducing sugars, but sucrose is not? (15.5)

CHALLENGE QUESTIONS

The following groups of questions are related to the topics in this chapter. However, they do not all follow the chapter order, and they require you to combine concepts and skills from several sections. These questions will help you increase your critical thinking skills and prepare for your next exam.

15.59 α-Cellobiose is a disaccharide obtained from the hydrolysis of cellulose. It is quite similar to maltose except it has a β(1 → 4)-glycosidic bond. Draw the Haworth structure for α-cellobiose. (15.3, 15.5)

15.60 The disaccharide trehalose found in mushrooms is composed of two α-D-glucose molecules joined by an α(1 → 1)-glycosidic bond. Draw the Haworth structure for trehalose. (15.3, 15.5)

15.61 Gentiobiose is found in saffron. (15.3, 15.4, 15.5)
  a. Gentiobiose contains two glucose molecules linked by a β(1 → 6)-glycosidic bond. Draw the Haworth structure for β-gentiobiose.
  b. Is gentiobiose a reducing sugar? Explain.

15.62 Identify the Fischer projection **A** to **D** that matches each of the following: (15.1, 15.2)
  a. the L enantiomer of mannose   **b.** a ketopentose
  c. an aldopentose   **d.** a ketohexose

(Fischer projections A, B, C, D shown at right)

A — aldohexose Fischer projection
B — aldohexose Fischer projection
C — ketohexose Fischer projection
D — ketohexose Fischer projection

ANSWERS

Answers to Selected Questions and Problems

15.1 Photosynthesis requires CO_2, H_2O, and the energy from the Sun. Respiration requires O_2 from the air and glucose from our foods.

15.3 Monosaccharides can be a chain of three to eight carbon atoms, one in a carbonyl group as an aldehyde or ketone, and the rest attached to hydroxyl groups. A monosaccharide cannot be split or hydrolyzed into smaller carbohydrates. A disaccharide consists of two monosaccharide units joined together that can be split.

15.5 Hydroxyl groups are found in all monosaccharides along with a carbonyl on the first or second carbon that gives an aldehyde or ketone functional group.

15.7 A ketopentose contains hydroxyl and ketone functional groups and has five carbon atoms.

15.9 a. ketohexose   **b.** aldopentose

15.11 a. D   **b.** D   **c.** L   **d.** D

15.13 a. (Fischer projection — aldotriose)
  b. (Fischer projection — ketopentose)
  c. (Fischer projection — aldohexose)
  d. (Fischer projection — aldohexose)

15.15

D-Glucose   L-Glucose

(Fischer projections of D-Glucose and L-Glucose)

15.17 In D-galactose, the —OH group on carbon 4 extends to the left. In D-glucose, this —OH group goes to the right.

15.19 a. glucose   **b.** galactose

15.21 In the cyclic structure of glucose, there are five carbon atoms and an oxygen atom.

15.23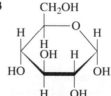

α-D-Glucose   β-D-Glucose

15.25 a. α anomer   **b.** α anomer

15.27 (Fischer projection)

D-Xylitol

15.29 Oxidation product: Reduction product:

HO⧵C⧸O
|
HO——H
|
H——OH
|
H——OH
|
CH₂OH

D-Arabinonic acid

CH₂OH
|
HO——H
|
H——OH
|
H——OH
|
CH₂OH

D-Arabitol

15.31 a. galactose and glucose; $\beta(1 \rightarrow 4)$-glycosidic bond; β-lactose
b. glucose and glucose; $\alpha(1 \rightarrow 4)$-glycosidic bond; α-maltose

15.33 a. is a reducing sugar   **b.** is a reducing sugar

15.35 a. sucrose   **b.** lactose
c. maltose   **d.** lactose

15.37 a. Amylose is an unbranched polymer of glucose units joined by $\alpha(1 \rightarrow 4)$-glycosidic bonds; amylopectin is a branched polymer of glucose joined by $\alpha(1 \rightarrow 4)$- and $\alpha(1 \rightarrow 6)$-glycosidic bonds.
b. Amylopectin, which is produced in plants, is a branched polymer of glucose, joined by $\alpha(1 \rightarrow 4)$- and $\alpha(1 \rightarrow 6)$-glycosidic bonds. The branches in amylopectin occur about every 25 glucose units. Glycogen, which is produced in animals, is a highly branched polymer of glucose, joined by $\alpha(1 \rightarrow 4)$- and $\alpha(1 \rightarrow 6)$-glycosidic bonds. The branches in glycogen occur about every 10 to 15 glucose units.

15.39 a. cellulose   **b.** amylose, amylopectin
c. amylose   **d.** glycogen

15.41 6.9 of glucose

15.43 a. Kate's breakfast had 73 g of carbohydrate. She still needs to cut down the amount of carbohydrate.
b. 290 kcal

15.45 a. disaccharide   **b.** α-D-glucose
c. $\alpha(1 \rightarrow 6)$-glycosidic bond   **d.** α
e. is a reducing sugar

15.47 a. trisaccharide
b. two glucose and one fructose
c. Melezitose has no free —OH groups on the glucose or fructose molecules; like sucrose it is not a reducing sugar.

15.49 D-Fructose is a ketohexose, whereas D-galactose is an aldohexose. In the Fischer projection of D-galactose, the —OH group on carbon 4 is drawn on the left; in fructose, the —OH group is drawn on the right.

15.51 L-Galactose is the mirror image of D-galactose. In the Fischer projection of D-galactose, the —OH groups on carbon 2 and carbon 5 are drawn on the right side, but they are drawn on the left for carbon 3 and carbon 4. In L-galactose, the —OH groups are reversed; carbons 2 and 5 have —OH groups drawn on the left, and carbons 3 and 4 have —OH groups drawn on the right.

15.53 a.

H⧵C⧸O
|
HO——H
|
HO——H
|
H——OH
|
HO——H
|
CH₂OH

L-Gulose

b.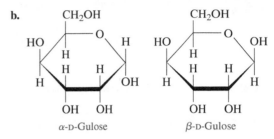

α-D-Gulose β-D-Gulose

15.55

CH₂OH
|
H——OH
|
HO——H
|
H——OH
|
H——OH
|
CH₂OH

15.57 When α-galactose forms an open-chain structure, it can close to form either α- or β-galactose.

15.59

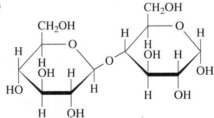

15.61 a.

[structure of gentiobiose]

b. Yes. Gentiobiose is a reducing sugar. The ring on the right can open up to form an aldehyde that can be oxidized.

Carboxylic Acids and Esters

MAUREEN, A SURGICAL TECHNICIAN, BEGINS

preparing for Robert's heart surgery. After Maureen places all of the surgical instruments into an autoclave for sterilization, she prepares the room by ensuring that all of the equipment is working properly. She also determines that the room is sterile, as this will minimize the chance of an infection. Right before surgery begins, Maureen shaves Robert's chest and disinfects the incision sites.

After the surgery, Maureen applies Indermil, which is a type of liquid bandage, to Robert's incision sites. Liquid bandages are tissue adhesives that seal surgical or wound incisions on a patient. Stitches and staples are not required and scarring is minimal. The polymer in a liquid bandage is typically dissolved in an alcohol-based solvent. The alcohol also acts as an antiseptic.

Indermil is a cyanoester or cyanoacrylate, as it contains a cyano group ($C\equiv N$) and an ester functional group. Esters have a carbonyl group ($C=O$), which has a single bond to a carbon group on one side of the carbonyl and an oxygen atom on the other side. The oxygen atom is then bonded to a carbon group by a single bond. Cyanoacrylates are a group of adhesives that include "Super Glue" and Indermil, which is butyl cyanoacrylate. The *ate* in butyl cyanoacrylate indicates that an ester is present in the molecule, and the *butyl* indicates the four-carbon group that is bonded to the oxygen atom.

In water and body fluids, these adhesives rapidly form strong chains that join the edges of surfaces and hold them in place.

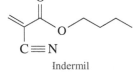

Indermil

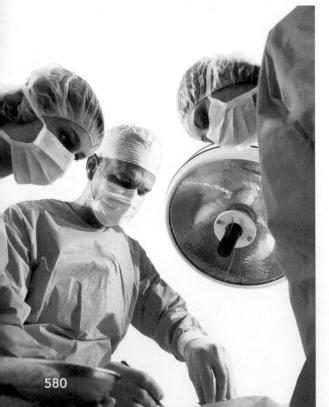

CAREER Surgical Technician

Surgical technicians prepare the operating room by creating a sterile environment. This includes setting up surgical instruments and equipment, and ensuring that all of the equipment is working properly. A sterile environment is critical to the patient's recovery, as it helps lower the chance of an infection. They also prepare patients for surgery by washing, shaving, and disinfecting incision sites. During the surgery, a surgical technician provides the sterile instruments and supplies to the surgeons and surgical assistants.

C arboxylic acids are weak acids. They have a sour or tart taste, produce hydronium ions in water, and neutralize bases. You encounter carboxylic acids when you use a salad dressing containing vinegar, which is a solution of acetic acid and water, or experience the sour taste of citric acid in a grapefruit or lemon. When a carboxylic acid combines with an alcohol, an ester and water are produced. Fats and oils are esters of glycerol and fatty acids, which are long-chain carboxylic acids. Esters produce the pleasant aromas and flavors of many fruits, such as bananas, strawberries, and oranges.

CHAPTER READINESS*

⚙ CORE CHEMISTRY SKILLS

- Writing Equations for Reactions of Acids and Bases (11.7)
- Naming and Drawing Alkanes (12.2)

*These Core Chemistry Skills from previous chapters are listed here for your review as you proceed to the new material in this chapter.

16.1 Carboxylic Acids

In a **carboxylic acid**, the carbon atom of a carbonyl group is attached to a hydroxyl group, which forms a **carboxyl group.** The carboxyl functional group may be attached to an alkyl group or an aromatic group. Some ways to represent the carboxyl group in carboxylic acids are the following:

LEARNING GOAL

Write the IUPAC and common names for carboxylic acids and draw their condensed and line-angle structural formulas.

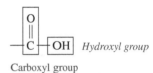

Carbonyl group

Carboxyl group

Hydroxyl group

$CH_3-\overset{\overset{O}{\|}}{C}-OH$

Ethanoic acid
(acetic acid)

(line-angle structure) OH

Propanoic acid
(propionic acid)

$CH_3-CH_2-CH_2-\overset{\overset{O}{\|}}{C}-OH$

Butanoic acid
(butyric acid)

⚙ CORE CHEMISTRY SKILL

Naming Carboxylic Acids

IUPAC Names of Carboxylic Acids

The IUPAC names of carboxylic acids replace the *e* of the corresponding alkane with *oic acid.* If there are substituents, the carbon chain is numbered beginning with the carboxyl carbon.

$H-\overset{\overset{O}{\|}}{C}-OH$

Methanoic acid

$CH_3-\overset{\overset{CH_3}{|}}{CH}-\overset{\overset{O}{\|}}{C}-OH$

2-Methylpropanoic acid

$CH_3-\overset{\overset{OH}{|}}{CH}-CH_2-\overset{\overset{O}{\|}}{C}-OH$

3-Hydroxybutanoic acid

The simplest aromatic carboxylic acid is named benzoic acid. With the carboxyl carbon bonded to carbon 1, the ring is numbered in the direction that gives substituents the smallest possible numbers. As before, the prefixes *ortho*, *meta*, and *para* may be used to show the position of one other substituent.

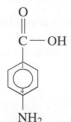

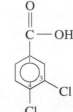

Benzoic acid

4-Aminobenzoic acid
(*p*-aminobenzoic acid;
PABA)

3,4-Dichlorobenzoic acid

Many carboxylic acids are still named by their common names, which use prefixes: *form, acet, propion, butyr*. When using the common names, the Greek letters alpha (α), beta (β), and gamma (γ) are assigned to the carbons adjacent to the carboxyl carbon.

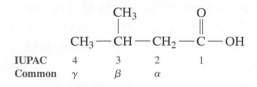

IUPAC	4	3	2	1
Common	γ	β	α	

Formic acid is injected under the skin during bee or red ant stings and other insect bites. Acetic acid is the oxidation product of the ethanol in wines and apple cider. The resulting solution of acetic acid and water is known as vinegar. Propionic acid is obtained from the fats of dairy products. Butyric acid gives the foul odor to rancid butter (see Table 16.1).

A red ant sting contains formic acid that irritates the skin.

TABLE 16.1 IUPAC and Common Names of Selected Carboxylic Acids

Condensed Structural Formula	IUPAC Name	Common Name	Ball-and-Stick Model
H—C—OH (with =O above C)	Methanoic acid	Formic acid	
CH_3—C—OH (with =O above C)	Ethanoic acid	Acetic acid	
CH_3—CH_2—C—OH (with =O above C)	Propanoic acid	Propionic acid	
CH_3—CH_2—CH_2—C—OH (with =O above C)	Butanoic acid	Butyric acid	

▶ SAMPLE PROBLEM 16.1 Naming Carboxylic Acids

Give the IUPAC and common name for the following carboxylic acid:

SOLUTION

	Given	Need
ANALYZE THE PROBLEM	carboxylic acid	IUPAC and common name

STEP **1** Identify the longest carbon chain and replace the *e* in the corresponding alkane name with *oic acid*. The IUPAC name of a carboxylic acid with four carbons is butanoic acid; the common name is butyric acid.

butanoic acid

(butyric acid)

STEP 2 Name and number any substituents by counting the carboxyl group as carbon 1. With a methyl group on the second carbon, the IUPAC name is 2-methylbutanoic acid. For the common name, the Greek letter α specifies the carbon atom next to the carboxyl carbon, α-methylbutyric acid.

Guide to Naming Carboxylic Acids

STEP 1
Identify the longest carbon chain and replace the *e* in the corresponding alkane name with *oic acid*.

STEP 2
Name and number any substituents by counting the carboxyl group as carbon 1.

2-methylbutanoic acid

(α-methylbutyric acid)

4 3 2 1
γ β α

STUDY CHECK 16.1

Give the IUPAC and common name for the following:

ANSWER

3-chlorobenzoic acid (*m*-chlorobenzoic acid)

Preparation of Carboxylic Acids

Carboxylic acids can be prepared from primary alcohols or aldehydes. For example, when ethyl alcohol in wine is exposed to oxygen in the air, vinegar is produced. The oxidation process converts the ethyl alcohol (1° alcohol) to acetaldehyde, and then to acetic acid, the carboxylic acid in vinegar.

The sour taste of vinegar is because of ethanoic acid (acetic acid).

$$CH_3-CH_2 \xrightarrow{[O]} CH_3-\overset{\displaystyle O}{\overset{\displaystyle \|}{C}}-H \xrightarrow{[O]} CH_3-\overset{\displaystyle O}{\overset{\displaystyle \|}{C}}-OH$$
|
OH

Ethanol   Ethanal   Ethanoic acid
(ethyl alcohol)   (acetaldehyde)   (acetic acid)

 # Chemistry Link to **Health**
Alpha Hydroxy Acids

Alpha hydroxy acids (AHAs), found in fruits, milk, and sugar cane, are naturally occurring carboxylic acids with a hydroxyl group (—OH) on the carbon atom that is adjacent to the carboxyl group. Cleopatra, Queen of Egypt, reportedly bathed in sour milk to smooth her skin. Dermatologists have been using products with high concentrations (20 to 70%) of AHAs to remove acne scars and in skin peels to reduce irregular pigmentation and age spots. Lower concentrations (8 to 10%) of AHAs are added to skin care products for the

purpose of smoothing fine lines, improving skin texture, and cleansing pores. Several different AHAs may be found in skin care products singly or in combination. Glycolic acid and lactic acid are most frequently used.

Recent studies indicate that products with AHAs increase sensitivity of the skin to sun and UV radiation. It is recommended that a sunscreen with a sun protection factor (SPF) of at least 15 be used when treating the skin with products that include AHAs. Products containing AHAs at concentrations under 10% and pH values greater than 3.5 are generally considered safe. However, the Food and Drug Administration (FDA) has received reports of AHAs causing skin irritation including blisters, rashes, and discoloration of the skin. The FDA does not require product safety reports from cosmetic manufacturers, although they are responsible for marketing safe products. The FDA advises that you test any product containing AHAs on a small area of skin before you use it on a large area.

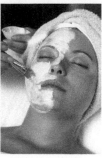

Alpha hydroxy carboxylic acids are used in many skin care products.

Alpha Hydroxy Acid (Source)	Condensed Structural Formula
Glycolic acid (sugar cane)	$HO-CH_2-\overset{\overset{O}{\|\|}}{C}-OH$
Lactic acid (sour milk)	$CH_3-\overset{\overset{OH}{\|}}{CH}-\overset{\overset{O}{\|\|}}{C}-OH$
Tartaric acid (grapes)	$HO-\overset{\overset{O}{\|\|}}{C}-\overset{\overset{OH}{\|}}{CH}-\overset{\overset{OH}{\|}}{CH}-\overset{\overset{O}{\|\|}}{C}-OH$
Malic acid (apples)	$HO-\overset{\overset{O}{\|\|}}{C}-CH_2-\overset{\overset{OH}{\|}}{CH}-\overset{\overset{O}{\|\|}}{C}-OH$
Citric acid (citrus fruits)	$\begin{array}{c} CH_2-COOH \\ \| \\ HO-C-COOH \\ \| \\ CH_2-COOH \end{array}$

QUESTIONS AND PROBLEMS

16.1 Carboxylic Acids

LEARNING GOAL Write the IUPAC and common names for carboxylic acids and draw their condensed and line-angle structural formulas.

16.1 What carboxylic acid is responsible for the pain of an ant sting?

16.2 What carboxylic acid is found in vinegar?

16.3 Draw the condensed structural formula and give the IUPAC name for each of the following:
   a. a carboxylic acid that has the formula $C_6H_{12}O_2$, with no substituents
   b. a carboxylic acid that has the formula $C_6H_{12}O_2$, with one ethyl substituent

16.4 Draw the condensed structural formula and give the IUPAC name for each of the following:
   a. a carboxylic acid that has the formula $C_5H_{10}O_2$, with no substituents
   b. a carboxylic acid that has the formula $C_5H_{10}O_2$, with two methyl substituents

16.5 Give the IUPAC and common name, if any, for each of the following carboxylic acids:

   a. $CH_3-\overset{\overset{O}{\|\|}}{C}-OH$

   b. (line-angle structure) with $\overset{O}{\|\|}$ and OH

   c. (line-angle structure) with $\overset{O}{\|\|}$ and OH

   d. (line-angle structure) with $\overset{O}{\|\|}$, C—OH, and Br, Br substituents

16.6 Give the IUPAC and common name, if any, for each of the following carboxylic acids:

   a. $H-\overset{\overset{O}{\|\|}}{C}-OH$

   b. (line-angle structure) with $\overset{O}{\|\|}$, OH and Br

   c. (benzene ring structure) with $\overset{O}{\|\|}$, C—OH and Cl

   d. $CH_3-CH_2-\overset{\overset{CH_3}{\|}}{CH}-\overset{\overset{O}{\|\|}}{C}-OH$

16.7 Draw the condensed structural formula for each of the following carboxylic acids:
   a. 2-chloroethanoic acid
   b. 3-hydroxypropanoic acid
   c. α-methylbutyric acid
   d. 3,5-dibromoheptanoic acid

16.8 Draw the condensed structural formula for each of the following carboxylic acids:
   a. pentanoic acid
   b. 3-ethylbenzoic acid
   c. α-hydroxyacetic acid
   d. 2,4-dibromobutanoic acid

16.9 Draw the condensed or line-angle structural formula for the carboxylic acid formed by the oxidation of each of the following:

a. CH_3-OH

b. $CH_3-\overset{\overset{\displaystyle O}{\|}}{C}-H$

c. (line-angle structure ending in OH)

d. (cyclopentane with CH₂OH)

16.10 Draw the condensed or line-angle structural formula for the carboxylic acid formed by the oxidation of each of the following:

a. (line-angle structure ending in OH)

b. (line-angle structure ending in aldehyde H)

c. $CH_3-\overset{\overset{\displaystyle CH_3}{|}}{CH}-CH_2-\overset{\overset{\displaystyle O}{\|}}{C}-H$

d. (benzene ring with CH_2-CH_2-OH)

16.2 Properties of Carboxylic Acids

LEARNING GOAL

Describe the boiling points, solubility, dissociation, and neutralization of carboxylic acids.

Carboxylic acids are among the most polar organic compounds because their functional group consists of two polar groups: a hydroxyl group ($-OH$) and a carbonyl group ($C=O$). The $-OH$ group is similar to the functional group in alcohols, and the $C=O$ is similar to the functional group of aldehydes and ketones.

Boiling Points

The polar carboxyl groups allow carboxylic acids to form several hydrogen bonds with other carboxylic acid molecules. This effect of hydrogen bonds gives carboxylic acids higher boiling points than alcohols, ketones, and aldehydes of similar molar mass.

	$CH_3-CH_2-\overset{\overset{\displaystyle O}{\|}}{C}-H$	$CH_3-CH_2-CH_2-OH$	$CH_3-\overset{\overset{\displaystyle O}{\|}}{C}-OH$
Name	Propanal	1-Propanol	Ethanoic acid
Molar Mass	58	60	60
Family	Aldehyde	Alcohol	Carboxylic acid
bp	49 °C	97 °C	118 °C

Boiling Point Increases →

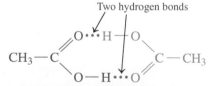

Two hydrogen bonds

A dimer of two ethanoic acid molecules

An important reason for the higher boiling points of carboxylic acids is that two carboxylic acids form hydrogen bonds between their carboxyl groups, resulting in a *dimer*. As a dimer, the mass of the carboxylic acid is effectively doubled, which means that a higher temperature is required to reach the boiling point. Table 16.2 lists the boiling points for some selected carboxylic acids.

▶ **SAMPLE PROBLEM 16.2 Boiling Points of Carboxylic Acids**

Match each of the compounds 2-butanol, pentane, propanoic acid with a boiling point of 141 °C, 100 °C, or 36 °C. (They have about the same molar mass.)

SOLUTION

The boiling point increases when the molecules of a compound can form hydrogen bonds or have dipole–dipole attractions. Pentane has the lowest boiling point, 36 °C,

Acetic acid crystals form at a freezing point of 16.5 °C.

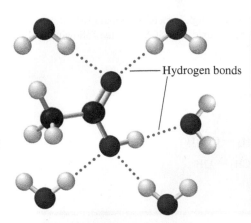

FIGURE 16.1 ▶ Acetic acid forms hydrogen bonds with water molecules.

Ⓠ Why do the atoms in the carboxyl group form hydrogen bonds with water molecules?

because alkanes cannot form hydrogen bonds or dipole–dipole attractions. 2-Butanol has a higher boiling point, 100 °C, than pentane because an alcohol can form hydrogen bonds. Propanoic acid has the highest boiling point, 141 °C, because carboxylic acids can form stable dimers through hydrogen bonding to increase their effective molar mass and therefore their boiling points.

STUDY CHECK 16.2

Why would methanoic acid (molar mass 46, bp 101 °C) have a higher boiling point than ethanol (molar mass 46, bp 78 °C)?

ANSWER

Two methanoic acid molecules form a dimer, which gives an effective molar mass that is double that of a single acid molecule. Thus, a higher boiling point is required than for ethanol.

Solubility in Water

Carboxylic acids with one to five carbons are soluble in water because the carboxyl group forms hydrogen bonds with several water molecules (see Figure 16.1). However, as the length of the hydrocarbon chain increases, the nonpolar portion reduces the solubility of the carboxylic acid in water. Carboxylic acids having more than five carbons are not very soluble in water. Table 16.2 lists the solubility for some selected carboxylic acids.

TABLE 16.2 Boiling Points, Solubilities, and Acid Dissociation Constants for Selected Carboxylic Acids

IUPAC Name	Condensed Structural Formula	Boiling Point (°C)	Solubility in Water	Acid Dissociation Constant (at 25 °C)
Methanoic acid	$H-\overset{\displaystyle O}{\overset{\|}{C}}-OH$	101	Soluble	1.8×10^{-4}
Ethanoic acid	$CH_3-\overset{\displaystyle O}{\overset{\|}{C}}-OH$	118	Soluble	1.8×10^{-5}
Propanoic acid	$CH_3-CH_2-\overset{\displaystyle O}{\overset{\|}{C}}-OH$	141	Soluble	1.3×10^{-5}
Butanoic acid	$CH_3-CH_2-CH_2-\overset{\displaystyle O}{\overset{\|}{C}}-OH$	164	Soluble	1.5×10^{-5}
Pentanoic acid	$CH_3-CH_2-CH_2-CH_2-\overset{\displaystyle O}{\overset{\|}{C}}-OH$	187	Soluble	1.5×10^{-5}
Hexanoic acid	$CH_3-CH_2-CH_2-CH_2-CH_2-\overset{\displaystyle O}{\overset{\|}{C}}-OH$	205	Slightly soluble	1.4×10^{-5}
Benzoic acid	$\overset{\displaystyle O}{\overset{\|}{C}}-OH$ (attached to benzene ring)	250	Slightly soluble	6.4×10^{-5}

Acidity of Carboxylic Acids

An important property of carboxylic acids is their dissociation in water. When a carboxylic acid dissociates in water, H^+ is transferred to a water molecule to form a negatively charged **carboxylate ion** and a positively charged hydronium ion (H_3O^+). Carboxylic acids are more acidic than most other organic compounds including phenols. However, they are weak acids. The acid dissociation constants of some carboxylic acids are given in Table 16.2.

Carboxylic Acid   **Carboxylate Ion**

$$CH_3 - \overset{\overset{\displaystyle O}{\|}}{C} - OH + H_2O \;\rightleftharpoons\; CH_3 - \overset{\overset{\displaystyle O}{\|}}{C} - O^- + H_3O^+$$

Ethanoic acid   Ethanoate ion   Hydronium
(acetic acid)   (acetate ion)   ion

▶ **SAMPLE PROBLEM 16.3 Dissociation of Carboxylic Acids in Water**

Write the balanced chemical equation for the dissociation of propanoic acid in water.

SOLUTION

ANALYZE THE PROBLEM	**Given**	**Need**
	propanoic acid	chemical equation for dissociation in water

A chemical equation for the dissociation of a carboxylic acid includes the reactants, a carboxylic acid and water, and the products, carboxylate and hydronium ions.

$$CH_3 - CH_2 - \overset{\overset{\displaystyle O}{\|}}{C} - OH + H_2O \;\rightleftharpoons\; CH_3 - CH_2 - \overset{\overset{\displaystyle O}{\|}}{C} - O^- + H_3O^+$$

Propanoic acid   Propanoate ion
(propionic acid)   (propionate ion)

STUDY CHECK 16.3

Write the balanced chemical equation for the dissociation of formic acid in water.

ANSWER

$$H - \overset{\overset{\displaystyle O}{\|}}{C} - OH + H_2O \;\rightleftharpoons\; H - \overset{\overset{\displaystyle O}{\|}}{C} - O^- + H_3O^+$$

Neutralization of Carboxylic Acids

Because carboxylic acids are weak acids, they are completely neutralized by strong bases such as NaOH and KOH. The products are a **carboxylate salt** and water. The carboxylate ion is named by replacing the *ic acid* ending of the acid name with *ate*.

$$H - \overset{\overset{\displaystyle O}{\|}}{C} - OH + NaOH \;\longrightarrow\; H - \overset{\overset{\displaystyle O}{\|}}{C} - O^- Na^+ + H_2O$$

Methanoic acid   Sodium methanoate
(formic acid)   (sodium formate)

$$\text{(benzoic acid)} - \overset{\overset{\displaystyle O}{\|}}{C} - OH + KOH \;\longrightarrow\; \text{(ring)} - \overset{\overset{\displaystyle O}{\|}}{C} - O^- K^+ + H_2O$$

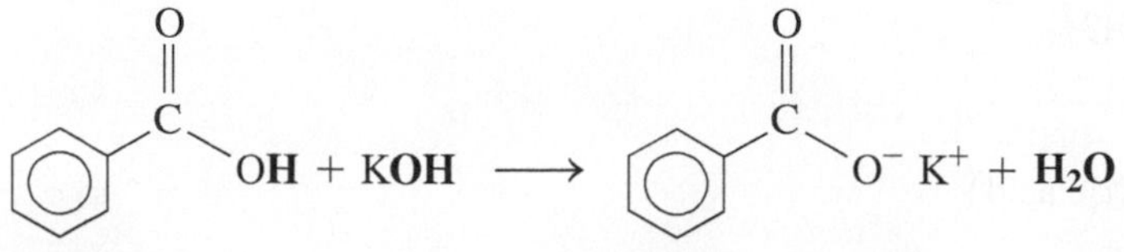

Benzoic acid   Potassium benzoate

FIGURE 16.2 ▶ Carboxylate salts are often used as preservatives and flavor enhancers in soups and seasonings.

◉ What is the carboxylate salt produced by the neutralization of butanoic acid and lithium hydroxide?

Sodium propionate, a preservative, is added to bread, cheeses, and bakery items to inhibit the spoilage of the food by microorganisms. Sodium benzoate, an inhibitor of mold and bacteria, is added to juices, margarine, relishes, salads, and jams. Monosodium glutamate (MSG) is added to meats, fish, vegetables, and bakery items to enhance flavor, although it causes headache in some people (see Figure 16.2).

$$CH_3-CH_2-\overset{\displaystyle O}{\overset{\|}{C}}-O^-\ Na^+$$

Sodium propanoate
(sodium propionate)

Sodium benzoate

$$HO-\overset{\displaystyle O}{\overset{\|}{C}}-CH_2-CH_2-\overset{NH_2}{\overset{|}{C}H}-\overset{\displaystyle O}{\overset{\|}{C}}-O^-\ Na^+$$

Monosodium glutamate

Carboxylate salts are ionic compounds with strong attractions between positively charged metal ions such as Li^+, Na^+, and K^+ and the negatively charged carboxylate ion. Like most salts, the carboxylate salts are solids at room temperature, have high melting points, and are usually soluble in water.

▶ **SAMPLE PROBLEM 16.4 Neutralization of Carboxylic Acid**

Write the balanced chemical equation for the neutralization of propanoic acid (propionic acid) with sodium hydroxide.

SOLUTION

ANALYZE THE PROBLEM	Given	Need
	propanoic acid	neutralization equation

A chemical equation for the neutralization of carboxylic acid includes the reactants, a carboxylic acid and a base, and the products, a carboxylate salt and water.

$$CH_3-CH_2-\overset{\displaystyle O}{\overset{\|}{C}}-OH + NaOH \longrightarrow CH_3-CH_2-\overset{\displaystyle O}{\overset{\|}{C}}-O^-\ Na^+ + H_2O$$

Propanoic acid   Sodium   Sodium propanoate
(propionic acid)   hydroxide   (sodium propionate)

STUDY CHECK 16.4

What carboxylic acid will give potassium butanoate (potassium butyrate) when it is neutralized by KOH?

ANSWER

butanoic acid (butyric acid)

Chemistry Link to **Health**
Carboxylic Acids in Metabolism

Several carboxylic acids are part of the metabolic processes within our cells. For example, during glycolysis, a molecule of glucose is broken down into two molecules of pyruvic acid, or actually, its carboxylate ion, pyruvate. During strenuous exercise when oxygen levels are low (anaerobic), pyruvic acid is reduced to give lactic acid or the lactate ion.

$$CH_3-\overset{O}{\overset{||}{C}}-\overset{O}{\overset{||}{C}}-OH + 2H \xrightarrow{\text{Reduction}} CH_3-\overset{OH}{\overset{|}{C}H}-\overset{O}{\overset{||}{C}}-OH$$

Pyruvic acid   Lactic acid

During exercise, pyruvic acid is converted to lactic acid in the muscles.

In the *citric acid cycle*, also called the Krebs cycle, di- and tricarboxylic acids are oxidized and decarboxylated (loss of CO_2) to produce energy for the cells of the body. These carboxylic acids are normally referred to by their common names. At the start of the citric acid cycle, citric acid with six carbons is converted to five-carbon α-ketoglutaric acid. Citric acid is also the acid that gives the sour taste to citrus fruits such as lemons and grapefruits.

$$HO-\overset{\overset{\displaystyle COOH}{|}\overset{\displaystyle CH_2}{|}}{\underset{\overset{\displaystyle CH_2}{|}\underset{\displaystyle COOH}{|}}{C}}-COOH \xrightarrow{[O]} \overset{\overset{\displaystyle COOH}{|}\overset{\displaystyle CH_2}{|}\overset{\displaystyle CH_2}{|}}{\underset{\overset{\displaystyle C=O}{|}}{\underset{\displaystyle COOH}{|}}} + CO_2$$

Citric acid α-Ketoglutaric acid

The citric acid cycle continues as α-ketoglutaric acid loses CO_2 to give a four-carbon succinic acid. Then a series of reactions converts succinic acid to oxaloacetic acid. We see that some of the functional groups we have studied, along with reactions such as hydration and oxidation, are part of the metabolic processes that take place in our cells.

$$\overset{\overset{\displaystyle COOH}{|}}{\underset{\overset{\displaystyle CH_2}{|}\overset{\displaystyle CH_2}{|}\overset{\displaystyle COOH}{|}}{}} \xrightarrow{[O]} \overset{\overset{\displaystyle COOH}{|}}{\underset{\overset{\displaystyle C-H}{||}\underset{\displaystyle H-C}{\underset{\displaystyle COOH}{|}}}{}} \xrightarrow{H_2O} \overset{\overset{\displaystyle COOH}{|}}{HO-\underset{\overset{\displaystyle C-H}{|}\underset{\displaystyle CH_2}{|}\underset{\displaystyle COOH}{|}}{}} \xrightarrow{[O]} \overset{\overset{\displaystyle COOH}{|}}{\underset{\overset{\displaystyle C=O}{||}\underset{\displaystyle CH_2}{|}\underset{\displaystyle COOH}{|}}{}}$$

Succinic acid   Fumaric acid   Malic acid   Oxaloacetic acid

At the pH of the aqueous environment in the cells, the carboxylic acids are dissociated, which means it is actually the carboxylate ions that take part in the reactions of the citric acid cycle. For example, in water, succinic acid is in equilibrium with its carboxylate ion, succinate.

$$\overset{\overset{\displaystyle COOH}{|}\overset{\displaystyle CH_2}{|}\overset{\displaystyle CH_2}{|}\overset{\displaystyle COOH}{|}}{} + 2H_2O \rightleftharpoons \overset{\overset{\displaystyle COO^-}{|}\overset{\displaystyle CH_2}{|}\overset{\displaystyle CH_2}{|}\overset{\displaystyle COO^-}{|}}{} + 2H_3O^+$$

Succinic acid   Succinate ion

Citric acid gives the sour taste to citrus fruits.

QUESTIONS AND PROBLEMS

16.2 Properties of Carboxylic Acids

LEARNING GOAL Describe the boiling points, solubility, dissociation, and neutralization of carboxylic acids.

16.11 Identify the compound in each of the following pairs that has the higher boiling point. Explain.
   a. ethanoic acid (acetic acid) or butanoic acid
   b. 1-propanol or propanoic acid
   c. butanone or butanoic acid

16.12 Identify the compound in each of the following pairs that has the higher boiling point. Explain.
   a. propanone (acetone) or propanoic acid
   b. propanoic acid or hexanoic acid
   c. ethanol or ethanoic acid (acetic acid)

16.13 Identify the compound in each of the following groups that is most soluble in water. Explain.
  a. propanoic acid, hexanoic acid, benzoic acid
  b. pentane, 1-hexanol, propanoic acid

16.14 Identify the compound in each of the following groups that is most soluble in water. Explain.
  a. butanone, butanoic acid, butane
  b. acetic acid, pentanoic acid, octanoic acid

16.15 Write the balanced chemical equation for the dissociation of each of the following carboxylic acids in water:
  a. butanoic acid

$$CH_3-\overset{\overset{\displaystyle CH_3}{|}}{C}H-\overset{\overset{\displaystyle O}{\|}}{C}-OH$$

  b. (as drawn above)

16.16 Write the balanced chemical equation for the dissociation of each of the following carboxylic acids in water:

$$\textbf{a.}\ \ CH_3-CH_2-CH_2-CH_2-\overset{\overset{\displaystyle O}{\|}}{C}-OH$$

  b. α-hydroxyacetic acid

16.17 Write the balanced chemical equation for the reaction of each of the following carboxylic acids with NaOH:
  a. pentanoic acid
  b. 2-chloropropanoic acid
  c. benzoic acid

16.18 Write the balanced chemical equation for the reaction of each of the following carboxylic acids with KOH:
  a. hexanoic acid
  b. 2-methylbutanoic acid
  c. p-chlorobenzoic acid

16.19 Give the IUPAC and common names, if any, of the carboxylate salts produced in problem 16.17.

16.20 Give the IUPAC and common names, if any, of the carboxylate salts produced in problem 16.18.

LEARNING GOAL

Write a balanced chemical equation for the formation of an ester.

16.3 Esters

A carboxylic acid reacts with an alcohol to form an **ester** and water. In an ester, the —H of the carboxylic acid is replaced by an alkyl group. Fats and oils in our diets contain esters of glycerol and fatty acids, which are long-chain carboxylic acids. The aromas and flavors of many fruits including bananas, oranges, and strawberries are due to esters.

Carboxylic Acid

$$CH_3-\overset{\overset{\displaystyle O}{\|}}{C}-O-H$$
Ethanoic acid
(acetic acid)

Ester

$$CH_3-\overset{\overset{\displaystyle O}{\|}}{C}-O-CH_3$$
Methyl ethanoate
(methyl acetate)

Esterification

In a reaction called **esterification**, an ester is produced when a carboxylic acid and an alcohol react in the presence of an acid catalyst (usually H_2SO_4) and heat. In esterification, the —OH group from the carboxylic acid and the —H from the alcohol combine to form water. An excess of the alcohol reactant is used to shift the equilibrium in the direction of the formation of the ester product.

$$CH_3-\overset{\overset{\displaystyle O}{\|}}{C}-OH + H-O-CH_3 \underset{}{\overset{H^+,\ heat}{\rightleftharpoons}} CH_3-\overset{\overset{\displaystyle O}{\|}}{C}-O-CH_3 + H-OH$$

Ethanoic acid   Methanol   Methyl ethanoate
(acetic acid)   (methyl alcohol)   (methyl acetate)

For example, the ester propyl ethanoate, which has the flavor and odor of pears, can be prepared using ethanoic acid and 1-propanol. The equation for this esterification is written as

$$CH_3-\overset{\overset{\displaystyle O}{\|}}{C}-OH + H-O-CH_2-CH_2-CH_3 \underset{}{\overset{H^+,\ heat}{\rightleftharpoons}} CH_3-\overset{\overset{\displaystyle O}{\|}}{C}-O-CH_2-CH_2-CH_3 + H_2O$$

Ethanoic acid   1-Propanol   Propyl ethanoate
(acetic acid)   (propyl alcohol)   (propyl acetate)

▶ **SAMPLE PROBLEM 16.5** Writing Esterification Equations

An ester that has the smell of pineapple can be synthesized from butanoic acid and methanol. Write the balanced chemical equation for the formation of this ester.

SOLUTION

ANALYZE THE PROBLEM	Given	Need
	butanoic acid, methanol	esterification equation

In an esterification equation, a carboxylic acid and an alcohol react to form an ester and water. The ester product of the esterification of butanoic acid and methanol is methyl butanoate.

$$CH_3-CH_2-CH_2-\overset{\overset{\displaystyle O}{\|}}{C}-OH + H-O-CH_3 \underset{}{\overset{H^+,\ heat}{\rightleftarrows}} CH_3-CH_2-CH_2-\overset{\overset{\displaystyle O}{\|}}{C}-O-CH_3 + H_2O$$

Butanoic acid   Methanol   Methyl butanoate

STUDY CHECK 16.5

The ester that smells like plums can be synthesized from methanoic acid and 1-butanol. Write the balanced chemical equation for the formation of this ester.

ANSWER

$$H-\overset{\overset{\displaystyle O}{\|}}{C}-OH + H-O-CH_2-CH_2-CH_2-CH_3 \overset{H^+,\ heat}{\rightleftarrows}$$

$$H-\overset{\overset{\displaystyle O}{\|}}{C}-O-CH_2-CH_2-CH_2-CH_3 + H_2O$$

 # Chemistry Link to **Health**

Salicylic Acid from a Willow Tree

For many centuries, relief from pain and fever was obtained by chewing on the leaves or a piece of bark from the willow tree. By the 1800s, chemists discovered that salicin was the agent in the bark responsible for the relief of pain. However, the body converts salicin to salicylic acid, which has a carboxyl group and a hydroxyl group that irritates the stomach lining. In 1899, the Bayer chemical company in Germany produced an ester of salicylic acid and acetic acid, called acetylsalicylic acid (aspirin), which is less irritating. In some aspirin preparations, a buffer is added to neutralize the carboxylic acid group. Today, aspirin is used as an analgesic (pain reliever), antipyretic (fever reducer), and anti-inflammatory agent. Many people take a daily low-dose aspirin, which has been found to lower the risk of heart attack and stroke.

The discovery of salicin in the leaves and bark of the willow tree led to the development of aspirin.

Salicylic acid · Acetic acid ⇌ Acetylsalicylic acid (aspirin) + H_2O

Oil of wintergreen, or methyl salicylate, has a pungent, minty odor and flavor. Because it can pass through the skin, methyl salicylate is used in skin ointments, where it acts as a counterirritant, producing heat to soothe sore muscles.

Salicylic acid + Methyl alcohol ⇌ Methyl salicylate (oil of wintergreen) + H_2O

Ointments containing methyl salicylate are used to soothe sore muscles.

Chemistry Link to the Environment
Plastics

Terephthalic acid (an aromatic acid with two carboxyl groups) is produced in large quantities for the manufacture of polyesters such as Dacron. When terephthalic acid reacts with ethylene glycol, ester bonds form on both ends of the molecules, allowing many molecules to combine into a long polyester polymer.

Dacron, a synthetic material first produced by DuPont in the 1960s, is a polyester used to make permanent press fabrics, carpets, and clothes. Permanent press is a chemical process in which fabrics are permanently shaped and treated for wrinkle resistance. In medicine, artificial blood vessels and valves are made of Dacron, which is biologically inert and does not clot the blood.

Dacron is a polyester used in permanent press clothing.

Terephthalic acid + $HO-CH_2-CH_2-OH$ ⇌ (H⁺, heat)

A section of the polyester Dacron — Ester bonds

The polyester can also be made into a film called Mylar and a plastic known as PETE (polyethyleneterephthalate). PETE is used for plastic soft drink and water bottles as well as for peanut butter jars, containers of salad dressings, shampoos, and dishwashing liquids. Today, PETE (recycling symbol "1") is the most widely recycled of all the plastics. Every year, more than 1.5×10^9 lb (6.8×10^8 kg) of PETE is being recycled. After PETE is separated from other plastics, it is used to make useful items, including polyester fabric for T-shirts and coats, carpets, fill for sleeping bags, doormats, and containers for tennis balls.

Polyester, in the form of the plastic PETE, is used to make soft drink bottles.

QUESTIONS AND PROBLEMS

16.3 Esters

LEARNING GOAL Write a balanced chemical equation for the formation of an ester.

16.21 Identify each of the following as an aldehyde, a ketone, a carboxylic acid, or an ester:

a. $CH_3-\overset{\overset{\displaystyle O}{\|}}{C}-H$

b. $CH_3-\overset{\overset{\displaystyle O}{\|}}{C}-O-CH_3$

c.

d. $CH_3-CH_2-\overset{\overset{\displaystyle O}{\|}}{C}-OH$

16.22 Identify each of the following as an aldehyde, a ketone, a carboxylic acid, or an ester:

a. $CH_3-\overset{\overset{\displaystyle O}{\|}}{C}-OH$

b. $CH_3-\overset{\overset{\displaystyle O}{\|}}{C}-O-CH_2-CH_3$

c. (line-angle structure with $\overset{O}{\|}$ and H)

d. $CH_3-\overset{\overset{\displaystyle CH_3}{|}}{CH}-\overset{\overset{\displaystyle O}{\|}}{C}-O-CH_2-CH_3$

16.23 Draw the condensed structural formula for the ester formed when each of the following reacts with ethyl alcohol:
a. acetic acid   **b.** butyric acid
c. benzoic acid

16.24 Draw the condensed structural formula for the ester formed when each of the following reacts with methyl alcohol:
a. formic acid   **b.** propionic acid
c. 2-methylpentanoic acid

16.25 Draw the condensed or line-angle structural formula for the ester formed in each of the following reactions:

a. (line-angle acid with $\overset{O}{\|}$) $OH + HO$ (propyl chain) $\xrightarrow{H^+,\ heat}$

b.

$CH_3-CH_2-CH_2-CH_2-\overset{\overset{\displaystyle O}{\|}}{C}-OH + HO-\overset{\overset{\displaystyle CH_3}{|}}{CH}-CH_3 \xrightarrow{H^+,\ heat}$

16.26 Draw the condensed or line-angle structural formula for the ester formed in each of the following reactions:

a. (line-angle with $\overset{O}{\|}$) $OH + HO$ (ethyl) $\xrightarrow{H^+,\ heat}$

b. (benzene ring)$-\overset{\overset{\displaystyle O}{\|}}{C}-OH + HO-CH_2-CH_2-CH_2-CH_3 \xrightarrow{H^+,\ heat}$

16.27 Give the IUPAC and common names, if any, of the carboxylic acid and alcohol needed to produce each of the following esters:

a. $H-\overset{\overset{\displaystyle O}{\|}}{C}-O-CH_3$

b. $CH_3-CH_2-\overset{\overset{\displaystyle O}{\|}}{C}-O-CH_2-CH_3$

c. (line-angle structure with $\overset{O}{\|}$ and O)

d. $CH_3-\overset{\overset{\displaystyle CH_3}{|}}{CH}-CH_2-\overset{\overset{\displaystyle O}{\|}}{C}-O-CH_2-CH_3$

16.28 Give the IUPAC and common names, if any, of the carboxylic acid and alcohol needed to produce each of the following esters:

a. $CH_3-CH_2-\overset{\overset{\displaystyle O}{\|}}{C}-O-CH_2-CH_3$

b. (line-angle structure with $\overset{O}{\|}$ and O)

c. $CH_3-CH_2-\overset{\overset{\overset{\displaystyle O}{\|}}{C}}{\underset{\underset{\displaystyle CH_3}{|}}{CH}}-O-CH_3$

d. (line-angle structure with $\overset{O}{\|}$ and O)

16.4 Naming Esters

LEARNING GOAL

The name of an ester consists of two words that are derived from the names of the alcohol and the acid in that ester. The first word indicates the *alkyl* part from the alcohol. The second word is the *carboxylate* from the carboxylic acid. The IUPAC names of esters use the IUPAC names of the acids, while the common names of esters use the common names of the acids. Let's take a look at the following ester, which has a fruity odor. We start by separating the ester bond to identify the alkyl part from the alcohol and the carboxylate part from the acid. Then we name the ester as an alkyl carboxylate.

LEARNING GOAL
Write the IUPAC and common names for esters; draw condensed and line-angle structural formulas.

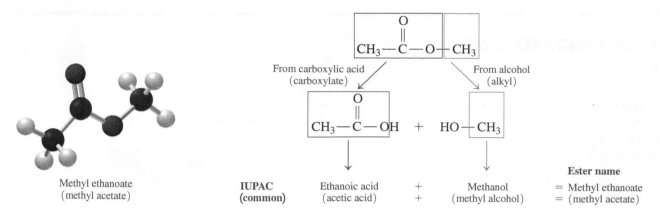

Methyl ethanoate
(methyl acetate)

From carboxylic acid
(carboxylate)

From alcohol
(alkyl)

Ester name
= Methyl ethanoate
= (methyl acetate)

IUPAC
(common)

Ethanoic acid
(acetic acid)

+
+

Methanol
(methyl alcohol)

The following examples of some typical esters show the IUPAC as well as the common names of esters:

Ethyl ethanoate
(ethyl acetate)

Methyl propanoate
(methyl propionate)

Ethyl benzoate

Many of the fragrances of perfumes and flowers, and the flavors of fruits, are due to esters. Small esters are volatile so we can smell them and soluble in water so we can taste them. Several esters and their flavors and odor are listed in Table 16.3.

TABLE 16.3 Some Esters in Fruits and Flavorings

Condensed Structural Formula and Name	Flavor/Odor
$CH_3-C(=O)-O-CH_2-CH_2-CH_3$ Propyl ethanoate (propyl acetate)	Pears
$CH_3-C(=O)-O-CH_2-CH_2-CH_2-CH_2-CH_3$ Pentyl ethanoate (pentyl acetate)	Bananas
$CH_3-C(=O)-O-CH_2-CH_2-CH_2-CH_2-CH_2-CH_2-CH_2-CH_3$ Octyl ethanoate (octyl acetate)	Oranges
$CH_3-CH_2-CH_2-C(=O)-O-CH_2-CH_3$ Ethyl butanoate (ethyl butyrate)	Pineapples
$CH_3-CH_2-CH_2-C(=O)-O-CH_2-CH_2-CH_2-CH_2-CH_3$ Pentyl butanoate (pentyl butyrate)	Apricots

Esters such as ethyl butanoate provide the odor and flavor of many fruits such as pineapples.

► **SAMPLE PROBLEM 16.6 Naming Esters**

What are the IUPAC and common names of the following ester?

$$CH_3-CH_2-\overset{\overset{\displaystyle O}{\|}}{C}-O-CH_2-CH_2-CH_3$$

SOLUTION

	Given	Need
ANALYZE THE PROBLEM	ester	IUPAC and common names

STEP 1 Write the name for the carbon chain from the alcohol as an *alkyl* group. The alcohol part of the ester is from propanol (propyl alcohol). The alkyl group is propyl.

$$CH_3-CH_2-\overset{\overset{\displaystyle O}{\|}}{C}-O-CH_2-CH_2-CH_3 \qquad \text{propyl}$$

STEP 2 Change the *ic acid* of the acid name to *ate.* The carboxylic acid part of the ester is from propanoic (propionic) acid, which becomes propanoate (propionate). The ester is named propyl propanoate (propyl propionate). Replacing the *ic acid* in the common name propionic acid with *ate* gives propionate. The common name for the ester is propyl propionate.

$$CH_3-CH_2-\overset{\overset{\displaystyle O}{\|}}{C}-O-CH_2-CH_2-CH_3 \qquad \text{propyl propanoate}$$
$$\text{(propyl propionate)}$$

Guide to Naming Esters

STEP 1
Write the name for the carbon chain from the alcohol as an *alkyl* group.

STEP 2
Change the *ic acid* of the acid name to *ate.*

STUDY CHECK 16.6

Draw the line-angle structural formula for ethyl heptanoate that gives odor and flavor to grapes.

ANSWER

The odor of grapes is due to ethyl heptanoate.

QUESTIONS AND PROBLEMS

16.4 Naming Esters

LEARNING GOAL Write the IUPAC and common names for esters; draw condensed and line-angle structural formulas.

16.29 Give the IUPAC name and common names, if any, for each of the following esters:

a. $H-\overset{\overset{\displaystyle O}{\|}}{C}-O-CH_3$

b. $CH_3-CH_2-\overset{\overset{\displaystyle O}{\|}}{C}-O-CH_2-CH_3$

c.

d. $CH_3-CH_2-CH_2-CH_2-\overset{\overset{\displaystyle O}{\|}}{C}-O-CH_2-\overset{\overset{\displaystyle CH_3}{|}}{CH}-CH_3$

16.30 Give the IUPAC name and common names, if any, for each of the following esters:

a. $CH_3-CH_2-CH_2-\overset{\overset{\displaystyle O}{\|}}{C}-O-CH_2-CH_3$

b. $CH_3-CH_2-CH_2-CH_2-CH_2-\overset{\overset{\displaystyle O}{\|}}{C}-O-CH_3$

c.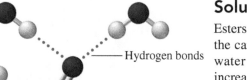

d. $CH_3-CH_2-\overset{\overset{\displaystyle O}{\|}}{C}-O-CH_2-CH_2-CH_2-CH_3$

16.31 Draw the condensed structural formula for each of the following:
  a. methyl acetate   b. butyl formate
  c. ethyl pentanoate   d. 2-bromopropyl propanoate

16.32 Draw the condensed structural formula for each of the following:
  a. hexyl acetate   b. propyl formate
  c. ethyl 2-hydroxybutanoate   d. methyl benzoate

16.33 What is the ester responsible for the flavor and odor of each of the following fruits?
  a. banana   b. orange
  c. apricot

16.34 What flavor would you notice if you smelled or tasted each of the following?
  a. ethyl butanoate   b. propyl acetate
  c. octyl acetate

Describe the boiling points and solubility of esters; draw the condensed structural formulas for the hydrolysis products.

16.5 Properties of Esters

Esters have boiling points higher than those of alkanes and ethers, but lower than those of alcohols and carboxylic acids of similar mass. Because ester molecules do not have hydroxyl groups, they cannot hydrogen bond to each other.

$$CH_3-CH_2-CH_2-CH_3 \qquad H-\overset{\overset{\displaystyle O}{\|}}{C}-O-CH_3 \qquad CH_3-CH_2-CH_2-OH \qquad CH_3-\overset{\overset{\displaystyle O}{\|}}{C}-OH$$

Name	Butane	Methyl methanoate	1-Propanol	Ethanoic acid
Molar Mass	58	60	60	60
Family	Alkane	Ester	Alcohol	Carboxylic acid
bp	0 °C	32 °C	97 °C	118 °C

Boiling Point Increases →

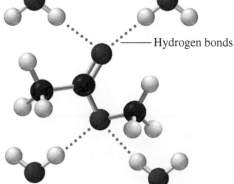

Esters with 2 to 5 carbon atoms are soluble because they form hydrogen bonds with water.

Hydrogen bonds

Solubility in Water

Esters with two to five carbon atoms are soluble in water. The partially negative oxygen of the carbonyl group forms hydrogen bonds with the partially positive hydrogen atoms of water molecules. The solubility of esters decreases as the number of carbon atoms increases.

Acid Hydrolysis of Esters

When esters are heated with water in the presence of a strong acid, usually H_2SO_4 or HCl, *hydrolysis* occurs. In **hydrolysis**, water reacts with the ester to form a carboxylic acid and an alcohol. Therefore, hydrolysis is the reverse of the esterification reaction. During acid hydrolysis, a water molecule provides the —OH group to convert the carbonyl group of the ester to a carboxyl group. A large quantity of water is used to shift the equilibrium in the direction of the carboxylic acid and alcohol products. When hydrolysis of biological esters occurs in the cells, an enzyme replaces the acid as the catalyst.

$$CH_3-\overset{\overset{\displaystyle O}{\|}}{C}-O-CH_3 + H-OH \underset{}{\overset{H^+,\ heat}{\rightleftharpoons}} CH_3-\overset{\overset{\displaystyle O}{\|}}{C}-OH + HO-CH_3$$

Methyl ethanoate   Water   Ethanoic acid   Methanol
(methyl acetate)   (acetic acid)   (methyl alcohol)

▶ **SAMPLE PROBLEM 16.7 Acid Hydrolysis of Esters**

Aspirin that has been stored for a long time may undergo hydrolysis in the presence of water and heat. What are the hydrolysis products of aspirin?

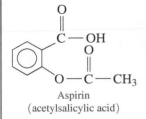

Aspirin
(acetylsalicylic acid)

Aspirin stored in a warm, humid place may undergo hydrolysis.

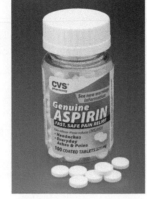

⚛ **CORE CHEMISTRY SKILL**

Hydrolyzing Esters

SOLUTION

ANALYZE THE PROBLEM	Given	Need
	aspirin	hydrolysis products

To write the hydrolysis products, separate the compound at the ester bond. Complete the formula of the carboxylic acid by adding —OH (from water) to the carbonyl group and —H to complete the alcohol. The acetic acid in the products gives the odor of vinegar to a sample of aspirin that has hydrolyzed.

Aspirin + H—OH $\xrightleftharpoons{H^+, \text{ heat}}$ Salicylic acid + HO—C—CH₃ (Acetic acid)

Separate here

STUDY CHECK 16.7

What are the names of the products from the acid hydrolysis of ethyl propanoate (ethyl propionate)?

ANSWER

propanoic acid and ethanol (propionic acid and ethyl alcohol)

Base Hydrolysis of Esters (Saponification)

When an ester undergoes hydrolysis with a strong base such as NaOH or KOH, the products are the carboxylate salt and the corresponding alcohol. This base hydrolysis is also called **saponification**, which refers to the reaction of a long-chain fatty acid with NaOH to make soap. Thus, a carboxylic acid, which is produced in acid hydrolysis, is converted to its carboxylate salt when neutralized by a strong base.

Ester + strong base ⟶ carboxylate salt + alcohol

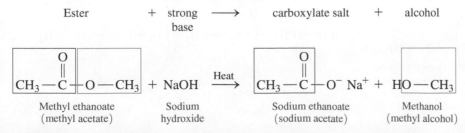

$$CH_3-C(=O)-O-CH_3 + NaOH \xrightarrow{\text{Heat}} CH_3-C(=O)-O^- Na^+ + HO-CH_3$$

Methyl ethanoate (methyl acetate)   Sodium hydroxide   Sodium ethanoate (sodium acetate)   Methanol (methyl alcohol)

Ethyl acetate is the solvent in fingernail polish.

> **SAMPLE PROBLEM 16.8   Base Hydrolysis of Esters**

Ethyl acetate is a solvent used in fingernail polish, plastics, and lacquers. Write the balanced chemical equation for the hydrolysis of ethyl acetate with NaOH.

SOLUTION

ANALYZE THE PROBLEM	Given	Need
	ester, base	carboxylate salt, alcohol

$$CH_3-\overset{\overset{\displaystyle O}{\|}}{C}-O-CH_2-CH_3 + NaOH \xrightarrow{\text{Heat}} CH_3-\overset{\overset{\displaystyle O}{\|}}{C}-O^- \ Na^+ + HO-CH_2-CH_3$$

Ethyl ethanoate (ethyl acetate)   Sodium ethanoate (sodium acetate)   Ethanol (ethyl alcohol)

Interactive Video

Hydrolysis of Esters

STUDY CHECK 16.8

Draw the condensed structural formulas for the products from the hydrolysis of methyl benzoate with KOH.

ANSWER

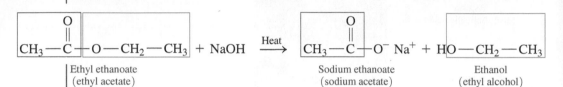

$+ \ HO-CH_3$

QUESTIONS AND PROBLEMS

16.5 Properties of Esters

LEARNING GOAL Describe the boiling points and solubility of esters; draw the condensed structural formulas for the hydrolysis products.

16.35 For each of the following pairs of compounds, select the compound that has the higher boiling point:

a. $CH_3-\overset{\overset{\displaystyle O}{\|}}{C}-O-CH_3$ or $CH_3-CH_2-\overset{\overset{\displaystyle O}{\|}}{C}-OH$

b. $CH_3-\overset{\overset{\displaystyle O}{\|}}{C}-O-CH_3$ or $CH_3-CH_2-CH_2-CH_2-OH$

c. [line-angle structure] or [ester line-angle structure]

16.36 For each of the following pairs of compounds, select the compound that has the higher boiling point:

a. $H-\overset{\overset{\displaystyle O}{\|}}{C}-O-CH_3$ or $CH_3-CH_2-CH_2-OH$

b. [formate ester structure] or [acetic acid structure]

c. $CH_3-O-CH_2-CH_3$ or $H-\overset{\overset{\displaystyle O}{\|}}{C}-O-CH_3$

16.37 Draw the condensed or line-angle structural formulas for the products from the acid- or base-catalyzed hydrolysis of each of the following compounds:

a. $CH_3-CH_2-\overset{\overset{\displaystyle O}{\|}}{C}-O-CH_3 + NaOH \xrightarrow{\text{Heat}}$

b. [ester line-angle structure] $+ H_2O \underset{}{\overset{H^+, \text{ heat}}{\rightleftharpoons}}$

c. $CH_3-CH_2-CH_2-\overset{\overset{\displaystyle O}{\|}}{C}-O-CH_2-CH_3 + H_2O \underset{}{\overset{H^+, \text{ heat}}{\rightleftharpoons}}$

d. [benzoate ester structure] $-\overset{\overset{\displaystyle O}{\|}}{C}-O-CH_2-CH_3 + NaOH \xrightarrow{\text{Heat}}$

e. [benzoate line-angle structure] $+ H_2O \underset{}{\overset{H^+, \text{ heat}}{\rightleftharpoons}}$

16.38 Draw the condensed or line-angle structural formulas for the products from the acid- or base-catalyzed hydrolysis of each of the following compounds:

a. $CH_3-CH_2-\overset{\overset{\displaystyle O}{\|}}{C}-O-CH_2-CH_2-CH_2-CH_3 + H_2O \underset{}{\overset{H^+, \text{ heat}}{\rightleftharpoons}}$

b. H [formate ester line-angle structure] $+ NaOH \xrightarrow{\text{Heat}}$

c. $CH_3-CH_2-\overset{\overset{\displaystyle O}{\|}}{C}-O-CH_3 + H_2O \xrightarrow{H^+, \text{ heat}} \rightleftharpoons$

e.  + NaOH $\xrightarrow{\text{Heat}}$

d. $CH_3-CH_2-\overset{\overset{\displaystyle O}{\|}}{C}-O-\hexagon + H_2O \xrightarrow{H^+, \text{ heat}} \rightleftharpoons$

Clinical Update
Liquid Bandages

The liquid bandage used to close Robert's surgical incisions is also available in pharmacies for home use in closing wounds. The liquid hardens quickly when it comes in contact with blood and tissue, stops bleeding, and holds the edges of the wound together as skin heals. In a few days, the plastic bandage sloughs off and there is no need to remove stitches or staples. Anyone applying liquid bandage needs to be aware that contact of the liquid with gloves or other surfaces will cause them to adhere. Persons with an allergy to plastic should not use liquid bandage products.

The polymer in the liquid bandage consists of repeating units of Indermil. Indermil can be produced by the esterification reaction of 2-cyano-2-propenoic acid and 1-butanol.

$$H_2C=\overset{\overset{\displaystyle CN}{|}}{C}-\overset{\overset{\displaystyle O}{\|}}{C}-OH$$
2-Cyano-2-propenoic acid

℞ Clinical Applications

16.39 a. Draw the condensed structural formulas for the reactants and products from the reaction between 2-cyano-2-propenoic acid and 1-butanol.
   b. What is the IUPAC name of the ester formed?

16.40 a. Draw the condensed structural formulas for the products from the acid hydrolysis of the ester in problem 16.39.
   b. Draw the condensed structural formulas for the products from the base hydrolysis with NaOH of the ester in problem 16.39.

A spray containing a liquid bandage applied to a wound closes the wound quickly and stops bleeding.

CONCEPT MAP

CARBOXYLIC ACIDS AND ESTERS

Carboxylic Acids

have a
Carboxyl Group

forms hydrogen bonds and are
Soluble in Water Up to 5 C Atoms

are
Polar

and dissociate as
Weak Acids

are neutralized by
Strong Bases

to form
Carboxylate Salts

and
Alcohols

combine to form   hydrolyze to form
Esters

saponify to form
Carboxylate Salts   and   **Alcohols**

CHAPTER REVIEW

16.1 Carboxylic Acids
LEARNING GOAL Write the IUPAC and common names for carboxylic acids and draw their condensed and line-angle structural formulas.

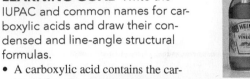

- A carboxylic acid contains the carboxyl functional group, which is a hydroxyl group connected to a carbonyl group.
- The IUPAC name of a carboxylic acid is obtained by replacing the *e* in the alkane name with *oic acid*.
- The common names of carboxylic acids with one to four carbon atoms are formic acid, acetic acid, propionic acid, and butyric acid.

16.2 Properties of Carboxylic Acids
LEARNING GOAL Describe the boiling points, solubility, dissociation, and neutralization of carboxylic acids.

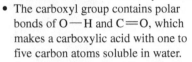
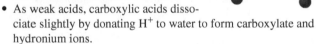

Hydrogen bonds

- The carboxyl group contains polar bonds of O—H and C=O, which makes a carboxylic acid with one to five carbon atoms soluble in water.
- As weak acids, carboxylic acids dissociate slightly by donating H^+ to water to form carboxylate and hydronium ions.
- Carboxylic acids are neutralized by base, producing a carboxylate salt and water.

16.3 Esters
LEARNING GOAL Write a balanced chemical equation for the formation of an ester.

- In an ester, an alkyl or aromatic group replaces the H of the hydroxyl group of a carboxylic acid.

- In the presence of a strong acid, a carboxylic acid reacts with an alcohol to produce an ester and a molecule of water from the —OH removed from the carboxylic acid, and the —H removed from the alcohol molecule.

16.4 Naming Esters
LEARNING GOAL Write the IUPAC and common names for esters; draw condensed and line-angle structural formulas.

Methyl ethanoate (methyl acetate)

- The names of esters consist of two words: the alkyl part from the alcohol and the name of the carboxylate obtained by replacing *ic acid* with *ate*.

16.5 Properties of Esters
LEARNING GOAL
Describe the boiling points and solubility of esters; draw the condensed structural formulas for the hydrolysis products.

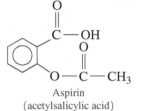

Aspirin (acetylsalicylic acid)

- Esters have boiling points that are lower than alcohols and carboxylic acids, but higher than alkanes.
- Esters with two to five carbon atoms are soluble in water.
- Esters undergo acid hydrolysis by adding water to yield the carboxylic acid and alcohol.
- Base hydrolysis, or saponification, of an ester produces the carboxylate salt and an alcohol.

SUMMARY OF NAMING

Family	Structure	IUPAC Name	Common Name
Carboxylic acid	$CH_3-\overset{\displaystyle O}{\overset{\|}{C}}-OH$	Ethanoic acid	Acetic acid
Carboxylate salt	$CH_3-\overset{\displaystyle O}{\overset{\|}{C}}-O^- \ Na^+$	Sodium ethanoate	Sodium acetate
Ester	$CH_3-\overset{\displaystyle O}{\overset{\|}{C}}-O-CH_3$	Methyl ethanoate	Methyl acetate

SUMMARY OF REACTIONS

The chapter sections to review are shown after the name of the reaction.

Dissociation of a Carboxylic Acid in Water (16.2)

$$CH_3-\overset{\overset{\displaystyle O}{\|}}{C}-OH + H_2O \rightleftharpoons CH_3-\overset{\overset{\displaystyle O}{\|}}{C}-O^- + H_3O^+$$

Ethanoic acid   Ethanoate ion   Hydronium
(acetic acid)   (acetate ion)   ion

Neutralization of a Carboxylic Acid (16.2)

$$CH_3-CH_2-\overset{\overset{\displaystyle O}{\|}}{C}-OH + NaOH \longrightarrow CH_3-CH_2-\overset{\overset{\displaystyle O}{\|}}{C}-O^- \, Na^+ + H_2O$$

Propanoic acid   Sodium   Sodium propanoate
(propionic acid)   hydroxide   (sodium propionate)

Esterification: Carboxylic Acid and an Alcohol (16.3)

$$CH_3-\overset{\overset{\displaystyle O}{\|}}{C}-OH + HO-CH_3 \underset{}{\overset{H^+, \, heat}{\rightleftharpoons}} CH_3-\overset{\overset{\displaystyle O}{\|}}{C}-O-CH_3 + H_2O$$

Ethanoic acid   Methanol   Methyl ethanoate
(acetic acid)   (methyl alcohol)   (methyl acetate)

Acid Hydrolysis of an Ester (16.5)

$$CH_3-\overset{\overset{\displaystyle O}{\|}}{C}-O-CH_3 + H-OH \underset{}{\overset{H^+, \, heat}{\rightleftharpoons}} CH_3-\overset{\overset{\displaystyle O}{\|}}{C}-OH + HO-CH_3$$

Methyl ethanoate   Ethanoic acid   Methanol
(methyl acetate)   (acetic acid)   (methyl alcohol)

Base Hydrolysis of an Ester (Saponification) (16.5)

$$CH_3-CH_2-\overset{\overset{\displaystyle O}{\|}}{C}-O-CH_3 + NaOH \overset{Heat}{\longrightarrow} CH_3-CH_2-\overset{\overset{\displaystyle O}{\|}}{C}-O^- \, Na^+ + HO-CH_3$$

Methyl propanoate   Sodium   Sodium propanoate   Methanol
(methyl propionate)   hydroxide   (sodium propionate)   (methyl alcohol)

KEY TERMS

acid hydrolysis The splitting of an ester molecule in the presence of a strong acid to produce a carboxylic acid and an alcohol.

base hydrolysis (saponification) The splitting of an ester molecule by a strong base to produce a carboxylate salt and an alcohol.

carboxyl group A functional group found in carboxylic acids composed of carbonyl and hydroxyl groups.

$$-\overset{\overset{\displaystyle O}{\|}}{C}-OH$$

Carboxyl group

carboxylate ion The anion produced when a carboxylic acid dissociates in water.

carboxylate salt The product of neutralization of a carboxylic acid, which is a carboxylate ion and a metal ion from the base.

carboxylic acid An organic compound containing the carboxyl group.

ester An organic compound in which an alkyl or aromatic group replaces the hydrogen atom in a carboxylic acid.

esterification The formation of an ester from a carboxylic acid and an alcohol with the elimination of a molecule of water in the presence of an acid catalyst.

⚛ CORE CHEMISTRY SKILLS

The chapter section containing each Core Chemistry Skill is shown in parentheses at the end of each heading.

Naming Carboxylic Acids (16.1)

- The IUPAC name of a carboxylic acid is obtained by replacing the *e* in the corresponding alkane name with *oic acid*.
- The common names of carboxylic acids with one to four carbon atoms are formic acid, acetic acid, propionic acid, and butyric acid.

Example: Give the IUPAC name for the following:

$$CH_3-\underset{\underset{CH_3}{|}}{\overset{\overset{CH_3}{|}}{CH}}-CH_2-\underset{\underset{CH_3}{|}}{\overset{\overset{Cl}{|}}{C}}-CH_2-\overset{\overset{O}{||}}{C}-OH$$

Answer: 3-chloro-3,5-dimethylhexanoic acid

Hydrolyzing Esters (16.5)

- Esters undergo acid hydrolysis by adding water to produce a carboxylic acid and an alcohol.
- Esters undergo base hydrolysis, or saponification, to produce a carboxylate salt and an alcohol.

Example: Draw the condensed structural formulas for the products from the **(a)** acid and **(b)** base hydrolysis (NaOH) of ethyl butanoate.

Answer:

a. $CH_3-CH_2-CH_2-\overset{\overset{O}{||}}{C}-OH + HO-CH_2-CH_3$

b. $CH_3-CH_2-CH_2-\overset{\overset{O}{||}}{C}-O^- \ Na^+ + HO-CH_2-CH_3$

UNDERSTANDING THE CONCEPTS

The chapter sections to review are shown in parentheses at the end of each question.

16.41 Draw the condensed structural formulas and give the IUPAC names of two structural isomers of the carboxylic acids that have the molecular formula $C_4H_8O_2$. (16.1)

16.42 Draw the condensed structural formulas and give the IUPAC names of four structural isomers of the carboxylic acids that have the molecular formula $C_5H_{10}O_2$. (16.1)

16.43 Draw the condensed structural formulas and give the IUPAC names of two structural isomers of the esters that have the molecular formula $C_3H_6O_2$. (16.3, 16.4)

16.44 Draw the condensed structural formulas and give the IUPAC names of four structural isomers of the esters that have the molecular formula $C_4H_8O_2$. (16.3, 16.4)

℞ Clinical Applications

16.45 A strawberry nutritional drink used for a liquid diet is flavored with methyl butanoate. (16.1, 16.3, 16.4, 16.5)
   a. Draw the condensed structural formula for methyl butanoate.

b. Give the IUPAC name of the carboxylic acid and the alcohol used to prepare methyl butanoate.
   c. Write a balanced chemical equation for the acid hydrolysis of methyl butanoate.
   d. Write a balanced chemical equation for the base hydrolysis of methyl butanoate with NaOH.

16.46 The drug cocaine hydrochloride hydrolyzes in air to give methyl benzoate. Its odor, which smells like pineapple guava, is used to train drug-sniffing dogs. (16.1, 16.3, 16.4, 16.5)

   a. Draw the condensed structural formula for methyl benzoate.
   b. Give the name of the carboxylic acid and alcohol used to prepare methyl benzoate.
   c. Write a balanced chemical equation for the acid hydrolysis of methyl benzoate.
   d. Write a balanced chemical equation for the base hydrolysis of methyl benzoate with NaOH.

ADDITIONAL QUESTIONS AND PROBLEMS

16.47 Give the IUPAC and common names, if any, for each of the following compounds: (16.1, 16.4)

a. $CH_3-\underset{\underset{CH_3}{|}}{\overset{\overset{CH_3}{|}}{CH}}-CH_2-\overset{\overset{O}{||}}{C}-OH$

b. benzene ring $-\overset{\overset{O}{||}}{C}-O-CH_2-CH_3$

c. $CH_3-CH_2-\overset{\overset{O}{||}}{C}-O-CH_2-CH_3$

d. benzene ring with $\overset{\overset{O}{||}}{C}-OH$ and Cl

e.

f. $CH_3-\overset{\overset{\displaystyle O}{\|}}{C}-O-\overset{\overset{\displaystyle CH_3}{|}}{CH}-CH_3$

16.48 Give the IUPAC and common names, if any, for each of the following compounds: (16.1, 16.4)

a. $CH_3-\overset{\overset{\displaystyle CH_3}{|}}{CH}-CH_2-CH_2-\overset{\overset{\displaystyle O}{\|}}{C}-OH$

b.

c.

d. $CH_3-CH_2-CH_2-\overset{\overset{\displaystyle O}{\|}}{C}-O-CH_3$

e. $CH_3-\overset{\overset{\displaystyle CH_3}{|}}{CH}-CH_2-\overset{\overset{\displaystyle O}{\|}}{C}-O-CH_2-CH_3$

f. $CH_3-\overset{\overset{\displaystyle CH_3}{|}}{CH}-CH_2-\overset{\overset{\displaystyle OH}{|}}{CH}-\overset{\overset{\displaystyle O}{\|}}{C}-OH$

16.49 Draw the line-angle structural formulas for two methyl esters that have the molecular formula $C_5H_{10}O_2$. (16.3)

16.50 Draw the line-angle structural formulas for the carboxylic acid and the ester that have the molecular formula $C_2H_4O_2$. (16.1, 16.3)

16.51 Draw the condensed structural formula for each of the following: (16.1, 16.4)
a. methyl hexanoate
b. *p*-chlorobenzoic acid
c. *β*-chloropropionic acid
d. ethyl butanoate
e. 3-methylpentanoic acid
f. ethyl benzoate

16.52 Draw the condensed structural formula for each of the following: (16.1, 16.4)
a. *α*-bromobutyric acid
b. ethyl butyrate
c. 2-methyloctanoic acid
d. 3,5-dimethylhexanoic acid
e. propyl acetate
f. 3,4-dibromobenzoic acid

16.53 For each of the following pairs, identify the compound that would have the higher boiling point. Explain. (16.2, 16.5)

a. $CH_3-CH_2-CH_2-OH$ or $CH_3-\overset{\overset{\displaystyle O}{\|}}{C}-OH$

b. $CH_3-CH_2-CH_2-CH_3$ or $CH_3-\overset{\overset{\displaystyle O}{\|}}{C}-OH$

16.54 For each of the following pairs, identify the compound that would have the higher boiling point. Explain. (16.2, 16.5)

a. $CH_3-\overset{\overset{\displaystyle OH}{|}}{CH}-CH_3$ or $H-\overset{\overset{\displaystyle O}{\|}}{C}-O-CH_3$

b. $H-\overset{\overset{\displaystyle O}{\|}}{C}-O-CH_3$ or $CH_3-CH_2-CH_2-CH_3$

16.55 Acetic acid, methyl formate, and 1-propanol all have the same molar mass. The possible boiling points are 32 °C, 97 °C, and 118 °C. Match the compounds with the boiling points and explain your choice. (16.2, 16.5)

16.56 Propionic acid, 1-butanol, and butyraldehyde all have the same molar mass. The possible boiling points are 76 °C, 118 °C, and 141 °C. Match the compounds with the boiling points and explain your choice. (16.2, 16.5)

16.57 Which of the following compounds are soluble in water? (16.2, 16.5)

a. $CH_3-CH_2-\overset{\overset{\displaystyle O}{\|}}{C}-O^-\ Na^+$

b.

c. $CH_3-CH_2-CH_2-OH$

d. $CH_3-CH_2-\overset{\overset{\displaystyle O}{\|}}{C}-OH$

16.58 Which of the following compounds are soluble in water? (16.2, 16.5)

a. $CH_3-CH_2-CH_2-\overset{\overset{\displaystyle O}{\|}}{C}-OH$

b. $CH_3-\overset{\overset{\displaystyle O}{\|}}{C}-O-CH_3$

c. $CH_3-CH_2-CH_2-CH_3$

d.

16.59 Draw the condensed structural formulas for the products from each of the following reactions: (16.2, 16.3)

a. $CH_3-CH_2-\overset{\overset{\displaystyle O}{\|}}{C}-OH + H_2O \rightleftharpoons$

b. $CH_3-CH_2-\overset{\overset{\displaystyle O}{\|}}{C}-OH + KOH \longrightarrow$

c. $\overset{H^+,\ heat}{\rightleftharpoons}$

d. $+\ HO-CH_2-CH_3 \overset{H^+,\ heat}{\rightleftharpoons}$

16.60 Draw the condensed structural formulas for the products from each of the following reactions: (16.2, 16.3)

a. $CH_3-\overset{\overset{\displaystyle O}{\|}}{C}-OH + NaOH \longrightarrow$

b. $CH_3-\overset{\overset{\displaystyle O}{\|}}{C}-OH + H_2O \rightleftharpoons$

c. $+ KOH \longrightarrow$

d. $CH_3-\overset{\overset{\displaystyle CH_3}{|}}{CH}-\overset{\overset{\displaystyle O}{\|}}{C}-OH + HO-CH_3 \underset{}{\overset{H^+, \text{ heat}}{\rightleftarrows}}$

16.61 Give the IUPAC names of the carboxylic acid and alcohol needed to produce each of the following esters: (16.3)

a. $CH_3-\overset{\overset{\displaystyle CH_3}{|}}{CH}-CH_2-\overset{\overset{\displaystyle O}{\|}}{C}-O-CH_3$

b. (structure: benzene ring with $\overset{\overset{\displaystyle O}{\|}}{C}-O-CH_2-CH_3$ group and Cl substituent)

c. (structure: pentanoate ester chain with ethyl group)

16.62 Give the IUPAC names of the carboxylic acid and alcohol needed to produce each of the following esters: (16.3)

a. $CH_3-CH_2-CH_2-\overset{\overset{\displaystyle O}{\|}}{C}-O-CH_2-CH_3$

b. (structure: propanoate ester bonded to benzene ring with Cl substituent)

c. $CH_3-\overset{\overset{\displaystyle CH_3}{|}}{CH}-\overset{\overset{\displaystyle CH_3}{|}}{CH}-\overset{\overset{\displaystyle O}{\|}}{C}-O-CH_3$

16.63 Draw the condensed structural formulas for the products from each of the following reactions: (16.5)

a. $CH_3-CH_2-\overset{\overset{\displaystyle O}{\|}}{C}-O-\overset{\overset{\displaystyle CH_3}{|}}{CH}-CH_3 + H_2O \underset{}{\overset{H^+, \text{ heat}}{\rightleftarrows}}$

b. $CH_3-\overset{\overset{\displaystyle CH_3}{|}}{CH}-\overset{\overset{\displaystyle O}{\|}}{C}-O-CH_2-CH_2-CH_3 + NaOH \overset{\text{Heat}}{\longrightarrow}$

16.64 Draw the condensed structural formulas for the products from each of the following reactions: (16.5)

a. $CH_3-CH_2-\overset{\overset{\displaystyle O}{\|}}{C}-O-\overset{\overset{\displaystyle CH_3}{|}}{CH}-CH_3 + NaOH \overset{\text{Heat}}{\longrightarrow}$

b. $CH_3-\overset{\overset{\displaystyle CH_3}{|}}{CH}-\overset{\overset{\displaystyle O}{\|}}{C}-O-CH_2-CH_2-CH_3 + H_2O \underset{}{\overset{H^+, \text{ heat}}{\rightleftarrows}}$

CHALLENGE QUESTIONS

The following groups of questions are related to the topics in this chapter. However, they do not all follow the chapter order, and they require you to combine concepts and skills from several sections. These questions will help you increase your critical thinking skills and prepare for your next exam.

16.65 Using the reactions we have studied, indicate how you might prepare the following from the starting substance given: (12.7, 16.1, 16.3)
    a. acetic acid from ethene
    b. butyric acid from 1-butanol

16.66 Using the reactions we have studied, indicate how you might prepare the following from the starting substance given: (16.1, 16.3)
    a. pentanoic acid from 1-pentanol
    b. ethyl acetate from two molecules of ethanol

16.67 Methyl benzoate is not soluble in water; however, when it is heated with KOH, the ester forms soluble products. When HCl is added to neutralize the basic solution, a white solid forms. Draw the condensed structural formulas for the reactants and products when methyl benzoate and KOH react. Explain what happens. (16.4, 16.5)

16.68 Hexanoic acid is not soluble in water. However, when hexanoic acid is added to a solution of NaOH, a soluble product forms. Draw the condensed structural formulas for the reactants and products when hexanoic acid and NaOH react. Explain what happens. (16.4, 16.5)

16.69 Propyl acetate is an ester that gives the odor and flavor of pears. (9.4, 16.3, 16.4, 16.5)

    a. Draw the condensed structural formula for propyl acetate.
    b. Write a balanced chemical equation for the formation of propyl acetate.
    c. Write a balanced chemical equation for the hydrolysis of propyl acetate with HCl.
    d. Write a balanced chemical equation for the hydrolysis of propyl acetate with NaOH.
    e. How many milliliters of a 0.208 M NaOH solution is needed to completely hydrolyze (saponify) 1.58 g of propyl acetate?

16.70 Ethyl octanoate is a flavor component of mangos. (9.4, 16.3, 16.4, 16.5)
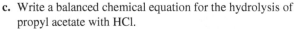
    a. Draw the condensed structural formula for ethyl octanoate.
    b. Write a balanced chemical equation for the formation of ethyl octanoate.
    c. Write a balanced chemical equation for the hydrolysis of ethyl octanoate with HCl.
    d. Write a balanced chemical equation for the hydrolysis of ethyl octanoate with NaOH.
    e. How many milliliters of a 0.315 M NaOH solution is needed to completely hydrolyze (saponify) 2.84 g of ethyl octanoate?

ANSWERS

Answers to Selected Questions and Problems

16.1 methanoic acid (formic acid)

16.3 a.

$$CH_3-CH_2-CH_2-CH_2-CH_2-\overset{O}{\overset{\|}{C}}-OH, \text{ hexanoic acid}$$

b. $CH_3-CH_2-\overset{\overset{\displaystyle CH_3-CH_2}{|}}{CH}-\overset{O}{\overset{\|}{C}}-OH, \text{ 2-ethylbutanoic acid}$

16.5 a. ethanoic acid (acetic acid)
b. butanoic acid (butyric acid)
c. 3-methylhexanoic acid
d. 3,4-dibromobenzoic acid

16.7 a. $Cl-CH_2-\overset{O}{\overset{\|}{C}}-OH$

b. $HO-CH_2-CH_2-\overset{O}{\overset{\|}{C}}-OH$

c. $CH_3-CH_2-\overset{\overset{}{|}}{\underset{\underset{\displaystyle CH_3}{|}}{CH}}-\overset{O}{\overset{\|}{C}}-OH$

d. $CH_3-CH_2-\underset{\underset{\displaystyle Br}{|}}{CH}-CH_2-\underset{\underset{\displaystyle Br}{|}}{CH}-CH_2-\overset{O}{\overset{\|}{C}}-OH$

16.9 a. $H-\overset{O}{\overset{\|}{C}}-OH$ **b.** $CH_3-\overset{O}{\overset{\|}{C}}-OH$

c.   **d.**

16.11 a. Butanoic acid has a greater molar mass and would have a higher boiling point.
b. Propanoic acid can form dimers, effectively doubling the molar mass, which gives propanoic acid a higher boiling point.
c. Butanoic acid can form dimers, effectively doubling the molar mass, which gives butanoic acid a higher boiling point.

16.13 a. Propanoic acid has the smallest alkyl group, which makes it most soluble.
b. Propanoic acid forms more hydrogen bonds with water, which makes it most soluble.

16.15 a. $CH_3-CH_2-CH_2-\overset{O}{\overset{\|}{C}}-OH + H_2O \rightleftarrows$

$$CH_3-CH_2-CH_2-\overset{O}{\overset{\|}{C}}-O^- + H_3O^+$$

b. $CH_3-\underset{\underset{\displaystyle CH_3}{|}}{CH}-\overset{O}{\overset{\|}{C}}-OH + H_2O \rightleftarrows$

$$CH_3-\underset{\underset{\displaystyle CH_3}{|}}{CH}-\overset{O}{\overset{\|}{C}}-O^- + H_3O^+$$

16.17 a.

$$CH_3-CH_2-CH_2-CH_2-\overset{O}{\overset{\|}{C}}-OH + NaOH \longrightarrow$$

$$CH_3-CH_2-CH_2-CH_2-\overset{O}{\overset{\|}{C}}-O^-\,Na^+ + H_2O$$

b. $CH_3-\underset{\underset{\displaystyle Cl}{|}}{CH}-\overset{O}{\overset{\|}{C}}-OH + NaOH \longrightarrow$

$$CH_3-\underset{\underset{\displaystyle Cl}{|}}{CH}-\overset{O}{\overset{\|}{C}}-O^-\,Na^+ + H_2O$$

c. $+ NaOH \longrightarrow$ $+ H_2O$

16.19 a. sodium pentanoate
b. sodium 2-chloropropanoate (sodium α-chloropropionate)
c. sodium benzoate

16.21 a. aldehyde   **b.** ester
c. ketone   **d.** carboxylic acid

16.23 a. $CH_3-\overset{O}{\overset{\|}{C}}-O-CH_2-CH_3$

b. $CH_3-CH_2-CH_2-\overset{O}{\overset{\|}{C}}-O-CH_2-CH_3$

c.

16.25 a.

b. $CH_3-CH_2-CH_2-CH_2-\overset{O}{\overset{\|}{C}}-O-\underset{\underset{\displaystyle CH_3}{|}}{CH}-CH_3$

16.27 a. methanoic acid (formic acid) and methanol (methyl alcohol)
b. propanoic acid (propionic acid) and ethanol (ethyl alcohol)
c. butanoic acid (butyric acid) and methanol (methyl alcohol)
d. 3-methylbutanoic acid (β-methylbutyric acid) and ethanol (ethyl alcohol)

16.29 a. methyl methanoate (methyl formate)
b. ethyl propanoate (ethyl propionate)
c. methyl butanoate (methyl butyrate)
d. 2-methylpropyl pentanoate

16.31 a. $CH_3-\overset{\overset{\displaystyle O}{\|}}{C}-O-CH_3$

b. $H-\overset{\overset{\displaystyle O}{\|}}{C}-O-CH_2-CH_2-CH_2-CH_3$

c. $CH_3-CH_2-CH_2-CH_2-\overset{\overset{\displaystyle O}{\|}}{C}-O-CH_2-CH_3$

d. $CH_3-CH_2-\overset{\overset{\displaystyle O}{\|}}{C}-O-CH_2-\overset{\overset{\displaystyle Br}{|}}{CH}-CH_3$

16.33 a. pentyl ethanoate (pentyl acetate)
b. octyl ethanoate (octyl acetate)
c. pentyl butanoate (pentyl butyrate)

16.35 a. $CH_3-CH_2-\overset{\overset{\displaystyle O}{\|}}{C}-OH$
b. $CH_3-CH_2-CH_2-CH_2-OH$

c.

16.37 a. $CH_3-CH_2-\overset{\overset{\displaystyle O}{\|}}{C}-O^-\ Na^+\ +\ HO-CH_3$

b.

c. $CH_3-CH_2-CH_2-\overset{\overset{\displaystyle O}{\|}}{C}-OH\ +\ HO-CH_2-CH_3$

d. $-\overset{\overset{\displaystyle O}{\|}}{C}-O^-\ Na^+\ +\ HO-CH_2-CH_3$

e.

16.39 a. $H_2C=\overset{\overset{\displaystyle CN}{|}}{C}-\overset{\overset{\displaystyle O}{\|}}{C}-OH\ +\ HO-CH_2-CH_2-CH_2-CH_3\ \underset{}{\overset{H^+,\ heat}{\rightleftharpoons}}$

$H_2C=\overset{\overset{\displaystyle CN}{|}}{C}-\overset{\overset{\displaystyle O}{\|}}{C}-O-CH_2-CH_2-CH_2-CH_3\ +\ H_2O$

b. butyl 2-cyano-2-propenoate

16.41 $CH_3-CH_2-CH_2-\overset{\overset{\displaystyle O}{\|}}{C}-OH$ $CH_3-\overset{\overset{\displaystyle CH_3}{|}}{CH}-\overset{\overset{\displaystyle O}{\|}}{C}-OH$
butanoic acid   2-methylpropanoic acid

16.43 $CH_3-\overset{\overset{\displaystyle O}{\|}}{C}-O-CH_3$ $H-\overset{\overset{\displaystyle O}{\|}}{C}-O-CH_2-CH_3$
methyl ethanoate   ethyl methanoate

16.45 a. $CH_3-CH_2-CH_2-\overset{\overset{\displaystyle O}{\|}}{C}-O-CH_3$
b. butanoic acid and methanol

c. $CH_3-CH_2-CH_2-\overset{\overset{\displaystyle O}{\|}}{C}-O-CH_3\ +\ H_2O\ \overset{H^+,\ heat}{\rightleftharpoons}$

$CH_3-CH_2-CH_2-\overset{\overset{\displaystyle O}{\|}}{C}-OH\ +\ HO-CH_3$

d. $CH_3-CH_2-CH_2-\overset{\overset{\displaystyle O}{\|}}{C}-O-CH_3\ +\ NaOH\ \overset{Heat}{\rightarrow}$

$CH_3-CH_2-CH_2-\overset{\overset{\displaystyle O}{\|}}{C}-O^-\ Na^+\ +\ HO-CH_3$

16.47 a. 3-methylbutanoic acid (β-methylbutyric acid)
b. ethyl benzoate
c. ethyl propanoate (ethyl propionate)
d. 2-chlorobenzoic acid (o-chlorobenzoic acid)
e. 4-hydroxypentanoic acid
f. 2-propyl ethanoate (isopropyl acetate)

16.49

16.51 a. $CH_3-CH_2-CH_2-CH_2-CH_2-\overset{\overset{\displaystyle O}{\|}}{C}-O-CH_3$

b.

c. $Cl-CH_2-CH_2-\overset{\overset{\displaystyle O}{\|}}{C}-OH$

d. $CH_3-CH_2-CH_2-\overset{\overset{\displaystyle O}{\|}}{C}-O-CH_2-CH_3$

e. $CH_3-CH_2-\overset{\overset{\displaystyle CH_3}{|}}{CH}-CH_2-\overset{\overset{\displaystyle O}{\|}}{C}-OH$

f.

16.53 a. Ethanoic acid has a higher boiling point than 1-propanol because two molecules of ethanoic acid hydrogen bond to form a dimer, which effectively doubles the molar mass and requires a higher temperature to reach the boiling point.
b. Ethanoic acid forms hydrogen bonds, but butane does not.

16.55 Of the three compounds, methyl formate would have the lowest boiling point since it only has dipole–dipole attractions. Both acetic acid and 1-propanol can form hydrogen bonds, but because acetic acid can form dimers and double the effective molar mass, it has the highest boiling point. Methyl formate, 32 °C; 1-propanol, 97 °C; acetic acid, 118 °C.

16.57 a, c, and **d** are soluble in water.

16.59 a. $CH_3-CH_2-\overset{\overset{\displaystyle O}{\|}}{C}-O^- + H_3O^+$

b. $CH_3-CH_2-\overset{\overset{\displaystyle O}{\|}}{C}-O^-\ K^+ + H_2O$

c. 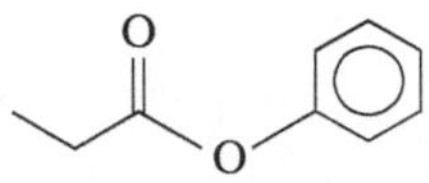 $+ H_2O$

d. 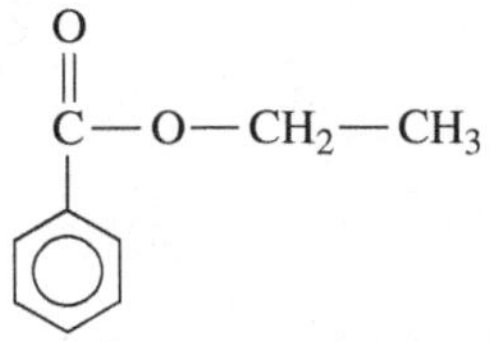 $+ H_2O$

16.61 a. 3-methylbutanoic acid and methanol
   b. 3-chlorobenzoic acid and ethanol
   c. hexanoic acid and ethanol

16.63 a. $CH_3-CH_2-\overset{\overset{\displaystyle O}{\|}}{C}-OH + HO-\overset{\overset{\displaystyle CH_3}{|}}{CH}-CH_3$

b. $CH_3-\overset{\overset{\displaystyle CH_3}{|}}{CH}-\overset{\overset{\displaystyle O}{\|}}{C}-O^-\ Na^+ + HO-CH_2-CH_2-CH_3$

16.65 a. $H_2C{=}CH_2 + H_2O \xrightarrow{\ H^+\ }$

$CH_3-CH_2-OH \xrightarrow{[O]} CH_3-\overset{\overset{\displaystyle O}{\|}}{C}-OH$

b. $CH_3-CH_2-CH_2-CH_2-OH \xrightarrow{[O]}$

$CH_3-CH_2-CH_2-\overset{\overset{\displaystyle O}{\|}}{C}-OH$

16.67 $+ KOH \xrightarrow{\text{Heat}}$

$K^+ + HO-CH_3$

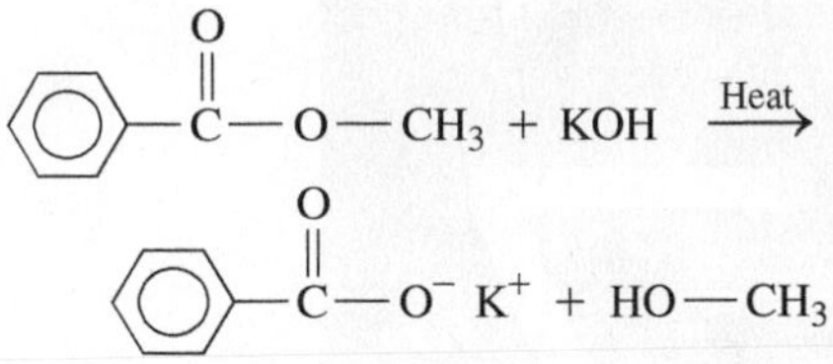

In KOH solution, the ester undergoes saponification to form the carboxylate salt, potassium benzoate, and methanol, which are soluble in water. When HCl is added, the salt is converted to benzoic acid, which is insoluble.

16.69 a. $CH_3-\overset{\overset{\displaystyle O}{\|}}{C}-O-CH_2-CH_2-CH_3$

b. $CH_3-\overset{\overset{\displaystyle O}{\|}}{C}-OH + HO-CH_2-CH_2-CH_3 \underset{}{\overset{H^+,\ \text{heat}}{\rightleftharpoons}}$

$CH_3-\overset{\overset{\displaystyle O}{\|}}{C}-O-CH_2-CH_2-CH_3 + H_2O$

c. $CH_3-\overset{\overset{\displaystyle O}{\|}}{C}-O-CH_2-CH_2-CH_3 + H_2O \underset{}{\overset{H^+,\ \text{heat}}{\rightleftharpoons}}$

$CH_3-\overset{\overset{\displaystyle O}{\|}}{C}-OH + HO-CH_2-CH_2-CH_3$

d. $CH_3-\overset{\overset{\displaystyle O}{\|}}{C}-O-CH_2-CH_2-CH_3 + NaOH \xrightarrow{\text{Heat}}$

$CH_3-\overset{\overset{\displaystyle O}{\|}}{C}-O^-\ Na^+ + HO-CH_2-CH_2-CH_3$

e. 74.4 mL of a 0.208 M NaOH solution

17

Lipids

REBECCA LEARNED OF HER FAMILY'S HYPER-
cholesterolemia after her mother died of a heart attack at 44. Her mother had a total cholesterol level of 600 mg/dL, which is three times the normal level. Rebecca learned that the lumps under her mother's skin and around the cornea of her eyes, called *xanthomas*, were caused by cholesterol that was stored throughout her body. In familial hypercholesterolemia (FH), genetic mutations prevent the removal of cholesterol from the bloodstream. As a result, low-density lipoprotein (LDL) accumulates in the blood and a person with FH can develop cardiovascular disease early in life. In adults with FH, cholesterol levels may be greater than 300 mg/dL, and LDL levels may be greater than 220 mg/dL. At the lipid clinic, Rebecca's blood tests showed that she had a total cholesterol level of 420 mg/dL and an LDL-cholesterol level of 275 mg/dL. Rebecca was diagnosed with FH. She learned that from birth, cholesterol has been accumulating throughout her arteries. FH is a genetic condition: If one parent has it, there is a 50 percent chance that a child will inherit the disorder. FH is caused by a mutation that blocks the removal of LDL-cholesterol from the blood resulting in the formation of cholesterol deposits on the arterial walls.

At age 39, Rebecca discovered a painful lump that was identified as calcified cholesterol. After her diagnosis, Rebecca met with Susan, a clinical lipid specialist at the lipid clinic where she informed Rebecca about managing risk factors that can lead to heart attack and stroke. Susan told Rebecca about medications she would prescribe, and then followed the results.

CAREER Clinical Lipid Specialist

Clinical lipid specialists work with patients who have lipid disorders such as high cholesterol, high triglycerides, coronary heart disease, obesity, and FH. At a lipid clinic, a clinical lipid specialist reviews a patient's lipid profile, which includes total cholesterol, high-density lipoprotein (HDL), and low-density lipoprotein (LDL). If a lipid disorder is identified, the lipid specialist assesses the patient's current diet and exercise program. The lipid specialist diagnoses and determines treatment including dietary changes such as reducing salt intake, increasing the amount of fiber in the diet, and lowering the amount of fat. He or she also discusses drug therapy using lipid-lowering medications that remove LDL-cholesterol to help patients achieve and maintain good health.

Allied health professionals such as nurses, nurse practitioners, pharmacists, and dietitians are certified by a clinical lipid specialist program for specialized care of patients with lipid disorders.

When we talk of fats and oils, waxes, steroids, and cholesterol, we are discussing lipids. Lipids are naturally occurring compounds that vary considerably in structure but share the common feature of being soluble in nonpolar solvents, but not in water. Fats, which are one family of lipids, have many functions in the body, such as storing energy and protecting and insulating internal organs. Because lipids are not soluble in water, they are important in cellular membranes that function to separate the internal contents of cells from the external environment. Other types of lipids are found in nerve fibers and in hormones, which act as chemical messengers.

Many people are concerned about the amounts of saturated fats and cholesterol in our diets. Researchers suggest that saturated fats and cholesterol are associated with diseases such as diabetes; cancers of the breast, pancreas, and colon; and *atherosclerosis*, a condition in which deposits of lipid materials called *plaque* accumulate in the coronary blood vessels. In atherosclerosis, plaque restricts the flow of blood to the tissue, causing necrosis (death). An accumulation of plaque in the heart could result in a *myocardial infarction* (heart attack).

The American Institute for Cancer Research (AICR) has recommended that we increase the fiber and starch content of our diets by adding more vegetables, fruits, and whole grains as well as foods with low levels of fat and cholesterol such as fish, poultry, lean meats, and low-fat dairy products. The AICR has also suggested that we limit our intake of foods high in fat and cholesterol such as eggs, nuts, fatty or organ meats, cheeses, butter, and coconut and palm oil.

CHAPTER READINESS*

⚛ CORE CHEMISTRY SKILLS

- Writing Equations for Hydrogenation, Hydration, and Polymerization (12.7)
- Naming Alcohols and Phenols (13.1)
- Naming Carboxylic Acids (16.1)
- Hydrolyzing Esters (16.5)

*These Core Chemistry Skills from previous chapters are listed here for your review as you proceed to the new material in this chapter.

17.1 Lipids

Lipids are a family of biomolecules that have the common property of being soluble in organic solvents but not in water. The word *lipid* comes from the Greek word *lipos*, meaning "fat" or "lard." Typically, the lipid content of a cell can be extracted using a nonpolar solvent such as ether or chloroform. Lipids are an important feature in cell membranes and steroid hormones.

Types of Lipids

Within the lipid family, there are specific structures that distinguish the different types of lipids. Lipids such as waxes, triacylglycerols, glycerophospholipids, and sphingolipids are esters that can be hydrolyzed to give fatty acids along with other molecules. Triacylglycerols and glycerophospholipids contain the alcohol *glycerol*, whereas sphingolipids contain the amino alcohol *sphingosine*. Steroids, which have a completely different structure, do not contain fatty acids and cannot be hydrolyzed. Steroids are characterized by the *steroid*

LEARNING GOAL

Describe the classes of lipids.

nucleus of four fused carbon rings. Figure 17.1 illustrates the types and general structure of lipids we will discuss in this chapter.

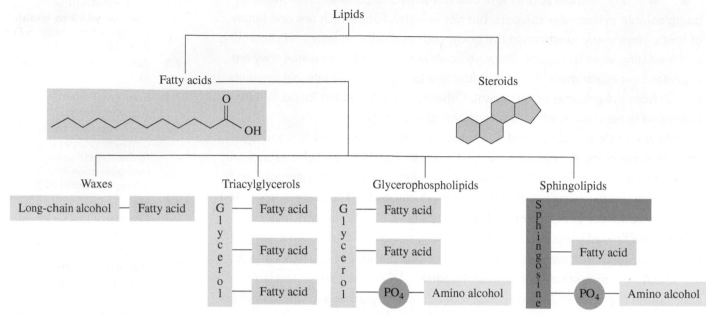

FIGURE 17.1 ▶ Lipids are naturally occurring compounds in cells and tissues, which are soluble in organic solvents but not in water.

ℚ What chemical property do waxes, triacylglycerols, and steroids have in common?

QUESTIONS AND PROBLEMS

17.1 Lipids

LEARNING GOAL Describe the classes of lipids.

17.1 Lipids are not soluble in water. Are lipids polar or nonpolar molecules?

17.2 Which of the following solvents might be used to dissolve an oil stain?
- **a.** water
- **b.** CCl₄
- **c.** diethyl ether
- **d.** benzene
- **e.** NaCl solution

℞ Clinical Applications

17.3 What are some functions of lipids in the body?

17.4 What are some of the different kinds of lipids?

LEARNING GOAL

Draw the condensed or line-angle structural formula for a fatty acid and identify it as saturated or unsaturated.

⚙ CORE CHEMISTRY SKILL

Identifying Fatty Acids

17.2 Fatty Acids

A **fatty acid** contains a long, unbranched carbon chain with a carboxylic acid group at one end. Although the carboxylic acid part is hydrophilic, the long hydrophobic carbon chain makes fatty acids insoluble in water.

Most naturally occurring fatty acids have an even number of carbon atoms, usually between 12 and 20. An example of a fatty acid is lauric acid, a 12-carbon acid found in coconut oil. In a line-angle structural formula of a fatty acid, the ends and bends of the line are the carbon atoms. The structural formula of lauric acid can be drawn in several forms.

Drawing Structural Formulas for Lauric Acid

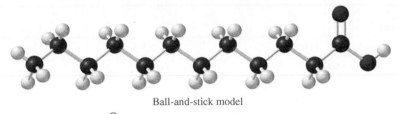

Ball-and-stick model

$$CH_3 - (CH_2)_{10} - \overset{\overset{\displaystyle O}{\|}}{C} - OH \qquad CH_3 - (CH_2)_{10} - COOH$$

$$CH_3 - CH_2 - CH_2 - CH_2 - CH_2 - CH_2 - CH_2 - CH_2 - CH_2 - CH_2 - CH_2 - \overset{\overset{\displaystyle O}{\|}}{C}$$
$$OH$$

Condensed structural formulas

Line-angle structural formula

A **saturated fatty acid (SFA)** contains only carbon–carbon single bonds, which make the properties of a long-chain fatty acid similar to those of an alkane. An **unsaturated fatty acid** contains one or more carbon–carbon double bonds. In a **monounsaturated fatty acid (MUFA)**, the long carbon chain has one double bond, which makes its properties similar to those of an alkene. A **polyunsaturated fatty acid (PUFA)** has at least two carbon–carbon double bonds. Table 17.1 lists some of the typical fatty acids in lipids. In the lipids of plants and animals, about half of the fatty acids are saturated and half are unsaturated.

Cis and Trans Isomers of Unsaturated Fatty Acids

Unsaturated fatty acids can be drawn as *cis* and *trans* isomers. For example, oleic acid, an 18-carbon monounsaturated fatty acid found in olives, has one double bond starting at carbon 9. We can show its cis and trans structures using its line-angle structural formulas. The cis structure is the more prevalent isomer found in naturally occurring unsaturated fatty acids. In the cis isomer, the carbon chain has a "kink" at the double bond site. The trans isomer of oleic acid, *elaidic acid*, is a straight chain without a kink at the double bond site.

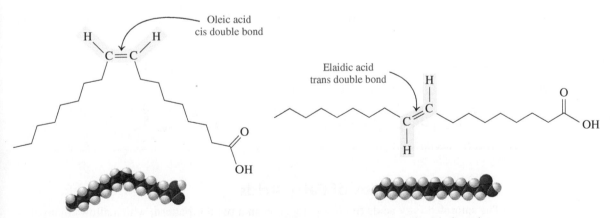

Almost all naturally occurring unsaturated fatty acids have one or more cis double bonds.

The human body is capable of synthesizing some fatty acids from carbohydrates or other fatty acids. However, humans cannot synthesize sufficient amounts of polyunsaturated fatty acids such as linoleic acid, linolenic acid, and arachidonic acid. Because they must be obtained from the diet, they are known as *essential fatty acids* (EFAs). In infants, a deficiency of EFAs can cause skin dermatitis. However, the role of fatty acids in adult nutrition is not well understood. Adults do not usually have a deficiency of EFAs.

Explore Your World
Solubility of Fats and Oils

Place some water in a small bowl. Add a drop of vegetable oil. Then add a few more drops of the oil. Record your observations. Now add a few drops of liquid soap and mix. Record your observations.

Place a small amount of fat such as margarine, butter, shortening, or vegetable oil on a dish or plate. Run water over it. Record your observations. Mix some soap with the fat substance and run water over it again. Record your observations.

Questions

1. Do the drops of oil in the water separate or do they come together? Explain.
2. How does the soap affect the oil layer?
3. Why don't the fats on the dish or plate wash off with water?
4. In general, what is the solubility of lipids in water?
5. Why does soap help to wash the fats off the plate?

TABLE 17.1 Structures and Melting Points of Common Fatty Acids

Name	Carbon Atoms: Double Bonds	Present in	Melting Point (°C)	Structures
Saturated Fatty Acids				
Lauric acid	12:0	Coconut	44	$CH_3-(CH_2)_{10}-COOH$
Myristic acid	14:0	Nutmeg	55	$CH_3-(CH_2)_{12}-COOH$
Palmitic acid	16:0	Palm	63	$CH_3-(CH_2)_{14}-COOH$
Stearic acid	18:0	Animal fat	69	$CH_3-(CH_2)_{16}-COOH$
Monounsaturated Fatty Acids				
Palmitoleic acid	16:1	Butter	0	$CH_3-(CH_2)_5-CH=CH-(CH_2)_7-COOH$
Oleic acid	18:1	Olives, pecan, grapeseed	14	$CH_3-(CH_2)_7-CH=CH-(CH_2)_7-COOH$
Polyunsaturated Fatty Acids				
Linoleic acid	18:2	Soybean, safflower, sunflower	−5	$CH_3-(CH_2)_4-CH=CH-CH_2-CH=CH-(CH_2)_7-COOH$
Linolenic acid	18:3	Corn	−11	$CH_3-CH_2-CH=CH-CH_2-CH=CH-CH_2-CH=CH-(CH_2)_7-COOH$
Arachidonic acid	20:4	Meat, eggs, fish	−50	$CH_3-(CH_2)_3-(CH_2-CH=CH)_4-(CH_2)_3-COOH$

Physical Properties of Fatty Acids

The saturated fatty acids fit closely together in a regular pattern, which allows many dispersion forces between the carbon chains. These normally weak intermolecular forces of attraction can be significant when molecules of fatty acids are close together. As a result, a significant amount of energy and high temperatures are required to separate the fatty acids before melting occurs. As the length of the carbon chain increases, more interactions occur between the fatty acids, requiring higher temperatures to melt. Saturated fatty acids are usually solids at room temperature (see Figure 17.2).

In unsaturated fatty acids, the cis double bonds cause the carbon chain to bend or kink, giving the molecules an irregular shape. As a result, unsaturated fatty acids cannot stack as closely as saturated fatty acids, and thus have fewer interactions between carbon

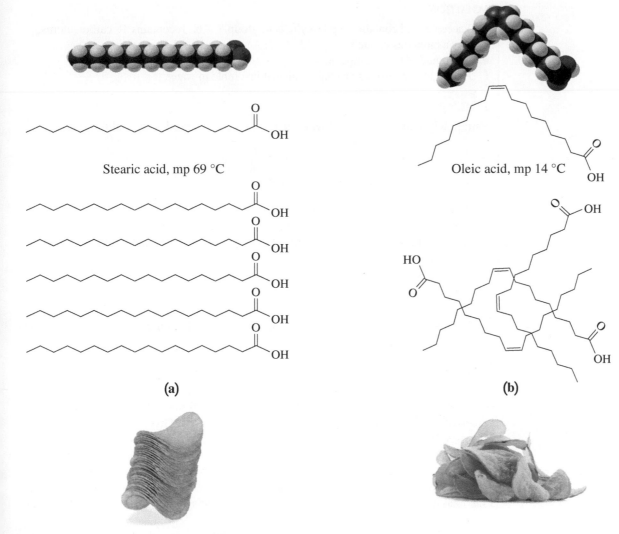

Stearic acid, mp 69 °C

Oleic acid, mp 14 °C

(a)

(b)

FIGURE 17.2 ▶ **(a)** In saturated fatty acids, the molecules fit closely together to give high melting points. **(b)** In unsaturated fatty acids, molecules cannot fit closely together, resulting in lower melting points.

🔍 Why does the cis double bond affect the melting points of unsaturated fatty acids?

chains. We might think of saturated fatty acids as chips with regular shapes that stack closely together in a can. Similarly, irregularly shaped chips would be like unsaturated fatty acids that do not fit closely together. Consequently, less energy is required to separate the molecules, making the melting points of unsaturated fats lower than those of saturated fats. Most unsaturated fats are liquid oils at room temperature.

SAMPLE PROBLEM 17.1 Structures and Properties of Fatty Acids

Consider the line-angle structural formula for vaccenic acid, a fatty acid found in dairy products and human milk.

a. Why is this substance an acid?
b. How many carbon atoms are in vaccenic acid?
c. Is the fatty acid saturated, monounsaturated, or polyunsaturated?
d. Give the shorthand notation for the number of carbon atoms and double bonds in vaccenic acid.
e. Is it most likely to be solid or liquid at room temperature?
f. Would it be soluble in water?

SOLUTION

a. Vaccenic acid contains a carboxylic acid group.   b. It contains 18 carbon atoms.

c. It is a monounsaturated fatty acid (MUFA).   d. 18:1

e. It is liquid at room temperature.

f. No. Its long hydrocarbon chain makes it insoluble in water.

STUDY CHECK 17.1

Palmitoleic acid is a fatty acid with the following condensed structural formula:

$$CH_3-(CH_2)_5-CH=CH-(CH_2)_7-\overset{\overset{\displaystyle O}{\|}}{C}-OH$$

a. How many carbon atoms are in palmitoleic acid?

b. Is the fatty acid saturated, monounsaturated, or polyunsaturated?

c. Give the shorthand notation for the number of carbon atoms and double bonds in palmitoleic acid.

d. Is it most likely to be solid or liquid at room temperature?

ANSWER

a. 16   b. monounsaturated   c. 16:1   d. liquid

Prostaglandins

Prostaglandins are hormone-like substances produced in small amounts in most cells of the body. The prostaglandins, also known as *eicosanoids*, are formed from arachidonic acid, the polyunsaturated fatty acid with 20 carbon atoms (*eicos* is the Greek word for 20). Swedish chemists first discovered prostaglandins and named them "prostaglandin E" (soluble in ether) and "prostaglandin F" (soluble in phosphate buffer or *fosfat* in Swedish). The various kinds of prostaglandins differ by the substituents attached to the five-carbon ring. Prostaglandin E (PGE) has a ketone group on carbon 9, whereas prostaglandin F (PGF) has a hydroxyl group. The number of double bonds is shown as a subscript 1 or 2.

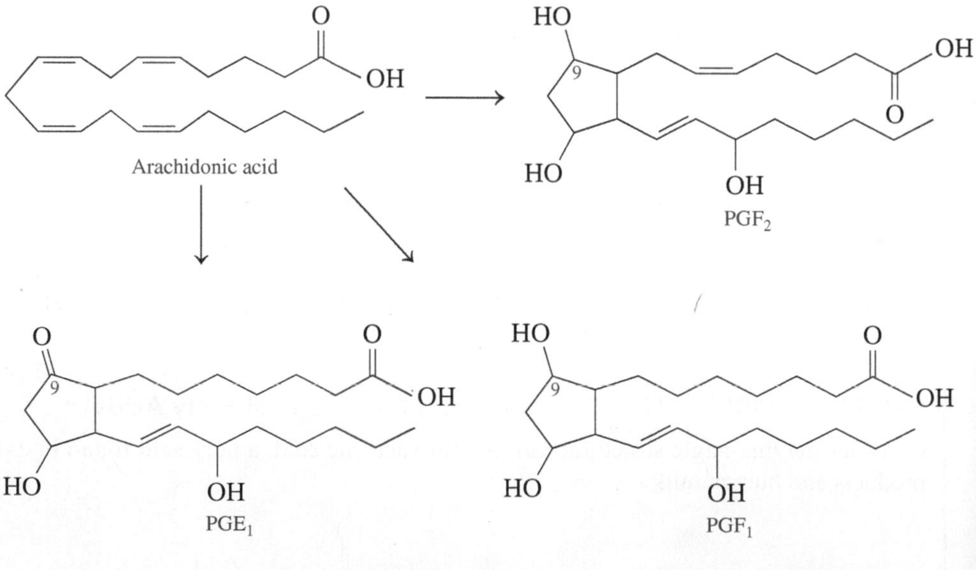

Arachidonic acid

PGF$_2$

PGE$_1$

PGF$_1$

Although prostaglandins are broken down quickly, they have potent physiological effects. Some prostaglandins increase blood pressure, and others lower blood pressure. Other prostaglandins stimulate contraction and relaxation in the smooth muscle of the uterus. When tissues are injured, arachidonic acid is converted to prostaglandins that produce inflammation and pain in the area.

When tissues are injured, prostaglandins are produced, which cause pain and inflammation.

The treatment of pain, fever, and inflammation is based on inhibiting the enzymes that convert arachidonic acid to prostaglandins. Several nonsteroidal anti-inflammatory drugs (NSAIDs), such as aspirin, block the production of prostaglandins and in doing so decrease pain and inflammation and reduce fever (antipyretics). Ibuprofen has similar anti-inflammatory and analgesic effects. Other NSAIDs include naproxen (Aleve and Naprosyn), ketoprofen (Actron), and nabumetone (Relafen). Although NSAIDs are helpful, their long-term use can result in liver, kidney, and gastrointestinal damage.

Aspirin   Ibuprofen (Advil, Motrin)   Naproxen (Aleve, Naprosyn)

♡ Chemistry Link to **Health**
Omega-3 Fatty Acids in Fish Oils

Because unsaturated fats are now recognized as being more beneficial to health than saturated fats, American diets have changed to include more unsaturated fats and less saturated fatty acids. This change is a response to research that indicates that atherosclerosis and heart disease are associated with high levels of fats in the diet. However, the Inuit people of Alaska have a diet with high levels of unsaturated fats as well as high levels of blood cholesterol, but a very low occurrence of atherosclerosis and heart attacks. The fats in the Inuit diet are primarily unsaturated fats from fish, rather than from land animals.

Both fish and vegetable oils have high levels of unsaturated fats. The fatty acids in vegetable oils are *omega-6 fatty acids* (ω-6 fatty acids), in which the first double bond occurs at carbon 6 counting from the methyl end of the carbon chain. Omega is the last letter in the Greek alphabet and is used to denote the end. Two common omega-6 acids are linoleic acid (LA) and arachidonic acid (AA). However, the fatty acids in fish oils are mostly the omega-3 type, in which the first double

Cold water fish are a good source of omega-3 fatty acids.

bond occurs at the third carbon counting from the methyl group. Three common *omega-3 fatty acids* (or *ω*-3 fatty acids) in fish are linolenic acid (ALA), eicosapentaenoic acid (EPA), and docosahexaenoic acid (DHA).

In atherosclerosis and heart disease, cholesterol forms plaques that adhere to the walls of the blood vessels. Blood pressure rises as blood has to squeeze through a smaller opening in the blood vessel. As more plaque forms, there is also a possibility of blood clots blocking the

blood vessels and causing a heart attack. Omega-3 fatty acids lower the tendency of blood platelets to stick together, thereby reducing the possibility of blood clots. However, high levels of omega-3 fatty acids can increase bleeding if the ability of the platelets to form blood clots is reduced too much. It does seem that a diet that includes fish such as salmon, tuna, and herring can provide higher amounts of the omega-3 fatty acids, which help lessen the possibility of developing heart disease.

Omega-6 Fatty Acids

Linoleic acid (LA)

Arachidonic acid (AA)

Omega-3 Fatty Acids

Linolenic acid (ALA)

Eicosapentaenoic acid (EPA)

Docosahexaenoic acid (DHA)

QUESTIONS AND PROBLEMS

17.2 Fatty Acids

LEARNING GOAL Draw the condensed or line-angle structural formula for a fatty acid and identify it as saturated or unsaturated.

17.5 Describe some similarities and differences in the structures of a saturated fatty acid and an unsaturated fatty acid.

17.6 Stearic acid and linoleic acid each have 18 carbon atoms. Why does stearic acid melt at 69 °C but linoleic acid melts at −5 °C?

17.7 Draw the line-angle structural formula for each of the following fatty acids:
a. palmitic acid
b. oleic acid

17.8 Draw the line-angle structural formula for each of the following fatty acids:
a. stearic acid
b. linoleic acid

17.9 For each of the following fatty acids, give the shorthand notation for the number of carbon atoms and double bonds, and classify as saturated, monounsaturated, or polyunsaturated:
a. lauric acid
b. linolenic acid
c. palmitoleic acid
d. stearic acid

17.10 For each of the following fatty acids, give the shorthand notation for the number of carbon atoms and double bonds, and classify as saturated, monounsaturated, or polyunsaturated:
a. linoleic acid
b. palmitic acid
c. myristic acid
d. oleic acid

17.11 How does the structure of a fatty acid with a cis double bond differ from the structure of a fatty acid with a trans double bond?

17.12 How does the double bond influence the dispersion forces that can form between the hydrocarbon chains of fatty acids?

℞ Clinical Applications

17.13 What is the difference in the location of the first double bond in an omega-3 and an omega-6 fatty acid (see Chemistry Link to Health "Omega-3 Fatty Acids in Fish Oils")?

17.14 What are some sources of omega-3 and omega-6 fatty acids (see Chemistry Link to Health "Omega-3 Fatty Acids in Fish Oils")?

17.15 Compare the structures and functional groups of arachidonic acid and prostaglandin PGE_1.

17.16 Compare the structures and functional groups of PGF_1 and PGF_2.

17.17 What are some effects of prostaglandins in the body?

17.18 How does an anti-inflammatory drug reduce inflammation?

17.3 Waxes and Triacylglycerols

Waxes are found in many plants and animals. Natural waxes are found on the surface of fruits, and on the leaves and stems of plants where they help prevent loss of water and damage from pests. Waxes on the skin, fur, and feathers of animals provide a waterproof coating. A **wax** is an ester of a saturated fatty acid and a long-chain alcohol, each containing from 14 to 30 carbon atoms.

The formulas of some common waxes are given in Table 17.2. Beeswax obtained from honeycombs and carnauba wax from palm trees are used to give a protective coating to furniture, cars, and floors. Jojoba wax is used in making candles and cosmetics such as lipstick. Lanolin, a mixture of waxes obtained from wool, is used in hand and facial lotions to aid retention of water, softening the skin.

TABLE 17.2 Some Typical Waxes

Type	Condensed Structural Formula	Source	Uses
Beeswax	$CH_3-(CH_2)_{14}-\overset{\overset{\textstyle O}{\|\|}}{C}-O-(CH_2)_{29}-CH_3$	Honeycomb	Candles, shoe polish, wax paper
Carnauba wax	$CH_3-(CH_2)_{24}-\overset{\overset{\textstyle O}{\|\|}}{C}-O-(CH_2)_{29}-CH_3$	Brazilian palm tree	Waxes for furniture, cars, floors, shoes
Jojoba wax	$CH_3-(CH_2)_{18}-\overset{\overset{\textstyle O}{\|\|}}{C}-O-(CH_2)_{19}-CH_3$	Jojoba bush	Candles, soaps, cosmetics

Triacylglycerols

In the body, fatty acids are stored as **triacylglycerols**, also called *triglycerides*, which are triesters of glycerol (a trihydroxy alcohol) and fatty acids. The general formula of a triacylglycerol follows:

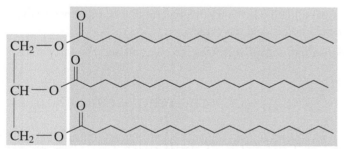

Triacylglycerol

In a triacylglycerol, three hydroxyl groups of glycerol form ester bonds with the carboxyl groups of three fatty acids. For example, glycerol and three molecules of stearic acid form a triacylglycerol. In the name, glycerol is named *glyceryl* and the fatty acids are named as carboxylates. For example, stearic acid is named as stearate, which gives the name glyceryl tristearate. The common name of this compound is tristearin.

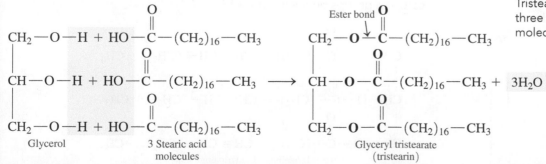

Glycerol   3 Stearic acid molecules   Glyceryl tristearate (tristearin)

LEARNING GOAL

Draw the condensed or line-angle structural formula for a wax or triacylglycerol produced by the reaction of a fatty acid and an alcohol or glycerol.

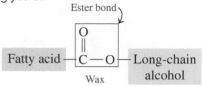

Waxes are esters of long-chain alcohols and fatty acids.

Jojoba wax is obtained from the seed of the jojoba bush.

Tristearin consists of glycerol with three ester bonds to stearic acid molecules.

⚛ CORE CHEMISTRY SKILL

Drawing Structures for
Triacylglycerols

Prior to hibernation, a polar bear
eats food with a high caloric content.

Triacylglycerols are used to
thicken creams and lotions.

Most naturally occurring triacylglycerols contain glycerol bonded to two or three different fatty acids, typically palmitic acid, oleic acid, linoleic acid, and stearic acid. For example, a mixed triacylglycerol might be made from stearic acid, oleic acid, and palmitic acid. One possible structure for this mixed triacylglycerol follows:

$$
\begin{array}{l}
\text{CH}_2\text{—O—}\overset{\displaystyle O}{\overset{\|}{\text{C}}}\text{—(CH}_2)_{16}\text{—CH}_3 \quad \text{Stearic acid}\\[2mm]
\text{CH—O—}\overset{\displaystyle O}{\overset{\|}{\text{C}}}\text{—(CH}_2)_7\text{—CH}=\text{CH—(CH}_2)_7\text{—CH}_3 \quad \text{Oleic acid}\\[2mm]
\text{CH}_2\text{—O—}\overset{\displaystyle O}{\overset{\|}{\text{C}}}\text{—(CH}_2)_{14}\text{—CH}_3 \quad \text{Palmitic acid}
\end{array}
$$

A mixed triacylglycerol

Triacylglycerols are the major form of energy storage for animals. Animals that hibernate eat large quantities of plants, seeds, and nuts that are high in calories. Prior to hibernation, these animals, such as polar bears, gain as much as 14 kg per week. As the external temperature drops, the animal goes into hibernation. The body temperature drops to nearly freezing, and cellular activity, respiration, and heart rate are drastically reduced. Animals that live in extremely cold climates hibernate for 4 to 7 months. During this time, stored fat is the only source of energy.

▶ **SAMPLE PROBLEM 17.2 Drawing the Structure for a Triacylglycerol**

Draw the condensed structural formula for glyceryl tripalmitoleate (tripalmitolein), which is used in cosmetic creams and lotions.

SOLUTION

ANALYZE THE PROBLEM	Given	Need
	glyceryl tripalmitoleate (tripalmitolein)	condensed structural formula

Glyceryl tripalmitoleate (tripalmitolein) is the triacylglycerol that contains ester bonds between glycerol and three palmitoleic acid molecules.

STEP 1 Draw the condensed structural formulas for glycerol and the fatty acids.

$$
\begin{array}{l}
\text{CH}_2\text{—OH} + \text{HO—}\overset{\displaystyle O}{\overset{\|}{\text{C}}}\text{—(CH}_2)_7\text{—CH}=\text{CH—(CH}_2)_5\text{—CH}_3 \quad \text{Palmitoleic acid}\\[2mm]
\text{CH—OH} + \text{HO—}\overset{\displaystyle O}{\overset{\|}{\text{C}}}\text{—(CH}_2)_7\text{—CH}=\text{CH—(CH}_2)_5\text{—CH}_3 \quad \text{Palmitoleic acid}\\[2mm]
\text{CH}_2\text{—OH} + \text{HO—}\overset{\displaystyle O}{\overset{\|}{\text{C}}}\text{—(CH}_2)_7\text{—CH}=\text{CH—(CH}_2)_5\text{—CH}_3 \quad \text{Palmitoleic acid}
\end{array}
$$

Glycerol

STEP 2 Form ester bonds between the hydroxyl groups on glycerol and the carboxyl groups on each fatty acid.

$$
\begin{array}{l}
\text{CH}_2\text{—O—}\overset{\displaystyle O}{\overset{\|}{\text{C}}}\text{—(CH}_2)_7\text{—CH}=\text{CH—(CH}_2)_5\text{—CH}_3\\[2mm]
\text{CH—O—}\overset{\displaystyle O}{\overset{\|}{\text{C}}}\text{—(CH}_2)_7\text{—CH}=\text{CH—(CH}_2)_5\text{—CH}_3\\[2mm]
\text{CH}_2\text{—O—}\overset{\displaystyle O}{\overset{\|}{\text{C}}}\text{—(CH}_2)_7\text{—CH}=\text{CH—(CH}_2)_5\text{—CH}_3
\end{array}
$$

Glyceryl tripalmitoleate (tripalmitolein)

Guide to Drawing Triacylglycerols

STEP 1
Draw the condensed structural formulas for glycerol and the fatty acids.

STEP 2
Form ester bonds between the hydroxyl groups on glycerol and the carboxyl groups on each fatty acid.

STUDY CHECK 17.2

Draw the condensed structural formula for the triacylglycerol containing three molecules of myristic acid (14:0).

ANSWER

$$
\begin{array}{l}
CH_2-O-\overset{\overset{\displaystyle O}{\|}}{C}-(CH_2)_{12}-CH_3 \\
\quad\quad\quad\quad\overset{\displaystyle O}{\|} \\
CH-O-\overset{}{C}-(CH_2)_{12}-CH_3 \\
\quad\quad\quad\quad\overset{\displaystyle O}{\|} \\
CH_2-O-\overset{}{C}-(CH_2)_{12}-CH_3
\end{array}
$$

Melting Points of Fats and Oils

A **fat** is a triacylglycerol that is solid at room temperature, and it usually comes from animal sources such as meat, whole milk, butter, and cheese.

An **oil** is a triacylglycerol that is usually a liquid at room temperature and is obtained from a plant source. Olive oil and peanut oil are monounsaturated because they contain large amounts of oleic acid. Oils from corn, cottonseed, safflower seed, and sunflower seed are polyunsaturated because they contain large amounts of fatty acids with two or more double bonds (see Figure 17.3).

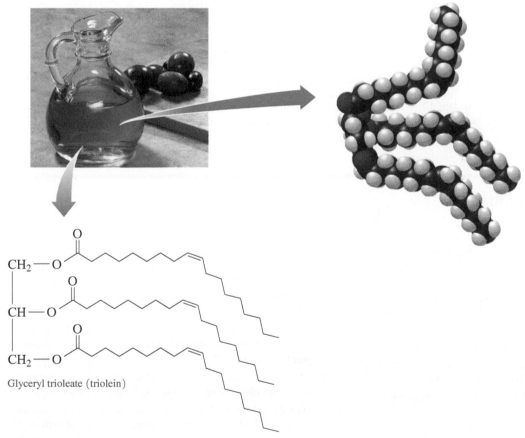

Glyceryl trioleate (triolein)

FIGURE 17.3 ▶ Vegetable oils such as olive oil, corn oil, and safflower oil contain unsaturated fats.

Why is olive oil a liquid at room temperature?

Palm oil and coconut oil are solids at room temperature because they consist mostly of saturated fatty acids. Coconut oil is 92% saturated fats, about half of which is lauric acid, which contains 12 carbon atoms rather than 18 carbon atoms found in the stearic acid of animal sources. Thus coconut oil has a melting point that is higher than typical vegetable oils, but not as high as fats from animal sources that contain stearic acid. The amounts of saturated, monounsaturated, and polyunsaturated fatty acids in some typical fats and oils are listed in Figure 17.4.

Saturated fatty acids have higher melting points than unsaturated fatty acids because they pack together more tightly. Animal fats usually contain more saturated fatty acids than do vegetable oils. Therefore, the melting points of animal fats are higher than those of vegetable oils.

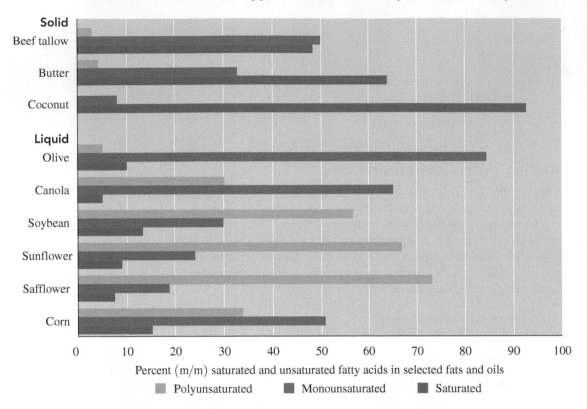

FIGURE 17.4 ▶ Vegetable oils are liquids at room temperature because they have a higher percentage of unsaturated fatty acids than do animal fats.

ⓠ Why is butter a solid at room temperature, whereas canola oil is a liquid?

QUESTIONS AND PROBLEMS

17.3 Waxes and Triacylglycerols

LEARNING GOAL Draw the condensed or line-angle structural formula for a wax or triacylglycerol produced by the reaction of a fatty acid and an alcohol or glycerol.

17.19 Draw the condensed structural formula for the ester in beeswax that is formed from myricyl alcohol, $CH_3-(CH_2)_{29}-OH$, and palmitic acid.

17.20 Draw the condensed structural formula for the ester in jojoba wax that is formed from arachidic acid, a 20-carbon saturated fatty acid, and 1-docosanol, $CH_3-(CH_2)_{21}-OH$.

17.21 Draw the condensed structural formula for a triacylglycerol that contains stearic acid and glycerol.

17.22 Draw the condensed structural formula for a mixed triacylglycerol that contains two palmitic acid molecules and one oleic acid molecule on the center carbon of glycerol.

℞ **Clinical Applications**

17.23 Caprylic acid is an 8-carbon saturated fatty acid that occurs in coconut oil (10%) and palm kernel oil (4%). Draw the condensed structural formula for glyceryl tricaprylate (tricaprylin).

17.24 Linoleic acid is a 18-carbon unsaturated fatty acid with two double bonds that occurs in many vegetable oils including safflower oil (75%) and poppyseed oil (75%). Draw the condensed structural formula for glyceryl trilinoleate (trilinolein).

17.25 Safflower oil is polyunsaturated, whereas olive oil is monounsaturated. Why would safflower oil have a lower melting point than olive oil?

17.26 Olive oil is monounsaturated, whereas butter fat is saturated. Why does olive oil have a lower melting point than butter fat?

17.27 How does the percentage of monounsaturated and polyunsaturated fatty acids in sunflower oil compare to that of safflower oil?

17.28 How does the percentage of monounsaturated and polyunsaturated fatty acids in olive oil compare to that of canola oil?

17.4 Chemical Properties of Triacylglycerols

The chemical reactions of triacylglycerols involve the hydrogenation of the double bonds in the fatty acids, and the hydrolysis and saponification of the ester bonds between glycerol and the fatty acids.

LEARNING GOAL

Draw the condensed or line-angle structural formula for the products of a triacylglycerol that undergoes hydrogenation, hydrolysis, or saponification.

Hydrogenation

In the **hydrogenation** reaction, hydrogen gas is bubbled through the heated oil typically in the presence of a nickel catalyst. As a result, H atoms add to one or more carbon–carbon double bonds to form carbon–carbon single bonds.

$$-CH{=}CH- + \ H_2 \xrightarrow{Ni} \begin{array}{c} H \ \ H \\ | \ \ \ | \\ -C-C- \\ | \ \ \ | \\ H \ \ H \end{array}$$

For example, when hydrogen adds to all of the double bonds of glyceryl trioleate (triolein) using a nickel catalyst, the product is the saturated fat glyceryl tristearate (tristearin).

Double bonds

$$CH_2-O-\overset{\overset{\displaystyle O}{\|}}{C}-(CH_2)_7-CH{=}CH-(CH_2)_7-CH_3$$
$$CH-O-\overset{\overset{\displaystyle O}{\|}}{C}-(CH_2)_7-CH{=}CH-(CH_2)_7-CH_3 \ + \ 3H_2$$
$$CH_2-O-\overset{\overset{\displaystyle O}{\|}}{C}-(CH_2)_7-CH{=}CH-(CH_2)_7-CH_3$$

Glyceryl trioleate
(triolein)

$\xrightarrow{Ni}$

Single bonds

$$CH_2-O-\overset{\overset{\displaystyle O}{\|}}{C}-(CH_2)_7-CH_2-CH_2-(CH_2)_7-CH_3$$
$$CH-O-\overset{\overset{\displaystyle O}{\|}}{C}-(CH_2)_7-CH_2-CH_2-(CH_2)_7-CH_3$$
$$CH_2-O-\overset{\overset{\displaystyle O}{\|}}{C}-(CH_2)_7-CH_2-CH_2-(CH_2)_7-CH_3$$

Glyceryl tristearate
(tristearin)

In commercial hydrogenation, the addition of hydrogen is stopped before all the double bonds in a liquid vegetable oil become completely saturated. Complete hydrogenation gives a very brittle product, whereas the partial hydrogenation of a liquid vegetable oil changes it to a soft, semisolid fat. As it becomes more saturated, the melting point increases, and the substance becomes more solid at room temperature. By controlling the amount of hydrogen, manufacturers can produce various types of products such as soft margarines, solid stick margarines, and solid shortenings (see Figure 17.5). Although these products now contain more saturated fatty acids than the original oils, they contain no cholesterol, unlike similar products from animal sources, such as butter and lard.

⚙ **CORE CHEMISTRY SKILL**

Drawing the Products for the Hydrogenation, Hydrolysis, and Saponification of a Triacylglycerol

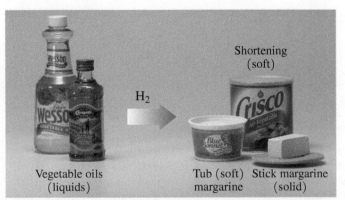

Vegetable oils (liquids) → H₂ → Shortening (soft); Tub (soft) margarine; Stick margarine (solid)

FIGURE 17.5 ▶ Many soft margarines, stick margarines, and solid shortenings are produced by the partial hydrogenation of vegetable oils.

❓ How does hydrogenation change the structure of the fatty acids in the vegetable oils?

Chemistry Link to Health

Converting Unsaturated Fats to Saturated Fats: Hydrogenation and Interesterification

During the early 1900s, margarine became a popular replacement for the highly saturated fats such as butter and lard. Margarine is produced by partially hydrogenating the unsaturated fats in vegetable oils such as safflower oil, corn oil, canola oil, cottonseed oil, and sunflower oil.

Hydrogenation and Trans Fats

In vegetable oils, the unsaturated fats usually contain cis double bonds. As hydrogenation occurs, double bonds are converted to single bonds. However, a small amount of the cis double bonds are converted to trans double bonds because they are more stable, which causes a change in the overall structure of the fatty acids. If the label on a product states that the oils have been "partially hydrogenated," that product will also contain trans fatty acids. In the United States, it is estimated that 2 to 4% of our total calories comes from trans fatty acids.

The concern about trans fatty acids is that their altered structure may make them behave like saturated fatty acids in the body. In the 1980s, research indicated that trans fatty acids have an effect on blood cholesterol similar to that of saturated fats, although study results vary. Several studies reported that trans fatty acids raise the levels of LDL-cholesterol, and lower the levels of HDL-cholesterol. (LDL and HDL are described in section 17.6.)

Foods containing naturally occurring trans fat include milk, beef, and eggs. Foods that contain trans fatty acids from the hydrogenation process include deep-fried foods, bread, baked goods, cookies, crackers, chips, stick and soft margarines, and vegetable shortening. The American Heart Association recommends that margarine should have no more than 2 g of saturated fat per tablespoon and a liquid vegetable oil should be the first ingredient. They also recommend the use of soft margarine, which is only slightly hydrogenated and therefore has fewer trans fatty acids. Currently, the amount of trans fats is included on the Nutrition Facts label on food products. In the United States, a food label for a product that has less than 0.5 g of trans fat in one serving can read "0 g of trans fat."

The best advice may be to reduce total fat in the diet by using fats and oils sparingly, cooking with little or no fat, substituting olive oil or canola oil for other oils, and limiting the use of coconut oil and palm oil, which are high in saturated fatty acids.

Nutrition Facts

Serving Size 5 oz. (144g)
Servings Per Container 4

Amount Per Serving

Calories 310   Calories from Fat 100

	% Daily Value*
Total Fat 15g	21%
Saturated Fat 2.6g	17%
Trans Fat 1g	
Cholesterol 118mg	39%
Sodium 560mg	28%
Total Carbohydrate 12g	4%
Dietary Fiber 1g	4%
Sugars 1g	
Protein 24g	

Nutrition Facts label includes the grams of trans fat in one serving.

cis-Fatty acid

H_2/Ni

Ni catalyst

H_2 Isomerization

Addition of H_2

Undesired side product (*trans*-fatty acid)

Desired saturated product

Interesterification

Interesterification is a newer process used to change unsaturated vegetable oils into products that have the properties of solid and semisolid saturated fats. During the process of interesterification, lipase enzymes are used to hydrolyze ester bonds in triacylglycerols of vegetable oils so that glycerol and fatty acids are formed. Then the saturated fatty acids recombine with glycerol. For example, an unsaturated oleic acid in a vegetable oil could be replaced by a saturated stearic acid, which results in a more saturated fat with a higher melting point. The saturated products in the mixture are separated by differences in melting points. As a result of bypassing the hydrogenation process of converting double bonds to single bonds, there are no trans fatty acids present in the solid or semisolid fats products. Such products may have a label that reads "no trans fats."

Simplified Example of Interesterification

Mixed triacylglycerols are unsaturated
and have lower melting points.

A new mixture of triacylglycerols includes
saturated triacylglycerols with higher melting
points, as well as unsaturated triacylglycerols.

Hydrolysis

Triacylglycerols are hydrolyzed (split by water) in the presence of strong acids such as
HCl or H_2SO_4, or digestive enzymes called *lipases*. The products of hydrolysis of the ester
bonds are glycerol and three fatty acids. The polar glycerol is soluble in water, but the fatty
acids with their long hydrocarbon chains are not.

Saponification

Saponification occurs when a fat is heated with a strong base such as NaOH to form glycerol and the sodium salts of the fatty acids, which is soap. When NaOH is used, a solid
soap is produced that can be molded into a desired shape; KOH produces a softer, liquid
soap. An oil that is polyunsaturated produces a softer soap. Names like "coconut" or
"avocado shampoo" tell you the sources of the oil used in the reaction.

Fat or oil   +   strong base $\xrightarrow{\text{Heat}}$ glycerol   +   salts of fatty acids (soap)

$$\begin{array}{l} CH_2-O-\overset{\overset{\displaystyle O}{\|}}{C}-(CH_2)_{14}-CH_3 \\[2mm] CH-O-\overset{\overset{\displaystyle O}{\|}}{C}-(CH_2)_{14}-CH_3 \;+\; \mathbf{3NaOH} \;\xrightarrow{\text{Heat}}\; \\[2mm] CH_2-O-\overset{\overset{\displaystyle O}{\|}}{C}-(CH_2)_{14}-CH_3 \end{array}$$

Glyceryl tripalmitate (tripalmitin)

$$\begin{array}{l} CH_2-OH \qquad Na^+\;{}^-O-\overset{\overset{\displaystyle O}{\|}}{C}-(CH_2)_{14}-CH_3 \\[2mm] CH-OH \;+\; Na^+\;{}^-O-\overset{\overset{\displaystyle O}{\|}}{C}-(CH_2)_{14}-CH_3 \\[2mm] CH_2-OH \qquad Na^+\;{}^-O-\overset{\overset{\displaystyle O}{\|}}{C}-(CH_2)_{14}-CH_3 \end{array}$$

Glycerol   3 Sodium palmitate (soap)

The reactions for fatty acids and triacylglycerols that are similar to the reactions of hydrogenation of alkenes, esterification, hydrolysis, and saponification are summarized in Table 17.3.

TABLE 17.3 Summary of Organic and Lipid Reactions

Reaction	Organic Reactants and Products	Lipid Reactants and Products
Esterification	Carboxylic acid + alcohol $\xrightarrow{H^+,\,heat}$ ester + water	3 Fatty acids + glycerol $\xrightarrow{Enzyme}$ triacylglycerol (fat) + 3 water
Hydrogenation	Alkene (double bond) + hydrogen $\xrightarrow{Pt}$ alkane (single bonds)	Unsaturated fat (double bonds) + hydrogen $\xrightarrow{Ni}$ saturated fat (single bonds)
Hydrolysis	Ester + water $\xrightarrow{H^+,\,heat}$ carboxylic acid + alcohol	Triacylglycerol (fat) + 3 water $\xrightarrow{Enzyme}$ 3 fatty acids + glycerol
Saponification	Ester + sodium hydroxide $\xrightarrow{Heat}$ sodium salt of carboxylic acid + alcohol	Triacylglycerol (fat) + 3 sodium hydroxide $\xrightarrow{Heat}$ 3 sodium salts of fatty acid (soaps) + glycerol

Explore Your World
Types of Fats

Read the labels on food products that contain fats, such as butter, margarine, vegetable oils, peanut butter, and potato chips. Look for terms such as saturated, monounsaturated, polyunsaturated, and partially or fully hydrogenated.

Questions

1. What type(s) of fats or oils are in the product?
2. How many grams of saturated, monounsaturated, and polyunsaturated fats are there in one serving of the product?
3. What percentage of the total fat is saturated fat? Unsaturated fat?

4. The label on a container of peanut butter states that the cottonseed and canola oils used to make the peanut butter have been fully hydrogenated. What are the typical products that would form when hydrogen is added?
5. For each packaged food, determine the following:
   a. How many grams of fat are in one serving of the food?
   b. Using the caloric value for fat (9 kcal/g), how many Calories (kilocalories) come from the fat in one serving?
   c. What is the percentage of fat in one serving?

Chemistry Link to the Environment

Biodiesel as an Alternative Fuel

Biodiesel is a name of a nonpetroleum fuel that can be used in place of diesel fuel. Biodiesel is produced from renewable biological resources such as vegetable oils (primarily soybean), waste vegetable oils from restaurants, and some animal fats. Biodiesel is nontoxic and biodegradable.

Biodiesel is prepared from triacylglycerols and alcohols (usually ethanol) to form ethyl esters and glycerol. The glycerol that separates from the fat is used in soaps and other products. The reaction of triacylglycerols is catalyzed by a base such as NaOH or KOH at low temperatures.

Triacylglycerol + 3 ethanol $\longrightarrow$

3 ethyl esters (biodiesel) + glycerol

Compared to diesel fuel from petroleum, biodiesel burns in an engine to produce much lower levels of carbon dioxide emissions, particulates, unburned hydrocarbons, and aromatic hydrocarbons that cause lung cancer. Because biodiesel has extremely low sulfur content, it does not contribute to the formation of the sulfur oxides that produce acid rain. The energy output from the combustion of biodiesel is almost the same as energy produced by the combustion of petroleum diesel.

In many cases, diesel engines need only slight modification to use biodiesel. Manufacturers of diesel cars, trucks, boats, and tractors have different suggestions for the percentage of biodiesel to use, ranging from 2% (B2) blended with standard diesel fuel to using 100% pure biodiesel (B100). For example, B20 is 20% biodiesel by volume, blended with 80% petroleum diesel by volume. In 2013, 4.9×10^9 L of biodiesel were produced in the United States. Fuel stations in Europe and the United States are now stocking biodiesel fuel.

Biodiesel 20 contains 20% ethyl esters and 80% standard diesel fuel.

$$CH_2-O-\overset{\displaystyle O}{\overset{\|}{C}}-(CH_2)_{12}-CH_3$$

$$CH-O-\overset{\displaystyle O}{\overset{\|}{C}}-(CH_2)_7-CH=CH-(CH_2)_7-CH_3 + 3CH_3-CH_2-OH \xrightarrow[\text{catalyst}]{\text{NaOH}}$$

$$CH_2-O-\overset{\displaystyle O}{\overset{\|}{C}}-(CH_2)_{16}-CH_3$$

Triacylglycerol from vegetable oil   Ethanol

$$CH_2-OH \qquad CH_3-CH_2-O-\overset{\displaystyle O}{\overset{\|}{C}}-(CH_2)_{12}-CH_3$$

$$CH-OH + CH_3-CH_2-O-\overset{\displaystyle O}{\overset{\|}{C}}-(CH_2)_7-CH=CH-(CH_2)_7-CH_3$$

$$CH_2-OH \qquad CH_3-CH_2-O-\overset{\displaystyle O}{\overset{\|}{C}}-(CH_2)_{16}-CH_3$$

Glycerol   Ethyl esters used for biodiesel

▶SAMPLE PROBLEM 17.3 Reactions of Lipids During Digestion

Write the equation for the reaction catalyzed by the enzyme lipase that hydrolyzes glyceryl trilaurate (trilaurin) during the digestion process.

SOLUTION

ANALYZE THE PROBLEM	Given	Need
	glyceryl trilaurate	chemical equation for hydrolysis

glyceryl trilaurate is an ester of glycerol and three lauric acid molecules (12:0). When the ester undergoes hydrolysis by lipase, the products are glycerol and three lauric acid molecules.

$$
\begin{array}{c}
\text{CH}_2\text{—O—}\overset{\displaystyle O}{\overset{\|}{\text{C}}}\text{—(CH}_2)_{10}\text{—CH}_3 \\[4pt]
\text{CH—O—}\overset{\displaystyle O}{\overset{\|}{\text{C}}}\text{—(CH}_2)_{10}\text{—CH}_3 \; + \; 3\text{H}_2\text{O} \quad\xrightarrow{\text{Lipase}}\quad \\[4pt]
\text{CH}_2\text{—O—}\overset{\displaystyle O}{\overset{\|}{\text{C}}}\text{—(CH}_2)_{10}\text{—CH}_3
\end{array}
$$

Glyceryl trilaurate (trilaurin)

$$
\begin{array}{c}
\text{CH}_2\text{—OH} \qquad \text{HO—}\overset{\displaystyle O}{\overset{\|}{\text{C}}}\text{—(CH}_2)_{10}\text{—CH}_3 \\[4pt]
\text{CH—OH} \; + \; \text{HO—}\overset{\displaystyle O}{\overset{\|}{\text{C}}}\text{—(CH}_2)_{10}\text{—CH}_3 \\[4pt]
\text{CH}_2\text{—OH} \qquad \text{HO—}\overset{\displaystyle O}{\overset{\|}{\text{C}}}\text{—(CH}_2)_{10}\text{—CH}_3
\end{array}
$$

Glycerol · 3 Lauric acid molecules

STUDY CHECK 17.3

What is the name of the product formed when a triacylglycerol containing oleic acid (18:1) and linoleic acid (18:2) is completely hydrogenated?

ANSWER

glyceryl tristearate (tristearin)

QUESTIONS AND PROBLEMS

17.4 Chemical Properties of Triacylglycerols

LEARNING GOAL Draw the condensed or line-angle structural formula for the products of a triacylglycerol that undergoes hydrogenation, hydrolysis, or saponification.

17.29 Identify each of the following processes as hydrogenation, hydrolysis, or saponification and give the products:
 a. the reaction of palm oil with KOH
 b. the reaction of glyceryl trilinoleate from safflower oil with water and HCl

17.30 Identify each of the following processes as hydrogenation, hydrolysis, or saponification and give the products:
 a. the reaction of corn oil and hydrogen (H_2) with a nickel catalyst
 b. the reaction of glyceryl tristearate with water in the presence of lipase enzyme

17.31 Write the balanced chemical equation for the hydrogenation of glyceryl tripalmitoleate, a fat containing glycerol and three palmitoleic acid molecules.

17.32 Write the balanced chemical equation for the hydrogenation of glyceryl trilinolenate, a fat containing glycerol and three linolenic acid molecules.

17.33 Write the balanced chemical equation for the acid hydrolysis of glyceryl trimyristate (trimyristin).

17.34 Write the balanced chemical equation for the acid hydrolysis of glyceryl trioleate (triolein).

17.35 Write the balanced chemical equation for the NaOH saponification of glyceryl trimyristate (trimyristin).

17.36 Write the balanced chemical equation for the NaOH saponification of glyceryl trioleate (triolein).

17.37 Draw the condensed structural formula for the product of the hydrogenation of the following triacylglycerol:

$$
\begin{array}{c}
\text{CH}_2\text{—O—}\overset{\displaystyle O}{\overset{\|}{\text{C}}}\text{—(CH}_2)_{16}\text{—CH}_3 \\[4pt]
\text{CH—O—}\overset{\displaystyle O}{\overset{\|}{\text{C}}}\text{—(CH}_2)_{7}\text{—CH}=\text{CH—(CH}_2)_{7}\text{—CH}_3 \\[4pt]
\text{CH}_2\text{—O—}\overset{\displaystyle O}{\overset{\|}{\text{C}}}\text{—(CH}_2)_{16}\text{—CH}_3
\end{array}
$$

17.38 Draw the condensed structural formulas for all the products that would be obtained when the triacylglycerol in problem 17.37 undergoes complete hydrolysis.

17.5 Phospholipids

LEARNING GOAL

Draw the structure of a phospholipid containing glycerol or sphingosine.

The **phospholipids** are a family of lipids similar in structure to triacylglycerols; they include glycerophospholipids and sphingomyelins. In a **glycerophospholipid**, two fatty acids form ester bonds with the first and second hydroxyl groups of glycerol. The third hydroxyl group forms an ester with phosphoric acid, which forms another phosphoester bond with an amino alcohol. In a *sphingomyelin*, sphingosine replaces glycerol. We can compare the general structures of a triacylglycerol, a glycerophospholipid, and a sphingolipid as follows:

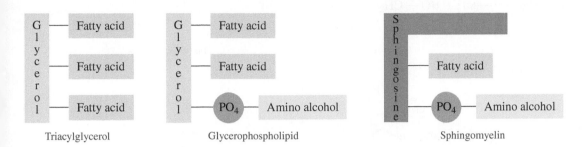

Triacylglycerol   Glycerophospholipid   Sphingomyelin

Amino Alcohols

Three amino alcohols found in glycerophospholipids are choline, serine, and ethanolamine. In the body, at a physiological pH of 7.4, these amino alcohols are ionized.

$$HO-CH_2-CH_2-\overset{+}{N}\underset{\underset{CH_3}{|}}{\overset{\overset{CH_3}{|}}{-}}CH_3 \qquad HO-CH_2-\overset{\overset{+}{NH_3}}{\underset{}{C}}H-\overset{\overset{O}{||}}{C}-O^- \qquad HO-CH_2-CH_2-\overset{+}{NH_3}$$

Choline   Serine   Ethanolamine

Lecithins and *cephalins* are two types of glycerophospholipids that are particularly abundant in brain and nerve tissues as well as in egg yolks, wheat germ, and yeast. Lecithins contain choline, and cephalins usually contain ethanolamine and sometimes serine. In the following structural formulas, the fatty acid that is used in each example is palmitic acid:

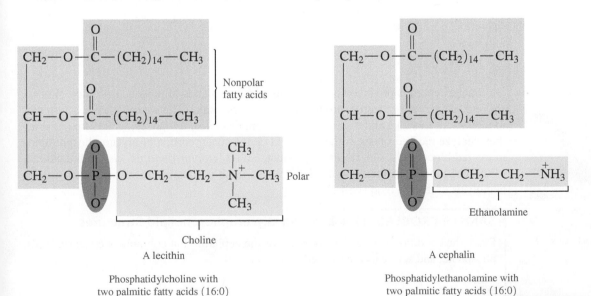

A lecithin

Phosphatidylcholine with two palmitic fatty acids (16:0)

A cephalin

Phosphatidylethanolamine with two palmitic fatty acids (16:0)

Glycerophospholipids contain both polar and nonpolar regions, which allow them to interact with both polar and nonpolar substances. The ionized amino alcohol and phosphate portion, called "the head," is polar and strongly attracted to water (see Figure 17.6). The hydrocarbon chains of the two fatty acids are the nonpolar "tails" of the glycerophospholipid, which are only soluble in other nonpolar substances, mostly lipids.

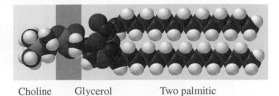

Choline   Glycerol   Two palmitic
Phosphate   fatty acids (16:0)

Choline

Phosphoric acid

Glycerol

Fatty acids

(a) Components of a typical glycerophospholipid

Nonpolar tails

Polar head

(b) Glycerophospholipid

Polar head

Nonpolar tails

(c) Simplified way to draw a glycerophospholipid

FIGURE 17.6 ▶ **(a)** The components of a typical glycerophospholipid: an amino alcohol, phosphoric acid, glycerol, and two fatty acids. **(b)** In a glycerophospholipid, a polar "head" contains the ionized amino alcohol and phosphate, while the hydrocarbon chains of two fatty acids make up the nonpolar "tails." **(c)** A simplified drawing indicates the polar region and the nonpolar region.

◎ Why are glycerophospholipids polar?

Poisonous snake venom contains phospholipases that hydrolyze phospholipids in red blood cells.

Snake venom is produced by the modified saliva glands of poisonous snakes. When a snake bites, venom is ejected through the fang of the snake. The venom of the eastern diamondback rattlesnake and the Indian cobra contains *phospholipases*, which are enzymes that catalyze the hydrolysis of the fatty acid on the center carbon of glycerophospholipids in the red blood cells. The resulting product, called *lysophospholipid*, causes breakdown of the red blood cell membranes. This makes them permeable to water, which causes hemolysis of the red blood cells.

▶ **SAMPLE PROBLEM 17.4 Drawing Glycerophospholipid Structures**

Draw the condensed structural formula for the cephalin that contains two stearic acids, phosphate, and serine as the ionized amino alcohol.

SOLUTION

ANALYZE THE PROBLEM	Given	Need
	cephalin, two stearic acids (18:0), phosphate, serine (ionized)	condensed structural formula

$$
\begin{array}{l}
\quad\quad\quad\quad O \\
\quad\quad\quad\quad \| \\
CH_2-O-C-(CH_2)_{16}-CH_3 \\
\quad\quad\quad\quad O \\
\quad\quad\quad\quad \| \\
Glycerol\ CH-O-C-(CH_2)_{16}-CH_3 \\
\quad\quad\quad\quad O \quad\quad\quad\quad \overset{+}{N}H_3 \quad O \\
\quad\quad\quad\quad \| \quad\quad\quad\quad | \quad\quad \| \\
CH_2-O-P-O-CH_2-CH-C-O^- \\
\quad\quad\quad\quad | \\
\quad\quad\quad\quad O^- \quad\quad\quad Serine \\
\quad\quad\quad Phosphate
\end{array}
$$

(Stearic acids)

STUDY CHECK 17.4

Draw the condensed structural formula for the lecithin that contains two myristic acids phosphate, and choline as the ionized amino alcohol.

ANSWER

$$
\begin{array}{l}
\quad\quad\quad\quad O \\
\quad\quad\quad\quad \| \\
CH_2-O-C-(CH_2)_{12}-CH_3 \\
\quad\quad\quad\quad O \\
\quad\quad\quad\quad \| \\
CH-O-C-(CH_2)_{12}-CH_3 \\
\quad\quad\quad\quad O \quad\quad\quad\quad\quad\quad CH_3 \\
\quad\quad\quad\quad \| \quad\quad\quad\quad\quad\quad | \\
CH_2-O-P-O-CH_2-CH_2-\overset{+}{N}-CH_3 \\
\quad\quad\quad\quad | \quad\quad\quad\quad\quad\quad | \\
\quad\quad\quad\quad O^- \quad\quad\quad\quad\quad\quad CH_3
\end{array}
$$

$$
\begin{array}{l}
HO-CH-CH=CH-(CH_2)_{12}-CH_3 \\
\quad\quad | \\
\quad\quad CH-NH_2 \\
\quad\quad | \\
\quad\quad CH_2-OH \\
\quad\quad\quad Sphingosine
\end{array}
$$

Sphingosine, found in sphingomyelins, is a long-chain amino alcohol, which replaces glycerol. In a **sphingomyelin**, the amine group of sphingosine forms an amide bond to a fatty acid and the hydroxyl group forms an ester bond with phosphate, which forms another phosphoester bond to choline or ethanolamine. The sphingomyelins are abundant in the white matter of the myelin sheath, a coating surrounding the nerve cells that increases the speed of nerve impulses and insulates and protects the nerve cells.

Amide bond

$$
\begin{array}{l}
HO-CH-CH=CH-(CH_2)_{12}-CH_3 \\
\quad\quad\quad\quad\quad H \quad O \\
\quad\quad\quad\quad\quad | \quad\quad \| \\
\quad\quad\quad CH-N-C-(CH_2)_{12}-CH_3 \\
\quad\quad\quad\quad\quad\quad O \quad\quad\quad\quad\quad\quad CH_3 \\
\quad\quad\quad\quad\quad\quad \| \quad\quad\quad\quad\quad\quad | \\
\quad\quad\quad CH_2-O-P-O-CH_2-CH_2-\overset{+}{N}-CH_3 \\
\quad Sphingosine \quad | \quad\quad\quad\quad\quad\quad | \\
\quad\quad\quad\quad\quad\quad O^- \quad\quad\quad\quad\quad\quad CH_3 \\
\quad\quad\quad Phosphate \\
\quad\quad\quad\quad\quad\quad\quad Choline\ (ionized)
\end{array}
$$

Fatty acid

A sphingomyelin containing myristic acid and choline

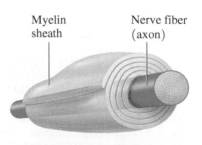

Myelin sheath   Nerve fiber (axon)

Normal myelin sheath

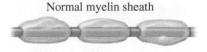

Damaged myelin sheath

When the myelin sheath loses sphingomyelin, it deteriorates and the transmission of nerve signals is impaired.

In multiple sclerosis, sphingomyelin is lost from the myelin sheath, which protects the neurons in the brain and spinal cord. As the disease progresses, the myelin sheath deteriorates. Scars form on the neurons and impair the transmission of nerve signals. The symptoms of multiple sclerosis include various levels of muscle weakness with loss of coordination and vision, depending on the amount of damage. The cause of multiple sclerosis is not yet known, although some researchers suggest that a virus is involved. Several studies also suggest that adequate levels of vitamin D may lessen the severity or lower the risk of developing multiple sclerosis.

▶SAMPLE PROBLEM 17.5 Sphingomyelin

The sphingomyelin found in eggs contains sphingosine, palmitic acid, the 16-carbon saturated fatty acid, and the ionized amino alcohol choline. Draw the condensed structural formula for this sphingomyelin.

SOLUTION

	Given	Need
ANALYZE THE PROBLEM	sphingosine, palmitic acid (16:0), choline (ionized)	condensed structural formula of the sphingomyelin

$$HO-CH-CH=CH-(CH_2)_{12}-CH_3$$

$$\underset{\text{Sphingosine}}{\begin{array}{c} | \\ CH-\underset{H}{N}-\overset{O}{\overset{||}{C}}-(CH_2)_{14}-CH_3 \quad \text{Palmitic acid} \\ | \\ CH_2-O-\overset{O}{\overset{||}{P}}-O-CH_2-CH_2-\overset{+}{\underset{|}{N}}-CH_3 \\ O^- \end{array}}$$

Choline

STUDY CHECK 17.5

Stearic acid is found in sphingomyelin in the brain. Draw the condensed structural formula for this sphingomyelin using ethanolamine as the ionized amino alcohol.

ANSWER

$$HO-CH-CH=CH-(CH_2)_{12}-CH_3$$

$$\begin{array}{c} | \\ CH-\underset{H}{N}-\overset{O}{\overset{||}{C}}-(CH_2)_{16}-CH_3 \\ | \\ CH_2-O-\overset{O}{\overset{||}{P}}-O-CH_2-CH_2-\overset{+}{N}H_3 \\ O^- \end{array}$$

Chemistry Link to Health

Infant Respiratory Distress Syndrome (IRDS)

When an infant is born, an important key to its survival is proper lung function. In the lungs, there are many tiny air sacs called *alveoli*, where the exchange of O_2 and CO_2 takes place. Upon birth of a mature infant, surfactant is released into the lung tissues where it lowers the surface tension in the alveoli, which helps the air sacs inflate. The production of a *pulmonary surfactant*, which is a mixture of phospholipids including lecithin and sphingomyelin produced by specific lung cells, occurs in a fetus after 24 to 28 weeks of pregnancy. If an infant is born prematurely before 28 weeks of gestation, the low level of surfactant and immature lung development lead to a high risk of *Infant Respiratory Distress Syndrome* (IRDS). Without sufficient surfactant, the air sacs collapse and have to reopen with each breath. As a result, alveoli cells are damaged, less oxygen is taken in, and more carbon dioxide is retained, which can lead to hypoxia and acidosis.

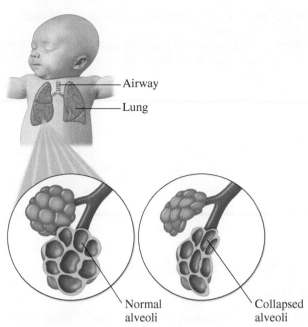

Airway

Lung

Normal alveoli

Collapsed alveoli

Without sufficient surfactant in the lungs of a premature infant, the alveoli collapse, which decreases pulmonary function.

One way to determine the maturity of the lungs of a fetus is to measure the *lecithin–sphingomyelin (L/S) ratio*. A ratio of 2.5 indicates mature fetal lung function, an L/S ratio of 2.4 to 1.6 indicates a low risk, and a ratio of less than 1.5 indicates a high risk of IRDS. Before the initiation of an early delivery, the L/S ratio of the amniotic fluid is measured. If the L/S ratio is low, steroids may be given to the mother to assist the lung development and production of surfactant in the fetus. Once a premature infant is born, treatment includes the use of steroids to help maturation of the lungs, the application of surfactants, and the administration of supplemental oxygen with ventilation to help minimize damage to the lungs.

A premature infant with respiratory distress is treated with a surfactant and oxygen.

QUESTIONS AND PROBLEMS

17.5 Phospholipids

LEARNING GOAL Draw the structure of a phospholipid containing glycerol or sphingosine.

17.39 Describe the similarities and differences between triacylglycerols and glycerophospholipids.

17.40 Describe the similarities and differences between lecithins and cephalins.

17.41 Draw the condensed structural formula for the cephalin that contains two palmitic acids, phosphate, and ethanolamine as the ionized amino alcohol.

17.42 Draw the condensed structural formula for the lecithin that contains two palmitic acids, phosphate, and choline as the ionized amino alcohol.

℞ Clinical Applications

17.43 Identify the following glycerophospholipid, which is found in nerves and spinal cord in the body, as a lecithin or cephalin, and list its components:

$$
\begin{array}{l}
CH_2-O-\overset{\displaystyle O}{\overset{\|}{C}}-(CH_2)_7-CH=CH-(CH_2)_7-CH_3 \\
CH-O-\overset{\displaystyle O}{\overset{\|}{C}}-(CH_2)_{16}-CH_3 \\
CH_2-O-\overset{\displaystyle O}{\underset{\underset{\displaystyle O^-}{\|}}{\overset{\|}{P}}}-O-CH_2-CH_2-\overset{+}{N}H_3
\end{array}
$$

17.44 Identify the following glycerophospholipid, which helps conduct nerve impulses in the body, as a lecithin or cephalin, and list its components:

$$
\begin{array}{l}
CH_2-O-\overset{\displaystyle O}{\overset{\|}{C}}-(CH_2)_{14}-CH_3 \\
CH-O-\overset{\displaystyle O}{\overset{\|}{C}}-(CH_2)_{16}-CH_3 \\
CH_2-O-\overset{\displaystyle O}{\underset{\underset{\displaystyle O^-}{\|}}{\overset{\|}{P}}}-O-CH_2-CH_2-\overset{\displaystyle CH_3}{\underset{\displaystyle CH_3}{\overset{+}{N}}}-CH_3
\end{array}
$$

17.45 Identify the following features of this phospholipid, which is abundant in the myelin sheath that surrounds nerve cells:

$$
\begin{array}{l}
HO-CH-CH=CH\sim\!\!\sim\!\!\sim\!\!\sim\!\!\sim \\
\qquad\quad \underset{\displaystyle CH-N-C}{\overset{\displaystyle H\ \ O}{|}}\sim\!\!\sim\!\!\sim\!\!\sim \\
\qquad\qquad\quad\ \ CH_2-O-\overset{\displaystyle O}{\underset{\underset{\displaystyle O^-}{\|}}{\overset{\|}{P}}}-O\sim\overset{+}{N}H_3
\end{array}
$$

a. Is the phospholipid formed from glycerol or sphingosine?
b. What is the fatty acid?
c. What type of bond connects the fatty acid?
d. What is the ionized amino alcohol?

17.46 Identify the following features of this phospholipid, which is needed for the brain and nerve tissues:

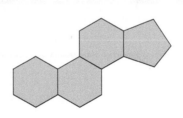

a. Is the phospholipid formed from glycerol or sphingosine?
b. What is the fatty acid?
c. What type of bond connects the fatty acid?
d. What is the ionized amino alcohol?

LEARNING GOAL

▼

Draw the structures of steroids.

17.6 Steroids: Cholesterol, Bile Salts, and Steroid Hormones

Steroids are compounds containing the *steroid nucleus*, which consists of three cyclohexane rings and one cyclopentane ring fused together. The four rings in the steroid nucleus are designated A, B, C, and D. The carbon atoms are numbered beginning with the carbons in ring A, and in steroids like cholesterol, ending with two methyl groups.

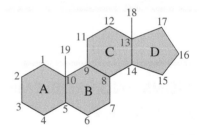

Steroid nucleus   Steroid numbering system

⚛ CORE CHEMISTRY SKILL

Identifying the Steroid Nucleus

Cholesterol

Cholesterol, which is one of the most important and abundant steroids in the body, is a *sterol* because it contains an oxygen atom as a hydroxyl group (—OH) on carbon 3. Like many steroids, cholesterol has a double bond between carbon 5 and carbon 6, methyl groups at carbon 10 and carbon 13, and a carbon chain at carbon 17. In other steroids, the oxygen atom forms a carbonyl group (C=O) at carbon 3.

Cholesterol is a component of cellular membranes, myelin sheath, and brain and nerve tissue. It is also found in the liver and bile salts; large quantities of it are found in the skin, and some of it becomes vitamin D when the skin is exposed to direct sunlight. In the adrenal gland, cholesterol is used to synthesize steroid hormones. The liver synthesizes sufficient cholesterol for the body from fats, carbohydrates, and proteins. Additional cholesterol is obtained from meat, milk, and eggs in the diet. There is no cholesterol in vegetable and plant products.

Cholesterol in the Body

If a diet is high in cholesterol, the liver produces less cholesterol. A typical daily American diet includes 400 to 500 mg of cholesterol, one of the highest in the world. The American Heart Association has recommended that we consume no more than 300 mg of cholesterol a day. Researchers suggest that saturated fats and cholesterol are associated with diseases such as diabetes; cancers of the breast, pancreas, and colon; and atherosclerosis. In atherosclerosis, deposits of a protein–lipid complex (plaque) accumulate in the coronary blood vessels, restricting the flow of blood to the tissue and causing necrosis (death) of the tissue (see Figure 17.7). In the heart, plaque accumulation could result in a *myocardial infarction* (heart attack). Other factors that may also increase the risk of heart disease are family history, lack of exercise, smoking, obesity, diabetes, gender, and age. The cholesterol contents of some typical foods are listed in Table 17.4.

TABLE 17.4 Cholesterol Content of Some Foods

Food	Serving Size	Cholesterol (mg)
Liver (beef)	3 oz	370
Large egg	1	200
Lobster	3 oz	175
Fried chicken	$3\frac{1}{2}$ oz	130
Hamburger	3 oz	85
Chicken (no skin)	3 oz	75
Fish (salmon)	3 oz	40
Whole milk	1 cup	35
Butter	1 tablespoon	30
Skim milk	1 cup	5
Margarine	1 tablespoon	0

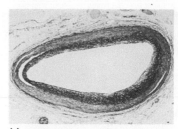
(a)

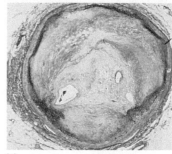
(b)

FIGURE 17.7 ▶ Excess cholesterol forms plaque that can block an artery, resulting in a heart attack. **(a)** A cross section of a normal, open artery shows no buildup of plaque. **(b)** A cross section of an artery that is almost completely clogged by atherosclerotic plaque.

◉ What property of cholesterol would cause it to form deposits along the coronary arteries?

Clinically, cholesterol levels are considered elevated if the total plasma cholesterol level exceeds 200 mg/dL. Saturated fats in the diet may stimulate the production of cholesterol by the liver. A diet that is low in foods containing cholesterol and saturated fats appears to be helpful in reducing the serum cholesterol level. The AICR has recommended that our diet contain more fiber and starch by adding more vegetables, fruits, whole grains, and moderate amounts of foods with low levels of fat and cholesterol such as fish, poultry, lean meats, and low-fat dairy products. AICR also suggests that we limit our intake of foods high in cholesterol such as eggs, nuts, French fries, fatty or organ meats, cheeses, butter, and coconut and palm oil.

▶SAMPLE PROBLEM 17.6 Cholesterol

Refer to the structure of cholesterol for each of the following questions:

a. What part of cholesterol is the steroid nucleus?
b. What features have been added to the steroid nucleus in cholesterol?
c. What classifies cholesterol as a sterol?

SOLUTION

a. The four fused rings form the steroid nucleus.
b. The cholesterol molecule contains a hydroxyl group (—OH) on the first ring, one double bond in the second ring, methyl groups (—CH₃) at carbons 10 and 13, and a branched carbon chain.
c. The hydroxyl group determines the sterol classification.

STUDY CHECK 17.6

Why is cholesterol in the lipid family?

ANSWER

Cholesterol is not soluble in water; it is classified with the lipid family.

Bile Salts

The *bile salts* in the body are synthesized from cholesterol in the liver and stored in the gallbladder. When bile is secreted into the small intestine, the bile salts mix with the water-insoluble fats and oils in our diets. The bile salts with their nonpolar and polar regions act

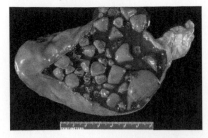

FIGURE 17.8 ▶ Gallstones form in the gallbladder when cholesterol levels are high.

🔘 What type of steroid is stored in the gallbladder?

much like soaps, breaking down large globules of fat into smaller droplets. The smaller droplets containing fat have a larger surface area to react with lipases, which are the enzymes that digest fat. The bile salts also help with the absorption of cholesterol into the intestinal mucosa.

When large amounts of cholesterol accumulate in the gallbladder, cholesterol can become solid, which forms gallstones (see Figure 17.8). Gallstones are composed of almost 100% cholesterol, with some calcium salts, fatty acids, and glycerophospholipids. Normally, small stones pass through the bile duct into the duodenum, the first part of the small intestine immediately beyond the stomach. If a large stone passes into the bile duct, it can get stuck, and the pain can be severe. If the gallstone obstructs the duct, bile cannot be excreted. Then bile pigments known as bilirubin will not be able to pass through the bile duct into the duodenum. They will back up into the liver and be excreted via the blood, causing jaundice (*hyperbilirubinemia*), which gives a yellow color to the skin and the whites of the eyes.

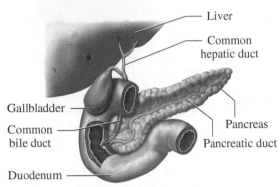

Gallstones formed in the gallbladder usually pass through the bile duct into the duodenum. If too large, they may obstruct the bile duct causing pain and blocking bile.

Lipoproteins: Transporting Lipids

In the body, lipids must be moved through the bloodstream to tissues where they are stored, used for energy, or used to make hormones. However, most lipids are nonpolar and insoluble in the aqueous environment of blood. They are made more soluble by combining them with phospholipids and proteins to form water-soluble complexes called **lipoproteins**. In general, lipoproteins are spherical particles with an outer surface of polar proteins and phospholipids that surround hundreds of nonpolar molecules of triacylglycerols and cholesteryl esters (see Figure 17.9). Cholesteryl esters are the prevalent form of cholesterol in the blood. They are formed by the esterification of the hydroxyl group in cholesterol with a fatty acid.

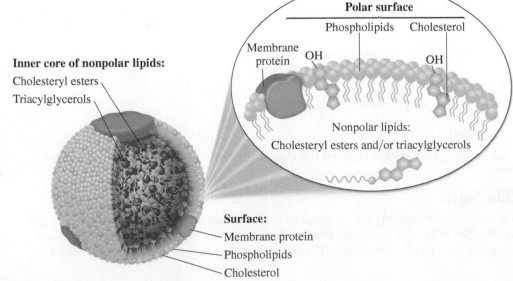

FIGURE 17.9 ▶ A spherical lipoprotein particle surrounds nonpolar lipids with polar lipids and protein for transport to body cells.

🔘 Why are the polar components on the surface of a lipoprotein particle and the nonpolar components at the center?

Ester bond

Cholesteryl ester

There are a variety of lipoproteins, which differ in density, lipid composition, and function. They include chylomicrons, very-low-density lipoproteins (VLDLs), low-density lipoproteins (LDLs), and high-density lipoproteins (HDLs). The density of the lipoproteins increases as the percentage of protein in each type also increases (see Table 17.5).

TABLE 17.5 Composition and Properties of Plasma Lipoproteins

	Chylomicrons	VLDL	LDL	HDL
Density (g/mL)	0.940	0.950–1.006	1.006–1.063	1.063–1.210
Composition (% by mass)				
Type of Lipid				
Triacylglycerols	86	55	6	4
Phospholipids	7	18	22	24
Cholesterol	2	7	8	2
Cholesteryl esters	3	12	42	15
Protein	2	8	22	55

Two important lipoproteins are the LDL and HDL, which transport cholesterol. The LDL carries cholesterol to the tissues where it can be used for the synthesis of cell membranes and steroid hormones. When the LDL exceeds the amount of cholesterol needed by the tissues, the LDL deposits cholesterol in the arteries (plaque), which can restrict blood flow and increase the risk of developing heart disease and/or myocardial infarctions (heart attacks). This is why LDL is called "bad" cholesterol. The HDL picks up cholesterol from the tissues and carries it to the liver, where it can be converted to bile salts, which are eliminated from the body. This is why HDL is called "good" cholesterol. Other lipoproteins include chylomicrons that carry triacylglycerols from the intestines to the liver, muscle, and adipose tissues, and VLDL that carries the triacylglycerols synthesized in the liver to the adipose tissues for storage (see Figure 17.10).

Because high cholesterol levels are associated with the onset of atherosclerosis and heart disease, a doctor may order a *lipid panel* as part of a health examination. A lipid panel is a blood test that measures serum lipid levels including cholesterol, triglycerides, HDL, and LDL. The results of a lipid panel are used to evaluate a patient's risk of heart disease and to help a doctor determine the type of treatment needed.

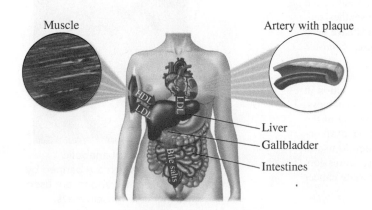

Muscle

Artery with plaque

Liver
Gallbladder
Intestines

FIGURE 17.10 ▶ High- and low-density lipoproteins transport cholesterol between the tissues and the liver.

◉ What type of lipoprotein transports cholesterol to the liver?

Lipid Panel	Recommended Level	Greater Risk of Heart Disease
Total Cholesterol	Less than 200 mg/dL	Greater than 240 mg/dL
Triglycerides (triacylglycerols)	Less than 150 mg/dL	Greater than 200 mg/dL
HDL ("good" cholesterol)	Greater than 60 mg/dL	Less than 40 mg/dL
LDL ("bad" cholesterol)	Less than 100 mg/dL	Greater than 160 mg/dL
Cholesterol/HDL Ratio	Less than 4	Greater than 7

Steroid Hormones

The word *hormone* comes from the Greek "to arouse" or "to excite." Hormones are chemical messengers that serve as a communication system from one part of the body to another. The *steroid* hormones, which include the sex hormones and the adrenocortical hormones, are closely related in structure to cholesterol and depend on cholesterol for their synthesis.

Two of the male sex hormones, *testosterone* and *androsterone*, promote the growth of muscle and facial hair, and the maturation of the male sex organs and of sperm.

The *estrogens*, a group of female sex hormones, direct the development of female sexual characteristics: the uterus increases in size, fat is deposited in the breasts, and the pelvis broadens. *Progesterone* prepares the uterus for the implantation of a fertilized egg. If an egg is not fertilized, the levels of progesterone and estrogen drop sharply, and menstruation follows. Synthetic forms of the female sex hormones are used in birth control pills. As with other kinds of steroids, side effects include weight gain and a greater risk of forming blood clots. The structures of some steroid hormones are shown below:

Testosterone (androgen)
(produced in testes)

Estradiol (estrogen)
(produced in ovaries)

Progesterone
(produced in ovaries)

Norethindrone
(synthetic progestin)

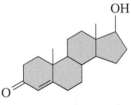

Chemistry Link to Health

Anabolic Steroids

Some of the physiological effects of testosterone are to increase muscle mass and decrease body fat. Derivatives of testosterone called *anabolic steroids* that enhance these effects have been synthesized. Although they have some medical uses, anabolic steroids have been used in high dosages by some athletes in an effort to increase muscle mass. Such use is banned by most sports organizations.

Use of anabolic steroids in attempting to improve athletic strength can cause numerous side effects: in males—a reduction in testicle size, low sperm count and infertility, male pattern baldness, and breast development; in females—facial hair, deepening of the voice, male pattern baldness, breast atrophy, and menstrual dysfunction. Possible long-term consequences of anabolic steroid use in both men and women include liver disease and tumors, depression, and heart complications, with an increased risk of prostate cancer for men.

High doses of anabolic steroids, which are banned by sports organizations, are used to increase muscle mass.

Methandienone   Oxandrolone   Nandrolone   Stanozolol

Adrenal Corticosteroids

The adrenal glands, located on the top of each kidney, produce a large number of compounds known as the *corticosteroids*. *Cortisone* increases the blood glucose level and stimulates the synthesis of glycogen in the liver. *Aldosterone* is responsible for the regulation of electrolytes and water balance by the kidneys. *Cortisol* is released under stress to increase blood sugar and regulate carbohydrate, fat, and protein metabolism. Synthetic corticosteroid drugs such as *prednisone* are derived from cortisone and used medically for reducing inflammation and treating asthma and rheumatoid arthritis, although health problems can result from long-term use.

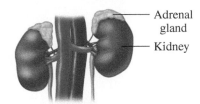

Adrenal gland

Kidney

The adrenal glands on the kidneys produce corticosteroids.

Cortisone
(produced in adrenal gland)

Aldosterone (mineralocorticoid)
(produced in adrenal gland)

Cortisol
(produced in adrenal cortex)

Prednisone
(synthetic corticoid)

QUESTIONS AND PROBLEMS

17.6 Steroids: Cholesterol, Bile Salts, and Steroid Hormones

LEARNING GOAL Draw the structures of steroids.

17.47 Draw the structure for the steroid nucleus.

17.48 Draw the structure for cholesterol.

℞ **Clinical Applications**

17.49 What is the function of bile salts in digestion?

17.50 Why are lipoproteins needed to transport lipids in the bloodstream?

17.51 How do chylomicrons differ from VLDL?

17.52 How does LDL differ from HDL?

17.53 Why is LDL called "bad" cholesterol?

17.54 Why is HDL called "good" cholesterol?

17.55 What are the similarities and differences between the steroid hormones estradiol and testosterone?

17.56 What are the similarities and differences between the adrenal hormone cortisone and the synthetic corticoid prednisone?

17.57 Which of the following are steroid hormones?
a. cholesterol   b. cortisol
c. estradiol   d. testosterone

17.58 Which of the following are adrenal corticosteroids?
a. prednisone   b. aldosterone
c. cortisol   d. testosterone

LEARNING GOAL

Describe the composition and function of the lipid bilayer in cell membranes.

17.7 Cell Membranes

The membrane of a cell separates the contents of a cell from the external fluids. It is *semipermeable* so that nutrients can enter the cell and waste products can leave. The main components of a cell membrane are the glycerophospholipids and sphingolipids. Earlier in this chapter, we saw that the phospholipids consist of a nonpolar region, or hydrocarbon "tail," with two long-chain fatty acids and a polar region, or ionic "head" of phosphate and an ionized amino alcohol.

In a cell (plasma) membrane, two layers of phospholipids are arranged with their hydrophilic heads at the outer and inner surfaces of the membrane, and their hydrophobic tails in the center. This double layer arrangement of phospholipids is called a **lipid bilayer** (see Figure 17.11). The outer layer of phospholipids is in contact with the external fluids, and the inner layer is in contact with the internal contents of the cell.

Most of the phospholipids in the lipid bilayer contain unsaturated fatty acids. Because of the kinks in the carbon chains at the cis double bonds, the phospholipids do not fit closely together. As a result, the lipid bilayer is not a rigid, fixed structure, but one that is dynamic and fluid-like. This liquid-like bilayer also contains proteins, carbohydrates, and cholesterol molecules. For this reason, the model of biological membranes is referred to as the **fluid mosaic model** of membranes.

In the fluid mosaic model, proteins known as *peripheral proteins* emerge on just one of the surfaces, outer or inner. The *integral proteins* extend through the entire lipid bilayer and appear on both surfaces of the membrane. Some proteins and lipids on the outer surface of the cell membrane are attached to carbohydrates. These carbohydrate chains project into the surrounding fluid environment where they are responsible for cell recognition and communication with chemical messengers such as hormones and neurotransmitters. In animals, cholesterol molecules embedded among the phospholipids make up 20 to 25% of the lipid bilayer. Because cholesterol molecules are large and rigid, they reduce the flexibility of the lipid bilayer and add strength to the cell membrane.

FIGURE 17.11 ▶ In the fluid mosaic model of a cell membrane, proteins and cholesterol are embedded in a lipid bilayer of phospholipids. The bilayer forms a membrane-type barrier with polar heads at the membrane surfaces and the nonpolar tails in the center away from the water.

Q What types of fatty acids are found in the phospholipids of the lipid bilayer?

Interactive Video

Membrane Structure

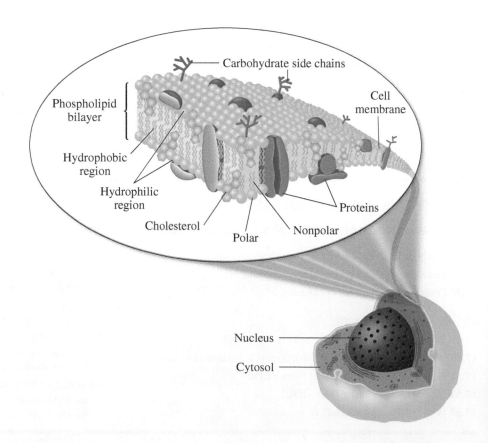

> **▶ SAMPLE PROBLEM 17.7** Lipid Bilayer in Cell Membranes
>
> Describe the role of phospholipids in the lipid bilayer.
>
> **SOLUTION**
>
> Phospholipids consist of polar and nonpolar parts. In a cell membrane, an alignment of the nonpolar sections toward the center with the polar sections on the outside produces a barrier that prevents the contents of a cell from mixing with the fluids on the outside of the cell.
>
> **STUDY CHECK 17.7**
>
> What is the function of cholesterol in the cell membrane?
>
> **ANSWER**
>
> Cholesterol adds strength and rigidity to the cell membrane.

Transport through Cell Membranes

Although a nonpolar membrane separates aqueous solutions, it is necessary that certain substances can enter and leave the cell. The main function of a cell membrane is to allow the movement (transport) of ions and molecules on one side of the membrane to the other side. This transport of materials into and out of a cell is accomplished in several ways.

Diffusion (Passive) Transport

In the simplest transport mechanism called *diffusion* or *passive transport*, molecules can diffuse from a higher concentration to a lower concentration. For example, small molecules such as O_2, CO_2, urea, and water diffuse via passive transport through cell membranes. If their concentrations are greater outside the cell than inside, they diffuse into the cell. If their concentrations are higher within the cell, they diffuse out of the cell.

Facilitated Transport

In *facilitated transport*, proteins that extend from one side of the bilayer membrane to the other provide a channel through which certain substances can diffuse more rapidly than by passive diffusion to meet cellular needs. These protein channels allow transport of chloride ion (Cl^-), bicarbonate ion (HCO_3^-), and glucose molecules in and out of the cell.

Active Transport

Certain ions such as K^+, Na^+, and Ca^{2+} move across a cell membrane *against* their concentration gradients. For example, the K^+ concentration is greater inside a cell, and the Na^+ concentration is greater outside. However, in the conduction of nerve impulses and contraction of muscles, K^+ moves into the cell, and Na^+ moves out by a process known as *active transport*.

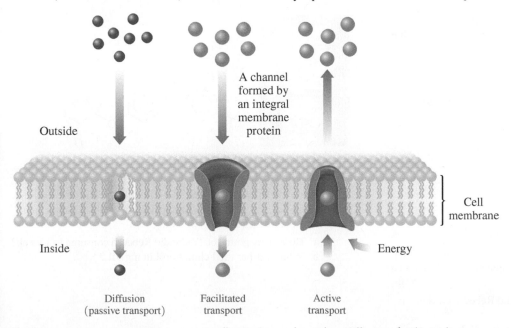

Substances are transported across a cell membrane by either diffusion, facilitated transport, or active transport.

QUESTIONS AND PROBLEMS

17.7 Cell Membranes

LEARNING GOAL Describe the composition and function of the lipid bilayer in cell membranes.

 Clinical Applications

17.59 What is the function of the lipid bilayer in a cell membrane?

17.60 Describe the structure of a lipid bilayer.

17.61 How do molecules of cholesterol affect the structure of cell membranes?

17.62 How do the unsaturated fatty acids in the phospholipids affect the structure of cell membranes?

17.63 Where are proteins located in cell membranes?

17.64 What is the difference between peripheral and integral proteins?

17.65 Identify the type of transport described by each of the following:
 a. A molecule moves through a protein channel.
 b. O_2 moves into the cell from a higher concentration outside the cell.

17.66 Identify the type of transport described by each of the following:
 a. An ion moves from low to high concentration in the cell.
 b. Carbon dioxide moves through a cell membrane.

Clinical Update

Rebecca's Program to Lower Cholesterol in Familial Hypercholesterolemia (FH)

At the lipid clinic, Susan told Rebecca how to maintain a diet with less beef and chicken, more fish with omega-3 oils, low-fat dairy products, no egg yolks, and no coconut or palm oils. Rebecca maintained her new diet containing lower quantities of fats and increased quantities of fiber for the next year. She also increased her exercise using a treadmill and cycling and lost 35 lb. When Rebecca returned to the lipid clinic to check her progress with Susan, a new set of blood tests indicated that her total cholesterol had dropped from 420 to 390 mg/dL and her LDL had dropped from 275 to 255 mg/dL.

Because Rebecca's changes in diet and exercise did not sufficiently lower her cholesterol level, Susan prescribed a medication to help lower blood cholesterol levels. The most common medications used

for treating high LDL-cholesterol are the statins lovastatin (Mevacor), pravastatin (Pravachol), simvastatin (Zocor), atorvastatin (Lipitor), and rosuvastatin (Crestor). For some FH patients, statin therapy may be combined with fibrates such as gemfibrozil or fenofibrate that reduce the synthesis of enzymes that break down fats in the blood.

Rebecca tried different statins, one at a time. One statin caused muscle aches and Susan prescribed pravastatin (Pravachol), 80 mg once a day, which was effective. Later, Susan added fenofibrate (TriCor), one 145-mg tablet, each day to the Pravachol. Rebecca understands that her medications and diet and exercise plan is a lifelong process and its impact is to help her live to a much older age than her mother. Because Rebecca was diagnosed with FH, both her children were tested for FH. Her older son was diagnosed with FH, and is also being treated with a statin. Her younger son does not have FH.

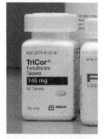

Pravastatin (Pravachol)

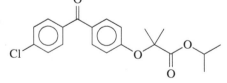

Fenofibrate (TriCor)

 Clinical Applications

17.67 Identify the functional groups in Pravachol.

17.68 Identify the functional groups in TriCor.

17.69 Six months after Rebecca was using the Pravachol, her blood test showed that a 5.0-mL blood sample contained a total cholesterol of 18 mg.
 a. How many grams of Pravachol did Rebecca consume in 1 week?
 b. What was her total cholesterol in mg/dL?

17.70 Five months later, Rebecca added the fibrate TriCor to the statin, her blood test showed that a 5.0-mL blood sample contained a total cholesterol of 14 mg.
 a. How many grams of TriCor did Rebecca consume in 1 week?
 b. What was her total cholesterol in mg/dL?

CONCEPT MAP

LIPIDS

contain

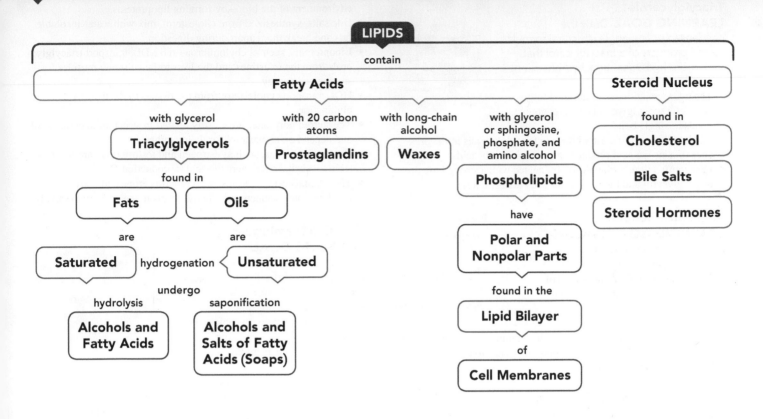

Fatty Acids · **Steroid Nucleus**

- with glycerol → **Triacylglycerols** → found in → **Fats** / **Oils**
  - Fats are **Saturated** ← hydrogenation → **Unsaturated** are Oils
  - Saturated undergo hydrolysis → **Alcohols and Fatty Acids**
  - saponification → **Alcohols and Salts of Fatty Acids (Soaps)**
- with 20 carbon atoms → **Prostaglandins**
- with long-chain alcohol → **Waxes**
- with glycerol or sphingosine, phosphate, and amino alcohol → **Phospholipids** → have → **Polar and Nonpolar Parts** → found in the → **Lipid Bilayer** → of → **Cell Membranes**
- Steroid Nucleus found in → **Cholesterol** / **Bile Salts** / **Steroid Hormones**

CHAPTER REVIEW

17.1 Lipids
LEARNING GOAL Describe the classes of lipids.
- Lipids are nonpolar compounds that are not soluble in water.
- Classes of lipids include waxes, triacylglycerols, glycerophospholipids, sphingolipids, and steroids.

17.2 Fatty Acids
LEARNING GOAL Draw the condensed or line-angle structural formula for a fatty acid and identify it as saturated or unsaturated.

- Fatty acids are unbranched carboxylic acids that typically contain an even number (12 to 20) of carbon atoms.

- Fatty acids may be saturated, monounsaturated with one double bond, or polyunsaturated with two or more double bonds.
- The double bonds in unsaturated fatty acids are almost always cis.

17.3 Waxes and Triacylglycerols
LEARNING GOAL Draw the condensed or line-angle structural formula for a wax or triacylglycerol produced by the reaction of a fatty acid and an alcohol or glycerol.

Triacylglycerol

- A wax is an ester of a long-chain fatty acid and a long-chain alcohol.
- The triacylglycerols are esters of glycerol with three long-chain fatty acids.
- Fats contain more saturated fatty acids and have higher melting points than most vegetable oils.

17.4 Chemical Properties of Triacylglycerols

LEARNING GOAL Draw the condensed or line-angle structural formula for the products of a triacylglycerol that undergoes hydrogenation, hydrolysis, or saponification.

- The hydrogenation of unsaturated fatty acids of a triacylglycerol converts double bonds to single bonds.
- The hydrolysis of the ester bonds in triacylglycerols in the presence of a strong acid produces glycerol and fatty acids.
- In saponification, a triacylglycerol heated with a strong base produces glycerol and the salts of the fatty acids (soap).

17.5 Phospholipids

LEARNING GOAL Draw the structure of a phospholipid containing glycerol or sphingosine.

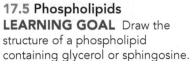

Phospholipid

- Glycerophospholipids are esters of glycerol with two fatty acids and a phosphate group attached to an ionized amino alcohol.
- In a sphingomyelin, the amino alcohol sphingosine forms an amide bond with a fatty acid, and phosphoester bonds to phosphate and an ionized amino alcohol.

17.6 Steroids: Cholesterol, Bile Salts, and Steroid Hormones

LEARNING GOAL Draw the structures of steroids.

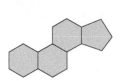

Steroid nucleus

- Steroids are lipids containing the steroid nucleus, which is a fused structure of four rings.
- Steroids include cholesterol, bile salts, and steroid hormones.

- Lipids, which are nonpolar, are transported through the aqueous environment of the blood by forming lipoproteins.
- Bile salts, synthesized from cholesterol, mix with water-insoluble fats and break them apart during digestion.
- Lipoproteins, such as chylomicrons and LDL, transport triacylglycerols from the intestines and the liver to fat cells and muscles for storage and energy.
- HDL transports cholesterol from the tissues to the liver for elimination.
- The steroid hormones are closely related in structure to cholesterol and depend on cholesterol for their synthesis.
- The sex hormones, such as estrogen and testosterone, are responsible for sexual characteristics and reproduction.
- The adrenal corticosteroids, such as aldosterone and cortisone, regulate water balance and glucose levels in the cells, respectively.

17.7 Cell Membranes

LEARNING GOAL Describe the composition and function of the lipid bilayer in cell membranes.

Phospholipid bilayer

- All animal cells are surrounded by a semipermeable membrane that separates the cellular contents from the external fluids.
- The membrane is composed of two rows of phospholipids in a lipid bilayer.
- Proteins and cholesterol are embedded in the lipid bilayer, and carbohydrates are attached to its surface.
- Nutrients and waste products move through the cell membrane using passive transport (diffusion), facilitated transport, or active transport.

SUMMARY OF REACTIONS

The chapter sections to review are shown after the name of the reaction.

Esterification (17.3)

Glycerol + 3 fatty acid molecules $\xrightarrow{\text{Enzyme}}$ triacylglycerol + $3H_2O$

Hydrogenation of Triacylglycerols (17.4)

Triacylglycerol (unsaturated) + H_2 $\xrightarrow{\text{Ni}}$ triacylglycerol (saturated)

Hydrolysis of Triacylglycerols (17.4)

Triacylglycerol + $3H_2O$ $\xrightarrow{\text{H}^+ \text{ or lipase}}$ glycerol + 3 fatty acid molecules

Saponification of Triacylglycerols (17.4)

Triacylglycerol + 3NaOH $\xrightarrow{\text{Heat}}$ glycerol + 3 sodium salts of fatty acids (soaps)

KEY TERMS

cholesterol The most prevalent of the steroid compounds; needed for cellular membranes and the synthesis of vitamin D, hormones, and bile salts.

fat A triacylglycerol that is solid at room temperature and usually comes from animal sources.

fatty acid A long-chain carboxylic acid found in many lipids.

fluid mosaic model The concept that cell membranes are lipid bilayer structures that contain an assortment of polar lipids and proteins in a dynamic, fluid arrangement.

glycerophospholipid A polar lipid of glycerol attached to two fatty acids and a phosphate group connected to an ionized amino alcohol such as choline, serine, or ethanolamine.

hydrogenation The addition of hydrogen to unsaturated fats.

lipid bilayer A model of a cell membrane in which phospholipids are arranged in two rows.

lipids A family of compounds that is nonpolar in nature and not soluble in water; includes prostaglandins, waxes, triacylglycerols, phospholipids, and steroids.

lipoprotein A polar complex composed of a combination of nonpolar lipids with glycerophospholipids and proteins to form a polar complex that can be transported through body fluids.

monounsaturated fatty acid (MUFA) A fatty acid with one double bond.

oil A triacylglycerol that is usually a liquid at room temperature and is obtained from a plant source.

phospholipid A polar lipid of glycerol or sphingosine attached to fatty acids and a phosphate group connected to an amino alcohol.

polyunsaturated fatty acid (PUFA) A fatty acid that contains two or more double bonds.

prostaglandins A number of compounds derived from arachidonic acid that regulate several physiological processes.

saturated fatty acid (SFA) A fatty acid that has no double bonds, which has a higher melting point than unsaturated lipids, and is usually solid at room temperature.

sphingomyelin A compound in which the amine group of sphingosine forms an amide bond to a fatty acid and the hydroxyl group forms an ester bond with phosphate, which forms another phosphoester bond to an ionized amino alcohol.

steroids Types of lipid containing a multicyclic ring system.

triacylglycerols A family of lipids composed of three fatty acids bonded through ester bonds to glycerol, a trihydroxy alcohol.

unsaturated fatty acid A fatty acid that contains one or more carbon–carbon double bonds, which has a lower melting point than saturated fatty acids, and is usually liquid at room temperature.

wax The ester of a long-chain alcohol and a long-chain saturated fatty acid.

⚛ CORE CHEMISTRY SKILLS

Chapter section containing each Core Chemistry Skill is shown in parentheses at the end of each heading.

Identifying Fatty Acids (17.2)

Fatty acids are unbranched carboxylic acids that typically contain an even number (12 to 20) of carbon atoms.

- Fatty acids may be saturated, monounsaturated with one double bond, or polyunsaturated with two or more double bonds.
- The double bonds in unsaturated fatty acids are almost always cis.

Example: State the number of carbon atoms, saturated or unsaturated, and name of the following:

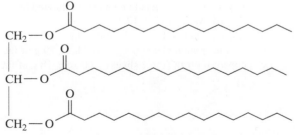

Answer: 16 carbon atoms, saturated, palmitic acid

Drawing Structures for Triacylglycerols (17.3)

- Triacylglycerols are esters of glycerol with three long-chain fatty acids.

Example: Draw and name the triacylglycerol formed from the esterification of glycerol and palmitic acid.

Answer:

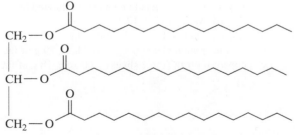

Glyceryl tripalmitate (tripalmitin)

Drawing the Products for the Hydrogenation, Hydrolysis, and Saponification of a Triacylglycerol (17.4)

- The hydrogenation of unsaturated fatty acids of a triacylglycerol in the presence of a Pt or Ni catalyst converts double bonds to single bonds.
- The hydrolysis of the ester bonds in triacylglycerols in the presence of a strong acid produces glycerol and fatty acids.
- In saponification, a triacylglycerol heated with a strong base produces glycerol and the salts of the fatty acids (soap).

Example: Identify each of the following as hydrogenation, hydrolysis, or saponification and state the products:

   a. the reaction of palm oil with NaOH

   b. the reaction of glyceryl trilinoleate from corn oil with water in the presence of an acid catalyst

   c. the reaction of corn oil and H_2 using a nickel catalyst

Answer: **a.** The reaction of palm oil with NaOH is saponification, and the products are glycerol and the potassium salts of the fatty acids, which is soap.

   b. In hydrolysis, glyceryl trilinoleate reacts with water in the presence of an acid catalyst, which splits the ester bonds to produce glycerol and three molecules of linoleic acid.

   c. In hydrogenation, H_2 adds to double bonds in corn oil, which produces a more saturated, and thus more solid, fat.

Identifying the Steroid Nucleus (17.6)

- The steroid nucleus consists of three cyclohexane rings and one cyclopentane ring fused together.

Example: Why are cholesterol, sodium glycocholate (a bile salt), and cortisone (a corticosteroid) all considered steroids?

Answer: They all contain the steroid nucleus of three six-carbon rings and one five-carbon ring fused together.

UNDERSTANDING THE CONCEPTS

The chapter sections to review are shown in parentheses at the end of each question.

17.71 Palmitic acid is obtained from palm oil as glyceryl tripalmitate (tripalmitin). Draw the condensed structural formula for glyceryl tripalmitate. (17.2, 17.3)

Palm fruit from palm trees are a source of palm oil.

17.72 Jojoba wax in candles consists of a 20-carbon saturated fatty acid and a 20-carbon saturated alcohol. Draw the condensed structural formula for jojoba wax. (17.2, 17.3)

Candles contain jojoba wax.

Clinical Applications

17.73 Identify each of the following as a saturated, monounsaturated, polyunsaturated, omega-3, or omega-6 fatty acid: (17.2)

a. $CH_3-(CH_2)_7-CH=CH-(CH_2)_7-\overset{\overset{\displaystyle O}{\|}}{C}-OH$

b. linoleic acid

c. $CH_3-CH_2-(CH=CH-CH_2)_5-CH_2-CH_2-\overset{\overset{\displaystyle O}{\|}}{C}-OH$

17.74 Identify each of the following as a saturated, monounsaturated, polyunsaturated, omega-3, or omega-6 fatty acid: (17.2)

a.
$CH_3-(CH_2)_4-CH=CH-CH_2-CH=CH-(CH_2)_7-\overset{\overset{\displaystyle O}{\|}}{C}-OH$

b. linolenic acid

c. $CH_3-(CH_2)_{14}-\overset{\overset{\displaystyle O}{\|}}{C}-OH$

Salmon is a good source of omega-3 unsaturated fatty acids.

ADDITIONAL QUESTIONS AND PROBLEMS

17.75 Among the ingredients in lipstick are beeswax, carnauba wax, hydrogenated vegetable oils, and glyceryl tricaprate (tricaprin). (17.1, 17.2, 17.3)
   a. What types of lipids have been used?
   b. Draw the condensed structural formula for glyceryl tricaprate (tricaprin). Capric acid is a saturated 10-carbon fatty acid.

17.76 Because peanut oil floats on the top of peanut butter, the peanut oil in many brands of peanut butter is hydrogenated and the solid is mixed into the peanut butter to give a solid product that does not separate. If a triacylglycerol in peanut oil that contains one oleic acid and two linoleic acids is completely hydrogenated, draw the condensed structural formula for the product. (17.3, 17.4)

17.77 Trans fats are produced during the hydrogenation of their unsaturated fatty acids. (17.2)
   a. What is the typical configuration of the double bond in a monounsaturated fatty acid?
   b. How does a trans fatty acid differ from a cis fatty acid?
   c. Draw the condensed structural formula for elaidic acid.

17.78 One mole of glyceryl trioleate (triolein) is completely hydrogenated. (7.6, 7.7, 8.6, 17.3, 17.4)
   a. Draw the condensed structural formula for the product.
   b. How many moles of hydrogen are required?
   c. How many grams of hydrogen are required?
   d. How many liters of hydrogen gas are needed if the reaction is run at STP?

Clinical Applications

17.79 The total kilocalories and grams of fat for some typical meals at fast-food restaurants are listed here. Calculate the number of kilocalories and the percentage of total kilocalories from fat (1 gram of fat = 9 kcal). Round answers to the tens place. Would you expect the fats to be mostly saturated or unsaturated? Why? (17.2, 17.3)
   a. a chicken dinner, 830 kcal, 46 g of fat
   b. a quarter-pound cheeseburger, 520 kcal, 29 g of fat
   c. pepperoni pizza (three slices), 560 kcal, 18 g of fat

17.80 The total kilocalories and grams of fat for some typical meals at fast-food restaurants are listed here. Calculate the number of kilocalories and the percentage of total kilocalories from fat (1 gram of fat = 9 kcal). Round answers to the tens place. Would you expect the fats to be mostly saturated or unsaturated? Why? (17.2, 17.3)
  a. a beef burrito, 470 kcal, 21 g of fat
  b. deep-fried fish (three pieces), 480 kcal, 28 g of fat
  c. a jumbo hot dog, 180 kcal, 18 g of fat

17.81 Identify each of the following as a fatty acid, soap, triacylglycerol, wax, glycerophospholipid, sphingolipid, or steroid: (17.1, 17.2, 17.3, 17.5, 17.6)
  a. beeswax
  b. cholesterol
  c. lecithin
  d. glyceryl tripalmitate (tripalmitin)
  e. sodium stearate
  f. safflower oil

17.82 Identify each of the following as a fatty acid, soap, triacylglycerol, wax, glycerophospholipid, sphingolipid, or steroid: (17.1, 17.2, 17.3, 17.5, 17.6)
  a. sphingomyelin
  b. whale blubber
  c. adipose tissue
  d. progesterone
  e. cortisone
  f. stearic acid

17.83 Identify the components (**1** to **6**) contained in each of the following lipids (**a** to **d**): (17.1, 17.2, 17.3, 17.5, 17.6)
  1. glycerol
  2. fatty acid
  3. phosphate
  4. amino alcohol
  5. steroid nucleus
  6. sphingosine

  a. estrogen
  b. cephalin
  c. wax
  d. triacylglycerol

17.84 Identify the components (**1** to **6**) contained in each of the following lipids (**a** to **d**): (17.1, 17.2, 17.3, 17.5, 17.6)
  1. glycerol
  2. fatty acid
  3. phosphate
  4. amino alcohol
  5. steroid nucleus
  6. sphingosine

  a. glycerophospholipid
  b. sphingomyelin
  c. aldosterone
  d. linoleic acid

17.85 Which of the following are found in cell membranes? (17.7)
  a. cholesterol
  b. triacylglycerols
  c. carbohydrates

17.86 Which of the following are found in cell membranes? (17.7)
  a. proteins
  b. waxes
  c. phospholipids

CHALLENGE QUESTIONS

The following groups of questions are related to the topics in this chapter. However, they do not all follow the chapter order, and they require you to combine concepts and skills from several sections. These questions will help you increase your critical thinking skills and prepare for your next exam.

17.87 Draw the condensed structural formula for a glycerophospholipid that contains two stearic acids and a phosphate bonded to ethanolamine. (17.2, 17.5)

17.88 Sunflower seed oil can be used to make margarine. A triacylglycerol in sunflower seed oil contains two linoleic acids and one oleic acid. (17.2, 17.3, 17.5)
  a. Draw the condensed structural formulas for two isomers of the triacylglycerol in sunflower seed oil.
  b. Using one of the isomers, write the reaction that would be used when sunflower seed oil is used to make solid margarine.

Sunflower oil is obtained from the seeds of the sunflower.

17.89 Match the lipoprotein (**1** to **4**) with its description (**a** to **d**). (17.6)
  1. chylomicrons
  2. VLDL
  3. LDL
  4. HDL

  a. "good" cholesterol
  b. transports most of the cholesterol to the cells
  c. carries triacylglycerols from the intestine to the fat cells
  d. transports cholesterol to the liver

17.90 Match the lipoprotein (**1** to **4**) with its description (**a** to **d**). (17.6)
  1. chylomicrons
  2. VLDL
  3. LDL
  4. HDL

  a. has the greatest abundance of protein
  b. "bad" cholesterol
  c. carries triacylglycerols synthesized in the liver to the muscles
  d. has the lowest density

17.91 A sink drain can become clogged with solid fat such as glyceryl tristearate (tristearin). (7.1, 7.6, 7.7, 9.4, 17.3, 17.4)
  a. How would adding lye (NaOH) to the sink drain remove the blockage?
  b. Write a balanced chemical equation for the reaction that occurs.
  c. How many milliliters of a 0.500 M NaOH solution are needed to completely saponify 10.0 g of glyceryl tristearate (tristearin)?

A sink drain can become clogged with saturated fats.

17.92 One of the triacylglycerols in olive oil is glyceryl tripalmitoleate (tripalmitolein). (7.1, 7.6, 7.7, 8.6, 9.4, 17.3, 17.4)
  a. Draw the condensed structural formula for glyceryl tripal-
    mitoleate (tripalmitolein).
  b. How many liters of H_2 gas at STP are needed to completely
    saturate 100 g of glyceryl tripalmitoleate (tripalmitolein)?
  c. How many milliliters of a 0.250 M NaOH solution are
    needed to completely saponify 100 g of glyceryl tripalmi-
    toleate (tripalmitolein)?

Olive oil contains glyceryl
tripalmitoleate (tripalmitolein).

ANSWERS

Answers to Selected Questions and Problems

17.1 Because lipids are not soluble in water, a polar solvent, they
are nonpolar molecules.

17.3 Lipids provide energy, protection, and insulation for the organs
in the body. Lipids are also an important part of cell
membranes.

17.5 All fatty acids contain a long chain of carbon atoms with a
carboxylic acid group. Saturated fatty acids contain only
carbon–carbon single bonds; unsaturated fatty acids contain
one or more double bonds.

17.7 **a.** palmitic acid

b. oleic acid

17.9 **a.** (12:0), saturated   **b.** (18:3), polyunsaturated
    c. (16:1), monounsaturated   **d.** (18:0), saturated

17.11 In a cis fatty acid, the hydrogen atoms are on the same side of
the double bond, which produces a kink in the carbon chain. In
a trans fatty acid, the hydrogen atoms are on opposite sides of
the double bond, which gives a carbon chain without any kink.

17.13 In an omega-3 fatty acid, there is a double bond beginning at
carbon 3, counting from the methyl group, whereas in an
omega-6 fatty acid, there is a double bond beginning at carbon 6,
counting from the methyl group.

17.15 Arachidonic acid and PGE_1 are both carboxylic acids with
20 carbon atoms. The differences are that arachidonic acid has
four cis double bonds and no other functional groups, whereas
PGE_1 has one trans double bond, one ketone functional group,
and two hydroxyl functional groups. In addition, a part of the
PGE_1 chain forms a cyclopentane ring.

17.17 Prostaglandins raise or lower blood pressure, stimulate contraction and relaxation of smooth muscle, and may cause
inflammation and pain.

17.19 $CH_3 - (CH_2)_{14} - \overset{\overset{\textstyle O}{\|}}{C} - O - (CH_2)_{29} - CH_3$

17.21

$$CH_2 - O - \overset{\overset{\textstyle O}{\|}}{C} - (CH_2)_{16} - CH_3$$
$$CH - O - \overset{\overset{\textstyle O}{\|}}{C} - (CH_2)_{16} - CH_3$$
$$CH_2 - O - \overset{\overset{\textstyle O}{\|}}{C} - (CH_2)_{16} - CH_3$$

17.23

$$CH_2 - O - \overset{\overset{\textstyle O}{\|}}{C} - (CH_2)_6 - CH_3$$
$$CH - O - \overset{\overset{\textstyle O}{\|}}{C} - (CH_2)_6 - CH_3$$
$$CH_2 - O - \overset{\overset{\textstyle O}{\|}}{C} - (CH_2)_6 - CH_3$$

17.25 Safflower oil has a lower melting point since it contains fatty
acids with two or three double bonds; olive oil contains a large
amount of oleic acid, which has only one double bond (monounsaturated).

17.27 Sunflower oil has about 24% monounsaturated fats, whereas
safflower oil has about 18%. Sunflower oil has about 66%
polyunsaturated fats, whereas safflower oil has about 73%.

17.29 **a.** The reaction of palm oil with KOH is saponification; the
    products are glycerol and the potassium salts of the fatty
    acids, which are soaps.
  b. The reaction of glyceryl trilinoleate from safflower oil with
    water and HCl is hydrolysis, which splits the ester bonds to
    produce glycerol and three molecules of linoleic acid.

17.31

$$CH_2 - O - \overset{\overset{\textstyle O}{\|}}{C} - (CH_2)_7 - CH = CH - (CH_2)_5 - CH_3$$
$$CH - O - \overset{\overset{\textstyle O}{\|}}{C} - (CH_2)_7 - CH = CH - (CH_2)_5 - CH_3 \ + \ 3H_2$$
$$CH_2 - O - \overset{\overset{\textstyle O}{\|}}{C} - (CH_2)_7 - CH = CH - (CH_2)_5 - CH_3$$

$$\xrightarrow{\text{Ni}}$$

$$CH_2 - O - \overset{\overset{\textstyle O}{\|}}{C} - (CH_2)_{14} - CH_3$$
$$CH - O - \overset{\overset{\textstyle O}{\|}}{C} - (CH_2)_{14} - CH_3$$
$$CH_2 - O - \overset{\overset{\textstyle O}{\|}}{C} - (CH_2)_{14} - CH_3$$

17.33

$$CH_2-O-\overset{\overset{\displaystyle O}{\|}}{C}-(CH_2)_{12}-CH_3$$
$$CH-O-\overset{\overset{\displaystyle O}{\|}}{C}-(CH_2)_{12}-CH_3 \;+\; 3H_2O \xrightarrow{\;H^+,\,heat\;}$$
$$CH_2-O-\overset{\overset{\displaystyle O}{\|}}{C}-(CH_2)_{12}-CH_3$$

$$CH_2-OH$$
$$CH-OH \;+\; 3HO-\overset{\overset{\displaystyle O}{\|}}{C}-(CH_2)_{12}-CH_3$$
$$CH_2-OH$$

17.35

$$CH_2-O-\overset{\overset{\displaystyle O}{\|}}{C}-(CH_2)_{12}-CH_3$$
$$CH-O-\overset{\overset{\displaystyle O}{\|}}{C}-(CH_2)_{12}-CH_3 \;+\; 3NaOH \xrightarrow{\;Heat\;}$$
$$CH_2-O-\overset{\overset{\displaystyle O}{\|}}{C}-(CH_2)_{12}-CH_3$$

$$CH_2-OH$$
$$CH-OH \;+\; 3Na^+ \;{}^-O-\overset{\overset{\displaystyle O}{\|}}{C}-(CH_2)_{12}-CH_3$$
$$CH_2-OH$$

17.37

$$CH_2-O-\overset{\overset{\displaystyle O}{\|}}{C}-(CH_2)_{16}-CH_3$$
$$CH-O-\overset{\overset{\displaystyle O}{\|}}{C}-(CH_2)_{16}-CH_3$$
$$CH_2-O-\overset{\overset{\displaystyle O}{\|}}{C}-(CH_2)_{16}-CH_3$$

17.39 A triacylglycerol consists of glycerol and three fatty acids. A glycerophospholipid also contains glycerol, but has only two fatty acids. The hydroxyl group on the third carbon of glycerol is attached by a phosphoester bond to an ionized amino alcohol.

17.41

$$CH_2-O-\overset{\overset{\displaystyle O}{\|}}{C}-(CH_2)_{14}-CH_3$$
$$CH-O-\overset{\overset{\displaystyle O}{\|}}{C}-(CH_2)_{14}-CH_3$$
$$CH_2-O-\overset{\overset{\displaystyle O}{\|}}{P}-O-CH_2-CH_2-\overset{+}{N}H_3$$
$$\;\;\;\;\;\;\;\;\;\;\;\;\overset{|}{O^-}$$

17.43 This glycerophospholipid is a cephalin. It contains glycerol, oleic acid, stearic acid, a phosphate, and ethanolamine.

17.45 a. sphingosine   **b.** palmitic acid
  c. an amide bond   **d.** ethanolamine

17.47

17.49 Bile salts act to emulsify fat globules, allowing the fat to be more easily digested.

17.51 Chylomicrons have a lower density than VLDLs. They pick up triacylglycerols from the intestine, whereas VLDLs transport triacylglycerols synthesized in the liver.

17.53 "Bad" cholesterol is the cholesterol carried by LDL that can form deposits in the arteries called plaque, which narrows the arteries.

17.55 Both estradiol and testosterone contain the steroid nucleus and a hydroxyl group. Testosterone has a ketone group, a double bond, and two methyl groups. Estradiol has an aromatic ring, a hydroxyl group in place of the ketone, and a methyl group.

17.57 b, c, and **d**

17.59 The lipid bilayer in a cell membrane surrounds the cell and separates the contents of the cell from the external fluids.

17.61 Because the molecules of cholesterol are large and rigid, they reduce the flexibility of the lipid bilayer and add strength to the cell membrane.

17.63 The peripheral proteins in the membrane emerge on the inner or outer surface only, whereas the integral proteins extend through the membrane to both surfaces.

17.65 Substances move through cell membranes by diffusion (passive transport), facilitated transport, and active transport.
  a. facilitated transport
  b. diffusion (passive transport)

17.67 alkene, alcohol, ester, carboxylic acid

17.69 a. 0.56 g of Pravachol   **b.** 360 mg/dL

17.71

$$CH_2-O-\overset{\overset{\displaystyle O}{\|}}{C}-(CH_2)_{14}-CH_3$$
$$CH-O-\overset{\overset{\displaystyle O}{\|}}{C}-(CH_2)_{14}-CH_3$$
$$CH_2-O-\overset{\overset{\displaystyle O}{\|}}{C}-(CH_2)_{14}-CH_3$$

17.73 a. monounsaturated
  b. polyunsaturated, omega-6
  c. polyunsaturated, omega-3

17.75 a. Beeswax and carnauba are waxes. Vegetable oil and glyceryl tricaprate (tricaprin) are triacylglycerols.

  b.
$$CH_2-O-\overset{\overset{\displaystyle O}{\|}}{C}-(CH_2)_8-CH_3$$
$$CH-O-\overset{\overset{\displaystyle O}{\|}}{C}-(CH_2)_8-CH_3$$
$$CH_2-O-\overset{\overset{\displaystyle O}{\|}}{C}-(CH_2)_8-CH_3$$
  Glyceryl tricaprate (tricaprin)

17.77 a. A typical unsaturated fatty acid has a cis double bond.
  b. A cis unsaturated fatty acid contains hydrogen atoms on the same side of each double bond. A trans unsaturated fatty acid has hydrogen atoms on opposite sides of the double bond that forms during hydrogenation.

  c.
$$CH_3-(CH_2)_6-CH_2 \underset{}{\overset{H}{\diagdown}} C=C \overset{CH_2-(CH_2)_6-\overset{\overset{\displaystyle O}{\|}}{C}-OH}{\diagup}$$

17.79 a. 410 kcal from fat; 49% fat
b. 260 kcal from fat; 50.% fat
c. 160 kcal from fat; 29% fat

17.81 a. Beeswax is a wax.
b. Cholesterol is a steroid.
c. Lecithin is a glycerophospholipid.
d. Glyceryl tripalmitate is a triacylglycerol.
e. Sodium stearate is a soap.
f. Safflower oil is a triacylglycerol.

17.83 a. 5   **b.** 1, 2, 3, 4
c. 2   **d.** 1, 2

17.85 a and c

17.87

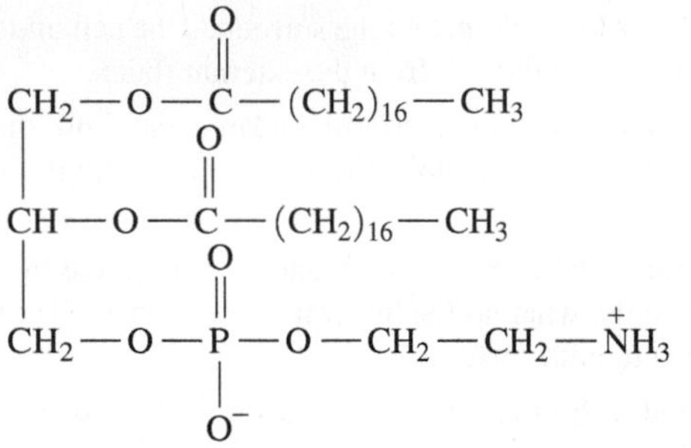

$$CH_2-O-\overset{\overset{\displaystyle O}{\|}}{C}-(CH_2)_{16}-CH_3$$
$$CH-O-\overset{\overset{\displaystyle O}{\|}}{C}-(CH_2)_{16}-CH_3$$
$$CH_2-O-\overset{\overset{\displaystyle O}{\|}}{\underset{\underset{\displaystyle O^-}{|}}{P}}-O-CH_2-CH_2-\overset{+}{N}H_3$$

17.89 a. (4) HDL   **b.** (3) LDL
c. (1) chylomicrons   **d.** (4) HDL

17.91 a. Adding NaOH would saponify lipids such as glyceryl tristearate (tristearin), forming glycerol and salts of the fatty acids that are soluble in water and would wash down the drain.

b.

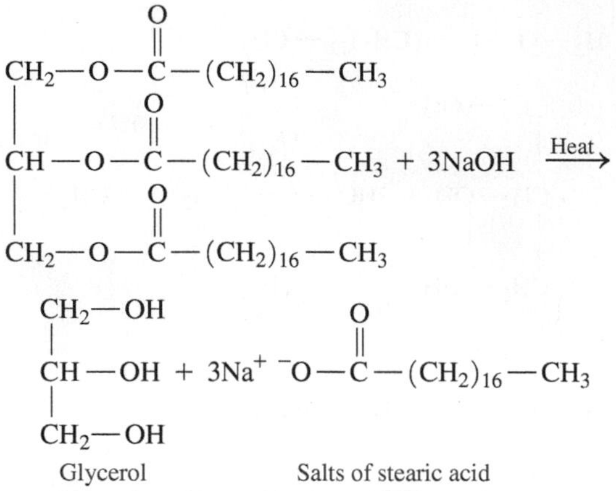

$$CH_2-O-\overset{\overset{\displaystyle O}{\|}}{C}-(CH_2)_{16}-CH_3$$
$$CH-O-\overset{\overset{\displaystyle O}{\|}}{C}-(CH_2)_{16}-CH_3 + 3NaOH \xrightarrow{\text{Heat}}$$
$$CH_2-O-\overset{\overset{\displaystyle O}{\|}}{C}-(CH_2)_{16}-CH_3$$

$$CH_2-OH$$
$$CH-OH + 3Na^+ \ ^-O-\overset{\overset{\displaystyle O}{\|}}{C}-(CH_2)_{16}-CH_3$$
$$CH_2-OH$$

     Glycerol   Salts of stearic acid

c. 67.3 mL of a 0.500 M NaOH solution

18

Amines and Amides

LANCE, AN ENVIRONMENTAL HEALTH PRACTITIONER,
is collecting soil and water samples at a ranch to test for the presence and concentration
of any pesticides and pharmaceuticals. Ranchers use pesticides to increase food
production and pharmaceuticals to treat and prevent animal-related diseases. Due to the
common use of these chemicals, they may pass into the soil and water supply, potentially
contaminating the environment and causing health problems.

Recently, the sheep on the ranch were treated with a pharmaceutical dewormer,
fenbendazole, to destroy any gastrointestinal worms. Fenbendazole contains several functional
groups: aromatic rings, an ester, an amine, and imidazole, a heterocyclic amine. Heterocyclic
amines are carbon-based rings where one or more of the carbon atoms have been replaced by
a nitrogen atom. Imidazole is a five-atom ring that contains two nitrogen atoms.

Lance detects small amounts of fenbendazole in the soil. He advises the rancher to
decrease the dosage he administers to his sheep in order to reduce the amounts currently being
detected in the soil. Lance then indicates he will be back in a month to re-test the soil and water.

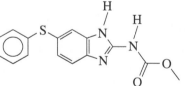

Fenbendazole   Imidazole

CAREER Environmental Health Practitioner

Environmental health practitioners (EHPs) monitor environmental
pollution to protect the health of the public. By using specialized
equipment, EHPs measure pollution levels in soil, air, and water,
as well as noise and radiation levels. EHPs can specialize in a
specific area, such as air quality or hazardous and solid waste.
For instance, air quality experts monitor indoor air for allergens,
mold, and toxins; they measure outdoor air pollutants created by
businesses, vehicles, and agriculture. Since EHPs obtain samples
with potentially hazardous materials, they must be knowledgeable
about safety protocols and wear personal protective equipment.
EHPs also recommend methods to diminish various pollutants, and
may assist in cleanup and remediation efforts. **649**

Amines and amides are organic compounds that contain nitrogen. Many nitrogen-containing compounds are important to life as components of amino acids, proteins, and nucleic acids (DNA and RNA). Many amines that exhibit strong physiological activity are used in medicine as decongestants, anesthetics, and sedatives. Examples include dopamine, histamine, epinephrine, and amphetamine.

Alkaloids such as caffeine, nicotine, cocaine, and digitalis, which demonstrate powerful physiological activity, are naturally occurring amines obtained from plants. In amides, the functional group consists of a carbonyl group attached to an amine. In biochemistry, the amide bond that links amino acids in a protein is called a peptide bond. Some medically important amides include acetaminophen (Tylenol) used to reduce fever; phenobarbital, a sedative and anticonvulsant medication; and penicillin, an antibiotic.

CHAPTER READINESS*

⚛ CORE CHEMISTRY SKILLS

• Writing Equations for Reactions of Acids and Bases (10.6)

• Naming and Drawing Alkanes (11.2)

*These Core Chemistry Skills from previous chapters are listed here for your review as you proceed to the new material in this chapter.

18.1 Amines

LEARNING GOAL

Name amines using IUPAC and common names; draw the condensed or line-angle structural formulas given the names. Classify amines as primary (1°), secondary (2°), or tertiary (3°).

Amines are derivatives of ammonia (NH_3) in which the nitrogen atom, which has one lone pair of electrons, has three bonds to hydrogen atoms. In an amine, the nitrogen atom is bonded to one, two, or three alkyl or aromatic groups.

Naming Amines

In the IUPAC names for amines, the *e* in the corresponding alkane name is replaced with *amine*.

$$CH_4 \qquad CH_3-NH_2 \qquad CH_3-CH_3 \qquad CH_3-CH_2-NH_2$$

Methane   Methan**amine**   Ethane   Ethan**amine**

When the amine has a chain of three or more carbon atoms, it is numbered to show the position of the $-NH_2$ group and any other substituents.

$$\underset{3}{CH_3}-\underset{2}{CH_2}-\underset{1}{CH_2}-NH_2 \qquad \underset{1}{CH_3}-\underset{2}{\overset{\overset{\displaystyle NH_2}{|}}{CH}}-\underset{3}{CH_3}$$

1-Propan**amine**   2-Propan**amine**

$$\underset{1}{CH_3}-\underset{2}{\overset{\overset{\displaystyle NH_2}{|}}{CH}}-\underset{3}{CH_2}-\underset{4}{CH_3} \qquad \underset{4}{CH_3}-\underset{3}{\overset{\overset{\displaystyle CH_3}{|}}{CH}}-\underset{2}{CH_2}-\underset{1}{CH_2}-NH_2$$

2-Butan**amine**   3-Methyl-1-butan**amine**

If there is an alkyl group attached to the nitrogen atom, the prefix *N*- and the alkyl name are placed in front of the amine name. If there are two alkyl groups bonded to the N atom, the prefix *N*- is used for each and they are listed alphabetically.

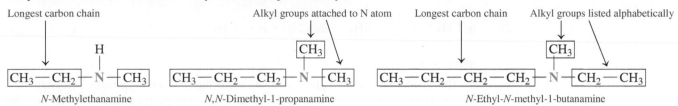

| Longest carbon chain | Alkyl groups attached to N atom | Longest carbon chain | Alkyl groups listed alphabetically |

N-Methylethanamine   *N,N*-Dimethyl-1-propanamine   *N*-Ethyl-*N*-methyl-1-butanamine

---

▶ SAMPLE PROBLEM 18.1 IUPAC Names for Amines

Give the IUPAC name for the following amine:

$$CH_3-CH_2-CH_2-CH_2-\overset{\overset{\displaystyle H}{|}}{N}-CH_3$$

SOLUTION

STEP 1 Name the longest carbon chain bonded to the N atom by replacing the *e* of its alkane name with *amine*. The longest carbon chain bonded to the N atom has four carbon atoms, which is named by replacing the *e* in the alkane name with *amine* to give butanamine.

$$CH_3-CH_2-CH_2-CH_2-\overset{\overset{\displaystyle H}{|}}{N}-CH_3 \qquad \text{butanamine}$$

STEP 2 Number the carbon chain to show the position of the amine group and other substituents. The N atom in the amine group is attached to carbon 1 of butanamine.

$$\underset{4}{CH_3}-\underset{3}{CH_2}-\underset{2}{CH_2}-\underset{1}{CH_2}-\overset{\overset{\displaystyle H}{|}}{N}-CH_3 \qquad \text{1-butanamine}$$

STEP 3 Any alkyl group attached to the nitrogen atom is indicated by the prefix *N*- and the alkyl name, which is placed in front of the amine name. Alkyl groups attached to the N atom are listed alphabetically.

$$\underset{4}{CH_3}-\underset{3}{CH_2}-\underset{2}{CH_2}-\underset{1}{CH_2}-\overset{\overset{\displaystyle H}{|}}{N}-CH_3 \qquad \textit{N}\text{-methyl-1-butanamine}$$

STUDY CHECK 18.1

Draw the condensed structural formula for *N*-ethyl-1-propanamine.

ANSWER

$$CH_3-CH_2-CH_2-\overset{\overset{\displaystyle H}{|}}{N}-CH_2-CH_3$$

> **Guide to the IUPAC Naming of Amines**
>
> **STEP 1**
> Name the longest carbon chain bonded to the N atom by replacing the *e* of its alkane name with *amine*.
>
> **STEP 2**
> Number the carbon chain to show the position of the amine group and other substituents.
>
> **STEP 3**
> Any alkyl group attached to the nitrogen atom is indicated by the prefix *N*- and the alkyl name, which is placed in front of the amine name.

Common Names of Amines

The common names of amines are often used when the alkyl groups are not branched. The alkyl groups bonded to the nitrogen atom are listed in alphabetical order. The prefixes *di* and *tri* are used to indicate two and three identical groups.

$$CH_3-NH_2 \qquad CH_3-\overset{\overset{\displaystyle H}{|}}{N}-CH_3 \qquad CH_3-CH_2-CH_2-\overset{\overset{\displaystyle CH_3}{|}}{N}-CH_2-CH_3$$

Methylamine   Dimethylamine   Ethylmethylpropylamine

> **SAMPLE PROBLEM 18.2 Common Names of Amines**
>
> Give a common name for each of the following amines:
>
> $$\text{a. } CH_3-CH_2-NH_2 \qquad \text{b. } CH_3-\underset{\underset{\displaystyle CH_3}{|}}{N}-CH_3$$
>
> **SOLUTION**
>
> **a.** This amine has one ethyl group attached to the nitrogen atom; its name is ethylamine.
> **b.** The common name for an amine with three methyl groups attached to the nitrogen atom is trimethylamine.
>
> **STUDY CHECK 18.2**
>
> Draw the condensed structural formula for butyldimethylamine.
>
> **ANSWER**
>
> $$CH_3-CH_2-CH_2-CH_2-\underset{\underset{\displaystyle CH_3}{|}}{N}-CH_3$$

Naming Compounds with Two Functional Groups

When a compound contains more than one functional group, we need to identify which group is used for the name of the compound and which group is named as a substituent. According to IUPAC rules for nomenclature, an oxygen-containing group will take priority over an $-NH_2$ group. Therefore, the $-NH_2$ group is named as the substituent, *amino*. Table 18.1 lists the priorities for the major functional groups, and the names of the functional groups as substituents. The functional group that is highest on the list is named as the compound, and any group lower on the list is named as a substituent. Examples are given for naming an alcohol, ketone, and carboxylic acid that also contain an amine group.

$$\underset{\text{2-Amino-1-propanol}}{CH_3-\underset{\underset{\displaystyle NH_2}{|}}{CH}-CH_2-OH} \qquad \underset{\text{4-Amino-2-pentanone}}{CH_3-\underset{\underset{\displaystyle NH_2}{|}}{CH}-CH_2-\overset{\overset{\displaystyle O}{||}}{C}-CH_3} \qquad \underset{\text{3-Aminobutanoic acid}}{CH_3-\underset{\underset{\displaystyle NH_2}{|}}{CH}-CH_2-\overset{\overset{\displaystyle O}{||}}{C}-OH}$$

TABLE 18.1 Priority of Functional Groups in IUPAC Names

	Functional Group	Name of Compound	Name as a Substituent
Highest Priority	carboxylic acid	oic acid	
	ester	oate	
	amide	amide	amido
	aldehyde	al	formyl
	ketone	one	oxo
	alcohol	ol	hydroxy
	amine	amine	amino
	alkane	ane	alkyl
Lowest Priority	halide		halo

> **SAMPLE PROBLEM 18.3 IUPAC Names for Compounds with Two Functional Groups**
>
> Give the IUPAC name for the following compound, which is used in the production of methadone:
>
> $$CH_3-\underset{\underset{\displaystyle OH}{|}}{CH}-CH_2-NH_2$$

SOLUTION

STEP 1 Identify the functional group with the highest priority and use the longest carbon chain to give the compound name. Because the hydroxyl group has a higher priority than the amine group, the compound is named as an alcohol.

$$CH_3-\overset{\overset{\displaystyle OH}{|}}{CH}-CH_2-NH_2 \qquad \boxed{propanol}$$

STEP 2 Number the carbon chain, and give the position and name of the main group and the substituent group on the carbon chain.

$$\underset{3}{CH_3}-\underset{2}{\overset{\overset{\displaystyle OH}{|}}{CH}}-\underset{1}{CH_2}-NH_2 \qquad 1\text{-amino-2-propanol}$$

Guide to Naming Compounds with Two Functional Groups

STEP 1 Identify the functional group with the highest priority and use the longest carbon chain to give the compound name.

STEP 2 Number the carbon chain, and give the position and name of the main group and the substituent group on the carbon chain.

STUDY CHECK 18.3

Draw the condensed structural formula for 3-aminopentanal.

ANSWER

$$CH_3-CH_2-\overset{\overset{\displaystyle NH_2}{|}}{CH}-CH_2-\overset{\overset{\displaystyle O}{||}}{C}-H$$

Aromatic Amines

The aromatic amines use the name *aniline*, which is approved by IUPAC. Aniline is the simplest aromatic amine; it is used to make many industrial chemicals.

Aniline · 4-Bromoaniline (*p*-bromoaniline) · *N*-Methylaniline · *N,N*-Dimethylaniline

Aniline, which was discovered in 1826 when it was first isolated from indigo plants, is used to make many dyes, which give color to wool, cotton, and silk fibers, as well as blue jeans. It is also used to make the polymer polyurethane and in the synthesis of the pain reliever acetaminophen.

Indigo

Indigo used in blue dyes can be obtained from tropical plants such as *Indigofera tinctoria*.

Classification of Amines

Amines are classified by counting the number of carbon atoms directly bonded to the nitrogen atom. In a primary (1°) amine, the nitrogen atom is bonded to one alkyl group. In a secondary (2°) amine, the nitrogen atom is bonded to two alkyl groups. In a tertiary (3°) amine, the nitrogen atom is bonded to three alkyl groups. In each of the following models of ammonia and amines, the atoms are arranged around the nitrogen atom (blue) in a trigonal pyramidal shape:

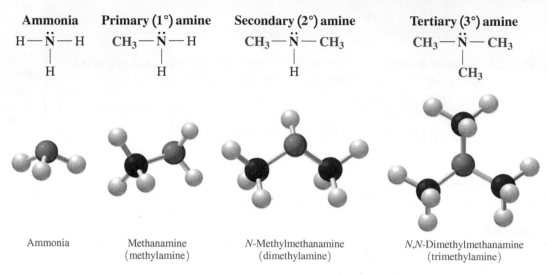

Ammonia

$H-\ddot{N}-H$
$|$
H

Primary (1°) amine

$CH_3-\ddot{N}-H$
$|$
H

Secondary (2°) amine

$CH_3-\ddot{N}-CH_3$
$|$
H

Tertiary (3°) amine

$CH_3-\ddot{N}-CH_3$
$|$
CH_3

Ammonia

Methanamine
(methylamine)

N-Methylmethanamine
(dimethylamine)

N,N-Dimethylmethanamine
(trimethylamine)

Line-Angle Structural Formulas for Amines

We can draw line-angle structural formulas for amines just as we have for other organic compounds. In the line-angle structural formula for an amine, we show the hydrogen atoms bonded to the N atom. For example, we can draw the following line-angle structural formulas and classify each:

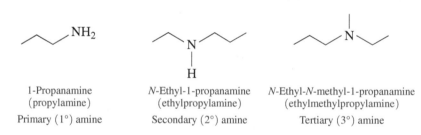

1-Propanamine
(propylamine)

Primary (1°) amine

N-Ethyl-1-propanamine
(ethylpropylamine)

Secondary (2°) amine

N-Ethyl-N-methyl-1-propanamine
(ethylmethylpropylamine)

Tertiary (3°) amine

▶ **SAMPLE PROBLEM 18.4 Classifying Amines**

Classify each of the following amines as primary (1°), secondary (2°), or tertiary (3°):

a.
NH₂ (on cyclohexane)

b. $CH_3-\overset{\overset{\displaystyle CH_3}{|}}{N}-CH_2-CH_3$

c. (phenyl)$-\overset{}{\underset{\underset{\displaystyle H}{|}}{N}}-CH_3$

d.

SOLUTION

a. This is a primary (1°) amine because there is one alkyl group (cyclohexyl) attached to the nitrogen atom.

b. This is a tertiary (3°) amine. There are three alkyl groups (two methyls and one ethyl) attached to the nitrogen atom.

c. This is a secondary (2°) amine with two carbon groups, methyl and phenyl, bonded to the nitrogen atom.

d. The nitrogen atom in this line-angle structural formula is bonded to two alkyl groups, which makes it a secondary (2°) amine.

STUDY CHECK 18.4

Classify the following amine as primary (1°), secondary (2°), or tertiary (3°):

$$CH_3-CH_2-\underset{\underset{CH_3}{|}}{N}-CH_2-CH_2-CH_3$$

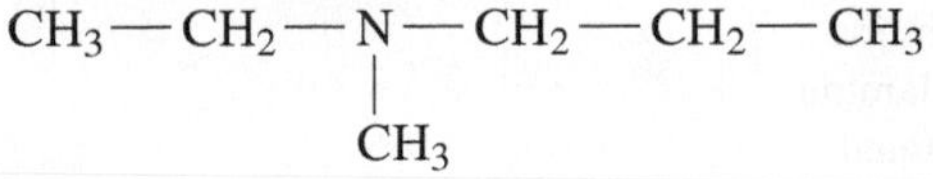

ANSWER

tertiary (3°)

QUESTIONS AND PROBLEMS

18.1 Amines

LEARNING GOAL Name amines using IUPAC and common names; draw the condensed or line-angle structural formulas given the names. Classify amines as primary (1°), secondary (2°), or tertiary (3°).

18.1 What is a primary amine?

18.2 What is a tertiary amine?

18.3 Classify each of the following amines as primary (1°), secondary (2°), or tertiary (3°):

a. $CH_3-CH_2-CH_2-NH_2$ **b.** 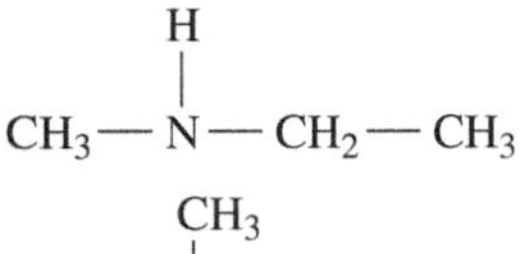 $CH_3-\underset{\underset{H}{|}}{N}-CH_2-CH_3$

c. 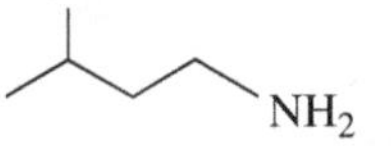 (line structure with NH_2)   **d.** 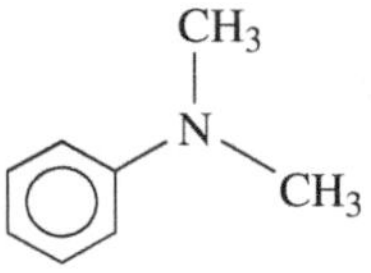 (benzene ring with $\underset{\underset{CH_3}{|}}{N}-CH_3$)

e. 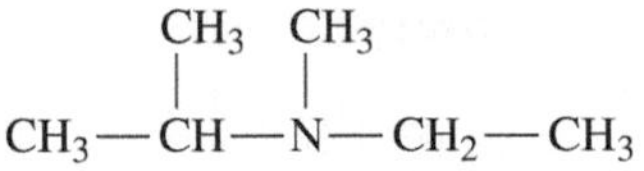 $CH_3-\underset{\underset{CH_3}{|}}{CH}-\underset{\underset{CH_3}{|}}{N}-CH_2-CH_3$

18.4 Classify each of the following amines as primary (1°), secondary (2°), or tertiary (3°):

a. 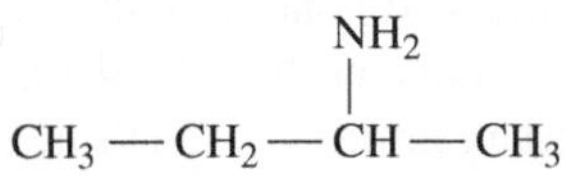 $CH_3-CH_2-\underset{\underset{NH_2}{|}}{CH}-CH_3$

b. 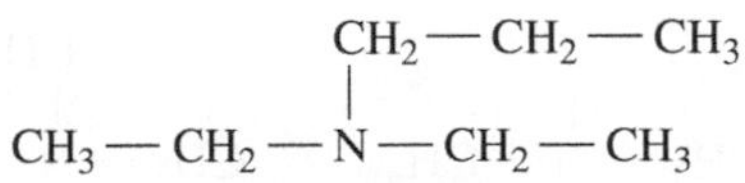 $CH_3-CH_2-\underset{\underset{CH_2-CH_2-CH_3}{|}}{N}-CH_2-CH_3$

c. 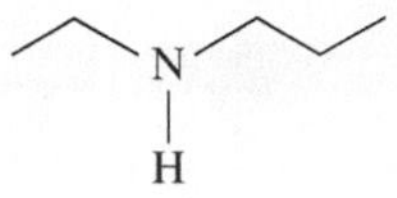 (line structure with N and H)

d. 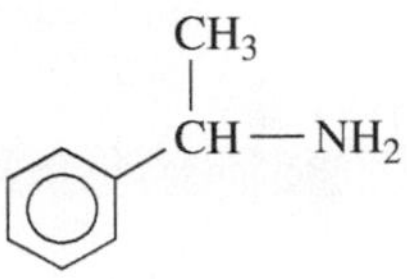 (benzene ring with $\underset{\underset{CH_3}{|}}{CH}-NH_2$)

e. 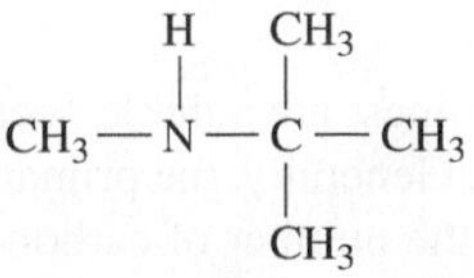 $CH_3-\underset{\underset{H}{|}}{N}-\underset{\overset{CH_3}{|}}{\underset{\underset{CH_3}{|}}{C}}-CH_3$

18.5 Write the IUPAC and common names for each of the following:

a. $CH_3-CH_2-NH_2$

b. 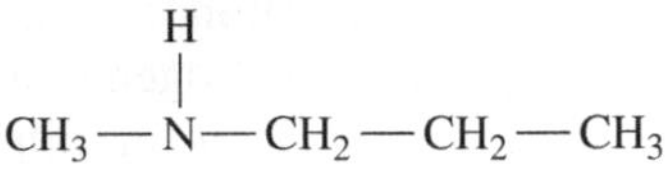 $CH_3-\underset{\underset{H}{|}}{\overset{H}{N}}-CH_2-CH_2-CH_3$

c. 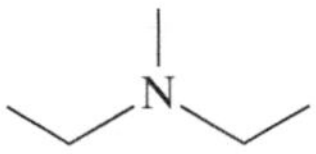 (line structure with N and NH_2)

d. 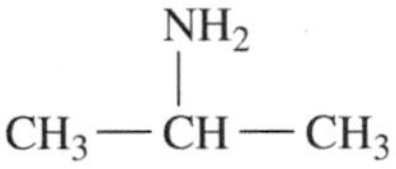 $CH_3-\underset{\underset{NH_2}{|}}{CH}-CH_3$

18.6 Write the IUPAC and common names for each of the following:

a. $CH_3-CH_2-CH_2-NH_2$

b. 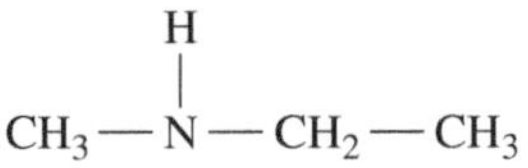 $CH_3-\underset{\underset{H}{|}}{\overset{H}{N}}-CH_2-CH_3$

c. 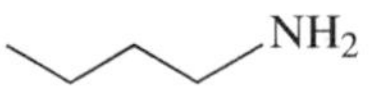 (line structure with NH_2)

d. 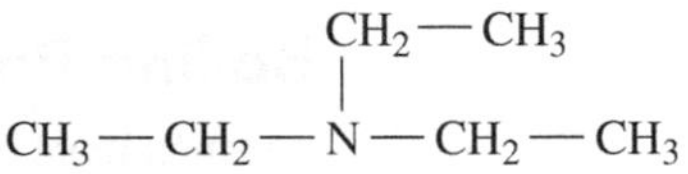 $CH_3-CH_2-\underset{\underset{CH_2-CH_3}{|}}{N}-CH_2-CH_3$

18.7 Write the IUPAC name for each of the following molecules that have two functional groups:

a. 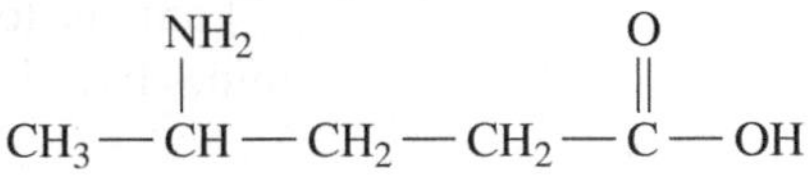 $CH_3-\underset{\underset{NH_2}{|}}{CH}-CH_2-CH_2-\overset{\overset{O}{\|}}{C}-OH$

b. (benzene ring with NH_2 and Cl)

c. $H_2N-CH_2-CH_2-\overset{\overset{O}{\|}}{C}-H$

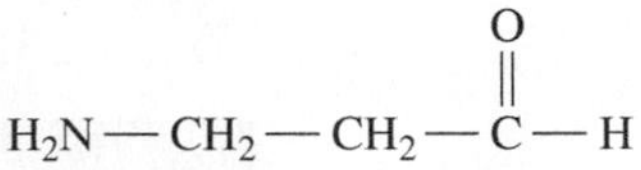

d. 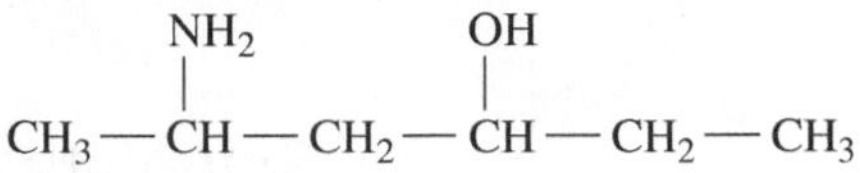 $CH_3-\underset{\underset{NH_2}{|}}{CH}-CH_2-\underset{\underset{OH}{|}}{CH}-CH_2-CH_3$

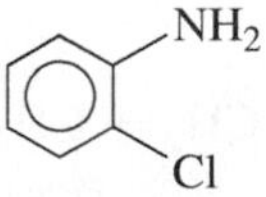

18.8 Write the IUPAC name for each of the following molecules that have two functional groups:

a. $CH_3 - \overset{\overset{\displaystyle O}{\|}}{C} - \overset{\overset{\displaystyle NH_2}{|}}{CH} - CH_3$

b. $CH_3 - \overset{\overset{\displaystyle NH_2}{|}}{CH} - CH_2 - CH_2 - CH_2 - OH$

c.

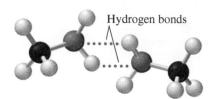

d. $CH_3 - \overset{\overset{\displaystyle NH_2}{|}}{CH} - \overset{\overset{\displaystyle O}{\|}}{C} - H$

18.9 Draw the condensed structural formula for each of the following amines:
   a. 2-chloroethanamine
   b. *N*-methylaniline
   c. butylpropylamine
   d. 2-aminobutanal

18.10 Draw the condensed structural formula for each of the following amines:
   a. dimethylamine
   b. *p*-chloroaniline
   c. *N,N*-diethylaniline
   d. 1-amino-3-pentanone

LEARNING GOAL

Describe the boiling points and solubility of amines; write equations for the dissociation and neutralization of amines.

18.2 Properties of Amines

Amines contain polar N—H bonds, which allow primary and secondary amines to form hydrogen bonds with each other, while all amines can form hydrogen bonds with water. However, nitrogen is not as electronegative as oxygen, which means that the hydrogen bonds in amines are weaker than the hydrogen bonds in alcohols.

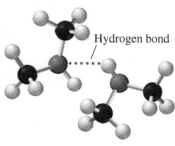

Most hydrogen bonds

Hydrogen bonds

Primary (1°) amine

Hydrogen bond

Secondary (2°) amine

No hydrogen bonds

Tertiary (3°) amine

Boiling Points of Amines

Amines have boiling points that are higher than alkanes but lower than alcohols. Primary (1°) amines, with two N—H bonds, can form more hydrogen bonds, and thus have higher boiling points than secondary (2°) amines of the same mass. It is not possible for tertiary (3°) amines to hydrogen bond with each other since they have no N—H bonds. Tertiary amines have lower boiling points than primary or secondary amines of the same mass.

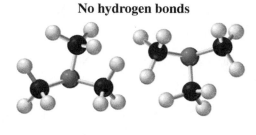

$CH_3 - CH_2 - CH_2 - NH_2$
Propylamine (1°)
bp 48 °C

$CH_3 - CH_2 - \overset{\overset{\displaystyle H}{|}}{N} - CH_3$
Ethylmethylamine (2°)
bp 37 °C

$CH_3 - \overset{\overset{\displaystyle CH_3}{|}}{N} - CH_3$
Trimethylamine (3°)
bp 3 °C

Boiling Point Decreases →

Solubility of Amines in Water

Amines with one to six carbon atoms, including tertiary amines, are soluble because they form several hydrogen bonds with water (see Figure 18.1). Generally, the primary amines are most soluble, and tertiary amines are least soluble. As the number of carbon atoms in an amine increases in the nonpolar alkyl portions, the effect of hydrogen bonding is diminished.

Most hydrogen bonds   **Fewest hydrogen bonds**

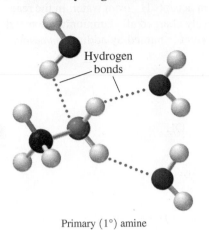

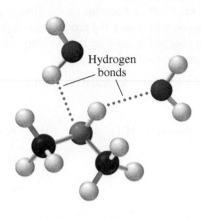

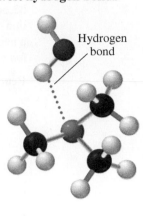

Hydrogen
bonds

Hydrogen
bonds

Hydrogen
bond

Primary (1°) amine   Secondary (2°) amine   Tertiary (3°) amine

FIGURE 18.1 ▶ Primary, secondary, and tertiary amines form hydrogen bonds with water molecules, but primary amines form the most and tertiary amines form the fewest.

◉ Why do tertiary (3°) amines form fewer hydrogen bonds with water than primary amines?

▶ **SAMPLE PROBLEM 18.5 Boiling Points and Solubility of Amines**

The compounds trimethylamine and ethylmethylamine have the same molar mass. Why is the boiling point of trimethylamine (3 °C) lower than that of ethylmethylamine (37 °C)?

SOLUTION

With polar N—H bonds, ethylmethylamine molecules form hydrogen bonds with each other. Thus, a higher temperature is required to break the hydrogen bonds and form a gas. However, trimethylamine, which is a tertiary amine, does not have N—H bonds and cannot hydrogen bond with other trimethylamine molecules. It does not need as high a temperature to form a gas.

STUDY CHECK 18.5

$$
\text{Why is } CH_3-CH_2-\overset{\overset{\textstyle H}{\mid}}{N}-CH_2-CH_3 \text{ more soluble in water than}
$$

$$
CH_3-CH_2-CH_2-CH_2-\overset{\overset{\textstyle H}{\mid}}{N}-CH_2-CH_2-CH_3?
$$

ANSWER

Hydrogen bonding makes amines with six or fewer carbon atoms soluble in water. When there are seven or more carbon atoms in the alkyl portions of an amine, the longer non-polar hydrocarbon chains diminish the solubility effect of the polar amine group.

Amines React as Bases in Water

Ammonia (NH_3) acts as a Brønsted–Lowry base by accepting H^+ from water to produce an ammonium ion (NH_4^+) and a hydroxide ion (OH^-).

$$
\text{H}-\overset{\overset{\textstyle H}{\mid}}{\underset{\underset{\textstyle H}{\mid}}{\ddot{N}}}-\text{H} + \text{HOH} \rightleftharpoons \text{H}-\overset{\overset{\textstyle H}{\mid}}{\underset{\underset{\textstyle H}{\mid}}{\overset{+}{N}}}-\text{H} + \text{OH}^-
$$

Ammonia   Ammonium   Hydroxide
                      ion   ion

All of the amines we have discussed in this chapter are also Brønsted–Lowry bases because the lone pair of electrons on the nitrogen atom accepts H^+ from water. In the reaction of an amine with water, the products are a positively charged alkylammonium ion and a negatively charged hydroxide ion. The organic product is named by adding *ammonium ion* to the name of its alkyl group.

Reaction of a Primary Amine with Water

$$CH_3-\overset{\cdot\cdot}{N}\!\!-\!\!H + H_2O \rightleftharpoons CH_3-\overset{H}{\underset{H}{\overset{|}{N^+}}}\!\!-\!\!H + OH^-$$

Methylamine   Methylammonium Hydroxide
ion   ion

Reaction of a Secondary Amine with Water

$$CH_3-\overset{\cdot\cdot}{\underset{H}{N}}\!\!-\!\!CH_3 + H_2O \rightleftharpoons CH_3-\overset{H}{\underset{H}{\overset{|}{N^+}}}\!\!-\!\!CH_3 + OH^-$$

Dimethylamine   Dimethylammonium Hydroxide
ion   ion

Reaction of a Tertiary Amine with Water

$$CH_3-\overset{\cdot\cdot}{\underset{CH_3}{N}}\!\!-\!\!CH_3 + H_2O \rightleftharpoons CH_3-\overset{H}{\underset{CH_3}{\overset{|}{N^+}}}\!\!-\!\!CH_3 + OH^-$$

Trimethylamine   Trimethylammonium Hydroxide
ion   ion

Neutralization of an Amine

When you squeeze lemon juice on fish, the "fishy" odor is removed by converting the amines to their ammonium salts. In a *neutralization reaction*, an amine acts as a base and reacts with an acid to form an **ammonium salt**. The lone pair of electrons on the nitrogen atom accepts H^+ from an acid to give an ammonium salt; no water is formed. An ammonium salt is named by using its alkylammonium ion name followed by the name of the negative ion.

The amines in fish react with the acid in lemon to neutralize the "fishy" odor.

Amine	Acid	Ammonium Salt

$$CH_3-\overset{\cdot\cdot}{\underset{H}{N}}\!\!-\!\!H + H-Cl \longrightarrow CH_3-\overset{H}{\underset{H}{\overset{|}{N^+}}}\!\!-\!\!H \; Cl^-$$

      Methylamine   Methylammonium chloride

$$CH_3-\overset{\cdot\cdot}{\underset{H}{N}}\!\!-\!\!CH_3 + H-Cl \longrightarrow CH_3-\overset{H}{\underset{H}{\overset{|}{N^+}}}\!\!-\!\!CH_3 \; Cl^-$$

      Dimethylamine   Dimethylammonium chloride

In a **quaternary ammonium salt**, a nitrogen atom is bonded to four carbon groups, which classifies it as a quaternary (4°) amine. As in other ammonium salts, the nitrogen atom has a positive charge. Choline, a component of glycerophospholipids, is a quaternary ammonium ion. The quaternary salts differ from other ammonium salts because the nitrogen atom is not bonded to an H atom.

Tetramethylammonium chloride

Choline

Properties of Ammonium Salts

Ammonium salts are ionic compounds with strong attractions between the positively charged ammonium ion and an anion, usually chloride. Like most salts, ammonium salts are solid at room temperature, odorless, and soluble in water and body fluids. For this reason, amines that are large molecules that are intended to be used as drugs are converted to their ammonium salts, which are soluble in water and body fluids. The ammonium salt of ephedrine is used as a bronchodilator and in decongestant products such as Sudafed. The ammonium salt of diphenhydramine is used in products such as Benadryl for relief of itching and pain from skin irritations and rashes (see Figure 18.2). In pharmaceuticals, the naming of the ammonium salt follows an older method of giving the amine name followed by the name of the acid.

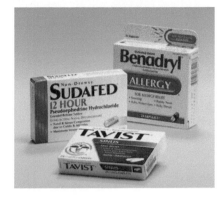

FIGURE 18.2 ▶ Decongestants and products that relieve itchy skin often contain ammonium salts.

Why are ammonium salts used in drugs rather than the biologically active amines?

Ephedrine hydrochloride
Ephedrine HCl
Sudafed

Diphenhydramine hydrochloride
Diphenylhydramine HCl
Benadryl

When an ammonium salt reacts with a strong base such as NaOH, it is converted back to the amine, which is also called the free amine or free base.

$$CH_3 \overset{+}{-} NH_3 \ Cl^- + NaOH \longrightarrow CH_3 - NH_2 + NaCl + H_2O$$

The narcotic cocaine is typically extracted from coca leaves using an acidic solution to give a white, solid ammonium salt, which is cocaine hydrochloride. It is the salt of cocaine (cocaine hydrochloride) that is smuggled and used illegally on the street. "Crack cocaine" is the free amine or free base of the amine obtained by treating the cocaine hydrochloride with NaOH and ether, a process known as "free-basing." The solid product is known as "crack cocaine" because it makes a cracking noise when heated. The free amine is rapidly absorbed when smoked and gives stronger highs than the cocaine hydrochloride, which makes crack cocaine more addictive.

Coca leaves are a source of cocaine.

Crack cocaine is obtained by treating cocaine hydrochloride with NaOH and ether.

Cocaine hydrochloride

Cocaine ("free base"; crack cocaine)

▶SAMPLE PROBLEM 18.6 Reactions of Amines

Write a balanced chemical equation that shows ethylamine:

a. acting as a weak base in water
b. neutralized by HCl

SOLUTION

a. $CH_3-CH_2-NH_2 + H_2O \rightleftharpoons CH_3-CH_2-\overset{+}{N}H_3 + OH^-$
b. $CH_3-CH_2-NH_2 + HCl \longrightarrow CH_3-CH_2-\overset{+}{N}H_3\ Cl^-$

STUDY CHECK 18.6

Draw the condensed structural formula for the ammonium salt formed by the reaction of trimethylamine and HCl.

ANSWER

$$CH_3-\overset{\overset{\displaystyle CH_3}{|}}{\underset{\underset{\displaystyle CH_3}{|}}{\overset{+}{N}}}-H\ Cl^-$$

QUESTIONS AND PROBLEMS

18.2 Properties of Amines

LEARNING GOAL Describe the boiling points and solubility of amines; write equations for the dissociation and neutralization of amines.

18.11 Identify the compound in each pair that has the higher boiling point. Explain.
   a. $CH_3-CH_2-NH_2$ or CH_3-CH_2-OH
   b. CH_3-NH_2 or $CH_3-CH_2-CH_2-NH_2$
   c. $CH_3-\overset{\overset{\displaystyle CH_3}{|}}{N}-CH_3$ or $CH_3-CH_2-CH_2-NH_2$

18.12 Identify the compound in each pair that has the higher boiling point. Explain.
   a. $CH_3-CH_2-CH_2-CH_3$ or $CH_3-CH_2-CH_2-NH_2$
   b. CH_3-NH_2 or $CH_3-CH_2-NH_2$
   c. $CH_3-CH_2-CH_2-OH$ or $CH_3-\overset{\overset{\displaystyle NH_2}{|}}{CH}-CH_3$

18.13 Propylamine (59 g/mole) has a boiling point of 48 °C, and ethylmethylamine (59 g/mole) has a boiling point of 37 °C. Butane (58 g/mole) has a much lower boiling point of −1 °C. Explain.

18.14 Assign the boiling point of 3 °C, 48 °C, or 97 °C to the appropriate compound: 1-propanol, propylamine, and trimethylamine.

18.15 Indicate if each of the following is soluble in water. Explain.
   a. $CH_3-CH_2-NH_2$
   b. $CH_3-\overset{\overset{\displaystyle H}{|}}{N}-CH_3$

c. $CH_3-CH_2-CH_2-\overset{\overset{\displaystyle CH_2-CH_2-CH_3}{|}}{\underset{\underset{\displaystyle NH_2}{|}}{N}}-CH_2-CH_2-CH_3$

   d. $CH_3-\overset{\overset{\displaystyle NH_2}{|}}{CH}-CH_2-CH_3$

18.16 Indicate if each of the following is soluble in water. Explain.
   a. $CH_3-CH_2-CH_2-NH_2$
   b. $CH_3-CH_2-CH_2-\overset{\overset{\displaystyle H}{|}}{N}-CH_2-CH_3$
   c. $CH_3-\overset{\overset{\displaystyle NH_2}{|}}{CH}-CH_3$
   d.

18.17 Write a balanced chemical equation for the dissociation of each of the following amines in water:
   a. methylamine   **b.** dimethylamine
   c. aniline

18.18 Write a balanced chemical equation for the dissociation of each of the following amines in water:
   a. diethylamine   **b.** propylamine
   c. N-methylaniline

18.19 Draw the condensed structural formula for the ammonium salt obtained when each of the amines in problem 18.17 reacts with HCl.

18.20 Draw the condensed structural formula for the ammonium salt obtained when each of the amines in problem 18.18 reacts with HCl.

℞ Clinical Applications

18.21 Novocain, a local anesthetic, is the ammonium salt of procaine.

Procaine

a. Draw the condensed structural formula for the ammonium salt (procaine hydrochloride) formed when procaine reacts with HCl. (*Hint*: The tertiary amine reacts with HCl.)
b. Why is procaine hydrochloride used rather than procaine?

18.22 Lidocaine (Xylocaine) is used as a local anesthetic and cardiac depressant.

Lidocaine (Xylocaine)

a. Draw the condensed structural formula for the ammonium salt formed when lidocaine reacts with HCl.
b. Why is the ammonium salt of lidocaine used rather than the amine?

18.3 Heterocyclic Amines

A **heterocyclic amine** is a cyclic organic compound that consists of a ring of five or six atoms, of which one or two are nitrogen atoms. Of the five-atom rings, the simplest one is pyrrolidine, which is a ring of four carbon atoms and one nitrogen atom, all with single bonds. Pyrrole is a five-atom ring with one nitrogen atom and two double bonds. Imidazole is a five-atom ring that contains two nitrogen atoms. Piperidine is a six-atom heterocyclic ring with a nitrogen atom. Some of the pungent aroma and taste of black pepper that we use to season our food is due to piperidine. Purine and pyrimidine rings are found in DNA and RNA. In purine, the structures of 6-atom pyrimidine and 5-atom imidazole are combined. Heterocyclic amines with two or three double bonds have aromatic properties similar to benzene.

5-Atom Heterocyclic Amines

Pyrrolidine

Pyrrole

Imidazole

6-Atom Heterocyclic Amines

Piperidine

Pyridine

Pyrimidine

Purine

The aroma of pepper is due to piperidine, a heterocyclic amine.

▶**SAMPLE PROBLEM 18.7 Heterocyclic Amines**

Identify the heterocyclic amines that are part of the structure of nicotine.

Nicotine

SOLUTION

Nicotine contains two heterocyclic rings. The 6-atom ring with one N atom and three double bonds is pyridine, and the 5-atom ring with one N atom and no double bonds is pyrrolidine. The N atom in the pyrrolidine ring is bonded to a methyl group ($-CH_3$).

STUDY CHECK 18.7

Sedamine is used as a sleep aid. Identify the heterocyclic amine that is part of the structure of sedamine.

Sedamine

ANSWER

piperidine

Alkaloids: Amines in Plants

Alkaloids are physiologically active nitrogen-containing compounds produced by plants. The term *alkaloid* refers to the "alkali-like" or basic characteristics we have seen for amines. Certain alkaloids are used in anesthetics, in antidepressants, and as stimulants, and many are habit forming.

As a stimulant, nicotine increases the level of adrenaline in the blood, which increases the heart rate and blood pressure. Nicotine is addictive because it activates pleasure centers in the brain. Nicotine has a simple alkaloid structure that includes a pyrrolidine ring. Coniine, which is obtained from poison hemlock, is an extremely toxic alkaloid that contains a piperidine ring.

Coniine, which causes respiratory paralysis, is a poisonous alkaloid from hemlock.

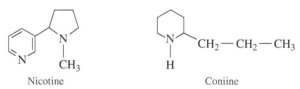

Nicotine   Coniine

Caffeine is a purine that is a central nervous system stimulant. Present in coffee, tea, soft drinks, energy drinks, chocolate, and cocoa, caffeine increases alertness, but it may cause nervousness and insomnia. Caffeine is also used in certain pain relievers to counteract the drowsiness caused by an antihistamine (see Figure 18.3).

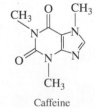

Caffeine

FIGURE 18.3 ▶ Caffeine is a stimulant found in coffee, tea, energy drinks, and chocolate.

◉ Why is caffeine an alkaloid?

Several alkaloids are used in medicine. Quinine, obtained from the bark of the cinchona tree, has been used to treat malaria since the 1600s. Atropine from nightshade (belladonna) is used in low concentrations to accelerate slow heart rates and to dilate the eyes during eye examinations.

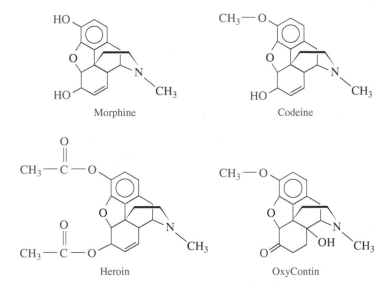

Quinine

Atropine

For many centuries, morphine and codeine, alkaloids found in the opium poppy plant, have been used as effective painkillers (see Figure 18.4). Codeine, which is structurally similar to morphine, is used in some prescription painkillers and cough syrups. Heroin, obtained by a chemical modification of morphine, is strongly addictive and is not used medically. The structure of the prescription drug OxyContin (oxycodone) used to relieve severe pain is similar to heroin. Today, there are an increasing number of deaths from Oxy-Contin abuse because its physiological effects are also similar to those of heroin.

Morphine

Codeine

Heroin

OxyContin

FIGURE 18.4 ▶ The green, unripe poppy seed capsule contains a milky sap (opium) that is the source of the alkaloids morphine and codeine.

◉ Where is the piperidine ring in the structures of morphine and codeine?

 Chemistry Link to **Health**

Synthesizing Drugs

One area of research in pharmacology is the synthesis of compounds that retain the anesthetic characteristic of naturally occurring alkaloids, such as cocaine and morphine, without the addictive side effects. For

example, cocaine is an effective anesthetic, but after taking it on a regular basis, the user can become addicted. Research chemists modified the structure of cocaine but kept the phenyl group and nitrogen atom. The synthetic products procaine and lidocaine retain the anesthetic qualities of the natural alkaloid without the addictive side effects.

The structure of morphine was also modified to make a synthetic alkaloid, meperidine, or Demerol, which acts as an effective painkiller.

Cocaine

Procaine (Novocain)

Lidocaine (Xylocaine)

Meperidine (Demerol)

QUESTIONS AND PROBLEMS

18.3 Heterocyclic Amines

LEARNING GOAL Identify heterocyclic amines; distinguish between the types of heterocyclic amines.

18.23 Name the heterocyclic amines in each of the following:

a.

b.

c.

18.24 Name the heterocyclic amines in each of the following:

a.

b.

c.

℞ **Clinical Applications**

18.25 Ritalin (methylphenidate) is a stimulant that may be prescribed for attention deficit hyperactivity disorder (ADHD). What is the heterocyclic amine in Ritalin?

Ritalin

18.26 Niacin, which is also known as vitamin B_3 and nicotinic acid, is found in many foods such as fish, beef, milk, and eggs. What is the heterocyclic amine in niacin?

Niacin

18.27 Low levels of serotonin in the brain appear to be associated with depressed states. What is the heterocyclic amine in serotonin?

Serotonin

18.28 Histamine causes inflammation and itchy skin in an allergic reaction. What is the heterocyclic amine in histamine?

Histamine

LEARNING GOAL

Describe the role of amines as neurotransmitters.

18.4 Neurotransmitters

A **neurotransmitter** is a chemical compound that transmits an impulse from a nerve cell (neuron) to a target cell such as another nerve cell, a muscle cell, or a gland cell. A typical neuron consists of a cell body and numerous filaments called *dendrites* at one end, and an axon that ends at the *axon terminal* at the opposite end. The axon terminals and the dendrites of other nerve cells form junctions called *synapses*. When an electrical signal reaches the axon terminal of a nerve cell, neurotransmitters are released into the synapse, which are taken up by the dendrites in nearby nerve cells. Thus, an alternating series of electrical impulses and chemical transmitters move information through a network of nerve cells in a very short period of time.

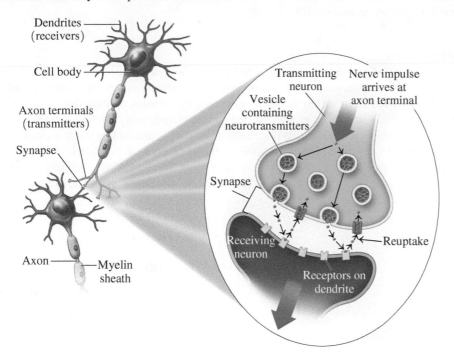

A nerve cell (neuron) consists of a cell body and filaments called axons and dendrites that form junctions (synapses) with nearby nerve cells to transmit nerve impulses.

Neurotransmitters at the Synapse

Within a nerve cell, a neurotransmitter is synthesized and stored in vesicles at the end of the axon terminal. There are many vesicles in a single filament, and each vesicle may contain several thousand molecules of a neurotransmitter. When a nerve impulse arrives at the nerve cell, it stimulates the vesicles to release the neurotransmitter into the synapse. The neurotransmitter molecules diffuse across the synapse to their receptor sites on the dendrites of another nerve cell. Neurotransmitters can be *excitatory*, which means they stimulate the receptors to send more nerve impulses, or *inhibitory*, which means they decrease the activity of the receptors. The binding of an excitatory neurotransmitter opens ion channels in nearby nerve cells. A flow of positive ions creates new electrical impulses that stimulate additional nerve cells to release the neurotransmitter from their vesicles into the synapse.

Termination of Neurotransmitter Action

Between nerve impulses, the neurotransmitters bound to the receptors are quickly removed to allow new signals to come from the adjacent nerve cells. The removal of neurotransmitters from the receptors can be done in different ways.

1. The neurotransmitter diffuses away from the synapse.
2. Enzymes in the receptors break down the neurotransmitter.
3. Reuptake returns the neurotransmitter to the vesicles where it is stored.

Amine Neurotransmitters

Neurotransmitters contain nitrogen atoms as amines and alkylammonium ions. Most are synthesized in a few steps from compounds such as amino acids obtained from our diets. The amino groups are usually ionized to form ammonium cations, and carboxyl groups are ionized to form carboxylate anions. Important amine neurotransmitters include acetylcholine, dopamine, norepinephrine (noradrenaline), epinephrine (adrenaline), serotonin, histamine, glutamate, and GABA.

Acetylcholine

Acetylcholine, the first neurotransmitter to be identified, communicates between the nervous system and the muscle, where it is involved in regulating muscle activation as well as learning and short-term memory. It is synthesized by forming an ester between choline and acetate, and is stored in the vesicles. When stimulated, acetylcholine is released into the synapse where it binds to receptors on the muscle cells and causes the muscles to contract. To enable continual nerve transmission, acetylcholine is quickly degraded by enzymes in the receptors that hydrolyze the ester bond. The loss of the acetylcholine at the receptors causes muscle cells to relax. The resulting choline and acetate are converted back to acetylcholine and stored in the vesicles.

$$CH_3-\overset{\overset{\displaystyle O}{\|}}{C}-O-CH_2-CH_2-\overset{\overset{\displaystyle CH_3}{|}}{\underset{\underset{\displaystyle CH_3}{|}}{\overset{+}{N}}}-CH_3 \xrightarrow{\text{Acetylcholinesterase}} CH_3-\overset{\overset{\displaystyle O}{\|}}{C}-O^- + HO-CH_2-CH_2-\overset{\overset{\displaystyle CH_3}{|}}{\underset{\underset{\displaystyle CH_3}{|}}{\overset{+}{N}}}-CH_3$$

Acetylcholine   Acetate   Choline

In older adults, a decrease in acetylcholine produces gaps in short-term memory. In Alzheimer's disease, the levels of acetylcholine may decrease by 90%, which causes severe loss of reasoning and motor function. Medications that are cholinesterase inhibitors such as Aricept are used to slow the breakdown of acetylcholine in order to maintain the acetylcholine levels in the brain.

Cholinesterase inhibitors, such as Aricept, slow the enzymatic breakdown of acetylcholine.

Donepezil hydrochloride (Aricept)

Nerve poisons such as Sarin, Soman, and Parathion bind to the acetylcholinesterase enzyme and inhibit its action. As a result, acetylcholine remains in the synapse and nerve transmissions stop. Because acetylcholine cannot be released, the muscles in the body cannot relax, and convulsions and respiratory failure soon occur.

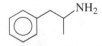

Amphetamine
(Benzedrine, Adderall)

Methamphetamine
(Methedrine)

Catecholamines

The word catecholamine refers to the catechol part (3,4-dihydroxyphenyl group) of these aromatic amines. The most important catecholamine neurotransmitters are dopamine, norepinephrine, and epinephrine, which are closely related in structure and all are synthesized from the amino acid tyrosine. In the diet, tyrosine is found in meats, nuts, eggs, and cheese.

Amphetamine and methamphetamine are synthetic central nervous system stimulants that increase the levels of excitatory catecholamine neurotransmitters particularly

Tyrosine

Catechol part
of structure

L-Dopa

Neurotransmitters dopamine, norepinephrine, and epinephrine
are synthesized from the amino acid tyrosine after it is converted
to L-dopa.

Dopamine

Norepinephrine (noradrenaline)

Epinephrine (adrenaline)

dopamine and norepinephrine. Amphetamine is used in the treatment of ADHD to improve
cognition and decrease hyperactivity.

Dopamine

Dopamine, which is produced in the nerve cells of the midbrain, works as a natural stimulant, to give us energy and feelings of enjoyment. It plays a role in controlling muscle movement, regulation of the sleep–wake cycle, and helps to improve cognition, attention, memory, and learning. High levels of dopamine may be involved in addictive behavior and schizophrenia. Cocaine and amphetamine block the reuptake of dopamine into the vesicles of the nerve cell. As a result, dopamine remains in the synapse longer. The addiction to cocaine may be a result of the extended exposure to high levels of dopamine in the synapses.

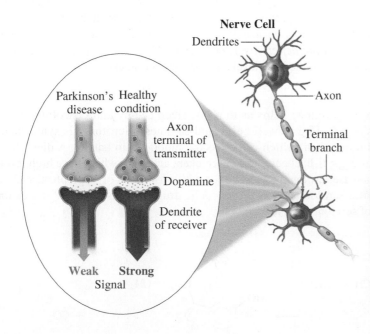

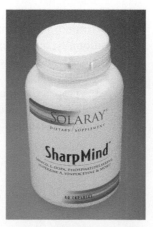

L-Dopa is used to increase
dopamine levels in the brain.

> **SAMPLE PROBLEM 18.8**
>
> Place the following in order of occurrence for nerve impulses:
>
> **a.** Neurotransmitters diffuse across synapse to receptors on dendrites.
> **b.** Neurotransmitters move away from receptors.
> **c.** An electrical signal reaches the axon terminal of a nerve cell.
> **d.** Reuptake moves neurotransmitters into the vesicles for storage.
> **e.** Vesicles release neurotransmitters into the synapse of nearby nerve cells.
> **f.** Neurotransmitters stimulate receptors to send new nerve impulse.
>
> **SOLUTION**
>
> **c, e, a, f, b, d**
>
> **STUDY CHECK 18.8**
>
> How does an excitatory neurotransmitter send a nerve impulse at the receptor?
>
> **ANSWER**
>
> When the neurotransmitter attaches to the receptor, ion channels open and positive ions flow to nearby nerve cells creating new electrical impulses.

In persons with Parkinson's disease, the midbrain nerve cells lose their ability to produce dopamine. As dopamine levels drop, there is a decrease in motor coordination, resulting in a slowing of movement and shuffling, rigidity of muscle, loss of cognition, and dementia. Although dopamine cannot cross the blood–brain barrier, persons with Parkinson's disease are given L-dopa, the precursor of dopamine, which does cross the blood–brain barrier.

Norepinephrine and Epinephrine

Norepinephrine (noradrenaline) and epinephrine (adrenaline) are hormonal neurotransmitters that play a role in sleep, attention and focus, and alertness. Epinephrine is synthesized from norepinephrine by the addition of a methyl group to the amine group. Norepinephrine (noradrenaline) and epinephrine (adrenaline) are normally produced in the adrenal glands, and are produced in large quantities when the stress of physical threat causes the fight-or-flight response. Then they cause an increase in blood pressure and heart rate, constrict blood vessels, dilate airways, and stimulate the breakdown of glycogen, which provides glucose and energy for the body. Because of its physiological effects, epinephrine is administered during cardiac arrest, and used as a bronchodilator during allergy or asthma attacks. As a neurotransmitter, low levels of norepinephrine as well as dopamine contribute to *attention deficit disorder* (ADD). Medications such as Ritalin or Dexedrine may be prescribed to increase levels of norepinephrine and dopamine.

Serotonin

Serotonin (5-hydroxytryptamine) helps us to relax, sleep deeply and peacefully, think rationally, and gives us a feeling of well-being and calmness. Serotonin is synthesized from the amino acid tryptophan, which can cross the blood–brain barrier. A diet which contains foods such as eggs, fish, cheese, turkey, chicken, and beef, which have high levels of tryptophan, will increase serotonin levels. Foods with a low level of tryptophan, such as whole wheat, will lower serotonin levels. Psychedelic drugs such as LSD and mescaline stimulate the action of serotonin at its receptors.

Tryptophan (amino acid) $\longrightarrow$ Serotonin $+ CO_2$

Low levels of serotonin in the brain may be associated with depression, anxiety disorders, obsessive–compulsive disorder, and eating disorders. Many antidepressant drugs, such as fluoxetine (Prozac) and paroxetine (Paxil), are selective serotonin reuptake inhibitors (SSRIs). When the reuptake of serotonin is slowed, it remains longer at the receptors, where it continues its action; the net effect is as if additional quantities of serotonin were taken.

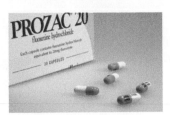

Prozac is one of the selective serotonin reuptake inhibitors (SSRIs) used to slow the reuptake of serotonin.

Fluoxetine hydrochloride (Prozac)

Paroxetine hydrochloride (Paxil)

Histamine

Histamine is synthesized in the nerve cells in the hypothalamus from the amino acid histidine, when a carboxylate group is converted to CO_2. Histamine is produced by the immune system in response to pathogens and invaders, or injury. When histamine combines with histamine receptors, it causes allergic reactions, which may include inflammation, watery eyes, itchy skin, and hay fever. Histamine can also cause smooth muscle constriction, such as the closing of the trachea in persons allergic to shellfish. Histamine is also stored and released in the cells of the stomach, where it stimulates acid production. Antihistamines, such as Benadryl, Zantac, and Tagamet, are used to block the histamine receptors and stop the allergic reactions.

Histidine $\xrightarrow{\text{Histidine decarboxylase}}$ Histamine $+ CO_2$

Histidine

Histamine

Glutamate

Glutamate is the most abundant neurotransmitter in the nervous system, where it is used to stimulate over 90% of the synapses. When glutamate binds to its receptor cells, it stimulates the synthesis of nitrogen oxide (NO), also a neurotransmitter in the brain. As NO reaches the transmitting nerve cells, more glutamate is released. Glutamate and NO are thought to be involved in learning and memory. Glutamate is used in many fast excitatory synapses in the brain and spinal cord. The reuptake of glutamate out of the synapse and back into the nerve cell occurs rapidly, which keeps glutamate levels low. If the reuptake of glutamate does not take place fast enough, a condition called *excitotoxicity* occurs in which excess glutamate at the receptors can destroy brain cells. In Lou Gehrig's disease (ALS), the production of an excessive amount of glutamate causes the degeneration of nerve cells in the spinal cord. As a result, a person with Lou Gehrig's disease suffers increasing weakness and muscular atrophy. When the reuptake of glutamate is too rapid, the levels of glutamate fall too low in the synapse, which may result in mental illness such as schizophrenia.

Glutamate

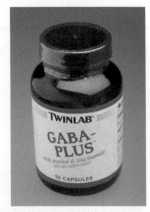

GABA is the major inhibitory neurotransmitter.

Gamma(γ)-Aminobutyric Acid or GABA

Gamma(γ)-aminobutyric acid or GABA, which is produced from glutamate, is the most common inhibitory neurotransmitter in the brain. GABA produces a calming effect and reduces anxiety by inhibiting the ability of nerve cells to send electrical signals to nearby nerve cells. It is involved in the regulation of muscle tone, sleep, and anxiety. GABA can be obtained as a nutritional supplement. Medications such as benzodiazepines, and barbiturates such as phenobarbital, are used to increase GABA levels at the GABA receptors. Alcohol, sedatives, and tranquilizers increase the inhibitory effects of GABA. Caffeine decreases the GABA levels in the synapses, leading to conditions of anxiety and sleep problems.

Table 18.2 summarizes the properties and functions of selected neurotransmitters we have discussed.

TABLE 18.2 Selected Neurotransmitters

Amine Transmitters	Synthesized from	Site of Synthesis	Function	Effect Enhanced by
Acetylcholine	Acetyl CoA and choline	Central nervous system	Excitatory: regulates muscle activation, learning, and short-term memory	Nicotine
Dopamine	Tyrosine	Central nervous system	Excitatory and inhibitory: regulates muscle movement, cognition, sleep, mood, and learning; deficiency leads to Parkinson's disease and schizophrenia	L-dopa, amphetamines, cocaine
Norepinephrine	Tyrosine	Central nervous system	Excitatory and inhibitory: sleep, focus, and alertness	Ritalin, Dexedrine
Epinephrine	Tyrosine	Adrenal glands	Excitatory: plays a role in sleep and being alert, and is involved in the fight-or-flight response	Ritalin, Dexedrine
Serotonin	Tryptophan	Central nervous system	Inhibitory: regulates anxiety, eating, mood, sleep, learning, and memory	LSD; Prozac and Paxil block its action to relieve anxiety
Histamine	Histidine	Central nervous system: hypothalamus	Inhibitory: involved in allergic reactions, inflammation, and hay fever	Antihistamines
Amino Acid Transmitters				
Glutamate		Central nervous system: spinal cord	Excitatory: involved in learning and memory; main excitatory neurotransmitter in brain	Alcohol
GABA	Glutamate	Central nervous system: brain, hypothalamus	Inhibitory: regulates muscle tone, sleep, and anxiety	Alcohol, sedatives, tranquilizers; synthesis blocked by antianxiety drugs (benzodiazepines); caffeine decreases GABA levels in synapse

QUESTIONS AND PROBLEMS

18.4 Neurotransmitters

LEARNING GOAL Describe the role of amines as neurotransmitters.

18.29 What is a neurotransmitter?

18.30 Where are the neurotransmitters stored in a neuron?

18.31 When is a neurotransmitter released into the synapse?

18.32 What happens to a neurotransmitter once it is in the synapse?

18.33 Why is it important to remove a neurotransmitter from its receptor?

18.34 What are three ways in which a neurotransmitter can be separated from a receptor?

℞ Clinical Applications

18.35 What is the role of acetylcholine?

18.36 What are some physiological effects of low levels of acetylcholine?

18.37 What is the function of dopamine in the body?

18.38 What are some physiological effects of low levels of dopamine?

18.39 What is the function of serotonin in the body?

18.40 What are the physiological effects of low serotonin?

18.41 What is the function of histamine in the body?

18.42 How do antihistamines stop the action of histamine?

18.43 Why is it important that the levels of glutamate in the synapse remain low?

18.44 What happens if there is an excess of glutamate in the synapse?

18.45 What is the function of GABA in the body?

18.46 What is the effect of caffeine on GABA levels?

18.5 Amides

The **amides** are derivatives of carboxylic acids in which an amino group replaces the hydroxyl group.

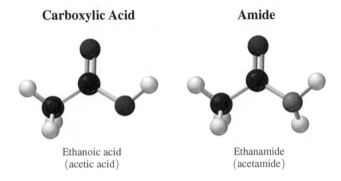

Carboxylic Acid

Ethanoic acid
(acetic acid)

Amide

Ethanamide
(acetamide)

Preparation of Amides

An amide is produced in a reaction called **amidation**, or *condensation*, in which a carboxylic acid reacts with ammonia or a primary (1°) or secondary (2°) amine. A molecule of water is eliminated, and the fragments of the carboxylic acid and amine molecules join to form the amide, much like the formation of an ester. Because a tertiary (3°) amine does not contain a hydrogen atom, it cannot undergo amidation.

Amide bond

$$CH_3-CH_2-\overset{\overset{\displaystyle O}{\|}}{C}-OH \ + \ H-\overset{\overset{\displaystyle H}{|}}{N}-H \ \xrightarrow{\text{Heat}} \ CH_3-CH_2-\overset{\overset{\displaystyle O}{\|}}{C}-\overset{\overset{\displaystyle H}{|}}{N}-H \ + \ H_2O$$

Propanoic acid (propionic acid) · Ammonia · Propanamide (propionamide)

$$CH_3-CH_2-\overset{\overset{\displaystyle O}{\|}}{C}-OH \ + \ H-\overset{\overset{\displaystyle H}{|}}{N}-CH_3 \ \xrightarrow{\text{Heat}} \ CH_3-CH_2-\overset{\overset{\displaystyle O}{\|}}{C}-\overset{\overset{\displaystyle H}{|}}{N}-CH_3 \ + \ H_2O$$

Propanoic acid (propionic acid) · Methylamine · *N*-Methylpropanamide (*N*-methylpropionamide)

▸ **SAMPLE PROBLEM 18.9 Amidation**

Draw the condensed structural formula for the amide product in each of the following reactions:

a.

$$\underset{\text{}}{\text{C}_6\text{H}_5}-\overset{\overset{\displaystyle O}{\|}}{C}-OH \ + \ NH_3 \ \xrightarrow{\text{Heat}}$$

b. $CH_3-\overset{\overset{\displaystyle O}{\|}}{C}-OH \ + \ H_2N-CH_2-CH_3 \ \xrightarrow{\text{Heat}}$

SOLUTION

The condensed structural formula for the amide product can be drawn by attaching the carbonyl group from the acid to the nitrogen atom of the amine. The —OH group is removed from the acid and —H from the amine to form water.

a.

$$\underset{\text{NH}_2}{\overset{\displaystyle \overset{\text{O}}{\parallel}}{\bigcirc\hspace{-0.6em}\text{C}}}$$

b. $CH_3 - \overset{\displaystyle \overset{\text{O}}{\parallel}}{C} - \overset{\displaystyle \overset{\text{H}}{|}}{N} - CH_2 - CH_3$

STUDY CHECK 18.9

Draw the condensed structural formulas for the carboxylic acid and amine needed to prepare the following amide. (*Hint*: Separate the N and C=O of the amide group, and add —H and —OH to give the original amine and carboxylic acid.)

$$H - \overset{\displaystyle \overset{\text{O}}{\parallel}}{C} - \overset{\displaystyle \overset{\text{CH}_3}{|}}{N} - CH_3$$

ANSWER

$$H - \overset{\displaystyle \overset{\text{O}}{\parallel}}{C} - OH \quad \text{and} \quad H - \overset{\displaystyle \overset{\text{CH}_3}{|}}{N} - CH_3$$

Naming Amides

In the IUPAC and common names for amides, the *oic acid* or *ic acid* from the corresponding carboxylic acid name is replaced with *amide*. We can diagram the name of an amide in the following way:

From butanoic acid (butyric acid) ⟶   From ammonia

$$CH_3 - CH_2 - CH_2 - \overset{\displaystyle \overset{\text{O}}{\parallel}}{C} \!\mid\! NH_2$$

IUPAC   Butanamide
Common   Butyramide

$$H - \overset{\displaystyle \overset{\text{O}}{\parallel}}{C} - NH_2$$
Methanamide
(formamide)

$$CH_3 - \overset{\displaystyle \overset{\text{O}}{\parallel}}{C} - NH_2$$
Ethanamide
(acetamide)

$$\underset{\text{NH}_2}{\overset{\displaystyle \overset{\text{O}}{\parallel}}{\bigcirc\hspace{-0.6em}\text{C}}}$$
Benzamide

When alkyl groups are attached to the nitrogen atom, the prefix *N-* or *N, N-* precedes the name of the amide, depending on whether there are one or two groups. We can diagram the name of a substituted amide in the following way:

From butanoic acid (butyric acid) ⟶   From dimethylamine

$$CH_3 - CH_2 - CH_2 - \overset{\displaystyle \overset{\text{O}}{\parallel}}{C} \!\mid\! \overset{\displaystyle \overset{\text{CH}_3}{|}}{N} - CH_3$$

IUPAC   *N,N*-Dimethylbutanamide
Common   *N,N*-Dimethylbutyramide

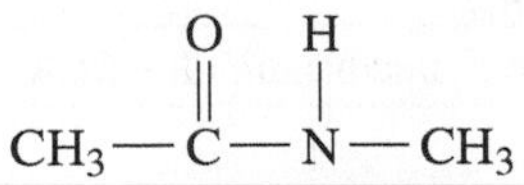

O H
‖ |
$CH_3-C-N-CH_3$
N-Methylethanamide
(*N*-methylacetamide)

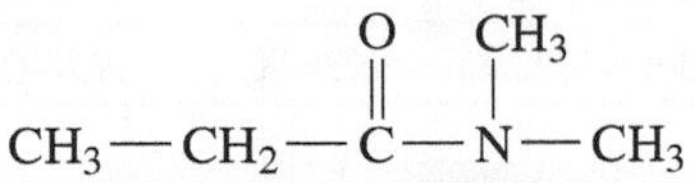

O CH_3
‖ |
$CH_3-CH_2-C-N-CH_3$
N,N-Dimethylpropanamide
(*N,N*-dimethylpropionamide)

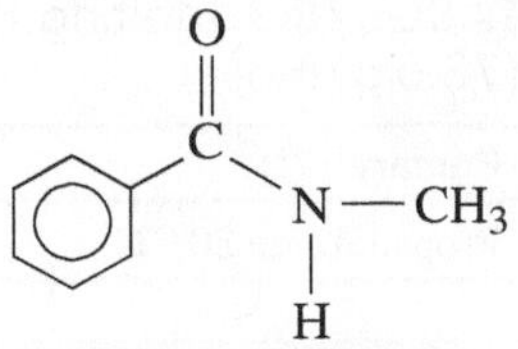

O
‖
C—N—CH_3
|
H
N-Methylbenzamide

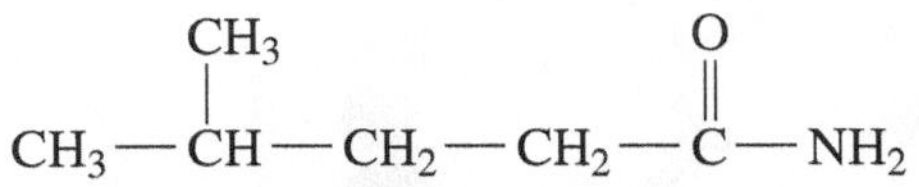

CH_3
|
$CH_3-CH-CH_2-CH_2-C-NH_2$
O
‖
4-Methylpentanamide

▶ **SAMPLE PROBLEM 18.10 Naming Amides**

Give the IUPAC name for the following amide:

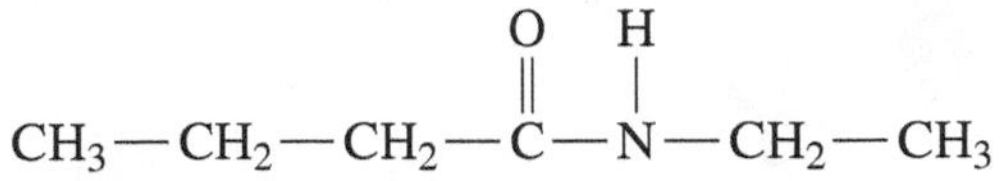

O H
‖ |
$CH_3-CH_2-CH_2-C-N-CH_2-CH_3$

SOLUTION

ANALYZE THE PROBLEM	Given	Need
	amide	IUPAC name

STEP 1 Replace *oic acid* (IUPAC) or *ic acid* (common) in the carboxyl name with *amide*.

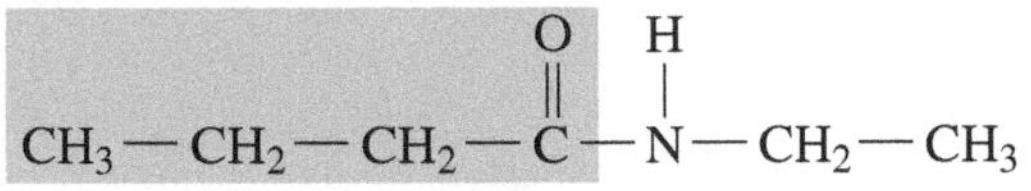

$CH_3-CH_2-CH_2-C-N-CH_2-CH_3$ butanamide

STEP 2 Name each substituent on the N atom using the prefix *N-* and the alkyl name.

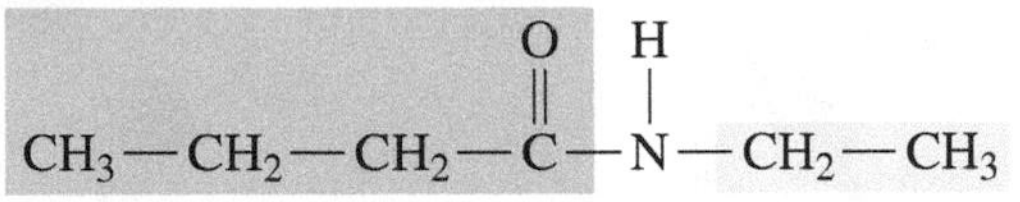

$CH_3-CH_2-CH_2-C-N-CH_2-CH_3$ *N*-ethyl butanamide

STUDY CHECK 18.10

Draw the condensed structural formula for *N,N*-dimethylbenzamide.

ANSWER

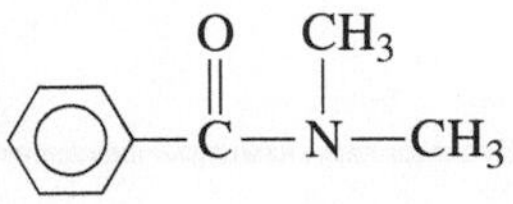

O CH_3
‖ |
C—N—CH_3

> **Guide to Naming Amides**
>
> **STEP 1**
> Replace *oic acid* (IUPAC) or *ic acid* (common) in the carboxyl name with *amide*.
>
> **STEP 2**
> Name each substituent on the N atom using the prefix *N-* and the alkyl name.

Physical Properties of Amides

The amides do not have the properties of bases that we saw for the amines. Only methanamide is a liquid at room temperature, while the other amides are solids. For primary (1°) amides, the —NH_2 group can form more hydrogen bonds, which gives primary amides the highest melting points. The melting points of the secondary (2°) amides are lower because they form fewer hydrogen bonds. Because tertiary (3°) amides cannot form hydrogen bonds, they have the lowest melting points (see Table 18.3).

TABLE 18.3 Melting Points of Selected Amides with the Same Molar Mass (73.0 g/mole)

Primary (1°)	Secondary (2°)	Tertiary (3°)
Propanamide 80. °C	*N*-Methylethanamide 28 °C	*N,N*-Dimethylmethanamide −61 °C

Melting Point Decreases →

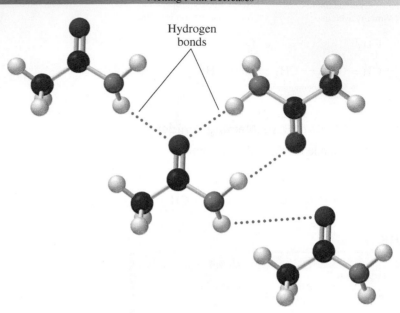

Hydrogen bonding between molecules of a primary amide.

The amides with one to five carbon atoms are soluble in water because they can hydrogen bond with water molecules.

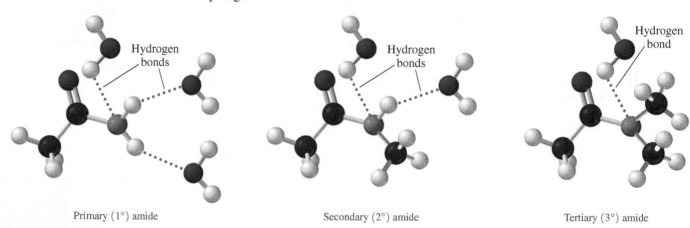

Primary (1°) amide

Secondary (2°) amide

Tertiary (3°) amide

In water, primary amides form more hydrogen bonds than secondary and tertiary amides.

♡ Chemistry Link to **Health**

Amides in Health and Medicine

The simplest natural amide is urea, an end product of protein metabolism in the body. The kidneys remove urea from the blood and excrete it in urine. If the kidneys malfunction, urea is not removed and builds to a toxic level, a condition called *uremia*. Urea is also used as a component of fertilizer to increase nitrogen in the soil.

Synthetic amides are used as substitutes for sugar. Saccharin is a very powerful sweetener and is used as a sugar substitute. The sweetener aspartame is made from two amino acids, aspartic acid and phenylalanine, joined by an amide bond.

$$H_2N - \overset{\overset{\displaystyle O}{\|}}{C} - NH_2$$

Urea

Saccharin

Amides are found in synthetic sweeteners, such as aspartame, and pain relievers, such as acetaminophen.

(Luminal), pentobarbital (Nembutal), and secobarbital (Seconal). Other amides, such as meprobamate and diazepam, act as sedatives and tranquilizers.

Phenobarbital
(Luminal)

Pentobarbital
(Nembutal)

Aspartic acid   Phenylalanine   Methyl ester

Aspartame

The compounds phenacetin and acetaminophen, which is used in Tylenol, reduce fever and pain, but they have little anti-inflammatory effect.

$CH_3—CH_2—O—$〈 〉$—N—C—CH_3$
with H and O

Phenacetin

Secobarbital
(Seconal)

$H_2N—C—O—CH_2—C—CH_2—O—C—NH_2$
with O, CH₃, and CH₂—CH₂—CH₃

Meprobamate
(Miltown)

$HO—$〈 〉$—N—C—CH_3$
with H and O

Acetaminophen

Many barbiturates are cyclic amides of barbituric acid that act as sedatives in small dosages or sleep inducers in larger dosages. They are often habit forming. Barbiturate drugs include phenobarbital

Diazepam
(Valium)

QUESTIONS AND PROBLEMS

18.5 Amides

LEARNING GOAL Draw the amide product from amidation, and give the IUPAC and common names.

18.47 Draw the condensed structural formula for the amide formed in each of the following reactions:

a. $CH_3—C—OH + NH_3 \xrightarrow{Heat}$
with O

b. $CH_3—C—OH + H_2N—CH_2—CH_3 \xrightarrow{Heat}$
with O

c. 〈 〉$—C—OH + H_2N—CH_2—CH_2—CH_3 \xrightarrow{Heat}$
with O

18.48 Draw the condensed structural formula for the amide formed in each of the following reactions:

a. $CH_3—CH_2—CH_2—CH_2—C—OH + NH_3 \xrightarrow{Heat}$
with O

b. $CH_3—CH—C—OH + H_2N—CH_2—CH_3 \xrightarrow{Heat}$
with CH₃ and O

c. $CH_3—CH_2—C—OH + H_2N—$〈 〉$\xrightarrow{Heat}$
with O

18.49 Give the IUPAC and common names (if any) for each of the following amides:

a. $CH_3-\overset{\overset{O}{\|}}{C}-\overset{\overset{H}{|}}{N}-CH_3$

b. (structure with) $\overset{O}{\|}$ ... NH_2

c. $H-\overset{\overset{O}{\|}}{C}-NH_2$

d. (benzene ring)$-\overset{\overset{O}{\|}}{C}-\overset{\overset{H}{|}}{N}-CH_3$

18.50 Give the IUPAC and common names (if any) for each of the following amides:

a. $CH_3-CH_2-\overset{\overset{O}{\|}}{C}-\overset{\overset{H}{|}}{N}-CH_2-CH_3$

b. (structure with) $\overset{O}{\|}$ ... NH_2

c. $CH_3-\overset{\overset{O}{\|}}{C}-\overset{\overset{CH_3}{|}}{N}-CH_2-CH_2-CH_3$

d. (benzene ring)$-\overset{\overset{O}{\|}}{C}-\overset{\overset{CH_2-CH_3}{|}}{N}-CH_2-CH_3$

18.51 Draw the condensed structural formula for each of the following amides:
a. propionamide
b. pentanamide
c. N-ethylbenzamide
d. N-ethylbutyramide

18.52 Draw the condensed structural formula for each of the following amides:
a. N-ethyl-N-methylbenzamide
b. 3-methylbutanamide
c. hexanamide
d. N-propylpentanamide

18.53 For each of the following pairs, identify the compound that has the higher melting point. Explain.
a. ethanamide or N-methylethanamide
b. butane or propionamide
c. N,N-dimethylpropanamide or N-methylpropanamide

18.54 For each of the following pairs, identify the compound that has the higher melting point. Explain.
a. propane or ethanamide
b. N-methylethanamide or propanamide
c. N-ethylethanamide or N,N-dimethylethanamide

18.6 Hydrolysis of Amides

In a reverse reaction of amidation, **hydrolysis** occurs when water and an acid or a base split an amide. In acid hydrolysis of an amide, the products are the carboxylic acid and the ammonium salt. In base hydrolysis, the products are the carboxylate salt and the amine or ammonia.

Acid Hydrolysis of Amides

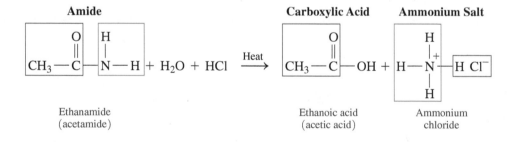

Amide		Carboxylic Acid	Ammonium Salt
Ethanamide (acetamide)		Ethanoic acid (acetic acid)	Ammonium chloride

Base Hydrolysis of Amides

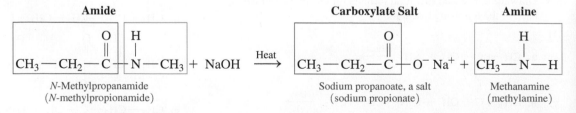

N-Methylpropanamide (N-methylpropionamide)   Sodium propanoate, a salt (sodium propionate)   Methanamine (methylamine)

▶ **SAMPLE PROBLEM 18.11 Hydrolysis of Amides**

Draw the condensed structural formulas and give the IUPAC names for the products of the hydrolysis of *N*-methylpentanamide with NaOH.

SOLUTION

	Given	Need
ANALYZE THE PROBLEM	hydrolysis of *N*-methylpentanamide with NaOH	products, condensed structural formulas, IUPAC names

In hydrolysis, the amide bond is broken between the carboxyl carbon atom and the nitrogen atom. When NaOH is used, the products are the carboxylate salt and an amine.

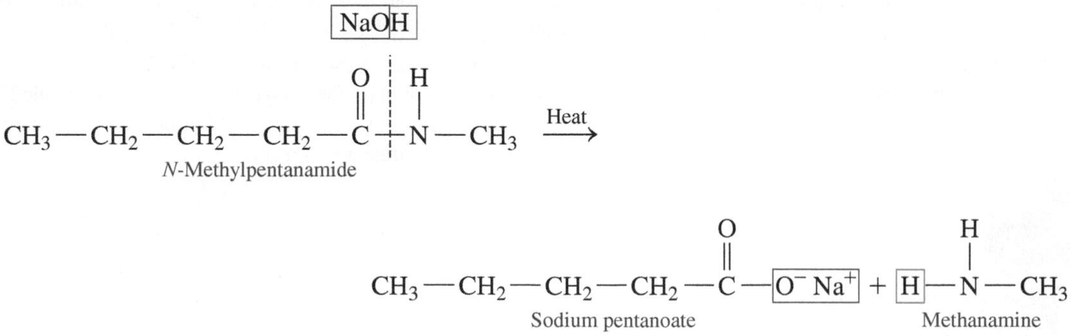

$$\boxed{NaOH}$$

$$CH_3-CH_2-CH_2-CH_2-\overset{\overset{O}{\|}}{C} \vdots \overset{\overset{H}{|}}{N}-CH_3 \xrightarrow{Heat}$$

N-Methylpentanamide

$$CH_3-CH_2-CH_2-CH_2-\overset{\overset{O}{\|}}{C}-\boxed{O^-Na^+} + \boxed{H}-\overset{\overset{H}{|}}{N}-CH_3$$

Sodium pentanoate   Methanamine

STUDY CHECK 18.11

Draw the condensed structural formulas for the products obtained from the hydrolysis of *N*-methylbutyramide with HBr.

ANSWER

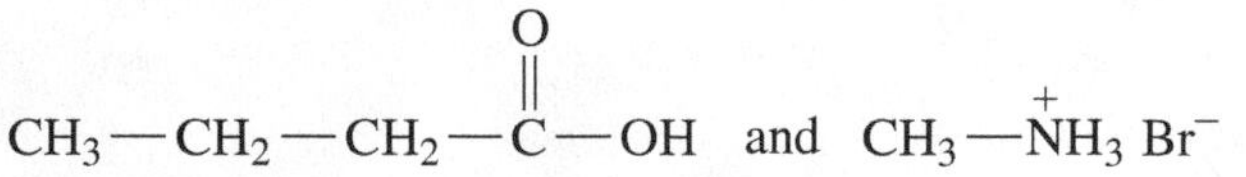

$$CH_3-CH_2-CH_2-\overset{\overset{O}{\|}}{C}-OH \text{ and } CH_3-\overset{+}{N}H_3\ Br^-$$

QUESTIONS AND PROBLEMS

18.6 Hydrolysis of Amides

LEARNING GOAL Write balanced chemical equations for the hydrolysis of amides.

18.55 Draw the condensed structural formulas for the products from the hydrolysis of each of the following with HCl:

a. 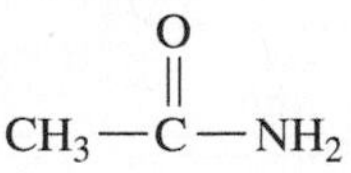 $CH_3-\overset{\overset{O}{\|}}{C}-NH_2$

b. $CH_3-CH_2-\overset{\overset{O}{\|}}{C}-NH_2$

c. $CH_3-CH_2-CH_2-\overset{\overset{O}{\|}}{C}-\overset{\overset{H}{|}}{N}-CH_3$

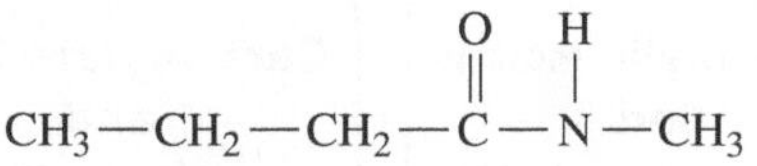

d. 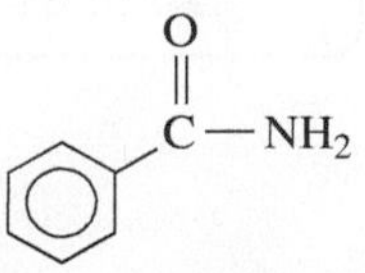 $\overset{\overset{O}{\|}}{\underset{\bigcirc}{C}}-NH_2$

18.56 Draw the condensed structural formulas for the products from the hydrolysis of each of the following with NaOH:

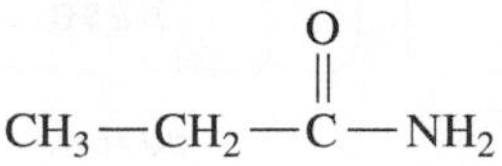

a. 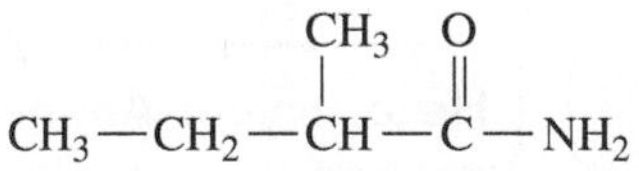 $CH_3-CH_2-\overset{\overset{CH_3}{|}}{CH}-\overset{\overset{O}{\|}}{C}-NH_2$

b. $CH_3-CH_2-CH_2-\overset{\overset{O}{\|}}{C}-\overset{\overset{CH_2-CH_3}{|}}{N}-CH_2-CH_3$

c. $\overset{\bigcirc}{}-\overset{\overset{O}{\|}}{C}-\overset{\overset{CH_3}{|}}{N}-CH_2-CH_2-CH_2-CH_3$

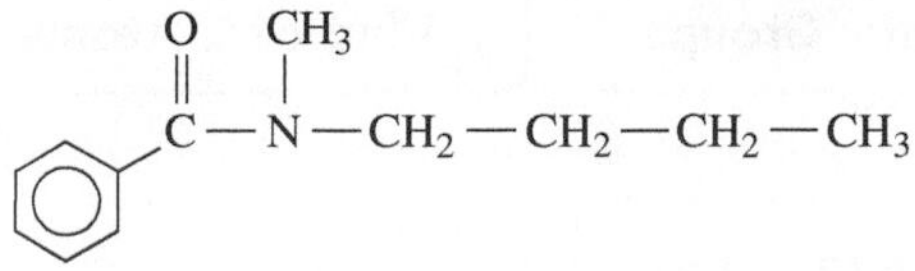

d. 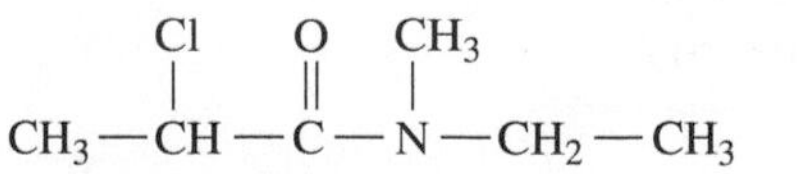 $CH_3-\overset{\overset{Cl}{|}}{CH}-\overset{\overset{O}{\|}}{C}-\overset{\overset{CH_3}{|}}{N}-CH_2-CH_3$

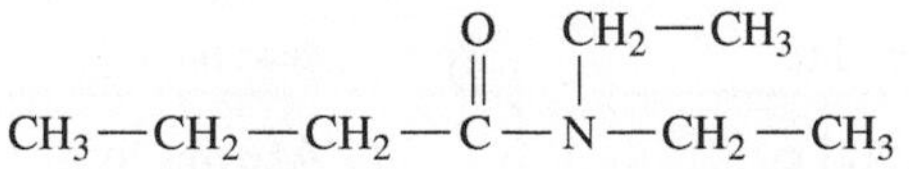

Clinical Update
Testing Soil and Water Samples for Chemicals

Lance, an environmental health practitioner, returned to the sheep ranch to obtain more soil and water samples. When he arrived at the ranch, he noticed that the owners were spraying the sheep because they had infestation of flies and maggots. Lance was told that the insecticide they were spraying on the sheep was called dicyclanil, a potent insect growth regulator. Lance was also informed that the sheep were being treated with enrofloxacin to counteract a respiratory infection.

Because high levels of these chemicals could be hazardous if they exceed acceptable environmental standards, Lance collected samples of soil and water to test for contaminants or breakdown products to evaluate in the laboratory. He will send the test results to the rancher,

A soil bag is filled with soil from areas where sheep were sprayed with dicyclanil.

who will use those results to adjust the levels of the drugs, order protective equipment, and do a cleanup, if necessary.

℞ Clinical Applications

18.57 Name the functional groups in dicyclanil. Identify the heterocyclic amine in dicyclanil.

18.58 Name the functional groups in enrofloxacin.

18.59 The recommended application for dicyclanil for an adult sheep is 65 mg/kg of body mass. If dicyclanil is supplied in a spray with a concentration of 50. mg/mL, how many milliliters of the spray are required to treat a 70.-kg adult sheep?

18.60 The recommended dose for enrofloxacin for sheep is 30. mg/kg of body mass for 5 days. Enrofloxacin is supplied in 50.-mL vials with a concentration of 100. mg/mL. How many vials are needed to treat a 64-kg sheep for 5 days?

Dicyclanil

Enrofloxacin

CONCEPT MAP

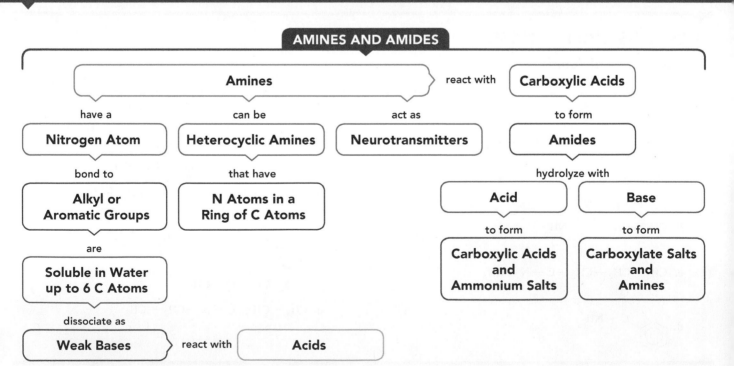

AMINES AND AMIDES

Amines —react with→ **Carboxylic Acids**

have a → **Nitrogen Atom**

can be → **Heterocyclic Amines**

act as → **Neurotransmitters**

to form → **Amides**

bond to → **Alkyl or Aromatic Groups**

that have → **N Atoms in a Ring of C Atoms**

hydrolyze with → **Acid** / **Base**

are → **Soluble in Water up to 6 C Atoms**

Acid — to form → **Carboxylic Acids and Ammonium Salts**

Base — to form → **Carboxylate Salts and Amines**

dissociate as → **Weak Bases** —react with→ **Acids**

CHAPTER REVIEW

18.1 Amines
LEARNING GOAL Name amines using IUPAC and common names; draw the condensed or line-angle structural formulas given the names. Classify amines as primary (1°), secondary (2°), or tertiary (3°).

Dimethylamine

- In the IUPAC system, name the longest carbon chain bonded to the N atom by replacing the *e* of its alkane name with *amine*. Groups attached to the nitrogen atom use the *N-* prefix.
- When other functional groups are present, the —NH_2 is named as an amino group.
- In the common names of simple amines, the alkyl groups are listed alphabetically followed by *amine*.
- A nitrogen atom attached to one, two, or three alkyl or aromatic groups forms a primary (1°), secondary (2°), or tertiary (3°) amine.

18.2 Properties of Amines
LEARNING GOAL Describe the boiling points and solubility of amines; write equations for the dissociation and neutralization of amines.

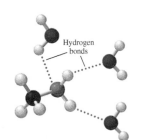
Hydrogen bonds

- Primary and secondary amines form hydrogen bonds, which make their boiling points higher than those of alkanes of similar mass, but lower than those of alcohols.
- Amines with up to six carbon atoms are soluble in water.
- In water, amines act as weak bases because the nitrogen atom accepts H^+ a proton from water to produce ammonium and hydroxide ions.
- When amines react with acids, they form ammonium salts. As ionic compounds, ammonium salts are solids, soluble in water, and odorless.
- Quaternary (4°) ammonium salts contain four carbon groups bonded to the nitrogen atom.

18.3 Heterocyclic Amines
LEARNING GOAL Identify heterocyclic amines; distinguish between the types of heterocyclic amines.

- Heterocyclic amines are cyclic organic compounds that contain one or more nitrogen atoms in the ring.

- Heterocyclic amines typically consist of five or six atoms and one or more nitrogen atoms.
- Many heterocyclic compounds are known for their physiological activity.
- Alkaloids such as caffeine and nicotine are physiologically active amines derived from plants.

18.4 Neurotransmitters
LEARNING GOAL Describe the role of amines as neurotransmitters.

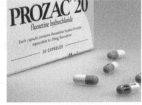

- Neurotransmitters are chemicals that transfer a signal between nerve cells.

18.5 Amides
LEARNING GOAL Draw the amide product from amidation, and give their IUPAC and common names.

Ethanamide (acetamide)

- Amides are derivatives of carboxylic acids in which the hydroxyl group is replaced by —NH_2 or a primary or secondary amine group.
- Amides are formed when carboxylic acids react with ammonia or primary or secondary amines in the presence of heat.
- Amides are named by replacing the *oic acid* or *ic acid* from the carboxylic acid name with *amide*. Any carbon group attached to the nitrogen atom is named using the *N-* prefix.

18.6 Hydrolysis of Amides
LEARNING GOAL Write balanced chemical equations for the hydrolysis of amides.

$$CH_3-\overset{\overset{\displaystyle O}{\|}}{C}-NH_2 + H_2O + HCl \longrightarrow CH_3-\overset{\overset{\displaystyle O}{\|}}{C}-OH + NH_4^+Cl^-$$

Ethanamide (acetamide)   Ethanoic acid (acetic acid)   Ammonium chloride

- Hydrolysis of an amide by an acid produces a carboxylic acid and an ammonium salt.
- Hydrolysis of an amide by a base produces the carboxylate salt and an amine.

SUMMARY OF NAMING

Family	Structure	IUPAC Name	Common Name
Amine	$CH_3-CH_2-NH_2$	Ethanamine	Ethylamine
	$CH_3-CH_2-NH-CH_3$	*N*-Methylethanamine	Ethylmethylamine
Ammonium salt	$CH_3-CH_2-\overset{+}{N}H_3\,Cl^-$	Ethylammonium chloride	Ethylammonium chloride
Amide	$CH_3-\overset{\overset{\displaystyle O}{\|}}{C}-NH_2$	Ethanamide	Acetamide

SUMMARY OF REACTIONS

The chapter sections to review are shown after the name of the reaction.

Dissociation of an Amine in Water (18.2)

$$CH_3-\underset{\underset{H}{|}}{\overset{\overset{H}{|}}{N}} + H_2O \rightleftharpoons CH_3-\underset{\underset{H}{|}}{\overset{\overset{H}{|}}{\overset{+}{N}}}-H + OH^-$$

Methylamine   Methylammonium   Hydroxide
                              ion   ion

Neutralization of an Amine (18.2)

$$CH_3-\underset{\underset{H}{|}}{\overset{\overset{H}{|}}{N}} + HCl \longrightarrow CH_3-\underset{\underset{H}{|}}{\overset{\overset{H}{|}}{\overset{+}{N}}}-H\ Cl^-$$

Methylamine   Methylammonium chloride

Amidation: Carboxylic Acid and an Amine (18.5)

$$CH_3-CH_2-\overset{\overset{O}{\|}}{C}-OH + H-\overset{\overset{H}{|}}{N}-H \xrightarrow{Heat} CH_3-CH_2-\overset{\overset{O}{\|}}{C}-\overset{\overset{H}{|}}{N}-H + H_2O$$

Propanoic acid   Ammonia   Propanamide
(propionic acid)   (propionamide)

$$CH_3-CH_2-\overset{\overset{O}{\|}}{C}-OH + H-\overset{\overset{H}{|}}{N}-CH_3 \xrightarrow{Heat} CH_3-CH_2-\overset{\overset{O}{\|}}{C}-\overset{\overset{H}{|}}{N}-CH_3 + H_2O$$

Propanoic acid   Methanamine   *N*-Methylpropanamide
(propionic acid)   (methylamine)   (*N*-methylpropionamide)

Acid Hydrolysis of an Amide (18.6)

$$CH_3-\overset{\overset{O}{\|}}{C}-NH_2 + H_2O + HCl \xrightarrow{Heat} CH_3-\overset{\overset{O}{\|}}{C}-OH + NH_4^+\ Cl^-$$

Ethanamide   Ethanoic acid   Ammonium
(acetamide)   (acetic acid)   chloride

Base Hydrolysis of an Amide (18.6)

$$CH_3-CH_2-\overset{\overset{O}{\|}}{C}-\overset{\overset{H}{|}}{N}-CH_3 + NaOH \xrightarrow{Heat} CH_3-CH_2-\overset{\overset{O}{\|}}{C}-O^-\ Na^+ + H_2N-CH_3$$

N-Methylpropanamide   Sodium propanoate   Methanamine
(*N*-methylpropionamide)   (sodium propionate)   (methylamine)

KEY TERMS

alkaloid An amine having physiological activity that is produced in plants.

amidation The formation of an amide from a carboxylic acid and ammonia or an amine.

amide An organic compound containing the carbonyl group attached to an amino group or a substituted nitrogen atom.

amine An organic compound containing a nitrogen atom attached to one, two, or three alkyl or aromatic groups.

ammonium salt An ionic compound produced from an amine and an acid.

heterocyclic amine A cyclic organic compound that contains one or more nitrogen atoms in the ring.

hydrolysis The splitting of a molecule by the addition of water. Amides yield the corresponding carboxylic acid and amine, or their salts.

neurotransmitter A chemical compound that transmits an impulse from a nerve cell (neuron) to a target cell such as another nerve cell, a muscle cell, or a gland cell.

quaternary ammonium salt An ammonium salt in which the nitrogen atom is bonded to four carbon groups.

⚛ CORE CHEMISTRY SKILLS

The chapter section containing each Core Chemistry Skill is shown in parentheses at the end of each heading.

Forming Amides (18.5)

- Amides are formed when carboxylic acids react with ammonia or primary or secondary amines in the presence of heat.

Example: Draw the condensed structural formula for the amide product of the reaction of 3-methylbutanoic acid and ethylamine.

Answer:

$$CH_3-\overset{\overset{\displaystyle CH_3}{|}}{CH}-CH_2-\overset{\overset{\displaystyle O}{\|}}{C}-\overset{\overset{\displaystyle H}{|}}{N}-CH_2-CH_3$$

Hydrolyzing Amides (18.6)

- An amide undergoes acid hydrolysis to produce a carboxylic acid and an ammonium salt.

- An amide undergoes base hydrolysis to produce the carboxylate salt and an amine.

Example: Draw the condensed structural formulas for the products from the **(a)** acid (HCl) and **(b)** base (NaOH) hydrolysis of *N*-ethylbutanamide.

Answer:

a. $CH_3-CH_2-CH_2-\overset{\overset{\displaystyle O}{\|}}{C}-OH + CH_3-CH_2-\overset{+}{N}H_3\ Cl^-$

b. $CH_3-CH_2-CH_2-\overset{\overset{\displaystyle O}{\|}}{C}-O^-\ Na^+ + CH_3-CH_2-NH_2$

UNDERSTANDING THE CONCEPTS

The chapter sections to review are shown in parentheses at the end of each question.

℞ Clinical Applications

18.61 The sweetener aspartame is made from two amino acids: aspartic acid and phenylalanine. Identify the functional groups in aspartame. (16.1, 16.3, 18.2, 18.5)

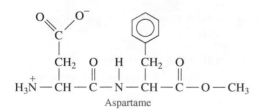

Aspartame

18.62 Some aspirin substitutes contain phenacetin to reduce fever. Identify the functional groups in phenacetin. (13.2, 18.5)

$$CH_3-CH_2-O-\bigcirc-\overset{\overset{\displaystyle H}{|}}{N}-\overset{\overset{\displaystyle O}{\|}}{C}-CH_3$$

Phenacetin

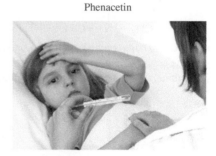

18.63 Neo-Synephrine is the active ingredient in some nose sprays used to reduce the swelling of nasal membranes. Identify the functional groups in Neo-Synephrine. (13.1, 18.1)

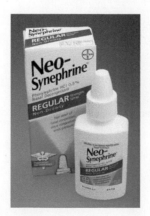

$$HO-\bigcirc-\overset{\overset{\displaystyle OH}{|}}{CH}-CH_2-\overset{\overset{\displaystyle H}{|}}{N}-CH_3$$

Neo-Synephrine

18.64 Melatonin is a naturally occurring compound in plants and animals, where it regulates the biological time clock. Melatonin is sometimes used to counteract jet lag. Identify the functional groups in melatonin. (13.2, 18.1, 18.5)

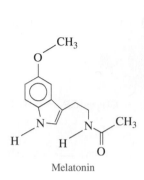

Melatonin

18.65 What is an excitatory neurotransmitter? (18.4)

18.66 What is an inhibitory neurotransmitter? (18.4)

18.67 Identify the structural components that are the same in dopamine, norepinephrine, and epinephrine. (18.4)

18.68 Identify the structural components that are different in dopamine, norepinephrine, and epinephrine. (18.4)

ADDITIONAL QUESTIONS AND PROBLEMS

18.69 Give the IUPAC and common names (if any) and classify each of the following compounds as a primary (1°), secondary (2°), tertiary (3°) amine, or as a quaternary (4°) ammonium salt: (18.1, 18.2)

a.
$$CH_3-CH_2-\overset{\underset{|}{CH_2-CH_3}}{\overset{+}{N}}-CH_2-CH_3 \ Br^-$$
$$\qquad\qquad\quad |$$
$$\qquad\qquad CH_2-CH_3$$

b. $CH_3-CH_2-CH_2-CH_2-CH_2-NH_2$

c.
$$CH_3-CH_2-CH_2-\overset{\overset{H}{|}}{N}-CH_2-CH_3$$

18.70 Give the IUPAC and common names (if any) and classify each of the following compounds as a primary (1°), secondary (2°), tertiary (3°) amine, or as a quaternary (4°) ammonium salt: (18.1, 18.2)

a.
$$\overset{\overset{CH_3}{|}}{N}-CH_2-CH_3$$
(attached to benzene ring)

b.
$$CH_3-\overset{\overset{CH_3}{|}}{CH}-CH_2-\overset{\overset{CH_3}{|}}{N}-CH_2-CH_3$$

c.
$$CH_3-\overset{\overset{CH_2-CH_3}{|}}{\underset{|}{\overset{+}{N}}}-CH_2-CH_3 \ Cl^-$$
$$\qquad\quad |$$
$$\qquad CH_3$$

18.71 Draw the condensed structural formula for each of the following compounds: (18.1, 18.2)
a. 3-pentanamine
b. cyclohexylamine
c. dimethylammonium chloride
d. triethylamine

18.72 Draw the condensed structural formula for each of the following compounds: (18.1, 18.2)
a. 3-amino-2-hexanol
b. tetramethylammonium bromide
c. *N,N*-dimethylaniline
d. butylethylmethylamine

18.73 In each of the following pairs, indicate the compound that has the higher boiling point. Explain. (18.1, 18.2)
a. 1-butanol or butanamine
b. ethylamine or dimethylamine

18.74 In each of the following pairs, indicate the compound that has the higher boiling point. Explain. (18.1, 18.2)
a. butylamine or diethylamine
b. butane or propylamine

18.75 In each of the following pairs, indicate the compound that is more soluble in water. Explain. (18.1, 18.2)
a. ethylamine or dibutylamine
b. trimethylamine or *N*-ethylcyclohexylamine

18.76 In each of the following pairs, indicate the compound that is more soluble in water. Explain. (18.1, 18.2, 18.5)
a. butylamine or pentane
b. butyramide or hexane

18.77 Give the IUPAC name for each of the following amides: (18.5)

a.
$$CH_3-\overset{\overset{O}{||}}{C}-\overset{\overset{H}{|}}{N}-CH_2-CH_3$$

b.
$$CH_3-CH_2-\overset{\overset{O}{||}}{C}-NH_2$$

c.
$$CH_3-\overset{\overset{CH_3}{|}}{CH}-CH_2-\overset{\overset{O}{||}}{C}-NH_2$$

18.78 Give the IUPAC name for each of the following amides: (18.5)

a. $CH_3-CH_2-CH_2-CH_2-\overset{\overset{\displaystyle O}{\|}}{C}-NH_2$

b. $CH_3-\overset{\overset{\displaystyle O}{\|}}{C}-\overset{\overset{\displaystyle CH_3}{|}}{N}-CH_2-CH_2-CH_2-CH_3$

c. $CH_3-\overset{\overset{\displaystyle O}{\|}}{C}-\overset{\overset{\displaystyle CH_3}{|}}{N}-CH_3$

18.79 Draw the condensed structural formulas for the products of the following reactions: (18.2)

a. $CH_3-CH_2-\overset{\overset{\displaystyle CH_3}{|}}{\underset{+}{N}H_2}\ Cl^- + NaOH \longrightarrow$

b. $CH_3-CH_2-NH-CH_3 + H_2O \rightleftharpoons$

18.80 Draw the condensed structural formulas for the products of the following reactions: (18.2)

a. $CH_3-CH_2-NH-CH_3 + HCl \longrightarrow$

b. $CH_3-CH_2-CH_2-\overset{+}{N}H_3\ Cl^- + NaOH \longrightarrow$

℞ Clinical Applications

18.81 Voltaren (diclofenac) is indicated for acute and chronic treatment of the symptoms of rheumatoid arthritis. Name the functional groups in the voltaren molecule. (18.1)

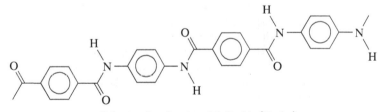

Voltaren

18.82 Toradol (ketorolac) is used in dentistry to relieve pain. Name the functional groups in toradol. (18.3, 18.5)

Toradol

18.83 Give the name of the alkaloid described in each of the following: (18.3)
a. from the bark of the cinchona tree and used in malaria treatment
b. found in tobacco
c. found in coffee and tea
d. a painkiller found in the opium poppy plant

18.84 Identify the heterocyclic amine(s) in each of the following: (18.3)
a. caffeine
b. Demerol (meperidine)
c. coniine
d. quinine

18.85 What is the structural difference between tryptophan and serotonin? (18.4)

18.86 What is the structural difference between histidine and histamine? (18.4)

18.87 What does the abbreviation SSRI signify? (18.4)

18.88 Give an example of an SSRI and its role in treating depression. (18.4)

CHALLENGE QUESTIONS

The following groups of questions are related to the topics in this chapter. However, they do not all follow the chapter order, and they require you to combine concepts and skills from several sections. These questions will help you increase your critical thinking skills and prepare for your next exam.

18.89 There are four amine isomers with the molecular formula C_3H_9N. Draw their condensed structural formulas. Give the common name and classify each as a primary (1°), secondary (2°), or tertiary (3°) amine. (18.1)

18.90 There are four amide isomers with the molecular formula C_3H_7NO. Draw their condensed structural formulas. (18.5)

℞ Clinical Applications

18.91 Use the Internet to look up the structural formula for the following medicinal drugs. List the functional groups in each compound. (18.1, 18.3, 18.5)
a. Keflex, an antibiotic (cefalexin)
b. Inderal, a β-channel blocker used to treat heart irregularities (propranolol)
c. Ibuprofen, an anti-inflammatory agent
d. Aldomet (methyldopa)
e. OxyContin (oxycodone), a narcotic pain reliever
f. Triamterene, a diuretic

18.92 Kevlar is a lightweight polymer used in tires and bulletproof vests. Part of the strength of Kevlar is due to hydrogen bonds between polymer chains. The polymer chain is: (16.1, 18.1, 18.5)

Poly-paraphenylene terephthalamide (Kevlar)

a. Draw the condensed structural formulas for the carboxylic acid and amine that polymerize to make Kevlar.
b. What feature of Kevlar will give the hydrogen bonds between the polymer chains?

18.93 Why is L-dopa, not dopamine, given to persons with low dopamine levels? (18.4)

18.94 How does cocaine increase the dopamine levels in the synapse? (18.4)

ANSWERS

Answers to Selected Questions and Problems

18.1 In a primary amine, there is one alkyl group (and two hydrogens) attached to a nitrogen atom.

18.3 a. primary (1°)   **b.** secondary (2°)
     c. primary (1°)   **d.** tertiary (3°)
     e. tertiary (3°)

18.5 a. ethanamine (ethylamine)
     b. N-methyl-1-propanamine (methylpropylamine)
     c. N-ethyl-N-methylethanamine (diethylmethylamine)
     d. 2-propanamine (isopropylamine)

18.7 a. 4-aminopentanoic acid
     b. 2-chloroaniline
     c. 3-aminopropanal
     d. 5-amino-3-hexanol

18.9 a. $Cl-CH_2-CH_2-NH_2$

b.

c. $CH_3-CH_2-CH_2-CH_2-\overset{\overset{\displaystyle H}{|}}{N}-CH_2-CH_2-CH_3$

d. $CH_3-CH_2-\overset{\overset{\displaystyle NH_2}{|}}{CH}-\overset{\overset{\displaystyle O}{||}}{C}-H$

18.11 a. CH_3-CH_2-OH has a higher boiling point because the $-OH$ group forms stronger hydrogen bonds than the $-NH_2$ group.
     b. $CH_3-CH_2-CH_2-NH_2$ has the higher boiling point because it has a greater molar mass.
     c. $CH_3-CH_2-CH_2-NH_2$ has the higher boiling point because it is a primary amine that forms hydrogen bonds. A tertiary amine cannot form hydrogen bonds with other tertiary amines.

18.13 As a primary amine, propylamine can form two hydrogen bonds, which gives it the highest boiling point. Ethylmethylamine, a secondary amine, can form one hydrogen bond, and butane cannot form hydrogen bonds. Thus, butane has the lowest boiling point of the three compounds.

18.15 a. Yes, amines with fewer than seven carbon atoms are soluble in water.
     b. Yes, amines with fewer than seven carbon atoms are soluble in water.
     c. No, an amine with nine carbon atoms is not soluble in water.
     d. Yes, amines with fewer than seven carbon atoms are soluble in water.

18.17 a. $CH_3-NH_2 + H_2O \rightleftarrows CH_3-\overset{+}{N}H_3 + OH^-$

b. $CH_3-\overset{\overset{\displaystyle H}{|}}{N}-CH_3 + H_2O \rightleftarrows CH_3-\overset{\overset{\displaystyle H}{|}}{\underset{\underset{\displaystyle H}{|}}{\overset{+}{N}}}-CH_3 + OH^-$

18.19 a. $CH_3-\overset{+}{N}H_3\ Cl^-$

b. $CH_3-\overset{+}{N}H_2-CH_3\ Cl^-$

c. (structure: benzene ring with $\overset{+}{N}H_3\ Cl^-$)

18.21 a. $H_2N-\bigcirc-\overset{\overset{\displaystyle O}{||}}{C}-O-CH_2-CH_2-\overset{\overset{\displaystyle CH_2-CH_3}{|}}{\underset{\underset{\displaystyle CH_2-CH_3}{|}}{\overset{+}{N}}}-H\ Cl^-$

     b. The ammonium salt (Novocain) is more soluble in aqueous body fluids than procaine.

18.23 a. piperidine   **b.** pyrimidine   **c.** pyrrole

18.25 piperidine

18.27 pyrrole

18.29 A neurotransmitter is a chemical compound that transmits an impulse from a nerve cell to a target cell.

18.31 When a nerve impulse reaches the axon terminal, it stimulates the release of neurotransmitters into the synapse.

18.33 A neurotransmitter must be removed from its receptor so that new signals can come from the nerve cells.

18.35 Acetylcholine is a neurotransmitter that communicates between the nervous system and muscle cells.

18.37 Dopamine is a neurotransmitter that controls muscle movement, regulates the sleep–wake cycle, and helps to improve cognition, attention, memory, and learning.

18.39 Serotonin is a neurotransmitter that helps to decrease anxiety, improve mood, learning, and memory; it also reduces appetite, and induces sleep.

18.41 Histamine is a neurotransmitter that causes allergic reactions, which may include inflammation, watery eyes, itchy skin, and hay fever.

18.43 Excess glutamate in the synapse can lead to destruction of brain cells.

18.45 GABA is a neurotransmitter that regulates muscle tone, sleep, and anxiety.

18.47 a. $CH_3-\overset{\overset{\displaystyle O}{||}}{C}-NH_2$

b. $CH_3-\overset{\overset{\displaystyle O}{||}}{C}-\overset{\overset{\displaystyle H}{|}}{N}-CH_2-CH_3$

c. $\bigcirc-\overset{\overset{\displaystyle O}{||}}{C}-\overset{\overset{\displaystyle H}{|}}{N}-CH_2-CH_2-CH_3$

18.49 a. N-methylethanamide (N-methylacetamide)
     b. butanamide (butyramide)
     c. methanamide (formamide)
     d. N-methylbenzamide

18.19 c. (continued reaction, top right)

$\bigcirc-NH_2 + H_2O \rightleftarrows \bigcirc-\overset{+}{N}H_3 + OH^-$

18.51 a. $CH_3-CH_2-\underset{\underset{O}{\|}}{C}-NH_2$

b. $CH_3-CH_2-CH_2-CH_2-\underset{\underset{O}{\|}}{C}-NH_2$

c. $\langle\bigcirc\rangle-\underset{\underset{O}{\|}}{C}-\underset{\overset{H}{|}}{N}-CH_2-CH_3$

d. $CH_3-CH_2-CH_2-\underset{\underset{O}{\|}}{C}-\underset{\overset{H}{|}}{N}-CH_2-CH_3$

18.53 a. Ethanamide has the higher melting point because it forms more hydrogen bonds as a primary amide than *N*-methylethanamide, which is a secondary amide.

b. Propionamide has the higher melting point because it forms hydrogen bonds, but butane does not.

c. *N*-methylpropanamide, a secondary amide, has a higher melting point because it can form hydrogen bonds, whereas *N,N*-dimethylpropanamide, a tertiary amide, cannot form hydrogen bonds.

18.55 a. $CH_3-\underset{\underset{O}{\|}}{C}-OH + NH_4^+\ Cl^-$

b. $CH_3-CH_2-\underset{\underset{O}{\|}}{C}-OH + NH_4^+\ Cl^-$

c. $CH_3-CH_2-CH_2-\underset{\underset{O}{\|}}{C}-OH + CH_3-\overset{+}{N}H_3\ Cl^-$

d. $\langle\bigcirc\rangle-\underset{\underset{O}{\|}}{C}-OH + NH_4^+\ Cl^-$

18.57 amine, pyrimidine

18.59 91 mL

18.61 amine, carboxylic acid, amide, aromatic, ester

18.63 amine, aromatic, alcohol, phenol

18.65 Excitatory neurotransmitters open ion channels and stimulate the receptors to send more signals.

18.67 Dopamine, norepinephrine, and epinephrine all have catechol (3,4-dihydroxyphenyl) and amine components.

18.69 a. tetraethylammonium bromide; quaternary (4°) ammonium salt

b. 1-pentanamine (pentylamine); primary (1°)

c. *N*-ethyl-1-propanamine; (ethylpropylamine); secondary (2°)

18.71 a. $CH_3-CH_2-\underset{\overset{NH_2}{|}}{CH}-CH_2-CH_3$

b. (cyclohexane with NH_2)

c. $CH_3-\underset{\overset{CH_3}{|}}{\overset{+}{N}}H_2\ Cl^-$

d. $CH_3-CH_2-\underset{\overset{CH_2-CH_3}{|}}{N}-CH_2-CH_3$

18.73 a. An alcohol with an $-OH$ group such as 1-butanol forms stronger hydrogen bonds than an amine, and has a higher boiling point than an amine.

b. Ethylamine, a primary amine, forms more hydrogen bonds and has a higher boiling point than dimethylamine, which forms fewer hydrogen bonds as a secondary amine.

18.75 a. Ethylamine is a small amine that is soluble because it forms hydrogen bonds with water. Dibutylamine has two large nonpolar alkyl groups that decrease its solubility in water.

b. Trimethylamine is a small tertiary amine that is soluble because it hydrogen bonds with water. *N*-ethylcyclohexylamine has a large nonpolar cycloalkyl group that decreases its solubility in water.

18.77 a. *N*-ethylethanamide **b.** propanamide

c. 3-methylbutanamide

18.79 a. $CH_3-CH_2-\underset{\overset{H}{|}}{N}-CH_3 + NaCl + H_2O$

b. $CH_3-CH_2-\overset{+}{N}H_2-CH_3 + OH^-$

18.81 carboxylate salt, aromatic, amine

18.83 a. quinine **b.** nicotine

c. caffeine **d.** morphine, codeine

18.85 Tryptophan contains a carboxylic acid group that is not present in serotonin. Serotonin has a hydroxyl group ($-OH$) on the aromatic ring that is not present in tryptophan.

18.87 SSRI stands for selective serotonin reuptake inhibitor.

18.89 $CH_3-CH_2-CH_2-NH_2$
Propylamine (1°)

$CH_3-CH_2-\underset{\overset{H}{|}}{N}-CH_3$
Ethylmethylamine (2°)

$CH_3-\underset{\overset{CH_3}{|}}{N}-CH_3$
Trimethylamine (3°)

$CH_3-\underset{\overset{CH_3}{|}}{CH}-NH_2$
Isopropylamine (1°)

18.91 a. aromatic, amine, amide, carboxylic acid, cycloalkene

b. aromatic, ether, alcohol, amine

c. aromatic, carboxylic acid

d. phenol, amine, carboxylic acid

e. aromatic, ether, alcohol, amine, ketone

f. aromatic, amine

18.93 Dopamine is needed in the brain, where it is important in controlling muscle movement. Since dopamine cannot cross the blood–brain barrier, persons with low levels of dopamine are given L-dopa, which can cross the blood–brain barrier, where it is converted to dopamine.

CI.35 The plastic known as PETE (**p**ol**y**ethylene**te**rephthalate) is used to make plastic soft drink bottles and containers for salad dressing, shampoos, and dishwashing liquids. PETE is a polymer of terephthalic acid and ethylene glycol. Today, PETE is the most widely recycled of all the plastics. In one year, 1.5×10^9 lb of PETE are recycled. After it is separated from other plastics, PETE can be used in polyester fabric, door mats, and tennis ball containers. The density of PETE is 1.38 g/mL. (2.5, 2.7, 16.3)

Terephthalic acid   Ethylene glycol

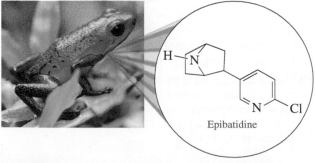

Plastic bottles made of PETE are ready to be recycled.

a. Draw the condensed structural formula for the ester formed from one molecule of terephthalic acid and one molecule of ethylene glycol.
b. Draw the condensed structural formula for the product formed when a second molecule of ethylene glycol reacts with the ester you drew in part **a**.
c. How many kilograms of PETE are recycled in one year?
d. What volume, in liters, of PETE is recycled in one year?
e. Suppose a landfill holds 2.7×10^7 L of recycled PETE. If all the PETE that is recycled in a year were placed instead in landfills, how many would it fill?

CI.36 Epibatidine is one of the alkaloids that the Ecuadorian poison dart frog (*Epipedobates tricolor*) secretes through its skin. Natives of the rainforest prepare poison darts by rubbing the tips on the skin of the poison dart frogs. The effect of a very small amount of the poison can paralyze or kill an animal. As a pain reliever, epibatidine is 200 times more effective than morphine. Although a therapeutic dose has been calculated as 2.5 mcg/kg, epibatidine has adverse effects. It is expected that

Epibatidine

Natives in the South American rainforests obtain poison for blow darts from the alkaloids secreted by poison dart frogs.

more research to chemically modify the epibatidine molecule will produce an important pain reliever. (7.4, 7.5, 18.3)

a. What two heterocyclic amines are in the structure of epibatidine?
b. What is the molecular formula of epibatidine?
c. What is the molar mass of epibatidine?
d. How many grams of epibatidine would be given to a 60.-kg person if the dose is 2.5 mcg/kg?
e. How many molecules of epibatidine would be given to a 60.-kg person for the dose in part **d**?

CI.37 The insect repellent DEET is an amide that can be made from the amidation of 3-methylbenzoic acid with diethylamine. A 6.0-fl oz can of DEET repellent contains 25% DEET (m/v)(1 qt = 32 fl oz). (7.4, 7.5, 9.4, 18.5)

a. Draw the condensed structural formula for DEET.
b. Give the molecular formula for DEET.
c. What is the molar mass of DEET?
d. How many grams of DEET are in one spray can?
e. How many molecules of DEET are in one spray can?

DEET is used in insect repellent.

CI.38 Glyceryl trimyristate (trimyristin) is found in the seeds of the nutmeg (*Myristica fragrans*). Trimyristin is used as a lubricant and fragrance in soaps and shaving creams. Isopropyl myristate is used to increase absorption of skin creams. Draw the condensed structural formula for each of the following: (16.1, 16.2, 16.3, 16.4, 16.5)

Nutmeg contains high levels of glyceryl trimyristate.

a. myristic acid (14:0)
b. glyceryl trimyristate (trimyristin)
c. isopropyl myristate
d. products from the hydrolysis of glyceryl trimyristate with an acid catalyst
e. products from the saponification of glyceryl trimyristate with KOH
f. reactant and product for oxidation of myristyl alcohol to myristic acid

CI.39 Panose is a trisaccharide that is being considered as a possible sweetener by the food industry. (15.4, 15.5, 15.6)

Panose

Hyaluronic acid

The shells of crabs and lobsters contain chitin.

a. What are the monosaccharide units **A**, **B**, and **C** in panose?
b. What type of glycosidic bond connects monosaccharides **A** and **B**?
c. What type of glycosidic bond connects monosaccharides **B** and **C**?
d. Is the structure drawn as α- or β-panose?
e. Why would panose be a reducing sugar?

CI.40 Hyaluronic acid (HA), a polymer of about 25 000 disaccharide units, is a natural component of eye and joint fluid as well as skin and cartilage. Due to the ability of HA to absorb water, it is used in skin care products and injections to smooth wrinkles and for treatment of arthritis. The repeating disaccharide units in HA consist of D-gluconic acid and N-acetyl-D-glucosamine. N-Acetyl-D-glucosamine is an amide derived from acetic acid and D-glucosamine, in which an amine group ($-NH_2$) replaces the hydroxyl on carbon 2 of D-glucose. Another natural polymer called chitin is found in the shells of crabs and lobsters. Chitin is made of repeating units of N-acetyl-D-glucosamine connected by $\beta(1 \rightarrow 4)$-glycosidic bonds. (15.4, 15.5, 15.6, 18.5)

a. Draw the Haworth structures for the product of the oxidation reaction of the hydroxyl group on carbon 6 in β-D-glucose to form β-D-gluconic acid.
b. Draw the Haworth structure for β-D-glucosamine.
c. Draw the Haworth structure for the amide of β-D-glucosamine and acetic acid.
d. What are the two types of glycosidic bonds that link the monosaccharides in hyaluronic acid?
e. Draw the structure for a section of chitin with two N-acetyl-D-glucosamine units linked by $\beta(1 \rightarrow 4)$-glycosidic bonds.

ANSWERS

CI.35 a. HO—C(=O)—C₆H₄—C(=O)—O—CH₂—CH₂—OH

b.

HO—CH₂—CH₂—O—C(=O)—C₆H₄—C(=O)—O—CH₂—CH₂—OH

c. 6.8×10^8 kg of PETE
d. 4.9×10^8 L of PETE
e. 18 landfills

CI.37 a.

C₆H₄(CH₃)—C(=O)—N(CH₂—CH₃)—CH₂—CH₃

b. $C_{12}H_{17}NO$
c. 191.3 g/mole
d. 44 g of DEET
e. 1.4×10^{23} molecules

CI.39 a. **A**, **B**, and **C** are all glucose.
b. An $\alpha(1 \rightarrow 6)$-glycosidic bond links **A** and **B**.
c. An $\alpha(1 \rightarrow 4)$-glycosidic bond links **B** and **C**.
d. β-panose
e. Panose is a reducing sugar because it has a free hydroxyl group on carbon 1 of structure **C**, which allows glucose **C** to form an aldehyde.

19

Amino Acids and Proteins

EDITH IS HAVING TROUBLE COMPLETING SIMPLE

daily tasks and even remembering who her husband is at times. Edith's doctor suspects that Edith may be in the early stages of Alzheimer's disease. Edith is referred to a neurologist who administers tests to assess her cognitive impairment. Victoria, a radiology technician, explains to Edith that she is scheduled for a positron emission tomography (PET) scan of her brain.

Patients with Alzheimer's have impaired brain function caused by the accumulation of beta-amyloid proteins that form clumps or plaques that block transmission in nerve cells. Proteins like beta-amyloid consist of chains of amino acids. There are 20 different amino acids commonly found in proteins. As the name implies, amino acids contain an amino (amine) functional group and a carboxylic acid group. Each amino acid has a unique side chain, or R group, which distinguishes it from the other amino acids that make up proteins.

CAREER Radiology Technician

Radiology technicians work with radiologists to produce images of the body that allow for the diagnosis and treatment of certain medical conditions. Technicians operate imaging equipment such as X-ray, computed tomography (CT), and positron emission tomography (PET). During the PET procedure, the technician works with the patient by explaining each step of the imaging procedure, answering questions, and monitoring the patient's physical condition. A patient is instructed to remove jewelry, clothing, and any other items that could interfere with the equipment. The technician positions the patient and covers parts of the body not being filmed. The technician may inject contrast agents to improve image quality. Radiology technicians maintain good radiation safety practice and serve as an important liaison between patient and physician. Once the imaging process is complete, the radiology technician reviews the images with radiologists, and makes additional images when necessary. A radiology technician may also maintain patient records.

Preparation for a career as a radiology technician involves a certificate program that takes one to two years, a two-year associate's degree, or a four-year bachelor's degree.

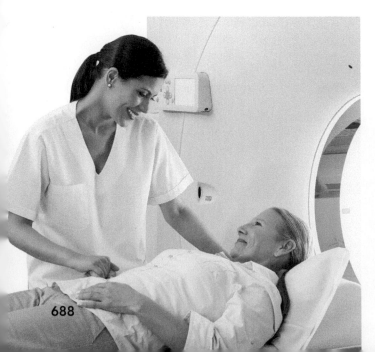

The word "protein" is derived from the Greek word *proteios*, meaning "first." Proteins are made up from 20 different amino acids arranged in a specific order. The ordering determines the characteristics of the protein and its biological action. Proteins provide structure in membranes, build cartilage and connective tissue, transport oxygen in blood and muscle, direct biological reactions as enzymes, defend the body against infection, and control metabolic processes as hormones. They can even be a source of energy.

All of these different protein functions depend on the structures and chemical behavior of amino acids, the building blocks of proteins. We will see how peptide bonds link amino acids and how the sequence of the amino acids in these protein polymers directs the formation of their unique three-dimensional structures.

CHAPTER READINESS*

🖩 KEY MATH SKILL
- Calculating pH from $[H_3O^+]$ (11.6)

⚛ CORE CHEMISTRY SKILLS
- Writing Equations for Reactions of Acids and Bases (11.7)
- Naming Carboxylic Acids (16.1)
- Forming Amides (18.5)

*This Key Math Skill and Core Chemistry Skills from previous chapters are listed here for your review as you proceed to the new material in this chapter.

19.1 Proteins and Amino Acids

Protein molecules, compared with many of the compounds we have studied, can be gigantic. Insulin has a molar mass of 5800, and hemoglobin has a molar mass of about 67 000. Some virus proteins are even larger, having molar masses of more than 40 million. Even though proteins can be huge, they all contain the same 20 amino acids. Every protein is a polymer built from these 20 different amino acid building blocks, repeated numerous times, with the specific sequence of the amino acids determining the characteristics of the protein and its biological action.

The many kinds of proteins perform different functions in the body. Some proteins form structural components such as cartilage, muscles, hair, and nails. Wool, silk, feathers, and horns in animals are made of proteins (see Figure 19.1). Proteins that function as enzymes regulate biological reactions such as digestion and cellular metabolism. Other proteins, such as hemoglobin and myoglobin, transport oxygen in the blood and muscle. Table 19.1 gives examples of proteins that are classified by their functions.

Amino Acids

Proteins are composed of building blocks called *amino acids*. The general structure of an **amino acid** consists of a central carbon atom called the α carbon, which is attached to an ammonium group ($-NH_3^+$) and a carboxylate group ($-COO^-$). The α carbon is also bonded to a hydrogen atom ($-H$) and a side chain called an R group. All of the 20 amino acids present in human proteins have this general structure except for proline in which the amine group is part of a ring structure. The differences in all of the 20 amino acids are due to the unique characteristics of the R groups.

LEARNING GOAL

Classify proteins by their functions. Give the name and abbreviations for an amino acid, and draw its zwitterion.

FIGURE 19.1 ▶ The horns of animals are made of proteins.

🅠 What class of protein would be in horns?

TABLE 19.1 Classification of Some Proteins and Their Functions

Class of Protein	Function	Examples
Structural	Provide structural components	*Collagen* is in tendons and cartilage. *Keratin* is in hair, skin, wool, and nails.
Contractile	Make muscles move	*Myosin* and *actin* contract muscle fibers.
Transport	Carry essential substances throughout the body	*Hemoglobin* transports oxygen. *Lipoproteins* transport lipids.
Storage	Store nutrients	*Casein* stores protein in milk. *Ferritin* stores iron in the spleen and liver.
Hormone	Regulate body metabolism and the nervous system	*Insulin* regulates blood glucose level. *Growth hormone* regulates body growth.
Enzyme	Catalyze biochemical reactions in the cells	*Sucrase* catalyzes the hydrolysis of sucrose. *Trypsin* catalyzes the hydrolysis of proteins.
Protection	Recognize and destroy foreign substances	*Immunoglobulins* stimulate immune responses.

At physiological pH, the ionized ammonium and carboxylate groups give an amino acid a balance of positive and negative charge, which gives an overall zero charge. This neutral amino acid, which is called a **zwitterion**, occurs at a specific pH value known as its **isoelectric point (pI)**. Because amino acids as zwitterions are charged, they have properties similar to salts: they have high melting points and are soluble in water, but not nonpolar solvents. In the zwitterion of alanine, the ammonium group (blue) has a positive charge, the carboxylate group (pink) has a negative charge, and the R group (yellow) is a methyl substituent, —CH₃.

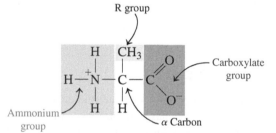

The zwitterion of alanine is neutral at its pI 6.0.

The ball-and-stick model of alanine shows the positively and negatively charged groups at its pI.

Classification of Amino Acids

We classify amino acids using their specific R groups, which determine their properties in aqueous solution. The **nonpolar amino acids** have hydrogen, alkyl, or aromatic R groups, which make them *hydrophobic* ("water fearing"). The **polar amino acids** have R groups that interact with water, which makes them *hydrophilic* ("water loving"). The *polar neutral* amino acids contain hydroxyl (—OH), thiol (—SH), or amide (—CONH₂) R groups. The R group of a polar **acidic amino acid** contains a carboxylate group (—COO⁻). The R group of a polar **basic amino acid** contains an ammonium group (—NH₃⁺). The structures of the 20 α-amino acids, their groups, names, three-letter and one-letter abbreviations, and pI values are listed in Table 19.2.

Using Table 19.2, we can summarize the different types of amino acid R groups, their polarity, and interaction with water as follows:

Type of Amino Acid	Number	Type of R Groups	Interaction with Water
Nonpolar	9	Nonpolar	Hydrophobic
Polar, neutral	6	Contain O and S atoms, but no charge	Hydrophilic
Polar, acidic	2	Contain carboxylate groups, negative charge	Hydrophilic
Polar, basic	3	Contain ammonium groups, positive charge	Hydrophilic

TABLE 19.2 Structures, Names, Abbreviations, and Isoelectric Points (pI) of 20 Common Amino Acids at Physiological pH (7.4)

Nonpolar Amino Acids (hydrophobic)

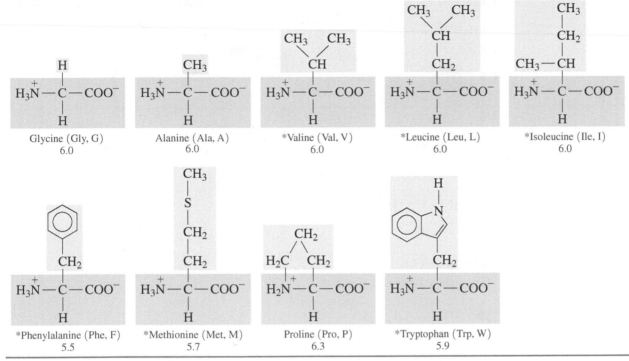

Glycine (Gly, G)
6.0

Alanine (Ala, A)
6.0

*Valine (Val, V)
6.0

*Leucine (Leu, L)
6.0

*Isoleucine (Ile, I)
6.0

*Phenylalanine (Phe, F)
5.5

*Methionine (Met, M)
5.7

Proline (Pro, P)
6.3

*Tryptophan (Trp, W)
5.9

Polar Amino Acids (hydrophilic)

Amino Acids with Neutral R Groups

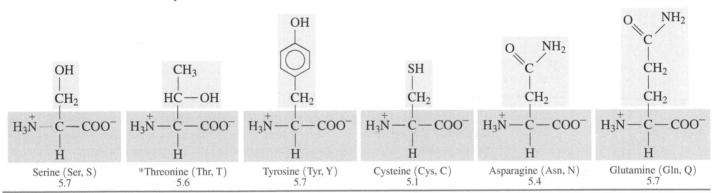

Serine (Ser, S)
5.7

*Threonine (Thr, T)
5.6

Tyrosine (Tyr, Y)
5.7

Cysteine (Cys, C)
5.1

Asparagine (Asn, N)
5.4

Glutamine (Gln, Q)
5.7

Amino Acids with Charged R Groups

Acidic (negative charge)

Basic (positive charge)

Aspartate (Asp, D)
2.8

Glutamate (Glu, E)
3.2

*Histidine (His, H)
7.6

*Lysine (Lys, K)
9.7

Arginine (Arg, R)
10.8

*Essential amino acids

▶ **SAMPLE PROBLEM 19.1 Structural Formulas of Amino Acids**

Draw the zwitterion for each of the following amino acids:

a. serine

b. aspartate

SOLUTION

ANALYZE THE PROBLEM	Given	Need
	serine, aspartate	draw the zwitterion for each

a.

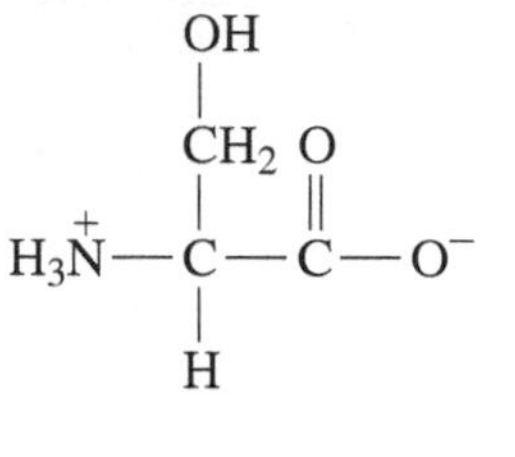

$$\text{H}_3\overset{+}{\text{N}}-\underset{\underset{\text{H}}{|}}{\overset{\overset{\text{OH}}{|}}{\underset{|}{\overset{|}{\text{C}}}}}-\overset{\overset{\text{O}}{||}}{\text{C}}-\text{O}^-$$

with CH₂ between C and OH

b.

$$\text{H}_3\overset{+}{\text{N}}-\underset{\underset{\text{H}}{|}}{\overset{\overset{\text{CH}_2}{|}}{\text{C}}}-\overset{\overset{\text{O}}{||}}{\text{C}}-\text{O}^-$$

with CH_2 attached to $\overset{\text{O}}{\underset{\overset{||}{\text{O}^-}}{\text{C}}}$

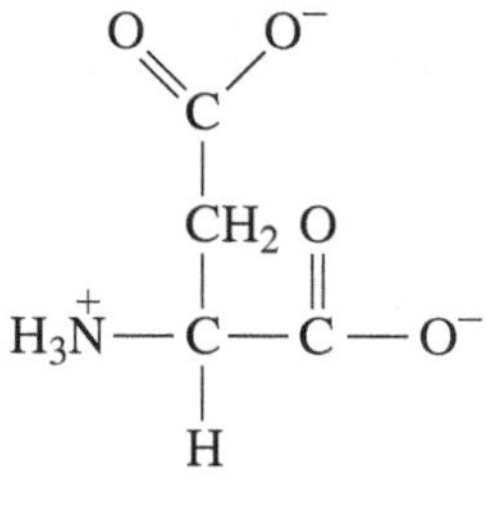

STUDY CHECK 19.1

Draw the zwitterion for leucine.

ANSWER

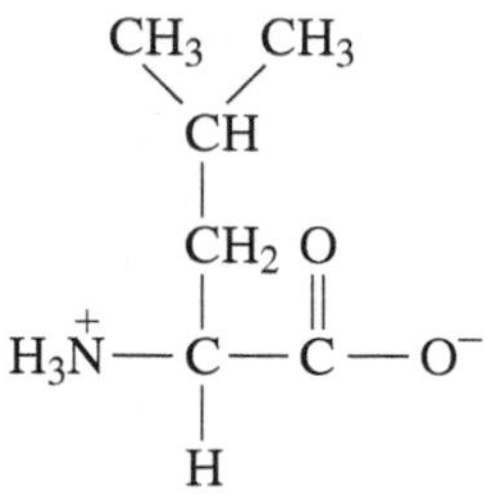

$$\text{H}_3\overset{+}{\text{N}}-\underset{\underset{\text{H}}{|}}{\overset{\overset{\text{CH}_2}{|}}{\text{C}}}-\overset{\overset{\text{O}}{||}}{\text{C}}-\text{O}^-$$

with CH₂ attached to CH, which bears two CH₃ groups

Amino Acid Abbreviations

Amino acids have both three-letter and one-letter abbreviations as seen in Table 19.2. The three-letter abbreviations, which were used initially, represent letters from the amino acid names as closely as possible. As scientists began to list the order of amino acids in longer chains of amino acids, the abbreviations were reduced to one letter to allow the faster transfer of data. Of the 20 amino acids, 11 have one-letter abbreviations that are the same as the first letter in their names. However, nine amino acids use different letters. Arginine R and tyrosine Y use the second letters in their names. Phenylalanine is F, which sounds like the first letters of its name. The other amino acids use single letters that are part of their names or have sounds similar to parts of their name. Lysine is K, which is near L in the alphabet.

▶ **SAMPLE PROBLEM 19.2 Classification of Amino Acids**

Using Table 19.2, indicate each of the following for the amino acid shown:

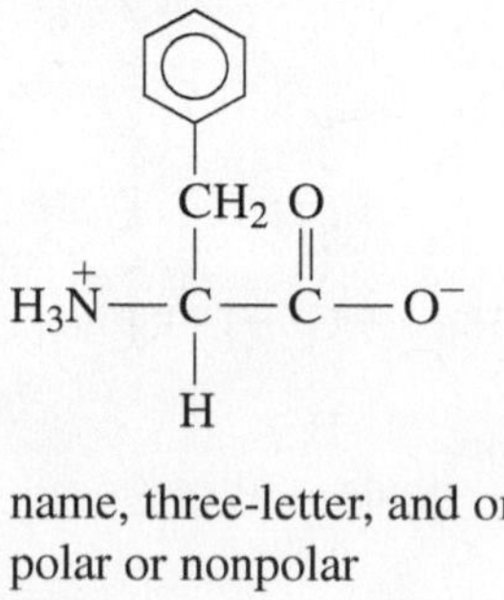

$$\text{H}_3\overset{+}{\text{N}}-\underset{\underset{\text{H}}{|}}{\overset{\overset{\text{CH}_2}{|}}{\text{C}}}-\overset{\overset{\text{O}}{||}}{\text{C}}-\text{O}^-$$

with CH₂ attached to a benzene ring

a. name, three-letter, and one-letter abbreviations

b. polar or nonpolar

c. has a neutral, acidic, or basic R group
d. interaction with water as hydrophobic or hydrophilic

SOLUTION
a. phenylalanine, Phe, F
b. nonpolar
c. neutral
d. hydrophobic

STUDY CHECK 19.2

Using Table 19.2, indicate each of the following for the amino acid shown:

$$H_3\overset{+}{N}-\underset{\underset{H}{|}}{\overset{\overset{CH_2}{|}}{\overset{\overset{\overset{OH}{|}}{}}{C}}}-\overset{\overset{O}{\|}}{C}-O^-$$

a. name, three-letter, and one-letter abbreviations
b. polar or nonpolar
c. has a neutral, acidic, or basic R group
d. interaction with water as hydrophobic or hydrophilic

ANSWER
a. serine, Ser, S
b. polar
c. neutral
d. hydrophilic

Amino Acid Stereoisomers

All of the α-amino acids except for glycine are chiral because the α carbon is attached to four different groups. Thus, amino acids can exist as D and L stereoisomers called *enantiomers*. We draw Fischer projections for α-amino acids by placing the carboxylate group at the top and the R group at the bottom. In the L enantiomer of an amino acid, the $-NH_3^+$ group is on the left, and in the D enantiomer, the $-NH_3^+$ group is on the right. In biological systems, the only amino acids incorporated into proteins are the L enantiomers. There are D amino acids found in nature, but not in proteins.

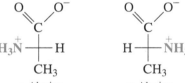

L-Alanine   D-Alanine

In the Fischer projections of amino acids such as alanine, the $-NH_3^+$ group appears on the left or right of the chiral carbon to give L or D enantiomers.

 # Chemistry Link to **Health**
Essential Amino Acids

Of the 20 amino acids typically used to build proteins in the body, only 11 can be synthesized in the body. The other nine amino acids, designated in Table 19.2 with asterisks and listed in Table 19.3, are called the **essential amino acids** because they must be obtained from the diet. In addition to the essential amino acids required by adults, infants and growing children also require arginine, cysteine, and tyrosine.

Complete proteins, which contain all of the essential amino acids, are found in most animal products, such as eggs, milk, meat, fish, and poultry. However, gelatin and plant proteins such as grains, beans, and nuts are *incomplete proteins* because they are deficient in one or more of the essential amino acids. Diets that rely on plant foods for protein must combine protein sources to obtain all the essential amino acids. Some examples of *complementary protein* sources include rice and beans, or a peanut butter sandwich on whole grain bread. Rice and wheat contain the amino acid methionine that is deficient in beans and

peanuts, whereas beans and peanuts are rich in lysine that is lacking in grain (see Table 19.4).

Complete proteins such as eggs, milk, meat, and fish contain all of the essential amino acids. Incomplete proteins from plants such as grains, beans, and nuts are deficient in one or more essential amino acids.

TABLE 19.3 Essential Amino Acids for Adults

Histidine (His, H)	Phenylalanine (Phe, F)
Isoleucine (Ile, I)	Threonine (Thr, T)
Leucine (Leu, L)	Tryptophan (Trp, W)
Lysine (Lys, K)	Valine (Val, V)
Methionine (Met, M)	

TABLE 19.4 Amino Acid Deficiencies in Selected Vegetables and Grains

Food Source	Amino Acid Deficiency
Wheat, rice, oats	Lysine
Corn	Lysine, tryptophan
Beans	Methionine, tryptophan
Peas, peanuts	Methionine
Almonds, walnuts	Lysine, tryptophan
Soy	Methionine

QUESTIONS AND PROBLEMS

19.1 Proteins and Amino Acids

LEARNING GOAL Classify proteins by their functions. Give the name and abbreviations for an amino acid, and draw its zwitterion.

19.1 Classify each of the following proteins according to its function:
  a. hemoglobin, oxygen carrier in the blood
  b. collagen, a major component of tendons and cartilage
  c. keratin, a protein found in hair
  d. amylases that catalyze the hydrolysis of starch

19.2 Classify each of the following proteins according to its function:
  a. insulin, which is needed for glucose utilization
  b. antibodies, disable foreign proteins
  c. casein, milk protein
  d. lipases that catalyze the hydrolysis of lipids

19.3 Draw the zwitterion and give the three- and one-letter abbreviation for each of the following amino acids:
  a. isoleucine   b. glutamine
  c. glutamate   d. proline

19.4 Draw the zwitterion and give the three- and one-letter abbreviation for each of the following amino acids:
  a. lysine   b. arginine
  c. methionine   d. tyrosine

19.5 Classify each of the amino acids in problem 19.3 as polar or nonpolar. If polar, indicate if the R group is neutral, acidic, or basic. Indicate if each is hydrophobic or hydrophilic.

19.6 Classify each of the amino acids in problem 19.4 as polar or nonpolar. If polar, indicate if the R group is neutral, acidic, or basic. Indicate if each is hydrophobic or hydrophilic.

℞ Clinical Applications

19.7 Give the name of the essential amino acid that has the following abbreviation:
  a. His   b. V   c. K   d. Ile

19.8 Give the name of the essential amino acid that has the following abbreviation:
  a. Trp   b. Met   c. F   d. W

19.9 Draw the Fischer projection for each of the following essential amino acids:
  a. L-serine   b. L-leucine

19.10 Draw the Fischer projection for each of the following essential amino acids:
  a. L-threonine   b. L-isoleucine

19.11 Explain why each of the following pairs are complementary proteins:
  a. corn and peas   b. rice and soy

19.12 Explain why each of the following pairs are complementary proteins:
  a. beans and oats   b. almonds and peanuts

19.2 Amino Acids as Acids and Bases

LEARNING GOAL

Using the zwitterion for an amino acid at its isoelectric point, draw its ionized structures at pH values above or below its isoelectric point.

The charged groups on an amino acid act as weak acids and bases, which means the groups can lose or gain H^+. Thus, the overall charge on an amino acid depends on the pH of the solution. At the isoelectric point (pI), an amino acid exists as a zwitterion with an overall charge of zero. However, an amino acid becomes a positive ion if it is placed in a more acidic solution (has a lower pH) than its pI. If that same amino acid is placed in a solution that is more basic (has a higher pH) than its pI, it becomes a negative ion.

The pI values for nonpolar and polar neutral amino acids range from pH 5.1 to 6. For example, alanine is a zwitterion at its pI of 6.0 with a carboxylate group ($-COO^-$) and an ammonium group ($-NH_3^+$), which give it an overall charge of zero. When alanine is placed in a solution that is more acidic, with a lower pH than its pI (pH < 6.0), the carboxylate group ($-COO^-$) of alanine gains H^+, which forms the carboxylic acid

(—COOH). Because the —NH$_3$$^+$ group retains a charge of 1+, alanine has an overall positive charge (1+) at a pH lower than its pI of 6.0.

Zwitterion of alanine
pH = 6.0
(charge = 0)

Alanine
pH < 6.0
(charge = 1+)

When alanine is placed in a solution that is more basic, with a higher pH than its pI (pH > 6.0), the —NH$_3$$^+$ group of alanine loses H$^+$ and forms an amino group (—NH$_2$), which has no charge. Because the carboxylate group (—COO$^-$) has a charge of 1−, alanine has an overall negative charge (1−) at a pH higher than 6.0.

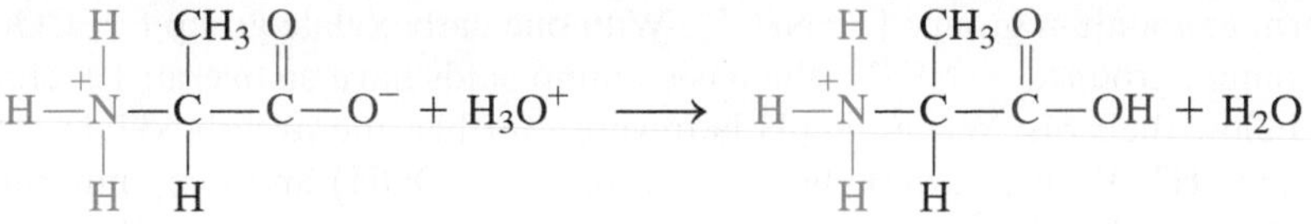

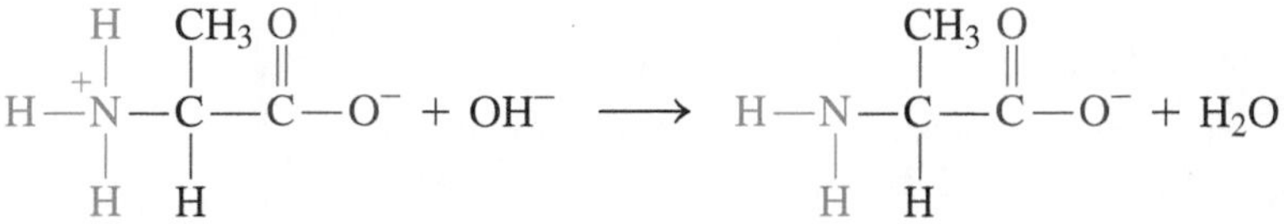

Zwitterion of alanine
pH = 6.0
(charge = 0)

Alanine
pH > 6.0
(charge = 1−)

The overall charge due to carboxylic acid or carboxylate groups and ammonium or amino groups for amino acids in solutions with pH below pI, at the pI, or above pI are summarized in Table 19.5.

TABLE 19.5 Ionized Forms of Nonpolar and Polar Neutral Amino Acids

Solution	pH < pI (acidic)	pH = pI	pH > pI (basic)
Change in H$^+$	[H$^+$] increases	No change	[H$^+$] decreases
Carboxylic Acid/Carboxylate	—COOH	—COO$^-$	—COO$^-$
Ammonium/Amino	—NH$_3$$^+$	—NH$_3$$^+$	—NH$_2$
Overall Charge	1+	0	1−

Ionized Forms of Polar Acidic and Polar Basic Amino Acids

The pI values of the polar acidic amino acids are around pH 3. For example, the aspartate zwitterion has a pI of 2.8. However, as pH values change, the ammonium group (—NH$_3$$^+$), the carboxylate group (—COO$^-$), and the carboxylic acid (—COOH) R group can lose or gain H$^+$, which changes the overall charge. For example, at pH 7, which is above the pI for aspartate, the R group loses H$^+$ to form carboxylate and gives aspartate an overall charge of 1−. When the pH value increases further, the ammonium group loses H$^+$, which gives aspartate an overall change of 2−. At pH values below 2.8, the carboxylate group on the α carbon gains H$^+$, which gives aspartate an overall 1+ charge.

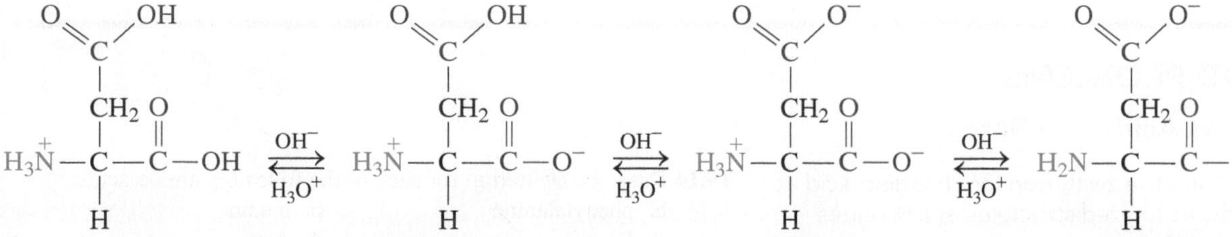

Aspartate
pH < 2.8
(charge = 1+)

Zwitterion of aspartate
pH = 2.8
(charge = 0)

Aspartate
pH = 7
(charge = 1−)

Aspartate
pH > 10
(charge = 2−)

The pI values of the polar basic amino acids (lysine, arginine, and histidine) are from pH 8 to 11. At pH values of 8 to 11, the amines in the R groups are not ionized, which gives an overall charge of zero. At lower pH values, the amines ($-NH_2$) in the R groups gain H^+ to form ammonium groups ($-NH_3^+$). With one carboxylate group ($-COO^-$) and two ammonium groups ($-NH_3^+$), the basic amino acids have an overall 1+ charge at pH values below their pIs. When the pH is lowered further, the α-carboxylate group ($-COO^-$) gains H^+. With a carboxylic acid group ($-COOH$) and two ammonium groups ($-NH_3^+$), the basic amino acids at very low pH values have an overall charge of 2+. If the pH increases above the pI, H^+ is lost to give ions with a 1- charge.

Ball-and-stick model of glycine at its pI of 6.0.

▶ **SAMPLE PROBLEM 19.3 Amino Acids in Acidic or Basic Solution**

The pI of glycine is 6.0. Draw the structural formula and state the overall charge for glycine at **a.** pH 6.0 and at **b.** pH 8.0.

SOLUTION

ANALYZE THE PROBLEM	Given	Need
	glycine, pI 6.0 **a.** pH 6.0, **b.** pH 8.0	structural formula, overall charge

a. At a pH of 6.0, glycine has an ammonium group and a carboxylate group, which give it an overall change of zero (0).

$$H_3\overset{+}{N}-\underset{\underset{H}{|}}{\overset{\overset{H}{|}}{C}}-\overset{\overset{O}{\|}}{C}-O^- \quad \text{Charge 0 at pH 6.0}$$

b. At a pH of 8.0 (basic solution), the $-NH_3^+$ group loses H^+ to become $-NH_2$, which has no charge. Because the carboxylate group ($-COO^-$) remains ionized, the overall charge of glycine at pH 8.0 is negative (1-).

$$H_2N-\underset{\underset{H}{|}}{\overset{\overset{H}{|}}{C}}-\overset{\overset{O}{\|}}{C}-O^- \quad \text{Charge 1- at pH 8.0}$$

STUDY CHECK 19.3

Draw the structural formula for glycine at pH 3.0 and give the overall charge.

ANSWER

$$H_3\overset{+}{N}-\underset{\underset{H}{|}}{\overset{\overset{H}{|}}{C}}-\overset{\overset{O}{\|}}{C}-OH \quad \text{Charge 1+ at pH 3.0}$$

QUESTIONS AND PROBLEMS

19.2 Amino Acids as Acids and Bases

LEARNING GOAL Using the zwitterion for an amino acid at its isoelectric point, draw its ionized structures at pH values above or below its isoelectric point.

19.13 Draw the zwitterion for each of the following amino acids:
   a. Val
   b. C
   c. threonine
   d. A

19.14 Draw the zwitterion for each of the following amino acids:
   a. phenylalanine
   b. leucine
   c. S
   d. Asn

19.15 Draw the ionized form for each of the amino acids in problem 19.13 at a pH below 1.0.

19.16 Draw the ionized form for each of the amino acids in problem 19.14 at a pH above 12.0.

19.17 Would each of the following ionized forms of valine exist at a pH above, below, or at its pI?

a. CH_3 CH_3 / CH O / $H_2N-C-C-O^-$ / H

b. CH_3 CH_3 / CH O / $H_3\overset{+}{N}-C-C-OH$ / H

c. CH_3 CH_3 / CH O / $H_3\overset{+}{N}-C-C-O^-$ / H

19.18 Would each of the following ionized forms of serine exist at a pH above, below, or at its pI?

a. OH / CH_2 O / $H_3\overset{+}{N}-C-C-O^-$ / H

b. OH / CH_2 O / $H_3\overset{+}{N}-C-C-OH$ / H

c. OH / CH_2 O / $H_2N-C-C-O^-$ / H

19.3 Formation of Peptides

When a carboxylic acid and an amine react through a condensation reaction, they form an amide bond. Because amino acids have the same functional groups, they also react to form an amide bond, called a **peptide bond**. The linking of two or more amino acids by peptide bonds forms a **peptide**. Two amino acids form a *dipeptide*, three amino acids form a *tripeptide*, and four amino acids form a *tetrapeptide*. A chain of five amino acids is a *pentapeptide*, and longer chains of amino acids are called *polypeptides*.

In the condensation reaction for the formation of the dipeptide glycylalanine (Gly–Ala, GA) (see Figure 19.2), the O atom is removed from the carboxylate group

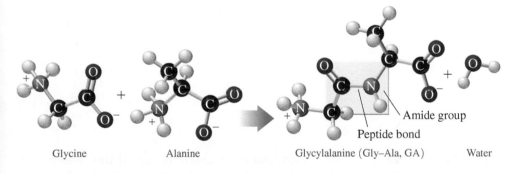

Glycine   Alanine   Glycylalanine (Gly–Ala, GA)   Water

FIGURE 19.2 ▶ A peptide bond between glycine and alanine as zwitterions forms the dipeptide glycylalanine.

🔘 What functional groups in glycine and alanine form the peptide bond?

($-COO^-$) of glycine, which combines with two H atoms removed from the ammonium group ($-NH_3^+$) of alanine to produce H_2O. When the peptide bonds have formed, the remaining parts of the amino acids are called *amino acid residues*.

In this dipeptide, the amino acid glycine written on the left with a free $-NH_3^+$ group is called the **N-terminal amino acid** or **N-terminus**. The amino acid alanine written on the right with a free $-COO^-$ group is called the **C-terminal amino acid** or **C-terminus**. By convention, chains of peptides are written starting with the N-terminal amino acid (the N-terminus) on the left, and ending with the C-terminal amino acid (or C-terminus) on the right.

N-terminus   Peptide bond   C-terminus

$$H-\underset{\underset{H}{|}}{\overset{\overset{H}{|}}{\overset{+}{N}}}-\underset{\underset{H}{|}}{\overset{\overset{H}{|}}{C}}-\overset{\overset{O}{||}}{C}-O^- + H-\underset{\underset{H}{|}}{\overset{\overset{H}{|}}{\overset{+}{N}}}-\underset{\underset{H}{|}}{\overset{\overset{CH_3}{|}}{C}}-\overset{\overset{O}{||}}{C}-O^- \longrightarrow H-\underset{\underset{H}{|}}{\overset{\overset{H}{|}}{\overset{+}{N}}}-\underset{\underset{H}{|}}{\overset{\overset{H}{|}}{C}}-\overset{\overset{O}{||}}{C}-\underset{\underset{H}{|}}{N}-\underset{\underset{H}{|}}{\overset{\overset{CH_3}{|}}{C}}-\overset{\overset{O}{||}}{C}-O^- + H_2O$$

Glycine   Alanine   Glycylalanine (Gly–Ala, GA)

Peptide bond

—N—C—C—N—C—C—

The backbone of a peptide consists of the repeating sequence —N—C—C—.

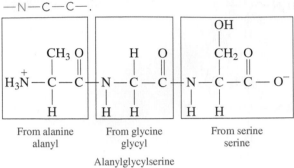

From alanine   From glycine   From serine
  alanyl   glycyl   serine

Alanylglycylserine
(Ala–Gly–Ser, AGS)

In the diagram of the dipeptide glycylalanine, the glycine residue is the N-terminus and the alanine residue is the C-terminus. The **backbone** of the dipeptide is the repeating sequence of the blue **N** from the ammonium group, the black **C** from the α carbon attached to an R group, and the magenta **C** from the carboxylate group.

Naming Peptides

The name of a peptide begins with the names of the N-terminal amino acid residue and all the following amino acid residues up to the C-terminal amino acid in which the *ine* or *ate* endings are replaced with *yl*. The C-terminal amino acid residue retains its complete amino acid name. For example, a tripeptide consisting of alanine, glycine, and serine residues is named as alan**yl**glyc**yl**serine. For convenience, the order of amino acids in the peptide is written from left to right as a sequence of three-letter or one-letter abbreviations.

▶ **SAMPLE PROBLEM 19.4 Drawing a Peptide**

Draw the structure and give the name for the tripeptide Gly–Ser–Met.

SOLUTION

ANALYZE THE PROBLEM	Given	Need
	Gly–Ser–Met	tripeptide structure, name

STEP 1 Draw the structures for each amino acid in the peptide, starting with the N-terminus.

Gly, G
N-terminus

Ser, S

Met, M
C-terminus

STEP 2 Remove the O atom from the carboxylate group of the N-terminus and two H atoms from the ammonium group in the adjacent amino acid. Repeat this process until the C-terminus is reached.

Gly, G
N-terminus

Ser, S

Met, M
C-terminus

Guide to Drawing a Peptide

STEP 1
Draw the structures for each amino acid in the peptide, starting with the N-terminus.

STEP 2
Remove the O atom from the carboxylate group of the N-terminus and two H atoms from the ammonium group in the adjacent amino acid.

STEP 3
Use peptide bonds to connect the amino acid residues.

STEP 3 Use peptide bonds to connect the amino acid residues.

The tripeptide is named by replacing the last syllable of each amino acid name with *yl*, starting with the N-terminus. The C-terminus retains its complete amino acid name.

> **N-terminus** glycine is named glycyl
>
> serine is named seryl
>
> **C-terminus** methionine keeps its full name

The tripeptide is named glycylserylmethionine.

STUDY CHECK 19.4

Draw the structure and give the name for Phe–Thr, a section in glucagon, which is a peptide hormone that increases blood glucose levels.

ANSWER

Phenylalanylthreonine

Chemistry Link to Health

Polypeptides in the Body

Enkephalins and endorphins are natural painkillers produced in the body. They are polypeptides that bind to receptors in the brain to give relief from pain. This effect appears to be responsible for the runner's high, for temporary loss of pain when severe injury occurs, and for the analgesic effects of acupuncture.

The *enkephalins*, which are found in the thalamus and the spinal cord, are pentapeptides, the smallest molecules with opiate activity. The short amino acid sequence of met-enkephalin is incorporated into the longer amino acid sequence of the endorphins.

Four groups of *endorphins* have been identified: α-endorphin contains 16 amino acids, β-endorphin contains 31 amino acids, γ-endorphin has 17 amino acids, and δ-endorphin has 27 amino acids.

Endorphins may produce their sedating effects by preventing the release of substance P, a polypeptide with 11 amino acids, which has been found to transmit pain impulses to the brain.

Two hormones produced by the pituitary gland are the nonapeptides (peptides with nine amino acids) oxytocin and vasopressin. Oxytocin stimulates uterine contractions in labor, and vasopressin is an antidiuretic hormone that regulates blood pressure by adjusting the amount of water reabsorbed by the kidneys. The structures of these nonapeptides are very similar. Only the amino acids in positions 3 and 8 are different. However, the difference of two amino acids greatly affects how the two hormones function in the body.

The structure of met-Enkephalin is shown with its amino acid residues. The chain reads:

$H_3\overset{+}{N}$—CH—C—NH—CH—C—NH—CH—C—NH—CH—C—NH—CH—C—O^-

with side chains: first residue has CH_2 connected to a phenol ring (OH); second and third residues have H; fourth residue has CH_2 connected to a benzene ring; fifth residue has CH_2—CH_2—S—CH_3. Each C is a carbonyl (=O).

met-Enkephalin

α-Endorphin

Tyr–Gly–Gly–Phe–Met–Thr–Ser–Glu–Lys–Ser–Gln–Thr–Pro–Leu–Val–Thr

met-Enkephalin

Leu

Glu–Gly–Lys–Lys–Tyr–Ala–Asn–Lys–Ile–Ile–Ala–Asn–Lys–Phe

β-Endorphin

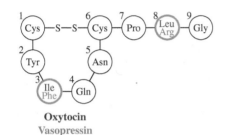

Oxytocin
Vasopressin

Oxytocin, a nonapeptide used to initiate labor, was the first hormone to be synthesized in the laboratory.

QUESTIONS AND PROBLEMS

19.3 Formation of Peptides

LEARNING GOAL Draw the structure for a peptide, give its three-letter and one-letter abbreviations, and name.

19.19 Draw the structure for each of the following peptides, and give the three-letter and one-letter abbreviations for their names:
  a. alanylcysteine
  b. serylphenylalanine
  c. glycylalanylvaline
  d. valylisoleucyltryptophan

19.20 Draw the structure for each of the following peptides, and give the three-letter and one-letter abbreviations for their names:
  a. prolylaspartate
  b. threonylleucine
  c. methionylglutaminyllysine
  d. histidylglycylglutamylisoleucine

℞ Clinical Applications

19.21 Refer to the structure of met-enkephalin (Chemistry Link to Health: Polypeptides in the Body) to answer each of the following:
  a. What is the C-terminus of met-enkephalin?
  b. What is the N-terminus of met-enkephalin?

  c. Write the amino acid order for met-enkephalin using single-letter abbreviations.

19.22 Refer to the structure of β-endorphin (Chemistry Link to Health: Polypeptides in the Body) to answer each of the following:
  a. What is the C-terminus of β-endorphin?
  b. What is the N-terminus of β-endorphin?
  c. Write the amino acid order for β-endorphin using single-letter abbreviations.

19.23 Peptides isolated from rapeseed that may lower blood pressure have the following sequence of amino acids. Draw the structure for each peptide and write the one-letter abbreviations.
  a. Arg–Ile–Tyr
  b. Val–Trp–Ile–Ser

19.24 Peptides from sweet potato with antioxidant properties have the following sequence of amino acids. Draw the structure for each peptide and write the one-letter abbreviations.
  a. Asp–Cys–Gly–Tyr
  b. Asn–Tyr–Asp–Glu–Tyr

19.4 Protein Structure: Primary and Secondary Levels

A **protein** is a polypeptide of 50 or more amino acids that has biological activity. Each protein in our cells has a unique sequence of amino acids that determines its three-dimensional structure and biological function.

Primary Structure

The **primary structure** of a protein is the particular sequence of amino acids held together by peptide bonds. For example, a hormone that stimulates the thyroid to release thyroxine is a tripeptide with the amino acid sequence Glu–His–Pro, EHP.

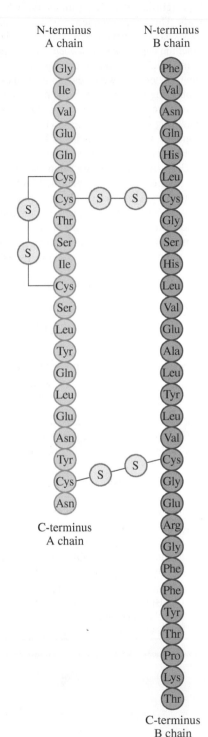

Although five other sequences of the same three amino acids are possible, such as His–Pro–Glu or Pro–His–Glu, they do not produce hormonal activity. Thus, the biological function of both peptides and proteins depends on the specific sequence of the amino acids.

The first protein to have its primary structure determined was insulin, which was accomplished by Frederick Sanger in 1953. Since that time, scientists have determined the amino acid sequences of many proteins. Insulin is a hormone that regulates the glucose level in the blood. In the primary structure of human insulin, there are two polypeptide chains. In chain A, there are 21 amino acids, and in chain B there are 30 amino acids. The polypeptide chains are held together by *disulfide bonds* formed by the thiol groups of the cysteine amino acids in each of the chains (see Figure 19.3). Today, human insulin with this exact structure is produced in large quantities through genetic engineering for the treatment of diabetes.

▶ **SAMPLE PROBLEM 19.5 Primary Structure**

What are the three-letter and one-letter abbreviations of the tetrapeptide that contains two valines, one proline, and one histidine if the N-terminus is histidine and the C-terminus is proline?

SOLUTION

The tetrapeptide starts with the N-terminus, histidine, followed by two valine residues, and ends with the C-terminus, proline.

   Three-letter abbreviations: His–Val–Val–Pro

   One-letter abbreviations: HVVP

STUDY CHECK 19.5

What are the three-letter and one-letter abbreviations of a tripeptide containing two glycines and one tyrosine, if the N-terminus is tyrosine?

ANSWER

Tyr–Gly–Gly (YGG)

FIGURE 19.3 ▶ The sequence of amino acids in human insulin is the primary structure.

◉ What kinds of bonds occur in the primary structure of a protein?

♡ Chemistry Link to Health

Protein Sequencing

A protein is a very large molecule, which has hundreds of amino acids. The unique sequence of amino acids in a primary structure allows us to predict the three-dimensional structure of a protein. Using a method called *protein sequencing*, scientists determine the order of amino acids. An enzyme or reagent is used to hydrolyze the protein into fragments for which the amino acid order (sequence) is obtained. Then using a different enzyme or reagent, the protein is hydrolyzed into different fragments, which are also sequenced. Finally, all the different fragments are arranged to find where they overlap. Only protein fragments of 20 amino acids or less can be accurately sequenced, so the large protein must be hydrolyzed into smaller pieces.

Digestive enzymes are often used to produce fragments because they hydrolyze specific peptide bonds. For example, the digestive enzyme trypsin only hydrolyzes peptide bonds after the basic amino acids arginine and lysine, whereas chymotrypsin hydrolyzes peptide bonds after the aromatic amino acids phenylalanine, tyrosine, and tryptophan. Table 19.6 shows some protein sequencing reagents and the amino acids after which hydrolysis occurs.

TABLE 19.6 Protein Sequencing Reagents

Reagent	Amino Acids Where Hydrolysis Occurs
Trypsin	After Arg and Lys (R or K)
Chymotrypsin	After Phe, Tyr, and Trp (F, Y, or W)
Cyanogen bromide (CNBr)	After Met (M)
Formic acid	After Asp (D)

Example of Protein Sequencing

The hormone α-melanotropin is a 13-amino acid peptide that stimulates cells to produce the pigment melanin. If the peptide is treated separately with chymotrypsin and cyanogen bromide, the fragments produced are shown.

Reagent	Fragments Produced
Chymotrypsin hydrolyzes peptide bonds after Phe, Tyr, and Trp.	Arg–Trp Ser–Tyr Gly–Lys–Pro–Val Ser–Met–Glu–His–Phe
Cyanogen bromide (CNBr) hydrolyzes peptide bonds after Met.	Ser–Tyr–Ser–Met Glu–His–Phe–Arg–Trp–Gly–Lys–Pro–Val

Now we can match the overlapping sections of amino acids from different fragments to determine their sequence in α-melanotropin. The pair Ser–Met is found in the fragments Ser–Tyr–Ser–Met and Ser–Met–Glu–His–Phe, which we can align in our series of fragments.

Ser–Tyr
Ser–Tyr–Ser–Met
        Ser–Met–Glu–His–Phe

From this group of fragments, we can write a sequence of seven amino acid residues as

Ser–Tyr–Ser–Met–Glu–His–Phe

The sequence Glu–His–Phe is also found in the longer fragment Glu–His–Phe–Arg–Trp–Gly–Lys–Pro–Val. By overlapping the two matching sections of amino acid residues, we obtain the complete sequence of amino acid residues.

Ser–Tyr–Ser–Met–Glu–His–Phe
        Glu–His–Phe–Arg–Trp–Gly–Lys–Pro–Val

Thus, the primary structure of the 13 amino acid residues in α-melanotropin is written as

Ser–Tyr–Ser–Met–Glu–His–Phe–Arg–Trp–Gly–Lys–Pro–Val

Now we can use this primary structure of α-melanotropin to see where chymotrypsin and CNBr reagent hydrolyzed peptide bonds to give the fragments we used to determine its sequence.

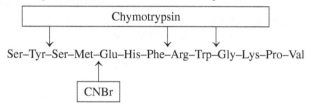

Secondary Structure

The **secondary structure** of a protein describes the structure that forms when amino acids form hydrogen bonds between the atoms in the backbone within a single polypeptide chain or between polypeptide chains. The most common types of secondary structures are the *alpha helix* and the *beta-pleated sheet*.

Alpha Helix

In an **alpha helix (α helix)**, hydrogen bonds form between the hydrogen atoms attached to the backbone nitrogen atoms (N—H), and the oxygen atoms in the backbone carbonyl (C=O) four amino acids away in the α helix (see Figure 19.4). The formation of many hydrogen bonds along the polypeptide chain gives the characteristic right-handed spiral shape of an alpha helix. All the residues of the different amino acids in the polypeptide extend to the outside of the helix.

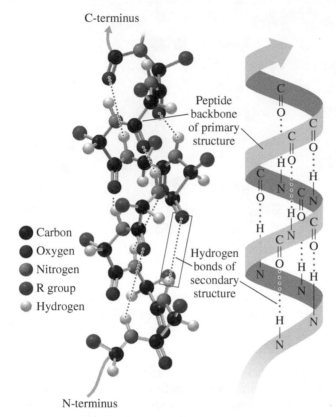

C-terminus

Peptide
backbone
of primary
structure

● Carbon
● Oxygen
● Nitrogen
● R group
● Hydrogen

Hydrogen
bonds of
secondary
structure

N-terminus

FIGURE 19.4 ▶ The α helix acquires a coiled shape of a right-handed spiral because of the hydrogen bonds between the hydrogen of the N—H group in one turn of the polypeptide and the oxygen in the C=O group in the next turn.

Q What are the partial charges of the H in N—H and the O in C=O that allows for hydrogen bonding?

Beta-Pleated Sheet

Another type of secondary structure found in proteins is the **beta-pleated sheet (β-pleated sheet)**. In a β-pleated sheet, short zigzagging lengths of polypeptide chain called β-strands are held together side by side by hydrogen bonds that form between oxygen atoms of the backbone carbonyl groups (C=O) in one section of the polypeptide chain, and the hydrogen atoms on the backbone nitrogen groups (N—H) in a nearby section of the polypeptide chain. A β-pleated sheet can form between adjacent polypeptide chains or within the same polypeptide chain when the rigid structure of the amino acid proline causes a bend in the polypeptide chain.

The tendency to form various kinds of secondary structures depends on the amino acids in a particular segment of the polypeptide chain. Typically, β-pleated sheets contain mostly amino acids with small residues such as glycine, valine, alanine, and serine, which extend above and below the β-pleated sheet. The α-helical regions in a protein have higher amounts of amino acids with large residues such as histidine, leucine, and methionine. The hydrogen bonds holding the β-pleated sheets tightly in place account for the strength and durability of fibrous proteins such as silk (see Figure 19.5).

In some proteins, the polypeptide chain consists mostly of α helices, whereas other proteins consist mostly of β-pleated sheets. However, in most proteins, there are sections of both α helices and β-pleated sheets. The sections of the polypeptide chain with no definite secondary structure are called *random coils*.

The secondary structure in silk is a β-pleated sheet.

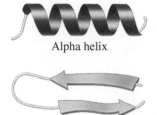
Alpha helix

Beta-pleated sheet

Protein with alpha helices
and beta-pleated sheets

A ribbon model of a protein shows
the regions of alpha helices and
beta-pleated sheets.

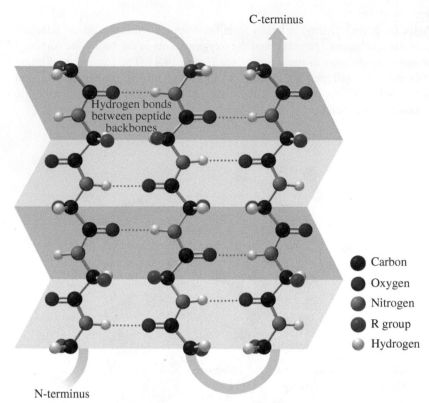

FIGURE 19.5 ▶ Hydrogen bonds between β-strands form a β-pleated sheet.

How do the hydrogen bonds differ between a β-pleated sheet and an α helix?

The regions of the α helices and β-pleated sheets are shown in a ribbon model in which the coiled portions represent the α helical backbone, and the long arrows that look like a piece of fettuccine represent the β-strands in a β-pleated sheet. Regions that are not α helices or β-pleated sheets are random regions indicated by thick lines.

Collagen

Collagen, the most abundant protein in the body, makes up as much as one-third of all protein in vertebrates. It is found in connective tissue, blood vessels, skin, tendons, ligaments, the cornea of the eye, and cartilage. The strong structure of collagen is a result of three helices woven together like a braid to form a **triple helix** (see Figure 19.6).

Collagen has a high content of glycine (33%), proline (22%), and alanine (12%), and smaller amounts of hydroxyproline and hydroxylysine, which are modified forms of proline and lysine. The —OH groups on these modified amino acids provide additional hydrogen bonds between the peptide chains to give strength to the collagen triple helix. When several triple helices wrap together as a braid, they form the fibrils that make up connective tissues and tendons. When a diet is deficient in vitamin C, collagen fibrils are weakened because the enzymes needed to form hydroxyproline and hydroxylysine require vitamin C. Collagen becomes less elastic as a person ages because additional bonds form between the fibrils. Bones, cartilage, and tendons become more brittle, and wrinkles are seen as the skin loses elasticity.

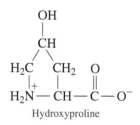
Hydroxyproline and hydroxylysine
provide additional hydrogen bonds
in the triple helices of collagen.

SAMPLE PROBLEM 19.6 Identifying Protein Structures

Identify the secondary structure (α helix, β-pleated sheet, or triple helix) described in each of the following statements:

a. a structure that has hydrogen bonds between adjacent polypeptide chains
b. three helical polypeptides woven together
c. a peptide chain with a coiled or corkscrew shape that is held in place by hydrogen bonds

SOLUTION

a. β-pleated sheet
b. triple helix
c. α helix

STUDY CHECK 19.6

Which attractive force holds secondary structures together in proteins?

ANSWER

hydrogen bonding

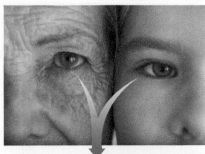

Triple helix   3 peptide chains

FIGURE 19.6 ► Collagen fibers are triple helices of polypeptide chains held together by hydrogen bonds.

Q What are some of the amino acids in collagen that form hydrogen bonds between the polypeptide chains?

 # Chemistry Link to **Health**

Protein Secondary Structures and Alzheimer's Disease

Alzheimer's disease is a form of dementia in which a person has increasing memory loss and inability to handle daily tasks. Alzheimer's usually occurs after age 60 and is irreversible. Although researchers are still investigating its causes, Alzheimer's patients have distinctly different brain tissue from people who do not have the disease. In the brain of a normal person, small beta-amyloid proteins, made up of 42 amino acids, exist in the alpha helical form. In the brain of a person with Alzheimer's, the beta-amyloid proteins change shape from the normal alpha helices that are soluble to insoluble, sticky beta-pleated sheets, forming clusters of protein fragments called *plaques*. The diagnosis of Alzheimer's disease is based on the presence of plaques and neurofibrillary tangles in the neurons that affect the transmission of nerve signals.

There is no cure for Alzheimer's disease, but there are medications that can slow its progression or lessen symptoms for a limited time. Medications like donepezil (Aricept) and rivastigmine (Exelon) help keep the levels of nerve transmitters high in the brain, which improves learning and memory in patients.

In patients with Alzheimer's disease, beta-amyloid proteins change from **(a)** a normal alpha-helical shape to **(b)** beta-pleated sheets that stick together and form plaques in the brain.

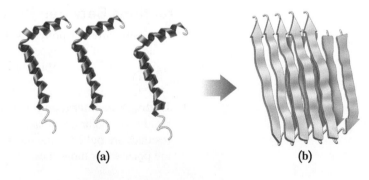

(a)   (b)

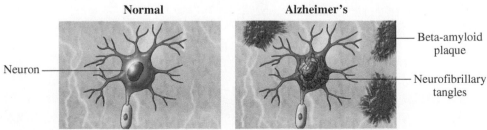

In an Alzheimer's brain, beta-amyloid plaques and neurofibrillary tangles damage the neurons and interfere with nerve signals.

QUESTIONS AND PROBLEMS

19.4 Protein Structure: Primary and Secondary Levels

LEARNING GOAL Describe the primary and secondary structures of a protein.

19.25 What type of bonding occurs in the primary structure of a protein?

19.26 How can two proteins with exactly the same number and type of amino acids have different primary structures?

19.27 Two peptides each contain one valine residue and two methionine residues. What are their possible primary structures?

19.28 What are the two different types of secondary protein structure?

19.29 What happens to the primary structure of a protein when a protein forms a secondary structure?

19.30 In an α helix, how does bonding occur between the amino acids in the polypeptide chain?

19.31 What is the difference in bonding between an α helix and a β-pleated sheet?

19.32 How is the structure of a β-pleated sheet different from that of a triple helix?

℞ Clinical Applications

19.33 Write the three-letter sequence for the amino acid residues in the octapeptide angiotensin II, a hormone involved in regulating blood pressure in humans, if treatment with chymotrypsin and trypsin gives the following fragments (see Chemistry Link to Health: Protein Sequencing):

Reagent	Fragments Produced
Chymotrypsin	Ile–His–Pro–Phe
	Asp–Arg–Val–Tyr
Trypsin	Asp–Arg
	Val–Tyr–Ile–His–Pro–Phe

19.34 Write the three-letter sequence for the amino acid residues in somatostatin, a peptide that inhibits the release of growth hormone, if treatment with chymotrypsin and trypsin gives the following fragments (see Chemistry Link to Health: Protein Sequencing):

Reagent	Fragments Produced
Chymotrypsin	Phe
	Trp
	Lys–Thr–Phe
	Thr–Ser–Cys
	Ala–Gly–Cys–Lys–Asn–Phe
Trypsin	Ala–Gly–Cys–Lys
	Asn–Phe–Phe–Trp–Lys
	Thr–Phe–Thr–Ser–Cys

LEARNING GOAL

Describe the tertiary and quaternary structures of a protein.

⚛ CORE CHEMISTRY SKILL

Identifying the Primary, Secondary, Tertiary, and Quaternary Structures of Proteins

19.5 Protein Structure: Tertiary and Quaternary Levels

The **tertiary structure** of a protein involves attractions and repulsions between the amino acid residues in the polypeptide chain. As interactions occur between the residues in different parts of the peptide chain, segments of the chain twist and bend to give the protein its specific three-dimensional shape.

Interactions Between Residues in Tertiary Structures

The tertiary structure of a protein is stabilized by interactions between the amino acid residues in one region of the polypeptide chain and the residues in other regions of the protein (see Figure 19.7). The stabilizing interactions of tertiary structures are detailed as follows:

1. **Hydrophilic interactions** occur between the external aqueous environment and the residues of polar amino acid residues. Sections of the polypeptide chain with polar residues are pulled to the outer surface of a protein where the residues interact with the polar water molecules.

2. **Hydrophobic interactions** occur between amino acid residues that have nonpolar residues. Within a protein, the amino acid residues with nonpolar residues are pushed toward each other and repelled by the hydrophilic interactions in water. This *hydrophobic effect* forms a nonpolar center at the interior of the protein.

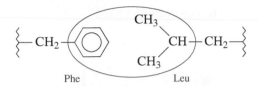

3. **Salt bridges** are ionic attractions between the charges of the acidic and basic residues of amino acid residues. For example, the positively charged residue of lysine forms a salt bridge (ionic bond) with the negatively charged residue of aspartate.

$$\{-CH_2-C\overset{O}{\underset{O^-}{\big<}} \quad H_3\overset{+}{N}-(CH_2)_4-\}$$

Asp   Lys

4. **Hydrogen bonds** form between the H of a polar residue and the O or N of a second polar amino acid residue. For example, a hydrogen bond occurs between the —OH groups of two serines or between the —OH of serine and the =O in asparagine.

$$\{-CH_2-O\overset{H\cdots\cdots O}{}\underset{NH_2}{C}-CH_2-\}$$

Ser   Asn

5. **Disulfide bonds** (—S—S—) are covalent bonds that form when the —SH groups of two cysteine residues are oxidized (H removed). In some proteins, there may be several disulfide bonds between the cysteine residues in the polypeptide chain; in others, there may be none.

$$\{-CH_2-S-S-CH_2-\}$$

Cys   Cys

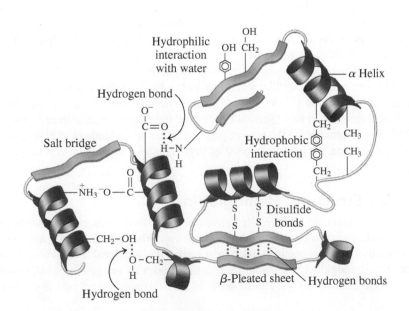

FIGURE 19.7 ▶ Interactions between amino acid residues fold a polypeptide into a specific three-dimensional shape called its tertiary structure.

◉ Why would one section of the polypeptide chain be pushed to the center whereas another section would be pulled to the surface?

> **SAMPLE PROBLEM 19.7** Interaction Between Residues in Tertiary Structures
>
> What type of interaction would you expect between the residues of each of the following amino acids in a tertiary structure of a protein?
>
> **a.** cysteine and cysteine   **b.** glutamate and lysine
> **c.** tyrosine and water
>
> **SOLUTION**
>
> | ANALYZE THE PROBLEM | Given | Need |
> |---|---|---|
> | | pairs of amino acids | type of interaction between residues |
>
> **a.** Two cysteines, each containing —SH, will form a disulfide bond.
> **b.** The interaction of the —COO⁻ in the residue of glutamate and the —NH₃⁺ in the residue of lysine will form an ionic bond called a salt bridge.
> **c.** The residue in tyrosine has an —OH group that is attracted to water by hydrophilic interactions.
>
> **STUDY CHECK 19.7**
>
> Would you expect to find valine and leucine on the outside or the inside of the tertiary structure? Why?
>
> **ANSWER**
>
> Both valine and leucine have nonpolar residues and would be found on the nonpolar inside of the tertiary structure.

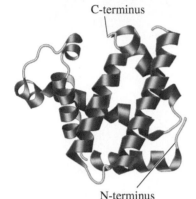

C-terminus

N-terminus

FIGURE 19.8 ▶ The ribbon model represents the tertiary structure of the polypeptide chain of myoglobin, a globular protein.

◉ Would hydrophilic amino acids be found on the outside or inside of the myoglobin structure?

α Helix

α-Keratin

FIGURE 19.9 ▶ The fibrous proteins of α-keratin wrap together to form fibrils of hair and wool.

◉ Why does hair have a large amount of cysteine amino acids?

Globular and Fibrous Proteins

A group of proteins known as **globular proteins** have compact, spherical shapes because sections of the polypeptide chain fold over on top of each other due to the various interactions between amino acid residues. It is the globular proteins that carry out the work of the cells: functions such as synthesis, transport, and metabolism.

Myoglobin is a globular protein that stores oxygen in skeletal muscle. High concentrations of myoglobin are found in the muscles of sea mammals, such as seals and whales allowing them to stay under the water for a long time. Myoglobin contains 153 amino acids in a single polypeptide chain with about three-fourths of the chain in the α helix secondary structure. The polypeptide chain, including its helical regions, forms a compact tertiary structure by folding upon itself (see Figure 19.8). Within the tertiary structure, oxygen (O_2) binds to an iron ion located in an organic compound called a *heme* within the protein.

The **fibrous proteins** are proteins that consist of long, thin, fiber-like shapes. They are typically involved in the structure of cells and tissues. Two types of fibrous protein are the α- and β-keratins. The α-keratins are the proteins that make up hair, wool, skin, and nails. In hair, three α helices coil together like a braid to form a fibril. Within the fibril, the α helices are held together by disulfide (—S—S—) linkages between the residues of the many cysteine amino acid residues in hair. Several fibrils bind together to form a strand of hair (see Figure 19.9). The β-keratins are the type of proteins found in the feathers of birds and scales of reptiles. In β-keratins, the proteins consist of large amounts of a β-pleated sheet structure.

Quaternary Structure: Hemoglobin

Although many proteins are biologically active as tertiary structures, most proteins require two or more tertiary structures to be biologically active. When a biologically active protein consists of two or more polypeptide chains or subunits, the structural level is called **quaternary structure**. Hemoglobin, a globular protein that transports oxygen in blood, consists of four polypeptide chains: two α-chains with 141 amino acids, and two β-chains with

146 amino acids. Although the α-chains and β-chains have different sequences of amino acids, they both form similar tertiary structures with similar shapes (see Figure 19.10).

In the quaternary structure, the subunits are held together by the same interactions that stabilize their tertiary structures, such as hydrogen bonds and salt bridges between R groups of amino acid residues, disulfide bonds, and hydrophobic interactions. Each subunit of hemoglobin is a globular protein with an embedded heme group, which contains one iron ion that can bind an oxygen molecule. In the adult hemoglobin molecule, all four subunits ($\alpha_2\beta_2$) *must* be combined for hemoglobin to properly function as an oxygen carrier. Therefore, the complete quaternary structure of hemoglobin can bind and transport up to four molecules of oxygen.

Hemoglobin and myoglobin have similar biological functions. Hemoglobin carries oxygen in the blood, whereas myoglobin carries oxygen in muscle. Myoglobin, a single polypeptide chain with a molar mass of 17 000, has about one-fourth the molar mass of hemoglobin (67 000). The tertiary structure of the single polypeptide myoglobin is almost identical to the tertiary structure of each of the subunits of hemoglobin. Myoglobin carries one molecule of oxygen, whereas hemoglobin carries four oxygen molecules. The similarity in tertiary structures allows each protein to bind and release oxygen in a similar manner. Table 19.7 and Figure 19.11 summarize the structural levels of proteins.

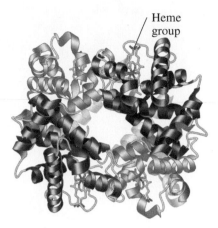

FIGURE 19.10 ▶ In the ribbon model of hemoglobin, the quaternary structure is made up of four polypeptide subunits—two (orange) are α-chains and two (red) are β-chains. The heme groups (green) in the four subunits bind oxygen.

Q What is the difference between a tertiary structure and a quaternary structure?

TABLE 19.7 Summary of Structural Levels in Proteins

Structural Level	Characteristics
Primary	Peptide bonds join amino acids in a specific sequence in a polypeptide.
Secondary	The α helix or β-pleated sheet, forms by hydrogen bonding between the backbone atoms in the peptide bonds along the chain.
Tertiary	A polypeptide folds into a compact, three-dimensional shape stabilized by interactions (hydrogen bonds, salt bridges, hydrophobic, hydrophilic, disulfide) between amino acid residues to form a biologically active protein.
Quaternary	Two or more protein subunits combine and are stabilized by interactions (hydrogen bonds, salt bridges, hydrophobic) between amino acid residues to form a biologically active protein.

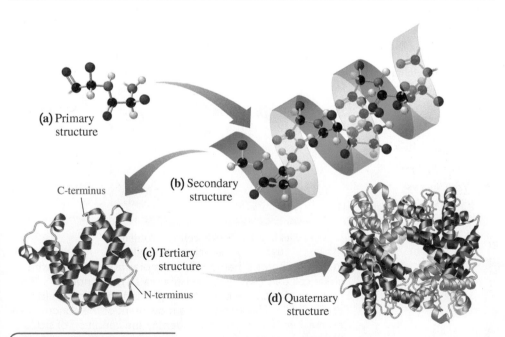

(a) Primary structure

(b) Secondary structure

C-terminus

(c) Tertiary structure

N-terminus

(d) Quaternary structure

FIGURE 19.11 ▶ Proteins consist of (a) primary, (b) secondary, (c) tertiary, and often times (d) quaternary structural levels.

Q What is the difference between a primary structure and a tertiary structure?

Interactive Video

Different Levels of Protein Structure

▶ **SAMPLE PROBLEM 19.8 Identifying Protein Structure**

Indicate whether the following interactions are responsible for primary, secondary, tertiary, or quaternary protein structures:

a. disulfide bonds that form between portions of a protein chain
b. peptide bonds that form a chain of amino acids
c. hydrogen bonds between the H of a peptide bond and the O of a peptide bond four amino acids away

SOLUTION

ANALYZE THE PROBLEM	Given	Need
	interactions of amino acid residues	identify structural level of protein

a. Disulfide bonds are a type of interaction between amino acid residues found in the tertiary and quaternary levels of protein structure.

b. The peptide bonds in the sequence of amino acids form the primary level of protein structure.

c. The hydrogen bonds between the peptide bonds along the polypeptide chain form the secondary structures of α helix or β-pleated sheet.

STUDY CHECK 19.8

What structural level is represented by the hydrophobic side chains of the amino acid residues at the center of a globular protein?

ANSWER

tertiary structure

Chemistry Link to **Health**
Sickle Cell Anemia

Sickle cell anemia is a disease caused by an abnormality in the shape of one of the subunits of the hemoglobin protein. In the β-chain, the sixth amino acid, glutamate, which is polar acidic, is replaced by valine, a nonpolar amino acid.

Because valine has a nonpolar residue, it is attracted to the nonpolar regions within the beta hemoglobin chains. The affected red blood cells (RBCs) change from a rounded shape to a crescent shape, which interferes with their ability to transport adequate quantities of oxygen. Hydrophobic interactions also cause sickle cell hemoglobin molecules to stick together. They form insoluble fibers of sickle cell hemoglobin that clog capillaries, where they cause inflammation, pain, and organ damage. Critically low oxygen levels may occur in the affected tissues.

In sickle cell anemia, both genes for the altered hemoglobin must be inherited. However, both sickled cells and normal cells are found in persons who carry one gene for sickle cell hemoglobin, a condition known as *sickle cell trait* that provides some resistance to malaria.

Normal β-chain: Val–His–Leu–Thr–Pro–Glu–Glu–Lys–   ← Polar acidic amino acid

Sickled β-chain: Val–His–Leu–Thr–Pro–Val–Glu–Lys–   ← Nonpolar amino acid

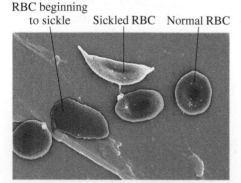

RBC beginning to sickle   Sickled RBC   Normal RBC

Diagnosing Sickle Cell Anemia—Electrophoresis

Proteins can be isolated from each other and used to diagnose diseases such as sickle cell anemia by a technique called *electrophoresis*. In electrophoresis, used to identify and diagnose sickle cell anemia, samples containing normal hemoglobin and sickle cell hemoglobin proteins are placed on a gel and an electric current is applied. The proteins move along the gel based on their charge, size, and shape.

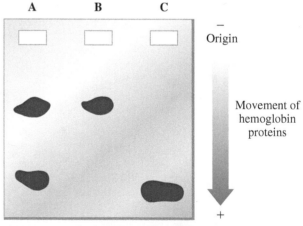

In electrophoresis, hemoglobin samples from patients with sickle cell trait (**A**), sickle cell anemia (**B**), and normal hemoglobin (**C**) are placed on a gel and an electric field is applied. The differences in the movement of the abnormal and normal hemoglobin proteins identify the condition of sickle cell trait or anemia.

QUESTIONS AND PROBLEMS

19.5 Protein Structure: Tertiary and Quaternary Levels

LEARNING GOAL Describe the tertiary and quaternary structures of a protein.

19.35 What type of interaction would you expect between the following groups in a tertiary structure?
  a. cysteine and cysteine
  b. glutamate and lysine
  c. serine and aspartate
  d. leucine and leucine

19.36 What type of interaction would you expect between the following groups in a tertiary structure?
  a. phenylalanine and isoleucine
  b. aspartate and histidine
  c. asparagine and tyrosine
  d. alanine and proline

19.37 A portion of a polypeptide chain contains the following sequence of amino acids:

  –Leu–Val–Cys–Asp–

  a. Which amino acid can form a disulfide bond?
  b. Which amino acids are likely to be found on the inside of the protein structure? Why?
  c. Which amino acids would be found on the outside of the protein? Why?
  d. How does the primary structure of a protein affect its tertiary structure?

19.38 About one-half of the 153 amino acids in myoglobin have nonpolar residues.
  a. Where would you expect those amino acids to be located in the tertiary structure?
  b. Where would you expect the polar residues to be in the tertiary structure?
  c. Why is myoglobin more soluble in water than silk or wool?

19.39 Indicate whether each of the following statements describes the primary, secondary, tertiary, or quaternary protein structure:
  a. Residues interact to form disulfide bonds or ionic bonds.
  b. Peptide bonds join the amino acids in a polypeptide chain.
  c. Several polypeptides in a β-pleated sheet are held together by hydrogen bonds between adjacent chains.
  d. Hydrogen bonding between amino acid residues in the same polypeptide gives a coiled shape to the protein.

19.40 Indicate whether each of the following statements describes the primary, secondary, tertiary, or quaternary protein structure:
  a. Hydrophobic amino acid residues seeking a nonpolar environment move toward the inside of the folded protein.
  b. Hydrophilic amino acid residues move to the polar aqueous environment outside the protein.
  c. An active protein contains four tertiary subunits.
  d. In sickle cell anemia, valine replaces glutamate in the β-chain.

19.6 Protein Hydrolysis and Denaturation

LEARNING GOAL

Describe the hydrolysis and denaturation of proteins.

Recall that peptide bonds are formed through condensation reactions. Similarly, they can be broken through hydrolysis reactions yielding individual amino acids. This process occurs in the stomach when enzymes such as pepsin or trypsin catalyze the hydrolysis of proteins to give amino acids. This hydrolysis breaks up the primary structure by breaking the covalent peptide bonds that link the amino acids. In the digestion of proteins, the amino acids are absorbed through the intestinal walls and carried to the cells, where they can be used to synthesize new proteins.

Alanylglycylserine (Ala–Gly–Ser, AGS)

Hydrolysis

Alanine (Ala, A)   Glycine (Gly, G)   Serine (Ser, S)

Denaturation of Proteins

Denaturation of a protein occurs when there is a change that disrupts the interactions between residues that stabilize the secondary, tertiary, or quaternary structure. However, the covalent amide bonds of the primary structure are not affected.

The loss of secondary and tertiary structures occurs when conditions change, such as increasing the temperature or making the pH very acidic or basic. If the pH changes, the basic and acidic residues lose their ionic charges and cannot form salt bridges, which causes a change in the shape of the protein. Denaturation can also occur by adding certain organic compounds or heavy metal ions, or through mechanical agitation. When the interactions between the residues are disrupted, a globular protein unfolds like a wet spaghetti noodle. With the loss of its overall shape (tertiary structure), the protein is no longer biologically active (see Figure 19.12).

FIGURE 19.12 ▶ Denaturation of a protein occurs when the interactions of residues that stabilize secondary, tertiary, or quaternary structures are disrupted, which destroys the shape and renders the protein biologically inactive.

Q What are some ways in which proteins are denatured?

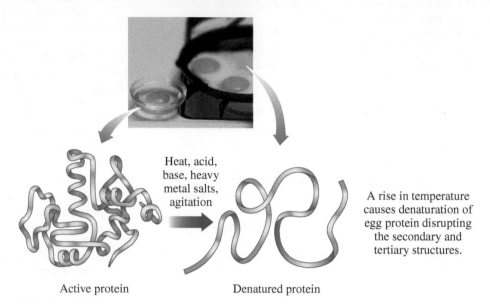

Heat, acid, base, heavy metal salts, agitation

A rise in temperature causes denaturation of egg protein disrupting the secondary and tertiary structures.

Active protein   Denatured protein

Heat

Whenever you cook food, you are using heat to denature protein. Hydrogen bonds and hydrophobic interactions between nonpolar residues are disrupted. Few proteins can remain biologically active above 50 °C. The nutritional value of the proteins in food is not changed, but they are more digestible. High temperatures are also used to disinfect surgical instruments and gowns by denaturing the proteins of any bacteria present.

Acids and Bases

Like a cooked egg, the denatured proteins in milk form more of a semisolid when denatured. In the preparation of yogurt and cheese, bacteria that produce lactic acid are added to denature the proteins by changing the pH. A change in pH breaks down hydrogen bonds and disrupts the ionic bonds (salt bridges). Tannic acid, a weak acid used in burn ointments, is applied to the site of the burn to coagulate proteins, which forms a protective cover and prevents further loss of fluid from the burn.

Organic Compounds

Ethanol and isopropyl alcohol act as disinfectants by exchanging the bacterial protein's hydrogen bonds to water with their own and disrupting the side chain intramolecular hydrogen bonding. An alcohol swab is used to clean wounds or to prepare the skin for an injection because the alcohol passes through the cell walls and coagulates the proteins inside the bacteria.

Heavy Metal Ions

In hospitals, a dilute (1%) solution of $AgNO_3$ is placed in the eyes of newborn babies to destroy the bacteria that cause gonorrhea. Heavy metal ions such as Ag^+, Pb^{2+}, and Hg^{2+} denature protein by forming bonds with ionic residues or reacting with disulfide ($-S-S-$) bonds. If heavy metals are ingested, they act as poisons by severely denaturing body proteins and disrupting metabolic reactions. An antidote is a high-protein food, such as milk, eggs, or cheese, that combines with the heavy metal ions until the stomach can be pumped.

Agitation

The whipping of cream and the beating of egg whites are examples of using mechanical agitation to denature protein. The whipping action stretches the polypeptide chains until the stabilizing interactions are disrupted. Table 19.8 summarizes protein denaturation.

TABLE 19.8 Protein Denaturation

Denaturing Agent	Bonds Disrupted	Examples
Heat Above 50 °C	Hydrogen bonds; hydrophobic interactions between nonpolar residues	Cooking food and autoclaving surgical items
Acids and Bases	Hydrogen bonds between polar residues; salt bridges	Lactic acid from bacteria, which denatures milk protein in the preparation of yogurt and cheese
Organic Compounds	Hydrophobic interactions	Ethanol and isopropyl alcohol, which disinfect wounds and prepare the skin for injections
Heavy Metal Ions Ag^+, Pb^{2+}, and Hg^{2+}	Disulfide bonds in proteins by forming ionic bonds	Mercury and lead poisoning
Agitation	Hydrogen bonds and hydrophobic interactions by stretching polypeptide chains and disrupting stabilizing interactions	Whipped cream, meringue made from egg whites

▶ SAMPLE PROBLEM 19.9 Denaturation of Proteins

Describe the denaturation process in each of the following:

a. An appetizer known as ceviche is prepared without heat by placing slices of raw fish in a solution of lemon or lime juice. After 3 or 4 h, the fish appears to be "cooked."
b. When baking scalloped potatoes, the added milk curdles (forms solids).

SOLUTION

a. The acids in lemon or lime juice break down the hydrogen bonds between polar residues and disrupt salt bridges, which denature the proteins of the fish.
b. The heat during baking breaks apart hydrogen bonds and hydrophobic interactions between nonpolar residues in the milk proteins. When the milk denatures, the proteins become insoluble and form solids called curds.

STUDY CHECK 19.9

Why is a dilute solution of $AgNO_3$ used to disinfect the eyes of newborn infants?

ANSWER

The heavy metal Ag^+ denatures the proteins in bacteria that cause gonorrhea.

Explore Your World

Denaturation of Milk Protein

Pour some milk in five glasses. Add the following to the milk samples in glasses 1 to 4. The fifth glass of milk is a reference sample.

1. Vinegar, drop by drop. Stir.
2. One-half teaspoon of meat tenderizer. Stir.
3. One teaspoon of fresh pineapple juice. (Canned juice has been heated and cannot be used.)
4. One teaspoon of fresh pineapple juice after the juice is heated to boiling.

Questions

1. How did the appearance of the milk change in each of the samples?
2. What enzyme is listed on the package label of the tenderizer?
3. How does the effect of the heated pineapple juice compare with that of the fresh juice? Explain.
4. Why is cooked pineapple used when making gelatin (a protein) desserts?

QUESTIONS AND PROBLEMS

19.6 Protein Hydrolysis and Denaturation

LEARNING GOAL Describe the hydrolysis and denaturation of proteins.

19.41 What products would result from the complete hydrolysis of Gly–Ala–Ser?

19.42 Would the hydrolysis products of the tripeptide Ala–Ser–Gly be the same or different from the products in problem 19.41? Explain.

19.43 What dipeptides could be produced from the partial hydrolysis of His–Met–Gly–Val?

19.44 What tripeptides could be produced from the partial hydrolysis of Ser–Leu–Gly–Gly–Ala?

19.45 What structural level of a protein is affected by hydrolysis?

19.46 What structural level of a protein is affected by denaturation?

Clinical Applications

19.47 Indicate the changes in the secondary and tertiary structural levels of proteins for each of the following:
   a. An egg placed in water at 100 °C is soft-boiled after 3 min.
   b. Prior to giving an injection, the skin is wiped with an alcohol swab.
   c. Surgical instruments are placed in a 120 °C autoclave.
   d. During surgery, a wound is closed by cauterization (heat).

19.48 Indicate the changes in the secondary and tertiary structural levels of proteins for each of the following:
   a. Tannic acid is placed on a burn.
   b. Milk is heated to 60 °C to make yogurt.
   c. To avoid spoilage, seeds are treated with a solution of $HgCl_2$.
   d. Hamburger is cooked at high temperatures to destroy *E. coli* bacteria that may cause intestinal illness.

Clinical Update
Alzheimer's Diagnosis

In preparation for the PET scan, Victoria gives Edith an injection of a radioactive fluorine compound called Vizamyl (flutemetamol F-18). The activity of the F-18 was 4.0 mCi. The PET scan for Edith started 90 min following the IV injection.

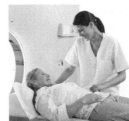

Vizamyl

Fluorine-18, which has a half-life of 110 min, decays by positron emission to stable oxygen-18. Vizamyl specifically binds to the beta-amyloid proteins, which are detected by the PET scans.

Beta-amyloid refers to proteins containing 40 amino acid residues, which are found as amyloid plaque in the brains of Alzheimer's patients.

Edith and her husband return to the clinic to learn the results of her PET scan. A PET scan of the brain indicates the level of plaque formation in the brain of adults with cognitive declines. Victoria shows Edith and her husband the PET scan images and points out dark regions in the brain where the Vizamyl has identified beta-amyloid plaque formation. Edith is diagnosed with early Alzheimer's.

Edith is prescribed an acetylcholinesterase inhibitor that can slow the progression of the disease by keeping levels of the neurotransmitter acetylcholine high, but will not cure it. Edith's husband is relieved to have a diagnosis so that he can better assist Edith in the future.

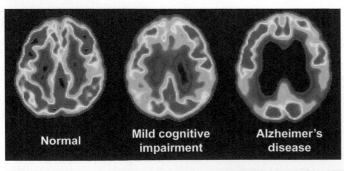

Normal / Mild cognitive impairment / Alzheimer's disease

Clinical Applications

19.49 When Edith leaves the clinic 5.5 h after her injection of Vizamyl F-18, what is the activity of the radioisotope in her body?

19.50 Write the balanced nuclear equation for the positron emission by F-18 to form O-18.

19.51 What is the difference between the secondary structures of the beta-amyloid protein in a normal adult brain and the brain of an adult with Alzheimer's disease?

19.52 What causes the formation of beta-amyloid plaques in Alzheimer's disease?

19.53 Determine the amino acid sequence of a peptide section of beta-amyloid containing 10 amino acid residues when it is treated with chymotrypsin and trypsin to give the following fragments:

Reagent	Fragments Produced from Hydrolysis
Chymotrypsin	Glu–Phe Glu–Val Arg–His–Asp–Ser–Gly–Tyr
Trypsin	Glu–Phe–Arg His–Asp–Ser–Gly–Tyr–Glu–Val

19.54 Determine the amino acid sequence of a peptide section of beta-amyloid containing 10 amino acid residues when it is treated with chymotrypsin and trypsin to give the following fragments:

Reagent	Fragments Produced from Hydrolysis
Chymotrypsin	Phe Ala–Glu–Asp His–His–Gln–Lys–Leu–Val–Phe
Trypsin	His–His–Gln–Lys Leu–Val–Phe–Phe–Ala–Glu–Asp

CONCEPT MAP

AMINO ACIDS AND PROTEINS

Proteins

contain
Amino Acids

that have
Ammonium, Carboxylate, and R Groups

that form
Zwitterions

at their
Isoelectric Points (pI)

contain peptide bonds between
Amino Acids

in a specific order as the
Primary Structure

and hydrogen bonds as the
Secondary Structure

with interactions that give
Tertiary and Quaternary Structures

undergo
Hydrolysis

to give
Amino Acids

or
Denaturation

when
Proteins Change 2°, 3°, 4° Shape

from
Heat, Acids and Bases, Organic Compounds, Heavy Metal Ions, or Agitation

CHAPTER REVIEW

19.1 Proteins and Amino Acids
LEARNING GOAL Classify proteins by their functions. Give the name and abbreviations for an amino acid, and draw its zwitterion.

- Some proteins are enzymes or hormones, whereas others are important in structure, transport, protection, storage, and muscle contraction.
- A group of 20 amino acids provides the molecular building blocks of proteins.
- Attached to the central α carbon of each amino acid are a hydrogen atom, an ammonium group, a carboxylate group, and a unique R group.
- The R group gives an amino acid the property of being nonpolar, polar, acidic, or basic.

19.2 Amino Acids as Acids and Bases
LEARNING GOAL Using the zwitterion for an amino acid at its isoelectric point, draw its ionized structures at pH values above or below its isoelectric point.

- Amino acids exist as positive ions at pH values below their pI values, and as negative ions at pH values above their pI values.
- At the isoelectric point, ionized amino acids have an overall charge of zero.

19.3 Formation of Peptides
LEARNING GOAL Draw the structure for a peptide, give its three-letter and one-letter abbreviations, and name.

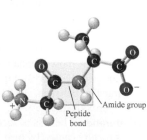

- Peptides form when an amide bond links the carboxylate group of one amino acid and the ammonium group of a second amino acid.
- Long chains of amino acids that are biologically active are called proteins.
- The primary structure of a protein is its sequence of amino acids joined by peptide bonds.
- Peptides are named from the N-terminus by replacing the last syllable of each amino acid name with *yl* followed by the amino acid name of the C-terminus.

19.4 Protein Structure: Primary and Secondary Levels

LEARNING GOAL Describe the primary and secondary structures of a protein.

- Amino acid sequences can be determined by examining overlapping peptide fragments.
- In the secondary structure, hydrogen bonds between atoms in the peptide bonds produce a characteristic shape such as an α helix or β-pleated sheet.
- The most abundant form of protein in the body is collagen, which is composed of fibrils of triple helices that are hydrogen bonded.

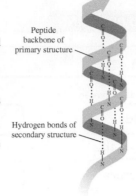

Peptide backbone of primary structure

Hydrogen bonds of secondary structure

19.5 Protein Structure: Tertiary and Quaternary Levels

LEARNING GOAL Describe the tertiary and quaternary structures of a protein.

- In globular proteins, the polypeptide chain, including α helical and β-pleated sheet regions, folds upon itself to form a tertiary structure.

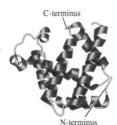

C-terminus

N-terminus

- A tertiary structure is stabilized by interactions that push amino acids with hydrophobic residues to the center and pull amino acids with hydrophilic residues to the surface, and by interactions between amino acids with residues that form hydrogen bonds, disulfide bonds, and salt bridges.
- In a quaternary structure, two or more tertiary subunits are joined together for biological activity, held by the same interactions found in tertiary structures.

19.6 Protein Hydrolysis and Denaturation

LEARNING GOAL Describe the hydrolysis and denaturation of proteins.

- Hydrolysis of a protein occurs when peptide bonds in the primary structure are broken by enzyme action to produce amino acids.

Heat, acid, base, heavy metal salts, agitation

Active protein → Denatured protein

- Denaturation of a protein destroys the secondary, tertiary, or quaternary structures of a protein with a loss of biological activity.
- Denaturation is caused by high temperatures, acids or bases, organic compounds, metal ions, or agitation.

KEY TERMS

acidic amino acid An amino acid that has an R group with a carboxylate group ($-COO^-$).

α(alpha) helix A secondary level of protein structure, in which hydrogen bonds connect the $N-H$ of one peptide bond with the $C=O$ of a peptide bond farther along in the chain to form a coiled or corkscrew structure.

amino acid The building block of proteins, consisting of a hydrogen atom, an ammonium group, a carboxylate group, and a unique R group attached to the α carbon.

backbone The repeating sequence of $N-C-C$ atoms from the amino acid residues in a protein.

basic amino acid An amino acid that contains an amine R group.

β(beta)-pleated sheet A secondary level of protein structure that consists of hydrogen bonds between peptide links in parallel polypeptide chains.

C-terminus (C-terminal amino acid) The end amino acid in a peptide chain with a free carboxylate group ($-COO^-$).

collagen The most abundant form of protein in the body, which is composed of fibrils of triple helices that are hydrogen bonded together between $-OH$ groups of hydroxyproline and hydroxylysine.

denaturation The loss of secondary, tertiary, and quaternary protein structure caused by heat, acids, bases, organic compounds, heavy metals, and/or agitation.

disulfide bond Covalent $-S-S-$ bond that forms between the $-SH$ groups of two cysteines in a protein, which stabilizes tertiary and quaternary structures.

essential amino acid Amino acid that must be supplied by the diet because it is not synthesized by the body.

fibrous protein A protein that is insoluble in water; consisting of polypeptide chains with α helices or β-pleated sheets, and comprising the fibers of hair, wool, skin, nails, and silk.

globular protein Protein that acquires a compact shape from attractions between the residues of the amino acids in the protein.

hydrogen bond The interaction between water and the polar residues such as $-OH$, $-NH_3^+$, and $-COO^-$ on the outside surface of a polypeptide chain.

hydrophilic interaction The attraction between polar residues on the protein surface and water.

hydrophobic interaction The attraction between nonpolar residues on the inside of a globular protein.

isoelectric point (pI) The pH at which an amino acid exists as a zwitterion with a net charge of zero.

N-terminus (N-terminal amino acid) The first amino acid in a peptide with a free $-NH_3^+$ group.

nonpolar amino acid Amino acid with a nonpolar R group containing only C and H atoms.

peptide The combination of two or more amino acids joined by peptide bonds; dipeptide, tripeptide, and so on.

peptide bond The amide bond in peptides that joins the carboxylate group of one amino acid with the ammonium group in the next amino acid.

polar amino acid (neutral) Amino acid with a polar R group.

primary structure The specific sequence of the amino acid residues in a protein.

protein A polypeptide of 50 or more amino acid residues that has biological activity.

quaternary structure A protein structure in which two or more protein subunits form an active protein.

salt bridge The attraction between the ionized residues of basic and acidic amino acids in the tertiary structure of a protein.

secondary structure The formation of an α helix or β-pleated sheet by hydrogen bonds.

tertiary structure The folding of the secondary structure of a protein into a compact structure that is stabilized by the interactions of residues such as ionic and disulfide bonds.

triple helix The protein structure found in collagen consisting of three helical polypeptide chains woven together like a braid.

zwitterion The ionized form of an amino acid at its pI that has an ammonium group ($-NH_3^+$) and a carboxylate group ($-COO^-$).

⚛ CORE CHEMISTRY SKILLS

The chapter section containing each Core Chemistry Skill is shown in parentheses at the end of each heading.

Drawing the Zwitterion for an Amino Acid (19.1)

- The central α carbon of each amino acid is bonded to an ammonium group ($—NH_3^+$), a carboxylate group ($—COO^-$), a hydrogen atom, and a unique R group.
- The R group gives an amino acid the property of being nonpolar, polar, acidic, or basic.
- At the isoelectric point (pI), an amino acid has an overall charge of zero.
- Amino acids exist as positive ions at pH values below their pI values, and as negative ions at pH values above their pI values.

Example: Draw the zwitterion for cysteine.

Answer:

$$\begin{array}{c} SH \\ | \\ CH_2 \quad O \\ | \qquad || \\ H_3\overset{+}{N}—C—C—O^- \\ | \\ H \end{array}$$

Identifying the Primary, Secondary, Tertiary, and Quaternary Structures of Proteins (19.4, 19.5)

- The primary structure of a protein is the sequence of amino acids joined by peptide bonds.

- In the secondary structures of proteins, hydrogen bonds between atoms in the peptide bonds produce an alpha helix or a beta-pleated sheet.
- The tertiary structure of a protein is stabilized by residues that form hydrogen bonds, disulfide bonds, and salt bridges, and hydrophobic residues that move to the center and hydrophilic residues that move to the surface.
- In a quaternary structure, two or more tertiary subunits are combined for biological activity, held by the same interactions found in tertiary structures.

Example: Identify the following as characteristic of the primary, secondary, tertiary, or quaternary structure of a protein:
   a. The residues of two amino acids interact to form a salt bridge.
   b. Eight amino acids form peptide bonds.
   c. A polypeptide forms an alpha helix.
   d. Two amino acids with hydrophobic residues move toward the inside of the folded protein.
   e. A protein with biological activity contains four tertiary polypeptide subunits.

Answer: **a.** tertiary, quaternary
   b. primary
   c. secondary
   d. tertiary
   e. quaternary

UNDERSTANDING THE CONCEPTS

The chapter sections to review are shown in parentheses at the end of each question.

19.55 Seeds and vegetables are often deficient in one or more essential amino acids. The following table shows which essential amino acids are present in each food. (19.1)

Source	Lysine	Tryptophan	Methionine
Oatmeal	No	Yes	Yes
Rice	No	Yes	Yes
Garbanzo beans	Yes	No	Yes
Lima beans	Yes	No	No
Cornmeal	No	No	Yes

Use the table to decide if each food combination provides the essential amino acids lysine, tryptophan, and methionine.
   a. rice and garbanzo beans
   b. lima beans and cornmeal
   c. a salad of garbanzo beans and lima beans

19.56 Use the table in problem 19.55 to decide if each food combination provides the essential amino acids lysine, tryptophan, and methionine. (19.1)
   a. rice and lima beans
   b. rice and oatmeal
   c. oatmeal and lima beans

Oatmeal is deficient in the essential amino acid lysine.

Use the following condensed structural formulas of cysteine (**1** to **4**) to answer problems 19.57 and 19.58:

$$\begin{array}{c} SH \\ | \\ CH_2 \quad O \\ | \qquad || \\ H_2N—CH—C—O^- \\ \textbf{(1)} \end{array} \qquad \begin{array}{c} SH \\ | \\ CH_2 \quad O \\ | \qquad || \\ H_3\overset{+}{N}—CH—C—OH \\ \textbf{(2)} \end{array}$$

$$\begin{array}{c} SH \\ | \\ CH_2 \quad O \\ | \qquad || \\ H_3\overset{+}{N}—CH—C—O^- \\ \textbf{(3)} \end{array} \qquad \begin{array}{c} SH \\ | \\ CH_2 \quad O \\ | \qquad || \\ H_2N—CH—C—OH \\ \textbf{(4)} \end{array}$$

19.57 If cysteine, an amino acid prevalent in hair, has a pI of 5.1, which condensed structural formula would it have in solutions with each the following pH values? (19.2)
a. pH = 10.5   **b.** pH = 5.1
c. pH = 1.8

The proteins in hair contain many cysteine residues that form disulfide bonds.

19.58 If cysteine, an amino acid prevalent in hair, has a pI of 5.1, which condensed structural formula would it have in solutions with each of the following pH values? (19.2)
a. pH = 2.0   **b.** pH = 3.5
c. pH = 9.1

19.59 Each of three peptides contains one valine residue and two serine residues. Use their three-letter and one-letter abbreviations to write the three possible peptides. (19.3, 19.4)

19.60 Each of three peptides contains one glycine residue, one alanine residue, and two isoleucine residues. In this peptide, the N-terminus is glycine. Use their three-letter and one-letter abbreviations to write the three possible peptides. (19.3, 19.4)

19.61 Identify the amino acids and the type of interaction that occurs between the following amino acid residues in a tertiary protein structure: (19.5)

a.
$$-CH_2-\overset{\overset{\displaystyle O}{\|}}{C}-NH_2 \quad \text{and} \quad HO-CH_2-$$

b. $-CH_2-SH \quad \text{and} \quad HS-CH_2-$

c.
$$-CH_2-\overset{\overset{\displaystyle CH_3}{|}}{CH}-CH_3 \quad \text{and} \quad CH_3-$$

19.62 What type of interaction would you expect between the residues of the following amino acids in a tertiary structure? (19.2, 19.5)
a. threonine and glutamine
b. valine and alanine
c. arginine and glutamate

ADDITIONAL QUESTIONS AND PROBLEMS

19.63 Draw the condensed structural formula for each of the following amino acids at pH 4.0: (19.1, 19.2)
a. serine   **b.** alanine   **c.** lysine

19.64 Draw the condensed structural formula for each of the following amino acids at pH 11.0 : (19.1, 19.2)
a. cysteine   **b.** aspartate   **c.** valine

19.65 a. Draw the structure for –Ser–Lys–Asp–. (19.3, 19.4, 19.5)
b. Would you expect to find this segment at the center or at the surface of a globular protein? Why?

19.66 a. Draw the structure for –Val–Ala–Leu–. (19.3, 19.4, 19.5)
b. Would you expect to find this segment at the center or at the surface of a globular protein? Why?

19.67 a. Where in the body is collagen found? (19.4)
b. What type of structure is used to form collagen?

19.68 a. What are some functions of collagen? (19.4)
b. What amino acids give strength to collagen?

19.69 Would you expect a polypeptide with a high content of His, Met, and Leu to have more α-helical sections or β-pleated sheet sections? (19.4)

19.70 Why would a polypeptide with a high content of Val, Pro, and Ser be likely to have more α-helical sections than β-pleated sheet sections? (19.4)

19.71 If serine was replaced by valine in a protein, how would the tertiary structure be affected? (19.5)

19.72 If glycine was replaced by alanine in a protein, how would the tertiary structure be affected? (19.5)

19.73 The amino acids lysine, proline, and glutamate are found in a protein. Which of these amino acids would: (19.5)
a. be found in hydrophobic regions?
b. be found in hydrophilic regions?
c. form salt bridges?

19.74 The amino acids histidine, phenylalanine, and serine are found in a protein. Which of these amino acids would: (19.5)
a. be found in hydrophobic regions?
b. be found in hydrophilic regions?
c. form hydrogen bonds?

19.75 In the preparation of meringue for a pie, a few drops of lemon juice are added and the egg whites are whipped. What causes the meringue to form? (19.6)

19.76 How does denaturation of a protein differ from its hydrolysis? (19.6)

℞ Clinical Applications

19.77 Aspartame, which is used in artificial sweeteners, contains the following dipeptide: (19.3)

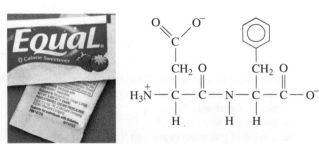

Aspartame is an artificial sweetener.

a. What are the amino acid residues in the dipeptide?
b. How would you name the dipeptide in aspartame?
c. Give the three-letter and one-letter abbreviations for the dipeptide in aspartame.

19.78 The tripeptide shown has a strong attraction for Cu^{2+} and is present in human blood and saliva.

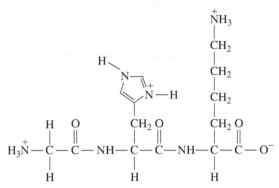

a. What are the amino acid residues?
b. How would you name this tripeptide?
c. Give the three-letter and one-letter abbreviations for the tripeptide.

CHALLENGE QUESTIONS

The following groups of questions are related to the topics in this chapter. However, they do not all follow the chapter order, and they require you to combine concepts and skills from several sections. These questions will help you increase your critical thinking skills and prepare for your next exam.

19.79 Indicate the overall charge of each amino acid at the following pH values as 0, 1+, or 1−. (19.1, 19.2)
a. serine at pH 5.7   b. threonine at pH 2.0
c. isoleucine at pH 3.0   d. leucine at pH 9.0

19.80 Indicate the overall charge of each amino acid at the following pH values as 0, 1+, or 1−. (19.1, 19.2)
a. tyrosine at pH 3.0   b. glycine at pH 10.0
c. phenylalanine at pH 8.5 d. methionine at pH 5.7

19.81 What are some differences between each of the following? (19.1, 19.2, 19.3, 19.4, 19.5)
a. secondary and tertiary protein structures
b. essential and nonessential amino acids
c. polar and nonpolar amino acids
d. dipeptides and tripeptides

19.82 What are some differences between each of the following? (19.1, 19.2, 19.3, 19.4, 19.5)
a. an ionic bond (salt bridge) and a disulfide bond
b. fibrous and globular proteins
c. α helix and β-pleated sheet
d. tertiary and quaternary structures of proteins

ANSWERS

Answers to Selected Questions and Problems

19.1 a. transport   **b.** structural
    c. structural   **d.** enzyme

19.3 a.

$$CH_3$$
$$|$$
$$CH_2$$
$$|$$
$$CH-CH_3$$
$$| \quad O$$
$$| \quad \|$$
$$H_3\overset{+}{N}-C-C-O^-$$
$$|$$
$$H$$
Ile, I

b.

$$O \diagdown \diagup NH_2$$
$$C$$
$$|$$
$$CH_2$$
$$|$$
$$CH_2 \quad O$$
$$| \quad \|$$
$$H_3\overset{+}{N}-C-C-O^-$$
$$|$$
$$H$$
Gln, Q

c.

$$O \diagdown \diagup O^-$$
$$C$$
$$|$$
$$CH_2$$
$$|$$
$$CH_2 \quad O$$
$$| \quad \|$$
$$H_3\overset{+}{N}-C-C-O^-$$
$$|$$
$$H$$
Glu, E

d.

$$CH_2$$
$$H_2C \diagup \diagdown CH_2 \quad O$$
$$| \qquad | \quad \|$$
$$H_2\overset{+}{N}-C-C-O^-$$
$$|$$
$$H$$
Pro, P

19.5 a. nonpolar; hydrophobic
    b. polar, neutral; hydrophilic
    c. polar, acidic; hydrophilic
    d. nonpolar; hydrophobic

19.7 a. histidine   **b.** valine
    c. lysine   **d.** isoleucine

19.9 a.

$$O \diagdown \diagup O^-$$
$$C$$
$$H_3\overset{+}{N}-\!\!\!\!\!\!-H$$
$$|$$
$$CH_2$$
$$|$$
$$OH$$

b.

$$O \diagdown \diagup O^-$$
$$C$$
$$H_3\overset{+}{N}-\!\!\!\!\!\!-H$$
$$|$$
$$CH_2$$
$$|$$
$$CH$$
$$H_3C \diagup \diagdown CH_3$$

19.11 a. Lysine and tryptophan are lacking in corn but supplied by peas; methionine is lacking in peas but supplied by corn.
    b. Lysine is lacking in rice but supplied by soy; methionine is lacking in soy but supplied by rice.

19.13 a.

$$CH_3 \; CH_3$$
$$\diagdown \diagup$$
$$CH \quad O$$
$$| \quad \|$$
$$H_3\overset{+}{N}-C-C-O^-$$
$$|$$
$$H$$

b.

$$SH$$
$$|$$
$$CH_2 \quad O$$
$$| \quad \|$$
$$H_3\overset{+}{N}-C-C-O^-$$
$$|$$
$$H$$

c.
$$HO-CH-CH_3$$
(CH_3, HO—CH, O; H_3N^+—C—C—O^-; H)

d.
(CH_3, O; H_3N^+—C—C—O^-; H)

19.15 a.
(CH_3 CH_3, CH, O; H_3N^+—C—C—OH; H)

b.
(SH, CH_2, O; H_3N^+—C—C—OH; H)

c.
(CH_3, HO—CH, O; H_3N^+—C—C—OH; H)

d.
(CH_3, O; H_3N^+—C—C—OH; H)

19.17 a. above its pI   **b.** below its pI   **c.** at its pI

19.19 a.
(CH_3, O; SH, CH_2, O; H_3N^+—C—C—NH—C—C—O^-; H   H)
Ala–Cys, AC

b.
(OH, CH_2, O; CH_2, O; H_3N^+—C—C—NH—C—C—O^-; H   H)
Ser–Phe, SF

c.
(H, O; CH_3, O; CH_3 CH_3, CH, O; H_3N^+—C—C—NH—C—C—NH—C—C—O^-; H   H   H)
Gly–Ala–Val, GAV

d.
(CH_3 CH_3, CH, O; CH_3—CH, O; CH_2, O; H_3N^+—C—C—NH——C—C—NH—C—C—O^-; H   H   H)
Val–Ile–Trp, VIW

19.21 a. Methionine, Met, is the C-terminus of met-enkephalin.
b. Tyrosine, Tyr, is the N-terminus of met-enkephalin.
c. YGGFM

19.23 a.
(NH_2, C=NH_2^+, NH, CH_2, CH_2, CH_2, O; CH_3, CH_2, O; OH, CH_2, O; H_3N^+—CH—C—NH—CH—C—NH—CH—C—O^-)
RIY

b.
(CH_3 CH_3, CH, O; CH_2(indole), O; CH_3—CH, O; OH, CH_2, O; H_3N^+—CH—C—NH—CH—C—NH—CH—C—NH—CH—C—)
VWIS

19.25 Amide bonds, which are covalent, form to connect the amino acids that make up the protein.

19.27 Val–Met–Met, VMM; Met–Val–Met, MVM; Met–Met–Val, MMV

19.29 The primary structure remains unchanged and intact as hydrogen bonds form between carbonyl oxygen atoms and amino hydrogen atoms in the secondary structure.

19.31 In the α helix, hydrogen bonds form between the carbonyl oxygen atom and the amino hydrogen atom in the next turn of the helix. In the β-pleated sheet, hydrogen bonds occur between parallel peptides or sections of a long polypeptide chain.

19.33 Asp–Arg–Val–Tyr–Ile–His–Pro–Phe

19.35 a. disulfide bond   **b.** salt bridge
c. hydrogen bond   **d.** hydrophobic interaction

19.37 a. cysteine
b. Leucine and valine will be found on the inside of the protein because they are hydrophobic.
c. The cysteine and aspartate would be on the outside of the protein because they are polar.
d. The order of the amino acids (the primary structure) provides the residues whose interactions determine the tertiary structure of the protein.

19.39 a. tertiary and quaternary   **b.** primary
c. secondary   **d.** secondary

19.41 The products would be the amino acids glycine, alanine, and serine.

19.43 His–Met, Met–Gly, Gly–Val

19.45 Hydrolysis splits the peptide bonds in the primary structure.

19.47 a. Placing an egg in boiling water coagulates the proteins of the egg because the heat disrupts hydrogen bonds and hydrophobic interactions.

    b. The alcohol on the swab coagulates the proteins of any bacteria present by forming hydrogen bonds and disrupting hydrophobic interactions.

    c. The heat from an autoclave will coagulate the proteins of any bacteria on the surgical instruments by disrupting hydrogen bonds and hydrophobic interactions.

    d. Heat will coagulate the surrounding proteins to close the wound by disrupting hydrogen bonds and hydrophobic interactions.

19.49 0.50 mCi

19.51 The secondary structure of beta-amyloid protein in the brain of a normal person is alpha-helical whereas the secondary structure in the brain of a person with Alzheimer's changes to beta-pleated sheet.

19.53 Glu–Phe–Arg–His–Asp–Ser–Gly–Tyr–Glu–Val

19.55 a. yes   **b.** no   **c.** no

19.57 a. (1)   **b.** (3)   **c.** (2)

19.59 Val–Ser–Ser (VSS), Ser–Ser–Val (SSV), Ser–Val–Ser (SVS)

19.61 a. asparagine and serine, hydrogen bond

    b. cysteine and cysteine, disulfide bond

    c. leucine and alanine, hydrophobic interaction

19.63 a.

$$\overset{+}{H_3N} - \underset{\underset{H}{|}}{\overset{\overset{CH_2OH}{|}}{C}} - \overset{\overset{O}{||}}{C} - OH$$

    b.

$$\overset{+}{H_3N} - \underset{\underset{H}{|}}{\overset{\overset{CH_3}{|}}{C}} - \overset{\overset{O}{||}}{C} - OH$$

    c.

$$\overset{+}{H_3N} - \underset{\underset{H}{|}}{\overset{\overset{CH_2-CH_2-CH_2-CH_2-\overset{+}{N}H_3}{|}}{C}} - \overset{\overset{O}{||}}{C} - OH$$

19.65 a.

$$\overset{+}{H_3N} - \underset{\underset{H}{|}}{\overset{\overset{CH_2OH}{|}}{C}} - \overset{\overset{O}{||}}{C} - NH - \underset{\underset{H}{|}}{\overset{\overset{CH_2-CH_2-CH_2-\overset{+}{N}H_3}{|}}{C}} - \overset{\overset{O}{||}}{C} - NH - \underset{\underset{H}{|}}{\overset{\overset{CH_2-C(=O)-O^-}{|}}{C}} - \overset{\overset{O}{||}}{C} - O^-$$

    b. This segment contains polar residues, which would be found on the surface of a globular protein where they hydrogen bond with water.

19.67 a. Collagen is found in connective tissue, blood vessels, skin, tendons, ligaments, the cornea of the eye, and cartilage.

    b. A triple helix is the structure found in collagen.

19.69 α helical

19.71 Serine is a polar amino acid, whereas valine is a nonpolar amino acid. Serine would move to the outside surface of the protein where it can form hydrogen bonds with water. However, valine, which is nonpolar, would be pushed to the center of the tertiary structure where it is stabilized by forming hydrophobic interactions.

19.73 a. proline   **b.** lysine, glutamate

    c. lysine, glutamate

19.75 The acid from the lemon juice and the mechanical whipping (agitation) denature the proteins of the egg white, which turn into solids as meringue.

19.77 a. aspartate and phenylalanine

    b. aspartylphenylalanine

    c. Asp–Phe, DF

19.79 a. 0   **c.** 1+

    b. 1+   **d.** 1−

19.81 a. In the secondary structure of proteins, hydrogen bonds form an alpha helix or a pleated sheet; the tertiary structure is determined by hydrogen bonds as well as by disulfide bonds and salt bridges.

    b. Nonessential amino acids can be synthesized by the body; essential amino acids must be supplied by the diet.

    c. Polar amino acids have hydrophilic R groups, whereas nonpolar amino acids have hydrophobic R groups.

    d. A dipeptide contains two amino acids, but a tripeptide contains three amino acids.

20

Enzymes and Vitamins

NOAH, A 6-YEAR-OLD BOY, IS HAVING SEVERE

diarrhea, abdominal pain, and intestinal growling two hours after he eats. Noah is also underweight for his age. His mother makes an appointment for Noah to see Emma, his physician assistant. Emma suspects that Noah may be lactose intolerant, which occurs due to an enzyme deficiency of lactase. A hydrogen breath test (HBT) is scheduled for Noah in a few days. Until then, Emma suggests that Noah's mother limit the amount of milk and milk products in Noah's diet.

The disaccharide in milk is lactose, which is broken down by *lactase* in the intestinal tract to glucose and galactose that are a source of energy. The enzyme lactase is a biological catalyst that is also a protein. When there is a lack of the enzyme, lactose is not broken down and remains in the intestinal tract. In the intestines, the lactose undergoes fermentation by bacteria to products that include gases such as H_2, CH_4, and CO_2, causing nausea, abdominal cramps, and diarrhea. The severity of the symptoms depends on how much lactose is present in the food and how much lactase a person produces.

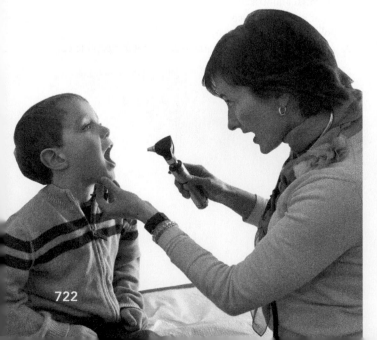

CAREER Physician Assistant

A physician assistant, commonly referred to as a PA, helps a doctor by examining and treating patients, as well as prescribing medications. Many physician assistants take on the role of the primary caregiver. Their duties would also include obtaining patient medical records and histories, diagnosing illnesses, educating and counseling patients, and referring the patient, when needed, to a specialist. Due to this diversity, physician assistants must be knowledgeable about a variety of medical conditions. Physician assistants may also help the doctor during major surgery.

Physician assistants can work in clinics, hospitals, health maintenance organizations, private practices, or take on a more administrative role that involves hiring new PAs and acting as the go-between for the hospital and patient or their family.

Every second, thousands of chemical reactions occur in the cells of our body. For example, many reactions occur to digest the food we eat, convert the products to chemical energy, and synthesize proteins and other macromolecules in our cells. In the laboratory, we can carry out chemical reactions that hydrolyze polysaccharides, fats, or proteins, but we must use a strong acid or base, high temperatures, and long reaction times. In the cells of our body, these reactions must take place at much faster rates that meet our physiological and metabolic needs. To make this happen, enzymes catalyze the chemical reactions in our cells, with a different enzyme for each reaction. Digestive enzymes in the mouth, stomach, and small intestine catalyze the hydrolysis of carbohydrate, fats, and proteins. Enzymes in the mitochondria extract energy from biomolecules to give us energy.

Every enzyme responds to what comes into the cells and to what the cells need. Enzymes keep reactions going when our cells need certain products, and turn off reactions when those products are not needed.

Many enzymes require cofactors to function properly. Cofactors are inorganic metal ions (minerals) or organic compounds such as vitamins. We obtain minerals such as zinc (Zn^{2+}) and iron (Fe^{3+}) and vitamins from our diets. A lack of minerals and vitamins can lead to certain nutritional diseases. For example, rickets is a deficiency of vitamin D, and scurvy occurs when a diet is low in vitamin C.

CHAPTER READINESS*

⚛ CORE CHEMISTRY SKILLS

- Interpreting Graphs (1.4E)

- Identifying the Primary, Secondary, Tertiary, and Quaternary Structures of Proteins (19.4, 19.5)

*These Core Chemistry Skills from previous chapters are listed here for your review as you proceed to the new material in this chapter.

20.1 Enzymes and Enzyme Action

Biological catalysts known as **enzymes** are needed for most chemical reactions that take place in the body. A *catalyst* increases the rate of a reaction by changing the way a reaction takes place but is itself not changed at the end of the reaction. An uncatalyzed reaction in a cell may take place eventually, but not at a rate fast enough for survival. For example, the acid in our stomachs would hydrolyze proteins in our diets without a catalyst, but without digestive enzymes, we would be unable to form amino acids fast enough to meet the body's requirements. The chemical reactions in our cells occur at incredibly fast rates under the mild conditions of pH 7.4 and a body temperature of 37 °C.

Enzymes act as catalysts by lowering the activation energy for a chemical reaction (see Figure 20.1). Less energy is required to convert reactant molecules to products, which increases the rate of a biochemical reaction compared to the rate of the uncatalyzed reaction. The rates of enzyme-catalyzed reactions are much faster than the rates of the uncatalyzed reactions. Some enzymes can increase the rate of a biological reaction by a factor of a billion, a trillion, or even a hundred million trillion compared to the rate of the uncatalyzed reaction. For example, an enzyme in the blood called carbonic anhydrase catalyzes the rapid interconversion of carbon dioxide and water to bicarbonate and H^+. In one second, one molecule of carbonic anhydrase can catalyze the reaction of about one million molecules of carbon dioxide. Carbonic anhydrase also catalyzes the reverse reaction, converting bicarbonate and H^+ to carbon dioxide and water.

$$CO_2 + H_2O \underset{\text{anhydrase}}{\overset{\text{Carbonic}}{\rightleftharpoons}} HCO_3^- + H^+$$

LEARNING GOAL

Describe enzymes and their role in enzyme-catalyzed reactions.

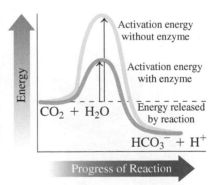

FIGURE 20.1 ▶ The enzyme carbonic anhydrase lowers the activation energy for the reversible reaction that converts CO_2 and H_2O to bicarbonate and H^+.

Q Why are enzymes needed in biological reactions?

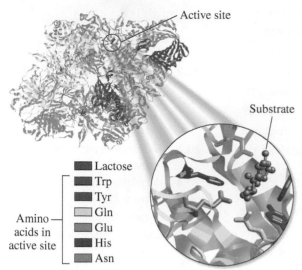

Lactose
Trp
Tyr
Amino — Gln
acids in Glu
active site His
Asn

FIGURE 20.2 ▶ Enzymes like lactase have an active site where the substrate fits for catalysis to occur. The quaternary structure of lactase consists of four subunits. The substrate, lactose (gray), is held in place in the active site by hydrogen bonds with amino acid side chains.

Q Why does an enzyme catalyze a reaction for only certain substrates?

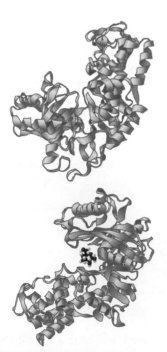

This ribbon representation shows the change in the shape of the enzyme hexokinase as the glucose molecule binds to its active site where it undergoes phosphorylation.

Enzymes and Active Sites

Nearly all enzymes are globular proteins. Each has a unique three-dimensional shape that recognizes and binds a small group of reacting molecules, which are called **substrates**. The tertiary structure of an enzyme plays an important role in how that enzyme catalyzes reactions.

In a catalyzed reaction, an enzyme must bind to a substrate in a way that favors catalysis. A typical enzyme is much larger than its substrate. However, within the enzyme's tertiary structure is a region called the **active site**, in which the substrate or substrates are held while the reaction takes place. The active site is often a small pocket within the larger tertiary structure that closely fits the substrate. Within the active site of an enzyme, residues of specific amino acids interact with functional groups of the substrate to form hydrogen bonds, salt bridges, and hydrophobic interactions.

Figure 20.2 shows the folded structure of the enzyme lactase. Lactase hydrolyzes the disaccharide lactose to the monosaccharides glucose and galactose. The protein backbone of lactase is represented by a ribbon. As lactase folds into its tertiary structure, the pocket that forms in one part of its surface is its active site. This is where the hydrolysis of lactose occurs. At least six residues are involved in the binding of the lactose substrate to the lactase enzyme.

Like a hand in a glove, lactose, the substrate for lactase, fits snugly into its active site. Other disaccharides will not fit into the active site. Enzymes demonstrate various types of *substrate specificity*. Three categories of substrate specificity are outlined in Table 20.1.

TABLE 20.1 Types of Substrate Specificity

Type	Reaction Type	Example
Absolute	catalyzes one type of reaction for one substrate	Urease catalyzes only the hydrolysis of urea.
Group	catalyzes one type of reaction for similar substrates	Hexokinase adds a phosphate group to hexoses.
Linkage	catalyzes one type of reaction for a specific type of bond	Chymotrypsin catalyzes the hydrolysis of peptide bonds.

SAMPLE PROBLEM 20.1 The Enzyme Active Site

What is the function of the active site in an enzyme?

SOLUTION

The R groups of amino acid residues within the active site of an enzyme bind the substrate by forming hydrogen bonds, salt bridges, and hydrophobic interactions and catalyze the reaction.

STUDY CHECK 20.1

Which is a larger molecule, glucose or hexokinase?

ANSWER

Hexokinase. Typically, enzymes are large protein molecules containing many amino acid residues, and substrates are small molecules such as the monosaccharide glucose.

Enzyme-Catalyzed Reaction

The combination of an enzyme and a substrate within the active site forms an **enzyme–substrate (ES) complex** that catalyzes the reaction with lower activation energy. Within the active site, R groups on the amino acid residues catalyze the reaction to form the **enzyme–product (EP) complex**. Then the products are released from the enzyme so it can bind to another substrate molecule. We can write the catalyzed reaction of an enzyme (E) with a substrate (S) to form product (P) as follows:

E + S ⇌ ES complex ⟶ EP complex ⟶ E + P

Enzyme and Substrate   Enzyme–Substrate Complex   Enzyme–Product Complex   Enzyme and Product

In the hydrolysis of the disaccharide lactose by the enzyme lactase, a molecule of lactose binds to the active site of lactase. In this ES complex, the glycosidic bond of lactose is in a position that is favorable for *hydrolysis*, which is the splitting by water of a large molecule into smaller parts. Groups on the amino acid residues in the active site then catalyze the hydrolysis of lactose, which produces the monosaccharides glucose and galactose. Because the structures of the products are no longer attracted to the active site, they are released, which allows the enzyme lactase to react with another lactose molecule (see Figure 20.3).

E + S ⇌ ES complex ⟶ EP complex ⟶ E + P

Lactase + Lactose   Lactase–Lactose Complex   Lactase–Glucose–Galactose Complex   Lactase + Glucose + Galactose

Models of Enzyme Action

An early theory of enzyme action, called the *lock-and-key model*, described the active site as having a rigid, nonflexible shape. According to the lock-and-key model, the shape of the active site was analogous to a lock, and its substrate was the key that specifically fit that lock. However, this model was a static one that did not include the flexibility of the tertiary shape of an enzyme and the way we now know that the active site can adjust to the shape of a substrate.

In the dynamic model of enzyme action, called the **induced-fit model**, the flexibility of the active site allows it to adapt to the shape of the substrate. At the same time, the shape of the substrate may be modified to better fit the geometry of the active site. As a result, the fit of both the active site and the substrate provides the best alignment for the catalysis of the substrate. In the induced-fit model, substrate and enzyme work together to acquire a geometrical arrangement that lowers the activation energy (see Figure 20.3).

Describing Enzyme Action

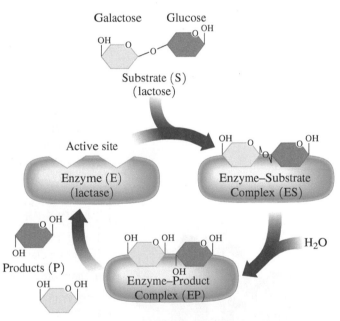

FIGURE 20.3 ▶ A flexible active site in lactase and the flexible substrate lactose adjust to provide the best fit for the hydrolysis reaction. Once the disaccharide is hydrolyzed, the monosaccharide products are released from the enzyme, which is ready to bind another lactose.

Ⓠ Why does the enzyme-catalyzed hydrolysis of lactose go faster than the hydrolysis of lactose in a test tube?

SAMPLE PROBLEM 20.2 The Induced-Fit Model

How does the induced-fit model explain the binding of the substrate at the active site?

SOLUTION

In the induced-fit model, the shapes of the substrate and the active site adjust so that the substrate is in the optimum position needed for the enzyme to carry out reaction catalysis.

STUDY CHECK 20.2

How does the lock-and-key model explain the binding of the substrate at an active site?

ANSWER

In the lock-and-key model, the substrate fits perfectly into the active site of the enzyme similar to a key fitting into a lock. We know today that most enzymes do not have a rigid active site and that the active site flexes to accommodate the chemical reaction being catalyzed.

QUESTIONS AND PROBLEMS

20.1 Enzymes and Enzyme Action

LEARNING GOAL Describe enzymes and their role in enzyme-catalyzed reactions.

20.1 Why do chemical reactions in the body require enzymes?

20.2 How do enzymes make chemical reactions in the body proceed at faster rates?

20.3 Match the terms, (1) enzyme–substrate complex, (2) enzyme, and (3) substrate, with each of the following:
  a. has a tertiary structure that recognizes the substrate
  b. the combination of an enzyme with the substrate
  c. has a structure that fits the active site of an enzyme

20.4 Match the terms, (1) active site, (2) induced-fit model, and (3) lock-and-key model with each of the following:
  a. an active site that has a rigid shape
  b. the portion of an enzyme where catalytic activity occurs
  c. an active site that adapts to the shape of a substrate

20.5 **a.** Write an equation that represents an enzyme-catalyzed reaction.
  b. How is the active site different from the whole enzyme structure?

20.6 **a.** How does an enzyme speed up the reaction of a substrate?
  b. After the products have formed, what happens to the enzyme?

LEARNING GOAL

Classify enzymes and give their names.

⚛ CORE CHEMISTRY SKILL

Classifying Enzymes

The ribbon structure for alanine transaminase, an aminotransferase, contains 495 amino acid residues.

20.2 Classification of Enzymes

The names of enzymes describe the compound or the reaction that is catalyzed. The actual names of enzymes are derived by replacing the end of the name of the reaction or reacting compound with the suffix *ase*. For example, an *oxidase* is an enzyme that catalyzes an oxidation reaction, and a *dehydrogenase* removes hydrogen atoms. These enzymes are classified as *oxidoreductases* because they catalyze the loss or gain of hydrogen or oxygen.

Often the name of the enzyme can be used to predict its class and function. The enzyme *sucrase* is a catalyst in the hydrolysis of sucrose, and *lipase* catalyzes reactions that hydrolyze lipids. Some enzymes use names that end in the suffix *in*, such as *papain* found in papaya; *rennin* found in milk; and *pepsin* and *trypsin*, enzymes that catalyze the hydrolysis of proteins. These enzymes are classified as *hydrolases* because they use water to split large molecules into smaller ones.

The Enzyme Commission of the International Union of Biochemistry and Molecular Biology systematically classifies enzymes according to the six general types of reactions they catalyze (see Table 20.2).

> **SAMPLE PROBLEM 20.3** Classifying Enzymes
>
> Using Table 20.2, identify the chemical reaction each of the following enzymes catalyzes and classify the enzyme:
>
> **a.** aminotransferase   **b.** lactate dehydrogenase
>
> **SOLUTION**
>
> | ANALYZE THE PROBLEM | Given | Need |
> |---|---|---|
> | | name of the enzyme | type of reaction catalyzed, class of enzyme |
>
> **a.** An aminotransferase catalyzes the transfer of an amino group between two substrates, which is classified as a transferase.
> **b.** Lactate dehydrogenase catalyzes the removal of two H atoms from lactate, which is classified as an oxidoreductase.
>
> **STUDY CHECK 20.3**
>
> What is the name and classification of the enzyme that catalyzes the hydrolysis of lipids?
>
> **ANSWER**
>
> An enzyme that hydrolyzes a lipid is a lipase, which is classified as a hydrolase.

TABLE 20.2 Classification of Enzymes

Class	Examples of Reaction Catalyzed
1. Oxidoreductases	
Catalyze oxidation–reduction reactions	*Oxidases* catalyze the oxidation of a substrate.
	Dehydrogenases catalyze the removal or addition of two H atoms and utilize a coenzyme.

$$CH_3-CH_2-OH + NAD^+ \xrightarrow{\text{Alcohol dehydrogenase}} CH_3-\overset{\overset{\text{O}}{\|}}{C}-H + NADH + H^+$$

Ethanol   Coenzyme   Ethanal   Coenzyme

2. Transferases	
Catalyze the transfer of a functional group between two compounds	*Transaminases* catalyze the transfer of an amino group from one substrate to another ATP is utilized.
	Kinases catalyze the transfer of phosphate groups from one substrate to another.

$$CH_3-\overset{\overset{+}{NH_3}}{\underset{\|}{CH}}-COO^- + {}^-OOC-\overset{\overset{\text{O}}{\|}}{C}-CH_2-CH_2-COO^- \underset{\text{transaminase}}{\overset{\text{Alanine}}{\rightleftharpoons}} CH_3-\overset{\overset{\text{O}}{\|}}{C}-COO^- + {}^-OOC-\overset{\overset{+}{NH_3}}{\underset{\|}{CH}}-CH_2-CH_2-COO^-$$

Alanine   α-Ketoglutarate   Pyruvate   Glutamate

3. Hydrolases	
Catalyze hydrolysis (add H_2O) reactions that split a compound into two products	*Proteases* catalyze the hydrolysis of peptide bonds in proteins.
	Lipases catalyze the hydrolysis of ester bonds in lipids.
	Nucleases catalyze the hydrolysis of the phosphate ester bonds in nucleic acids.

$$-NH-\overset{\overset{R}{\|}}{CH}-\overset{\overset{\text{O}}{\|}}{C}-NH-\overset{\overset{R}{\|}}{CH}-COO^- + H_2O \xrightarrow{\text{Protease}} -NH-\overset{\overset{R}{\|}}{CH}-\overset{\overset{\text{O}}{\|}}{C}-O^- + H_3\overset{+}{N}-\overset{\overset{R}{\|}}{CH}-COO^-$$

Polypeptide   Shorter polypeptide   Amino acid

4. Lyases	
Catalyze the addition or removal of a group without hydrolysis	*Decarboxylases* catalyze the removal of CO_2 from a substrate.
	Deaminases catalyze the removal of NH_3 from a substrate.
	Dehydratases catalyze the removal of H_2O from a substrate.
	Hydratases catalyze the addition of H_2O to a substrate.

$$CH_3-\overset{\overset{\text{O}}{\|}}{C}-COO^- + H^+ \xrightarrow{\text{Pyruvate decarboxylase}} CH_3-\overset{\overset{\text{O}}{\|}}{C}-H + CO_2$$

Pyruvate   Ethanal   Carbon dioxide

5. Isomerases	
Catalyze the rearrangement (isomerization) of atoms within a substrate	*Isomerases* catalyze rearrangement reactions.
	Epimerases catalyze rearrangements between carbohydrates.

$$\underset{H}{\overset{{}^-OOC}{>}}C=C\underset{H}{\overset{COO^-}{<}} \underset{\text{isomerase}}{\overset{\text{Maleate}}{\rightleftharpoons}} \underset{H}{\overset{{}^-OOC}{>}}C=C\underset{COO^-}{\overset{H}{<}}$$

Maleate   Fumarate

6. Ligases	
Catalyze the joining of two substrates using ATP energy (see Section 22.2)	*Synthetases* catalyze the formation of a bond between two substrates utilizing the energy of ATP.
	Carboxylases catalyze the formation of a bond between CO_2 and a substrate utilizing the energy of ATP.

$${}^-OOC-\overset{\overset{\text{O}}{\|}}{C}-CH_3 + CO_2 + ATP \xrightarrow{\text{Pyruvate carboxylase}} {}^-OOC-\overset{\overset{\text{O}}{\|}}{C}-CH_2-COO^- + ADP + P_i + H^+$$

Pyruvate   Oxaloacetate

Chemistry Link to Health

Isoenzymes As Diagnostic Tools

Isoenzymes are different forms of an enzyme that catalyze the same reaction in different cells or tissues of the body. They consist of quaternary structures with slight variations in the amino acids in the polypeptide subunits. For example, there are five isoenzymes of *lactate dehydrogenase* (LDH) that catalyze the conversion between lactate and pyruvate.

$$\underset{\text{Lactate}}{CH_3-\overset{\overset{\displaystyle OH}{|}}{CH}-COO^-} + NAD^+ \underset{\xrightarrow{\hspace{1.2cm}}}{\overset{\text{Lactate}}{\underset{\text{dehydrogenase}}{\xleftarrow{\hspace{1.2cm}}}}} \underset{\text{Pyruvate}}{CH_3-\overset{\overset{\displaystyle O}{\|}}{C}-COO^-} + NADH + H^+$$

A myocardial infarction may be indicated by an increase in the levels of creatine kinase (CK) and lactate dehydrogenase (LDH).

Graph: Enzyme Activity in Blood Serum (y-axis) vs Days Following Myocardial Infarction (x-axis, 1–8). Two curves labeled CK and LDH.

Each LDH isoenzyme contains a mix of polypeptide subunits, M and H. In the liver and muscle, lactate is converted to pyruvate by the LDH_5 isoenzyme with four M subunits designated M_4. In the heart, the same reaction is catalyzed by the LDH_1 isoenzyme (H_4) containing four H subunits. Different combinations of the M and H subunits are found in the LDH isoenzymes of the brain, red blood cells, kidneys, and white blood cells.

The different forms of an enzyme allow a medical diagnosis of damage or disease to a particular organ or tissue. In healthy tissues, isoenzymes function within the cells. However, when a disease damages a particular organ, cells die, which releases their contents including the isoenzymes into the blood. Measurements of the elevated levels of specific isoenzymes in the blood serum help to identify the disease and its location in the body. For example, an elevation in serum LDH_5, M_4, indicates liver damage or disease. When a *myocardial infarction* or heart attack damages heart muscle, an increase in the level of LDH_1 (H_4) isoenzyme is detected in the blood serum (see Table 20.3).

Isoenzymes of Lactate Dehydrogenase	Highest Levels Found in the Following:
H_4 (LDH_1)	Heart, kidneys
H_3M (LDH_2)	Red blood cells, heart, kidney, brain
H_2M_2 (LDH_3)	Brain, lung, white blood cells
HM_3 (LDH_4)	Lung, skeletal muscle
M_4 (LDH_5)	Skeletal muscle, liver

The different isoenzymes of lactate dehydrogenase (LDH) indicate damage to different organs in the body.

Another isoenzyme used diagnostically is creatine kinase (CK), which consists of two types of polypeptide subunits. Subunit B is prevalent in the brain, and subunit M predominates in muscle. Normally CK_3 (subunits MM) is present at low levels in the blood serum. However, in a patient who has suffered a myocardial infarction, the level of CK_2 (subunits MB) is elevated within 4 to 6 h and reaches a peak in about 24 h. Table 20.4 lists some enzymes used to diagnose tissue damage and diseases of certain organs.

TABLE 20.3 Isoenzymes of Lactate Dehydrogenase and Creatine Kinase

Isoenzyme	Abundant in	Subunits
Lactate Dehydrogenase (LDH)		
LDH_1	Heart, kidneys	H_4
LDH_2	Red blood cells, heart, kidney, brain	H_3M
LDH_3	Brain, lung, white blood cells	H_2M_2
LDH_4	Lung, skeletal muscle	HM_3
LDH_5	Skeletal muscle, liver	M_4
Creatine Kinase (CK)		
CK_1	Brain, lung	BB
CK_2	Heart muscle	MB
CK_3	Skeletal muscle, red blood cells	MM

TABLE 20.4 Serum Enzymes Used in Diagnosis of Tissue Damage

Condition	Diagnostic Enzymes Elevated
Heart attack or liver disease (cirrhosis, hepatitis)	Lactate dehydrogenase (LDH) Aspartate transaminase (AST)
Heart attack	Creatine kinase (CK)
Hepatitis	Alanine transaminase (ALT)
Liver (carcinoma) or bone disease (rickets)	Alkaline phosphatase (ALP)
Pancreatic disease	Pancreatic amylase (PA) Cholinesterase (CE) Lipase (LPS)
Prostate carcinoma	Acid phosphatase (ACP) Prostate-specific antigen (PSA)

QUESTIONS AND PROBLEMS

20.2 Classification of Enzymes

LEARNING GOAL Classify enzymes and give their names.

20.7 What type of reaction is catalyzed by each of the following classes of enzymes?
  a. oxidoreductases   **b.** transferases
  c. hydrolases

20.8 What type of reaction is catalyzed by each of the following classes of enzymes?
  a. lyases   **b.** isomerases
  c. ligases

20.9 What is the name of the class of enzymes that catalyzes each of the following reactions?
  a. hydrolyzing sucrose
  b. adding oxygen
  c. converting glucose-6-phosphate to fructose-6-phosphate
  d. moving an amino group from one molecule to another

20.10 What is the name of the class of enzymes that catalyzes each of the following reactions?
  a. adding water to a double bond
  b. removing hydrogen atoms from a substrate
  c. splitting peptide bonds in proteins
  d. converting a tertiary alcohol to a secondary alcohol

20.11 Classify the enzyme that catalyzes each of the following reactions:

a. $CH_3-\overset{\overset{\textstyle O}{\|}}{C}-COO^- + H^+ \longrightarrow CH_3-\overset{\overset{\textstyle O}{\|}}{C}-H + CO_2$

b. $CH_3-\overset{\overset{\textstyle \overset{+}{N}H_3}{|}}{C}H-COO^- + {}^-OOC-\overset{\overset{\textstyle O}{\|}}{C}-CH_2-CH_3 \rightleftharpoons$
$CH_3-\overset{\overset{\textstyle O}{\|}}{C}-COO^- + {}^-OOC-\overset{\overset{\textstyle \overset{+}{N}H_3}{|}}{C}H-CH_2-CH_3$

20.12 Classify the enzyme that catalyzes each of the following reactions:

a. $CH_3-\overset{\overset{\textstyle O}{\|}}{C}-COO^- + CO_2 + ATP \longrightarrow$
${}^-OOC-CH_2-\overset{\overset{\textstyle O}{\|}}{C}-COO^- + ADP + P_i + H^+$

b. $CH_3-CH_2-OH + NAD^+ \longrightarrow$
$CH_3-\overset{\overset{\textstyle O}{\|}}{C}-H + NADH + H^+$

20.13 Predict the name of the enzyme that catalyzes each of the following reactions:
  a. oxidizes succinate
  b. combines glutamate and ammonia to form glutamine
  c. removes 2H from an alcohol

20.14 Predict the name of the enzyme that catalyzes each of the following reactions:
  a. hydrolyzes sucrose
  b. transfers an amino group from aspartate
  c. removes a carboxylate group from pyruvate

℞ Clinical Applications

20.15 Name the enzyme that is indicated by each of the following abbreviations:
  a. PSA   **b.** CK   **c.** CE

20.16 Name the enzyme that is indicated by each of the following abbreviations:
  a. ALP   **b.** AST   **c.** PA

20.17 What are isoenzymes?

20.18 How is the LDH isoenzyme in the heart different from the LDH isoenzyme in the liver?

20.19 A patient arrives in the emergency room complaining of chest pains. What enzymes might be present in the patient's blood serum?

20.20 A patient who is an alcoholic has elevated levels of LDH and AST. What condition might be indicated?

20.3 Factors Affecting Enzyme Activity

The **activity** of an enzyme describes how fast an enzyme catalyzes the reaction that converts a substrate to product. This activity is strongly affected by reaction conditions, which include the temperature, pH, concentration of the enzyme, and concentration of the substrate.

Temperature

Enzymes are very sensitive to temperature. At low temperatures, most enzymes show little activity because there is not a sufficient amount of energy for the catalyzed reaction to take place. At higher temperatures, enzyme activity increases as reacting molecules move faster causing more collisions with enzymes. Enzymes are most active at **optimum temperature**, which is 37 °C, or body temperature, for most enzymes (see Figure 20.4). At temperatures above 50 °C, the tertiary structures, and thus the shapes of most proteins are

LEARNING GOAL

Describe the effect of changes of temperature, pH, concentration of enzyme, and concentration of substrate on enzyme activity.

⚙ CORE CHEMISTRY SKILL

Identifying Factors Affecting Enzyme Activity

Thermophiles survive in the high temperatures (50 °C to 120 °C) of a hot spring.

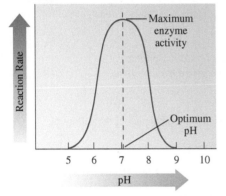

FIGURE 20.5 ▶ Enzymes are most active at their optimum pH. At a higher or lower pH, denaturation of the enzyme causes a loss of catalytic activity.

◉ Why does the digestive enzyme pepsin have an optimum pH of 2.0?

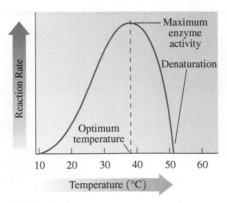

FIGURE 20.4 ▶ An enzyme attains maximum activity at its optimum temperature, usually 37 °C. Lower temperatures slow the rate of reaction, and temperatures above 50 °C denature most enzymes, with a loss of catalytic activity.

◉ Why is 37 °C the optimum temperature for many enzymes?

destroyed causing a loss of enzyme activity. For this reason, equipment in hospitals and laboratories is sterilized in autoclaves where the high temperatures denature the enzymes in harmful bacteria.

Certain organisms, known as thermophiles, live in environments where temperatures range from 50 °C to 120 °C. In order to survive in these extreme conditions, thermophiles have enzymes with tertiary structures that are not destroyed by such high temperatures. Some research shows that their enzymes are very similar to ordinary enzymes except that they contain more hydrogen bonds and salt bridges that stabilize their tertiary structures at high temperatures and resist unfolding and the loss of enzymatic activity.

pH

Enzymes are most active at their **optimum pH**, the pH that maintains the proper tertiary structure of the protein (see Figure 20.5). If a pH value is above or below the optimum pH, the interactions between the R groups of amino acid residues are disrupted, which destroys the tertiary structure and the active site. As a result, the enzyme no longer binds substrate, and no catalysis occurs. Small changes in pH are reversible, which allows an enzyme to regain its tertiary or quaternary structure and biological activity. However, large variations from optimum pH permanently destroy the structure of the enzyme.

Enzymes in most cells have optimum pH values at physiological pH around 7.4. However, enzymes in the stomach have a low optimum pH because they hydrolyze proteins at the acidic pH in the stomach. For example, pepsin, a digestive enzyme in the stomach, has an optimum pH of 1.5 to 2.0. Between meals, the pH in the stomach is 4 to 5, and pepsin shows little or no digestive activity. When food enters the stomach, the secretion of HCl lowers the pH to about 2, which activates the digestive enzyme pepsin. Table 20.5 lists the optimum pH values for selected enzymes.

TABLE 20.5 Optimum pH for Selected Enzymes

Enzyme	Location	Substrate	Optimum pH
Pepsin	stomach	peptide bonds	1.5–2.0
Lactase	GI tract	lactose	6.0
Sucrase	small intestine	sucrose	6.2
Amylase	pancreas	amylose	6.7–7.0
Urease	liver	urea	7.0
Trypsin	small intestine	peptide bonds	7.7–8.0
Lipase	pancreas	lipid (ester bonds)	8.0
Arginase	liver	arginine	9.7

Enzyme and Substrate Concentration

In any catalyzed reaction, the substrate must first bind with the enzyme to form the enzyme–substrate complex. For a particular substrate concentration, an increase in enzyme concentration increases the rate of the catalyzed reaction. At higher enzyme concentrations, more molecules are available to bind substrate and catalyze the reaction. As long as the substrate concentration is greater than the enzyme concentration, there is a direct relationship between the enzyme concentration and enzyme activity (see Figure 20.6a). In most enzyme-catalyzed reactions, the concentration of the substrate is much greater than the concentration of the enzyme.

When the enzyme concentration is kept constant, the addition of more substrate will increase the rate of the reaction. If the substrate concentration is high, the substrate can bind with all of the available enzyme molecules. Then the rate of the reaction reaches its maximum, and the addition of more substrate does not increase the rate further (see Figure 20.6b).

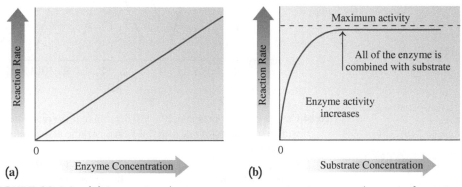

FIGURE 20.6 ▶ (a) Increasing the enzyme concentration increases the rate of reaction. (b) Increasing the substrate concentration increases the rate of reaction until all the enzyme molecules are combined with substrate.

◉ What happens to the rate of reaction when all the available enzymes are attached to substrate molecules?

Explore Your World
Enzyme Activity

The enzymes on the surface of a freshly cut apple, avocado, or banana react with oxygen in the air to turn the surface brown. An antioxidant, such as vitamin C in lemon juice, prevents the browning reaction. Cut an apple, an avocado, or a banana into several slices. Place one slice in a plastic zipper bag, squeeze out all the air, and close the zipper lock. Dip another slice in lemon juice. Sprinkle another slice with a crushed vitamin C tablet. Leave another slice alone as a control. Observe the surface of each of your samples. Record your observations immediately, then every hour for 6 h or longer.

Questions

1. Which slice(s) shows the most oxidation (a brown color)?
2. Which slice(s) shows little or no oxidation?
3. How was the browning reaction on each slice affected by treatment with an antioxidant?

▶ **SAMPLE PROBLEM 20.4 Factors Affecting Enzymatic Activity**

Describe the effect each of the following changes would have on the rate of the reaction that is catalyzed by urease:

$$H_2N - \overset{\overset{\displaystyle O}{\|}}{C} - NH_2 + H_2O \xrightarrow{\text{Urease}} 2NH_3 + CO_2$$
Urea

a. increasing the urea concentration   **b.** lowering the temperature to 10 °C

SOLUTION

a. An increase in urea concentration will increase the rate of reaction until all the enzyme molecules bind to urea. Then no further increase in rate occurs.

b. Because 10 °C is lower than the optimum temperature of 37 °C, there is a decrease in the rate of the reaction.

STUDY CHECK 20.4

If urease has an optimum pH of 7.0, what is the effect of lowering the pH of a urease sample to 3.0?

ANSWER

At a pH lower than the optimum pH, the hydrogen bonds and salt bridges of urease will be disrupted, resulting in the denaturation of the enzyme, loss of tertiary and quaternary structure, and a decrease in its biological activity.

QUESTIONS AND PROBLEMS

20.3 Factors Affecting Enzyme Activity

LEARNING GOAL Describe the effect of changes of temperature, pH, concentration of enzyme, and concentration of substrate on enzyme activity.

℞ Clinical Applications

20.21 Trypsin, a protease that hydrolyzes polypeptides, functions in the small intestine at an optimum pH of 7.7 to 8.0. How is the rate of a trypsin-catalyzed reaction affected by each of the following conditions?
   a. lowering the concentration of polypeptides
   b. changing the pH to 3.0
   c. running the reaction at 75 °C
   d. adding more trypsin

20.22 Pepsin, a protease that hydrolyzes polypeptides, functions in the stomach at an optimum pH of 1.5 to 2.0. How is the rate of a pepsin-catalyzed reaction affected by each of the following conditions?

Trypsin, a protease containing 247 amino acid residues, hydrolyzes peptides after lysine or arginine residues.

   a. increasing the concentration of polypeptides
   b. changing the pH to 5.0
   c. running the reaction at 0 °C
   d. using less pepsin

20.23 Use the graph to estimate the optimum pH for pepsin, lactase, sucrase, and trypsin.

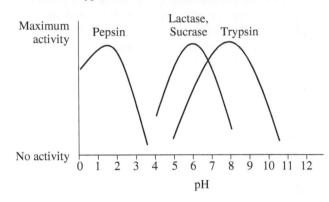

20.24 Use the graph in problem 20.23 to determine if the reaction rate will be the optimum rate or not for each enzyme at the following pH values:
   a. trypsin, pH 5.0   **b.** lactase, pH 5.0
   c. pepsin, pH 4.0   **d.** trypsin, pH 8.0
   e. sucrase, pH 2.0

LEARNING GOAL

Describe the role of allosteric enzymes, feedback control, and covalent modification in regulating enzyme activity.

20.4 Regulation of Enzyme Activity

In enzyme-catalyzed reactions, substances are produced in the amounts and at the times they are needed in a cell. Therefore the rates of enzyme-catalyzed reactions are controlled by regulatory enzymes that increase the reaction rate when more of a particular substance is needed, and decrease the reaction rate when that substance is not needed. Enzyme activity can be regulated by allosteric enzymes, feedback control, and covalent modifications.

Positive Allosteric Regulation

Allosteric site Active site   Substrate

Products   Products

Negative Allosteric Regulation

Enzyme   Substrate

FIGURE 20.7 ▶ A positive regulator changes the shape of the active site allowing the substrate to bind more effectively and increasing the reaction rate. A negative regulator changes the shape of the active site preventing the binding of the substrate and decreasing the reaction rate.

Allosteric Enzymes

Many enzymes are **allosteric enzymes**, which bind with a regulator molecule that is different from the substrate. The regulator binds to the enzyme at an *allosteric site*, which is a different location than the active site. As a result, the shape of the enzyme changes, which causes a change in the shape of the active site. There are both positive and negative regulators. A *positive regulator* changes the shape of the active site to allow the substrate to bind more effectively, which increases the rate of the catalyzed reaction. A *negative regulator* changes the shape of the active site to prevent the proper binding of the substrate, which decreases the rate of the catalyzed reaction (see Figure 20.7).

Feedback Control

In **feedback control**, the end product of a series of reactions acts as a negative regulator (see Figure 20.8). When the end product is present in sufficient amounts for the needs of the cell, end product molecules act as negative regulators and bind to the allosteric site within the first enzyme (E_1) in the reaction series. Then the substrate cannot bind to the active site and production of all of the intermediate compounds in the subsequent reaction sequence stops.

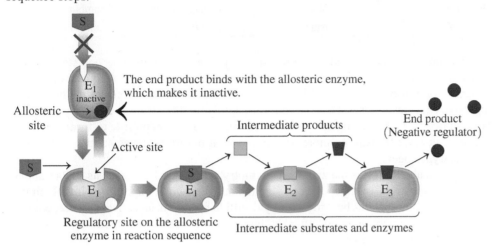

Allosteric site

The end product binds with the allosteric enzyme, which makes it inactive.

Active site

Intermediate products

End product (Negative regulator)

Regulatory site on the allosteric enzyme in reaction sequence

Intermediate substrates and enzymes

FIGURE 20.8 ▶ In feedback control, the end product binds to a regulatory site on the allosteric (first) enzyme in the reaction sequence, which prevents the formation of all intermediate compounds needed in the synthesis of the end product.

◉ Do the intermediate enzymes in a reaction sequence have regulatory sites?

When the level of end product is low, the regulator dissociates from the allosteric enzyme (E_1), which unblocks the active site allowing the enzyme to bind with the initial substrate once again. Feedback control allows the enzyme-catalyzed reactions to operate only when the end product is needed by the cell. Thus, feedback control prevents the accumulation of intermediate products as well as end product, thereby conserving energy and materials in the cell.

An example of feedback control is the reaction sequence in which the amino acid threonine is converted to the amino acid isoleucine. When the level of isoleucine is high in the cell, some of the isoleucine binds to the allosteric enzyme threonine deaminase (E_1). The binding of isoleucine changes the shape of the threonine deaminase, which prevents threonine from binding to its active site. As a result, the entire reaction sequence does not function. As isoleucine is utilized in the cell and its concentration decreases, isoleucine molecules are released from the allosteric site on threonine deaminase. The shape of the deaminase returns to its active form, which allows the enzyme-catalyzed reaction sequence to convert threonine to isoleucine.

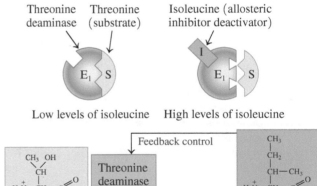

Threonine deaminase   Threonine (substrate)   Isoleucine (allosteric inhibitor deactivator)

Low levels of isoleucine   High levels of isoleucine

Feedback control

Threonine

Threonine deaminase

Isoleucine

Covalent Modification

Covalent modification is another way in which enzymes are modified when covalent bonds to a group on the polypeptide chain are formed or broken. As a regulatory mechanism, covalent modification is reversible.

Zymogens (Proenzymes)

Many enzymes are active as soon as they are synthesized and fold into their tertiary or quaternary structures. However, **zymogens**, or *proenzymes*, are produced as inactive forms and stored for later use. Zymogens include digestive enzymes, protein hormones, such as insulin, and blood clotting enzymes (see Table 20.6). For example, proteases, which are digestive enzymes that hydrolyze protein, are produced as larger, inactive forms. Once a zymogen is formed, it is transported to the part of the body where the active form is needed. Then the zymogen is converted to its active form by a covalent modification, typically the removal of a polypeptide section, which uncovers its active site. The pancreatic zymogens are stored in *zymogen granules*, which have membranes that are resistant to enzymatic digestion while in the pancreas. If zymogen activation should occur in the pancreas, the proteins within the tissues of the pancreas would undergo digestion, which would cause inflammation and could result in a painful condition called *pancreatitis*.

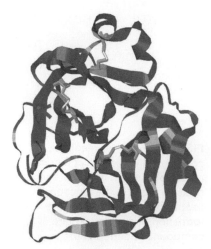

The ribbon representation of chymotrypsin shows six cysteines (green) that form three disulfide bonds (yellow).

TABLE 20.6 Examples of Zymogens and Their Active Forms

Zymogen (Inactive Enzyme)	Produced in	Activated in	Enzyme (Active)
Chymotrypsinogen	pancreas	small intestine	chymotrypsin
Pepsinogen	gastric chief cells	stomach	pepsin
Trypsinogen	pancreas	small intestine	trypsin
Fibrinogen	blood	damaged tissues	fibrin
Prothrombin	blood	damaged tissues	thrombin
Proinsulin	pancreas	pancreas	insulin

The proteases trypsin and chymotrypsin are produced as zymogens and stored in the pancreas. After food is ingested, hormones trigger the release of the zymogens from the pancreas for transport to the small intestine. There the zymogens are converted into active digestive enzymes by proteases that remove peptide sections from the protein chains. A hexapeptide from the zymogen trypsinogen is removed by a peptidase to form the active digestive enzyme trypsin. As more trypsin forms, it in turn removes peptide sections to activate trypsinogen.

Trypsin also activates the zymogen chymotrypsinogen, which consists of 245 amino acids, by removing two dipeptides to give the active enzyme chymotrypsin, which has three polypeptide sections held together by disulfide bonds. As an active protease, chymotrypsin splits the peptide bonds after the hydrophobic amino acid residues tryptophan, tyrosine, and phenylalanine.

Once formed, trypsin catalyzes the removal of dipeptides from inactive chymotrypsinogen and trypsinogen to give the active proteases chymotrypsin and trypsin.

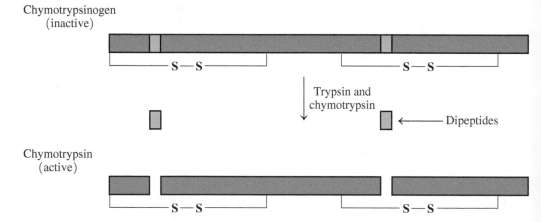

The protein hormone insulin is initially synthesized in the pancreas as a zymogen called proinsulin. When the polypeptide chain of 33 amino acids is removed by peptidases, insulin becomes biologically active.

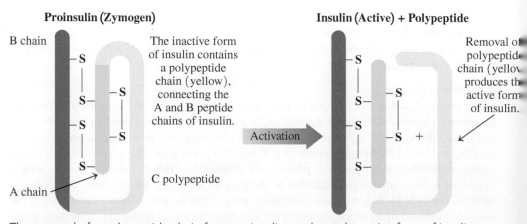

The removal of a polypeptide chain from proinsulin produces the active form of insulin.

Phosphorylation

Another common covalent modification is the addition or removal of a phosphate group, which can induce a structural change in an enzyme and change its catalytic activity. Almost one-third of all enzymes are regulated through addition or removal of a phosphate group. An inactive enzyme can be activated by the addition of a phosphate from ATP in a reaction catalyzed by a kinase (see Figure 20.9a). For enzymes that are inactive when phosphorylated, a phosphatase catalyzes the hydrolysis of phosphate and that enzyme becomes active (see Figure 20.9b).

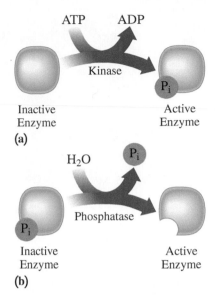

FIGURE 20.9 ▶ Phosphorylation is a type of covalent modification in which an enzyme is deactivated or activated. **(a)** A kinase can activate an inactive enzyme by phosphorylation. **(b)** A phosphatase can activate an inactive enzyme by removal of phosphate.

Q What is the difference between a kinase and a phosphatase if they both transfer phosphates?

▶ SAMPLE PROBLEM 20.5 Enzyme Regulation

How is the rate of a reaction sequence regulated in feedback control?

SOLUTION

When the end product of a reaction sequence is produced at sufficient levels for the cell, some product molecules bind to the allosteric enzyme (E_1) in the sequence, which shuts down all the reactions that follow and stops the synthesis of intermediate products.

STUDY CHECK 20.5

Why is pepsin, a digestive enzyme, produced as a zymogen?

ANSWER

Pepsin hydrolyzes proteins in the foods we ingest. It is synthesized as a zymogen, pepsinogen, to prevent its digestion of the proteins that make up the organs in the body.

QUESTIONS AND PROBLEMS

20.4 Regulation of Enzyme Activity

LEARNING GOAL Describe the role of allosteric enzymes, feedback control, and covalent modification in regulating enzyme activity.

20.25 How does an allosteric enzyme function as a regulatory enzyme?

20.26 What is the difference between a negative regulator and a positive regulator?

20.27 In feedback control, how does the end product of a reaction sequence regulate enzyme activity?

20.28 Why are the second or third enzymes in a reaction sequence not used as regulatory enzymes?

℞ Clinical Applications

20.29 Indicate if the following statements describe enzyme regulation by (1) an allosteric enzyme, (2) a zymogen, or (3) covalent modification:
a. The enzyme activity increases due to phosphorylation.
b. Fibrinogen in the blood forms fibrin in damaged tissues.
c. A positive regulator stimulates enzyme action.

20.30 Indicate if the following statements describe enzyme regulation by (1) an allosteric enzyme, (2) a zymogen, or (3) covalent modification:
a. An end product attaches to the regulatory site of the first enzyme in the reaction sequence.
b. Proinsulin forms in the pancreas.
c. Phosphorylase kinase deactivates pyruvate dehydrogenase.

20.31 Why is the active form of thrombin, which helps blood clot, produced from prothrombin only when injury and bleeding occur?

20.32 The zymogen trypsinogen produced in the pancreas is activated in the small intestine, where it catalyzes the digestion of proteins. Explain how the activation of the zymogen in the pancreas can lead to an inflammation of the pancreas called pancreatitis.

20.5 Enzyme Inhibition

Inhibitors are substances that cause enzymes to lose catalytic activity. Although inhibitors act differently, they all prevent the active site from binding with a substrate. An enzyme with a *reversible inhibitor* can regain enzymatic activity, but an *irreversible inhibitor* causes the permanent loss of enzymatic activity.

LEARNING GOAL

Describe competitive and noncompetitive inhibition, and reversible and irreversible inhibition.

Reversible Inhibition

In **reversible inhibition**, the inhibitor causes a loss of enzymatic activity that can be reversed. A reversible inhibitor can act in different ways but does not form covalent bonds with the enzyme. Reversible inhibition can be competitive or noncompetitive. In *competitive inhibition*, an inhibitor competes for the active site, whereas in *noncompetitive inhibition*, the inhibitor acts on another site that is not the active site.

Competitive Inhibitors

A **competitive inhibitor** has a chemical structure and polarity that is similar to that of the substrate. Thus, a competitive inhibitor competes with the substrate for the active site on the enzyme. When the inhibitor occupies the active site, the substrate cannot bind to the enzyme and no reaction can occur (see Figure 20.10). As long as the concentration of the inhibitor is substantial, there is a loss of enzyme activity. However, adding more substrate displaces the competitive inhibitor. As more enzyme molecules bind to substrate (ES), enzyme activity is regained.

FIGURE 20.10 ▶ With a structure similar to the substrate of an enzyme, a competitive inhibitor (I) also fits the active site and competes with the substrate when both are present.

Q Why does increasing the substrate concentration reverse the inhibition by a competitive inhibitor?

Active Site
E + S → Enzyme–Substrate Complex (ES) → Enzyme–Product Complex (EP) → E + P Products (P)

Active Site
E + I → Enzyme–Inhibitor Complex (EI)
Competitive inhibitor in the active site prevents the binding of substrate.

Malonate, which has a structure and polarity similar to that of succinate, competes for the active site on the enzyme succinate dehydrogenase. As long as malonate, a competitive inhibitor, occupies the active site, no reaction occurs. When more of the substrate succinate is added, malonate is displaced from the active site, and the inhibition is reversed.

Some bacterial infections are treated with competitive inhibitors called *antimetabolites*. Sulfanilamide, one of the first sulfa drugs, competes with *p*-aminobenzoic acid (PABA), which is an essential substance (metabolite) in the growth cycle of bacteria.

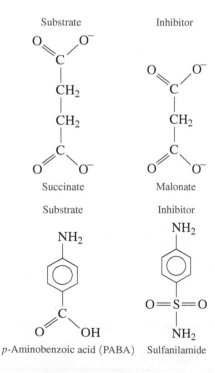

Succinate — Malonate
p-Aminobenzoic acid (PABA) — Sulfanilamide

Noncompetitive Inhibitors

The structure of a **noncompetitive inhibitor** does not resemble the substrate and does not compete for the active site. Instead, a noncompetitive inhibitor binds to a site on the enzyme that is not the active site. When bonded, the noncompetitive inhibitor distorts the shape of the enzyme. Inhibition occurs because the substrate cannot fit in the altered active site or it does not fit properly. Without the proper alignment of substrate, no catalysis can take place (see Figure 20.11). A noncompetitive inhibitor prevents catalysis in a similar manner as a negative regulator of an allosteric enzyme. Because a noncompetitive inhibitor is not competing for the active site, the addition of more substrate does not reverse the effect of a noncompetitive inhibitor. Examples of noncompetitive inhibitors are the heavy metal ions Pb^{2+}, Ag^+, and Hg^{2+} that bond with amino acid side groups such as $—COO^-$ or $—OH$. However, the effect of a metallic noncompetitive inhibitor can be reversed by using chemical reagents known as *chelators*, which bind these heavy metals, and remove them from the body. Then the enzyme regains biological activity.

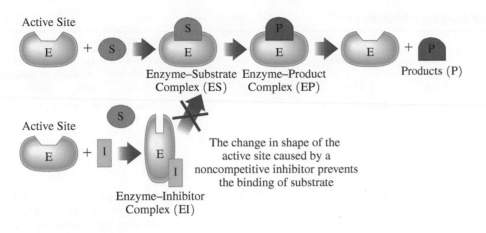

FIGURE 20.11 ▶ A noncompetitive inhibitor (I) binds to an enzyme at a site other than the active site, which distorts the enzyme and active site and prevents the proper binding and catalysis of the substrate at the active site.

◉ Why does an increase in the substrate concentration not reverse inhibition by a noncompetitive inhibitor?

Irreversible Inhibition

In irreversible inhibition, a molecule causes an enzyme to lose all enzymatic activity. Most **irreversible inhibitors** are toxic substances that destroy enzymes. Usually an irreversible inhibitor forms a covalent bond with an amino acid side group within the active site, which prevents the substrate from binding to the active site, thereby preventing catalytic activity.

Insecticides and nerve gases act as irreversible inhibitors of acetylcholinesterase, an enzyme needed for nerve conduction. The compound diisopropyl fluorophosphate (DFP) forms a covalent bond with the —CH₂OH group of a serine residue in the active site. When acetylcholinesterase is inhibited, the transmission of nerve impulses is blocked, and paralysis occurs.

Antibiotics produced by bacteria, mold, or yeast are irreversible inhibitors used to stop bacterial growth. For example, penicillin inhibits an enzyme needed for the formation of cell walls in bacteria, but not human cell membranes. With an incomplete cell wall, bacteria cannot survive and the infection is stopped. However, some bacteria are resistant to penicillin because they produce penicillinase, an enzyme that breaks down penicillin. The penicillinase hydrolyzes the four-atom ring converting penicillin to penicillinoic acid, which is inactive. Over the years, derivatives of penicillin to which bacteria have not yet become resistant have been produced. Examples of some irreversible enzyme inhibitors are listed in Table 20.7.

TABLE 20.7 Examples of Irreversible Enzyme Inhibitors

Name	Structure	Source	Inhibitory Action
Cyanide	CN^-	bitter almonds	bonds to iron in the heme group of cytochrome c oxidase, an enzyme in electron transport
Allopurinol		drug	inhibits xanthine oxidase from forming uric acid
Parathion		insecticide	inhibits cholinesterase from breaking down acetylcholine, resulting in continual nerve transmission
Penicillin		*Penicillium* fungus	inhibits enzymes that build cell walls in bacteria

R Groups for Penicillin Derivatives (Penicillin G, Penicillin V, Ampicillin, Amoxicillin)

A summary of competitive, noncompetitive, and irreversible inhibitor characteristics is shown in Table 20.8.

TABLE 20.8 Summary of Competitive, Noncompetitive, and Irreversible Inhibitors

Characteristics	Competitive	Noncompetitive	Irreversible
Shape of Inhibitor	similar shape to the substrate	does not have a similar shape to the substrate	does not have a similar shape to the substrate
Binding to Enzyme	competes for and binds at the active site	binds away from the active site to change the shape of the enzyme and its activity	forms a covalent bond with the enzyme
Reversibility	adding more substrate reverses the inhibition	not reversed by adding more substrate, but by a chemical change that removes the inhibitor	permanent, not reversible

Guide to Determining Type of Enzyme Inhibition

STEP 1 Compare the structure of the inhibitor to that of the substrate.

STEP 2 Describe the characteristics of the inhibitor.

STEP 3 Assign the type of inhibition based on the characteristics.

▶ SAMPLE PROBLEM 20.6 Enzyme Inhibition

State the type of inhibition in the following:

a. The inhibitor has a structure similar to that of the substrate.
b. The inhibitor binds to the surface of the enzyme, changing its shape in such a way that it cannot bind to substrate.

SOLUTION

a. STEP 1 Compare the structure of the inhibitor to that of the substrate. This inhibitor has a structure similar to that of the substrate.

STEP 2 Describe the characteristics of the inhibitor. This inhibitor would compete with the substrate for the active site.

STEP 3 Assign the type of inhibition based on the characteristics. This type of inhibition is competitive inhibition, which is reversed by increasing the concentration of the substrate.

b. STEP 1 Compare the structure of the inhibitor to that of the substrate. This inhibitor does not have a structure similar to the substrate.

STEP **2** Describe the characteristics of the inhibitor. This inhibitor binds to the surface of the enzyme where it changes the shape of the enzyme and the active site.

STEP **3** Assign the type of inhibition based on the characteristics. This type of inhibition is noncompetitive inhibition.

STUDY CHECK 20.6

What type of inhibition occurs when aspirin, also called acetylsalicylic acid, forms a covalent bond with serine in the active site of the enzyme cyclooxygenase?

ANSWER

irreversible inhibition

QUESTIONS AND PROBLEMS

20.5 Enzyme Inhibition

LEARNING GOAL Describe competitive and noncompetitive inhibition, and reversible and irreversible inhibition.

20.33 Indicate whether each of the following describes a competitive or a noncompetitive enzyme inhibitor:
   a. The inhibitor has a structure similar to the substrate.
   b. The effect of the inhibitor cannot be reversed by adding more substrate.
   c. The inhibitor competes with the substrate for the active site.
   d. The structure of the inhibitor is not similar to the substrate.
   e. The addition of more substrate reverses the inhibition.

20.34 Oxaloacetate is an inhibitor of succinate dehydrogenase.
   a. Would you expect oxaloacetate to be a competitive or a noncompetitive inhibitor? Why?
   b. Would oxaloacetate bind to the active site or elsewhere on the enzyme?
   c. How would you reverse the effect of the inhibitor?

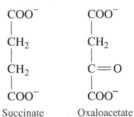

Succinate   Oxaloacetate

R Clinical Applications

20.35 Methanol and ethanol are oxidized by alcohol dehydrogenase. In methanol poisoning, ethanol is given intravenously to prevent the formation of formaldehyde that has toxic effects.
   a. Draw the condensed structural formulas for methanol and ethanol.
   b. Would ethanol compete with methanol for the active site or bind to a different site on the enzyme?
   c. Would ethanol be a competitive or noncompetitive inhibitor of methanol oxidation?

20.36 In humans, the antibiotic amoxicillin (a type of penicillin) is used to treat certain bacterial infections.
   a. Does the antibiotic inhibit human enzymes?
   b. Why does the antibiotic kill bacteria but not humans?
   c. Is amoxicillin a reversible or irreversible inhibitor?

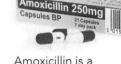

Amoxicillin is a derivative of the antibiotic penicillin.

20.6 Enzyme Cofactors and Vitamins

For many enzymes, their polypeptide chains are biologically active. However, there are also enzymes in which the polypeptide chain is inactive and cannot catalyze a reaction. An inactive enzyme becomes active when it combines with a **cofactor**, which is a nonprotein component such as a vitamin or a metal ion. If the cofactor is an organic molecule, it is known as a **coenzyme**. A cofactor binds to an enzyme in a way that prepares the active site to take part in the catalysis of its substrate.

Metal Ions as Cofactors

The metal ions from the minerals that we obtain from foods in our diet have various functions in enzyme catalysis. Metal ion cofactors such as Fe^{2+} and Cu^{2+} are often required by enzymes involved in the loss or gain of electrons (oxidoreductases). Other metal ions such as Zn^{2+} stabilize the amino acid residues in the active site of hydrolases. Some of the metal ion cofactors that are required by enzymes are listed in Table 20.9.

The enzyme carboxypeptidase is produced in the pancreas and moves into the small intestine where it catalyzes the hydrolysis of the C-terminal amino acid with an aromatic residue in a protein (see Figure 20.12).

LEARNING GOAL

Describe the types of cofactors found in enzymes.

TABLE 20.9 Enzymes and the Metal Ions Required as Cofactors

Metal Ion	Enzymes Requiring Metal Ion Cofactors
Cu^{2+}/Cu^{+}	Cytochrome oxidase
Fe^{2+}/Fe^{3+}	Catalase Cytochrome oxidase
Zn^{2+}	Alcohol dehydrogenase Carbonic anhydrase Carboxypeptidase A
Mg^{2+}	Glucose-6-phosphatase Hexokinase
Mn^{2+}	Arginase
Ni^{2+}	Urease

FIGURE 20.12 ▶
Carboxypeptidase requires a Zn^{2+} cofactor for the hydrolysis of the peptide bond of a C-terminal aromatic amino acid.

Ⓠ Why is Zn^{2+} a cofactor for carboxypeptidase?

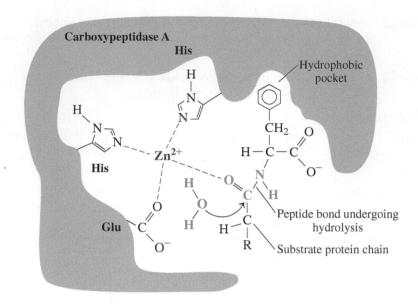

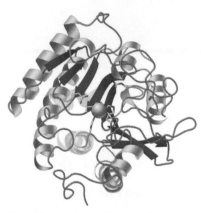

The ribbon representation of carboxypeptidase shows a Zn^{2+} cofactor (orange sphere) in the center of the active site, held in place by amino acid residues in the active site.

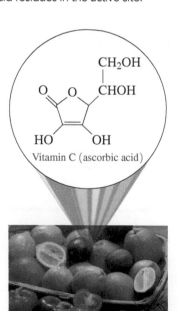

Vitamin C (ascorbic acid)

FIGURE 20.13 ▶ Oranges, lemons, peppers, and tomatoes contain the water-soluble vitamin, vitamin C (ascorbic acid), which is an antioxidant.

Ⓠ What happens to the excess vitamin C that may be consumed in one day?

The active site includes a pocket that fits the bulky hydrophobic amino acid residue on a protein substrate. In the center of the active site, a Zn^{2+} cofactor is bonded to the nitrogen atom in each of two histidine residues, and an oxygen atom in the residue of glutamic acid. The Zn^{2+} promotes the hydrolysis of the peptide bond by stabilizing the partial negative charge of the oxygen in the carbonyl group of the peptide bond undergoing hydrolysis.

▶ SAMPLE PROBLEM 20.7 Cofactors

Indicate whether each of the following enzymes is active with or without a cofactor:

a. an enzyme that needs Mg^{2+} for catalytic activity
b. a polypeptide chain that is biologically active
c. an enzyme that binds to vitamin B_6 to become active

SOLUTION

a. The enzyme would be active with the metal ion Mg^{2+} cofactor.
b. An active enzyme that is only a polypeptide chain does not require a cofactor.
c. An enzyme that requires vitamin B_6 is active with a cofactor.

STUDY CHECK 20.7

Which cofactor for the enzymes in Sample Problem 20.7 would be called a coenzyme?

ANSWER

vitamin B_6

Vitamins and Coenzymes

Vitamins are organic molecules that are essential for normal health and growth. They are required in trace amounts and need to be obtained from the diet because vitamins are not synthesized in the body. Before vitamins were discovered, it was known that lime juice prevented the disease scurvy in sailors, and that cod liver oil could prevent rickets. In 1912, scientists found that in addition to carbohydrates, fats, and proteins, certain other factors called vitamins must be obtained from the diet. Vitamin B_1 (thiamine) was the first B vitamin to be identified, thus the abbreviation B_1.

Vitamins are classified into two groups by solubility: water-soluble and fat-soluble. **Water-soluble vitamins** have polar groups such as —OH and —COOH, which make them soluble in the aqueous environment of the cells. The **fat-soluble vitamins** are nonpolar compounds, which are soluble in the fat (lipid) components of the body such as fat deposits and cell membranes.

Water-Soluble Vitamins

Because water-soluble vitamins cannot be stored in the body, any excess amounts are excreted in the urine each day. Therefore, the water-soluble vitamins must be in the foods of our daily diets (see Figure 20.13). Because many water-soluble vitamins are easily destroyed by heat, oxygen, and ultraviolet light, care must be taken in food preparation, processing, and storage. Because refining grains such as wheat causes a loss of vitamins, during the 1940s, the Committee on Food and Nutrition of the National Research Council began to recommend dietary enrichment of cereal grains. Vitamin B_1 (thiamine), vitamin B_2 (riboflavin), and iron were in the first group of added nutrients recommended. The Recommended Daily Allowance (RDA) for many vitamins and minerals appears on food product labels. Individuals eating balanced meals including fresh produce and whole grains can readily achieve the U.S. RDAs.

Many of the water-soluble vitamins are precursors of cofactors required by many enzymes to carry out certain aspects of catalytic action (see Table 20.10). The coenzymes do not remain bonded to a particular enzyme, but are used repeatedly by different enzyme molecules to facilitate an enzyme-catalyzed reaction (see Figure 20.14). Thus, only small amounts of coenzymes are required in the cells. Table 20.11 gives the structures of the water-soluble vitamins.

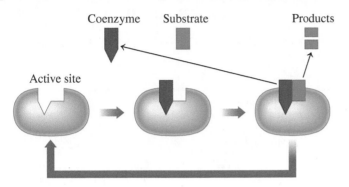

⚛ CORE CHEMISTRY SKILL

Describing the Role of Cofactors

FIGURE 20.14 ▶ A coenzyme is required so that an enzyme can become active.

🅠 What is the function of water-soluble vitamins in enzymes?

TABLE 20.10 Water-Soluble Vitamins, Coenzymes, Functions, Sources and RDA, and Deficiency Symptoms

Vitamin	Coenzyme	Transfer Function	Sources and RDA (Adults)	Deficiency Symptoms
B_1 (Thiamine)	Thiamine pyrophosphate (TPP)	aldehyde groups	liver, yeast, whole grain bread, cereals, milk (1.2 mg)	beriberi: fatigue, poor appetite, weight loss
B_2 (Riboflavin)	Flavin adenine dinucleotide (FAD); flavin mononucleotide (FMN)	electrons	beef, liver, chicken, eggs, green leafy vegetables, dairy foods, peanuts, whole grains (1.2 to 1.8 mg)	dermatitis; dry skin; red, sore tongue; cataracts
B_3 (Niacin)	Nicotinamide adenine dinucleotide (NAD^+); nicotinamide adenine dinucleotide phosphate ($NADP^+$)	electrons	brewer's yeast, chicken, beef, fish, liver, brown rice, whole grains (14 to 18 mg)	pellagra: dermatitis, muscle fatigue, loss of appetite, diarrhea, mouth sores
B_5 (Pantothenic acid)	Coenzyme A	acetyl groups	salmon, beef, liver, eggs, brewer's yeast, whole grains, fresh vegetables (5 mg)	fatigue, retarded growth, muscle cramps, anemia
B_6 (Pyridoxine)	Pyridoxal phosphate (PLP)	amino groups	meat, liver, fish, nuts, whole grains, spinach (1.3 to 2.0 mg)	dermatitis, fatigue, anemia, retarded growth
B_9 (Folic acid)	Tetrahydrofolate (THF)	methyl groups	green leafy vegetables, beans, meat, seafood, yeast, asparagus, whole grains enriched with folic acid (400 mcg)	abnormal red blood cells, anemia, intestinal tract disturbances, loss of hair, growth impairment, depression
B_{12} (Cobalamin)	Methylcobalamin	methyl groups, hydrogen	liver, beef, kidney, chicken, fish, milk products (2.0 to 2.6 mcg)	pernicious anemia, malformed red blood cells, nerve damage
C (Ascorbic acid)	Ascorbic acid	electrons	blueberries, citrus fruits, strawberries, cantaloupe, tomatoes, peppers, broccoli, cabbage, spinach (75 to 90 mg)	scurvy: bleeding gums, weakened connective tissues, slow-healing wounds, anemia
H (Biotin)	Biocytin	carbon dioxide	liver, yeast, nuts, eggs (30 mcg)	dermatitis, loss of hair, fatigue, anemia, depression

TABLE 20.11 Structures of Water-Soluble Vitamins

B₁ (Thiamine)

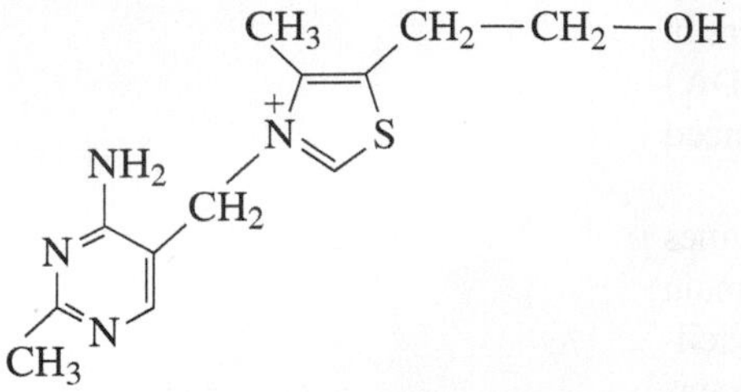

B₂ (Riboflavin)

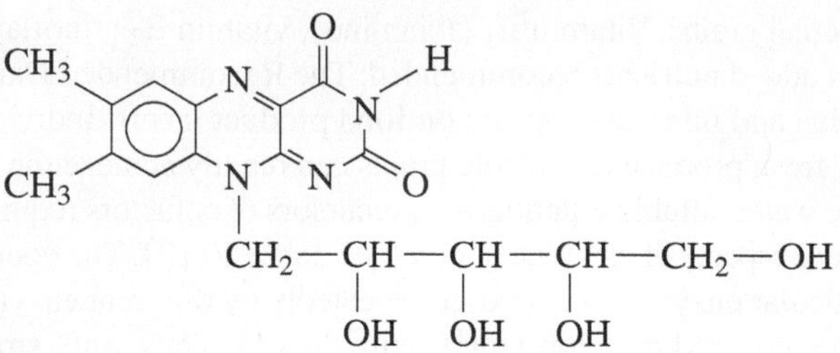

B₃ (Niacin)

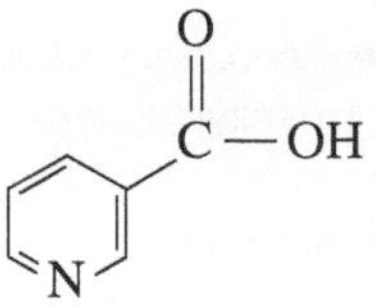

B₅ (Pantothenic acid)

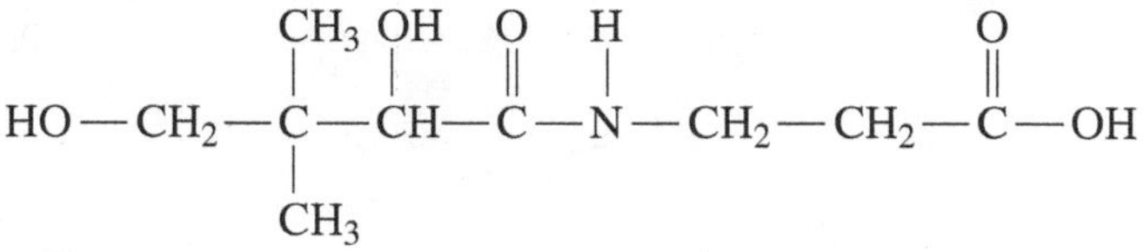

B₆ (Pyridoxine)

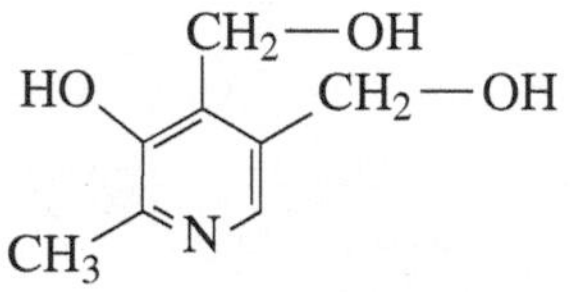

B₁₂ (Cobalamin)

C (Ascorbic acid)

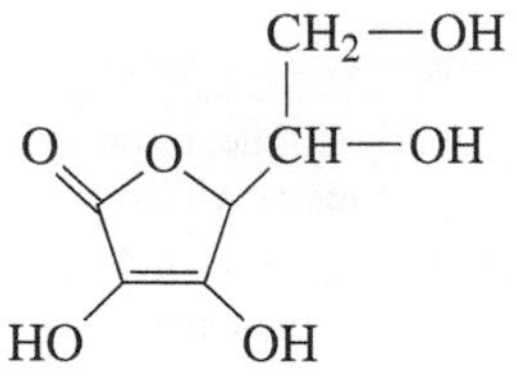

H (Biotin)

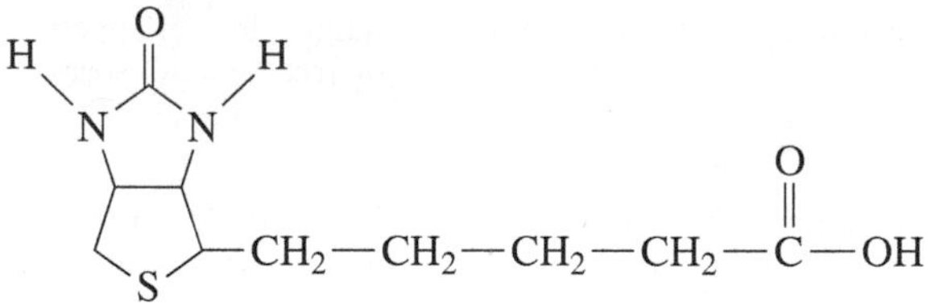

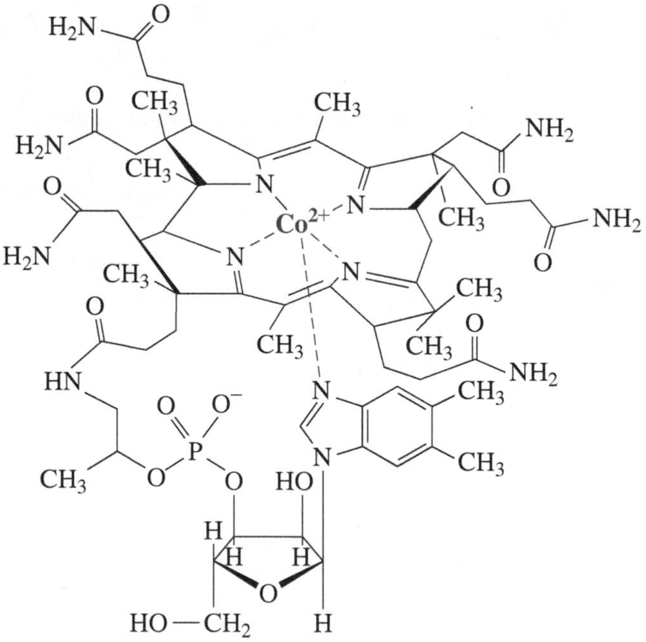

B₉ (Folic acid)

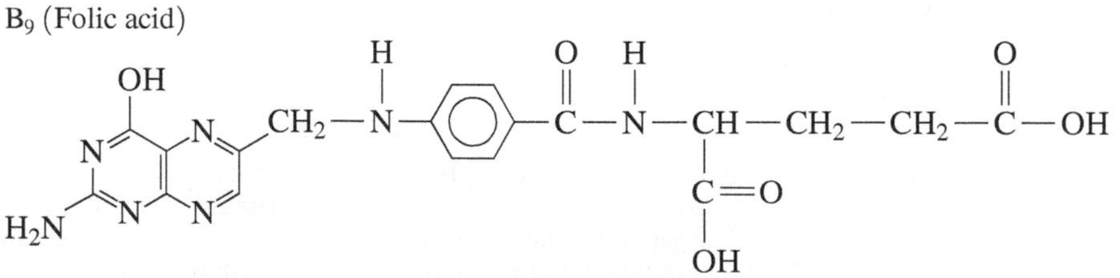

Fat-Soluble Vitamins

The fat-soluble vitamins—A, D, E, and K—are not involved as coenzymes in catalytic reactions, but they are important in processes such as vision, formation of bone, protection from oxidation, and proper blood clotting (see Table 20.12). Because the fat-soluble vitamins are stored in the body, and not eliminated, it is possible to take too much, which could be toxic primarily in the liver and fatty tissues. Table 20.13 gives the structures of the fat-soluble vitamins.

TABLE 20.12 Function, Sources and RDA, and Deficiency Symptoms of Fat-Soluble Vitamins

Vitamin	Function	Sources and RDA (Adults)	Deficiency Symptoms
A (Retinol)	formation of visual pigments, synthesis of RNA	yellow and green fruits and vegetables (800 mcg)	night blindness, immune system repression, slowed growth, rickets
D (Cholecalciferol)	regulation of absorption of P and Ca during bone growth	sunlight, cod liver oil, enriched milk, eggs (5 to 10 mcg)	rickets, weak bone structure, osteomalacia
E (Tocopherol)	antioxidant; prevents oxidation of vitamin A and unsaturated fatty acids	meats, whole grains, vegetables (15 mg)	hemolysis, anemia
K (Menaquinone)	synthesis of zymogen prothrombin for blood clotting	liver, spinach, cauliflower (9 to 120 mcg)	prolonged bleeding time, bruising

TABLE 20.13 Structures of Fat-Soluble Vitamins

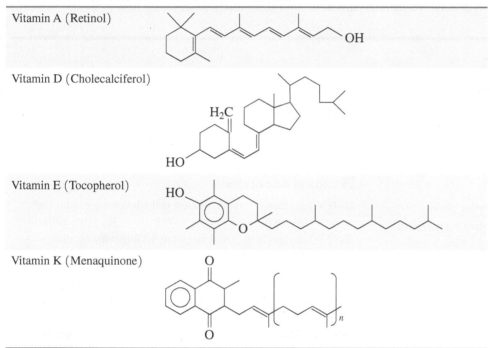

Vitamin A (Retinol)

Vitamin D (Cholecalciferol)

Vitamin E (Tocopherol)

Vitamin K (Menaquinone)

The orange pigment (carotene) in carrots is used to synthesize vitamin A (retinol), an antioxidant, in the body.

Sunflower seeds, almonds, and spinach contain vitamin E, which is an antioxidant.

Antioxidants

The production of energy by cells occurs through chemical oxidation. During this process, reactive oxygen compounds called *free radicals*, such as $NO^{\bullet}$, $OH^{\bullet}$, and $O_2^{\bullet-}$ are formed. These molecules are called free radicals because they have an unpaired electron. Because electrons are more stable when they are paired, free radicals react readily. An overabundance of free radicals can cause cellular and DNA damage such as aging, inflammation, cataracts, and cancer.

The body uses *antioxidants* to defend against free radicals. These antioxidants include vitamins C, E, and beta-carotene, a precursor to vitamin A. Many face creams and serums contain vitamin E to protect against free radicals. The tannins and flavonoids found in tea leaves and wine have been shown to have antioxidant properties.

The body also produces antioxidant enzymes such as superoxide dismutase that reacts with free radicals damaging membranes, proteins, and neurons. A genetic mutation in this enzyme is responsible for the disease *Amyotrophic Lateral Sclerosis* (ALS) commonly called Lou Gehrig's disease. Another antioxidant enzyme is glutathione peroxidase, which uses the micronutrient selenium as a cofactor.

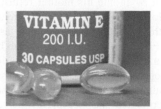

Vitamins and other small molecules in foods act as antioxidants, which can prevent oxidative damage to cells.

> ► **SAMPLE PROBLEM 20.8 Vitamins**
>
> Why is it more important to get regular, daily amounts of vitamins B_1 and B_2, but not vitamins A or D?
>
> **SOLUTION**
>
> Water-soluble vitamins like vitamin B_1 (thiamine) and vitamin B_2 (riboflavin) are not stored in the body, whereas fat-soluble vitamins such as vitamin A (retinol) and vitamin D (cholecalciferol) are stored in the liver and body fat. Any excess of thiamine or riboflavin is eliminated in the urine and must be replenished each day from the diet.
>
> **STUDY CHECK 20.8**
>
> Why are fresh fruits rather than cooked fruits recommended as a source of vitamin C?
>
> **ANSWER**
>
> Water-soluble vitamins such as vitamin C are easily destroyed by heat.

QUESTIONS AND PROBLEMS

20.6 Enzyme Cofactors and Vitamins

LEARNING GOAL Describe the types of cofactors found in enzymes.

20.37 Is the enzyme described in each of the following statements active with or without a cofactor?
   a. requires vitamin B_1 (thiamine)
   b. needs Zn^{2+} for catalytic activity
   c. its active form consists of two polypeptide chains

20.38 Is the enzyme described in each of the following statements active with or without a cofactor?
   a. requires vitamin B_2 (riboflavin)
   b. its active form is composed of 155 amino acid residues
   c. uses Cu^{2+} during catalysis

20.39 Identify the vitamin that is a component of each of the following coenzymes:
   a. coenzyme A   **b.** tetrahydrofolate (THF)
   c. NAD^+

20.40 Identify the vitamin that is a component of each of the following coenzymes:
   a. thiamine pyrophosphate   **b.** FAD
   c. pyridoxal phosphate

℞ Clinical Applications

20.41 What vitamin may be deficient in the following conditions?
   a. rickets   **b.** scurvy   **c.** pellagra

20.42 What vitamin may be deficient in the following conditions?
   a. poor night vision   **b.** pernicious anemia
   c. beriberi

20.43 The RDA for vitamin B_6 (pyridoxine) is 1.3 to 2.0 mg. Why will it not improve your nutrition to take 100 mg of pyridoxine daily?

20.44 The RDA for vitamin C (ascorbic acid) is 75 to 90 mg. If you take 1000 mg of vitamin C daily, what happens to the vitamin C you do not need?

℞ Clinical Update

Noah's Diet for Lactose Intolerance

When Noah and his mother return to the clinic, Emma administers the hydrogen breath test (HBT) after Noah has fasted for 8 h. First, the technician has Noah breathe into a balloon to determine a base level of hydrogen (H_2). Then Noah drinks a solution containing lactose and more breath samples are collected and measured for hydrogen over the next 3 h. Hydrogen is present in the breath when the bacteria in the colon are fermenting lactose and producing hydrogen (H_2).

Lactose intolerance is confirmed if the hydrogen levels rise 20 ppm above baseline levels over a 3-h period after ingesting the lactose solution. The results of the test shown as the black line on the graph show that Noah's levels were 130 ppm, so Emma and the attending physician concluded that Noah has a problem digesting lactose, which means he has *lactose intolerance*.

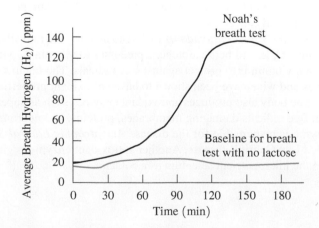

Treatment of Lactose Intolerance

Emma tells Noah's mother that he will need to avoid products that contain lactose, including milk and milk products such as cheese, butter, and ice cream. A person who is lactose intolerant should also know that some foods that are not dairy products contain lactose. For example, many baked goods, cereals, breakfast drinks, salad dressings, and even lunchmeat can contain lactose. Food labels must be read carefully to see if the ingredients include "milk" or "lactose."

Another way to combat lactose intolerance is to use the enzyme lactase with meals. Lactase is available in many forms, such as tablets that are taken with meals, or drops that are added to milk. When lactase is added to milk that is left in the refrigerator for 24 h, the lactose level is reduced by 70 to 90%. Lactase pills or chewable tablets are taken when a person begins to eat a meal that contains dairy foods.

Lactaid contains lactase that aids the digestion of lactose.

℞ Clinical Applications

20.45 Using the graph for the average hydrogen breath test, estimate
   a. the baseline ppm at 60 min
   b. the hydrogen ppm for Noah at 60 min

20.46 Using the graph for the average hydrogen breath test, estimate
   a. the baseline ppm at 90 min
   b. the hydrogen ppm for Noah at 90 min

20.47 Noah's mother makes him some hot chocolate, to which she adds a tablet of lactase. A few hours after Noah drinks the hot chocolate, he has symptoms of lactose intolerance. Explain why the lactase was ineffective.

20.48 Noah's mother adds a tablet of lactase to a glass of milk and places it in the refrigerator for 24 h. The next day Noah drinks the milk and has no symptoms of lactose intolerance. Explain why the lactase was effective.

CONCEPT MAP

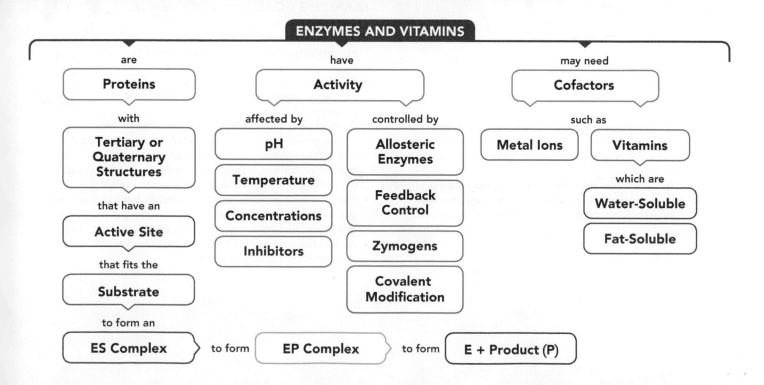

CHAPTER REVIEW

20.1 Enzymes and Enzyme Action
LEARNING GOAL Describe enzymes and their role in enzyme-catalyzed reactions.

- Enzymes are globular proteins that act as biological catalysts by lowering activation energy and accelerating the rate of cellular reactions.
- Within the tertiary structure of an enzyme, a small pocket called the active site binds the substrate.
- In the lock-and-key model, an early theory of enzyme action, a substrate precisely fits the shape of the active site.
- In the induced-fit model, both the active site and the substrate undergo changes in their shapes to give the best fit for efficient catalysis.
- In the enzyme–substrate complex, catalysis takes place when amino acid residues in the active site of an enzyme react with a substrate.
- When the products of catalysis are released, the enzyme can bind to another substrate molecule.

20.2 Classification of Enzymes
LEARNING GOAL Classify enzymes and give their names.

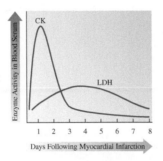

- The names of most enzymes ending in *ase* describe the compound or reaction catalyzed by the enzyme.
- Enzymes are classified by the type of reaction they catalyze, such as oxidoreductase, transferase, or isomerase.

20.3 Factors Affecting Enzyme Activity
LEARNING GOAL Describe the effect of changes of temperature, pH, concentration of enzyme, and concentration of substrate on enzyme activity.

- The optimum temperature at which most enzymes are effective is usually 37 °C, and the optimum pH is usually 7.4.
- The rate of an enzyme-catalyzed reaction decreases as temperature and pH go above or below the optimum temperature and pH values.
- An increase in the enzyme concentration increases the rate of reaction.
- An increase in substrate concentration increases the reaction rate of an enzyme-catalyzed reaction, but a maximum rate is reached when all of the enzyme molecules are combined with substrate.

20.4 Regulation of Enzyme Activity
LEARNING GOAL Describe the role of allosteric enzymes, feedback control, and covalent modification in regulating enzyme activity.

- Allosteric enzymes change their activity when they bind to regulator molecules.
- In feedback control, the end product of an enzyme-catalyzed reaction acts as a negative regulator and binds with the first enzyme of the reaction sequence.
- Covalent modification regulates enzymes by adding or removing a covalently bonded group.
- Insulin and most digestive enzymes are produced as inactive forms called zymogens.
- Production of zymogens and phosphorylation are types of covalent modification.

20.5 Enzyme Inhibition
LEARNING GOAL Describe competitive and noncompetitive inhibition, and reversible and irreversible inhibition.

Enzyme–Substrate Complex

- An inhibitor reduces the activity of an enzyme or makes it inactive.
- An inhibitor can be reversible or irreversible.
- A competitive inhibitor has a structure similar to the substrate and competes for the active site.
- When the active site is occupied, the enzyme cannot catalyze the reaction of the substrate.
- A noncompetitive inhibitor attaches to the enzyme away from the active site, changing the shape of both the enzyme and its active site.
- An irreversible inhibitor forms a covalent bond within the active site that permanently prevents catalytic activity.

20.6 Enzyme Cofactors and Vitamins
LEARNING GOAL Describe the types of cofactors found in enzymes.

Coenzyme   Products

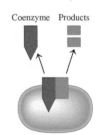

- Some enzymes are biologically active as proteins only, whereas other enzymes require a nonprotein component called a cofactor.
- A cofactor may be a metal ion, such as Cu^{2+} or Fe^{2+}, or an organic molecule or a vitamin called a coenzyme.
- A vitamin is a small organic molecule needed for health and normal growth that is obtained in small amounts from the diet.
- The water-soluble vitamins are B and C, and they function as coenzymes. Vitamin B is essential for the workings of certain enzymes in the body, and vitamin C is an antioxidant.
- The fat-soluble vitamins are A, D, E, and K. Vitamin A is important for vision, vitamin D for proper bone growth, vitamin E is an antioxidant, and vitamin K is required for proper blood clotting.
- Antioxidants neutralize the highly reactive oxygen free radicals generated during oxidative processes.

KEY TERMS

active site A pocket in a part of the tertiary enzyme structure that binds to a substrate and catalyzes a reaction.

activity The rate at which an enzyme catalyzes the reaction that converts a substrate to a product.

allosteric enzyme An enzyme that regulates the rate of a reaction when a regulator molecule attaches to a site other than the active site.

antibiotic A substance usually produced by bacteria, mold, or yeast that inhibits the growth of bacteria.

coenzyme An organic molecule, usually a vitamin, required as a cofactor in enzyme action.

cofactor A metal ion or an organic molecule that is necessary for a biologically functional enzyme.

competitive inhibitor A molecule that has a structure similar to a substrate and that inhibits enzyme action by competing for the active site.

covalent modification Regulation of an enzyme that involves forming or breaking covalent bonds to a group on the polypeptide chain.

enzyme A globular protein, sometimes with a cofactor, that catalyzes a biological reaction.

enzyme–product (EP) complex An intermediate consisting of an enzyme that binds to a product in an enzyme-catalyzed reaction.

enzyme–substrate (ES) complex An intermediate consisting of an enzyme that binds to a substrate in an enzyme-catalyzed reaction.

fat-soluble vitamin A vitamin that is not soluble in water and can be stored in the liver and body fat.

feedback control A type of inhibition in which an end product inhibits the first enzyme in a sequence of enzyme-catalyzed reactions.

induced-fit model A model of enzyme action in which the shape of a substrate and the active site of the enzyme adjust to give an optimal fit.

inhibitor A substance that makes an enzyme inactive by interfering with its ability to react with a substrate.

irreversible inhibitor A compound or metal ion that causes the loss of enzymatic activity by forming a covalent bond near or at the active site.

noncompetitive inhibitor An inhibitor that does not resemble the substrate and attaches to the enzyme away from the active site to prevent the binding of the substrate.

optimum pH The pH at which an enzyme is most active.

optimum temperature The temperature at which an enzyme is most active.

reversible inhibition The loss of enzymatic activity by an inhibitor whose effect can be reversed.

substrate The molecule that reacts in the active site in an enzyme-catalyzed reaction.

vitamin An organic molecule that is essential for normal health and growth, and obtained in small amounts from the diet.

water-soluble vitamin A vitamin that is soluble in water; cannot be stored in the body; is easily destroyed by heat, ultraviolet light, and oxygen; and functions as a coenzyme.

zymogen An inactive form of an enzyme that is activated by the removal of a peptide portion from one end of the protein.

⚛ CORE CHEMISTRY SKILLS

Describing Enzyme Action (20.1)

- Enzymes are biological catalysts that lower the activation energy and accelerate the rate of cellular reactions.
- Within the tertiary structure of an enzyme, a small pocket called the active site binds the substrate.
- In the induced-fit model of enzyme action, the active site and the substrate change their shapes for efficient catalysis.
- When the products of catalysis are released, the enzyme can bind to another substrate molecule.

Example: Match the terms (1) enzyme, (2) substrate, (3) active site, and (4) induced-fit model with each of the following:
  a. an active site that adapts to the shape of a substrate
  b. has a structure that fits the active site of an enzyme
  c. the portion of an enzyme where catalytic activity occurs
  d. has a tertiary structure that recognizes the substrate

Answer: **a.** (4) induced-fit model **b.** (2) substrate
  c. (3) active site **d.** (1) enzyme

Classifying Enzymes (20.2)

An enzyme can be classified from its name or the equation for the catalyzed reaction. Enzymes have six general classes: oxidoreductase, transferase, hydrolase, lyase, isomerase, and ligase.

Example: Match the enzyme names (1) DNA ligase, (2) HIV protease, (3) protein kinase, and (4) glucose oxidase with one of the following classifications:
  a. oxidoreductase **b.** transferase
  c. hydrolase **d.** ligase

Answer: **a.** (4) glucose oxidase **b.** (3) protein kinase
  c. (2) HIV protease **d.** (1) DNA ligase

Identifying Factors Affecting Enzyme Activity (20.3)

- The activity of many enzymes is regulated by allosteric enzymes, feedback control, and covalent modification including production of zymogens and phosphorylation.
- The rate of an enzyme-catalyzed reaction is affected by changes in temperature, pH, enzyme, and substrate concentration.
- Molecules called inhibitors decrease enzyme activity by binding in the active site (competitive inhibition) or at another site on the enzyme (noncompetitive inhibition).

Example: Lactase, the enzyme that hydrolyzes lactose, operates at an optimal pH of 6.0 and an optimal temperature of 37 °C. Would the following changes increase, decrease, or have no effect on the activity of lactase?
  a. lowering the pH to 2
  b. raising the temperature above 65 °C
  c. greatly increasing the amount of lactose available
  d. introducing a competitive inhibitor of lactase

Answer: **a.** decrease **b.** decrease **c.** increase **d.** decrease

Describing the Role of Cofactors (20.6)

- Metal ions can be cofactors that stabilize the active site of enzymes and are vital for catalysis.
- Many vitamins are coenzymes necessary for catalysis by some enzymes.

Example: Match the coenzymes (1) NAD^+, (2) FAD, (3) coenzyme A, and (4) THF with one of the following vitamins:
  a. riboflavin (B_2)   **b.** niacin (B_3)
  c. folic acid (B_9)   **d.** pantothenic acid (B_5)

Answer: **a.** (2) FAD   **b.** (1) NAD^+
  c. (4) THF   **d.** (3) coenzyme A

UNDERSTANDING THE CONCEPTS

The chapter sections to review are shown in parentheses at the end of each question.

20.49 Fresh pineapple contains the enzyme bromelain that degrades proteins. (20.3)
  a. The directions on a gelatin (protein) package say not to add fresh pineapple. However, canned pineapple that has been heated to high temperatures can be added. Why?
  b. Fresh pineapple can be used as a marinade to tenderize tough meat. Why?

Fresh pineapple contains the enzyme bromelain.

20.50 Vitamin C, also called ascorbic acid, can act as a coenzyme and an antioxidant. (20.6)
  a. Is vitamin C a water-soluble or a fat-soluble vitamin? How do you know?
  b. How do antioxidants protect cells from damage?

Rose hips are rich in vitamin C.

℞ Clinical Applications

20.51 Ethylene glycol (HO—CH_2—CH_2—OH) is a major component of antifreeze. If ingested, it is first converted to $HOOC$—CHO (oxoethanoic acid) and then to $HOOC$—$COOH$ (oxalic acid), which is toxic. (20.1, 20.4)

  a. What class of enzyme catalyzes both of the reactions of ethylene glycol?
  b. The treatment for the ingestion of ethylene glycol is an intravenous solution of ethanol. How might this help prevent toxic levels of oxalic acid in the body?

Ethylene glycol is added to a radiator to prevent freezing and boiling.

20.52 Adults who are lactose intolerant cannot break down the disaccharide in milk products. To help digest dairy food, a product known as Lactaid can be ingested prior to eating dairy products. (20.1, 20.3)
  a. What is the name of the enzyme present in Lactaid, and what is the major class of this enzyme?
  b. What might happen to the enzyme if the digestion product were stored in a warm area?
  c. A label on a bottle of Lactaid recommends it is stored at room temperature (68 °F to 77 °F) and kept away from heat and moisture. Why should Lactaid be stored at cool temperatures and dry conditions?

The disaccharide lactose is present in milk products.

ADDITIONAL QUESTIONS AND PROBLEMS

20.53 Why do the cells in the body have so many enzymes? (20.1)

20.54 Are all the possible enzymes present at the same time in a cell? (20.1)

20.55 How are enzymes different from the catalysts used in chemistry laboratories? (20.1)

20.56 Why do enzymes function only under mild conditions? (20.1)

20.57 How does an enzyme change the activation energy for a reaction in a cell? (20.1)

20.58 Why do most enzyme-catalyzed reactions proceed quickly? (20.1)

20.59 How does the lock-and-key model explain that sucrose hydrolyzes sucrose but not lactose? (20.1)

20.60 How does the induced-fit model of enzyme action allow an enzyme to catalyze a reaction of a group of substrates? (20.1)

20.61 Indicate whether each of the following would be a substrate (S) or an enzyme (E): (20.2)
  a. lactose   **b.** lactase   **c.** lipase
  d. trypsin   **e.** pyruvate   **f.** transaminase

20.62 Indicate whether each of the following would be a substrate (S) or an enzyme (E): (20.2)
  a. glucose   **b.** hydrolase   **c.** maleate isomerase
  d. alanine   **e.** amylose   **f.** amylase

20.63 Give the substrate for each of the following enzymes: (20.2)
  a. urease   **b.** succinate dehydrogenase
  c. aspartate transaminase   **d.** phenylalanine hydroxylase

20.64 Give the substrate for each of the following enzymes: (20.2)
  a. maltase   **b.** fructose oxidase
  c. phenolase   **d.** sucrase

20.65 Predict the major class for each of the following enzymes: (20.2)
  a. acyltransferase   **b.** oxidase
  c. lipase   **d.** decarboxylase

20.66 Predict the major class for each of the following enzymes: (20.2)
  a. cis–trans isomerase   **b.** reductase
  c. carboxylase   **d.** peptidase

20.67 What is meant by the optimum temperature for an enzyme? (20.3)

20.68 What is meant by the optimum pH for an enzyme? (20.3)

20.69 Indicate how each of the following will affect an enzyme-catalyzed reaction if the enzyme has an optimum temperature of 37 °C and an optimum pH of 7.0: (20.3)
  a. heating the reaction mixture to 100 °C
  b. placing the reaction mixture in ice
  c. adjusting the pH of the reaction mixture to pH 2.0

20.70 Indicate how each of the following will affect an enzyme-catalyzed reaction if the enzyme has an optimum temperature of 37 °C and an optimum pH of 8.0: (20.3)
  a. decreasing the temperature of the reaction mixture from 37 °C to 15 °C
  b. adjusting the pH of the reaction mixture to pH 5.0
  c. adjusting the pH of the reaction mixture to pH 10.0

20.71 Indicate whether the enzyme is saturated or not saturated with substrate in each of the following conditions: (20.3)
  a. adding more substrate does not increase the rate of reaction
  b. doubling the substrate concentration doubles the rate of reaction

20.72 Indicate whether each of the following enzymes would be functional: (20.3)
  a. pepsin, a digestive enzyme, at pH 2.0
  b. an enzyme at 37 °C, if the enzyme is from a type of thermophilic bacteria that has an optimum temperature of 100 °C

20.73 What is an allosteric enzyme? (20.4)

20.74 Why can some regulator molecules speed up a reaction, whereas others slow it down? (20.4)

20.75 In feedback control, what type of regulator slows down the catalytic activity of the reaction series? (20.4)

20.76 Why is covalent modification used to regulate the activity of an enzyme? (20.4)

20.77 How does reversible inhibition differ from irreversible inhibition? (20.5)

20.78 How does competitive reversible inhibition differ from noncompetitive reversible inhibition? (20.5)

20.79 Match the type of inhibitor (**1** to **3**) with the following statements (**a** to **d**): (20.5)
  1. competitive inhibitor
  2. noncompetitive inhibitor
  3. irreversible inhibitor

  a. forms a covalent bond with an amino acid residue in the active site
  b. has a structure similar to the substrate
  c. the addition of more substrate reverses the inhibition
  d. bonds to the surface of the enzyme, causing a change in the shape of the enzyme and active site

20.80 Match the type of inhibitor (**1** to **3**) with the following statements (**a** to **d**): (20.5)
  1. competitive inhibitor
  2. noncompetitive inhibitor
  3. irreversible inhibitor

  a. has a structure that is not similar to the substrate
  b. the addition of more substrate does not reverse the inhibition, but the removal of the inhibitor by chemical reaction can return activity to the enzyme
  c. the inhibition is permanent, and it cannot be reversed
  d. competes with the substrate for the active site

20.81 Which of the following statements describe an enzyme that requires a cofactor? (20.6)
  a. contains Mg^{2+} in the active site
  b. has catalytic activity as a tertiary protein structure
  c. requires folic acid for catalytic activity

20.82 Which of the following statements describes an enzyme that requires a cofactor? (20.6)
  a. contains riboflavin (vitamin B_2)
  b. has four subunits of polypeptide chains
  c. requires Fe^{3+} in the active site for catalytic activity

℞ Clinical Applications

20.83 Match the following coenzymes (**1** to **3**) with their vitamins (**a** to **c**): (20.6)
  1. NAD^+ **2.** thiamine pyrophosphate (TPP)
  3. coenzyme A

  a. pantothenic acid (B_5) **b.** niacin (B_3)
  c. thiamine (B_1)

20.84 Match the following coenzymes (**1** to **3**) with their vitamins (**a** to **c**): (20.6)
1. pyridoxal phosphate   **2.** tetrahydrofolate (THF)
3. FAD

   a. folic acid   **b.** riboflavin (B_2)   **c.** pyridoxine

20.85 Why are only small amounts of vitamins needed in the cells when there are several enzymes that require coenzymes? (20.6)

20.86 Why is there a daily requirement for vitamins? (20.6)

20.87 Match each of the following symptoms or conditions (**1** to **3**) with a vitamin deficiency (**a** to **c**): (20.6)
1. night blindness   **2.** weak bone structure   **3.** pellagra

   a. niacin   **b.** vitamin A   **c.** vitamin D

20.88 Match each of the following symptoms or conditions (**1** to **3**) with a vitamin deficiency (**a** to **c**): (20.6)
1. bleeding   **2.** anemia   **3.** scurvy

   a. cobalamin   **b.** vitamin C   **c.** vitamin K

20.89 If a blood test indicates a high level of LDH and CK, what could be the cause? (20.2)

20.90 If a blood test indicates a high level of ALT, what could be the cause? (20.2)

20.91 Many drugs are competitive inhibitors of enzymes. When scientists design inhibitors to serve as drugs, why do you suppose they choose to design competitive inhibitors instead of noncompetitive inhibitors? (20.5)

20.92 When lead acts as a poison, it can do so by either replacing another ion (such as zinc) in the active site of an enzyme or it can react with cysteine side chains to form covalent bonds. Which of these is irreversible and why? (20.5)

20.93 **a.** What type of an inhibitor is the antibiotic ampicillin? (20.5)
   b. Why is ampicillin used to treat bacterial infections?

20.94 A gardener using Parathion develops a headache, dizziness, nausea, blurred vision, excessive salivation, and muscle twitching. (20.5)
   a. What might be happening to the gardener?
   b. Why must humans be careful when using insecticides?

20.95 The zymogen pepsinogen is produced in the gastric chief cells of the stomach. (20.4)
   a. How and where does pepsinogen become the active form, pepsin?
   b. Why are proteases such as pepsin produced in inactive forms?

20.96 Thrombin is an enzyme that helps produce blood clotting when an injury and bleeding occur. (20.4)
   a. What would be the name of the zymogen of thrombin?
   b. Why would the active form of thrombin be produced only when an injury to tissue occurs?

CHALLENGE QUESTIONS

The following groups of questions are related to the topics in this chapter. However, they do not all follow the chapter order, and they require you to combine concepts and skills from several sections. These questions will help you increase your critical thinking skills and prepare for your next exam.

20.97 Lactase is an enzyme that hydrolyzes lactose to glucose and galactose. (20.1, 20.2)
   a. What are the reactants and products of the reaction?
   b. Draw an energy diagram for the reaction with and without lactase.
   c. How does lactase make the reaction go faster?

20.98 Maltase is an enzyme that hydrolyzes maltose into two glucose molecules. (20.1, 20.2)
   a. What are the reactants and products of the reaction?
   b. Draw an energy diagram for the reaction with and without maltase.
   c. How does maltase make the reaction go faster?

20.99 What class of enzyme would catalyze each of the following reactions? (20.2)

   a. $CH_3-\overset{\displaystyle O}{\overset{\displaystyle \|}{C}}-H \longrightarrow CH_3-\overset{\displaystyle O}{\overset{\displaystyle \|}{C}}-OH$

   b. $\overset{+}{H_3N}-CH_2-\overset{\displaystyle O}{\overset{\displaystyle \|}{C}}-\overset{\displaystyle H}{\overset{\displaystyle |}{N}}-\overset{\displaystyle CH_3}{\overset{\displaystyle |}{CH}}-\overset{\displaystyle O}{\overset{\displaystyle \|}{C}}-O^- + H_2O \longrightarrow$

   $\overset{+}{H_3N}-CH_2-\overset{\displaystyle O}{\overset{\displaystyle \|}{C}}-O^- + \overset{+}{H_3N}-\overset{\displaystyle CH_3}{\overset{\displaystyle |}{CH}}-\overset{\displaystyle O}{\overset{\displaystyle \|}{C}}-O^-$

   c. $CH_3-CH=CH-CH_3 + H_2O \longrightarrow$

   $CH_3-CH_2-\overset{\displaystyle OH}{\overset{\displaystyle |}{CH}}-CH_3$

20.100 What class of enzyme would catalyze each of the following reactions? (20.2)

   a. $CH_3-\overset{\displaystyle O}{\overset{\displaystyle \|}{C}}-\overset{\displaystyle O}{\overset{\displaystyle \|}{C}}-OH \longrightarrow CH_3-\overset{\displaystyle O}{\overset{\displaystyle \|}{C}}-OH + CO_2$

   b. $CH_3-\overset{\displaystyle O}{\overset{\displaystyle \|}{C}}-\overset{\displaystyle O}{\overset{\displaystyle \|}{C}}-OH + CO_2 + ATP \longrightarrow$

   $HO-\overset{\displaystyle O}{\overset{\displaystyle \|}{C}}-CH_2-\overset{\displaystyle O}{\overset{\displaystyle \|}{C}}-\overset{\displaystyle O}{\overset{\displaystyle \|}{C}}-OH + ADP + P_i$

   c. glucose-6-phosphate $\longrightarrow$ fructose-6-phosphate

℞ Clinical Applications

20.101 Cadmium is a poisonous metal used in industries that produce batteries and plastics. Cadmium ions (Cd^{2+}) are inhibitors of the enzyme hexokinase. Increasing the concentration of glucose or ATP, the substrates of hexokinase, or Mg^{2+}, the cofactor of hexokinase, does not change the rate of the cadmium-inhibited reaction. Is cadmium a competitive or noncompetitive inhibitor? Explain. (20.5, 20.6)

20.102 Beano contains an enzyme that breaks down polysaccharides into smaller, more digestible sugars, which diminishes the intestinal gas formation that can occur after eating foods such as vegetables and beans. (20.1, 20.2, 20.5)
   a. The label says "contains alpha-galactosidase." What class of enzyme is this?
   b. What is the substrate for the enzyme?
   c. The directions indicate you should not cook with or heat Beano. Why?

Beano contains an enzyme that breaks down carbohydrates.

ANSWERS TO SELECTED QUESTIONS AND PROBLEMS

20.1 Chemical reactions can occur without enzymes, but the rates are too slow. Catalyzed reactions, which are many times faster, provide the amounts of products needed by the cell at a particular time.

20.3 **a.** (2) enzyme
   b. (1) enzyme–substrate complex
   c. (3) substrate

20.5 **a.** $E + S \rightleftharpoons ES \longrightarrow EP \longrightarrow E + P$
   b. The active site is a region or pocket within the tertiary structure of an enzyme that accepts the substrate, aligns the substrate for reaction, and catalyzes the reaction.

20.7 **a.** oxidation–reduction
   b. transfer of a group from one substance to another
   c. hydrolysis (splitting) of molecules with the addition of water

20.9 **a.** hydrolase   **b.** oxidoreductase
   c. isomerase   **d.** transferase

20.11 **a.** lyase   **b.** transferase

20.13 **a.** succinate oxidase
   b. glutamine synthetase
   c. alcohol dehydrogenase

20.15 **a.** prostate-specific antigen   **b.** creatine kinase
   c. cholinesterase

20.17 Isoenzymes are slightly different forms of an enzyme that catalyze the same reaction in different organs and tissues of the body.

20.19 A doctor might run tests for the enzymes CK and LDH to determine if the patient had a heart attack.

20.21 **a.** The reaction will be slower.
   b. The reaction will slow or stop because the enzyme will be denatured at low pH.
   c. The reaction will slow or stop because the high temperature will denature the enzyme.
   d. The reaction will go faster as long as there are polypeptides to react.

20.23 pepsin, pH 2; lactase, pH 6; sucrase, pH 6; trypsin, pH 8

20.25 When a regulator molecule binds to an allosteric site, the shape of the enzyme is altered, which makes the active site more reactive or less reactive, and thereby increases or decreases the rate of the reaction.

20.27 In feedback control, the product binds to the first enzyme in a series and changes the shape of the active site. If the active site can no longer bind the substrate effectively, the reaction will stop.

20.29 **a.** (3) covalent modification   **b.** (2) a zymogen
   c. (1) an allosteric enzyme

20.31 In order to conserve material and energy and to prevent clotting in the bloodstream, thrombin is produced from prothrombin only at a wound site.

20.33 **a.** competitive   **b.** noncompetitive
   c. competitive   **d.** noncompetitive
   e. competitive

20.35 **a.** methanol, CH_3-OH; ethanol, CH_3-CH_2-OH
   b. Ethanol competes with methanol for the active site in the enzyme.
   c. Ethanol is a competitive inhibitor.

20.37 **a.** active with a cofactor
   b. active with a cofactor
   c. does not require a cofactor

20.39 **a.** pantothenic acid (vitamin B_5)
   b. folic acid
   c. niacin (vitamin B_5)

20.41 **a.** vitamin D (cholecalciferol)
   b. vitamin C (ascorbic acid)
   c. vitamin B_3 (niacin)

20.43 Vitamin B_6 is a water-soluble vitamin, which means that each day any excess of vitamin B_6 is eliminated from the body.

20.45 **a.** 20 ppm H_2 **b.** 40 ppm H_2

20.47 Heating the milk in the hot chocolate will denature the protein enzyme, lactase. Since the enzyme is no longer active, Noah will suffer from the symptoms of lactose intolerance.

20.49 **a.** The enzyme bromelain found in fresh pineapple breaks down protein, which means that the gelatin dessert would not turn solid upon cooking. The high temperatures used to prepare canned pineapple denature the enzyme so it no longer catalyzes the hydrolysis of protein.
   b. The enzyme in fresh pineapple juice can be used to tenderize tough meat because the enzyme breaks down proteins.

20.51 **a.** oxidoreductase
   b. Ethanol competes with ethylene glycol for the active site of the alcohol dehydrogenase enzyme, saturating the active site, which allows ethylene glycol to be removed from the body without producing oxalic acid.

20.53 The many different reactions that take place in cells require different enzymes because enzymes react with only a certain type of substrate.

20.55 Enzymes are catalysts that are proteins and function only at mild temperature and pH. Catalysts used in chemistry laboratories are usually inorganic materials that function at high temperatures and in strongly acidic or basic conditions.

20.57 An enzyme lowers the activation energy for a reaction.

20.59 Sucrose fits the shape of the active site in sucrose, but lactose does not.

20.61 **a.** S   **b.** E   **c.** E
         d. E   **e.** S   **f.** E

20.63 **a.** urea   **b.** succinate
         c. aspartate   **d.** phenylalanine

20.65 **a.** transferase   **b.** oxidoreductase
         c. hydrolase   **d.** lyase

20.67 The optimum temperature for an enzyme is the temperature at which the enzyme is fully active and most effective.

20.69 **a.** The rate of catalysis will slow and stop as a high temperature denatures the enzyme.
         b. The rate of the catalyzed reaction will slow as temperature is lowered.
         c. The enzyme will not be functional at pH 2.0.

20.71 **a.** saturated   **b.** unsaturated

20.73 An allosteric enzyme contains sites for regulators that alter the structure of the active site of an enzyme, which speeds up or slows down the rate of the catalyzed reaction.

20.75 In feedback control, a negative regulator slows down the catalytic activity.

20.77 In reversible inhibition, the inhibitor can dissociate from the enzyme, whereas in irreversible inhibition, the inhibitor forms a strong covalent bond with the enzyme and does not dissociate. Irreversible inhibitors act as poisons to enzymes.

20.79 **a.** (3) irreversible inhibitor
         b. (1) competitive inhibitor
         c. (1) competitive inhibitor
         d. (2) noncompetitive inhibitor

20.81 **a.** requires a cofactor
         b. does not require a cofactor
         c. requires a cofactor (coenzyme)

20.83 **a.** (3) coenzyme A   **b.** (1) NAD^+
         c. (2) thiamine pyrophosphate (TPP)

20.85 A vitamin combines with an enzyme only when the enzyme and coenzyme are needed to catalyze a reaction. When the enzyme is not needed, the vitamin dissociates for use by other enzymes in the cell.

20.87 **a.** niacin, (3) pellagra
         b. vitamin A, (1) night blindness
         c. vitamin D, (2) weak bone structure

20.89 A heart attack may be the cause.

20.91 When designing an inhibitor, the substrate of an enzyme usually is known even if the structure of the enzyme is not. It is easier to design a molecule that resembles the substrate (competitive) than to find an inhibitor that binds to a second site on an enzyme (noncompetitive).

20.93 **a.** Antibiotics such as ampicillin are irreversible inhibitors.
         b. Antibiotics inhibit enzymes needed to form cell walls in bacteria, not humans.

20.95 **a.** When pepsinogen enters the stomach, the low pH cleaves a peptide from its protein chain to form pepsin.
         b. An active protease would digest the proteins of the stomach rather than the proteins in foods.

20.97 **a.** The reactants are lactose and water and the products are glucose and galactose.
         b.

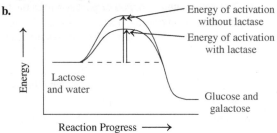

         c. By lowering the energy of activation, the enzyme furnishes a lower energy pathway by which the reaction can take place.

20.99 **a.** oxidoreductase   **b.** hydrolase
         c. lyase

20.101 Cadmium would be a noncompetitive inhibitor because increasing the substrate and cofactor has no effect on the rate. This implies that the cadmium is binding to another site on the enzyme.

21

Nucleic Acids and Protein Synthesis

ELLEN HAS FOUND A PEA-SIZED LUMP IN HER

breast. A needle biopsy confirms that Ellen has breast cancer. She undergoes a lumpectomy, during which the surgeon removes the tumor along with a small margin of surrounding normal tissue. The surgeon also makes an incision under her arm and removes the sentinel lymph nodes. Because cancer cells are found in the sentinel node, more lymph nodes are removed. He sends the excised tumor and lymph nodes to Lisa, a histology technician.

Lisa prepares the tissue sample to be viewed by a pathologist. Tissue preparation requires Lisa to cut the tissue into very thin sections, normally 0.001 mm, which are mounted onto microscope slides. She treats the tissue on the slides with a dye to stain the cells, which enables the pathologist to distinguish abnormal cells more easily.

When a person's DNA (deoxyribonucleic acid) is damaged, it may result in mutations that promote the abnormal cell growth found in cancer. Cancer as well as genetic diseases can be a result of mutations caused by environmental and hereditary factors.

CAREER Histology Technician

A histology technician studies the microscopic make-up of tissues, cells, and bodily fluids with the purpose of detecting and identifying the presence of a specific disease. They determine blood types and the concentrations of drugs and other substances in the blood. Histologists also help establish a rationale for why a patient may not be responding to his or her treatment. Sample preparation is a critical component of a histologist's job, as they prepare tissue samples from humans, animals, and plants. The tissue samples are cut, using specialized equipment, into extremely thin sections which are then mounted, and stained using various chemical dyes. The dyes provide contrast for the cells to be viewed and help highlight any abnormalities that may exist. Utilization of various dyes requires the histologist to be familiar with solution preparation and the handling of potentially hazardous chemicals.

Nucleic acids are large molecules found in the nuclei of cells that store information and direct activities for cellular growth and reproduction. Deoxyribonucleic acid (DNA), the genetic material in the nucleus of a cell, contains all the information needed for the development of a complete living organism. The way you grow, your hair, your eyes, your physical appearance, and all the activities of all the cells in your body are determined by a set of directions contained within the DNA of your cells.

All of the genetic information in the cell is called the *genome*. Every time a cell divides, the information in the genome is copied and passed on to the new cells. This replication process must duplicate the genetic instructions exactly. Some sections of DNA called *genes* contain the information to make a particular protein.

When a cell requires protein, another type of nucleic acid, ribonucleic acid (RNA), interprets the genetic information in DNA and carries that information to the ribosomes, where the synthesis of protein takes place. However, mistakes may occur that lead to mutations that affect the synthesis of a certain protein.

CHAPTER READINESS*

⚛ CORE CHEMISTRY SKILLS

- Forming Amides (18.5)
- Drawing the Zwitterion for an Amino Acid (19.1)

- Identifying the Primary, Secondary, Tertiary, and Quaternary Structures of Proteins (19.4, 19.5)
- Identifying Factors Affecting Enzyme Activity (20.3)

*These Core Chemistry Skills from previous chapters are listed here for your review as you proceed to the new material in this chapter.

LEARNING GOAL

Describe the bases and ribose sugars that make up the nucleic acids DNA and RNA.

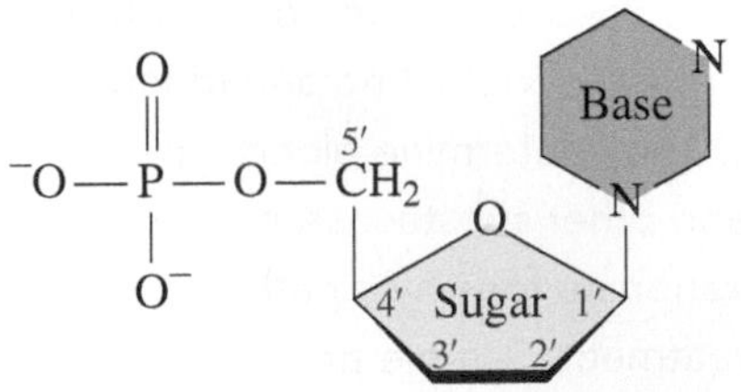

FIGURE 21.1 ▶ The general structure of a nucleotide includes a nitrogen-containing base, a sugar, and a phosphate group.

Q In a nucleotide, what types of groups are bonded to a five-carbon sugar?

21.1 Components of Nucleic Acids

There are two closely related types of nucleic acids: *deoxyribonucleic acid* (**DNA**) and *ribonucleic acid* (**RNA**). Both are unbranched polymers of repeating monomer units known as *nucleotides*. Each nucleotide has three components: a base that contains nitrogen, a five-carbon sugar, and a phosphate group (see Figure 21.1). A DNA molecule may contain several million nucleotides; smaller RNA molecules may contain up to several thousand.

Bases

The nitrogen-containing **bases** in nucleic acids are derivatives of the heterocyclic amines *pyrimidine* or *purine*. A pyrimidine has a single ring with two nitrogen atoms, and a purine has two rings each with two nitrogen atoms. They are basic because the nitrogen atoms are H⁺ acceptors.

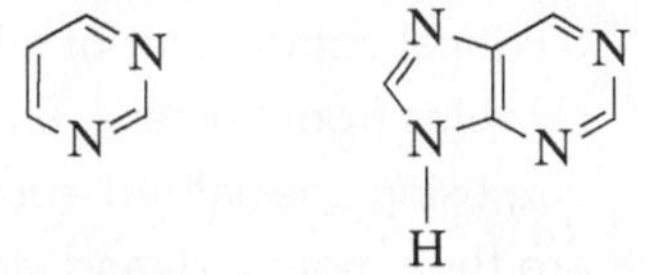

Pyrimidine   Purine

In DNA, the purine bases with double rings are adenine (A) and guanine (G), and the pyrimidine bases with single rings are cytosine (C) and thymine (T). RNA contains the same bases, except thymine (5-methyluracil) is replaced by uracil (U) (see Figure 21.2).

Pyrimidines

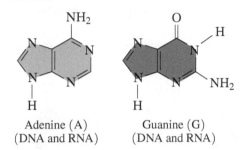

Cytosine (C)
(DNA and RNA)

Uracil (U)
(RNA only)

Thymine (T)
(DNA only)

Purines

Adenine (A)
(DNA and RNA)

Guanine (G)
(DNA and RNA)

FIGURE 21.2 ▶ DNA contains the bases A, G, C, and T; RNA contains A, G, C, and U.

◉ Which bases are found in DNA?

Pentose Sugars

In RNA, the five-carbon sugar is *ribose*, which gives the letter R in the abbreviation RNA. The atoms in the pentose sugars are numbered with primes ($1'$, $2'$, $3'$, $4'$, and $5'$) to differentiate them from the atoms in the bases. In DNA, the five-carbon sugar is *deoxyribose*, which is similar to ribose except that there is no hydroxyl group ($-OH$) on $C2'$. The *deoxy* prefix means "without oxygen" and provides the letter D in DNA.

Nucleosides and Nucleotides

A **nucleoside** is composed of one of the nitrogen-containing bases and one of the sugars, either ribose or deoxyribose. A nitrogen atom of the base is connected by a β-*N*-glycosidic bond to the $C1'$ of the sugar. For example, the combination of adenine, a purine, and ribose forms the nucleoside adenosine.

Pentose Sugars in RNA and DNA

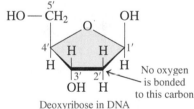

Ribose in RNA

Deoxyribose in DNA

The five-carbon pentose sugar found in RNA is ribose and in DNA, deoxyribose.

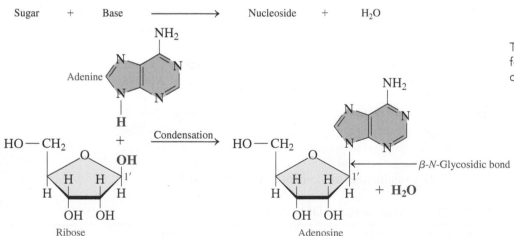

A base forms a β-*N*-glycosidic bond with ribose or deoxyribose to form a nucleoside.

When a phosphate group adds to a nucleoside, a *nucleotide* is produced. Thus, a **nucleotide** is composed of a base, a sugar, and a phosphate group, which forms a phosphoester bond with the $C5'$ OH group of the sugar. Other hydroxyl groups on ribose can also form phosphate esters, but only $5'$ monophosphate nucleotides are found in RNA and DNA. All the nucleotides in RNA and DNA are shown in Figure 21.3.

Phosphate + Nucleoside $\longrightarrow$ Nucleotide + H_2O

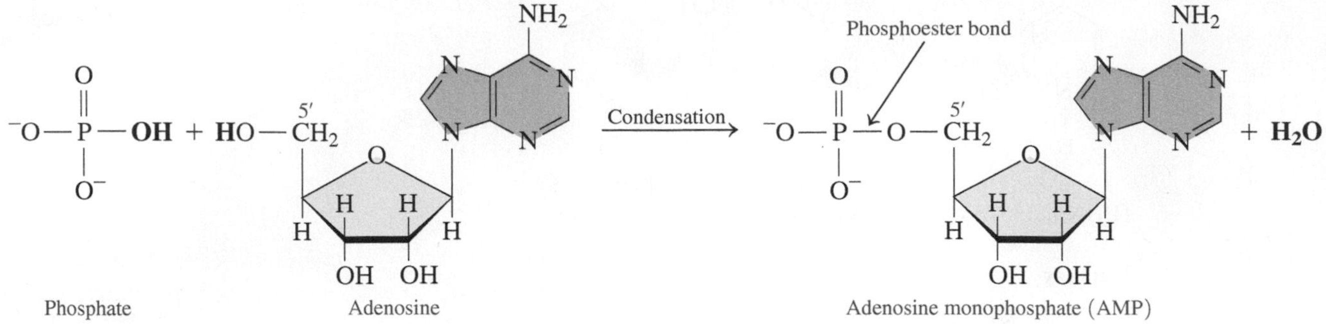

The addition of a phosphate group to a nucleoside (adenosine) forms a nucleotide (adenosine monophosphate, AMP).

Adenosine monophosphate (AMP)
Deoxyadenosine monophosphate (dAMP)

Guanosine monophosphate (GMP)
Deoxyguanosine monophosphate (dGMP)

Cytidine monophosphate (CMP)
Deoxycytidine monophosphate (dCMP)

Uridine monophosphate (UMP)

Deoxythymidine monophosphate (dTMP)

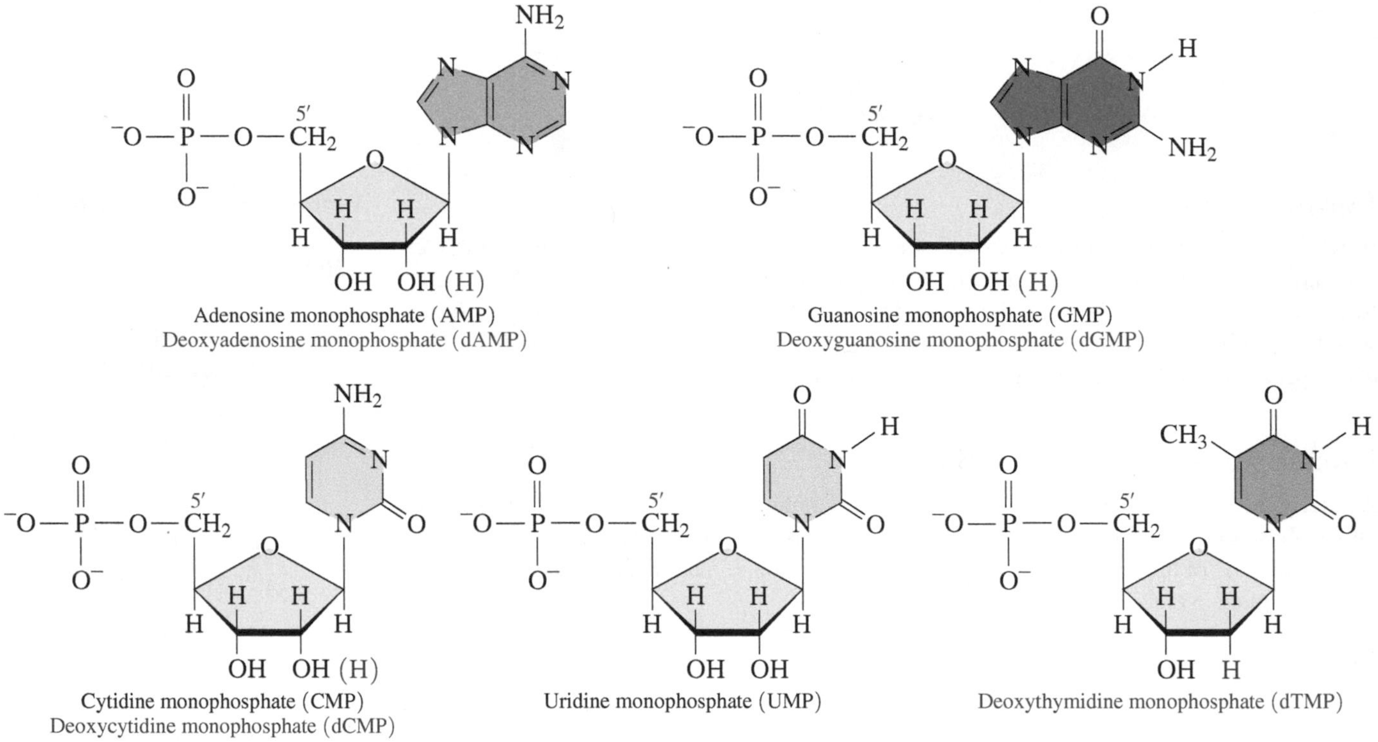

FIGURE 21.3 ▶ The nucleotides of RNA (shown in black) are similar to those of DNA (shown in magenta), except in DNA the sugar is deoxyribose and deoxythymidine replaces uridine.

◉ What are two differences in the nucleotides of RNA and DNA?

Table 21.1 summarizes the components in DNA and RNA.

TABLE 21.1 Components in DNA and RNA

Component	DNA	RNA
Bases	A, G, C, and T	A, G, C, and U
Sugar	Deoxyribose	Ribose
Nucleoside	Base + deoxyribose	Base + ribose
Nucleotide	Base + deoxyribose + phosphate	Base + ribose + phosphate
Nucleic Acid	Polymer of deoxyribose nucleotides	Polymer of ribose nucleotides

Naming Nucleosides and Nucleotides

The name of a nucleoside that contains a purine ends with *osine*, whereas a nucleoside that contains a pyrimidine ends with *idine*. The names of nucleosides of DNA add *deoxy* to the beginning of their names. The corresponding nucleotides in RNA and DNA are named by adding *monophosphate* to the end of the nucleoside name. Although the letters A, G, C, U, and T represent the bases, they are often used in the abbreviations of the respective nucleosides and nucleotides. The names of the bases, nucleosides, and nucleotides in DNA and RNA and their abbreviations are listed in Table 21.2.

TABLE 21.2 Nucleosides and Nucleotides in DNA and RNA

Base	Nucleosides	Nucleotides
DNA		
Adenine (A)	Deoxyadenosine (A)	Deoxyadenosine monophosphate (dAMP)
Guanine (G)	Deoxyguanosine (G)	Deoxyguanosine monophosphate (dGMP)
Cytosine (C)	Deoxycytidine (C)	Deoxycytidine monophosphate (dCMP)
Thymine (T)	Deoxythymidine (T)	Deoxythymidine monophosphate (dTMP)
RNA		
Adenine (A)	Adenosine (A)	Adenosine monophosphate (AMP)
Guanine (G)	Guanosine (G)	Guanosine monophosphate (GMP)
Cytosine (C)	Cytidine (C)	Cytidine monophosphate (CMP)
Uracil (U)	Uridine (U)	Uridine monophosphate (UMP)

Formation of Di- and Triphosphonucleotides

When one or two more phosphate groups add to a monophosphate nucleotide, a di- or triphosphate nucleotide is produced. For example, adding one phosphate group to AMP gives ADP (*adenosine diphosphate*). Adding another phosphate group to ADP gives ATP (*adenosine triphosphate*) (see Figure 21.4). Of the triphosphates, ATP is of particular interest because it is the major source of energy for most energy-requiring activities in the cell. In other examples, phosphate is added to GMP to yield GDP and GTP, which is part of the citric acid cycle.

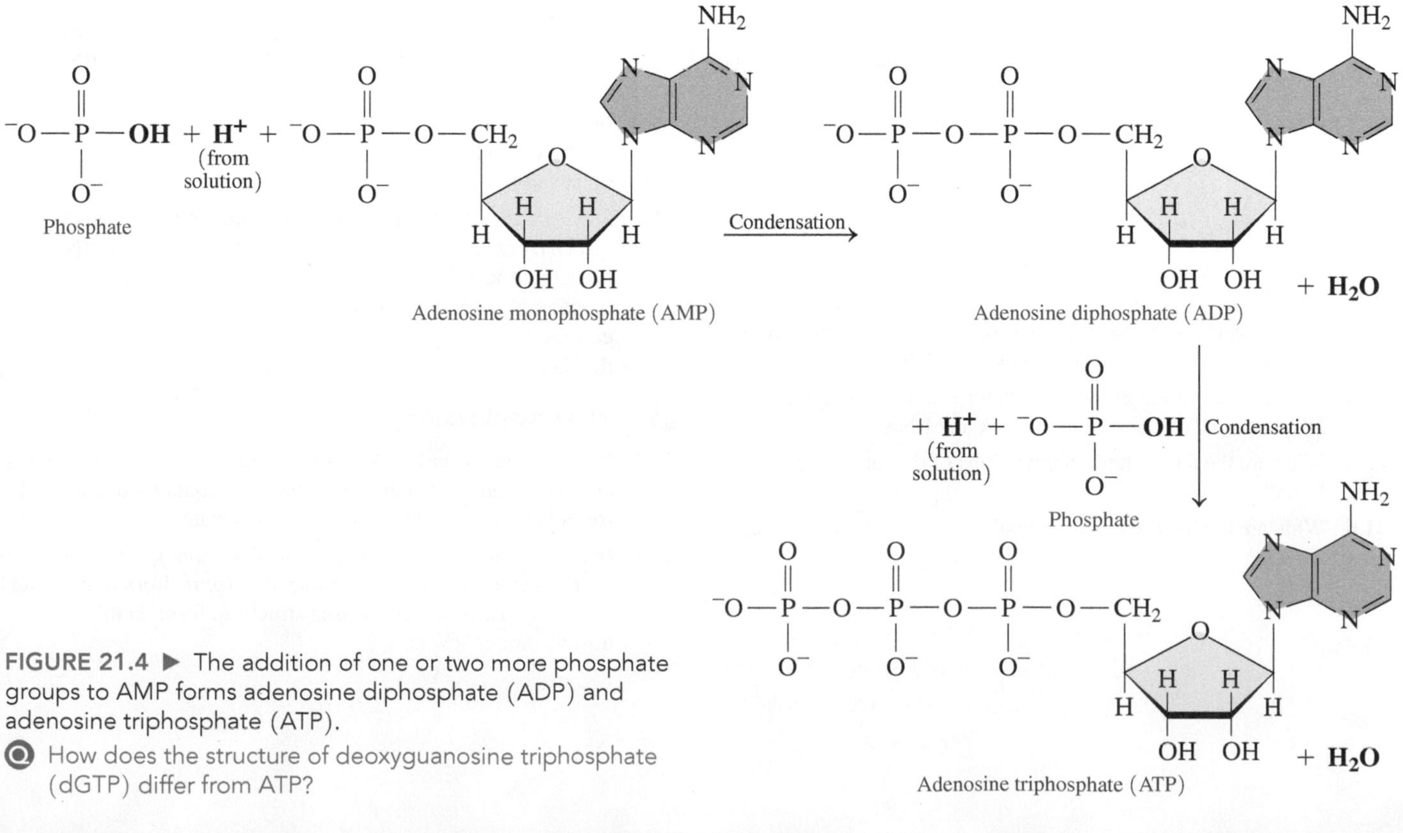

FIGURE 21.4 ▶ The addition of one or two more phosphate groups to AMP forms adenosine diphosphate (ADP) and adenosine triphosphate (ATP).

How does the structure of deoxyguanosine triphosphate (dGTP) differ from ATP?

> ▶**SAMPLE PROBLEM 21.1 Nucleotides**
>
> For each of the following nucleotides, identify the components and whether the nucleotide is found in DNA only, RNA only, or both DNA and RNA:
>
> **a.** deoxyguanosine monophosphate (dGMP)
> **b.** adenosine monophosphate (AMP)
>
> **SOLUTION**
>
> **a.** This nucleotide of deoxyribose, guanine, and a phosphate group is only found in DNA.
> **b.** This nucleotide of ribose, adenine, and a phosphate group is only found in RNA.
>
> **STUDY CHECK 21.1**
>
> What is the name and abbreviation of the DNA nucleotide of cytosine?
>
> **ANSWER**
>
> deoxycytidine monophosphate (dCMP)

QUESTIONS AND PROBLEMS

21.1 Components of Nucleic Acids

LEARNING GOAL Describe the bases and ribose sugars that make up the nucleic acids DNA and RNA.

21.1 Identify each of the following bases as a purine or a pyrimidine:
  a. thymine
  b.

21.2 Identify each of the following bases as a purine or a pyrimidine:
  a. guanine
  b.

21.3 Identify each of the bases in problem 21.1 as a component of DNA only, RNA only, or both DNA and RNA.

21.4 Identify each of the bases in problem 21.2 as a component of DNA only, RNA only, or both DNA and RNA.

21.5 What are the names and abbreviations of the four nucleotides in DNA?

21.6 What are the names and abbreviations of the four nucleotides in RNA?

21.7 Identify each of the following as a nucleoside or a nucleotide:
  a. adenosine
  b. deoxycytidine
  c. uridine
  d. cytidine monophosphate

21.8 Identify each of the following as a nucleoside or a nucleotide:
  a. deoxythymidine
  b. guanosine
  c. deoxyadenosine monophosphate
  d. uridine monophosphate

21.9 State whether each of the following components is present in (1) DNA only, (2) RNA only, or (3) both DNA and RNA:
  a. phosphate
  b. ribose
  c. deoxycytidine monophosphate
  d. adenine

21.10 State whether each of the following components is present in (1) DNA only, (2) RNA only, or (3) both DNA and RNA:
  a. deoxyribose
  b. guanosine monophosphate
  c. uracil
  d. UMP

℞ Clinical Applications

21.11 In the genetic disease *adenosine deaminase deficiency*, there is an accumulation of adenosine. Draw the condensed structural formula for deoxyadenosine monophosphate.

21.12 In the genetic disease *uridine monophosphate synthase deficiency*, symptoms include anemia, cardiac malformations, and infections. Draw the condensed structural formula for uridine monophosphate.

21.13 In Lesch–Nyhan syndrome, a deficiency of *guanine transferase* causes an overproduction of uric acid. Draw the condensed structural formula for guanosine monophosphate.

21.14 A deficiency of *adenine transferase* causes a lack of adenine for purine synthesis and a high level of adenine in the urine. Draw the condensed structural formula for adenosine monophosphate.

21.2 Primary Structure of Nucleic Acids

LEARNING GOAL

Describe the primary structures of RNA and DNA.

The **nucleic acids** are polymers of many nucleotides in which the 3′ hydroxyl group of the sugar in one nucleotide bonds to the phosphate group on the 5′ carbon atom in the sugar of the next nucleotide. This connection between a phosphate and sugars in adjacent nucleotides is referred to as a **phosphodiester linkage**. As more nucleotides are added, a backbone forms that consists of alternating sugar and phosphate groups. The bases, which are attached to each sugar, extend out from the sugar–phosphate backbone.

A phosphodiester linkage forms between the 3′ hydroxyl group in the sugar of one nucleotide and the phosphate group on the 5′ carbon atom in the sugar of the next nucleotide.

Each nucleic acid has its own unique sequence of bases, which is known as its **primary structure**. It is this sequence of bases that carries the genetic information. In any nucleic acid, the sugar at one end has an unreacted or free 5′ phosphate terminal end, and the sugar at the other end has a free 3′ hydroxyl group.

A nucleic acid sequence is read from the sugar with the free 5′ phosphate to the sugar with the free 3′ hydroxyl group. The order of nucleotides in a nucleic acid is often written using the letters of the bases. For example, the nucleotide sequence starting with adenine (free 5′ phosphate end) in the section of RNA shown in Figure 21.5 is A C G U.

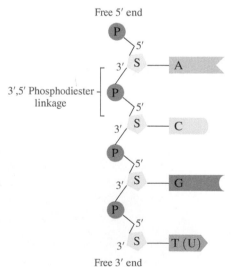

In the primary structure of nucleic acids, each sugar in a sugar–phosphate backbone is attached to a base.

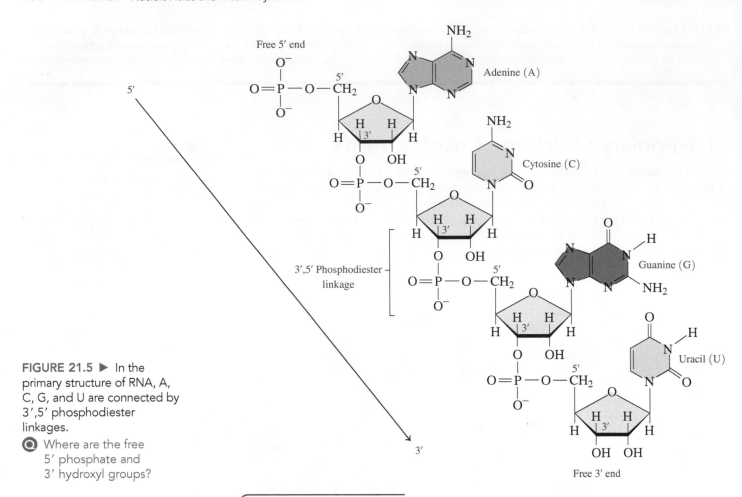

FIGURE 21.5 ▶ In the primary structure of RNA, A, C, G, and U are connected by 3′,5′ phosphodiester linkages.

🔘 Where are the free 5′ phosphate and 3′ hydroxyl groups?

▶ **SAMPLE PROBLEM 21.2 Bonding of Nucleotides**

Draw the condensed structural formula for an RNA dinucleotide formed by joining the 3′ OH group of adenosine monophosphate and the 5′ phosphate group of cytidine monophosphate.

SOLUTION

The dinucleotide is drawn by connecting the 3′ hydroxyl group on the adenosine 5′ monophosphate with the 5′ phosphate group on the cytidine monophosphate.

STUDY CHECK 21.2

What type of linkage connects the two nucleotides in Sample Problem 21.2?

ANSWER

A 3′,5′ phosphodiester linkage connects the 3′ OH group in the ribose of AMP and the 5′ carbon in the ribose of CMP.

QUESTIONS AND PROBLEMS

21.2 Primary Structure of Nucleic Acids

LEARNING GOAL Describe the primary structures of RNA and DNA.

21.15 What nucleic acid subunits are connected in a 3′,5′ phosphodiester linkage in a polynucleotide?

21.16 What is the difference in the 3′ end and the 5′ end of a polynucleotide chain?

21.17 What components join together to form the backbone of a nucleic acid?

21.18 What component in the backbone of a nucleic acid is bonded to a nitrogen base?

21.19 What component in a nucleic acid determines the 5′ free end?

21.20 What component in a nucleic acid determines the 3′ free end?

21.21 Draw the condensed structural formula for the dinucleotide 5′ G C 3′ that would be in RNA.

21.22 Draw the condensed structural formula for the dinucleotide 5′ A T 3′ that would be in DNA.

21.3 DNA Double Helix

During the 1940s, biologists determined that the bases in DNA from a variety of organisms had a specific relationship: the amount of adenine (A) was equal to the amount of thymine (T), and the amount of guanine (G) was equal to the amount of cytosine (C) (see Table 21.3). Eventually, scientists determined that adenine is paired (1:1) with thymine, and guanine is paired (1:1) with cytosine. This relationship, known as *Chargaff's rules*, can be summarized as follows:

Number of purine molecules = Number of pyrimidine molecules

Adenine (A) = Thymine (T)

Guanine (G) = Cytosine (C)

TABLE 21.3 Percentages of Bases in the DNAs of Selected Organisms

Organism	%A	%T	%G	%C
Human	30	30	20	20
Chicken	28	28	22	22
Salmon	28	28	22	22
Corn (maize)	27	27	23	23
Neurospora	23	23	27	27

In 1953, James Watson and Francis Crick proposed that DNA was a **double helix** that consisted of two polynucleotide strands winding about each other like a spiral staircase. The sugar–phosphate backbones are analogous to the outside railings of the stairs, with the bases arranged like steps along the inside. One strand goes from the 5′ to 3′ direction, and the other strand goes in the 3′ to 5′ direction.

Complementary Base Pairs

Each of the bases along one polynucleotide strand forms hydrogen bonds to only one specific base on the opposite DNA strand. Adenine forms hydrogen bonds to thymine only, and guanine bonds to cytosine only (see Figure 21.6). The pairs AT and GC are called **complementary base pairs**. Because of structural limitations, there are only two kinds of stable base pairs. The bases that bind utilizing two hydrogen bonds are adenine and thymine, and the bases that bind utilizing three hydrogen bonds are cytosine and guanine. *No other stable base pairs occur.* For example, adenine does not form hydrogen bonds with cytosine or guanine; cytosine does not form hydrogen bonds with adenine or thymine. This explains why DNA has equal amounts of A and T bases and equal amounts of G and C.

LEARNING GOAL

Describe the double helix of DNA.

⚛ **CORE CHEMISTRY SKILL**

Writing the Complementary DNA Strand

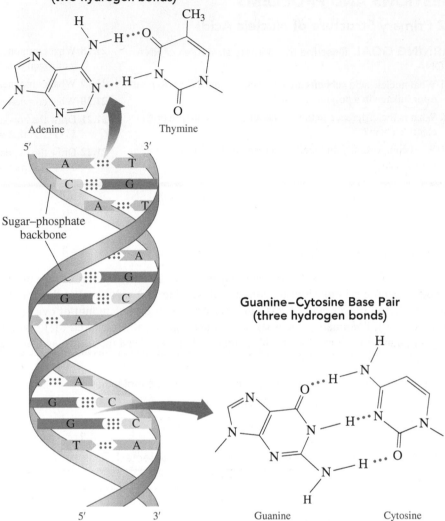

Adenine–Thymine Base Pair
(two hydrogen bonds)

Adenine   Thymine

Sugar–phosphate
backbone

Guanine–Cytosine Base Pair
(three hydrogen bonds)

Guanine   Cytosine

FIGURE 21.6 ▶ In the model shown, the sugar–phosphate backbone is represented by a ribbon with hydrogen bonds between complementary base pairs.

◉ Why are GC base pairs more stable than AT base pairs?

▶**SAMPLE PROBLEM 21.3 Complementary Base Pairs**

Write the complementary base sequence for the following segment of a strand of DNA:

5′A C G A T C T 3′

SOLUTION

ANALYZE THE PROBLEM	Given	Need
	5′ A C G A T C T 3′	complementary base sequence

The complementary base pairs are A–T and C–G. The complementary strand is written in the opposite direction, from the 3′ end to the 5′ end.

Original segment of DNA: 5′A   C   G   A   T   C   T 3′
                                 ⋮   ⋮   ⋮   ⋮   ⋮   ⋮   ⋮
Complementary segment: 3′T   G   C   T   A   G   A 5′

STUDY CHECK 21.3

What sequence of bases is complementary to a DNA segment with a base sequence of
5' G G T T A A C C 3'?

ANSWER

3' C C A A T T G G 5'

QUESTIONS AND PROBLEMS

21.3 DNA Double Helix

LEARNING GOAL Describe the double helix of DNA.

21.23 List three structural characteristics of DNA.

21.24 What is meant by double helix?

21.25 How are the two strands of nucleic acid in DNA held together?

21.26 What is meant by complementary base pairing?

21.27 Write the base sequence in a complementary DNA segment if each original segment has the following base sequence:
  a. 5' A A A A A A 3'
  b. 5' G G G G G G 3'
  c. 5' A G T C C A G G T 3'
  d. 5' C T G T A T A C G T T A 3'

21.28 Write the base sequence in a complementary DNA segment if each original segment has the following base sequence:
  a. 5' T T T T T T 3'
  b. 5' C C C C C C C C C 3'
  c. 5' A T G G C A 3'
  d. 5' A T A T G C G C T A A A 3'

21.4 DNA Replication

The function of DNA in the cells of animals and plants as well as in bacteria is to preserve genetic information. As cells divide, copied strands of DNA are produced that transfer genetic information to the new cells.

LEARNING GOAL

Describe the process of DNA replication.

DNA Replication

In DNA **replication**, the strands in the original or *parent* DNA molecule separate to allow the synthesis of complementary DNA strands. The process begins with the unwinding of a portion of the double helix by breaking the hydrogen bonds between the complementary bases. The resulting single strands act as templates for the synthesis of new complementary strands of DNA (see Figure 21.7).

Within the nucleus, nucleoside triphosphates of the four types of bases (dATP, dTTP, dGTP, and dCTP) are available so that each exposed base on the template strand can form hydrogen bonds with its complementary base. For example, T in the template strand hydrogen bonds with A, and G on the template strand hydrogen bonds with C. As the hydrogen bonds form base pairs, phosphodiester linkages are formed between the nucleotides.

Eventually, the entire double helix of the parent DNA is copied. In each new DNA, one strand of the double helix is from the parent DNA, and one is a newly synthesized DNA strand. This process produces two new daughter DNA strands, which are exact copies of the parent DNA. In DNA replication, complementary base pairing ensures the correct placement of bases in the daughter DNA strands.

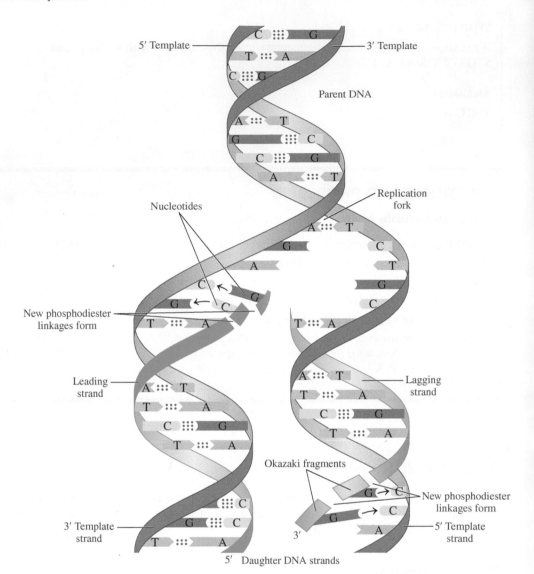

FIGURE 21.7 ▶ In DNA replication, the separate strands of the parent DNA are the templates for the synthesis of complementary strands, producing two exact copies of DNA.

🎯 How many strands of the parent DNA are contained in each of the daughter DNA?

Direction of Replication

Now that we have seen the overall process, we can take a look at some of the details of DNA replication, which requires the interaction of many enzymes and proteins as well as the parent DNA strands (see Figure 21.8). The unwinding of DNA by *helicase* occurs simultaneously in several sections along the parent DNA molecule. The separated strands are held open by a small protein called *single-strand binding protein* so that *DNA polymerase* can bind to the exposed bases. As a result, DNA polymerase can catalyze the replication process at each of these open DNA sections called **replication forks**. However, DNA polymerase only moves in the 5′ to 3′ direction, which means it catalyzes the formation of phosphodiester linkages between the hydroxyl group at the end of the growing nucleic acid and the phosphate group of a nucleoside triphosphate. The new DNA strand that grows in the 5′ to 3′ direction, the *leading strand*, is synthesized continuously.

However, the other new DNA strand, which is the *lagging strand*, is synthesized discontinuously in short, separate segments. To initiate synthesis on the lagging strand, the enzyme *primase* produces short complementary RNA fragments, called *primers*. These RNA primers serve as starting points for DNA polymerase to begin extending the complementary DNA fragments at the 3′ end until the polymerase reaches the next primer. As a result, DNA replication on the lagging strand consists of DNA segments called **Okazaki fragments**. Eventually DNA polymerase replaces the RNA primers in each segment with the corresponding DNA. Finally *DNA ligase* connects the Okazaki fragments by phosphodiester linkages, forming a daughter lagging strand, which matches the leading DNA strand. The enzymes and proteins required for replication are summarized in Table 21.4.

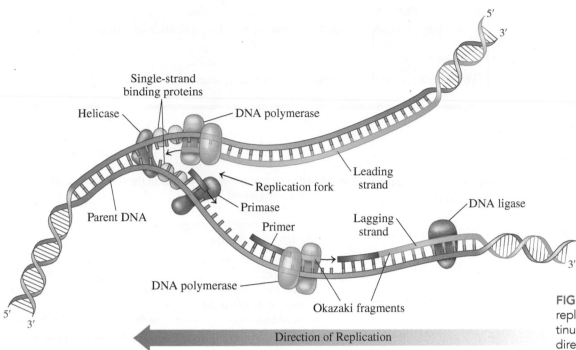

FIGURE 21.8 ▶ DNA replication occurs continuously in the 5′ to 3′ direction on the leading strand and discontinuously on the lagging strand in the 5′ to 3′ direction. Smaller Okazaki fragments are joined by DNA ligase.

Q Why are the Okazaki fragments formed only for the lagging strand?

TABLE 21.4 Enzymes and Proteins in DNA Replication

Enzymes and Proteins		
1. Helicase	Helicase breaks the hydrogen bonds of the parent DNA strands at the *replication forks*, which gives two separate DNA strands.	
2. Single-strand Binding Protein	Single-strand binding proteins attach to the separated parent strands to keep them apart and the bases exposed.	
	Leading Strand 5′ to 3′	**Lagging Strand 3′ to 5′**
3. Primase		Primase synthesizes short RNA segments called primers that are starting points for DNA polymerase.
4. DNA Polymerase	DNA polymerase catalyzes the formation of phosphodiester linkages on the new DNA strands between the 3′ ends of the growing chains and available complementary nucleotides (dATP, dTTP, dGTP, and dCTP).	
	DNA polymerase adds nucleotides continuously in the 5′ to 3′ direction to a growing DNA chain.	At each primer, DNA polymerase forms short, separate segments (Okazaki fragments) until it reaches the next primer and stops.
5. DNA Ligase		DNA ligase joins the Okazaki fragments.

▶SAMPLE PROBLEM 21.4 Direction of DNA Replication

In an original DNA strand, a segment has the base sequence 5′ A G T C C G 3′.

a. What is the sequence of nucleotides in the daughter DNA strand that is complementary to this segment?

b. Why would the complementary sequence in the daughter DNA strand be synthesized as Okazaki fragments that require a DNA ligase?

SOLUTION

a. Only one possible nucleotide can pair with each base in the original segment. Thymine will pair only with adenine, whereas cytosine pairs only with guanine to give the complementary base sequence: 3′ T C A G G C 5′.

b. Because DNA polymerase only adds nucleotides in the 5′ to 3′ direction, DNA on the lagging strand is synthesized as short Okazaki fragments, which are joined by DNA ligase.

STUDY CHECK 21.4

How many daughter strands are formed during the replication of DNA?

ANSWER

Two daughter strands are formed, one from each strand of the DNA double helix.

QUESTIONS AND PROBLEMS

21.4 DNA Replication

LEARNING GOAL Describe the process of DNA replication.

21.29 What is the function of the enzyme helicase in DNA replication?

21.30 What is the function of the enzyme DNA polymerase in DNA replication?

21.31 What process ensures that the replication of DNA produces identical copies?

21.32 Why are Okazaki fragments formed in the synthesis of the lagging strand?

21.33 Match each component with one of the following descriptions:
(1) lagging strand
(2) helicase
(3) primase
(4) replication fork

a. unwinds the DNA helix
b. synthesizes primers at the replication fork
c. point in DNA where nucleotides add to daughter DNA strand
d. daughter DNA synthesized from short sections called Okazaki fragments

21.34 Match each component with one of the following descriptions:
(1) leading strand
(2) DNA ligase
(3) single-strand binding protein
(4) DNA polymerase

a. catalyzes the formation of phosphodiester linkages between nucleotides
b. daughter DNA synthesized continuously in 5′ to 3′ direction
c. attaches to unwound strands to keep them open
d. combines Okazaki fragments to form daughter DNA strand

21.35 Answer each of the following for a segment of a template strand 3′ G C T C C A T G 5′:
a. Write the sequence of the new DNA segment.
b. Will the production of this new DNA segment require the synthesis of Okazaki fragments?

21.36 Answer each of the following for a segment of a template strand 5′ A A G T C G T G 3′:
a. Write the sequence of the new DNA segment.
b. Will the production of this new DNA segment require the synthesis of Okazaki fragments?

LEARNING GOAL

Identify the different types of RNA; describe the synthesis of mRNA.

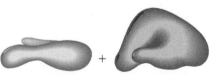

Small subunit   +   Large subunit

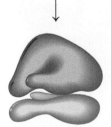

Ribosome

FIGURE 21.9 ▶ A typical ribosome consists of a small subunit and a large subunit. The subunit shapes shown contain both protein and rRNA.

Ⓠ Why would there be many thousands of ribosomes in a cell?

21.5 RNA and Transcription

Ribonucleic acid, RNA, which makes up most of the nucleic acid found in the cell, is involved with transmitting the genetic information needed to operate the cell. Similar to DNA, RNA molecules are unbranched polymers of nucleotides. However, RNA differs from DNA in several important ways:

1. The sugar in RNA is ribose rather than the deoxyribose found in DNA.
2. In RNA, the base uracil replaces thymine.
3. RNA molecules are single stranded, not double stranded.
4. RNA molecules are much smaller than DNA molecules.

Types of RNA

There are three major types of RNA in the cells: *messenger RNA*, *ribosomal RNA*, and *transfer RNA*. Ribosomal RNA (**rRNA**), the most abundant type of RNA, is combined with proteins to form ribosomes. Ribosomes, which are the sites for protein synthesis, consist of two subunits: a large subunit and a small subunit (see Figure 21.9). Cells that synthesize large numbers of proteins have thousands of ribosomes.

Messenger RNA (**mRNA**) carries genetic information from the DNA, located in the nucleus of the cell, to the ribosomes, located in the *cytosol*, the liquid outside the nucleus. A *gene* is a segment of DNA that produces a separate mRNA used to synthesize a protein needed in the cell.

Transfer RNA (**tRNA**), the smallest of the RNA molecules, interprets the genetic information in mRNA and brings specific amino acids to the ribosome for protein synthesis. Only tRNA can translate the genetic information in the mRNA into the amino acid sequence that makes a protein. There can be more than one tRNA for each of the 20 amino acids. The structures of all of the transfer RNAs are similar, consisting of 70 to 90 nucleotides. Hydrogen bonds between some complementary bases in the strand produce loops that give some double-stranded regions. The types of RNA molecules in humans are summarized in Table 21.5.

TABLE 21.5 Types of RNA Molecules in Humans

Type	Abbreviation	Percentage of Total RNA	Function in the Cell
Ribosomal RNA	rRNA	80	major component of the ribosomes; site of protein synthesis
Messenger RNA	mRNA	5	carries information for protein synthesis from the DNA to the ribosomes
Transfer RNA	tRNA	15	brings specific amino acids to the site of protein synthesis

Although the structure of tRNA in three dimensions is complex, we can draw tRNA as a two-dimensional cloverleaf (see Figure 21.10a). In the three-dimensional model, the RNA chain has more twists that shows the L-shape of tRNA (see Figure 21.10b). All tRNA molecules have a 3′ end with the nucleotide sequence ACC, which is known as the *acceptor stem*. An enzyme attaches an amino acid to the 3′ end of the acceptor stem by forming an ester bond with the free —OH group of the acceptor stem. Each tRNA contains an **anticodon**, which is a series of three bases that complements three bases on mRNA.

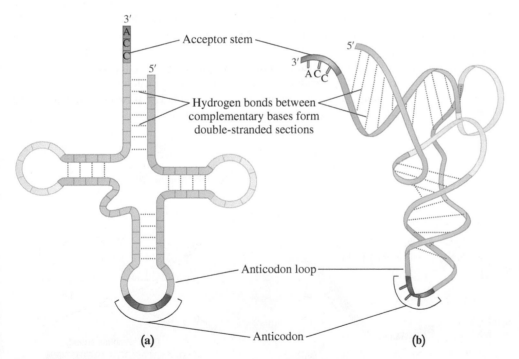

FIGURE 21.10 ▶ A typical tRNA molecule has an acceptor stem at the 3′ end that attaches to an amino acid and an anticodon loop that complements a codon on mRNA.

Ⓠ Why will different tRNAs have different bases in the anticodon loop?

RNA and Protein Synthesis

We now look at the overall processes involved in transferring genetic information encoded in the DNA to the production of proteins. In the nucleus, genetic information for the synthesis of a protein is copied from a gene in DNA to make mRNA, a process called **transcription**. The mRNA molecules move out of the nucleus into the cytosol, where they bind with the ribosomes. Then in a process called **translation**, tRNA molecules convert the information in the mRNA into amino acids, which are placed in the proper sequence to synthesize a protein (see Figure 21.11).

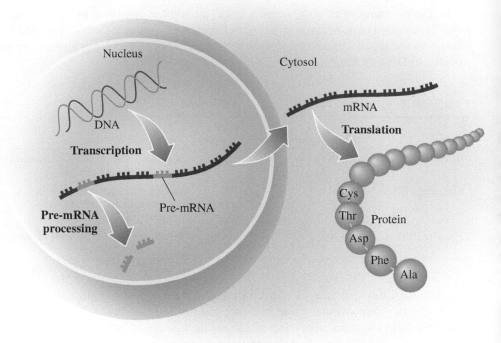

FIGURE 21.11 ▶ The genetic information in DNA is replicated in cell division and used to produce messenger RNA that codes for amino acids used in protein synthesis at the ribosomes.

Q What is the difference between transcription and translation?

Transcription: Synthesis of mRNA

Transcription begins when the section of a DNA molecule that contains the gene to be copied unwinds. Within this unwound portion of DNA called a *transcription bubble*, the 5′ to 3′ open strand is the *DNA informational strand*, whereas the 3′ to 5′ is the *DNA template strand*. *RNA polymerase* uses the DNA template strand to form the new mRNA using bases that are complementary to the DNA template: C and G form pairs, T (in DNA) pairs with A (in mRNA), and A (in DNA) pairs with U (in mRNA). When the RNA polymerase reaches the termination site (a sequence of nucleotides that is a stop signal), transcription ends, and the new mRNA is released. The unwound portion of the DNA returns to its double helix structure (see Figure 21.12).

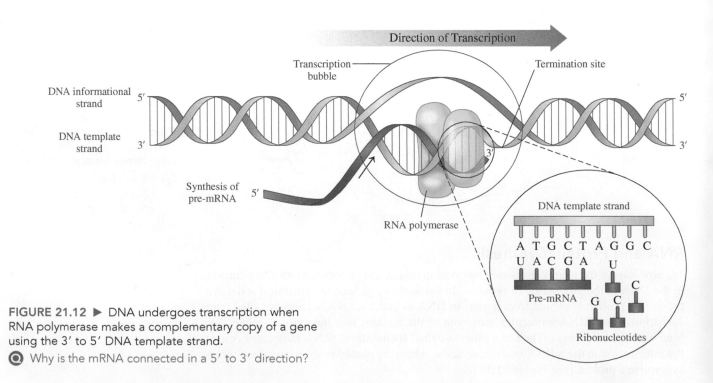

FIGURE 21.12 ▶ DNA undergoes transcription when RNA polymerase makes a complementary copy of a gene using the 3′ to 5′ DNA template strand.

Q Why is the mRNA connected in a 5′ to 3′ direction?

▶**SAMPLE PROBLEM 21.5 RNA Synthesis**

The sequence of bases in a part of the DNA template strand is 3′ C G A T C A 5′. What corresponding mRNA is produced?

SOLUTION

To form the mRNA, the bases in the DNA template are paired with their complementary bases: G with C, C with G, T with A, and A with U.

DNA template strand: 3′ C G A T C A 5′

            Transcription: ↓ ↓ ↓ ↓ ↓ ↓

Complementary base sequence in mRNA: 5′ G C U A G U 3′

STUDY CHECK 21.5

What is the DNA template strand segment that codes for the mRNA segment with the nucleotide sequence 5′ G G G U U U A A A 3′?

ANSWER

3′ C C C A A A T T T 5′

CORE CHEMISTRY SKILL

Writing the mRNA Segment for a DNA Template

Processing of mRNA

The DNA in plants and animals (eukaryotes) contains sections known as *exons* and *introns*. **Exons**, which code for proteins, are mixed in with sections called **introns** that do not code for proteins. A newly formed mRNA called a *pre-mRNA* or *heterogeneous nuclear RNA* (hnRNA) is a copy of the entire DNA template, including the noncoding introns. However, the pre-mRNA exists for only a short time before it is processed. The introns are cut out and the remaining exons spliced together by *spliceosome*. The function of introns is not well understood. They may regulate transcription to allow different proteins to be synthesized from the same gene or have a role in genetic expression. This processing of pre-mRNA produces a mature mRNA that leaves the nucleus to deliver the genetic information to the ribosomes for the synthesis of protein (see Figure 21.13). The removal of introns in eukaryotes offers the cell another chance to check the mRNA before it exits the nucleus, preserving the DNA sequence.

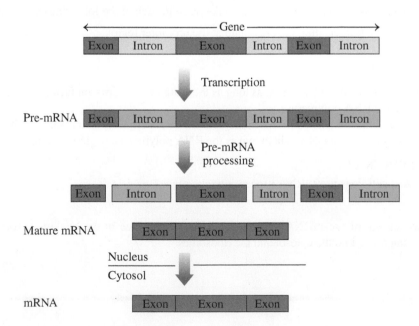

FIGURE 21.13 ▶ A pre-mRNA, containing copies of the exons and introns from the gene, is processed to remove the introns to form a mature mRNA that codes for a protein.

❓ What is the difference between exons and introns?

Regulation of Transcription: Transcription Factors

The synthesis of mRNA occurs when cells require a particular protein; it does not occur randomly. The regulation of mRNA synthesis is controlled at the transcription level.

In eukaryotes (plants and animals), the transcription of a gene requires the RNA polymerase to bind to DNA. However, RNA polymerase cannot do this alone. A group of

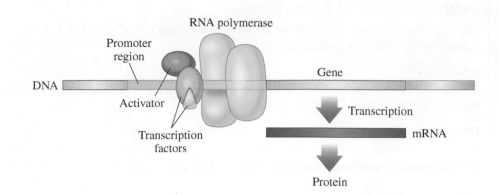

Transcription factors at the promoter region bind RNA polymerase to DNA, which activates the transcription of a gene.

protein complexes called a **transcription factor** must first recognize and bind to a *promoter region* (small nucleotide sequences) in front of the start site for the gene. Proteins called *activators* bind with the transcription factor complex; the function of the activators is to increase the rate of RNA transcription. Thus transcription factors and activators work together to regulate the binding and activity of RNA polymerase at the specific gene for the transcription of a particular mRNA for that protein. Sometimes, another regulatory protein called a *repressor* blocks the activator and slows down the rate of transcription. Although all cells have the same set of genes, different transcription factors activate different genes that produce proteins for different tissues and organs. Transcription factors have a role in cancer if they activate genes that cause cell division. Mutations in transcription factors may lead to diabetes, inflammation, cancer, and auto-immune diseases.

▶ **SAMPLE PROBLEM 21.6 Transcription**

Describe why transcription will or will not take place in each of the following conditions:

a. There are no transcription factors bound at the promoter region.
b. An activator binds to a transcription factor.

SOLUTION

a. Transcription will not take place as long as there are no transcription factors to bind and activate the RNA polymerase.
b. Transcription will take place when the activated transcription factor binds to the promoter region on the DNA, which makes the RNA polymerase begin transcription.

STUDY CHECK 21.6

Where in a cell does pre-mRNA processing take place?

ANSWER

The processing of pre-mRNA to mature mRNA takes place in the nucleus before the mRNA can move into the cytosol and the ribosomes.

QUESTIONS AND PROBLEMS

21.5 RNA and Transcription

LEARNING GOAL Identify the different types of RNA; describe the synthesis of mRNA.

21.37 What are the three different types of RNA?

21.38 What are the functions of each type of RNA?

21.39 What is the composition of a ribosome?

21.40 What is the smallest RNA?

21.41 What is meant by the term "transcription"?

21.42 What bases in mRNA are used to complement the bases A, T, G, and C in DNA?

21.43 Write the corresponding section of mRNA produced from the following section of DNA template strand:

   3′ C C G A A G G T T C A C 5′

21.44 Write the corresponding section of mRNA produced from the following section of DNA template strand:

   3′ T A C G G C A A G C T A 5′

21.45 What are introns and exons?

21.46 What kind of processing do pre-mRNA molecules undergo before they leave the nucleus?

21.47 A pre-mRNA segment has the following base sequence. If underlined sections **A**, **C**, and **D** are introns, and **B**, **E**, and **F** are exons, what is the base sequence of the mature mRNA produced after pre-mRNA processing?

5′	ACC	GGC	ACA	UUC	GGA	UCG	3′
	A	B	C	D	E	F	

21.48 A pre-mRNA segment has the following base sequence. If underlined sections **B**, **D**, and **F** are introns, and **A**, **C**, and **E** are exons, what is the base sequence of the mature mRNA produced after pre-mRNA processing?

5′	GAC	UAU	GGC	AAC	GGC	GUC	3′
	A	B	C	D	E	F	

21.49 What is a transcription factor?

21.50 How do transcription factors control protein synthesis at the transcription level?

21.51 What is an activator?

21.52 What is a repressor?

21.6 The Genetic Code and Protein Synthesis

The overall function of the different types of RNA in the cell is to facilitate the task of synthesizing proteins. After the genetic information encoded in DNA is transcribed and processed into mature mRNA molecules, they move out of the nucleus to the ribosomes in the cytosol. At the ribosomes, the genetic information in the mRNA is translated into a sequence of amino acids in protein.

Genetic Code

The **genetic code** consists of a series of three nucleotides (triplets) in mRNA called **codons** that specify the amino acids and their sequence in a protein. Early work on protein synthesis showed that repeating triplets of uracil (UUU) produced a polypeptide that contained only phenylalanine. Therefore, a sequence of 5′ UUU UUU UUU 3′ codes for three phenylalanines.

Codons in mRNA: 5′ UUU   UUU   UUU 3′

         ↓   ↓   ↓

Amino acid sequence: Phe — Phe — Phe

Codons have been determined for all 20 amino acids. A total of 64 codons are possible from the triplet combinations of A, G, C, and U. Three of these, UGA, UAA, and UAG, are stop signals that code for the termination of protein synthesis. All the other three-base codons shown in Table 21.6 specify amino acids. Thus one amino acid can have several codons. For example, glycine has four codons: GGU, GGC, GGA, and GGG. The triplet AUG has two roles in protein synthesis. At the beginning of an mRNA, the codon AUG signals the start of protein synthesis. In the middle of a series of codons, the AUG codon specifies the amino acid methionine.

Translation

Once an mRNA is synthesized and processed, it migrates out of the nucleus into the cytosol to the ribosomes. In the *translation* process, tRNA molecules, amino acids, and enzymes convert the mRNA codons into amino acids to build a protein.

Activation of tRNA

Each tRNA molecule contains a loop called the *anticodon*, which is a triplet of bases that complements a codon in mRNA. An amino acid is attached to the acceptor stem of each tRNA by an enzyme called *aminoacyl–tRNA synthetase*. Each amino acid has a different synthetase (see Figure 21.14). Activation of tRNA occurs when aminoacyl–tRNA synthetase forms an ester bond between the carboxylate group of its amino acid and the hydroxyl group on the acceptor stem. Each synthetase then checks the tRNA–amino acid combination and hydrolyzes any incorrect combinations.

LEARNING GOAL

Use the genetic code to write the amino acid sequence for a segment of mRNA.

Interactive Video

Protein Synthesis

⚙ CORE CHEMISTRY SKILL

Writing the Amino Acid for an mRNA Codon

TABLE 21.6 Codons in mRNA: The Genetic Code for Amino Acids

First Letter	Second Letter				Third Letter
	U	**C**	**A**	**G**	
U	UUU ⎱ Phe (F) UUC ⎰	UCU ⎱ UCC ⎰ Ser (S)	UAU ⎱ Tyr (Y) UAC ⎰	UGU ⎱ Cys (C) UGC ⎰	U C
	UUA ⎱ Leu (L) UUG ⎰	UCA UCG	UAA STOP[b] UAG STOP[b]	UGA STOP[b] UGG Trp (W)	A G
C	CUU CUC Leu (L) CUA CUG	CCU CCC Pro (P) CCA CCG	CAU ⎱ His (H) CAC ⎰ CAA ⎱ Gln (Q) CAG ⎰	CGU CGC Arg (R) CGA CGG	U C A G
A	AUU AUC Ile (I) AUA AUG START[a]/ Met (M)	ACU ACC Thr (T) ACA ACG	AAU ⎱ Asn (N) AAC ⎰ AAA ⎱ Lys (K) AAG ⎰	AGU ⎱ Ser (S) AGC ⎰ AGA ⎱ Arg (R) AGG ⎰	U C A G
G	GUU GUC Val (V) GUA GUG	GCU GCC Ala (A) GCA GCG	GAU ⎱ Asp (D) GAC ⎰ GAA ⎱ Glu (E) GAG ⎰	GGU GGC Gly (G) GGA GGG	U C A G

START[a] codon signals the initiation of a peptide chain.
STOP[b] codons signal the end of a peptide chain.

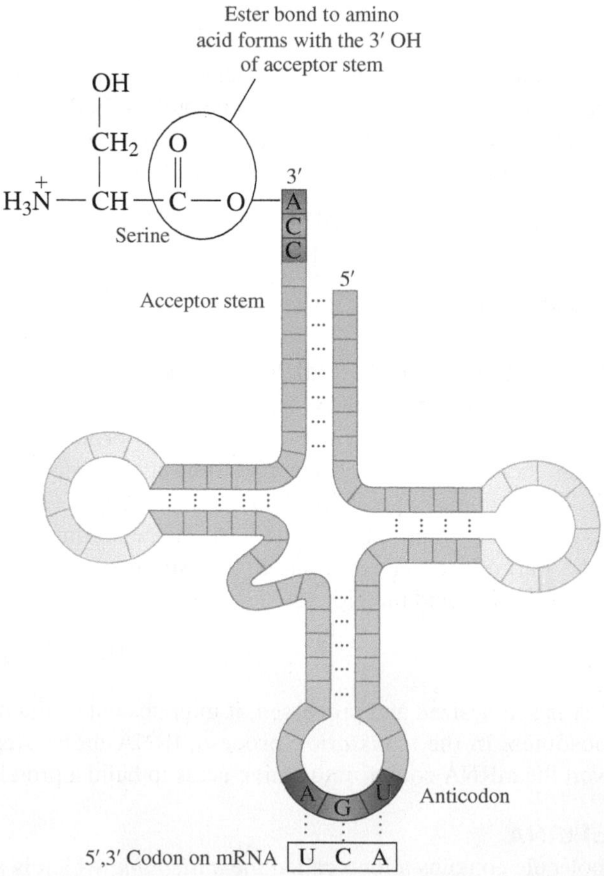

FIGURE 21.14 ▶ An activated tRNA with anticodon AGU bonds to serine at the acceptor stem.

ⓠ What is the codon for serine for this tRNA?

Initiation and Chain Elongation

Protein synthesis begins when mRNA binds to a ribosome. The first codon in an mRNA is a *start codon*, AUG, which forms hydrogen bonds with methionine–tRNA. Another tRNA hydrogen bonds to the next codon, placing a second amino acid adjacent to methionine. A peptide bond forms between the C terminus of methionine and the N terminus of the second amino acid (see Figure 21.15). The initial tRNA detaches from the ribosome,

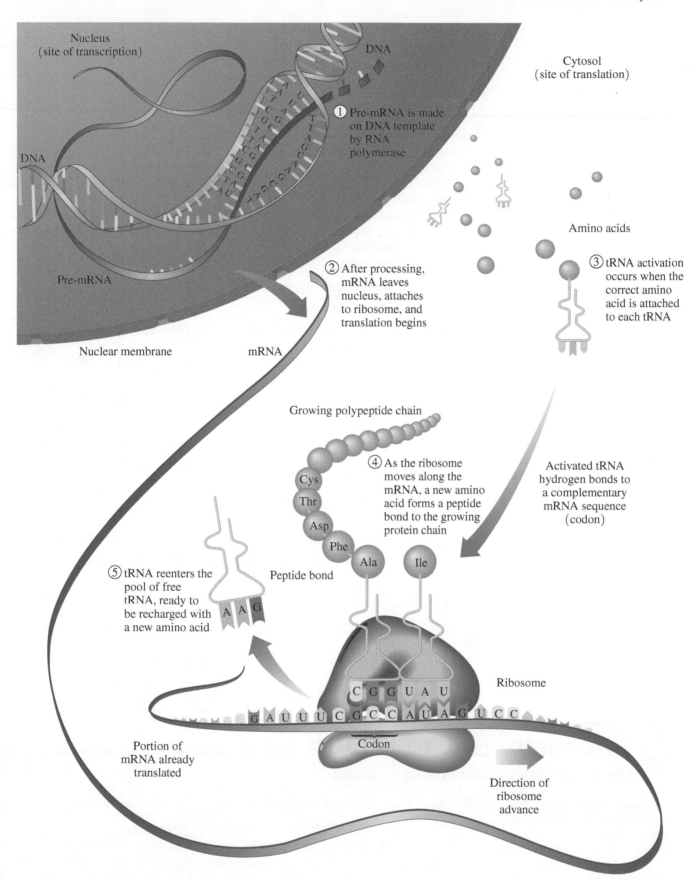

FIGURE 21.15 ▶ In the translation process, the mRNA synthesized by transcription attaches to a ribosome, and tRNAs pick up their amino acids, bind to the appropriate codon, and place them in a growing peptide chain.

Q How is the correct amino acid placed in the peptide chain?

which shifts to the next available codon, a process called *translocation*. During *chain elongation*, the ribosome moves along the mRNA from codon to codon so that the tRNAs can attach new amino acids to the growing polypeptide chain. Sometimes several ribosomes, called a polysome, translate the same strand of mRNA to produce several copies of the polypeptide at the same time.

Chain Termination

Eventually, a ribosome encounters a codon—UAA, UGA, or UAG—that has no corresponding tRNAs. These are *stop codons*, which signal the termination of polypeptide synthesis and the release of the polypeptide chain from the ribosome. The initial amino acid, methionine, is usually removed from the beginning of the polypeptide chain. The R groups on the amino acid residues in the new polypeptide chain form hydrogen bonds to give the secondary structures of α helices, β-pleated sheets, or triple helices and form interactions such as salt bridges and disulfide bonds to produce tertiary and quaternary structures, which make it a biologically active protein.

Table 21.7 summarizes the steps in protein synthesis.

TABLE 21.7 Steps in Protein Synthesis

Step	Site: Materials	Process
1. DNA Transcription	Nucleus: nucleotides, RNA polymerase	A DNA template is used to produce mRNA.
2. Translation of mRNA	Ribosome: mRNA	mRNA binds to ribosomes where translation begins.
3. Activation of tRNA	Cytosol: amino acids, tRNAs, aminoacyl–tRNA synthetase	Molecules of tRNA pick up specific amino acids according to their anticodons.
4. Initiation and Chain Elongation	Ribosome: Met–tRNA, mRNA, aminoacyl–tRNAs	A start codon binds the first tRNA carrying the amino acid methionine to the mRNA. Successive tRNAs bind to and detach from the ribosome as they add an amino acid to the polypeptide.
5. Chain Termination	Ribosome: stop codon on mRNA	The protein is released from the ribosome.

Table 21.8 summarizes the nucleotide and amino acid sequences in protein synthesis.

TABLE 21.8 Complementary Sequences in DNA, mRNA, tRNA, and Peptides

Nucleus	
DNA informational strand	5′ GCG AGT GGA TAC 3′
DNA template strand	3′ CGC TCA CCT ATG 5′
Ribosome (cytosol)	
mRNA	5′ GCG AGU GGA UAC 3′
tRNA anticodons	3′ CGC UCA CCU AUG 5′
Polypeptide amino acids	Ala — Ser — Gly — Tyr

Chemistry Link to **Health**

Many Antibiotics Inhibit Protein Synthesis

Several antibiotics stop bacterial infections by interfering with the synthesis of proteins needed by the bacteria. Some antibiotics act only on bacterial cells, binding to the ribosomes in bacteria but not those in human cells. A description of some of these antibiotics is given in Table 21.9.

TABLE 21.9 Antibiotics That Inhibit Protein Synthesis in Bacterial Cells

Antibiotic	Effect on Ribosomes to Inhibit Protein Synthesis
Chloramphenicol	Inhibits peptide bond formation and prevents the binding of tRNA
Erythromycin	Inhibits peptide chain growth by preventing the translocation of the ribosome along the mRNA
Puromycin	Causes release of an incomplete protein by ending the growth of the polypeptide early
Streptomycin	Prevents the proper attachment of the initial tRNA
Tetracycline	Prevents the binding of tRNA

▶**SAMPLE PROBLEM 21.7 Protein Synthesis**

Use three-letter and one-letter abbreviations to write the amino acid sequence for the peptide from the mRNA sequence of 5′ UCA AAA GCC CUU 3′.

SOLUTION

Each of the codons specifies a particular amino acid. Using Table 21.6, we write a peptide with the following amino acid sequence:

mRNA codons: 5′ UCA AAA GCC CUU 3′

Amino acid sequence: Ser — Lys — Ala — Leu , SKAL

STUDY CHECK 21.7

Use three-letter and one-letter abbreviations to write the amino acid sequence for the peptide from the mRNA sequence of 5′ GGG AGC AGU GAG GUU 3′.

ANSWER

Gly–Ser–Ser–Glu–Val, GSSEV

QUESTIONS AND PROBLEMS

21.6 The Genetic Code and Protein Synthesis

LEARNING GOAL Use the genetic code to write the amino acid sequence for a segment of mRNA.

21.53 What is a codon?

21.54 What is the genetic code?

21.55 What amino acid is coded for by each of the following mRNA codons?
a. CUU **b.** UCA **c.** GGU **d.** AGG

21.56 What amino acid is coded for by each of the following mRNA codons?
a. AAA **b.** UUC **c.** CGG **d.** GCA

21.57 When does the codon AUG signal the start of a protein? When does it code for the amino acid methionine?

21.58 The codons UGA, UAA, and UAG do not code for amino acids. What is their role as codons in mRNA?

21.59 What is the difference between a *codon* and an *anticodon*?

21.60 Why are there at least 20 different tRNAs?

21.61 What are the three steps of translation?

21.62 Where does protein synthesis take place?

21.63 Use three-letter and one-letter abbreviations to write the amino acid sequence for the peptide from each of the following mRNA sequences:
a. 5′ ACC ACA ACU 3′
b. 5′ UUU CCG UUC CCA 3′
c. 5′ UAC GGG AGA UGU 3′

21.64 Use three-letter and one-letter abbreviations to write the amino acid sequence for the peptide from each of the following mRNA sequences:
a. 5′ AAA CCC UUG GCC 3′
b. 5′ CCU CGC AGC CCA UGA 3′
c. 5′ AUG CAC AAG GAA GUA CUG 3′

21.65 How is a peptide chain extended?

21.66 What is meant by "translocation"?

21.67 The following sequence is a portion of the DNA template strand:

3′ GCT TTT CAA AAA 5′

a. Write the corresponding mRNA segment.
b. What are the anticodons of the tRNAs?
c. Write the three-letter and one-letter abbreviations for this segment in the peptide chain.

21.68 The following sequence is a portion of the DNA template strand:

3′ TGT GGG GTT ATT 5′

a. Write the corresponding mRNA segment.
b. What are the anticodons of the tRNAs?
c. Write the three-letter and one-letter abbreviations for this segment in the peptide chain.

℞ **Clinical Applications**

21.69 The following is a segment of the DNA template that codes for human insulin:

3′ TTT GTG AAC CAA CAC CTG 5′

a. Write the corresponding mRNA segment.
b. Write the three-letter and one-letter abbreviations for this corresponding peptide segment.

21.70 The following is a segment of the DNA template that codes for human insulin:

3′ TGC GGC TCA CAC CTG GTG 5′

a. Write the corresponding mRNA segment.
b. Write the three-letter and one-letter abbreviations for the corresponding peptide segment.

Identify the type of change in DNA for a point mutation, a deletion mutation, and an insertion mutation.

21.7 Genetic Mutations

A **mutation** is a change in the nucleotide sequence of DNA. Such a change may alter the sequence of amino acids, affecting the structure and function of a protein in a cell. Mutations may result from X-rays, overexposure to sun (ultraviolet (UV) light), chemicals called *mutagens*, and possibly some viruses. If a mutation occurs in a somatic cell (a cell other than a reproductive cell), the altered DNA is limited to that cell and its daughter cells. If the mutation affects DNA that controls the growth of the cell, cancer could result. If a mutation occurs in a germ cell (egg or sperm), then all DNA produced will contain the same genetic change. When a mutation severely alters proteins or enzymes, the new cells may not survive or the person may exhibit a disease or condition that is a result of a genetic defect.

Types of Mutations

Consider a triplet of bases CCG in the template strand of DNA, which produces the codon GGC in mRNA. At the ribosome, tRNA would place the amino acid glycine in the peptide chain (see Figure 21.16a). Now, suppose that T replaces the first C in the DNA triplet, which gives TCG as the triplet. Then the codon produced in the mRNA is AGC, which brings the tRNA with the amino acid serine to add to the peptide chain. The replacement of one base in the template strand of DNA with another is called a **point mutation**. When there is a change of a nucleotide in the codon, a different amino acid may be inserted into the polypeptide. However, if a point mutation does not change the amino acid, it is a *silent mutation*. A point mutation is the most common way in which mutations occur (see Figure 21.16b).

In a **deletion mutation**, a base is deleted from the normal order of bases in the template strand of DNA. Suppose that an A is deleted from the triplet AAA giving a new triplet of AAC (see Figure 21.16c). The next triplet becomes CGA rather than CCG, and so on. All the triplets shift by one base, which changes all the codons that follow and leads to a different sequence of amino acids from that point.

In an **insertion mutation**, a base is inserted into the normal order of bases in the template strand of DNA. Suppose a T is inserted into the triplet AAA, which gives a new triplet of AAT. The next triplet becomes ACC rather than CCG, and so on. All the triplets shift by one base, which changes all the codons that follow and leads to a different sequence of amino acids from that point.

Explore Your World

A Model for DNA Replication and Mutation

1. Cut out 16 rectangular pieces of paper. Using 8 rectangular pieces for DNA strand 1, label two each of the following nucleotide symbols: A═, T═, G≡, and C≡.
2. Using the other 8 rectangular pieces for DNA strand 2, label two of each of the following nucleotide symbols: ═A, ═T, ≡G, and ≡C.
3. Place the pieces for strand 1 in random order.
4. Using the DNA segment strand 1 you made in part 3, select the correct bases to build the complementary segment of DNA strand 2.
5. Using the rectangular pieces for nucleotides, put together a DNA segment using a template strand of A T T G C C. What is the mRNA that would form from this segment of DNA? What is the dipeptide that would form from this mRNA?
6. In the DNA segment of part 5, change the G to an A. What is the mRNA that would form from this segment of DNA? What is the dipeptide that forms? How could this change in codons lead to a mutation?

▶**SAMPLE PROBLEM 21.8 Mutations**

An mRNA has the sequence of codons 5′ CCC AGA GCC 3′. If a point mutation in the DNA changes the mRNA codon of AGA to GGA, how is the amino acid sequence affected in the resulting protein?

SOLUTION

The mRNA sequence 5′ CCC AGA GCC 3′ codes for the following amino acids: proline, arginine, and alanine. When the point mutation occurs, the new sequence of the mRNA codons is 5′ CCC GGA GCC 3′, which codes for proline, glycine, and alanine. The basic amino acid arginine is replaced by the nonpolar amino acid glycine.

	Normal			After Point Mutation		
mRNA codons:	5′ CCC	AGA	GCC 3′	5′ CCC	GGA	GCC 3′
Amino acid sequence:	Pro	—Arg—	Ala	Pro—	Gly	— Ala

STUDY CHECK 21.8

How might the protein made from this mRNA be affected by this mutation?

ANSWER

Because the point mutation replaces a polar basic amino acid with a nonpolar neutral amino acid, the tertiary structure may be altered sufficiently to cause the resulting protein to be less effective or nonfunctional.

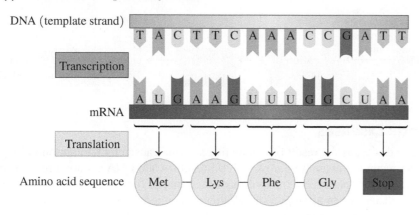

(a) Normal DNA and protein synthesis

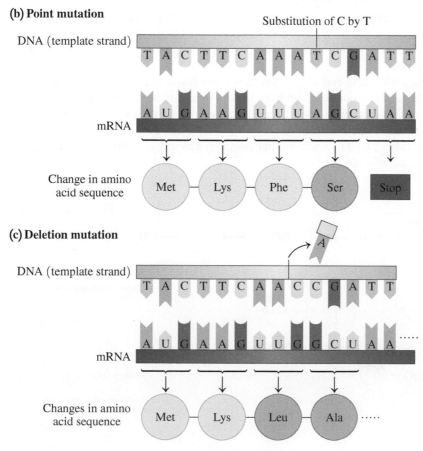

(b) Point mutation

(c) Deletion mutation

FIGURE 21.16 ▶ An alteration in the DNA template strand produces a change in the sequence of amino acids in the protein, which may result in a mutation. **(a)** A normal DNA leads to the correct amino acid order in a protein. **(b)** In a point mutation, the change of a base in DNA leads to a change in the mRNA codon and possibly a change in one amino acid. **(c)** The deletion of a base causes a deletion mutation, which changes the mRNA codons that follow the mutation and produces a different amino acid sequence.

Q When would a point mutation cause protein synthesis to stop?

Effect of Mutations

Some mutations do not cause a significant change in the primary structure of a protein and the protein is able to maintain biological activity. However, if the mutation causes a change to an amino acid critical to protein structure or function, the protein loses biological activity. If the protein is an enzyme, it may no longer bind to its substrate or react with the substrate at the active site. When an altered enzyme cannot catalyze a reaction, certain substances may accumulate until they act as poisons in the cell, or substances vital to survival may not be synthesized. If a defective enzyme occurs in a major metabolic pathway or is involved in the building of a cell membrane, the mutation can be lethal. When a protein deficiency is hereditary, the condition is called a **genetic disease**.

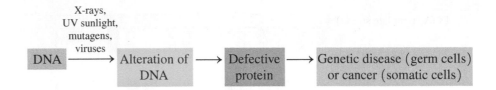

Genetic Diseases

A genetic disease is the result of a defective enzyme caused by a mutation in its genetic code. For example, *phenylketonuria* (PKU) results when DNA cannot direct the synthesis of the enzyme phenylalanine hydroxylase, required for the conversion of phenylalanine to tyrosine. In an attempt to break down the phenylalanine, other enzymes in the cells convert it to phenylpyruvate. If phenylalanine and phenylpyruvate accumulate in the blood of an infant, it can lead to severe brain damage and mental retardation. If PKU is detected in a newborn baby, a diet is prescribed that eliminates all foods that contain phenylalanine. Preventing the buildup of phenylpyruvate ensures normal growth and development.

The amino acid tyrosine is needed in the formation of melanin, the pigment that gives the color to our skin and hair. If the enzyme that converts tyrosine to melanin is defective, no melanin is produced and a genetic disease known as *albinism* results. Persons and animals with no melanin have no skin, eye, or hair pigment (see Figure 21.17). Table 21.10 lists some other common genetic diseases and the type of metabolism or area affected.

FIGURE 21.17 ▶ A peacock with albinism does not produce the melanin needed to make bright colors for its feathers.

Q Why are traits such as albinism related to the gene?

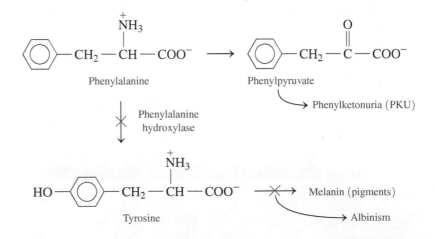

TABLE 21.10 Some Genetic Diseases

Genetic Disease	Result
Galactosemia	In galactosemia, the transferase enzyme required for the metabolism of galactose-1-phosphate is absent, resulting in the accumulation of galactose-1-phosphate, which leads to cataracts and mental retardation. Galactosemia occurs in about 1 in every 50 000 births.
Cystic fibrosis (CF)	Cystic fibrosis is caused by a mutation in the gene for the protein that regulates the production of stomach fluids and mucus. CF is one of the most common inherited diseases in children, in which thick mucus secretions make breathing difficult and block pancreatic function.
Down syndrome	Down syndrome is the leading cause of mental retardation, occurring in about 1 of every 800 live births; the mother's age strongly influences its occurrence. Mental and physical problems, including heart and eye defects, are the result of the formation of three chromosomes (trisomy), usually number 21, instead of a pair.
Familial hypercholesterolemia (FH)	Familial hypercholesterolemia occurs when there is a mutation of a gene on chromosome 19, which produces high cholesterol levels that lead to early coronary heart disease in people 30 to 40 years old.
Muscular dystrophy (MD) (Duchenne)	Muscular dystrophy, Duchenne form, is caused by a mutation in the X chromosome. This muscle-destroying disease appears at about age 5, with death by age 20, and occurs in about 1 of 10 000 males.
Huntington's disease (HD)	Huntington's disease affects the nervous system, leading to total physical impairment. It is the result of a mutation in a gene on chromosome 4, which can now be mapped to test people in families with a history of HD. There are about 30 000 people with Huntington's disease in the United States.
Sickle cell anemia	Sickle cell anemia is caused by a defective form of hemoglobin resulting from a mutation in a gene on chromosome 11. It decreases the oxygen-carrying ability of red blood cells, which take on a sickled shape, causing anemia and plugged capillaries from red blood cell aggregation. In the United States, about 72 000 people are affected by sickle cell anemia.
Hemophilia	Hemophilia is the result of one or more defective blood clotting factors that lead to poor coagulation, excessive bleeding, and internal hemorrhages. There are about 20 000 hemophilia patients in the United States.
Tay–Sachs disease	Tay–Sachs disease is the result of a defective hexosaminidase A, which causes an accumulation of gangliosides and leads to mental retardation, loss of motor control, and early death.

QUESTIONS AND PROBLEMS

21.7 Genetic Mutations

LEARNING GOAL Identify the type of change in DNA for a point mutation, a deletion mutation, and an insertion mutation.

21.71 What is a point mutation?

21.72 How does a point mutation for an enzyme affect the order of amino acids in that protein?

21.73 What is the effect of a deletion mutation on the amino acid sequence of a polypeptide?

21.74 How can a mutation decrease the activity of a protein?

21.75 How is protein synthesis affected if the normal base sequence TTT in the DNA template strand is changed to TTC?

21.76 How is protein synthesis affected if the normal base sequence CCC in the DNA template strand is changed to ACC?

21.77 Consider the following segment of mRNA produced by the normal order of DNA nucleotides:

5' ACA UCA CGG GUA 3'

a. What is the amino acid order produced from this mRNA?
b. What is the amino acid order if a point mutation changes UCA to ACA?
c. What is the amino acid order if a point mutation changes CGG to GGG?
d. What happens to protein synthesis if a point mutation changes UCA to UAA?

e. What is the amino acid order if an insertion mutation adds a G to the beginning of the mRNA segment?
f. What is the amino acid order if a deletion mutation removes the A at the beginning of the mRNA segment?

21.78 Consider the following segment of mRNA produced by the normal order of DNA nucleotides:

5' CUU AAA CGA GUU 3'

a. What is the amino acid order produced from this mRNA?
b. What is the amino acid order if a point mutation changes CUU to CCU?
c. What is the amino acid order if a point mutation changes CGA to AGA?
d. What happens to protein synthesis if a point mutation changes AAA to UAA?
e. What is the amino acid order if an insertion mutation adds a G to the beginning of the mRNA segment?
f. What is the amino acid order if a deletion mutation removes the C at the beginning of the mRNA segment?

℞ Clinical Applications

21.79 a. A point mutation changes a codon in the mRNA for an enzyme from GCC to GCA. Why is there no change in the amino acid order in the protein?

b. In sickle cell anemia, a point mutation in the mRNA for hemoglobin results in the replacement of glutamate with valine in the resulting hemoglobin molecule. Why does the replacement of one amino acid cause such a drastic change in biological function?

21.80 a. A point mutation in the mRNA for an enzyme results in the replacement of leucine with alanine in the resulting enzyme molecule. Why does this change in amino acids have little effect on the biological activity of the enzyme?

b. A point mutation in mRNA replaces cytosine in the codon UCA with adenine. How would this substitution affect the amino acid order in the protein?

LEARNING GOAL

Describe the preparation and uses of recombinant DNA.

21.8 Recombinant DNA

Techniques in the field of genetic engineering permit scientists to cut and recombine DNA fragments to form **recombinant DNA**. The technology of recombinant DNA is used to produce important medicines like human insulin for diabetics, the antiviral substance interferon, blood clotting factor VIII, and human growth hormone.

Preparing Recombinant DNA

Much of the work with recombinant DNA is done with *Escherichia coli* (*E. coli*) bacteria. Some of the DNA in bacterial cells exists as small, circular double-stranded DNA structures called *plasmids*, which are easy to isolate and capable of replication. Initially, *E. coli* cells are soaked in a detergent solution to disrupt the plasma membrane releasing the plasmids. A *restriction enzyme* is used to cut the double strands of DNA between specific bases in the DNA sequence (see Figure 21.18). For example, the restriction enzyme EcoR1 (pronounced "Echo-R-One") recognizes the base sequences GAATTC on both strands, and cuts both DNA strands between the G and A.

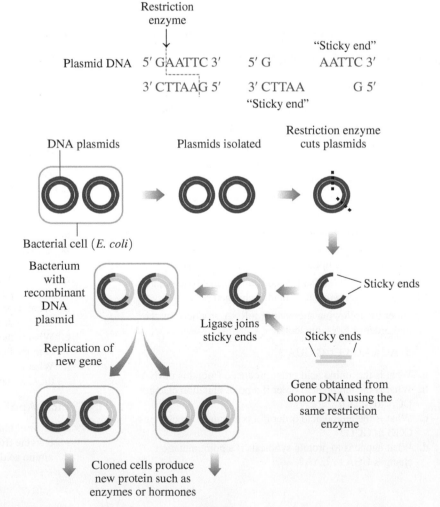

FIGURE 21.18 ▶ Recombinant DNA is formed by placing a gene from another organism in a plasmid DNA of the bacterium, which causes the bacterium to produce a nonbacterial protein such as insulin or growth hormone.

Q How can recombinant DNA help a person with a genetic disease?

The same restriction enzymes are used to cut a piece of DNA called donor DNA from a gene of a different organism, such as the gene that produces insulin or growth hormone. When the donor DNA is mixed with the cut plasmids, the nucleotides in their "sticky ends" join by forming complementary base pairs to make *recombinant DNA*. The resulting altered plasmids containing the recombinant DNA are placed in a fresh culture of *E. coli* bacteria. The *E. coli* that take up the plasmids are then selected. As the recombined cells divide and replicate, they produce the protein from the inserted gene in the plasmids.

Plasmid DNA	Donor DNA	Recombinant DNA
5′ G	AATTC 3′ ⟶	5′ GAATTC 3′
3′ CTTAA	G 5′ ⟶	3′ CTTAAG 5′

In a single day, one *E. coli* bacterium is capable of producing a million copies of itself including the recombinant DNA, a process known as *gene cloning*. If the inserted DNA codes for the human insulin protein, the altered plasmids begin to synthesize human insulin. Bacterial cells with the recombinant DNA can produce large quantities of the insulin protein, which is then collected and purified. Table 21.11 lists some of the products developed through recombinant DNA technology that are now used therapeutically.

TABLE 21.11 Therapeutic Products of Recombinant DNA

Product	Therapeutic Use
Human insulin	Treat diabetes
Erythropoietin (EPO)	Treat anemia; stimulate production of erythrocytes
Human growth hormone (HGH)	Stimulate growth
Interferon	Treat cancer and viral disease
Tumor necrosis factor (TNF)	Destroy tumor cells
Monoclonal antibodies	Transport drugs needed to treat cancer and transplant rejection
Epidermal growth factor (EGF)	Stimulate healing of wounds and burns
Human blood clotting factor VIII	Treat hemophilia; allows blood to clot normally
Interleukins	Stimulate immune system; treat cancer
Prourokinase	Destroy blood clots; treat myocardial infarctions
Influenza vaccine	Prevent influenza
Hepatitis B virus (HBV) vaccine	Prevent viral hepatitis

Polymerase Chain Reaction

Before gene cloning can occur, a purified gene has to be isolated. In 1987, a process called the **polymerase chain reaction (PCR)** made it possible to produce multiple copies of a gene (amplify) in a short time. In the PCR technique, a sequence of a DNA molecule is selected to copy, and the DNA is heated to separate the strands. RNA primers hydrogen bond to a small group of complementary nucleotides on each strand end of the sequence to be copied. The DNA strands with their primers are mixed with a heat-stable DNA polymerase and the four deoxyribonucleotides, and undergo repeated cycles of heating and cooling to produce complementary strands for the DNA section. Then the process is repeated with the new batch of DNA. After several cycles of the PCR process, millions of copies of the initial DNA section are produced (see Figure 21.19).

Genetic Testing

PCR allows screening for defective genes whose sequence is known. For example, there are several defects in two known breast cancer genes, called BRCA1 and BRCA2, that correlate to a higher risk of breast cancer. Patients are screened for the defects in these genes by using a DNA sample from their blood or saliva. PCR amplifies the defective genes while incorporating a fluorescent label which is visible if the test is positive.

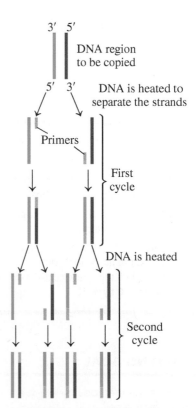

FIGURE 21.19 ▶ Each cycle of the polymerase chain reaction doubles the number of copies of the DNA section.

Why are the DNA strands heated at the start of each cycle?

FIGURE 21.20 ▶ Bands on film represent DNA fingerprints that can be used to identify a person involved in a crime.

Q What causes DNA fragments to appear on X-ray film?

DNA Fingerprinting

DNA fingerprinting or *DNA profiling* uses PCR to identify individuals based on a set of 13 hereditary traits. The chance that two individuals of the same ethnic background have the same 13 genetic traits is 1 in 575 trillion unless they are identical twins. Only a very small sample size is needed from blood, skin, saliva, or semen. Fluorescent or radioactive isotopes are incorporated into the amplified DNA during the PCR process. The DNA is cut into smaller pieces by restriction enzymes, which are placed on a gel and separated using electrophoresis. The banding pattern on the gel is called a DNA fingerprint.

One application of DNA fingerprinting is in forensic science, where DNA samples are used to connect a suspect with a crime (see Figure 21.20). Recently, DNA fingerprinting has been used to gain the release of individuals who were wrongly convicted. Other applications of DNA fingerprinting are determining the biological parents of a child, establishing the identity of a deceased person, and matching recipients with organ donors.

The Human Genome

The Human Genome Project, completed in 2003, showed that our DNA is composed of 3 billion bases and 21 000 genes coding for protein, but represents only 3% of the total DNA. Since then researchers have identified stretches of DNA that code for other RNA molecules. Much of our DNA regulates genes and serves as recognition sites for proteins like transcription factors and polymerase enzymes. To date, almost 80% of our genome has been assigned a function allowing scientists to better understand human diseases caused by errors in DNA replication, transcription, or regulation.

QUESTIONS AND PROBLEMS

21.8 Recombinant DNA

LEARNING GOAL Describe the preparation and uses of recombinant DNA.

21.81 Why are *E. coli* bacteria used in recombinant DNA procedures?

21.82 What is a plasmid?

21.83 How are plasmids obtained from *E. coli*?

21.84 Why are restriction enzymes mixed with the plasmids?

21.85 How is a gene for a particular protein inserted into a plasmid?

21.86 Why is DNA polymerase useful in criminal investigations?

21.87 What is a DNA fingerprint?

21.88 What beneficial proteins are produced from recombinant DNA technology?

21.89 The Acl1 restriction enzyme will cleave DNA between A and C (A/C) in the 5′ to 3′ direction. Draw the resulting DNA sections with the "sticky ends" when the following DNA segment is cleaved by Acl1:

5′ A A C G T T 3′
3′ T T G C A A 5′

21.90 The Pci1 restriction enzyme will cleave DNA between A and C (A/C) in the 5′ to 3′ direction. Draw the resulting DNA sections with the "sticky ends" when the following DNA segment is cleaved by Pci1:

5′ A C A T G T 3′
3′ T G T A C A 5′

21.91 Write the DNA sequence for each of the following "sticky ends":
a. 5′ G G C T 3′   b. 5′ A A T G C G 3′
c. 5′ T T C C G A 3′

21.92 Write the DNA sequence for each of the following "sticky ends":
a. 5′ T C C T C T 3′   b. 5′ G G C A C T T 3′
c. 5′ T A G C A T 3′

LEARNING GOAL

Describe the methods by which a virus infects a cell.

21.9 Viruses

Viruses are small particles of 3 to 200 genes that cannot replicate without a host cell. A typical virus contains a nucleic acid, DNA or RNA, but not both, inside a protein coat. A virus does not have the necessary material such as nucleotides and enzymes to make proteins and grow. The only way a virus can replicate (make additional copies of itself) is to invade a host cell and take over the machinery and materials necessary for protein synthesis and growth. Some infections caused by viruses invading human cells are listed in Table 21.12. There are also viruses that attack bacteria, plants, and animals.

TABLE 21.12 Some Diseases Caused by Viral Infection

Disease	Virus
Common cold	Coronavirus (over 100 types), rhinovirus (over 110 types)
Influenza	Orthomyxovirus
Warts	Papovavirus
Herpes	Herpesvirus
HPV	Human papilloma virus
Leukemia, cancers, AIDS	Retrovirus
Hepatitis	Hepatitis A virus (HAV), hepatitis B virus (HBV), hepatitis C virus (HCV)
Mumps	Paramyxovirus
Epstein–Barr	Epstein–Barr virus (EBV)
Chicken pox (shingles)	*Varicella zoster* virus (VZV)

A viral infection begins when an enzyme in the protein coat of the virus makes a hole in the outside of the host cell, allowing the viral nucleic acid to enter and mix with the materials in the host cell (see Figure 21.21). If the virus contains DNA, the host cell begins to replicate the viral DNA in the same way it would replicate normal DNA. Viral DNA produces viral RNA, and a protease processes proteins to produce a protein coat to form a viral particle that leaves the cell. The cell synthesizes so many virus particles that it eventually releases new viruses to infect more cells.

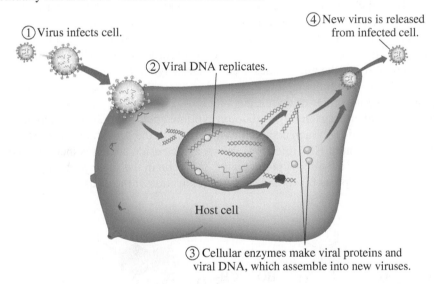

① Virus infects cell.

② Viral DNA replicates.

③ Cellular enzymes make viral proteins and viral DNA, which assemble into new viruses.

④ New virus is released from infected cell.

Host cell

FIGURE 21.21 ▶ After a virus attaches to the host cell, it injects its viral DNA and uses the host cell's machinery and materials to make viral mRNA, new viral DNA, and viral proteins. The newly assembled viruses are released to infect other cells.

Q Why does a virus need a host cell for replication?

Vaccines are inactive forms of viruses that boost the immune response by causing the body to produce antibodies to the virus. Several childhood diseases, such as polio, mumps, chicken pox, and measles, can be prevented through the use of vaccines.

Reverse Transcription

A virus that contains RNA as its genetic material is a **retrovirus**. Once inside the host cell, it must first make viral DNA using a process known as *reverse transcription*. A retrovirus contains a polymerase enzyme called *reverse transcriptase* that uses the viral RNA template to synthesize complementary strands of DNA. Once produced, the single DNA strands form double-stranded DNA using the nucleotides present in the host cell. This newly formed viral DNA, called a *provirus*, integrates with the DNA of the host cell (see Figure 21.22).

AIDS

During the early 1980s, a disease called *acquired immune deficiency syndrome*, commonly known as AIDS, began to claim an alarming number of lives. We now know that the HIV virus (human immunodeficiency virus) causes the disease (see Figure 21.23). HIV is a retrovirus that infects and destroys T4 lymphocyte cells, which are involved in the immune response. After the HIV binds to receptors on the surface of a T4 cell, the virus injects viral RNA into the

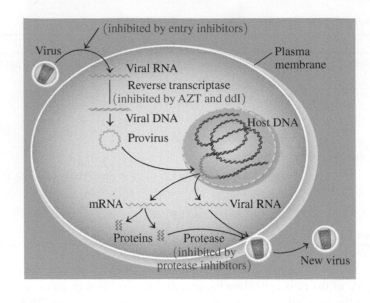

FIGURE 21.22 ▶ After a retrovirus injects its viral RNA into a cell, it forms a DNA strand by reverse transcription. The single-stranded DNA forms a double-stranded DNA called a provirus, which is incorporated into the host cell DNA. When the cell replicates, the provirus produces the viral RNA needed to produce more virus particles.

Q What is reverse transcription?

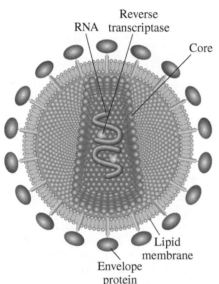

FIGURE 21.23 ▶ The HIV virus causes AIDS, which destroys the immune system in the body.

Q Is HIV a DNA virus or an RNA retrovirus?

host cell. As a retrovirus, the genes of the viral RNA direct the formation of viral DNA, which is then incorporated into the host's genome so it can replicate as part of the host cell's DNA. The gradual depletion of T4 cells reduces the ability of the immune system to destroy harmful organisms. The AIDS syndrome is characterized by opportunistic infections such as *Pneumocystis carinii*, which causes pneumonia, and *Kaposi's sarcoma*, a skin cancer.

Treatment for AIDS is based on attacking the HIV at different points in its life cycle, including cell entry, reverse transcription, and protein synthesis. Nucleoside analogs mimic the structures of the nucleosides used for DNA synthesis, and are able to successfully inhibit the reverse transcriptase enzyme. For example, the drug AZT (3′-azido-2′-deoxythymidine) is similar to thymidine, and ddI (2′,3′-dideoxyinosine) is similar to guanosine. Two other drugs are 2′,3′-dideoxycytidine (ddC) and 2′,3′-didehydro-2′,3′-dideoxythymidine (d4T). Such compounds are found in the "cocktails" that are providing extended remission of HIV infections. When a nucleoside analog is incorporated into viral DNA, the lack of a hydroxyl group on the 3′ carbon in the sugar prevents the formation of the sugar–phosphate bonds and stops the replication of the virus.

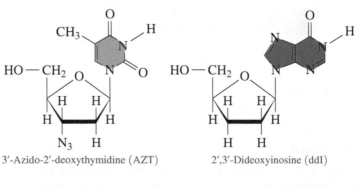

3′-Azido-2′-deoxythymidine (AZT)   2′,3′-Dideoxyinosine (ddI)

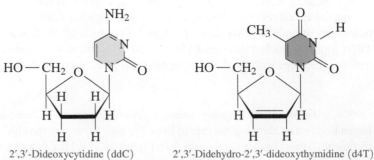

2′,3′-Dideoxycytidine (ddC)   2′,3′-Didehydro-2′,3′-dideoxythymidine (d4T)

Today, people with HIV and AIDS are treated with a combination of drugs that include entry inhibitors, reverse transcriptase inhibitors, and protease inhibitors. Entry inhibitors attach to the surface of either the lymphocyte or HIV virus, which blocks entry into the cell. Entry inhibitors include enfuvirtide (Fuzeon) and maraviroc (Selzentry). Protease inhibitors prevent the proper cutting and formation of proteins used by the virus to make more copies of its own proteins. Protease inhibitors include saquinavir (Invirase), ritonavir (Norvir), fosamprenavir (Lexiva), and several others. When patients become resistant to certain drugs, different combinations are used to prolong life expectancy.

Lexiva metabolizes slowly to provide amprenavir, an HIV-protease inhibitor.

▶ **SAMPLE PROBLEM 21.9 Viruses**

Why are viruses unable to replicate on their own?

SOLUTION

Viruses contain only packets of DNA or RNA, but not the necessary replication machinery that includes enzymes and nucleosides.

STUDY CHECK 21.9

What are the essential parts of a virus?

ANSWER

nucleic acid (DNA or RNA) and a protein coat

Chemistry Link to **Health**
Cancer

Normally, cells in the body undergo an orderly and controlled cell division. When cells begin to grow and multiply without control, they invade neighboring cells and appear as a tumor. If these tumors are limited, they are benign. When they invade other tissues and interfere with normal functions of the body, the tumors are cancerous. Cancer can be caused by chemical and environmental substances, by ultraviolet or medical radiation, or by *oncogenic viruses*, which are associated with human cancers.

Some reports estimate that 70 to 80% of all human cancers are initiated by chemical and environmental substances. A *carcinogen* is any substance that increases the chance of inducing a tumor. Known

carcinogens include aniline dyes, cigarette smoke, and asbestos. More than 90% of all persons with lung cancer are smokers. A carcinogen causes cancer by reacting with molecules in a cell, probably DNA, and altering the growth of that cell. Some known carcinogens are listed in Table 21.13.

TABLE 21.13 Some Chemical and Environmental Carcinogens

Carcinogen	Tumor Site
Aflatoxin	Liver
Aniline dyes	Bladder
Arsenic	Skin, lungs
Asbestos	Lungs, respiratory tract
Cadmium	Prostate, kidneys
Chromium	Lungs
Nickel	Lungs, sinuses
Nitrites	Stomach
Vinyl chloride	Liver

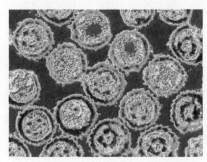
Epstein–Barr virus (EBV), herpesvirus 4, causes cancer in humans.

Skin cancer has become one of the most prevalent forms of cancer. It appears that DNA damage in the areas of the skin exposed to ultraviolet radiation may eventually cause mutations. The cells lose their ability to control protein synthesis. This type of uncontrolled cell division becomes skin cancer. The incidence of *malignant melanoma*, one of the most serious skin cancers, has been rapidly increasing. Some possible factors for this increase may be the popularity of sun tanning as well as the reduction of the ozone layer, which absorbs much of the harmful radiation from sunlight.

Oncogenic viruses cause cancer when cells are infected. Several viruses associated with human cancers are listed in Table 21.14. Some cancers such as retinoblastoma and breast cancer appear to occur more frequently within families. There is some indication that a missing or defective gene may be responsible.

TABLE 21.14 Human Cancers Caused by Oncogenic Viruses

Virus	Disease
RNA Viruses	
Human T-cell lymphotropic virus-type 1 (HTLV-1)	Leukemia
DNA Viruses	
Epstein–Barr virus (EBV)	Burkitt's lymphoma (cancer of white blood B cells) Nasopharyngeal carcinoma Hodgkin's disease
Hepatitis B virus (HBV)	Liver cancer
Herpes simplex virus (HSV, type 2)	Cervical and uterine cancer
Papilloma virus (HPV)	Cervical and colon cancer, genital warts

QUESTIONS AND PROBLEMS

21.9 Viruses

LEARNING GOAL Describe the methods by which a virus infects a cell.

21.93 What type of genetic information is found in a virus?

21.94 Why do viruses need to invade a host cell?

 Clinical Applications

21.95 A specific virus contains RNA as its genetic material.
  a. Why would reverse transcription be used in the life cycle of this type of virus?
  b. What is the name of this type of virus?

21.96 What is the purpose of a vaccine?

21.97 How do nucleoside analogs disrupt the life cycle of the HIV virus?

21.98 How do protease inhibitors disrupt the life cycle of the HIV virus?

Clinical Update
Ellen's Medical Treatment Following Breast Cancer Surgery

Ellen's oncologist told Ellen that the cells in her breast tumor and surrounding tissue tested positive for estrogen receptor (ER), which verified that she had breast cancer. Many breast tumors are estrogen positive because they require estrogen for their growth. Estrogen is a hormone that travels through the bloodstream and activates estrogen receptors in the cells of the breast and ovaries. The bonding of estrogen (activator) and the estrogen receptor (transcription factor) to DNA increase the production of mammary cells and potential mutations that can lead to cancer. High levels of the estrogen receptor appear in more than 60% of all breast cancer cases.

Because Ellen is 45 years old and has a family history of breast and ovarian cancer, she was also tested for altered genes BRCA1 and BRCA2. Normally, these genes suppress tumor growth by repairing DNA defects. However, if the mutated genes are inherited, a person's cells lose the ability to suppress tumor growth, and the risk for breast and ovarian as well as other cancers becomes much greater. Both parents can carry a BRCA mutation and pass it on to their sons and daughters. Ellen was relieved that her test results for mutated BRCA1 and BRCA2 were negative.

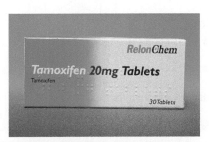

The estrogen receptor is a dimer with a binding region for estrogen or tamoxifen.

After Ellen completed a radiation series, she discussed the choice of drugs available for the treatment of breast cancer. Drugs such as tamoxifen and raloxifene block the binding of estrogen to the estrogen receptor, which prevents the growth of cancers that are estrogen positive. Other drugs such as anastrozole (Arimidex) and letrozole (Femara) are aromatase inhibitors (AIs) that prevent the growth of new tumors by blocking the synthesis of aromatase (estrogen synthetase), an enzyme that produces estrogen. Aromatase inhibitors are used primarily for post-menopausal women whose ovaries no longer produce estrogen. Ellen and her oncologist agreed upon the use of tamoxifen, which she will take for the next five years to prevent breast cancer from recurring after her surgery.

℞ Clinical Applications

21.99 What are estrogen receptors?

21.100 How do estrogen and the estrogen receptor influence cancer growth of mammary cells?

21.101 How does tamoxifen reduce the potential of breast cancer?

21.102 How does letrozole reduce the potential of breast cancer?

21.103 The following is a segment of the template strand of human BRCA1 gene:

3′ TGG AAT TAT CTG CTC TTC GCG 5′

a. Write the corresponding mRNA segment.

b. Write the three-letter and one-letter abbreviations for the corresponding peptide segment.

c. If there is a point mutation in the fourth nucleotide triplet and A replaces **G**, what is the change, if any, in the amino acid sequence?

21.104 The following is a segment of the template strand of human BRCA1 gene:

3′ ACA TAT TTT GCA AAT TTT GCA 5′

a. Write the corresponding mRNA segment.

b. Write the three-letter and one-letter abbreviations for the corresponding peptide segment.

c. If there is a point mutation in the second nucleotide triplet and C replaces **A**, what is the change, if any, in the amino acid sequence?

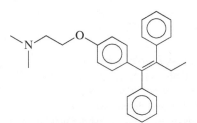

Tamoxifen slows down transcription by blocking the binding of estrogen to estrogen receptors.

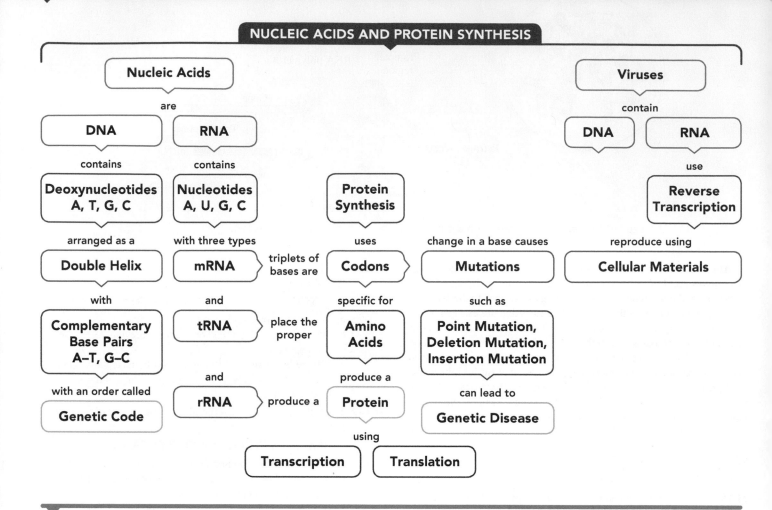

NUCLEIC ACIDS AND PROTEIN SYNTHESIS

- **Nucleic Acids** are
  - **DNA** contains
    - **Deoxynucleotides A, T, G, C** arranged as a
      - **Double Helix** with
        - **Complementary Base Pairs A–T, G–C** with an order called
          - **Genetic Code**
  - **RNA** contains
    - **Nucleotides A, U, G, C** with three types
      - **mRNA** — triplets of bases are
      - **tRNA** — place the proper
      - **rRNA** — produce a
- **Protein Synthesis** uses
  - **Codons** specific for
    - **Amino Acids** produce a
      - **Protein** using
        - **Transcription** **Translation**
- change in a base causes **Mutations** such as
  - **Point Mutation, Deletion Mutation, Insertion Mutation** can lead to
    - **Genetic Disease**
- **Viruses** contain
  - **DNA**
  - **RNA** use
    - **Reverse Transcription** reproduce using
      - **Cellular Materials**

CHAPTER REVIEW

21.1 Components of Nucleic Acids
LEARNING GOAL Describe the bases and ribose sugars that make up the nucleic acids DNA and RNA.

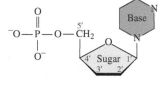

- Nucleic acids, such as deoxyribonucleic acid (DNA) and ribonucleic acid (RNA), are polymers of nucleotides.
- A nucleoside is a combination of a pentose sugar and a base.
- A nucleotide is composed of three parts: a pentose sugar, a base, and a phosphate group.
- In DNA, the sugar is deoxyribose and the base can be adenine, thymine, guanine, or cytosine.
- In RNA, the sugar is ribose, and uracil replaces thymine.

21.2 Primary Structure of Nucleic Acids
LEARNING GOAL Describe the primary structures of RNA and DNA.

- Each nucleic acid has its own unique sequence of bases known as its primary structure.

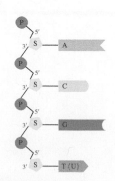

- In a nucleic acid polymer, the 3′ OH group of each ribose in RNA or deoxyribose in DNA forms a phosphodiester linkage to the phosphate group of the 5′ carbon atom of the sugar in the next nucleotide to give a backbone of alternating sugar and phosphate groups.
- There is a free 5′ phosphate at one end of the polymer and a free 3′ OH group at the other end.

21.3 DNA Double Helix
LEARNING GOAL Describe the double helix of DNA.

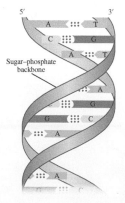

- A DNA molecule consists of two strands of nucleotides that are wound around each other like a spiral staircase.
- The two strands are held together by hydrogen bonds between complementary base pairs, A with T, and G with C.

21.4 DNA Replication
LEARNING GOAL Describe the process of DNA replication.

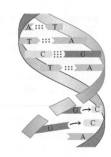

- During DNA replication, DNA polymerase makes new DNA strands along each of the original DNA strands that serve as templates.
- Complementary base pairing ensures the correct pairing of bases to give identical copies of the original DNA.

21.5 RNA and Transcription
LEARNING GOAL Identify the different types of RNA; describe the synthesis of mRNA.

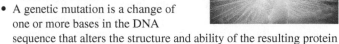

RNA polymerase

- The three types of RNA differ by function in the cell: ribosomal RNA makes up most of the structure of the ribosomes, messenger RNA carries genetic information from the DNA to the ribosomes, and transfer RNA places the correct amino acids in a growing peptide chain.
- Transcription is the process by which RNA polymerase produces mRNA from one strand of DNA.
- Transcription factors at the promoter region bind RNA polymerase to DNA, which activates the transcription of a gene.
- The bases in the mRNA are complementary to the DNA, except A in DNA is paired with U in RNA.
- The production of mRNA occurs when certain proteins are needed in the cell.

21.6 The Genetic Code and Protein Synthesis
LEARNING GOAL Use the genetic code to write the amino acid sequence for a segment of mRNA.

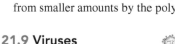

- The genetic code consists of a series of codons, which are sequences of three bases that specify the order for the amino acids in a protein.
- There are 64 codons for the 20 amino acids, which means there are multiple codons for most amino acids.
- The codon AUG signals the start of transcription, and codons UAG, UGA, and UAA signal it to stop.
- Proteins are synthesized at the ribosomes in a translation process that includes three steps: initiation, chain elongation, and termination.

- During translation, tRNAs bring the appropriate amino acids to the ribosome, and peptide bonds form to join the amino acids in a peptide chain.
- When the polypeptide is released, it takes on its secondary and tertiary structures and becomes a functional protein in the cell.

21.7 Genetic Mutations
LEARNING GOAL Identify the type of change in DNA for a point mutation, a deletion mutation, and an insertion mutation.

- A genetic mutation is a change of one or more bases in the DNA sequence that alters the structure and ability of the resulting protein to function properly.
- In a point mutation, one codon is altered, and in an insertion mutation or a deletion mutation, a base is added or removed, which changes all the codons after the base change.

21.8 Recombinant DNA
LEARNING GOAL Describe the preparation and uses of recombinant DNA.

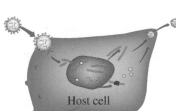

- A recombinant DNA is prepared by inserting a DNA segment—a gene—into plasmid DNA present in *E. coli* bacteria.
- As the altered bacterial cells replicate, the protein expressed by the foreign DNA segment is produced.
- In criminal investigation, large quantities of DNA are obtained from smaller amounts by the polymerase chain reaction.

21.9 Viruses
LEARNING GOAL Describe the methods by which a virus infects a cell.

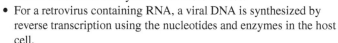

Host cell

- Viruses containing DNA or RNA must invade host cells to use the machinery within the cell for the synthesis of more viruses.
- For a retrovirus containing RNA, a viral DNA is synthesized by reverse transcription using the nucleotides and enzymes in the host cell.
- In the treatment of AIDS, entry inhibitors block the virus from entering the cell, nucleoside analogs inhibit the reverse transcriptase of the HIV virus, and protease inhibitors disrupt the catalytic activity of protease needed to produce proteins for the synthesis of more viruses.

KEY TERMS

anticodon The triplet of bases in the center loop of tRNA that is complementary to a codon on mRNA.

base A nitrogen-containing compound found in DNA and RNA: adenine (A), thymine (T), cytosine (C), guanine (G), and uracil (U).

codon A sequence of three bases in mRNA that specifies a certain amino acid to be placed in a protein. A few codons signal the start or stop of protein synthesis.

complementary base pairs In DNA, adenine is always paired with thymine (A and T or T and A), and guanine is always paired with cytosine (G and C or C and G). In forming RNA, adenine is always paired with uracil (A and U or U and A).

deletion mutation A mutation that deletes a base from a DNA sequence.

DNA Deoxyribonucleic acid; the genetic material of all cells containing nucleotides with deoxyribose, phosphate, and the four bases: adenine, thymine, guanine, and cytosine.

double helix The helical shape of the double chain of DNA that is like a spiral staircase with a sugar–phosphate backbone on the outside and base pairs like stair steps on the inside.

exons The sections in a DNA template that code for proteins.

genetic code The sequence of codons in mRNA that specifies the amino acid order for the synthesis of protein.

genetic disease A physical malformation or metabolic dysfunction caused by a mutation in the base sequence of DNA.

insertion mutation A mutation that inserts a base in a DNA sequence.

introns The sections in DNA that do not code for proteins.

mRNA Messenger RNA; produced in the nucleus from DNA to carry the genetic information to the ribosomes for the construction of a protein.

mutation A change in the DNA base sequence that alters the formation of a protein in the cell.

nucleic acid A large molecule composed of nucleotides; found as a double helix in DNA and as the single strands of RNA.

nucleoside The combination of a pentose sugar and a base.

nucleotide Building block of a nucleic acid consisting of a base, a pentose sugar (ribose or deoxyribose), and a phosphate group.

Okazaki fragment A short segment formed by DNA polymerase in the daughter DNA strand that runs in the 3' to 5' direction.

phosphodiester linkage The phosphate link that joins the 3' hydroxyl group in one nucleotide to the phosphate group on the 5' carbon atom in the next nucleotide.

point mutation A mutation that replaces one base in a DNA with a different base.

polymerase chain reaction (PCR) A procedure in which a strand of DNA is copied many times by mixing it with primers, DNA polymerase and a mixture of deoxyribonucleotides and subjecting it to repeated cycles of heating and cooling.

primary structure The sequence of nucleotides in nucleic acids.

recombinant DNA DNA combined from different organisms to form new, synthetic DNA.

replication The process of duplicating DNA by pairing the bases on each parent strand with their complementary bases.

replication forks The open sections in unwound DNA strands where DNA polymerase begins the replication process.

retrovirus A virus that contains RNA as its genetic material and that synthesizes a complementary DNA strand inside a cell.

RNA Ribonucleic acid; a type of nucleic acid that is a single strand of nucleotides containing ribose, phosphate, and the four bases: adenine, cytosine, guanine, and uracil.

rRNA Ribosomal RNA; the most prevalent type of RNA and a major component of the ribosomes.

transcription The transfer of genetic information from DNA by the formation of mRNA.

transcription factor A protein that binds to DNA and controls transcription. It often binds with an activator.

translation The interpretation of the codons in mRNA as amino acids in a peptide.

tRNA Transfer RNA; an RNA that places a specific amino acid into a peptide chain at the ribosome so that a protein can be made. There is one or more tRNA for each of the 20 different amino acids.

virus A small particle containing DNA or RNA in a protein coat that requires a host cell for replication.

⚛ CORE CHEMISTRY SKILLS

The chapter section containing each Core Chemistry Skill is shown in parentheses at the end of each heading.

Writing the Complementary DNA Strand (21.3)

• During DNA replication, new DNA strands are made along each of the original DNA strands.

• The new strand of DNA is made by forming hydrogen bonds with the bases in the template strand: A with T and T with A; C with G and G with C.

Example: Write the complementary base sequence for the following DNA segment:

5' A T T C G G T A C 3'

Answer: 3' T A A G C C A T G 5'

Writing the mRNA Segment for a DNA Template (21.5)

• Transcription is the process that produces mRNA from one strand of DNA.

• The bases in the mRNA are complementary to the DNA, expect that A in DNA is paired with U in RNA.

Example: What is the mRNA produced for the DNA segment 5' C G C A T G T C A 3'?

Answer: 3' G C G U A C A G U 5'

Writing the Amino Acid for an mRNA Codon (21.6)

• The genetic code consists of a sequence of three bases (codons) that specifies the order for the amino acids in a protein.

• The codon AUG signals the start of transcription and codons UAG, UGA, and UAA signal it to stop.

Example: Use three-letter and one-letter abbreviations to write the amino acid sequence you would expect in a peptide for the mRNA sequence 5' CCG UAU GGG 3'.

Answer: Pro–Tyr–Gly, PYG

UNDERSTANDING THE CONCEPTS

The chapter sections to review are given in parentheses at the end of each question.

21.105 Answer the following questions for the given section of DNA: (21.4, 21.5, 21.6)

a. Complete the bases in the parent and new strands.

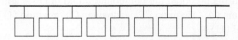

Parent strand: A ☐ G T ☐ ☐ C T
New strand: ☐ C ☐ G C G ☐ ☐

b. Using the new strand as a template, write the mRNA sequence.

c. Write the three-letter symbols for the amino acids that would go into the peptide from the mRNA you wrote in part **b**.

21.106 Suppose a mutation occurs in the DNA section in problem 21.105, and the first base in the parent chain, adenine, is replaced by guanine. (21.4, 21.5, 21.6, 21.7)
  a. What type of mutation has occurred?
  b. Using the new strand that results from this mutation, write the order of bases in the altered mRNA.

c. Write the three-letter symbols for the amino acids that would go into the peptide from the mRNA you wrote in part **b**.

d. What effect, if any, might this mutation have on the structure and/or function of the resulting protein?

ADDITIONAL QUESTIONS AND PROBLEMS

21.107 Identify each of the following bases as a pyrimidine or a purine: (21.1)
  a. cytosine   **b.** adenine
  c. uracil   **d.** thymine
  e. guanine

21.108 Indicate if each of the bases in problem 21.107 is found in DNA only, RNA only, or both DNA and RNA. (21.1)

21.109 Identify the base and sugar in each of the following nucleosides: (21.1)
  a. deoxythymidine   **b.** adenosine
  c. cytidine   **d.** deoxyguanosine

21.110 Identify the base and sugar in each of the following nucleotides: (21.1)
  a. CMP   **b.** dAMP
  c. dTMP   **d.** UMP

21.111 How do the bases thymine and uracil differ? (21.1)

21.112 How do the bases cytosine and uracil differ? (21.1)

21.113 Draw the condensed structural formula for CMP. (21.1)

21.114 Draw the condensed structural formula for dGMP. (21.1)

21.115 What is similar about the primary structure of RNA and DNA? (21.2)

21.116 What is different about the primary structure of RNA and DNA? (21.2)

21.117 If the DNA double helix in salmon contains 28% adenine, what is the percentage of thymine, guanine, and cytosine? (21.3)

21.118 If the DNA double helix in humans contains 20% cytosine, what is the percentage of guanine, adenine, and thymine? (21.3)

21.119 In DNA, how many hydrogen bonds form between adenine and thymine? (21.3)

21.120 In DNA, how many hydrogen bonds are formed between guanine and cytosine? (21.3)

21.121 Write the complementary base sequence for each of the following DNA segments: (21.4)
  a. 5′ G A C T T A G G C 3′
  b. 3′ T G C A A A C T A G C T 5′
  c. 5′ A T C G A T C G A T C G 3′

21.122 Write the complementary base sequence for each of the following DNA segments: (21.4)
  a. 5′ T T A C G G A C C G C 3′
  b. 5′ A T A G C C C T T A C T G G 3′
  c. 3′ G G C C T A C C T T A A C G A C G 5′

21.123 In DNA replication, what is the difference between the synthesis of the leading strand and the synthesis of the lagging strand? (21.4)

21.124 How are the Okazaki fragments joined to the growing DNA strand? (21.4)

21.125 After the replication of a DNA, where are the original DNA strands located in the daughter DNA molecules? (21.4)

21.126 How can replication occur at several places along a DNA double helix? (21.4)

21.127 Match the following statements with rRNA, mRNA, or tRNA: (21.5)
  a. is the smallest type of RNA
  b. makes up the highest percentage of RNA in the cell
  c. carries genetic information from the nucleus to the ribosomes

21.128 Match the following statements with rRNA, mRNA, or tRNA: (21.5)
  a. combines with proteins to form ribosomes
  b. brings amino acids to the ribosomes for protein synthesis
  c. acts as a template for protein synthesis

21.129 What are the possible codons for each of the following amino acids? (21.6)
  a. threonine   **b.** serine
  c. cysteine

21.130 What are the possible codons for each of the following amino acids? (21.6)
  a. valine   **b.** arginine
  c. histidine

21.131 What is the amino acid for each of the following codons? (21.6)
  a. AAG   **b.** AUU   **c.** CGA

21.132 What is the amino acid for each of the following codons? (21.6)
  a. CAA   **b.** GGC   **c.** AAC

21.133 What is the anticodon on tRNA for each of the following codons in an mRNA? (21.6)
  a. AGC   **b.** UAU   **c.** CCA

21.134 What is the anticodon on tRNA for each of the following codons in an mRNA? (21.6)
  a. GUG   **b.** CCC   **c.** GAA

℞ Clinical Applications

21.135 Endorphins are polypeptides that reduce pain. What is the amino acid order for the endorphin leucine enkephalin (leu-enkephalin), which has the following mRNA? (21.5, 21.6)

    5′ AUG UAC GGU GGA UUU CUA UAA 3′

21.136 Endorphins are polypeptides that reduce pain. What is the amino acid order for the endorphin methionine enkephalin (met-enkephalin), which has the following mRNA? (21.5, 21.6)

    5′ AUG UAC GGU GGA UUU AUG UAA 3′

CHALLENGE QUESTIONS

The following groups of questions are related to the topics in this chapter. However, they do not all follow the chapter order, and they require you to combine concepts and skills from several sections. These questions will help you increase your critical thinking skills and prepare for your next exam.

21.137 Oxytocin is a peptide that contains nine amino acids. How many nucleotides would be found in the mRNA for this peptide? (21.6)

21.138 A polypeptide contains 36 amino acids. How many nucleotides would be found in the mRNA for this polypeptide? (21.6)

21.139 What is the difference between a DNA virus and a retrovirus? (21.9)

21.140 Why are there no base pairs in DNA between adenine and guanine or thymine and cytosine? (21.3)

21.141 Match each of the following processes (**1** to **5**) with one of the items (**a** to **e**): (21.4, 21.5, 21.6)

(1) replication of DNA   (2) transcription
(3) translation   (4) recombinant DNA
(5) reverse transcription

a. Okazaki fragments
b. mRNA is synthesized from nuclear DNA
c. viruses
d. restriction enzymes
e. tRNA molecules bond to anticodons

21.142 Match each of the following processes (**1** to **5**) with one of the items (**a** to **e**): (21.4, 21.5, 21.6)

(1) replication of DNA   (2) transcription
(3) translation   (4) recombinant DNA
(5) reverse transcription

a. amino acids are linked together
b. RNA template is used to synthesize DNA
c. helicase unwinds DNA
d. genetic information is transferred from DNA
e. sticky ends join new DNA segment

ANSWERS

Answers to Selected Questions and Problems

21.1 a. pyrimidine   b. pyrimidine

21.3 a. DNA   b. both DNA and RNA

21.5 deoxyadenosine monophosphate (dAMP), deoxythymidine monophosphate (dTMP), deoxycytidine monophosphate (dCMP), and deoxyguanosine monophosphate (dGMP)

21.7 a. nucleoside   b. nucleoside
       c. nucleoside   d. nucleotide

21.9 a. (3) both DNA and RNA
      b. (2) RNA only
      c. (1) DNA only
      d. (3) both DNA and RNA

21.11

21.13

21.15 The nucleotides in nucleic acid polymers are held together by phosphodiester linkages between the 3' OH group of a sugar (ribose or deoxyribose) and a phosphate group on the 5' carbon of another sugar.

21.17 –sugar–phosphate–sugar–phosphate–

21.19 the free 5' phosphate on the 5' carbon of ribose or deoxyribose of a nucleic acid

21.21

21.23 Structural features of DNA include that it is shaped like a double helix, it contains a sugar–phosphate backbone, the nitrogen-containing bases are hydrogen bonded between strands, and the strands run in opposite directions. A forms two hydrogen bonds to T, and G forms three hydrogen bonds to C.

21.25 The two DNA strands are held together by hydrogen bonds between the complementary bases in each strand.

21.27 a. 3' T T T T T T 5'   b. 3' C C C C C C 5'
      c. 3' T C A G G T C C A 5'
      d. 3' G A C A T A T G C A A T 5'

21.29 The enzyme helicase unwinds the DNA helix so that the parent DNA strands can be replicated into daughter DNA strands.

21.31 Once the DNA strands separate, the DNA polymerase pairs each of the bases with its complementary base and produces two exact copies of the original DNA.

21.33 a. (2) helicase **b.** (3) primase
c. (4) replication fork **d.** (1) lagging strand

21.35 a. 5′ CGAGGTAC 3′ **b.** No

21.37 ribosomal RNA, messenger RNA, and transfer RNA

21.39 A ribosome consists of a small subunit and a large subunit that contain rRNA combined with proteins.

21.41 In transcription, the sequence of nucleotides on a DNA template (one strand) is used to produce the base sequence of a messenger RNA.

21.43 5′ GGC UUC CAA GUG 3′

21.45 In eukaryotic cells, genes contain sections called exons that code for proteins and sections called introns that do not code for proteins.

21.47 5′ GGC GGA UCG 3′

21.49 A transcription factor is a molecule that binds to DNA and regulates transcription.

21.51 An activator binds to transcription factors and increases the rate of RNA transcription.

21.53 A codon is a three-base sequence in mRNA that codes for a specific amino acid in a protein.

21.55 a. leucine (Leu) **b.** serine (Ser)
c. glycine (Gly) **d.** arginine (Arg)

21.57 When AUG is the first codon, it signals the start of protein synthesis. Thereafter, AUG codes for methionine.

21.59 A codon is a base triplet in the mRNA. An anticodon is the complementary triplet on a tRNA for a specific amino acid.

21.61 initiation, chain elongation, and termination

21.63 a. Thr–Thr–Thr, TTT
b. Phe–Pro–Phe–Pro, FPFP
c. Tyr–Gly–Arg–Cys, YGRC

21.65 The new amino acid is joined by a peptide bond to the growing peptide chain. The ribosome moves to the next codon, which attaches to a tRNA carrying the next amino acid.

21.67 a. 5′ CGA AAA GUU UUU 3′
b. GCU, UUU, CAA, AAA
c. Arg–Lys–Val–Phe, RKVF

21.69 a. 5′AAA CAC UUG GUU GUG GAC 3′
b. Lys–His–Leu–Val–Val–Asp, KHLVVD

21.71 In a point mutation, a base in DNA is replaced by a different base.

21.73 In a deletion mutation caused by the deletion of a base, all the codons from the mutation onward are changed, which changes the order of amino acids in the rest of the polypeptide chain.

21.75 The normal triplet TTT forms a codon AAA, which codes for lysine. The mutation TTC forms a codon AAG, which also codes for lysine. There is no effect on the amino acid sequence.

21.77 a. Thr–Ser–Arg–Val
b. Thr–Thr–Arg–Val
c. Thr–Ser–Gly–Val
d. Thr — STOP. Protein synthesis would terminate early. If this occurs early in the formation of the polypeptide, the resulting protein will probably be nonfunctional.
e. The new protein will contain the sequence Asp–Ile–Thr–Gly.
f. The new protein will contain the sequence His–His–Gly.

21.79 a. GCC and GCA both code for alanine.
b. A vital ionic interaction in the tertiary structure of hemoglobin cannot be formed when the polar glutamic acid is replaced by valine, which is nonpolar. The resulting hemoglobin is malformed and less capable of carrying oxygen.

21.81 *E. coli* bacterial cells contain several small circular plasmids of DNA that can be isolated easily. After the recombinant DNA is formed, *E. coli* multiply rapidly, producing many copies of the recombinant DNA in a relatively short time.

21.83 *E. coli* can be soaked in a detergent solution that disrupts the plasma membrane and releases the cell contents, including the plasmids, which are collected.

21.85 When a gene has been obtained using a restriction enzyme, it is mixed with plasmids that have been cut by the same enzyme. When mixed together, the sticky ends of the DNA fragments bond with the sticky ends of the plasmid DNA to form a recombinant DNA.

21.87 In DNA fingerprinting, restriction enzymes cut a sample DNA into fragments, which are sorted by size using gel electrophoresis. A radioactive probe that adheres to specific DNA sequences exposes an X-ray film and creates a pattern of dark and light bands called a DNA fingerprint.

21.89 The bold sections represent the "sticky ends" of the cleaved bases.

5′ AA **CGTT** 3′
3′ **TTGC** AA 5′

21.91 a. 3′ CCGA 5′ **b.** 3′ TTACGC 5′
c. 3′ AAGGCT 5′

21.93 DNA or RNA, but not both

21.95 a. A viral RNA is used to synthesize a viral DNA to produce the proteins for the protein coat, which allows the virus to replicate and leave the cell.
b. retrovirus

21.97 Nucleoside analogs such as AZT and ddI are similar to the nucleosides required to make viral DNA in reverse transcription. However, they interfere with the ability of the DNA to form and thereby disrupt the life cycle of the HIV virus.

21.99 Estrogen receptors are transcription factors that bind to DNA and increase the production of mammary cells, which can lead to mutations and cancer.

21.101 Tamoxifen blocks the binding of estrogen to the estrogen receptor, which prevents binding and activation of the gene.

21.103 a. 5′ ACC UUA AUA GAC GAG AAG CGC 3′
b. Thr–Leu–Ile–Asp–Glu–Lys–Arg, TLIDEKR
c. There is no change, Asp is still the fourth amino acid residue.

21.105 a.

Parent strand:	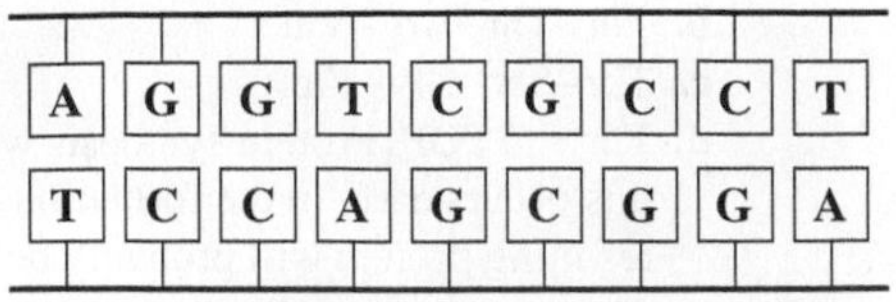 A	G	G	T	C	G	C	C	T
New strand:	T	C	C	A	G	C	G	G	A

b.

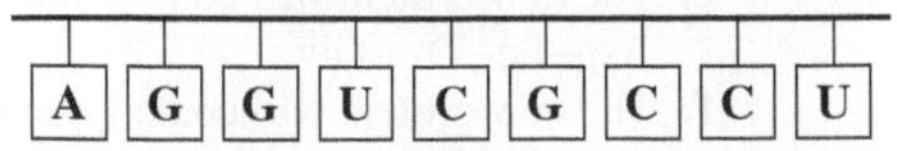

A	G	G	U	C	G	C	C	U

c. Arg — Ser — Pro

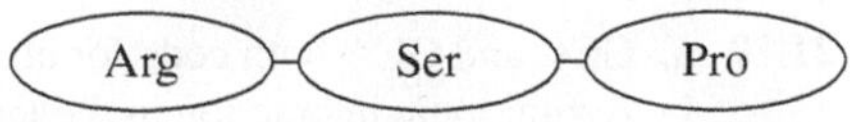

21.107 a. pyrimidine   **b.** purine
     c. pyrimidine   **d.** purine
     e. pyrimidine

21.109 a. thymine and deoxyribose
     b. adenine and ribose
     c. cytosine and ribose
     d. guanine and deoxyribose

21.111 They are both pyrimidines, but thymine has a methyl group.

21.113

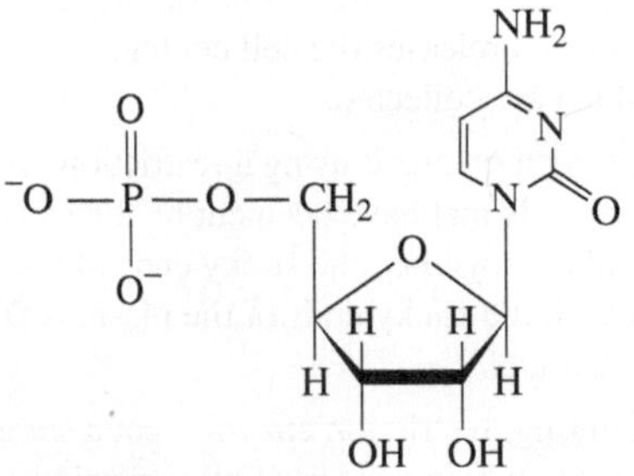

21.115 They are both polymers of nucleotides connected through phosphodiester linkages between alternating sugar and phosphate groups, with bases extending out from each sugar.

21.117 28% T, 22% G, and 22% C

21.119 two

21.121 a. 3′ C T G A A T C C G 5′
     b. 5′ A C G T T T G A T C G A 3′
     c. 3′ T A G C T A G C T A G C 5′

21.123 DNA polymerase synthesizes the leading strand continuously in the 5′ to 3′ direction. The lagging strand is synthesized in small segments called Okazaki fragments because it must grow in the 3′ to 5′ direction and DNA polymerase can only work in the 5′ to 3′ direction.

21.125 One strand of the parent DNA is found in each of the two copies of the daughter DNA molecule.

21.127 a. tRNA   **b.** rRNA   **c.** mRNA

21.129 a. ACU, ACC, ACA, and ACG
     b. UCU, UCC, UCA, UCG, AGU, and AGC
     c. UGU and UGC

21.131 a. lysine   **b.** isoleucine   **c.** arginine

21.133 a. UCG   **b.** AUA   **c.** GGU

21.135 START–Tyr–Gly–Gly–Phe–Leu–STOP

21.137 Three nucleotides are needed to code for each amino acid, plus the start and stop codons consisting of three nucleotides each, which makes a minimum total of 33 nucleotides.

21.139 A DNA virus attaches to a cell and injects viral DNA that uses the host cell to produce copies of the DNA to make viral RNA. A retrovirus injects viral RNA from which complementary DNA is produced by reverse transcription.

21.141 a. (1) replication of DNA
     b. (2) transcription
     c. (5) reverse transcription
     d. (4) recombinant DNA
     e. (3) translation

CI.41 Aromasin is a drug that is used to inhibit the activity of the enzyme aromatase (estrogen synthetase). In the ovaries and mammary glands, aromatase converts testosterone to estrogen. Aromasin is used to treat breast cancer because it binds irreversibly to the active site of the enzyme, preventing the synthesis of estrogen and slowing the growth of estrogen-related cancers. Aromasin has the molecular formula $C_{20}H_{24}O_2$. (7.5, 12.5, 13.1, 14.1, 17.6, 20.1, 20.4)

Aromasin

a. What are the functional groups in aromasin?
b. What are the functional groups in testosterone?
c. What are the functional groups in estrogen?
d. Why is the enzyme that converts testosterone to estrogen called aromatase?
e. Why would aromasin compete with testosterone, the precursor of estrogen?
f. What is the molar mass of aromasin?
g. If one tablet contains 25 mg of aromasin and there are 30 tablets in a package, how many moles of aromasin are in the package?

Testosterone $\xrightarrow{\text{Aromatase}}$ Estrogen

CI.42 Thalassemia is an inherited genetic mutation that limits the production of the beta chain needed for the formation of hemoglobin. If low levels of the beta chain are produced, there is a shortage of red blood cells (anemia). As a result, the body does not have sufficient amounts of oxygen. In one form of thalassemia, a single nucleotide is deleted in the DNA that codes for the beta chain. This mutation involves the deletion of thymine (T) from section 91 in the following informational strand of normal DNA: (21.4, 21.5, 21.6, 21.7, 21.8)

89	90	91	92	93	94
AGT	GAG	CTG	CAC	TGT	GAC A ...

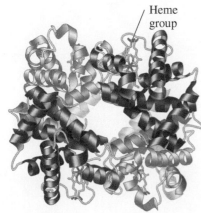

The ribbon structure of hemoglobin shows the four polypeptide subunits; two (orange) are α-chains and two (red) are β-chains. The heme groups (green) in the four subunits bind oxygen.

a. Write the complementary (template) strand for this normal DNA segment.
b. Write the mRNA sequence from normal DNA using the template strand in part **a**.
c. What amino acids are placed in the beta chain by this portion of mRNA?
d. What is the order of nucleotides in the mutation?
e. Write the template strand for the mutated DNA segment.
f. Write the mRNA sequence from the mutated DNA segment using the template strand in part **e**.
g. What amino acids are placed in the beta chain by the mutated DNA segment?
h. What type of mutation occurs in this form of thalassemia?
i. How might the properties of this segment of the beta chain be different from the properties of the normal protein?
j. How might the level of structure in hemoglobin be affected if beta chains are not produced?

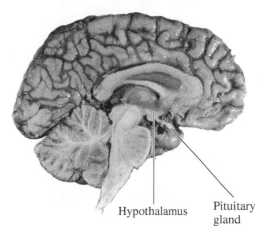

The hypothalamus secretes GnRF.

Use the following information for CI.43 and CI.44:
In response to signals from the nervous system, the hypothalamus secretes a polypeptide hormone known as gonadotropin-releasing factor (GnRF), which stimulates the pituitary gland to release other hormones into the bloodstream. Two of these hormones are luteinizing hormone (LH) and follicle-stimulating hormone (FSH).

The mRNA for the GnRF contains the codon sequence: 5' GAA CAC UGG UCC UAU GGC CUU AGG CCA GGA 3' (19.1, 19.3, 19.4, 20.5, 21.6, 21.7)

CI.43 a. Write the three-letter abbreviations for the sequence of amino acid residues in the decapeptide GnRF.
b. Write the one-letter abbreviations for the decapeptide GnRF.
c. If the fourth triplet UCC is changed to UUC, what type of mutation has occurred in the mRNA?
d. What is the change in the amino acid sequence in the mutated GnRF?
e. How could the tertiary structure and biological behavior of the mutated GnRF change?
f. When the level of LH or FSH is high in the bloodstream, the hypothalamus stops secreting GnRF. What type of regulation of proteins does this represent?

CI.44 Use the amino acid sequence you determined in CI.43 for the GnRF to answer the following: (19.1, 19.2, 19.3, 19.4)
  a. What amino acid is the N-terminus?
  b. What amino acid is the C-terminus?
  c. Which amino acids in GnRF are nonpolar?
  d. Which amino acids in GnRF are polar neutral?
  e. Draw the condensed structural formulas for the acidic amino acids at physiological pH.
  f. Draw the condensed structural formulas for the basic amino acids at physiological pH.

CI.45 A segment of the DNA template from BRCA1 mutated gene has the nucleotide sequence: 3′ A C A T A T T T T G C A A A T T T T G C A T G C 5′ (21.5, 21.6, 21.7)
  a. Write the corresponding section of mRNA produced from the segment of the BRCA1 mutated gene.
  b. What are the tRNA anticodons?
  c. Write the three-letter abbreviations for the amino acid residues in the peptide for this segment.

CI.46 A segment of the DNA template from BRCA2 mutated gene has the nucleotide sequence: 3′ T T C A A A G A G C A A G G G C T G A C T C T G 5′ (21.5, 21.6, 21.7)
  a. Write the corresponding section of mRNA produced from the segment of the BRCA2 mutated gene.
  b. What are the tRNA anticodons?
  c. Write the three-letter abbreviations for the amino acid residues in the peptide for this segment.

ANSWERS

CI.41 **a.** ketone, alkene, cycloalkene
  b. alkene, cycloalkene, alcohol, ketone
  c. phenol, alcohol
  d. The enzyme aromatase converts a six-carbon cycloalkene into an aromatic ring.
  e. Aromasin has a steroid structure similar to that of testosterone, which binds with aromatase at the active site.
  f. 296.4 g/mole
  g. 2.5×10^{-3} mole

CI.43 **a.** Glu–His–Trp–Ser–Tyr–Gly–Leu–Arg–Pro–Gly
  b. EHWSYGLRRPG
  c. a point mutation
  d. serine is replaced with phenylalanine

  e. Serine has a polar —OH group, whereas phenylalanine is nonpolar. The polar serine would have been on the outside of the normal peptide, whereas the phenylalanine will move to the inside of the mutated GnRF. This could change the tertiary structure of the decapeptide, and possibly cause a loss in biological activity.
  f. feedback control

CI.45 **a.** 5′ UGU AUA AAA CGU UUA AAA CGU ACG 3′
  b. ACA UAU UUU GCA AAU UUU GCA UGC
  c. Cys–Ile–Lys–Arg–Leu–Lys–Arg–Thr

22

Metabolic Pathways for Carbohydrates

PHILIP, WHO IS 8 MONTHS OLD, WAS BROUGHT TO
the hepatology unit with symptoms that included convulsions, lethargy, difficulty breathing, and diarrhea. Blood tests indicated that Philip had very low blood glucose, low blood pH, high lactate levels, and high liver glycogen. During examination, Barbara, a clinical lipid specialist, noted that Philip was small for his age, had a doll-like face from fat deposits, and a very large liver causing an extended abdomen. Because of his characteristic doll-like face and large amount of glycogen in his liver, Philip was diagnosed with a glycogen storage disease type I (GSD I), also known as *von Gierke's disease*, in which a genetic disorder produces a defective enzyme *glucose-6-phosphatase*. Without this enzyme, glucose-6-phosphate cannot be degraded to glucose but is stored as glycogen in large amounts in the liver.

CAREER Hepatology Nurse

Hepatology nursing is a specialty of nursing that emphasizes liver health, prevention of illness, and the care of clients with liver-related health problems that can have viral, genetic, and metabolic causes.

The hepatology nurse provides care for patients with liver-related conditions in clinics, outreach centers, or hospitals. Nursing care involves diagnosing illnesses, ordering and analyzing laboratory tests, developing appropriate treatment plans, providing patient education, and giving instruction in preventative care. In addition, a hepatology nurse may be responsible for documenting patient medical records, clinical research, and drug testing.

When we eat food, the polysaccharides, lipids, and proteins are digested to smaller molecules that can be absorbed into the cells of our body. As the glucose, fatty acids, and amino acids are broken down further, the energy is transferred to molecules in our cells such as adenosine triphosphate (ATP). Our cells use the energy stored in ATP when they do work such as contracting muscles, synthesizing large molecules, sending nerve impulses, and moving substances across cell membranes.

All the chemical reactions that take place in cells to break down or build molecules are known as *metabolism*. A *metabolic pathway* is a series of linked reactions each catalyzed by a specific enzyme. In this and the following chapters, we will look at these pathways and the way they produce energy and cellular compounds.

CHAPTER READINESS*

⚛ CORE CHEMISTRY SKILLS

- Identifying D- and L-Fischer Projections (15.2)
- Describing Enzyme Action (20.1)
- Classifying Enzymes (20.2)
- Identifying Factors Affecting Enzyme Activity (20.3)
- Describing the Role of Cofactors (20.6)

*These Core Chemistry Skills from previous chapters are listed here for your review as you proceed to the new material in this chapter.

LEARNING GOAL

Describe the three stages of catabolism, the structure of ATP, and the role of ATP.

22.1 Metabolism and Energy

The term **metabolism** refers to all the chemical reactions that provide energy and the substances required for continued cell growth. There are two types of metabolic reactions: *catabolic* and *anabolic*. In **catabolic reactions**, complex molecules are broken down to small ones with an accompanying release of energy. In **anabolic reactions**, energy in the cell is used to join small molecules to build large ones. We can think of catabolism as consisting of three stages (see Figure 22.1).

Stage 1 Catabolism begins with the processes of **digestion** in which enzymes in the digestive tract hydrolyze large molecules into smaller ones. The polysaccharides break down to monosaccharides, fats break down to glycerol and fatty acids, and the proteins yield amino acids. These digestion products diffuse into the bloodstream for transport to cells.

Stage 2 Within the cells, catabolic reactions continue as the digestion products are broken down further to yield two- and three-carbon compounds such as pyruvate and acetyl CoA.

Stage 3 The major production of energy takes place in the mitochondria, as the two-carbon acetyl group is oxidized in the citric acid cycle, which produces reduced coenzymes NADH, NADPH, and FADH₂. As long as the cells have oxygen, the hydrogen ions and electrons from the reduced coenzymes are transferred to electron transport to synthesize ATP.

Stages of Catabolism

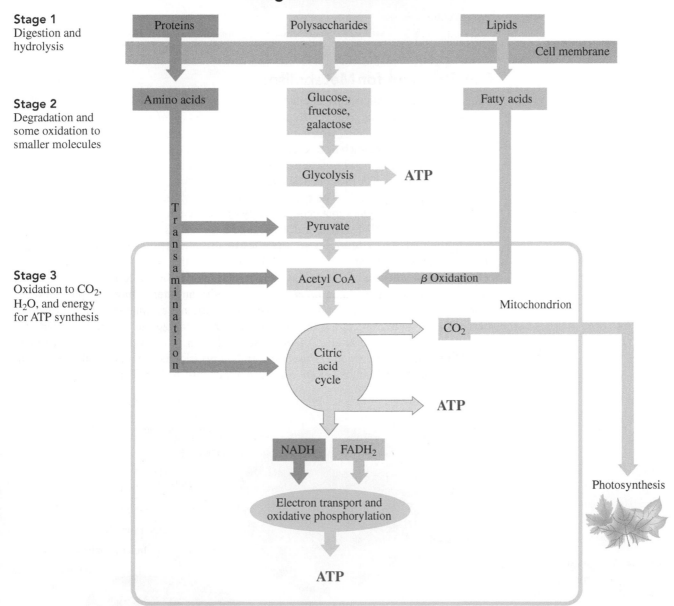

FIGURE 22.1 ▶ In the three stages of catabolism, large molecules from foods are digested and degraded to give smaller molecules that can be oxidized to produce energy.

Q Where is most of the ATP energy produced in the cells?

▶SAMPLE PROBLEM 22.1 Metabolism

Identify each of the following as catabolic or anabolic:

a. digestion of lipids
b. synthesis of lactase
c. hydrolysis of sucrose
d. synthesis of adenine monophosphate from adenine, ribose, and phosphate

SOLUTION

a. The breakdown of large molecules involves catabolic reactions.
b. The synthesis of large molecules involves anabolic reactions.
c. The breakdown of sucrose to smaller molecules is a catabolic reaction.
d. The combination of small molecules to give a large molecule is an anabolic reaction.

STUDY CHECK 22.1

Identify the oxidation of glucose to CO_2 and H_2O as catabolic or anabolic.

ANSWER

catabolic

Cell Structure for Metabolism

To understand the relationships among metabolic reactions, we need to look at where these metabolic reactions take place in the cells of plants and animals. The cells in plants and animals are *eukaryotic* cells, which have a nucleus that contains DNA (see Figure 22.2). Single-celled organisms such as bacteria are *prokaryotic* cells, which have no nucleus.

In animals, a *cell membrane* separates the materials inside the cell from the aqueous environment surrounding the cell. The *nucleus* contains the genes that control DNA replication and protein synthesis. The **cytosol**, the fluid part of the cell, is an aqueous solution of electrolytes and enzymes that catalyze many of the chemical reactions in the cell.

Within the cytosol are small structures called *organelles* that carry out specific functions in the cell. The *ribosomes* are the sites of protein synthesis. *Lysosomes* contain enzymes that break down recyclable cellular structures that are no longer needed by the cell. The **mitochondria** are the energy-producing factories of the cells. A mitochondrion has an outer membrane and an inner membrane, with an intermembrane space between them. The fluid section surrounded by the inner membrane is called the *matrix*. Enzymes located in the matrix and along the inner membrane catalyze the oxidation of carbohydrates, fats, and amino acids. All of these oxidation pathways eventually produce CO_2, H_2O, and energy, which are used to form energy-rich compounds. Table 22.1 summarizes some of the functions of the cellular components in animal cells.

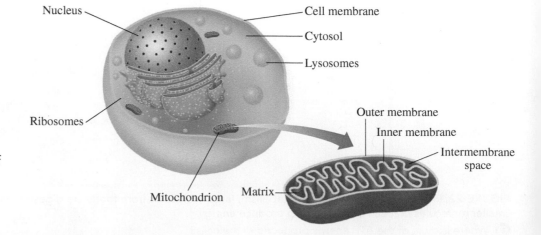

FIGURE 22.2 ▶ The diagram illustrates the major components of a typical eukaryotic cell of animals and plants.

Ⓠ What is the function of the mitochondrion in a cell?

TABLE 22.1 Functions of Components in Animal Cells

Component	Description and Function
Cell membrane	Separates the contents of a cell from the external environment and contains structures that communicate with other cells
Cytosol	Is the fluid part of the cytoplasm that contains enzymes for many of the cell's chemical reactions
Lysosome	Contains hydrolytic enzymes that digest and recycle old cell structures
Mitochondrion	Contains the structures for the synthesis of ATP from energy-producing reactions
Nucleus	Contains genetic information for the replication of DNA and the synthesis of protein
Ribosome	Is the site of protein synthesis using mRNA templates

In our cells, the energy released from the oxidation of the food we eat is stored in the form of a "high-energy" compound called *adenosine triphosphate* (ATP). The **ATP** molecule is composed of the base adenine, a ribose sugar, and three phosphate groups (see Figure 22.3).

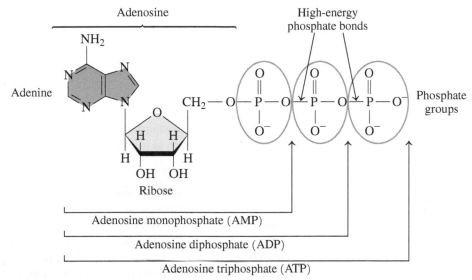

FIGURE 22.3 ▶ Adenosine triphosphate (ATP) hydrolyzes to form ADP and AMP, along with a release of energy.

◉ How many phosphate groups are in adenosine monophosphate (AMP)?

Hydrolysis of ATP Yields Energy

Adenosine triphosphate undergoes hydrolysis, which breaks one of its phosphodiester linkages, to yield adenosine diphosphate (**ADP**), an inorganic phosphate group HPO_4^{2-}, abbreviated P_i, and energy needed for cellular metabolism. The hydrolysis of ATP molecules can provide 7.3 kcal/mole (31 kJ/mole).

$$ATP \longrightarrow ADP + P_i + 7.3 \text{ kcal/mole (31 kJ/mole)}$$

We can draw the hydrolysis of ATP as an exothermic reaction on an energy curve.

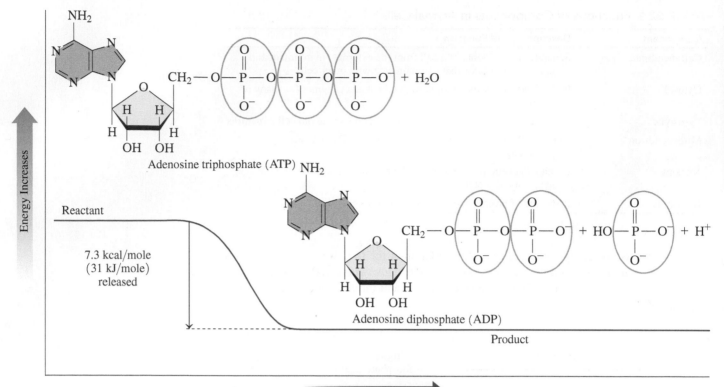

Energy Increases →

Reactant

7.3 kcal/mole
(31 kJ/mole)
released

Adenosine triphosphate (ATP)

Adenosine diphosphate (ADP)

Product

Progress of Reaction →

The ADP can also hydrolyze to form adenosine monophosphate (AMP) and an inorganic phosphate (P_i). The abbreviated equation is written as follows:

$$ADP \longrightarrow AMP + P_i + 7.3 \text{ kcal/mole } (31 \text{ kJ/mole})$$

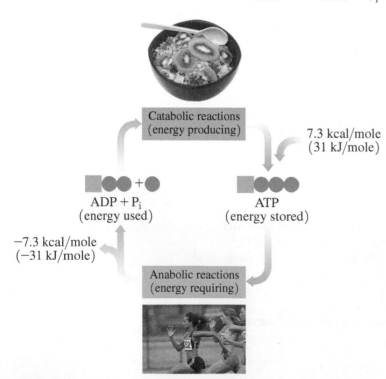

Catabolic reactions
(energy producing)

7.3 kcal/mole
(31 kJ/mole)

ADP + P_i
(energy used)

ATP
(energy stored)

−7.3 kcal/mole
(−31 kJ/mole)

Anabolic reactions
(energy requiring)

FIGURE 22.4 ▶ ATP, the energy-storage molecule, links energy-producing reactions with energy-requiring reactions in the cells.

Q What type of reaction provides energy for ATP synthesis?

Every time we contract muscles, move substances across cellular membranes, send nerve signals, or synthesize an enzyme, we use energy from ATP hydrolysis. In a cell that is doing work (anabolic processes), 1 to 2 million ATP molecules may be hydrolyzed in one second. The amount of ATP hydrolyzed in one day can be as much as our body mass, even though only about 1 g of ATP is present in all our cells at any given time.

When we take in food, the resulting catabolic reactions provide energy to regenerate ATP in our cells. Then 7.3 kcal/mole (31 kJ/mole) is used to synthesize ATP from ADP and P_i (see Figure 22.4).

$$ADP + P_i + 7.3 \text{ kcal/mole } (31 \text{ kJ/mole}) \longrightarrow ATP$$

ATP Drives Reactions

Many of the reactions essential to a cell do not proceed spontaneously, but they can be made to proceed by combining them with a reaction that releases energy for their use. Often the energy released by the hydrolysis of ATP is used to run a reaction that requires energy. For example, the glucose obtained from the digestion of carbohydrates must add a phosphate group to start its breakdown in the cell. However, the energy needed to add a phosphate group to glucose is 3.3 kcal/mole (14 kJ/mole), which means that the reaction does not occur spontaneously. When this energy-requiring reaction is paired with the energy-releasing hydrolysis of ATP, which releases 7.3 kcal/mole of energy, the reaction can take place.

ATP	$\longrightarrow$ ADP + P_i + 7.3 kcal/mole (31 kJ/mole)	Provides energy
Glucose + P_i + 3.3 kcal/mole (14 kJ/mole) $\longrightarrow$	glucose-6-phosphate	Requires energy
Overall: ATP + glucose	$\longrightarrow$ ADP + glucose-6-phosphate + 4.0 kcal/mole (17 kJ/mole)	

▶SAMPLE PROBLEM 22.2 ATP and Energy

The reaction of glutamate (Glu) with ammonia (NH_3) produces the amino acid glutamine (Gln). The reaction requires 3.4 kcal/mole.

a. Is the formation of glutamine a catabolic or an anabolic reaction?
b. Write the equation for the formation of glutamine (Gln) including the energy.
c. Write the equation for the hydrolysis of ATP including the energy.
d. Write the overall equation for the combined reactions including the net energy change.

SOLUTION

a. anabolic
b. Glu + NH_3 + 3.4 kcal/mole $\longrightarrow$ Gln
c. ATP $\longrightarrow$ ADP + P_i + 7.3 kcal/mole
d. Glu + NH_3 + ATP $\longrightarrow$ Gln + ADP + P_i + 3.9 kcal/mole

STUDY CHECK 22.2

Why are anabolic reactions that require energy coupled with the hydrolysis of a high-energy compound such as ATP?

ANSWER

The hydrolysis of a high-energy compound such as ATP provides energy to drive reactions that require energy.

 # Chemistry Link to **Health**

ATP Energy and Ca^{2+} Needed to Contract Muscles

Our muscles consist of thousands of parallel fibers. Within these muscle fibers are filaments composed of two kinds of proteins, myosin and actin. Arranged in alternating rows, the thick filaments of the protein myosin overlap the thin filaments containing the protein actin. During muscle contraction, the thin filaments (actin) slide inward over the thick filaments (myosin), which shortens the muscle fibers.

The calcium ion, Ca^{2+}, and ATP play an important role in muscle contraction. An increase in the Ca^{2+} concentration in the muscle fibers causes the filaments to slide, whereas a decrease stops the process. In a relaxed muscle, the Ca^{2+} concentration is low. When a nerve impulse reaches the muscle, the calcium channels in the membrane surrounding the muscle fibers open to allow Ca^{2+} to flow into the fluid surrounding the filaments. The muscle contracts as myosin binds to actin and pulls the filaments inward. The energy for the contraction is provided by the hydrolysis of ATP to ADP + P_i.

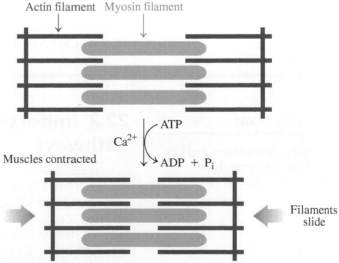

Muscles contract when myosin binds to actin.

Muscle contraction continues as long as both ATP and Ca^{2+} levels are high around the filaments. When the nerve impulse ends, the calcium channels close. The Ca^{2+} concentration decreases as energy from ATP pumps the remaining Ca^{2+} out of the filaments, back across the membrane, causing the muscle to relax. In *rigor mortis*, Ca^{2+} concentration remains high within the muscle fibers, causing a continued state of rigidity. After approximately 72 h, the Ca^{2+} concentration decreases due to cellular deterioration, and the muscles relax.

Muscle contraction uses the energy from the breakdown of ATP.

QUESTIONS AND PROBLEMS

22.1 Metabolism and Energy

LEARNING GOAL Describe the three stages of catabolism, the structure of ATP, and the role of ATP.

22.1 What stage of catabolism involves the digestion of polysaccharides?

22.2 What stage of catabolism involves the conversion of small molecules to CO_2, H_2O, and energy for the synthesis of ATP?

22.3 What is meant by a catabolic reaction in metabolism?

22.4 What is meant by an anabolic reaction in metabolism?

22.5 Identify each of the following as a catabolic or an anabolic reaction:
a. synthesis of lipids from glycerol and fatty acids
b. glucose adds P_i to form glucose-6-phosphate
c. hydrolysis of ATP to ADP and P_i
d. digestion of proteins in the stomach

22.6 Identify each of the following as a catabolic or an anabolic reaction:
a. digestion of fats to fatty acids and glycerol
b. hydrolysis of proteins into amino acids
c. synthesis of nucleic acids from nucleotides
d. glucose and galactose form the disaccharide lactose

22.7 Why is ATP considered an energy-rich compound?

22.8 What is meant when we say that the hydrolysis of ATP is used to "drive" a reaction?

22.9 Phosphoenolpyruvate (PEP) is a high-energy compound that releases 14.8 kcal/mole of energy when it hydrolyzes to pyruvate and P_i. This reaction can be coupled with the synthesis of ATP from ADP and P_i.
a. Write an equation for the energy-releasing reaction of PEP.
b. Write an equation for the energy-requiring reaction that forms ATP.
c. Write the overall equation for the combined reaction including the net energy change.

22.10 The phosphorylation of glycerol to glycerol-3-phosphate requires 2.2 kcal/mole and is driven by the hydrolysis of ATP.
a. Write an equation for the energy-releasing reaction of ATP.
b. Write an equation for the energy-requiring reaction that forms glycerol-3-phosphate.
c. Write the overall equation for the combined reaction including the net energy change.

℞ Clinical Applications

22.11 A 185-lb person bicycling vigorously on a stationary bicycle uses 2100 kJ. If the molar mass of ATP is 507 g/mole, how many grams of ATP are hydrolyzed to provide this amount of energy?

22.12 A 185-lb person bicycling moderately on a stationary bicycle uses 1300 kJ. If the molar mass of ATP is 507 g/mole, how many grams of ATP are hydrolyzed to provide this amount of energy?

LEARNING GOAL

Describe the components and functions of the coenzymes NAD^+, $NADP^+$, FAD, and coenzyme A.

22.2 Important Coenzymes in Metabolic Pathways

Several metabolic reactions that extract energy from our food involve oxidation and reduction reactions. Therefore, we will review several important coenzymes in their oxidized and reduced forms. In chemistry, oxidation is often association with the loss of H atoms, whereas reduction is associated with the gain of H atoms. Often, we represent two H atoms as two hydrogen ions ($2H^+$) and two electrons ($2\,e^-$). In both types of reactions, coenzymes are required to carry the hydrogen ions and electrons from or to the reacting substrate. A coenzyme that gains hydrogen ions and electrons is reduced, whereas a coenzyme that loses hydrogen ions and electrons to a substrate is oxidized.

In general, oxidation reactions produce energy, and reduction reactions require energy. Table 22.2 summarizes the characteristics of oxidation and reduction.

⊗ **CORE CHEMISTRY SKILL**

Identifying Important Coenzymes in Metabolism

TABLE 22.2 Characteristics of Oxidation and Reduction in Metabolic Pathways

Oxidation	Reduction
Loss of electrons (e^-)	Gain of electrons (e^-)
Loss of hydrogen (H or H^+ and e^-)	Gain of hydrogen (H or H^+ and e^-)
Gain of oxygen	Loss of oxygen
Produces energy	Requires energy input

NAD^+

NAD^+ (nicotinamide adenine dinucleotide) is an important coenzyme in which the vitamin *niacin* provides the *nicotinamide* group, which is bonded to ribose and the nucleotide adenosine diphosphate (ADP) (see Figure 22.5). The oxidized form of NAD^+ undergoes reduction when a carbon atom in the nicotinamide ring reacts with 2H (two hydrogen ions and two electrons), leaving one H^+.

The NAD^+ coenzyme is required in dehydrogenation reactions that produce carbon–oxygen (C=O) double bonds, such as the oxidation of alcohols to aldehydes and ketones. An example of an oxidation–reduction reaction is the oxidation of ethanol in the liver to ethanal and the reduction of NAD^+ to $NADH + H^+$.

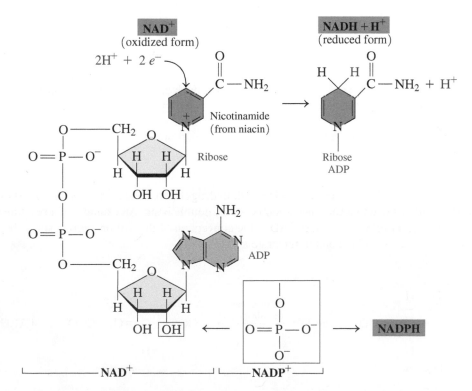

FIGURE 22.5 ▶ The coenzyme NAD^+ (nicotinamide adenine dinucleotide), which consists of adenosine diphosphate, nicotinamide from the vitamin niacin, and ribose, is reduced to $NADH + H^+$ by adding a hydrogen ion and two electrons to NAD^+. The coenzyme $NADP^+$ is similar to NAD^+ except that a 2' OH group is replaced by a phosphate. The reduced form of $NADP^+$ is NADPH.

❓ Why is the conversion of NAD^+ to NADH and H^+ called a reduction?

NADP$^+$ (nicotinamide adenine dinucleotide phosphate) is a coenzyme used in anabolic reactions, such as lipid and nucleic acid synthesis, which require a source of hydrogen ions and electrons. The coenzyme NADP$^+$ is similar to NAD$^+$ except that a 2' OH group is replaced by a phosphate group. The reduced form of NADP$^+$ is NADPH.

FAD

FAD (flavin adenine dinucleotide) is a coenzyme that contains the nucleotide adenosine diphosphate and riboflavin. Riboflavin, also known as vitamin B$_2$, consists of ribitol (a sugar alcohol) and flavin. The oxidized form of FAD undergoes reduction when the two nitrogen atoms in the flavin part of the FAD coenzyme react with two hydrogen atoms (2H$^+$ + 2 e^-), reducing FAD to FADH$_2$ (see Figure 22.6).

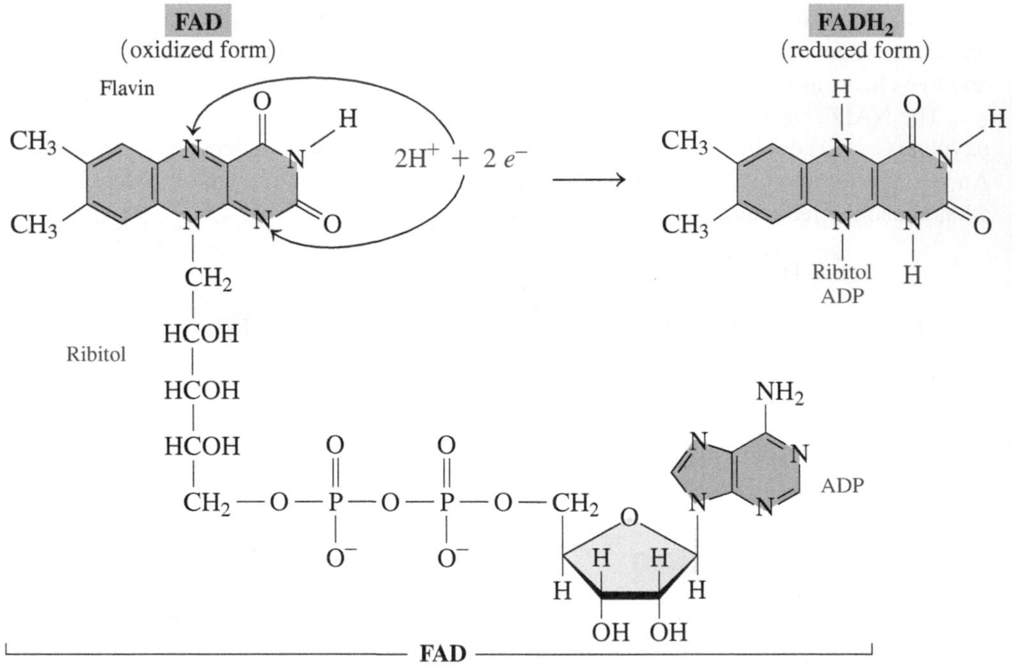

FIGURE 22.6 ▶ The coenzyme FAD (flavin adenine dinucleotide) made from riboflavin (vitamin B$_2$) and adenosine diphosphate is reduced to FADH$_2$ by adding two hydrogen atoms.

❓ What is the type of reaction in which FAD accepts hydrogen?

FAD is used as a coenzyme when a dehydrogenation reaction converts a carbon–carbon single bond to a carbon–carbon (C=C) double bond. An example of a reaction in the citric acid cycle that reduces FAD is the conversion of the carbon–carbon single bond in succinate to a double bond in fumarate and FADH$_2$.

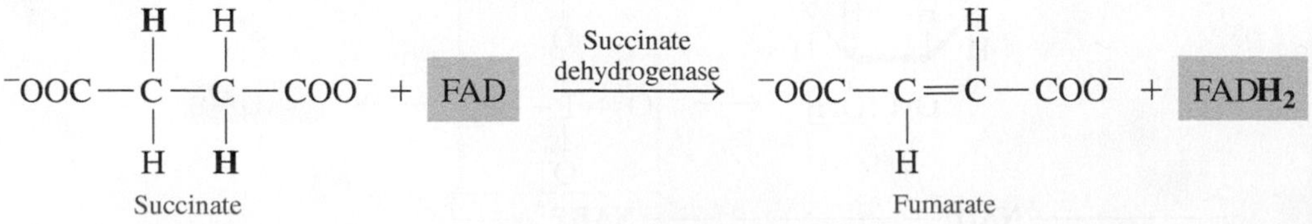

Coenzyme A

Coenzyme A (CoA) is made up of several components: pantothenic acid (vitamin B_5), phosphorylated ADP, and aminoethanethiol (see Figure 22.7).

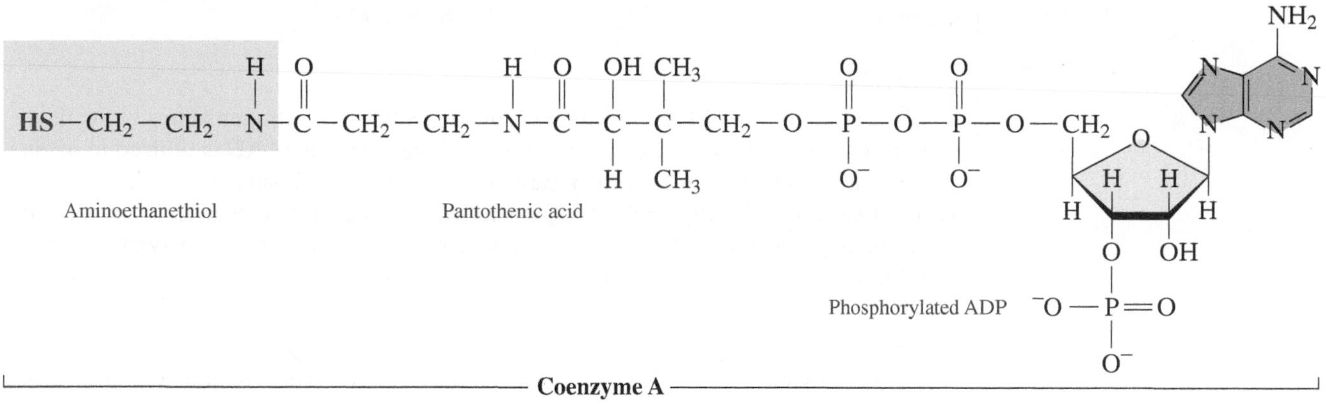

FIGURE 22.7 ▶ Coenzyme A is derived from a phosphorylated ADP and pantothenic acid bonded by an amide bond to aminoethanethiol, which contains the —SH reactive part of the molecule.

◉ What part of coenzyme A reacts with a two-carbon acetyl group?

An important function of coenzyme A is to prepare small acyl groups (represented by the letter A in the name), such as acetyl, for reactions with enzymes. The reactive feature of coenzyme A is the thiol group (—SH), which bonds to a two-carbon acetyl group to produce the energy-rich thioester **acetyl CoA**.

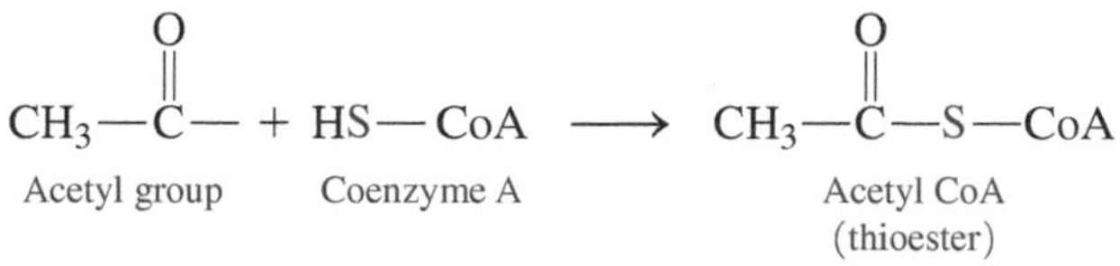

In biochemistry, several abbreviations are used for coenzyme A and acetyl coenzyme A. For discussions in this text, we will use CoA for coenzyme A and acetyl CoA when the acetyl group is bonded to the sulfur atom (—S—) in coenzyme A. In equations, we will show the —SH group in coenzyme A as HS—CoA.

Types of Metabolic Reactions

Many reactions within the cells are similar to the types of reactions in organic chemistry such as hydration, dehydration (condensation), hydrolysis, hydrogenation, oxidation, and reduction. In the laboratory, organic reactions typically require strong acids (low pH), high temperatures, and/or metallic catalysts. However, metabolic reactions take place at body temperature and physiological pH, only requiring enzymes and often a coenzyme. Table 22.3 gives some enzymes and coenzymes, as well as their metabolic reactions.

TABLE 22.3 Enzymes and Coenzymes in Metabolic Reactions

Reaction	Enzyme	Coenzyme
Oxidation	Dehydrogenase	NAD^+, $NADP^+$, FAD
Reduction	Dehydrogenase	$NADH + H^+$, $NADPH + H^+$, $FADH_2$
Hydration	Hydrase	
Dehydration	Dehydrase	
Rearrangement	Isomerase, epimerase	
Transfer of phosphate group	Phosphatase, kinase	ATP, GDP, ADP
Transfer of acetyl group	Acetyl CoA transferase	CoA
Decarboxylation	Decarboxylase	
Hydrolysis	Protease, lipase, synthetase	ADP, GDP

> ▶**SAMPLE PROBLEM 22.3 Coenzymes**
>
> Describe the reactive part of each of the following coenzymes and the way each participates in metabolic pathways:
>
> **a.** FAD   **b.** NAD^+
>
> **SOLUTION**
>
> **a.** The oxidized form of FAD undergoes reduction when two nitrogen atoms in the flavin part react with $2H^+$ and $2\ e^-$ to give $FADH_2$. The coenzyme FAD is utilized in oxidation reactions that produce carbon–carbon (C=C) double bonds.
> **b.** The oxidized form of NAD^+ undergoes reduction when a carbon atom in the nicotinamide part reacts with $2H^+$ and $2\ e^-$, to give NADH and H^+. The coenzyme NAD^+ is utilized in oxidation reactions that produce carbon–oxygen (C=O) double bonds.
>
> **STUDY CHECK 22.3**
>
> Describe the reactive part of coenzyme A and how it participates in metabolic reactions.
>
> **ANSWER**
>
> In coenzyme A, the thiol group (—SH) of aminoethanethiol combines with an acetyl group to form acetyl coenzyme A. The HS—CoA participates in the transfer of acyl groups, usually acetyl groups.

QUESTIONS AND PROBLEMS

22.2 Important Coenzymes in Metabolic Pathways

LEARNING GOAL Describe the components and functions of the coenzymes NAD^+, $NADP^+$, FAD, and coenzyme A.

22.13 Identify one or more coenzymes that contain each of the following components:
   a. pantothenic acid   **b.** niacin
   c. ribitol

22.14 Identify one or more coenzymes that contain each of the following components:
   a. riboflavin   **b.** adenine
   c. aminoethanethiol

22.15 Give the abbreviation for each of the following:
   a. the reduced form of NAD^+
   b. the oxidized form of $FADH_2$

22.16 Give the abbreviation for each of the following:
   a. the reduced form of FAD
   b. the oxidized form of NADPH

22.17 What coenzyme picks up hydrogen when a carbon–carbon double bond is formed?

22.18 What coenzyme picks up hydrogen when a carbon–oxygen double bond is formed?

LEARNING GOAL

Give the sites and products of the digestion of carbohydrates.

22.3 Digestion of Carbohydrates

In stage 1 of catabolism, foods undergo digestion, a process that converts large molecules to smaller ones that can be absorbed by the body.

Digestion of Carbohydrates

We begin the digestion of carbohydrates as soon as we chew food. Enzymes produced in the salivary glands hydrolyze some of the α-glycosidic bonds in amylose and amylopectin, producing maltose, glucose, and smaller polysaccharides called dextrins, which contain three to eight glucose units. After swallowing, the partially digested starches enter the acidic environment of our stomach, where the low pH stops further carbohydrate digestion (see Figure 22.8).

In the small intestine, which has a pH of about 8, enzymes produced in the pancreas hydrolyze the remaining dextrins to maltose and glucose. Then enzymes produced in the mucosal cells that line the small intestine hydrolyze maltose, lactose, and sucrose. The resulting monosaccharides are absorbed through the intestinal wall into the bloodstream, which carries them to the liver, where the hexoses fructose and galactose are converted to glucose. Glucose is the primary energy source for muscle contractions, red blood cells, and the brain.

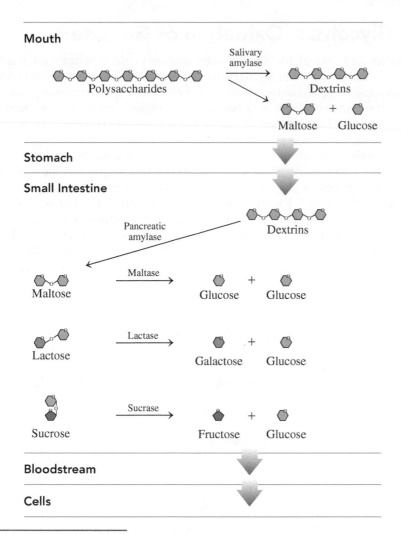

Mouth

Polysaccharides → (Salivary amylase) → Dextrins

Maltose + Glucose

Stomach

Small Intestine

Dextrins

(Pancreatic amylase)

Maltose → (Maltase) → Glucose + Glucose

Lactose → (Lactase) → Galactose + Glucose

Sucrose → (Sucrase) → Fructose + Glucose

Bloodstream

Cells

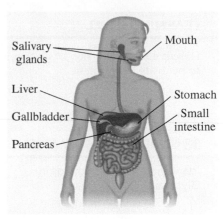

Carbohydrates begin digestion in the mouth, proteins in the stomach and small intestine, and lipids in the small intestine.

FIGURE 22.8 ▶ In stage 1 of catabolism, the digestion of carbohydrates begins in the mouth and is completed in the small intestine.

Q Why is there little or no digestion of carbohydrates in the stomach?

▶ **SAMPLE PROBLEM 22.4 Digestion of Carbohydrates**

Indicate the carbohydrate that undergoes digestion in each of the following sites:

a. mouth   **b.** stomach   **c.** small intestine

SOLUTION

a. starches amylose and amylopectin ($\alpha(1 \rightarrow 4)$-glycosidic bonds only)
b. essentially no digestion of carbohydrates   **c.** dextrins, maltose, sucrose, and lactose

STUDY CHECK 22.4

Describe the digestion of amylose, a polymer of glucose molecules joined by $\alpha(1 \rightarrow 4)$-glycosidic bonds.

ANSWER

The digestion of amylose begins in the mouth when salivary amylase hydrolyzes some of the $\alpha(1 \rightarrow 4)$-glycosidic bonds. In the small intestine, pancreatic amylase hydrolyzes more glycosidic bonds, and finally maltose is hydrolyzed by maltase to yield glucose.

QUESTIONS AND PROBLEMS

22.3 Digestion of Carbohydrates

LEARNING GOAL Give the sites and products of the digestion of carbohydrates.

22.19 What is the general type of reaction that occurs during the digestion of carbohydrates?

22.20 Why is α-amylase produced in the salivary glands and in the pancreas?

22.21 Complete the following equations by filling in the missing words:
a. _____ + H_2O ⟶ galactose + glucose
b. Sucrose + H_2O ⟶ _____ + _____
c. Maltose + H_2O ⟶ glucose + _____

22.22 Give the site and the enzyme for each of the reactions in problem 22.21.

22.4 Glycolysis: Oxidation of Glucose

The major source of energy for the body is the glucose produced when we digest the carbohydrates in our food or from glycogen, a polysaccharide stored in the liver and skeletal muscle. Glucose in the bloodstream enters our cells where it undergoes degradation in a pathway called *glycolysis*. Early organisms used glycolysis to produce energy from simple nutrients long before there was any oxygen in Earth's atmosphere. Glycolysis is an **anaerobic** process; no oxygen is required.

In **glycolysis**, a six-carbon glucose molecule is broken down to yield two molecules of three-carbon pyruvate. All the reactions in glycolysis take place in the cytosol of the cell where the enzymes for glycolysis are located. In the first five reactions (1 to 5), called the *energy-investing phase*, energy is obtained from the hydrolysis of two ATP, which is needed to form sugar phosphates (see Figure 22.9). In reactions 4 and 5, a six-carbon sugar phosphate is split to yield two molecules of three-carbon sugar phosphate. In the last five reactions (6 to 10), called the *energy-generating phase*, energy is obtained from the hydrolysis of the energy-rich phosphate compounds and used to synthesize four ATP.

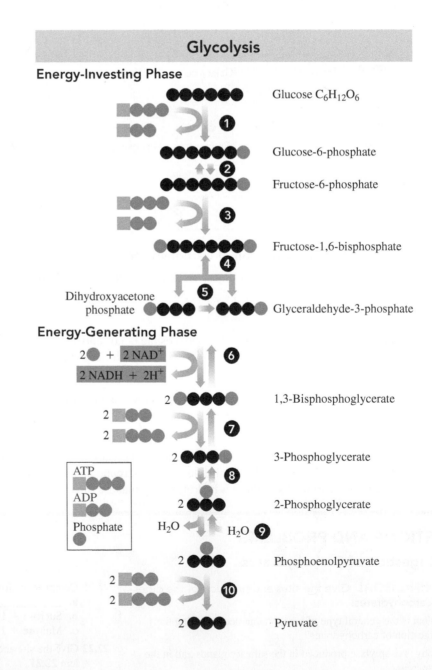

FIGURE 22.9 ▶ In glycolysis, the six-carbon glucose molecule is degraded to yield two three-carbon pyruvate molecules. A net of two ATP is produced along with two NADH.

❓ Where in the glycolysis pathway is glucose cleaved to yield two three-carbon compounds?

Energy-Investing Reactions: 1 to 5

As we describe the reactions in glycolysis, recall the names of enzymes that catalyze reactions as outlined in Table 22.3.

Reaction 1 Phosphorylation

In the initial reaction, a phosphate group is transferred from ATP to glucose producing glucose-6-phosphate and ADP. The enzyme that catalyzes this reaction is called a *hexokinase*, *hexo* because glucose is a hexose sugar and *kinase* because it uses the energy of ATP to transfer the phosphate group.

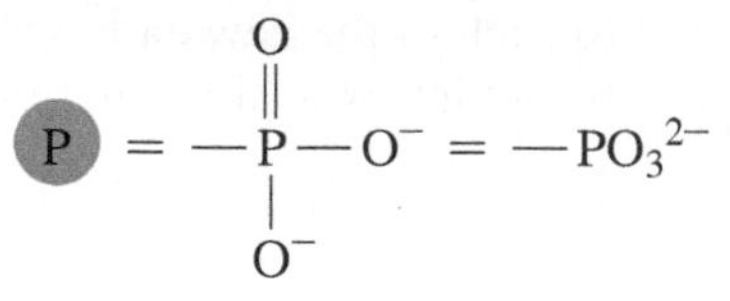

$$\text{P} = -\overset{\overset{\textstyle O}{\|}}{\underset{\underset{\textstyle O^-}{|}}{P}}-O^- = -PO_3{}^{2-}$$

Reaction 2 Isomerization

Glucose-6-phosphate, the aldose from reaction 1, is converted by *phosphoglucose isomerase* to fructose-6-phosphate, which is a ketose.

Reaction 3 Phosphorylation

The hydrolysis of another ATP provides a second phosphate group, which is transferred to fructose-6-phosphate producing fructose-1,6-bisphosphate. The word *bisphosphate* is used to show that the two phosphate groups are on different carbons in fructose and not connected to each other. This reaction is catalyzed by a second kinase enzyme called *phosphofructokinase*.

Reaction 4 Cleavage

Fructose-1,6-bisphosphate is split by *aldolase* into two three-carbon phosphate isomers: dihydroxyacetone phosphate and glyceraldehyde-3-phosphate.

Reaction 5 Isomerization

Because dihydroxyacetone phosphate is a ketone, it cannot react further. However, it undergoes isomerization by *triose phosphate isomerase* producing a second molecule of glyceraldehyde-3-phosphate, which can be oxidized. Now all six carbon atoms from glucose are contained in two identical triose phosphates.

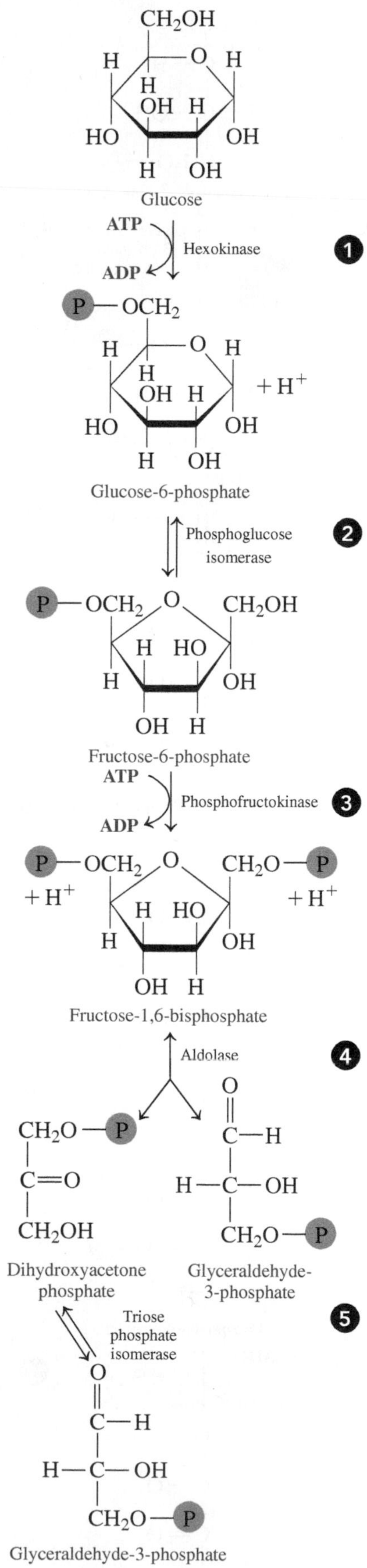

Glucose

ATP → Hexokinase → ADP ❶

Glucose-6-phosphate $+ H^+$

Phosphoglucose isomerase ❷

Fructose-6-phosphate

ATP → Phosphofructokinase → ADP ❸

Fructose-1,6-bisphosphate $+ H^+$

Aldolase ❹

Dihydroxyacetone phosphate   Glyceraldehyde-3-phosphate

Triose phosphate isomerase ❺

Glyceraldehyde-3-phosphate

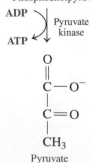

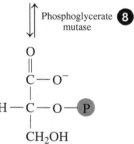

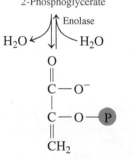

Energy-Generating Reactions: 6 to 10

In our discussion of glycolysis from this point, the two molecules of glyceraldehyde-3-phosphate produced in step 5 are undergoing the same reactions. For simplicity, we show the structures and reactions for only one three-carbon molecule for reactions 6 to 10.

Reaction 6 Oxidation and Phosphorylation

The aldehyde group of each glyceraldehyde-3-phosphate is oxidized by *glyceraldehyde-3-phosphate dehydrogenase* to a carboxyl group. The coenzyme NAD^+ is reduced to NADH and H^+. Then a phosphate group (P_i) is transferred to each of the new carboxyl groups to form two molecules of 1,3-bisphosphoglycerate, which is a high-energy compound.

Reaction 7 Phosphate Transfer

A phosphate group from each 1,3-bisphosphoglycerate is transferred to two ADP molecules by *phosphoglycerate kinase* yielding two molecules of the high-energy compound ATP. At this point in glycolysis, two ATP are produced, which balance the two ATP consumed in reactions 1 and 3.

Reaction 8 Isomerization

Two 3-phosphoglycerate molecules undergo isomerization by *phosphoglycerate mutase*, which moves the phosphate group from carbon 3 to carbon 2, yielding two molecules of 2-phosphoglycerate. The enzyme here is a specific type of isomerase called a *mutase* because the functional group merely shifts from one carbon to another.

Reaction 9 Dehydration

Each of the phosphoglycerate molecules undergoes dehydration (loss of water) by the enzyme *enolase* producing two phosphoenolpyruvate molecules, a high-energy compound.

Reaction 10 Phosphate Transfer

In a second direct substrate phosphorylation, phosphate groups from two phosphoenolpyruvate molecules are transferred by *pyruvate kinase* to yield two ADP, two pyruvate, and two ATP. Here, a fourth kinase enzyme is involved because a phosphate is transferred with ATP production.

Summary of Glycolysis

In the glycolysis pathway, a six-carbon glucose molecule is converted to two three-carbon pyruvates. Initially, two ATP are required to form fructose-1,6-bisphosphate. In later reactions (7 and 10), phosphate transfers produce a total of four ATP. Overall, glycolysis yields two ATP and two NADH when a glucose molecule is converted to two pyruvates.

$$C_6H_{12}O_6 + 2\,NAD^+ + 2\,ADP + 2P_i \longrightarrow 2CH_3\overset{\overset{\displaystyle O}{\|}}{-}C-COO^- + 2\,NADH + 2\,ATP + 4H^+ + 2H_2O$$

Glucose   Pyruvate

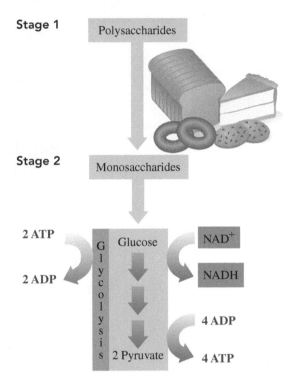

Glucose obtained from the digestion of polysaccharides is degraded in glycolysis to pyruvate.

▶**SAMPLE PROBLEM 22.5 Reactions in Glycolysis**

Identify each of the following reactions as an isomerization, phosphorylation, or dehydration:

a. A phosphate group is transferred to ADP to form ATP.
b. 3-Phosphoglycerate is converted to 2-phosphoglycerate.
c. A water molecule is removed from 2-phosphoglycerate.

SOLUTION

a. phosphorylation
b. isomerization
c. dehydration

STUDY CHECK 22.5

Indicate the reaction and enzyme that catalyzes each of the reactions in Sample Problem 22.5.

ANSWER

a. Phosphorylation in reaction 7 is catalyzed by phosphoglycerate kinase and in reaction 10 by pyruvate kinase.
b. Isomerization in reaction 8 is catalyzed by phosphoglycerate mutase.
c. Dehydration in reaction 9 is catalyzed by enolase.

Fructose and Galactose Enter Glycolysis

Other monosaccharides in our diet such as fructose and galactose also enter glycolysis, but first they must be converted to intermediates that can enter into the glycolytic pathway.

Fructose

In the muscles and kidneys, fructose is phosphorylated to fructose-6-phosphate, which enters glycolysis in reaction 3, where its movement through glycolysis is regulated by the enzyme phosphofructokinase. In the liver, fructose is converted to glyceraldehyde-3-phosphate, which enters glycolysis at reaction 6. Because this is after the main regulation at step 3, any fructose that enters the liver must continue through glycolysis.

Galactose

In a series of four enzymatic steps, galactose reacts with ATP to yield glucose-1-phosphate, which is converted to glucose-6-phosphate. Glucose-6-phosphate enters glycolysis at reaction 2.

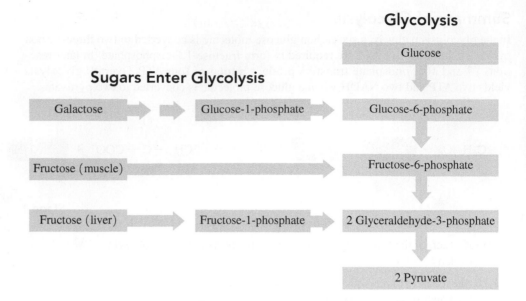

Galactose and fructose form intermediates that enter the glycolysis pathway to be metabolized.

Regulation of Glycolysis

Metabolic pathways such as glycolysis do not run at the same rates all the time. The amount of glucose that is broken down is controlled by the requirements in the cells for pyruvate, ATP, and other intermediates of glycolysis. Within the 10-step pathway of glycolysis, the three enzymatic reactions 1, 3, and 10 are irreversible. These irreversible reactions respond to the levels of ATP and other products.

Reaction 1 Hexokinase

The amount of glucose entering the glycolysis pathway decreases when high levels of glucose-6-phosphate are present in the cell. This phosphorylation product inhibits hexokinase, which prevents glucose from reacting with ATP. This inhibition of the first enzyme in a pathway is an example of feedback control, which is a type of enzyme regulation.

Reaction 3 Phosphofructokinase

The reaction catalyzed by phosphofructokinase is a major control point for glycolysis. Because this is an irreversible reaction, once fructose-1,6-bisphosphate is formed, it must continue through the remaining reactions to pyruvate. As an allosteric enzyme, phosphofructokinase is inhibited by high levels of ATP and activated by high levels of ADP and AMP. High levels of ADP and AMP indicate that the cell has used up much of its ATP. As a regulator, phosphofructokinase increases the rate of pyruvate production for ATP synthesis when the cell needs to replenish ATP, and slows or stops the reaction when ATP is plentiful.

Reaction 10 Pyruvate Kinase

In the last reaction of glycolysis, high levels of ATP as well as acetyl CoA inhibit pyruvate kinase, which is another allosteric enzyme.

Reactions 1, 3, and 10 of glycolysis are examples of how metabolic pathways shut off enzymes to stop the production of molecules that are not needed. Pyruvate, which can be used to synthesize ATP, responds to ATP levels in the cell. When ATP levels are high, enzymes in glycolysis slow or stop the synthesis of pyruvate. With phosphofructokinase and pyruvate kinase inhibited by ATP, glucose-6-phosphate accumulates and inhibits reaction 1, and glucose does not enter the glycolysis pathway. The glycolysis pathway is shut down until ATP is once again needed in the cell. When ATP levels are low or AMP/ADP levels are high, these enzymes are activated and pyruvate production starts again.

▶**SAMPLE PROBLEM 22.6 Regulation of Glycolysis**

How is glycolysis regulated by each of the following enzymes?

a. hexokinase   **b.** phosphofructokinase   **c.** pyruvate kinase

SOLUTION

a. High levels of glucose-6-phosphate inhibit hexokinase, which stops the addition of a phosphate group to glucose in reaction 1.
b. Phosphofructokinase, which catalyzes the formation of fructose-1,6-bisphosphate, is inhibited by high levels of ATP, and activated by high levels of ADP and AMP.
c. High levels of ATP or acetyl CoA inhibit pyruvate kinase, which stops the formation of pyruvate in reaction 10.

STUDY CHECK 22.6

Name the molecule that inhibits hexokinase by feedback regulation in step 1 of glycolysis.

ANSWER

glucose-6-phosphate

The Pentose Phosphate Pathway

The **pentose phosphate pathway** is an alternative pathway for the oxidation of glucose, which produces the coenzyme NADPH and five-carbon pentoses. The NADPH, which is the reduced form of $NADP^+$, is an important coenzyme required in the anabolic pathways such as the biosynthesis of nucleic acids, cholesterol, and fatty acids in the liver and fat (adipose) cells. The pentose phosphate pathway begins with glucose-6-phosphate from reaction 1 in glycolysis, which is converted to ribulose-5-phosphate and requires two $NADP^+$. Ribulose-5-phosphate is isomerized by *phosphopentose isomerase* to ribose-5-phosphate, an important component of nucleotides such as ATP, GTP, UTP, NAD^+, FAD, as well as RNA.

$$\text{Glucose-6-phosphate} + 2NADP^+ + H_2O \longrightarrow \text{ribose-5-phosphate} + 2NADPH + 2H^+ + CO_2$$

Several steps follow as ribose-5-phosphate is converted to sugar phosphates with three-, four-, five-, six-, and seven-carbon atoms, and eventually to fructose-6-phosphate (6C) and glyceraldehyde-3-phosphate (3C), both intermediates that can be metabolized in the glycolysis pathway. In this series of reactions, three ribose-5-phosphate molecules are converted to two hexose molecules and one triose molecule.

$$\text{3 Ribose-5-phosphate} \longrightarrow \text{2 fructose-6-phosphate} + \text{glyceraldehyde-3-phosphate}$$

We can write the overall reaction of the pentose phosphate pathway as

$$\text{3 Glucose-6-phosphate} + 6NADP^+ + 3H_2O \longrightarrow$$
$$\text{2 fructose-6-phosphate} + \text{glyceraldehyde-3-phosphate} + 6NADPH + 6H^+ + 3CO_2$$

The importance of the pentose phosphate pathway is to supply NADPH and pentose sugars for biosynthesis, and utilize the remaining three- and six-carbon intermediates in glycolysis.

Pentose phosphate pathway

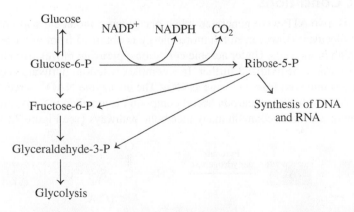

The pentose phosphate pathway converts glucose-6-P to ribose-5-P, which is needed for the synthesis of DNA and RNA. Ribose-5-P can also return to glycolysis as needed.

QUESTIONS AND PROBLEMS

22.4 Glycolysis: Oxidation of Glucose

LEARNING GOAL Describe the conversion of glucose to pyruvate in glycolysis.

22.23 What is the starting compound of glycolysis?

22.24 What is the three-carbon product of glycolysis?

22.25 How is ATP used in the initial steps of glycolysis?

22.26 How many ATP are used in the initial steps of glycolysis?

22.27 What three-carbon intermediates are obtained when fructose-1,6-bisphosphate splits?

22.28 Why does one of the three-carbon intermediates undergo isomerization?

22.29 How does substrate phosphorylation account for the production of ATP in glycolysis?

22.30 Why are there two ATP molecules formed for one molecule of glucose?

22.31 Indicate the enzyme(s) that catalyze(s) each of the following reactions in glycolysis:
a. phosphorylation
b. direct transfer of a phosphate group

22.32 Indicate the enzyme(s) that catalyze(s) each of the following reactions in glycolysis:
a. isomerization
b. formation of a three-carbon ketone and a three-carbon aldehyde

22.33 How many ATP or NADH are produced (or required) in each of the following steps in glycolysis?
a. glucose to glucose-6-phosphate
b. glyceraldehyde-3-phosphate to 1,3-bisphosphoglycerate
c. glucose to pyruvate

22.34 How many ATP or NADH are produced (or required) in each of the following steps in glycolysis?
a. 1,3-bisphosphoglycerate to 3-phosphoglycerate
b. fructose-6-phosphate to fructose-1,6-bisphosphate
c. phosphoenolpyruvate to pyruvate

22.35 Which step(s) in glycolysis involve(s) the following?
a. The first ATP molecule is hydrolyzed.
b. Direct substrate phosphorylation occurs.
c. Six-carbon sugar splits into two three-carbon molecules.

22.36 Which step(s) in glycolysis involve(s) the following?
a. Isomerization takes place.
b. NAD^+ is reduced.
c. A second ATP molecule is synthesized.

22.37 How do galactose and fructose, obtained from the digestion of carbohydrates, enter glycolysis?

22.38 What are three enzymes that regulate glycolysis?

22.39 Indicate whether each of the following would activate or inhibit phosphofructokinase:
a. low levels of ATP   **b.** high levels of ATP

22.40 Indicate whether each of the following would activate or inhibit pyruvate kinase:
a. low levels of ATP   **b.** high levels of ATP

22.41 What is the initial substrate for the pentose phosphate pathway?

22.42 What are the end products of the pentose phosphate pathway?

22.43 What is the purpose of producing NADPH in the pentose phosphate pathway?

22.44 What is the purpose of producing ribose-5-phosphate in the pentose phosphate pathway?

℞ Clinical Applications

22.45 Table sugar, which is the disaccharide sucrose, contains the monosaccharides glucose and fructose. After digestion of sucrose, how do each of the monosaccharides enter glycolysis?

22.46 Milk sugar, which is the disaccharide lactose, contains the monosaccharides glucose and galactose. After digestion of lactose, how do each of the monosaccharides enter glycolysis?

LEARNING GOAL

Give the conditions for the conversion of pyruvate to lactate, ethanol, and acetyl coenzyme A.

22.5 Pathways for Pyruvate

The pyruvate produced from glucose can now enter pathways that continue to extract energy. The available pathway depends on whether there is sufficient oxygen in the cell. Under **aerobic** conditions, oxygen is available to convert pyruvate to acetyl coenzyme A (acetyl CoA) and CO_2. When oxygen levels are low, pyruvate is reduced to lactate. In yeast cells, pyruvate is reduced to ethanol and CO_2.

Aerobic Conditions

In glycolysis, two ATP were generated when one glucose molecule was converted to two pyruvate molecules. However, much more energy is obtained from glucose when oxygen levels are high in the cells. Under aerobic conditions, pyruvate moves from the cytosol into the mitochondria to be oxidized further. In a complex reaction, pyruvate is oxidized, and a carbon atom is removed from pyruvate as CO_2. The coenzyme NAD^+ is reduced during the oxidation. The resulting two-carbon acetyl compound is attached to CoA, producing acetyl CoA, an important intermediate in many metabolic pathways (see Figure 22.10).

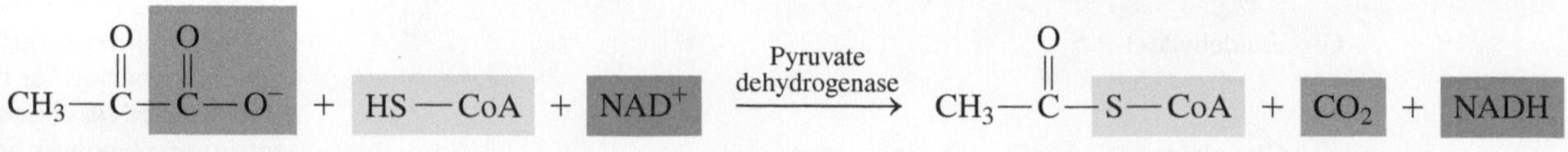

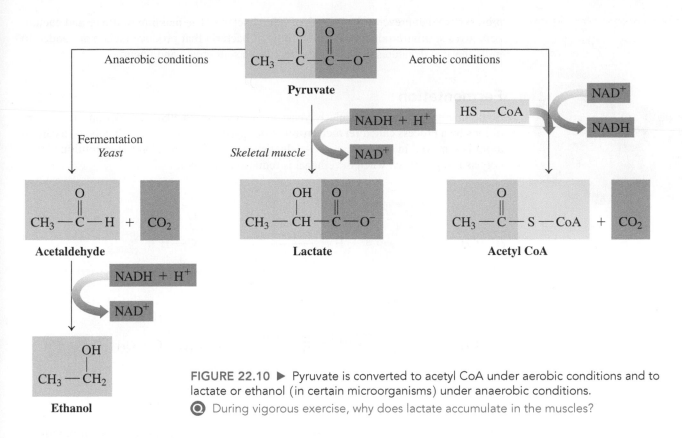

FIGURE 22.10 ▶ Pyruvate is converted to acetyl CoA under aerobic conditions and to lactate or ethanol (in certain microorganisms) under anaerobic conditions.

🔍 During vigorous exercise, why does lactate accumulate in the muscles?

Anaerobic Conditions

When we engage in strenuous exercise, the oxygen stored in our muscle cells is quickly depleted. Under anaerobic conditions, pyruvate remains in the cytosol where it is reduced to lactate. The product NAD^+ is used to oxidize glyceraldehyde-3-phosphate in the glycolysis pathway, which produces a small but needed amount of ATP.

$$CH_3-\overset{\overset{\text{O}}{\|}}{C}-\overset{\overset{\text{O}}{\|}}{C}-O^- + \boxed{NADH + H^+} \underset{}{\overset{\text{Lactate}}{\underset{\text{dehydrogenase}}{\rightleftarrows}}} CH_3-\overset{\overset{\text{OH}}{|}}{\underset{\text{H}}{C}}-\overset{\overset{\text{O}}{\|}}{C}-O^- + \boxed{NAD^+}$$

Pyruvate (oxidized)   Lactate (reduced)

The accumulation of lactate causes the muscles to tire and become sore. After exercise, a person continues to breathe rapidly to repay the *oxygen debt* incurred during exercise. Most of the lactate is transported to the liver, where it is converted back into pyruvate. Under anaerobic conditions, the only ATP production in glycolysis occurs during the steps that phosphorylate ADP directly, giving a net gain of only two ATP.

$$C_6H_{12}O_6 + \boxed{2\ ADP} + 2P_i \longrightarrow 2CH_3-\overset{\overset{\text{OH}}{|}}{CH}-COO^- + \boxed{2\ ATP}$$

Glucose   Lactate

After vigorous exercise, rapid breathing helps to repay the oxygen debt.

Bacteria also convert pyruvate to lactate under anaerobic conditions. In the preparation of kimchee and sauerkraut, cabbage is covered with salt brine. The glucose obtained from the starches in the cabbage is converted to lactate. The acid environment acts as a

Olives are cured in a vinegar and salt brine.

preservative that prevents the growth of other bacteria. The pickling of olives and cucumbers gives similar products. When cultures of bacteria that produce lactate are added to milk, the acid denatures the milk proteins to give sour cream and yogurt.

Fermentation

Some microorganisms, particularly yeast, convert sugars to ethanol under anaerobic conditions by a process called **fermentation**. After pyruvate is formed in glycolysis, a carbon atom is removed in the form of CO_2 (**decarboxylation**). The NAD^+ for continued glycolysis is regenerated when the ethanal is reduced to ethanol.

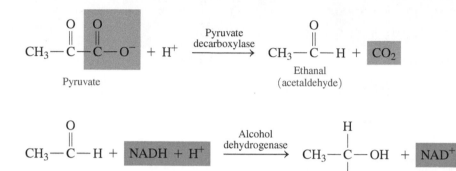

The process of fermentation by yeast is one of the oldest known chemical reactions. Enzymes in the yeast convert the sugars in a variety of carbohydrate sources to glucose and then to ethanol. The evolution of CO_2 gas produces bubbles in beer, sparkling wines, and champagne. The type of carbohydrate used determines the taste associated with a particular alcoholic beverage. Beer is made from the fermentation of barley malt, wine and champagne from the sugars in grapes, vodka from potatoes or grain, sake from rice, and whiskeys from corn or rye. Fermentation produces solutions of about 15% alcohol by volume. At this concentration, the alcohol kills the yeast and fermentation stops.

Beer is produced by the fermentation of pyruvate from barley malt, which gives carbon dioxide and ethanol.

▶SAMPLE PROBLEM 22.7 Pathways for Pyruvate

Identify the pathway(s) that has each of the following characteristics:

a. In this pathway, NAD^+ is reduced to $NADH + H^+$.
b. The product of this pathway contains three carbon atoms.
c. NADH is the oxidizing agent in this anaerobic pathway to give a two-carbon molecule.
d. CO_2 is a product of this aerobic pathway.

SOLUTION

a. NAD^+ is used to oxidize pyruvate to acetyl CoA with the loss of one carbon atom as CO_2.
b. Pyruvate is reduced to a three-carbon molecule of lactate by lactate dehydrogenase and NADH.
c. Under anaerobic conditions, pyruvate is reduced to ethanol, a two-carbon molecule, and CO_2 by NADH.
d. Under aerobic conditions, pyruvate is oxidized to acetyl CoA and CO_2 by NAD^+.

STUDY CHECK 22.7

After strenuous exercise, lactate is oxidized back to pyruvate by lactate dehydrogenase using NAD^+. Write an equation to show this reaction.

ANSWER

$$\underset{\substack{\text{OH} \quad \text{O} \\ | \qquad \| }}{CH_3-CH-C-O^-} + \boxed{NAD^+} \xrightarrow[\text{dehydrogenase}]{\text{Lactate}} \underset{\substack{\text{O} \quad \text{O} \\ \| \quad \| }}{CH_3-C-C-O^-} + \boxed{NADH + H^+}$$

QUESTIONS AND PROBLEMS

22.5 Pathways for Pyruvate

LEARNING GOAL Give the conditions for the conversion of pyruvate to lactate, ethanol, and acetyl coenzyme A.

22.47 What condition is needed in the cell to convert pyruvate to acetyl CoA?

22.48 What coenzymes are needed for the oxidation of pyruvate to acetyl CoA?

22.49 Write the overall equation for the conversion of pyruvate to acetyl CoA.

22.50 What are the possible products of pyruvate under anaerobic conditions?

22.51 Indicate which of the pathways for pyruvate (1) acetyl CoA, (2) lactate, and/or (3) ethanol occur under each of the following conditions:
   a. The reaction is catalyzed by alcohol dehydrogenase.
   b. NAD^+ is reduced.
   c. A three-carbon compound is produced.
   d. CO_2 is produced.

22.52 Indicate which of the pathways for pyruvate (1) acetyl CoA, (2) lactate, and/or (3) ethanol occur under each of the following conditions:
   a. NAD^+ is produced.
   b. $HS-CoA$ is required.
   c. NADH is required.
   d. The reaction is catalyzed by pyruvate decarboxylase.

22.53 In fermentation, a carbon atom is removed from pyruvate. What is the compound formed with that carbon atom?

22.54 In fermentation, what enzymes and coenzymes are used to produce ethanol?

℞ Clinical Applications

22.55 After a marathon, a runner has muscle pain and cramping. What might have occurred in the muscle cells to cause this?

22.56 Some students decided to make some wine by placing yeast and grape juice in a container with a tight lid. A few weeks later, the container exploded. What reaction could account for the explosion?

22.57 A defective *pyruvate dehydrogenase* causes a buildup of lactate in the body and lactic acidosis, which lead to neurological problems. In addition, the production of cellular energy is diminished. Write the chemical equation for the conversion of pyruvate to lactate.

22.58 Defective *pyruvate decarboxylase*, an enzyme in the pyruvate dehydrogenase complex, is a rare disorder that occurs in infancy and leads to an elevated level of pyruvate and lactate in the blood and urine. The inability to convert pyruvate to acetyl CoA and CO_2 leads to lack of energy, general weakness, and developmental delay. Write the chemical equation for the conversion of pyruvate to acetyl CoA.

22.6 Glycogen Synthesis and Degradation

LEARNING GOAL

Describe the synthesis and breakdown of glycogen.

You have just eaten a large meal that supplies you with all the glucose you need to produce pyruvate and ATP by glycolysis. Any excess glucose is used to replenish your energy reserves by synthesizing glycogen, which is stored in your muscles and liver. Glycogen is a polymer of glucose with $\alpha(1 \rightarrow 4)$-glycosidic bonds and multiple branches attached by $\alpha(1 \rightarrow 6)$-glycosidic bonds. When glycogen stores are full, any remaining glucose is converted to triacylglycerols and stored as body fat. When your diet does not supply sufficient glucose and your blood glucose is low, the glycogen in your muscles is converted to glucose for energy, and the glucose from glycogen in your liver is released into the bloodstream to raise your blood glucose levels. During conditions of fasting, glycogen breakdown supplies nearly all the glucose for the body.

Glycogen Synthesis: Glycogenesis

Glycogenesis is the metabolic process of converting glucose molecules into glycogen. When glucose-6-phosphate, which is produced in reaction 1 of glycolysis, is not needed in the cell, it can be stored as glycogen.

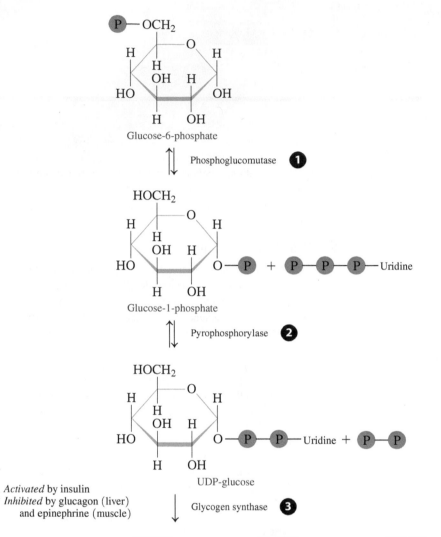

Glucose-6-phosphate

Phosphoglucomutase ❶

Glucose-1-phosphate

Pyrophosphorylase ❷

UDP-glucose

▲ *Activated* by insulin
▼ *Inhibited* by glucagon (liver) and epinephrine (muscle)

Glycogen synthase ❸

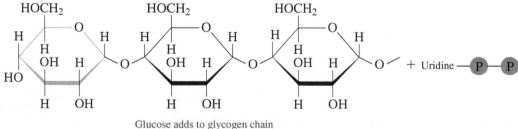

Glucose adds to glycogen chain

FIGURE 22.11 ▶ In glycogenesis, glucose is used to synthesize glycogen.

◉ What is the function of UTP in glycogen synthesis?

⚛ CORE CHEMISTRY SKILL

Identifying the Compounds and Enzymes in Glycogenesis and Glycogenolysis

Reaction 1 Isomerization

Glycogen synthesis begins when the enzyme *phosphoglucomutase* converts glucose-6-phosphate to the isomer glucose-1-phosphate. A mutase is a type of isomerase that shifts the phosphate functional group between carbon atoms (see Figure 22.11).

Reaction 2 Activation

Before glucose-1-phosphate can be added to the glycogen chain, it must be activated. Energy is released when *pyrophosphorylase* catalyzes the reaction of the high-energy compound UTP (uridine triphosphate), which transfers UMP to glucose-1-phosphate to give UDP-glucose (uridine diphosphate-glucose) and pyrophosphate, PP_i.

Reaction 3 Glycogen Synthesis (Glucose Transfer to Glycogen)

Glycogen synthase catalyzes the breaking of the phosphate bond to glucose in UDP-glucose, releasing glucose, which forms an $\alpha(1 \rightarrow 4)$-glycosidic bond with the end of a glycogen chain.

Glycogenolysis

Glycogen is a highly branched polysaccharide of glucose monomers with both $\alpha(1 \rightarrow 4)$- and $\alpha(1 \rightarrow 6)$-glycosidic bonds. Glucose is the primary energy source for muscle contractions, red blood cells, and the brain. When blood glucose is depleted, the glycogen stored in the muscle and liver is converted to glucose molecules in a process called **glycogenolysis**.

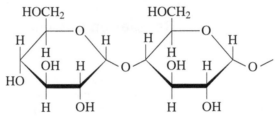

Glycogen

Glycogen phosphorylase **1** and **2**

▲ *Activated* by glucagon (liver) and epinephrine (muscle)
▼ *Inhibited* by insulin

Reaction 1 Phosphorolysis (Hydrolysis and Phosphorylation)

Glucose molecules are removed one by one from the ends of the glycogen chain and phosphorylated by *glycogen phosphorylase* to yield glucose-1-phosphate.

Reaction 2 Hydrolysis $\alpha(1 \rightarrow 6)$

Glycogen phosphorylase continues to cleave $\alpha(1 \rightarrow 4)$-links until one glucose remains bonded to the main chain by an $\alpha(1 \rightarrow 6)$-glycosidic bond. A debranching enzyme $\alpha(1 \rightarrow 6)$-*glycosidase* breaks $\alpha(1 \rightarrow 6)$-glycosidic bonds so that branches of glucose molecules can be hydrolyzed by reaction 1.

Glucose-1-phosphate   +   Glycogen with one glucose removed

Phosphoglucomutase **3**

Reaction 3 Isomerization

The glucose-1-phosphate molecules are converted to glucose-6-phosphate molecules, which enter the glycolysis pathway at reaction 2.

Glucose-6-phosphate   ⟶ Glycolysis

Glucose-6-phosphatase **4** Liver and kidney only

Reaction 4 Dephosphorylation

Free glucose is needed for energy by the brain and muscle. Although glucose can diffuse across cell membranes, charged glucose phosphate cannot. Only cells in the liver and kidneys have a *glucose-6-phosphatase* that hydrolyzes the glucose-6-phosphate to yield free glucose.

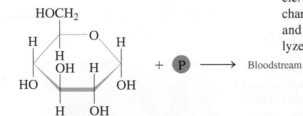

Glucose   + P ⟶ Bloodstream

Glucose

> **SAMPLE PROBLEM 22.8** Glycogen Metabolism
>
> Identify each of the following as part of the reaction pathways of glycogenolysis or glycogenesis:
>
> **a.** Glucose-1-phosphate is converted to glucose-6-phosphate.
> **b.** Glucose-1-phosphate forms UDP-glucose.
> **c.** The pathway that is activated by insulin.
>
> **SOLUTION**
>
> **a.** glycogenolysis   **b.** glycogenesis   **c.** glycogenesis
>
> **STUDY CHECK 22.8**
>
> Why do cells in the liver and kidneys provide glucose to raise blood glucose levels, but cells in skeletal muscle do not?
>
> **ANSWER**
>
> Only the cells in the liver and kidneys provide glucose-6-phosphatase, which is needed to catalyze the hydrolysis of glucose-6-phosphate to yield free glucose.

Regulation of Glycogen Metabolism

The brain, skeletal muscles, and red blood cells require large amounts of glucose every day to function properly. To protect the brain, hormones with opposing actions control blood glucose levels. When glucose is low, *glucagon*, a hormone produced in the pancreas, is secreted into the bloodstream. Glucagon signals cells in the liver to increase the rate of glycogenolysis, which raises blood glucose levels. At the same time, glucagon inhibits the synthesis of glycogen.

Glycogen in skeletal muscle is broken down quickly when the body requires a "burst of energy," often referred to as "fight or flight." *Epinephrine* released from the adrenal glands converts glycogen phosphorylase from an inactive to an active form. The secretion of only a few molecules of epinephrine results in the breakdown of a huge number of glycogen molecules.

Soon after we eat and digest a meal, our blood glucose level rises, which stimulates the pancreas to secrete the hormone *insulin* into our bloodstream. Insulin signals cells to use glucose by increasing glycogen synthesis and oxidation reactions such as glycolysis. At the same time, insulin inhibits the synthesis of glucose, which we will discuss in the next section.

 Chemistry Link to **Health**
Glycogen Storage Diseases (GSDs)

Glycogen storage diseases (GSDs) occur when a defective enzyme is involved in a pathway for glycogen storage or degradation. Different types of GSDs are listed in Table 22.4. For example, in Hers' disease (GSD VI), liver phosphorylase is deficient and glycogen cannot be completely degraded to glucose. As a result, glycogen accumulates in the liver and a person with Hers' disease has hypoglycemia. Severe GSDs are detected in infancy, and life expectancy is usually short. Less severe types are detected in adulthood.

There are no cures for GSDs, although diet therapy may be used to treat symptoms. For some GSD III patients, liver transplantation has been successful.

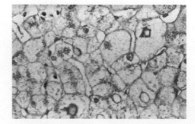

A micrograph shows an excess of stored glycogen (blue) in a liver biopsy of a patient with Cori's disease.

TABLE 22.4 Types of Glycogen Storage Diseases (GSDs)

Type	Organ	Defective Enzyme	Disease	Specifics
0	Liver, muscle	Glycogen synthase	Glycogen synthase deficiency	Liver type severe, lack of muscle glycogen, exercise intolerant
I	Liver, kidneys	Glucose-6-phosphatase	*von Gierke's*, cannot convert glucose-6-phosphate to glucose	Glycogen accumulation, liver enlargement, hypoglycemic, short life expectancy
II	Lysosomes of all organs	$\alpha(1 \rightarrow 4)$-phosphatase	*Pompe's*	Glycogen accumulation heart, heart failure, significant muscle weakness, short life expectancy
III	Liver, muscle	Glycogen debranching enzyme	*Cori's*, cannot completely degrade glycogen to glucose	Lack of glycogen degradation, cannot hydrolyze $\alpha(1 \rightarrow 6)$-glycosidic bonds, hypoglycemic, muscle weakness
IV	Liver	Glycogen branching enzyme	*Andersen's*, cannot form $\alpha(1 \rightarrow 6)$-glycogen branches	Abnormal, unbranched glycogen accumulation, short life expectancy due to heart or liver failure
V	Muscle	Glycogen phosphorylase	*McArdle's*, cannot degrade glycogen in muscle to glucose	Exercise intolerant, muscle cramps due to exercise
VI	Liver	Glycogen phosphorylase	*Hers'*, cannot degrade glycogen in liver to glucose	Mild impact

A summary of the processes of glycogenesis and glycogenolysis indicates that glucose-6-phosphate and glucose-1-phosphate are intermediates of both processes, but UDP-glucose is only involved in glycogenesis.

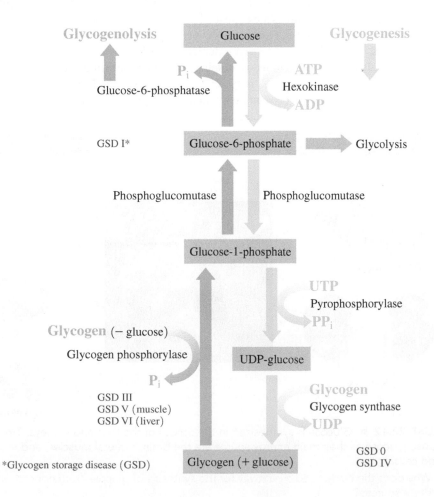

Glucose-6-phosphate and glucose-1-phosphate are intermediates of both glycogenesis and glycogenolysis.

QUESTIONS AND PROBLEMS

22.6 Glycogen Synthesis and Degradation

LEARNING GOAL Describe the synthesis and breakdown of glycogen.

22.59 What is meant by the term *glycogenesis*?

22.60 What is meant by the term *glycogenolysis*?

22.61 How do muscle cells use glycogen to provide energy?

22.62 How does the liver raise blood glucose levels?

22.63 What is the function of glycogen phosphorylase?

22.64 Why is the enzyme phosphoglucomutase used in both glycogenolysis and glycogenesis?

22.65 Indicate whether each of the following hormones activates or inhibits glycogenesis:
    a. insulin   **b.** glucagon   **c.** epinephrine

22.66 Indicate whether each of the following hormones activates or inhibits glycogenolysis:
    a. insulin   **b.** glucagon   **c.** epinephrine

℞ Clinical Applications

22.67 Diabetics often substitute fructose for glucose. Why is it acceptable for diabetics to include fructose in their diet?

22.68 Glycogen storage diseases are the result of a defective enzyme involved in pathways for glycogen storage or degradation. What is the effect of a defective debranching enzyme in *Cori's disease* (GSD III)?

22.69 Glycogen storage diseases are the result of a defective enzyme involved in pathways for glycogen storage or degradation. What is the effect of a defective liver *glycogen phosphorylase* in *Hers' disease* (GSD VI)?

22.70 Glycogen storage diseases are the result of a defective enzyme involved in pathways for glycogen storage or degradation. What is the effect of a defective *glycogen synthase enzyme* (GSD 0)?

LEARNING GOAL

Describe how glucose is synthesized from noncarbohydrate molecules.

22.7 Gluconeogenesis: Glucose Synthesis

Glycogen stored in our liver and muscles can supply us with about one day's requirement of glucose. However, glycogen stores are depleted in 10 to 12 h if we fast for more than one day or participate in heavy exercise. Glucose is the primary source of energy for the brain and red blood cells. If our glycogen stores are depleted, our liver cells synthesize glucose by **gluconeogenesis** from carbon atoms we obtain from noncarbohydrate compounds such as pyruvate, lactate, glycerol from fats, fatty acids, and amino acids. Most glucose is synthesized in the cytosol of the liver cells and some in the kidneys (see Figure 22.12).

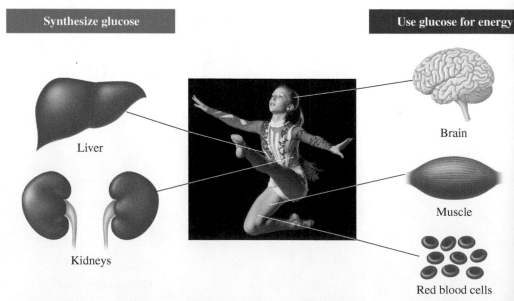

FIGURE 22.12 ▶ Glucose is synthesized in the tissues of the liver and kidneys. Tissues that use glucose as their main energy source are the brain, skeletal muscles, and red blood cells.

◉ Why does the body need a pathway for the synthesis of glucose from noncarbohydrate sources?

To begin the metabolic process of gluconeogenesis, the carbon atoms from noncarbohydrate food sources are converted to pyruvate. Many of the compounds and reactions in gluconeogenesis are the same in glycolysis and catalyzed by the same enzymes. There are 10 reactions in glycolysis and 11 reactions in gluconeogenesis. Three reactions (1, 3, and 10) in glycolysis, which are irreversible reactions, are catalyzed by different enzymes in gluconeogenesis.

Converting Pyruvate to Phosphoenolpyruvate

To start the synthesis of glucose from pyruvate, two catalyzed reactions are needed to replace reaction 10 in glycolysis. In the first step, *pyruvate carboxylase* uses the energy of ATP hydrolysis to catalyze the addition of CO_2 to pyruvate to produce a four-carbon compound oxaloacetate. In the second step, *phosphoenolpyruvate carboxykinase* uses the energy of hydrolysis of the high-energy compound GTP to convert oxaloacetate to phosphoenolpyruvate. Molecules of phosphoenolpyruvate now use the same enzymes of the next several reverse reactions in glycolysis to form fructose-1,6-bisphosphate.

Converting Fructose-1,6-Bisphosphate to Fructose-6-Phosphate

The second irreversible reaction in glycolysis (reaction 3) is bypassed when *fructose-1,6-bisphosphatase* cleaves a phosphate group from fructose-1,6-bisphosphate by hydrolysis with water. The product fructose-6-phosphate undergoes the reversible reaction 2 of glycolysis to yield glucose-6-phosphate.

Converting Glucose-6-Phosphate to Glucose (Reaction 1)

In the final irreversible reaction, the phosphate group of glucose-6-phosphate is hydrolyzed by a different enzyme *glucose-6-phosphatase* to form glucose.

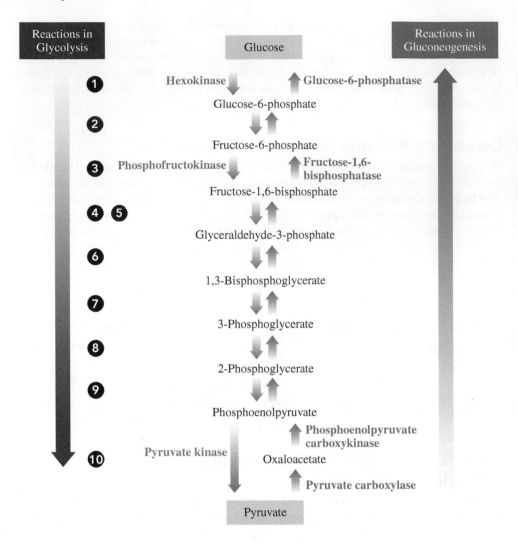

FIGURE 22.13 ▶ In gluconeogenesis, four different enzymes (in blue) are used to replace the enzymes that catalyze the three irreversible reactions of glycolysis (1, 3, and 10). All the other reactions are catalyzed in both directions by the same enzymes used for glycolysis.

Ⓠ Why are 11 enzymes required for gluconeogenesis and only 10 for glycolysis?

A summary of the reactions and different enzymes in gluconeogenesis and glycolysis is shown in Figure 22.13. The overall equation for gluconeogenesis is written as follows:

$$2 \text{ Pyruvate } + 4\text{ ATP} + 2\text{ GTP} + 2\text{ NADH} + 2\text{H}^+ + 6\text{H}_2\text{O} \longrightarrow$$
$$\text{glucose} + 4\text{ ADP} + 2\text{ GDP} + 6\text{P}_i + 2\text{ NAD}^+$$

Energy Cost of Gluconeogenesis

The pathway of gluconeogenesis consists of seven reversible reactions of glycolysis and four new reactions that replace the three irreversible reactions. If all the reactions were simply the reverse of glycolysis, gluconeogenesis would not be energetically favorable. However, by using energy obtained from four ATP, two GTP, and two NADH, gluconeogenesis can take place.

Lactate and the Cori Cycle

When a person exercises vigorously, anaerobic conditions in the muscle reduce pyruvate to lactate. At the same time, NADH is converted to NAD^+, so that a small amount of ATP is formed when oxygen is lacking. Lactate is an important source of carbon atoms for gluconeogenesis. In the **Cori cycle**, lactate is transported to the liver where it is oxidized to pyruvate, which is used to synthesize glucose. Glucose enters the bloodstream and returns to the muscle to rebuild glycogen stores. The Cori cycle is very active when a person has just completed a period of vigorous exercise (see Figure 22.14).

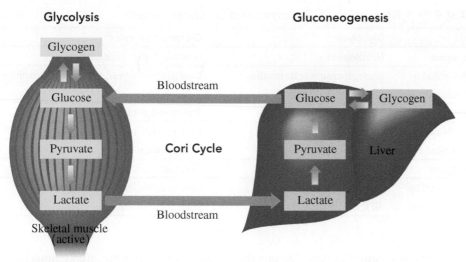

FIGURE 22.14 ▶ In the Cori cycle, lactate from glycolysis in the muscles enters the bloodstream and travels to the liver where it is converted to glucose. The glucose travels through the bloodstream to muscles to produce energy.

Ⓠ Why is lactate formed in the muscle converted to glucose in the liver?

SAMPLE PROBLEM 22.9 Gluconeogenesis

The conversion of fructose-1,6-bisphosphate to fructose-6-phosphate is an irreversible reaction using a glycolytic enzyme. How does gluconeogenesis make this reaction happen?

SOLUTION

This reaction is catalyzed by fructose-1,6-bisphosphatase, which cleaves a phosphate group using a hydrolysis reaction, a reaction that is energetically favorable.

STUDY CHECK 22.9

Why is hexokinase in glycolysis replaced by glucose-6-phosphatase in gluconeogenesis?

ANSWER

The reaction catalyzed by hexokinase in glycolysis is irreversible.

Regulation of Gluconeogenesis

Gluconeogenesis is a pathway that protects the brain and nervous system from experiencing a loss of glucose, which causes impairment of function. It is also a pathway that is utilized when vigorous activity depletes blood glucose and glycogen stores. Thus, the level of carbohydrate available from the diet controls gluconeogenesis. When a diet is high in carbohydrate, the gluconeogenesis pathway is not utilized. However, when a diet is low in carbohydrate, the pathway is very active.

As long as conditions in a cell favor glycolysis, there is no synthesis of glucose. But when the cell requires the synthesis of glucose, glycolysis is turned off. The same three reactions that control glycolysis also control gluconeogenesis, but with different enzymes. Let's look at how high levels of certain compounds activate or inhibit the two processes (see Table 22.5).

TABLE 22.5 Regulation of Glycolysis and Gluconeogenesis

	Glycolysis	Gluconeogenesis
Enzyme	Hexokinase	Glucose-6-phosphatase
Activated by	High glucose levels, insulin	Low glucose levels, glucose-6-phosphate
Inhibited by	Glucose-6-phosphate, epinephrine	
Enzyme	Phosphofructokinase	Fructose-1,6-bisphosphatase
Activated by	AMP, insulin	Low glucose levels, glucagon
Inhibited by	ATP, glucagon	AMP, insulin
Enzyme	Pyruvate kinase	Pyruvate carboxylase
Activated by	Fructose-1,6-bisphosphate	Low glucose levels, glucagon
Inhibited by	ATP, acetyl CoA	Insulin

The relationship between the metabolic reactions of glucose are summarized in Figure 22.15.

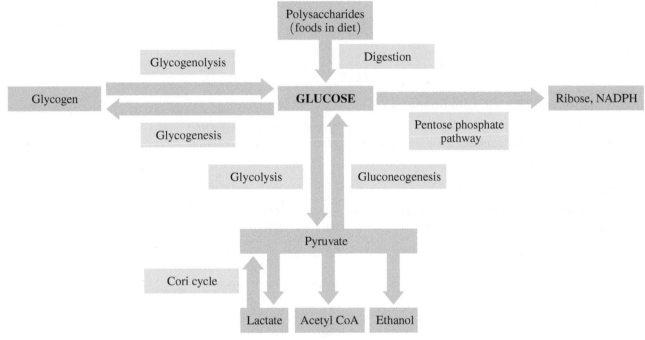

FIGURE 22.15 ▶ Glycolysis involves the breakdown of glucose, and gluconeogenesis involves the synthesis of glucose from noncarbohydrates. The pentose phosphate pathway converts glucose to ribose and provides NADPH. Glycogenolysis degrades glycogen to glucose whereas glycogenesis produces glycogen from glucose.

Q Why does glycogenesis occur after the digestion of a meal high in carbohydrates?

QUESTIONS AND PROBLEMS

22.7 Gluconeogenesis: Glucose Synthesis

LEARNING GOAL Describe how glucose is synthesized from noncarbohydrate molecules.

22.71 What is the function of gluconeogenesis in the body?

22.72 What enzymes in glycolysis are not used in gluconeogenesis?

22.73 What enzymes in glycolysis are used in gluconeogenesis?

22.74 How is the lactate produced in skeletal muscle used for glucose synthesis?

22.75 Indicate whether each of the following activates or inhibits gluconeogenesis:
   a. low glucose levels   **b.** glucagon
   c. insulin   **d.** AMP

22.76 Indicate whether each of the following activates or inhibits glycolysis:
   a. low glucose levels   **b.** insulin
   c. epinephrine   **d.** ATP

Clinical Applications

22.77 Low carbohydrate diets ask dieters to lower or eliminate their intake of carbohydrates. Since we need glucose to fuel the brain, gluconeogenesis will produce glucose under these conditions. What carbohydrate store is lowered (and the source of weight loss) in people who do not eat carbohydrates?

22.78 When would gluconeogenesis be most active, after a meal, or when you wake up in the morning? Explain your reasoning.

℞ Clinical Update
Philip's Diet for von Gierke's Disease

Much of the metabolism of carbohydrates depends on the storage and degradation of glycogen stored in the liver. If glucose-6-phosphatase is defective, the liver cannot provide the body with glucose. In *von Gierke's disease*, the huge amounts of glycogen that accumulate lead to an enlarged liver. Because Philip cannot produce sufficient glucose, he is hypoglycemic and weak.

The hepatology nurse, Barbara, began dietary management by giving Philip frequent feedings of glucose or starch by nasogastric tube to raise blood glucose levels. A stomach tube (gastrostomy tube) was also used. Philip showed a rapid improvement in physical behavior. During the day, Philip was fed cornstarch, which is easily digested to provide small, but continuous, amounts of glucose in the blood. Foods containing fructose or galactose were avoided because they are converted to glucose-6-phosphate, which Philip cannot metabolize. As Philip grows older, he can be physically active, but should not participate in contact sports to avoid damage to his liver. As a young child, Philip continues to thrive.

℞ Clinical Applications

22.79 What are some symptoms of *von Gierke's disease*?

22.80 Write the chemical equation for the reaction catalyzed by glucose-6-phosphatase.

22.81 What is the impact of a defective glucose-6-phosphatase in *von Gierke's disease* (GSD I) on blood glucose and stored glycogen?

22.82 Explain why Philip's condition requires that he is fed cornstarch every few hours.

CONCEPT MAP

METABOLIC PATHWAYS FOR CARBOHYDRATES

Digestion of Carbohydrates

yields

Glucose

reacts by

Pentose Phosphate Pathway

to yield

Nucleotides and NADPH

is oxidized by

Glycolysis

to yield

Pyruvate   **NADH**   **ATP**

is reduced to   undergoes oxidation to

Lactate   **Acetyl CoA**   **CO_2**

NADH

to give   undergoes

Gluconeogenesis

hydrolyzes glycogen to

undergoes

Glycogenesis

to store as

Glycogen

undergoes

Glycogenolysis

CHAPTER REVIEW

22.1 Metabolism and Energy

LEARNING GOAL Describe the three stages of catabolism, the structure of ATP, and the role of ATP.

- Metabolism includes all the catabolic and anabolic reactions that occur in the cells.
- Catabolic reactions degrade large molecules into smaller ones with an accompanying release of energy.
- Anabolic reactions require energy to synthesize larger molecules from smaller ones.
- The three stages of catabolism are digestion of food, degradation of monomers such as glucose to pyruvate, and the extraction of energy from the two- and three-carbon compounds from stage 2.
- Many of the metabolic enzymes are present in the cytosol of the cell where metabolic reactions take place.
- Energy obtained from catabolic reactions is stored primarily in adenosine triphosphate (ATP), a high-energy compound.
- ATP is hydrolyzed when energy is required by anabolic reactions in the cells.

22.2 Important Coenzymes in Metabolic Pathways

LEARNING GOAL Describe the components and functions of the coenzymes NAD^+, NADP, FAD, and coenzyme A.

- NAD^+, $NADP^+$, and FAD are the oxidized forms of coenzymes that participate in oxidation–reduction reactions.
- When NAD^+, $NADP^+$, and FAD pick up hydrogen ions and electrons, they are reduced to $NADH + H^+$, $NADPH + H^+$, and $FADH_2$.
- Coenzyme A contains a thiol group ($—SH$) that usually bonds with a two-carbon acetyl group (acetyl CoA).

22.3 Digestion of Carbohydrates

LEARNING GOAL Give the sites and products of the digestion of carbohydrates.

- The digestion of carbohydrates is a series of reactions that breaks down polysaccharides into hexose monomers such as glucose, galactose, and fructose.
- The hexose monomers are absorbed through the intestinal wall into the bloodstream to be carried to cells where they provide energy and carbon atoms for the synthesis of new molecules.

22.4 Glycolysis: Oxidation of Glucose

LEARNING GOAL Describe the conversion of glucose to pyruvate in glycolysis.

- Glycolysis, which occurs in the cytosol, consists of 10 reactions that degrade glucose (six carbons) to two pyruvate molecules (three carbons each).
- The overall series of reactions yields two molecules of the reduced coenzyme NADH and two ATP.
- The pentose phosphate pathway utilizes glucose-6-phosphate to supply NADPH for the biosynthesis of pentose sugars, fatty acids, cholesterol, and amino acids.

Glucose-6-phosphate

22.5 Pathways for Pyruvate

LEARNING GOAL Give the conditions for the conversion of pyruvate to lactate, ethanol, and acetyl coenzyme A.

- Under aerobic conditions, pyruvate is oxidized in the mitochondria to acetyl CoA.
- In the absence of oxygen, pyruvate is reduced to lactate and NAD^+ is regenerated for the continuation of glycolysis, whereas microorganisms such as yeast reduce pyruvate to ethanol, a process known as fermentation.

22.6 Glycogen Synthesis and Degradation

LEARNING GOAL Describe the synthesis and breakdown of glycogen.

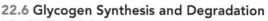

Glycogen

- When blood glucose levels are high, glycogenesis converts glucose to glycogen, which is stored in the liver.
- Glycogenolysis breaks down glycogen to glucose when glucose and ATP levels are low.

22.7 Gluconeogenesis: Glucose Synthesis

LEARNING GOAL Describe how glucose is synthesized from noncarbohydrate molecules.

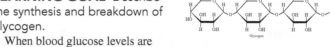

- When blood glucose levels are low and glycogen stores in the liver are depleted, gluconeogenesis occurs, which synthesizes glucose from noncarbohydrate compounds such as pyruvate.
- Gluconeogenesis utilizes many of the same enzymes as glycolysis.

SUMMARY OF KEY REACTIONS

The chapter sections to review are shown after the name of the reaction.

Hydrolysis of ATP (22.1)

$$ATP \longrightarrow ADP + P_i + 7.3 \text{ kcal/mole (31 kJ/mole)}$$

Hydrolysis of ADP (22.1)

$$ADP \longrightarrow AMP + P_i + 7.3 \text{ kcal/mole (31 kJ/mole)}$$

Formation of ATP (22.1)

$$ADP + P_i + 7.3 \text{ kcal/mole (31 kJ/mole)} \longrightarrow ATP$$

Reduction of NAD⁺, NADP⁺, and FAD (22.2)

$$NAD^+ + 2H^+ + 2\,e^- \longrightarrow NADH + H^+$$
$$NADP^+ + 2H^+ + 2\,e^- \longrightarrow NADPH + H^+$$
$$FAD + 2H^+ + 2\,e^- \longrightarrow FADH_2$$

Glycolysis (22.4)

$$C_6H_{12}O_6 + 2ADP + 2P_i + 2NAD^+ \longrightarrow$$
Glucose

$$\underset{\text{Pyruvate}}{2CH_3-\overset{\displaystyle O}{\overset{\|}{C}}-COO^-} + 2ATP + 2NADH + 4H^+$$

Pentose Phosphate Pathway (22.4)

$$\text{Glucose-6-P} + 2NADP^+ + H_2O \longrightarrow$$
$$\text{ribose-5-P} + 2NADPH + 2H^+ + CO_2$$

Oxidation of Pyruvate to Acetyl CoA (22.5)

$$\underset{\text{Pyruvate}}{CH_3-\overset{\displaystyle O}{\overset{\|}{C}}-COO^-} + NAD^+ + HS-CoA \xrightarrow[\text{dehydrogenase}]{\text{Pyruvate}}$$

$$\underset{\text{Acetyl CoA}}{CH_3-\overset{\displaystyle O}{\overset{\|}{C}}-S-CoA} + NADH + CO_2$$

Reduction of Pyruvate to Lactate (22.5)

$$\underset{\text{Pyruvate}}{CH_3-\overset{\displaystyle O}{\overset{\|}{C}}-COO^-} + NADH + H^+ \longrightarrow$$

$$\underset{\text{Lactate}}{CH_3-\overset{\displaystyle OH}{\overset{|}{CH}}-COO^-} + NAD^+$$

Oxidation of Glucose to Lactate (22.5)

$$\text{Glucose} + 2ADP + 2P_i \longrightarrow 2\text{lactate} + 2ATP$$

Reduction of Pyruvate to Ethanol (22.5)

$$\underset{\text{Pyruvate}}{CH_3-\overset{\displaystyle O}{\overset{\|}{C}}-COO^-} + NADH + 2H^+ \longrightarrow$$

$$\underset{\text{Ethanol}}{CH_3-CH_2-OH} + NAD^+ + CO_2$$

Glycogenesis (22.6)

$$\text{UDP-glucose} + \text{glycogen} \longrightarrow \text{glycogen–glucose} + UDP$$

Glycogenolysis (22.6)

$$\text{Glycogen–glucose} \longrightarrow \text{glycogen} + \text{glucose}$$

Gluconeogenesis (22.7)

$$2 \text{ Pyruvate} + 4ATP + 2GTP + 2NADH + 2H^+ + 6H_2O \longrightarrow$$
$$\text{glucose} + 4ADP + 2GDP + 6P_i + 2NAD^+$$

KEY TERMS

acetyl CoA The compound that forms when a two-carbon acetyl unit bonds to coenzyme A.

ADP Adenosine diphosphate, formed by the hydrolysis of ATP; consists of adenine, a ribose sugar, and two phosphate groups.

aerobic An oxygen-containing environment in the cells.

anabolic reaction A metabolic reaction that requires energy to build large molecules from small molecules.

anaerobic A condition in cells when there is no oxygen.

ATP Adenosine triphosphate, a high-energy compound that stores energy in the cells; consists of adenine, a ribose sugar, and three phosphate groups.

catabolic reaction A metabolic reaction that produces energy for the cell by the degradation and oxidation of glucose and other molecules.

coenzyme A (CoA) A coenzyme that transports acyl and acetyl groups.

Cori cycle A cyclic process in which lactate produced in muscle is transferred to the liver to be converted to glucose, which can be used again by muscle.

cytosol The fluid of the cell, which is an aqueous solution of electrolytes and enzymes.

decarboxylation The loss of a carbon atom in the form of CO_2.

digestion The processes in the gastrointestinal tract that break down large food molecules to smaller ones that pass through the intestinal membrane into the bloodstream.

FAD A coenzyme (flavin adenine dinucleotide) for dehydrogenase enzymes that forms carbon–carbon double bonds.

fermentation The anaerobic conversion of glucose by enzymes in yeast to yield alcohol and CO_2.

gluconeogenesis The synthesis of glucose from noncarbohydrate compounds.

glycogenesis The synthesis of glycogen from glucose molecules.

glycogenolysis The breakdown of glycogen into glucose molecules.

glycolysis The 10 oxidation reactions of glucose that yield two pyruvate molecules.

metabolism All the chemical reactions in living cells that carry out molecular and energy transformations.

mitochondrion The organelle of cells where energy-producing reactions take place.

NAD$^+$ The hydrogen acceptor used in oxidation reactions that form carbon–oxygen double bonds.

pentose phosphate pathway A metabolic pathway that oxidizes glucose to produce NADPH for anabolic reactions and five-carbon sugars required for the synthesis of nucleotides, DNA, and RNA.

⚛ CORE CHEMISTRY SKILLS

The chapter section containing each Core Chemistry Skill is shown in parentheses at the end of each heading.

Identifying Important Coenzymes in Metabolism (22.2)

- ATP is a nucleotide that transfers energy through metabolic reactions.
- NAD$^+$, NADP$^+$, and FAD are the oxidized forms of the coenzymes that move electrons and H$^+$ through metabolic reactions.
- CoA is a coenzyme that moves two-carbon acetyl groups through metabolic reactions.

Example: Provide the formulas of the reduced forms of the coenzymes that move electrons and H$^+$ through metabolism.

Answer: NADH, NADPH, and FADH$_2$

Identifying the Compounds in Glycolysis (22.4)

- Glycolysis, which occurs in the cytosol, consists of 10 reactions that degrade glucose (6C) to two pyruvate (3C).
- The overall series of reactions in glycolysis yields two NADH and two ATP.

Example: Identify the reaction(s) and compounds in glycolysis that have each of the following:

    a. requires ATP
    b. converts a six-carbon compound to two three-carbon compounds
    c. converts ADP to ATP

Answer: **a.** The phosphorylation of glucose in reaction 1 and fructose-6-phosphate in reaction 3 each require one ATP.

    b. In reaction 4, the six-carbon fructose-1,6-bisphosphate is cleaved into two three-carbon compounds.

    c. Phosphate transfer in reactions 7 and 10 converts ADP to ATP.

Identifying the Compounds and Enzymes in Glycogenesis and Glycogenolysis (22.6)

- Glucose undergoes glycogenesis when blood glucose levels are high and is stored as glycogen in the liver.
- Glycogenolysis breaks down glycogen to glucose when levels of glucose or ATP are low.

Example: Indicate which of the processes glycogenesis and/or glycogenolysis involve each of the following compounds:

    a. glucose-1-phosphate
    b. UDP-glucose
    c. glycogen phosphorylase
    d. UTP

Answer: **a.** glycogenesis, glycogenolysis
    b. glycogenesis
    c. glycogenolysis
    d. glycogenesis

UNDERSTANDING THE CONCEPTS

The chapter sections to review are given in parentheses at the end of each question.

22.83 On a hike, you expend 350 kcal/h. How many moles of ATP will you use if you hike for 2.5 h? (22.1)

Vigorous hiking can expend 350 kcal per hour.

22.84 Identify each of the following as a six-carbon or a three-carbon compound and arrange them in the order in which they occur in glycolysis: (22.4)
    a. 3-phosphoglycerate   **b.** pyruvate
    c. glucose-6-phosphate   **d.** glucose
    e. fructose-1,6-bisphosphate

22.85 Indicate whether each of the following enzymes is utilized in (1) glycogenesis but not glycogenolysis, (2) glycogenolysis but not glycogenesis, or (3) both glycogenesis and glycogenolysis: (22.6)
    a. pyrophosphorylase   **b.** phosphoglucomutase
    c. glycogen phosphorylase

22.86 Indicate whether each of the following enzymes is utilized in (1) glycogenesis but not glycogenolysis, (2) glycogenolysis but not glycogenesis, or (3) both glycogenesis and glycogenolysis: (22.6)
    a. glycogen synthase
    b. glucose-6-phosphatase
    c. debranching enzyme

22.87 Indicate whether each of the following enzymes is utilized in (1) glycolysis but not gluconeogenesis, (2) gluconeogenesis but not glycolysis, or (3) both glycolysis and gluconeogenesis: (22.4, 22.7)
    a. glucose-6-phosphatase   **b.** aldolase
    c. phosphofructokinase   **d.** phosphoglycerate mutase

22.88 Indicate whether each of the following enzymes is utilized in (1) glycolysis but not gluconeogenesis, (2) gluconeogenesis but not glycolysis, or (3) both glycolysis and gluconeogenesis: (22.4, 22.7)
    a. hexokinase   **b.** pyruvate kinase
    c. enolase   **d.** pyruvate carboxylase

ADDITIONAL QUESTIONS AND PROBLEMS

22.89 What is meant by the term metabolism? (22.1)

22.90 How do catabolic reactions differ from anabolic reactions? (22.1)

22.91 What stage of catabolism involves the digestion of large food polymers? (22.1)

22.92 What stage of catabolism degrades monomers such as glucose into smaller molecules? (22.1)

22.93 What type of cell has a nucleus? (22.1)

22.94 What is the function of each of the following cell components? (22.1)
a. cell membrane   b. mitochondria   c. cytosol

22.95 What is the full name of ATP? (22.1)

22.96 What is the full name of ADP? (22.1)

22.97 Write the abbreviated equation for the hydrolysis of ATP to ADP. (22.1)

22.98 Write the abbreviated equation for the hydrolysis of ADP to AMP. (22.1)

22.99 What are the high- and low-energy forms of the coenzyme FAD? (22.2)

22.100 What type of reaction uses FAD as the coenzyme? (22.2)

22.101 What are the high- and low-energy forms of the coenzyme NAD^+? (22.2)

22.102 What type of reaction uses NAD^+ as the coenzyme? (22.2)

22.103 Write the abbreviation for the reduced form of each of the following: (22.2)
a. FAD   b. NAD^+ c. $NADP^+$

22.104 What is the name of the vitamin in the structure of each of the following? (22.2)
a. FAD   b. NAD^+ c. coenzyme A

22.105 How and where does lactose undergo digestion in the body? What are the products? (22.3)

22.106 How and where does sucrose undergo digestion in the body? What are the products? (22.3)

22.107 What are the reactant and product of glycolysis? (22.4)

22.108 What is the coenzyme used in glycolysis? (22.4)

22.109 a. In glycolysis, which reactions involve phosphorylation? (22.4)
b. Which reactions involve a direct substrate phosphorylation to generate ATP?

22.110 How do ADP and ATP regulate the glycolysis pathway? (22.4)

22.111 What reaction and enzyme in glycolysis convert a hexose bisphosphate into two three-carbon intermediates? (22.4)

22.112 How does the investment and generation of ATP give a net gain of ATP for glycolysis? (22.4)

22.113 What compound is converted to fructose-6-phosphate by phosphoglucose isomerase? (22.4)

22.114 What product forms when glyceraldehyde-3-phosphate adds a phosphate group? (22.4)

22.115 When is pyruvate converted to lactate in the body? (22.5)

22.116 When pyruvate is used to form acetyl CoA or ethanol in fermentation, the product has only two carbon atoms. What happened to the third carbon? (22.5)

22.117 How does phosphofructokinase regulate the rate of glycolysis? (22.5)

22.118 How does pyruvate kinase regulate the rate of glycolysis? (22.5)

22.119 When does the rate of glycogenolysis increase in the cells? (22.6)

22.120 If glucose-1-phosphate is the product from glycogen breakdown, how does it enter glycolysis? (22.6)

℞ Clinical Applications

22.121 What is the end product of glycogenolysis in the liver? (22.6)

22.122 What is the end product of glycogenolysis in skeletal muscle? (22.6)

22.123 Indicate whether each of the following conditions would increase or decrease the rate of glycogenolysis in the liver: (22.6)
a. low blood glucose level
b. secretion of insulin
c. secretion of glucagon
d. high levels of ATP

22.124 Indicate whether each of the following conditions would increase or decrease the rate of glycogenesis in the liver: (22.6)
a. low blood glucose level
b. secretion of insulin
c. secretion of glucagon
d. high levels of ATP

22.125 Indicate whether each of the following conditions would increase or decrease the rate of gluconeogenesis: (22.7)
a. high blood glucose level
b. secretion of insulin
c. secretion of glucagon
d. high levels of ATP

22.126 Indicate whether each of the following conditions would increase or decrease the rate of glycolysis: (22.4)
a. high blood glucose level
b. secretion of insulin
c. secretion of glucagon
d. high levels of ATP

CHALLENGE QUESTIONS

The following groups of questions are related to the topics in this chapter. However, they do not all follow the chapter order, and they require you to combine concepts and skills from several sections. These questions will help you increase your critical thinking skills and prepare for your next exam.

22.127 Why is glucose provided by glycogenolysis in the liver but not in skeletal muscle? (22.6)

22.128 When does the rate of glycogenesis increase in the cells? (22.6)

22.129 How do the hormones insulin and glucagon affect the rates of glycogenesis, glycogenolysis, and glycolysis? (22.4, 22.6)

22.130 What is the function of gluconeogenesis? (22.7)

22.131 Where does the Cori cycle operate? (22.7)

22.132 Identify each of the following as part of glycolysis, glycogenolysis, glycogenesis, or gluconeogenesis: (22.4, 22.6, 22.7)
a. Glycogen is broken down to glucose in the liver.
b. Glucose is synthesized from noncarbohydrate sources.

c. Glucose is degraded to pyruvate.
d. Glycogen is synthesized from glucose.

22.133 The average daily diet of an adult woman is 2.0×10^3 kcal. The molar mass of ATP is 507 g/mole. (22.1)
a. If all the energy in her diet is converted to ATP, how many kg of ATP are synthesized in one day?
b. If the average amount of ATP in the body is 250 g, what is the lifetime, in minutes, of ATP?

22.134 A teaspoon containing 4.2 g of sucrose is added to a cup of tea. (22.1)
a. How much energy, in kilocalories, are in the sucrose if 1 g of sucrose provides 4 kcal?
b. How many grams of ATP (507 g/mole) are produced if all the energy in the sucrose is converted to ATP?

ANSWERS

Answers to Selected Questions and Problems

22.1 The digestion of polysaccharides takes place in stage 1.

22.3 In metabolism, a catabolic reaction breaks apart large molecules, releasing energy.

22.5 a. anabolic   **b.** anabolic
c. catabolic   **d.** catabolic

22.7 When a phosphate group is cleaved from ATP, sufficient energy is released for energy-requiring processes in the cell.

22.9 a. PEP $\longrightarrow$ pyruvate + P_i + 14.8 kcal/mole
b. ADP + P_i + 7.3 kcal/mole $\longrightarrow$ ATP
c. PEP + ADP $\longrightarrow$ ATP + pyruvate + 7.5 kcal/mole

22.11 3.4×10^4 g

22.13 a. coenzyme A   **b.** NAD$^+$, NADP$^+$
c. FAD

22.15 a. NADH   **b.** FAD

22.17 FAD

22.19 Hydrolysis is the main reaction involved in the digestion of carbohydrates.

22.21 a. lactose   **b.** glucose and fructose
c. glucose

22.23 glucose

22.25 ATP is required in phosphorylation reactions.

22.27 glyceraldehyde-3-phosphate and dihydroxyacetone phosphate

22.29 ATP is produced in glycolysis by transferring a phosphate group from 1,3-bisphosphoglycerate and from phosphoenolpyruvate directly to ADP.

22.31 a. hexokinase; phosphofructokinase
b. phosphoglycerate kinase; pyruvate kinase

22.33 a. 1 ATP required   **b.** 1 NADH produced
c. 2 ATP and 2 NADH produced

22.35 a. In reaction 1, a hexokinase uses ATP to phosphorylate glucose.

b. In reactions 7 and 10, phosphate groups are transferred from 1,3-bisphosphoglycerate and phosphoenolpyruvate directly to ADP to produce ATP.
c. In reaction 4, the six-carbon molecule fructose-1,6-bisphosphate is split into two three-carbon molecules, glyceraldehyde-3-phosphate and dihydroxyacetone phosphate.

22.37 In a series of enzymatic reactions, galactose is phosphorylated to yield glucose-1-phosphate, which is converted to glucose-6-phosphate, which enters glycolysis in reaction 2. In the muscles, fructose is phosphorylated to fructose-6-phosphate, which enters glycolysis in reaction 3, where its movement through glycolysis is regulated by the enzyme phosphofructokinase. In the liver, fructose is phosphorylated to fructose-1-phosphate, which is converted to glyceraldehyde-3-phosphate, which enters glycolysis at reaction 6.

22.39 a. activate   **b.** inhibit

22.41 Glucose-6-phosphate is the initial substrate for the pentose phosphate pathway.

22.43 The pentose phosphate pathway produces NADPH required for anabolic reactions.

22.45 Sucrose contains the monosaccharides glucose and fructose. Once hydrolyzed during digestion, glucose directly enters glycolysis at step 1 and fructose enters glycolysis either at step 3 in the muscle and kidney or step 6 in the liver.

22.47 Aerobic (oxygen) conditions are needed.

22.49 The oxidation of pyruvate converts NAD$^+$ to NADH and produces acetyl CoA and CO_2.

$$CH_3-\overset{\overset{\displaystyle O}{\|}}{C}-COO^- + NAD^+ + HS-CoA \xrightarrow{\text{Pyruvate dehydrogenase}}$$

$$CH_3-\overset{\overset{\displaystyle O}{\|}}{C}-S-CoA + NADH + CO_2$$

22.51 a. (3) ethanol   **b.** (1) acetyl CoA
c. (2) lactate   **d.** (1) acetyl CoA,
(3) ethanol

22.53 carbon dioxide, CO_2

22.55 During strenuous exercise, under anaerobic conditions, pyruvate is converted to lactate. The accumulation of lactate causes the muscles to tire and become sore.

22.57

$$CH_3-\overset{\overset{\displaystyle O}{\|}}{C}-\overset{\overset{\displaystyle O}{\|}}{C}-O^- + NADH + H^+ \longrightarrow$$

$$CH_3-\overset{\overset{\displaystyle OH}{|}}{CH}-\overset{\overset{\displaystyle O}{\|}}{C}-O^- + NAD^+$$

22.59 Glycogenesis is the synthesis of glycogen from glucose molecules.

22.61 Muscle cells break down glycogen to glucose-6-phosphate, which enters glycolysis.

22.63 Glycogen phosphorylase cleaves the glycosidic bonds at the ends of glycogen chains to remove glucose as glucose-1-phosphate.

22.65 a. activates   **b.** inhibits   **c.** inhibits

22.67 The movement of glucose out of the bloodstream and into the cells is regulated by insulin whereas fructose is not. Fructose can move into the cells and be degraded in glycolysis.

22.69 When the glycogen phosphorylase enzyme in the liver is defective, glycogen in the liver cannot be broken down to glucose.

22.71 When there are no glycogen stores remaining in the liver, gluconeogenesis synthesizes glucose from noncarbohydrate compounds such as pyruvate and lactate.

22.73 phosphoglucose isomerase, aldolase, triose phosphate isomerase, glyceraldehyde-3-phosphate dehydrogenase, phosphoglycerate kinase, phosphoglycerate mutase, and enolase

22.75 a. activates   **b.** activates
c. inhibits   **d.** inhibits

22.77 People on low carbohydrate diets do not store normal amounts of glycogen and therefore lose this weight and the water weight used to hydrolyze the glycogen.

22.79 Some of the symptoms of von Gierke's disease are: liver enlargement due to glycogen accumulation, and hypoglycemia, which can lead to a shortened life expectancy.

22.81 Glycogen cannot be degraded completely to glucose causing low blood glucose. Glycogen accumulates as stored glycogen in the liver. Lower insulin levels inhibits glycolysis and activates gluconeogenesis.

22.83 120 moles of ATP

22.85 a. (1) glycogenesis but not glycogenolysis
b. (3) both glycogenesis and glycogenolysis
c. (2) glycogenolysis but not glycogenesis

22.87 a. (2) gluconeogenesis but not glycolysis
b. (3) both glycolysis and gluconeogenesis
c. (1) glycolysis but not gluconeogenesis
d. (3) both glycolysis and gluconeogenesis

22.89 Metabolism includes all the reactions in cells that provide energy and material for cell growth.

22.91 stage 1

22.93 eukaryotic cell

22.95 adenosine triphosphate

22.97 $ATP \longrightarrow ADP + P_i + 7.3$ kcal/mole (31 kJ/mole)

22.99 High energy is the reduced form, $FADH_2$; low energy is the oxidized form, FAD.

22.101 High energy is the reduced form, NADH; low energy is the oxidized form, NAD^+.

22.103 a. $FADH_2$ **b.** $NADH + H^+$
c. $NADPH + H^+$

22.105 Lactose undergoes digestion in the small intestine to yield glucose and galactose.

22.107 Glucose is the reactant and pyruvate is the product of glycolysis.

22.109 a. Reactions 1 and 3 involve phosphorylation of hexoses with ATP.
b. Reactions 7 and 10 involve direct substrate phosphorylation that generates ATP.

22.111 Reaction 4, which converts fructose-1,6-bisphosphate into two three-carbon intermediates, is catalyzed by aldolase.

22.113 glucose-6-phosphate

22.115 Pyruvate is converted to lactate when oxygen is not present in the cell (anaerobic conditions) to regenerate NAD^+ for glycolysis.

22.117 Phosphofructokinase is an allosteric enzyme that is activated by high levels of AMP and ADP because the cell needs to produce more ATP. When ATP levels are high due to a decrease in energy needs, ATP inhibits phosphofructokinase, which reduces its catalysis of fructose-6-phosphate.

22.119 The rate of glycogenolysis increases when blood glucose levels are low and glucagon has been secreted, which accelerates the breakdown of glycogen.

22.121 glucose

22.123 a. increase   **b.** decrease
c. increase   **d.** decrease

22.125 a. decrease   **b.** decrease
c. increase   **d.** decrease

22.127 The cells in the liver, but not skeletal muscle, contain a phosphatase enzyme needed to convert glucose-6-phosphate to free glucose that can diffuse through cell membranes into the bloodstream. Glucose-6-phosphate, which is the end product of glycogenolysis in muscle cells, cannot diffuse easily across cell membranes.

22.129 Insulin increases the rate of glycogenesis and glycolysis and decreases the rate of glycogenolysis. Glucagon decreases the rate of glycogenesis and glycolysis and increases the rate of glycogenolysis.

22.131 The Cori cycle is a cyclic process that involves the transfer of lactate from muscle to the liver where glucose is synthesized, which can be used again by the muscle.

22.133 a. 140 kg   **b.** 2.6 min

23

Metabolism and Energy Production

NATALIE WAS RECENTLY DIAGNOSED WITH MILD
pulmonary emphysema due to secondhand cigarette smoke. She has been referred to
Angela, an exercise physiologist, who begins to assess Natalie's condition by connecting
her to an electrocardiogram (ECG or EKG), a pulse oximeter, and a blood pressure cuff.
The ECG records the electrical activity of Natalie's heart, which is used to measure the rate
and rhythm of her heartbeat, and possible presence of heart damage. The
pulse oximeter measures her pulse and the saturation level of oxygen in her
arterial blood (the percentage of hemoglobin that is saturated with O_2). The
blood pressure cuff determines the pressure exerted by the heart in pumping
her blood.

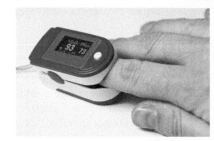

A pulse oximeter measures the
pulse and the O_2 saturation in the
blood.

To determine possible heart disease, Natalie has an exercise stress test
on a treadmill to measure how her heart rate and blood pressure respond
to exertion by walking faster as the slope of the treadmill is increased.
Electrical leads are attached to measure the heart rate and blood pressure
first at rest and then on the treadmill. Additional equipment using a face
mask collects expired air and measures Natalie's maximal volume of oxygen
uptake, or $V_{O_2\,max}$.

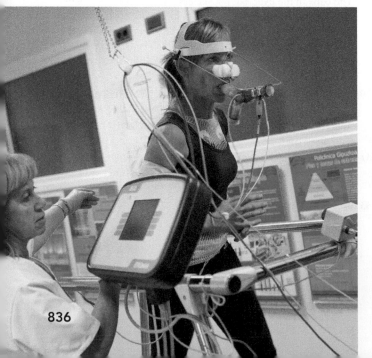

CAREER Exercise Physiologist

Exercise physiologists work with athletes as well as patients who
have been diagnosed with diabetes, heart disease, pulmonary
disease, or other chronic disabilities or diseases. Patients who
have been diagnosed with one of these diseases are often
prescribed exercise as a form of treatment, and they are referred
to an exercise physiologist. The exercise physiologist evaluates
the patient's overall health and then creates a customized
exercise program for that individual. The program for an athlete
might focus on reducing the number of injuries, whereas a
program for a cardiac patient would focus on strengthening
the heart muscles. The exercise physiologist also monitors
the patient for improvement and determines if the exercise is
helping to reduce or reverse the progression of the disease.

O xygen is necessary for catabolism and the production of ATP. In the mitochondria, the reactions associated with electron transport are coupled with oxidative phosphorylation to produce ATP. The pyruvate obtained from the degradation of glucose during glycolysis is converted to acetyl CoA when oxygen is plentiful in the cell and to lactate when oxygen levels are low. Although glycolysis produces a small amount of ATP, most of the ATP in the cells is produced in stage 3 of catabolism during the conversion of pyruvate. In a process known as *respiration*, oxygen is required to complete the oxidation of glucose to CO_2 and H_2O.

In the *citric acid cycle*, a series of catabolic reactions in the mitochondria oxidizes the two carbon atoms in the acetyl component of acetyl CoA to two molecules of carbon dioxide. The reduced coenzymes NADH and $FADH_2$ produced in the citric acid cycle enter *electron transport*, or the *respiratory chain*, where they provide hydrogen ions and electrons that combine with oxygen (O_2) to form H_2O. The energy transferred during electron transport is used to synthesize ATP from ADP.

CHAPTER READINESS*

⚙ CORE CHEMISTRY SKILLS

- Writing Equations for Hydrogenation, Hydration, and Polymerization (12.7)
- Classifying Enzymes (20.2)
- Identifying Important Coenzymes in Metabolism (22.2)
- Identifying the Compounds in Glycolysis (22.4)

*These Core Chemistry Skills from previous chapters are listed here for your review as you proceed to the new material in this chapter.

23.1 The Citric Acid Cycle

The citric acid cycle is a series of reactions that connects the intermediate acetyl CoA from the catabolic pathways in stage 2 with electron transport and the synthesis of ATP in stage 3. As a central pathway in metabolism, the **citric acid cycle** uses the two-carbon acetyl group of acetyl CoA to produce CO_2, and reduced coenzymes NADH and $FADH_2$ (see Figure 23.1).

The citric acid cycle is named for the six-carbon citrate ion from citric acid $(C_6H_8O_7)$, a tricarboxylic acid, which forms in the first reaction. The citric acid cycle is also known as the *tricarboxylic acid (TCA) cycle* or the *Krebs cycle*, named for H. A. Krebs, who recognized it in 1937 as the major pathway for the production of energy.

LEARNING GOAL

Describe the oxidation of acetyl CoA in the citric acid cycle.

Overview of the Citric Acid Cycle

Six carbons move through the eight reactions of the citric acid cycle, with each turn producing oxaloacetate (four carbons) and $2CO_2$ (see Figure 23.2). Each turn of the cycle contains four oxidation reactions producing the reduced coenzymes NADH and $FADH_2$ from the energy released during the reactions. One GTP (converted to ATP in the cell) is also produced during the citric acid cycle from the energy transferred during coenzyme A hydrolysis.

Eight reactions take place in the citric acid cycle that oxidize acetyl CoA from pyruvate or fatty acids and produce CO_2 and the high-energy compounds $FADH_2$, NADH, and GTP (see Figure 23.3). Reactions involved in the citric acid cycle include condensation (dehydration), hydration, oxidation, reduction, and hydrolysis.

⚙ CORE CHEMISTRY SKILL

Describing the Reactions in the Citric Acid Cycle

Stages of Catabolism

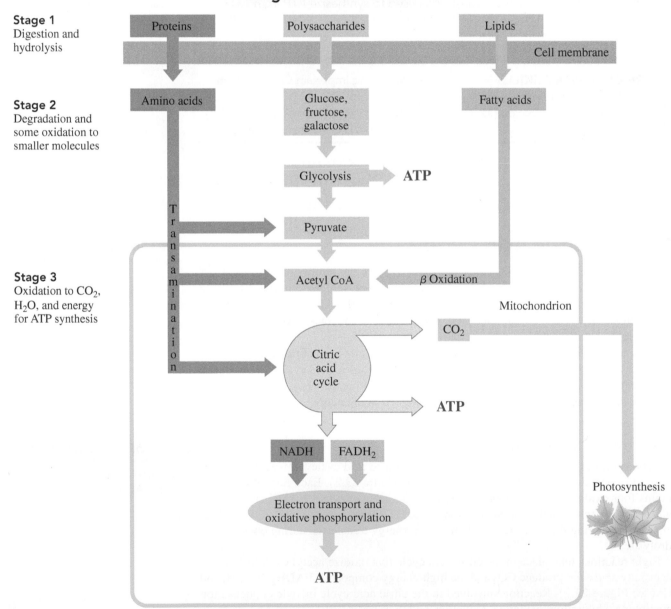

Stage 1
Digestion and
hydrolysis

Stage 2
Degradation and
some oxidation to
smaller molecules

Stage 3
Oxidation to CO_2,
H_2O, and energy
for ATP synthesis

FIGURE 23.1 ▶ The citric acid cycle connects the catabolic pathways that begin with the digestion and degradation of foods in stages 1 and 2 with the oxidation of substrates in stage 3 that generates most of the energy for ATP synthesis.

Ⓠ Why is the citric acid cycle called a central metabolic pathway?

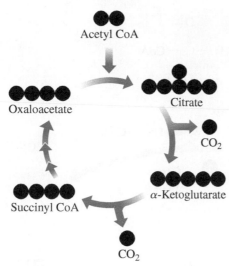

FIGURE 23.2 ▶ In the citric acid cycle, two carbon atoms are removed as CO_2 from six-carbon citrate to give four-carbon succinyl CoA, which is converted to four-carbon oxaloacetate.

Q How many carbon atoms are removed in one turn of the citric acid cycle?

Reaction 1 Formation of Citrate

In the first reaction, *citrate synthase* catalyzes the condensation of an acetyl group (2C) from acetyl CoA with oxaloacetate (4C) to yield citrate (6C) and coenzyme A. The energy to form citrate is provided by the hydrolysis of the high-energy thioester bond in acetyl CoA.

Citric acid (citrate) provides the sour taste of citrus fruits such as lemons, limes, oranges, and grapefruits.

$$
\begin{array}{c}
\underset{\text{Acetyl CoA}}{\text{CH}_3-\overset{\overset{\text{O}}{\|}}{\text{C}}-\text{S}-\text{CoA}}
+
\underset{\text{Oxaloacetate}}{\underset{\text{COO}^-}{\overset{\text{COO}^-}{\text{C}=\text{O}}}}
+ \text{H}_2\text{O}
\xrightarrow{\text{Citrate synthase}}
\underset{\text{Citrate}}{\text{HO}-\overset{\overset{\text{COO}^-}{\overset{|}{\text{CH}_2}}}{\underset{\text{CH}_2}{\underset{\text{COO}^-}{\text{C}}}}-\text{COO}^-}
+ \text{HS}-\text{CoA} + \text{H}^+
\end{array}
$$

Reaction 2 Isomerization

The citrate formed in reaction 1 is a tertiary alcohol, which cannot be oxidized. In reaction 2, citrate is rearranged to its isomer isocitrate, a secondary alcohol that can be oxidized. Initially, *aconitase* catalyzes the dehydration of citrate (tertiary alcohol) to yield *cis*-aconitate, which is followed by a hydration that forms isocitrate (secondary alcohol).

$$
\underset{\substack{\text{Citrate}\\(3°\ \text{alcohol})}}{
\text{HO}-\overset{\overset{\text{COO}^-}{\overset{|}{\text{CH}_2}}}{\underset{\underset{\text{COO}^-}{|}}{\underset{\text{H}-\text{C}-\text{H}}{\text{C}}}}-\text{COO}^-}
\xrightarrow[\text{H}_2\text{O}]{\text{Aconitase}}
\underset{\substack{\textit{cis}\text{-Aconitate}}}{
\overset{\overset{\text{COO}^-}{\overset{|}{\text{CH}_2}}}{\underset{\underset{\text{COO}^-}{|}}{\underset{\text{C}-\text{H}}{\text{C}}}}-\text{COO}^-}
\xrightarrow[\text{H}_2\text{O}]{\text{Aconitase}}
\underset{\substack{\text{Isocitrate}\\(2°\ \text{alcohol})}}{
\text{H}-\overset{\overset{\text{COO}^-}{\overset{|}{\text{CH}_2}}}{\underset{\underset{\text{COO}^-}{|}}{\underset{\text{HO}-\text{C}-\text{H}}{\text{C}}}}-\text{COO}^-}
$$

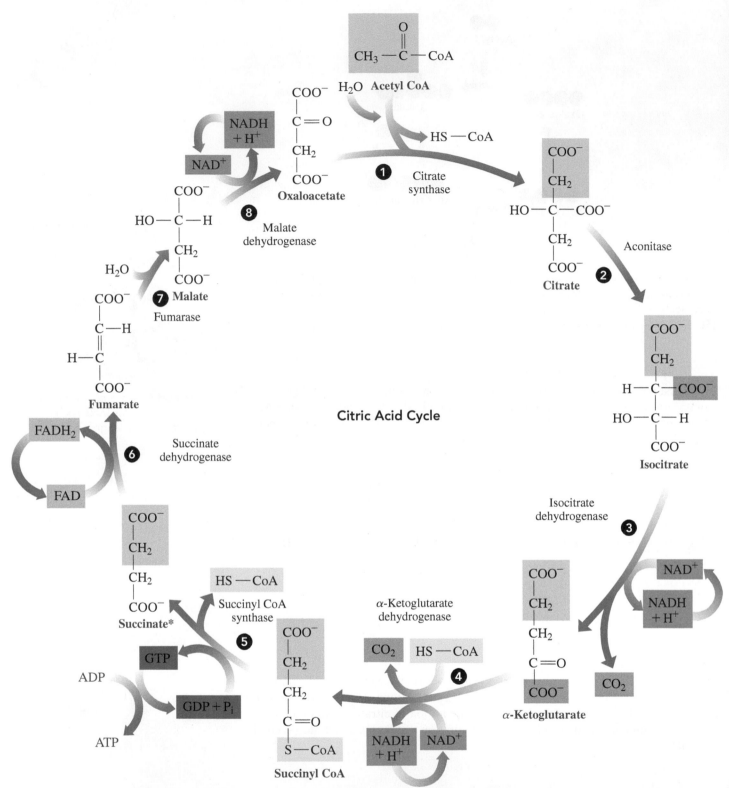

*Succinate is a symmetrical compound.

FIGURE 23.3 ▶ In the citric acid cycle, oxidation reactions produce two CO_2 and reduced coenzymes NADH and $FADH_2$, GTP, and regenerate oxaloacetate.

Q What type of enzyme in the citric acid cycle produces reduced coenzymes?

Reaction 3   Oxidation and Decarboxylation

In reaction 3, both an oxidation and a decarboxylation take place for the first time in the citric acid cycle. The secondary alcohol group in isocitrate (6C) is oxidized to a ketone by *isocitrate dehydrogenase*. A *decarboxylation* removes one carbon from isocitrate by converting a carboxylate group (COO^-) to a CO_2 molecule. The ketone product is named α-ketoglutarate (5C) because the ketone is next to (alpha to) the carboxyl group. During this oxidation, a dehydrogenase removes hydrogen ions and electrons, which are used to reduce NAD^+ to NADH and H^+.

Isocitrate   α-Ketoglutarate

Reaction 4   Decarboxylation and Oxidation

In a reaction catalyzed by *α-ketoglutarate dehydrogenase*, α-ketoglutarate (5C) undergoes decarboxylation. The four-carbon product combines with coenzyme A to yield succinyl CoA. The oxidation of the thiol group ($-SH$) in HS$-$CoA provides hydrogen that is transferred to NAD^+ to form a second molecule of NADH and H^+.

α-Ketoglutarate   Succinyl CoA

Reaction 5   Hydrolysis

In reaction 5, *succinyl CoA synthetase* catalyzes the hydrolysis of the thioester bond in succinyl CoA to yield succinate and HS$-$CoA. The energy from hydrolysis is transferred to the condensation of phosphate and GDP (guanosine diphosphate) forming GTP, a high-energy compound similar to ATP.

Succinyl CoA   Succinate

Eventually in the cell, the hydrolysis of GTP to GDP provides energy for the condensation of phosphate with ADP forming ATP. This reaction is the only time in the citric acid cycle that ATP is produced by a direct transfer of a phosphate group. The reaction between GTP and ADP regenerates GDP that is used again in the citric acid cycle.

$$GTP + ADP \longrightarrow GDP + ATP$$

Reaction 6   Oxidation

In reaction 6, *succinate dehydrogenase* catalyzes the oxidation of succinate to yield fumarate, a compound with a carbon–carbon ($C{=}C$) double bond. In this oxidation, the 2H lost from succinate are used to reduce the coenzyme FAD to $FADH_2$. This is the only reaction in the citric acid cycle in which FAD is reduced to $FADH_2$.

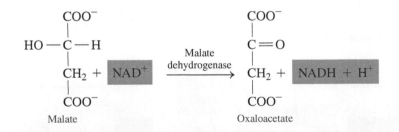

Reaction 7   Hydration

In reaction 7, a hydration catalyzed by *fumarase* adds water to the double bond of fumarate to yield malate, which is a secondary alcohol.

Reaction 8   Oxidation

In reaction 8, the last step of the citric acid cycle, *malate dehydrogenase* catalyzes the oxidation of the hydroxyl group ($-OH$) in malate to a carbonyl group ($C{=}O$) yielding oxaloacetate. For the third time in the citric acid cycle, an oxidation by a dehydrogenase provides hydrogen ions and electrons for the reduction of NAD^+ to NADH and H^+.

Malic acid (malate) produces the sour taste of green apples and rhubarb.

Products from One Turn of the Citric Acid Cycle
2 CO_2
3 NADH and $3H^+$
1 $FADH_2$
1 GTP (1 ATP)
1 HS—CoA

Summary of Products from the Citric Acid Cycle

We have seen that the citric acid cycle begins when a two-carbon acetyl group from acetyl CoA combines with four-carbon oxaloacetate to form six-carbon citrate. Through oxidation, reduction, and decarboxylation, two carbon atoms are removed to yield two CO_2 and a four-carbon compound that undergoes reactions to regenerate oxaloacetate.

In the four oxidation reactions for one turn of the citric acid cycle, three NAD^+ are reduced to three NADH and one FAD is reduced to one $FADH_2$. One GDP is converted to one GTP, which is used to convert one ADP and P_i to ATP. We can write an overall chemical equation for one complete turn of the citric acid cycle as follows:

$$Acetyl\ CoA\ +\ 3NAD^+\ +\ FAD\ +\ GDP\ (or\ ADP)\ +\ P_i\ +\ 2H_2O\ \longrightarrow$$

$$2CO_2\ +\ 3NADH\ +\ 3H^+\ +\ FADH_2\ +\ GTP\ (or\ ATP)\ +\ HS\!-\!CoA$$

Up to this point, we have seen that when a molecule of glucose undergoes oxidation, it yields two acetyl CoA that would go through two turns of the citric acid cycle producing several reduced coenzymes and 2 ATP in the process.

Regulation of the Citric Acid Cycle

The primary function of the citric acid cycle is to produce high-energy compounds like NADH and $FADH_2$ for ATP synthesis. When the cell needs energy, low levels of ATP or high levels of ADP stimulate the conversion of pyruvate to acetyl CoA, which increases the rate of the citric acid cycle. When ATP or NADH levels are high, citrate synthase is inhibited, and the production of acetyl CoA from pyruvate decreases.

In the citric acid cycle, the enzymes that catalyze reactions 3 and 4 respond to allosteric activation and feedback inhibition. In reaction 3, isocitrate dehydrogenase is activated by high levels of ADP and inhibited by high levels of ATP and NADH. In reaction 4, α-ketoglutarate dehydrogenase is activated by high levels of ADP and inhibited by high levels of NADH and succinyl CoA (see Figure 23.4).

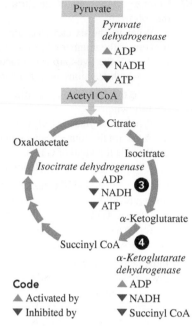

Code
▲ Activated by
▼ Inhibited by

FIGURE 23.4 ▶ High levels of ADP activate enzymes for the production of acetyl CoA and the citric acid cycle, whereas high levels of ATP, NADH, and succinyl CoA inhibit enzymes in the citric acid cycle.

Q How do high levels of ATP affect the rate of the citric acid cycle?

▶SAMPLE PROBLEM 23.1 The Citric Acid Cycle

When one acetyl CoA moves through one turn of the citric acid cycle, how many of each of the following is produced?

a. NADH   **b.** CO_2

SOLUTION

a. One turn of the citric acid cycle produces three molecules of NADH.
b. Two molecules of CO_2 are produced by the decarboxylation of isocitrate and α-ketoglutarate.

STUDY CHECK 23.1

When one acetyl CoA moves through one turn of the citric acid cycle, how many $FADH_2$ would be produced?

ANSWER

one $FADH_2$

QUESTIONS AND PROBLEMS

23.1 The Citric Acid Cycle

LEARNING GOAL Describe the oxidation of acetyl CoA in the citric acid cycle.

23.1 What other names are used for the citric acid cycle?

23.2 What compounds are needed to start the citric acid cycle?

23.3 What are the products from one turn of the citric acid cycle?

23.4 What compound is regenerated in each turn of the citric acid cycle?

23.5 Identify the reaction(s) of the citric acid cycle that involve(s)
a. oxidation and decarboxylation
b. dehydration
c. reduction of NAD^+

23.6 Identify the reaction(s) of the citric acid cycle that involve(s)
a. reduction of FAD
b. direct phosphate transfer
c. hydration

23.7 Refer to the diagram of the citric acid cycle to answer each of the following:
  a. What are the six-carbon compounds?
  b. How is the number of carbon atoms decreased?
  c. What is the five-carbon compound?
  d. In which reactions are secondary alcohols oxidized?

23.8 Refer to the diagram of the citric acid cycle to answer each of the following:
  a. What is the yield of CO_2 molecules?
  b. What are the four-carbon compounds?
  c. What is the yield of GTP molecules?
  d. What are the decarboxylation reactions?

23.9 Indicate the name of the enzyme that catalyzes each of the following reactions in the citric acid cycle:
  a. joins acetyl CoA to oxaloacetate
  b. forms a carbon–carbon double bond
  c. adds water to fumarate

23.10 Indicate the name of the enzyme that catalyzes each of the following reactions in the citric acid cycle:
  a. isomerizes citrate
  b. oxidizes and decarboxylates α-ketoglutarate
  c. hydrolyzes succinyl CoA

23.11 Indicate the coenzyme that accepts hydrogen in each of the following:
  a. isocitrate $\longrightarrow$ α-ketoglutarate
  b. succinate $\longrightarrow$ fumarate

23.12 Indicate the coenzyme that accepts hydrogen in each of the following:
  a. malate $\longrightarrow$ oxaloacetate
  b. α-ketoglutarate $\longrightarrow$ succinyl CoA

23.13 What enzymes in the citric acid cycle are allosteric enzymes?

23.14 Why does the rate of the oxidation of pyruvate affect the rate of the citric acid cycle?

23.15 How do high levels of ADP affect the rate of the citric acid cycle?

23.16 How do high levels of NADH affect the rate of the citric acid cycle?

℞ Clinical Applications

23.17 An enzyme deficiency in the citric acid cycle causes a buildup of malate. Symptoms of the enzyme deficiency include polycythemia, severe neurological problems, and seizures. Which enzyme in the citric acid cycle is deficient?

23.18 An enzyme deficiency in the citric acid cycle produces a large amount of α-ketoglutarate in the blood and urine. Symptoms of the enzyme deficiency include neurological degeneration, rigid muscles, and encephalopathy. Which enzyme in the citric acid cycle is deficient?

LEARNING GOAL

Describe the transfer of hydrogen ions and electrons in electron transport and the process of oxidative phosphorylation in ATP synthesis.

23.2 Electron Transport and ATP

At this point in stage 3 of catabolism, for each glucose molecule that completes glycolysis, the oxidation of two pyruvate, and the citric acid cycle, four ATP, ten NADH, and two $FADH_2$ are produced.

From One Glucose	ATP	Reduced Coenzymes	
Glycolysis	2	2 NADH	
Oxidation of 2 Pyruvate		2 NADH	
Citric Acid Cycle with 2 Acetyl CoA	2	6 NADH	$2 FADH_2$
Total for One Glucose	4	**10 NADH**	$2 FADH_2$

The reduced coenzymes NADH and $FADH_2$ produced from glycolysis, the oxidation of pyruvate, and the citric acid cycle are oxidized to provide the energy for the synthesis of significant amounts of ATP. In **electron transport**, or the *respiratory chain*, hydrogen ions and electrons from NADH and $FADH_2$ are passed from one electron acceptor or electron carrier to the next until they combine with oxygen to form H_2O. The energy released during electron transport is used to synthesize ATP from ADP and P_i, a process called *oxidative phosphorylation*. As long as oxygen is available for the mitochondria in the cell, electron transport and oxidative phosphorylation function to synthesize most of the ATP produced in the cell.

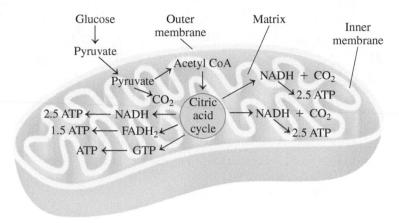

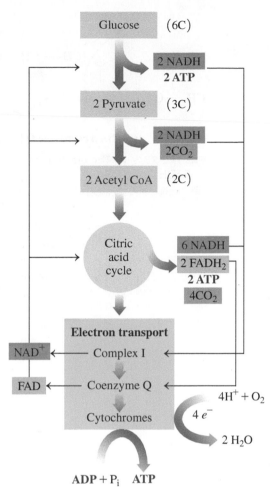

The enzymes and electron carriers for electron transport are located along the inner membrane of the mitochondria.

A mitochondrion contains an inner and outer membrane. Along the highly folded inner membrane are the enzymes and electron carriers required for electron transport. Embedded within these membranes are five distinct protein complexes, which are numbered I, II, III, IV, and V. Four of the protein complexes (I, III, IV, and V) extend through the inner mitochondrial membrane, with one end of each complex in the matrix and the other end in the intermembrane space. Two mobile electron carriers, coenzyme Q and cytochrome c, carry electrons between these protein complexes bound to the inner membrane (see Figure 23.5).

The reduced coenzymes NADH and $FADH_2$ that provide hydrogen ions and electrons in electron transport are regenerated as NAD^+ and FAD.

Complex I

Electron transport begins when hydrogen ions and electrons are transferred from NADH to complex I. The loss of hydrogen from NADH regenerates NAD^+, which becomes available to oxidize more substrates in oxidative

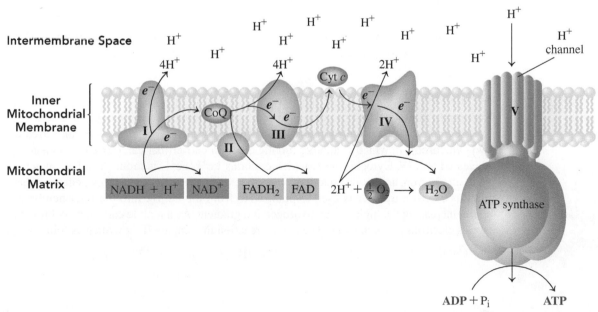

FIGURE 23.5 ▶ In electron transport, the oxidation of NADH and $FADH_2$ provides hydrogen ions and electrons that eventually react with oxygen to form water.

Q What pathway is the major source of NADH for electron transport?

Quinone

$(CH_2-CH=\overset{\overset{\displaystyle CH_3}{|}}{C}-CH_2)_{10}H$

CH_3-O

CH_3-O

$2H^+ + 2e^-$

Oxidized coenzyme Q (CoQ)

$(CH_2-CH=\overset{\overset{\displaystyle CH_3}{|}}{C}-CH_2)_{10}H$

CH_3-O

CH_3-O

OH

OH

Reduced coenzyme Q (CoQH$_2$)

FIGURE 23.6 ▶ The electron carrier CoQ is reduced to CoQH$_2$ when it accepts 2H$^+$ and 2 e$^-$ from NADH + H$^+$ or FADH$_2$.

◉ How does reduced coenzyme CoQH$_2$ compare to the oxidized form?

pathways such as the citric acid cycle. The hydrogen ions and electrons are transferred to the first mobile electron carrier **coenzyme Q (CoQ)**, which is not strongly associated with a particular complex. Thus, CoQH$_2$ can carry electrons from complexes I and II to complex III (see Figure 23.6).

During the electron transfer to CoQ, H$^+$ ions are pumped through complex I into the intermembrane space, producing a reservoir of H$^+$ called a **hydrogen ion gradient**. Each time two electrons pass from NADH to CoQ, a total of 4H$^+$ are pumped across the mitochondrial membrane. This movement of hydrogen ions produces a charge separation on opposite sides of the membrane. The overall reaction sequence in complex I is written as follows:

$$NADH + H^+ + CoQ \longrightarrow NAD^+ + CoQH_2$$

Complex II

Complex II consists of the enzyme succinate dehydrogenase from the citric acid cycle. In complex II, CoQ obtains hydrogen and electrons directly from FADH$_2$ that was generated by the conversion of succinate to fumarate in the citric acid cycle. This produces CoQH$_2$ and regenerates the oxidized coenzyme FAD, which becomes available again to oxidize more substrates in oxidative pathways. The overall reaction sequence in complex II is written as follows:

$$FADH_2 + CoQ \longrightarrow FAD + CoQH_2$$

Because complex II is at a lower energy than complex I, the electrons from FADH$_2$ enter electron transport at a lower energy level than those from NADH.

Complex III

In complex III, two electrons are transferred from the mobile carrier CoQH$_2$ to a series of iron-containing proteins called **cytochromes (cyt)**. Eventually, electrons are transferred to two cytochrome c, which is another mobile electron carrier that can move between complexes III and IV. Cytochrome c, which contains Fe^{3+}/Fe^{2+}, is reduced to Fe^{2+} when it gains an electron, and oxidized to Fe^{3+} when it loses an electron. The energy generated during this electron transfer is used to pump 4H$^+$ from the matrix into the intermembrane space, increasing the high-energy hydrogen ion gradient. As a mobile carrier, cytochrome c carries electrons to complex IV. The overall reaction in complex III is written as follows:

$$CoQH_2 + 2cyt\ c\ (Fe^{3+}) \longrightarrow CoQ + 2H^+ + 2cyt\ c\ (Fe^{2+})$$

(Oxidized)   (Reduced)

Complex IV

At complex IV, four electrons from four cytochrome c are passed to other electron carriers until the electrons combine with hydrogen ions and oxygen (O$_2$) to form two molecules of water. The overall reaction in complex IV is written as follows:

$$4\ e^- + 4H^+ + O_2 \longrightarrow 2H_2O$$

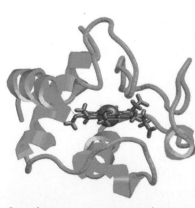

Cytochrome c carries one electron when Fe^{3+} is reduced to Fe^{2+} (orange sphere). The heme group (gray) holds the iron in place.

This equation may also be written as:

$$2\,e^- + 2H^+ + \tfrac{1}{2}O_2 \longrightarrow H_2O$$

At complex IV, energy is used to pump H^+ from the mitochondrial matrix into the intermembrane space, increasing the hydrogen ion gradient further. Overall, the reduced coenzymes NADH and $FADH_2$ from the citric acid cycle enter electron transport to provide hydrogen ions and electrons that react with oxygen, producing water and regenerating the oxidized coenzymes NAD^+ and FAD.

▶SAMPLE PROBLEM 23.2 Oxidation and Reduction

Identify each of the following steps in electron transport as oxidation or reduction:

a. $CoQH_2 \longrightarrow CoQ + 2H^+ + 2\,e^-$
b. cyt c $(Fe^{3+}) + e^- \longrightarrow$ cyt c (Fe^{2+})

SOLUTION

a. The loss of electrons is oxidation.
b. The gain of an electron is reduction.

STUDY CHECK 23.2

What is the final substance that accepts electrons in electron transport?

ANSWER

oxygen (O_2)

Chemistry Link to Health

Toxins: Inhibitors of Electron Transport

Several substances can inhibit the electron carriers in the different complexes of electron transport. Rotenone, a product from a plant root used as an insecticide, and the painkillers Amytal and Demerol block electron transport between complexes I and CoQ. Another inhibitor is the antibiotic antimycin A, which blocks the flow of electrons between complex III and cytochrome c. Another group of compounds, including cyanide (CN^-) and carbon monoxide, block the flow of electrons

between cytochrome c and complex IV. Oligomycin, a common antibiotic, inhibits electron carriers by blocking complex V, ATP synthase. Oligomycin, a common antibiotic, inhibits electron carriers by blocking complex V, ATP synthase. The toxic nature of these compounds makes it clear that organisms rely heavily on the process of electron transport.

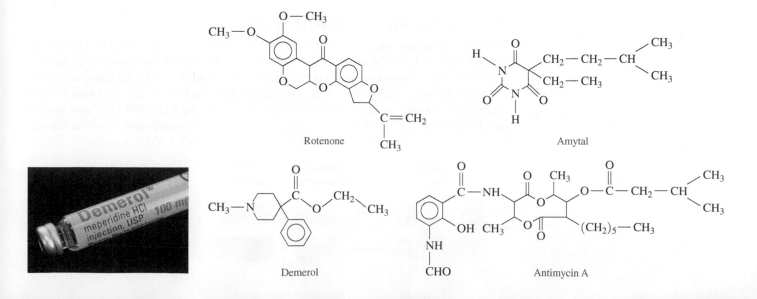

Rotenone

Amytal

Demerol

Antimycin A

When an inhibitor blocks a step in electron transport, the carriers preceding that step are unable to transfer electrons, and remain in their reduced forms. All the carriers after the blocked step remain oxidized without a source of electrons. Thus, any of these inhibitors can shut down electron transport. Consequently, respiration stops, and the cells die.

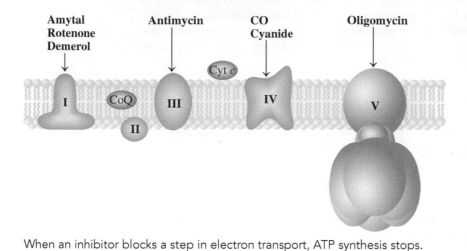

When an inhibitor blocks a step in electron transport, ATP synthesis stops.

Oxidative Phosphorylation

We have seen that energy is generated when electrons from the oxidation of substrates flow through electron transport. Now we will look at how that energy is coupled with the production of ATP in the process called **oxidative phosphorylation**.

In 1978, Peter Mitchell received the Nobel Prize in chemistry for his theory called the *chemiosmotic model*, which links the energy from electron transport to a hydrogen ion gradient that drives the synthesis of ATP. In the model, the complexes I, III, and IV act as hydrogen ion pumps by pushing H^+ ions out of the matrix and into the intermembrane space, producing a hydrogen ion gradient.

To equalize the pH and the electrical charge between the intermembrane space and the matrix, H^+ must return to the matrix. However, H^+ cannot move through the inner membrane. Instead, H^+ must return to the matrix by passing through a fifth protein complex in the inner membrane called **ATP synthase**, also called *complex V*. The flow of H^+ from the intermembrane space through the ATP synthase generates energy that is used to synthesize ATP from ADP and P_i. This process of oxidative phosphorylation couples the energy from electron transport to the synthesis of ATP.

$$ \boxed{ADP + P_i} + \text{energy} \xrightarrow{\text{ATP synthase}} \boxed{ATP} $$

Electron Transport and ATP Synthesis

When NADH enters electron transport at complex I, the energy transferred from its oxidation can be used to synthesize 2.5 ATP. When $FADH_2$ enters electron transport at complex II, which is at a lower energy level, its oxidation provides energy for the synthesis of 1.5 ATP. Old values of 3 ATP from NADH and 2 ATP from $FADH_2$ are still found in some chemistry texts and are often used in biology. However, the ATP values are now considered to be somewhat less than earlier calculations. Current research indicates that the oxidation of one NADH yields 2.5 ATP and one $FADH_2$ yields 1.5 ATP.

Reduced Coenzyme		Oxidized Coenzyme		ATP Output
$NADH + H^+$	$\longrightarrow$	NAD^+	+	2.5 ATP
$FADH_2$	$\longrightarrow$	FAD	+	1.5 ATP

> **SAMPLE PROBLEM 23.3 ATP Synthesis**
>
> Why does the oxidation of NADH provide energy for the formation of 2.5 ATP molecules, whereas $FADH_2$ produces 1.5 ATP molecules?
>
> **SOLUTION**
>
> The oxidation of NADH at complex I provides electrons and hydrogen ions (H^+), which are pumped from the matrix into the intermembrane space eventually producing enough energy for the synthesis of 2.5 ATP molecules. However, $FADH_2$ is oxidized at complex II, which provides energy for the synthesis of only 1.5 ATP molecules.
>
> **STUDY CHECK 23.3**
>
> How do hydrogen ions return to the matrix?
>
> **ANSWER**
>
> Hydrogen ions return to the matrix by passing through ATP synthase, complex V.

Chemistry Link to **Health**
Uncouplers of ATP Synthase

Some types of compounds called *uncouplers* separate the electron transport system from ATP synthase. They do this by providing an alternate route for hydrogen ions to return to the matrix. The electrons are transported to O_2 in electron transport, but ATP is not formed by ATP synthase.

Some uncouplers transport H^+ through the inner mitochondrial membrane, which is normally impermeable to H^+. Compounds such as dicumarol and 2,4-dinitrophenol (DNP) are hydrophobic and bind with H^+ to carry them across the inner membrane. An antibiotic, oligomycin, blocks the channel, which does not allow any H^+ ions to return to the matrix. By removing H^+ ions or blocking the channel, there is no H^+ flow to generate energy for ATP synthesis.

When there is no mechanism for ATP synthesis, the energy of electron transport is released as heat. Certain animals that are adapted to cold climates have developed their own uncoupling system, which allows them to use electron transport energy for heat production. These animals have large amounts of a tissue called *brown fat*, which contains a high concentration of mitochondria. This tissue is brown because of the color of iron in the cytochromes of the mitochondria. The hydrogen ion pumps still operate in brown fat, but a protein called thermogenin, embedded in the inner mitochondrial membrane of brown adipose tissues, allows the H^+ to bypass ATP synthase. Heat rather than ATP is produced.

Dicumarol

2,4-Dinitrophenol (DNP)

Oligomycin

In newborn babies, brown fat is used to generate heat because babies have a small mass but large surface area, and they need to produce more heat than do adults. The brown fat deposits are located near major blood vessels, which carry the warmed blood to the body. Most adults have little or no brown fat, although someone who works outdoors in a cold climate will develop some brown fat deposits.

Plants also use uncouplers. In early spring, heat is used to warm early shoots of plants under the snow, which helps them melt the snow around the plants. Some plants, such as skunk cabbage, use uncoupling agents to volatize fragrant compounds that attract insects to pollinate the plants.

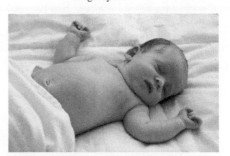

Brown fat helps babies to keep warm.

Regulation of Electron Transport and Oxidative Phosphorylation

Electron transport is regulated by the availability of ADP, P_i, oxygen (O_2), and NADH. Low levels of any of these compounds will decrease the activity of electron transport and the formation of ATP. When a cell is active and ATP is consumed rapidly, the elevated levels of ADP will activate the synthesis of ATP. Therefore, the activity of electron transport is strongly dependent on the availability of ADP for ATP synthesis.

QUESTIONS AND PROBLEMS

23.2 Electron Transport and ATP

LEARNING GOAL Describe the transfer of hydrogen ions and electrons in electron transport and the process of oxidative phosphorylation in ATP synthesis.

23.19 Is cyt c (Fe^{3+}) the abbreviation for the oxidized or reduced form of cytochrome c?

23.20 Is $FADH_2$ the abbreviation for the oxidized or reduced form of flavin adenine dinucleotide?

23.21 Identify each of the following as oxidation or reduction:
a. $NADH \longrightarrow NAD^+ + H^+ + 2\,e^-$
b. $CoQ + 2H^+ + 2\,e^- \longrightarrow CoQH_2$

23.22 Identify each of the following as oxidation or reduction:
a. cyt c (Fe^{2+}) $\longrightarrow$ cyt c (Fe^{3+}) $+ e^-$
b. $FAD + 2H^+ + 2\,e^- \longrightarrow FADH_2$

23.23 What reduced coenzyme provides hydrogen and electrons for electron transport at complex I?

23.24 What reduced coenzyme provides hydrogen and electrons for electron transport at complex II?

23.25 Arrange the following in the order in which they appear in electron transport: cytochrome c (Fe^{3+}), $FADH_2$, CoQ.

23.26 Arrange the following in the order in which they appear in electron transport: O_2, NAD^+, FAD.

23.27 How are electrons carried from complex I to complex III?

23.28 How are electrons carried from complex III to complex IV?

23.29 How is NADH oxidized in electron transport?

23.30 How is $FADH_2$ oxidized in electron transport?

23.31 Complete each of the following reactions in electron transport:
a. $NADH + H^+ + \underline{\hspace{1cm}} \longrightarrow \underline{\hspace{1cm}} + CoQH_2$
b. $CoQH_2 + 2cyt\,c\ (Fe^{3+}) \longrightarrow CoQ + \underline{\hspace{1cm}} + \underline{\hspace{1cm}}$

23.32 Complete each of the following reactions in electron transport:
a. $CoQ + \underline{\hspace{1cm}} \longrightarrow \underline{\hspace{1cm}} + FAD$
b. $4cyt\,c\ (Fe^{3+}) + 4H^+ + O_2 \longrightarrow 4cyt\,c\ (Fe^{2+}) + \underline{\hspace{1cm}}$

23.33 What is meant by the term oxidative phosphorylation?

23.34 How is the hydrogen ion gradient established?

23.35 According to the chemiosmotic model, how does the hydrogen ion gradient provide energy to synthesize ATP?

23.36 How does the phosphorylation of ADP occur?

23.37 How are glycolysis and the citric acid cycle linked to the production of ATP by electron transport?

23.38 Why does $FADH_2$ provide energy to synthesize 1.5 ATP via electron transport, whereas NADH provides energy to synthesize 2.5 ATP?

℞ Clinical Applications

23.39 Potassium cyanide is a potent poison that kills by inhibiting electron transport when CN^- binds to the Fe^{3+} in the cytochrome heme groups. Why would this stop electron transport?

23.40 Coenzyme Q is sold as a dietary supplement called CoQ10 with recommended doses of 22 mg to 400 mg. It is said to boost energy and recovery from exercise. Based on its role in electron transport, explain how this might be possible.

23.41 Increasing thermogenesis has been thought to be a way to lose weight. In fact, 2,4-dinitrophenol is available as a supplement most often used by bodybuilders to burn fat. This dangerous drug is also marketed as a pesticide and kills insects in a similar manner. What might be a side effect of using this compound?

23.42 Oligomycin is an antibiotic that inhibits ATP synthase. If ATP synthase is not operable, what happens to the energy from electron transport?

23.3 ATP Energy from Glucose

LEARNING GOAL

Account for the ATP produced by the complete oxidation of glucose.

The total ATP for the complete oxidation of glucose under aerobic conditions is calculated by combining the ATP produced from glycolysis, the oxidation of pyruvate, the citric acid cycle, and electron transport.

ATP from Glycolysis

In glycolysis, the oxidation of glucose stores energy in two NADH molecules, as well as two ATP molecules from direct phosphate transfer. From glycolysis, glucose produces a total of seven ATP: five ATP from two NADH (malate–aspartate shuttle), and two ATP from direct phosphate transfer.

$$\text{Glucose} \longrightarrow 2\ \text{pyruvate} + 2\ \text{ATP} + 2\ \text{NADH}\ (5\ \text{ATP})$$

Malate–Aspartate Shuttle

Because glycolysis occurs in the cytosol, the NADH it produces cannot pass through the mitochondrial inner membrane. However, the hydrogen ions and electrons from NADH in the cytosol of heart and liver cells can be transferred to compounds in the *malate–aspartate shuttle* called *transporters*, which can move in and out of the mitochondria. In the cytosol, *malate dehydrogenase* catalyzes the reaction of oxaloacetate and NADH to yield malate and NAD^+. Then a transporter binds the malate and carries it across the mitochondrial membrane into the matrix, where *malate dehydrogenase* in the matrix oxidizes malate back to oxaloacetate. The oxidation provides hydrogen ions and electrons that are used to reduce NAD^+ to NADH, which can now enter electron transport to synthesize ATP (see Figure 23.7). Because the oxaloacetate produced in the matrix cannot cross the mitochondrial membrane, it is converted back to aspartate, which moves out of matrix back into the cytosol, where transamination converts it to oxaloacetate. The resulting NAD^+ can participate again in glycolysis in the cytosol.

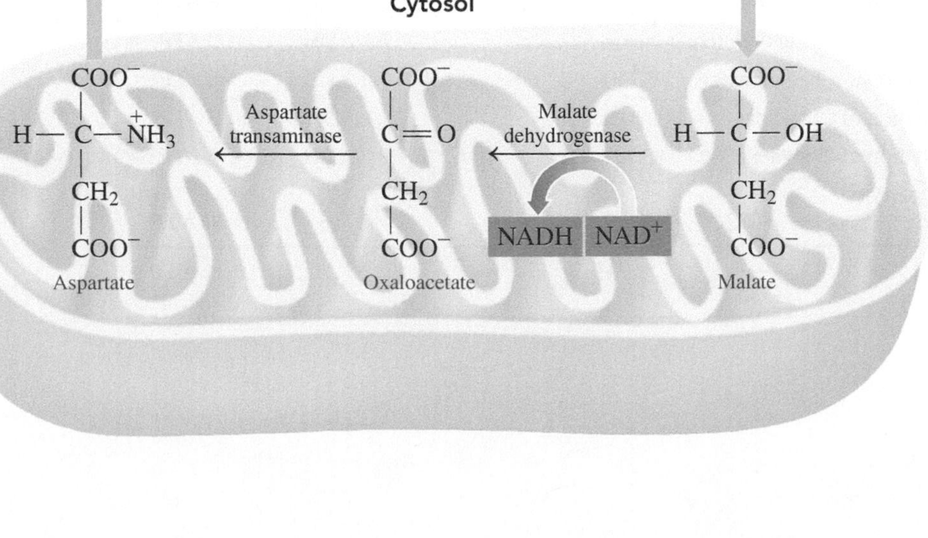

FIGURE 23.7 ▶ The malate–aspartate shuttle transfers the energy stored in NADH formed during glycolysis to transporters that move from the cytosol into the mitochondrial matrix where NADH is regenerated for use in electron transport.

Q Why does the NADH produced by glycolysis utilize the malate–aspartate shuttle?

ATP from the Oxidation of Two Pyruvate

Under aerobic conditions, pyruvate enters the mitochondria, where it is oxidized to give acetyl CoA, CO_2, and NADH. Because glucose yields two pyruvate, two NADH enter electron transport; thus the oxidation of two pyruvate leads to the production of five ATP.

$$2 \text{ Pyruvate} \longrightarrow 2 \text{ acetyl CoA} + 2CO_2 + \boxed{2 \text{ NADH} \quad (5 \text{ ATP})}$$

ATP from the Citric Acid Cycle

The two acetyl CoA produced from two pyruvate now enter the citric acid cycle. Each acetyl CoA makes one turn of the citric acid cycle and produces two CO_2, three NADH, one $FADH_2$, and one ATP (from GTP) by direct phosphate transfer. Thus, the two acetyl CoA initially from one glucose produce a total of six NADH, two $FADH_2$, and two ATP. In electron transport, six NADH produce 15 ATP, and two $FADH_2$ produce 3 ATP. In two turns of the citric acid cycle, a total of 20 ATP are produced.

$$
\begin{aligned}
6 \text{ NADH} \times 2.5 \text{ ATP/NADH} &= 15 \text{ ATP} \\
2 \text{ FADH}_2 \times 1.5 \text{ ATP/FADH}_2 &= 3 \text{ ATP} \\
2 \text{ GTP} \times 1 \text{ ATP/GTP} &= 2 \text{ ATP} \\
\hline
\text{Total (two turns)} &= 20 \text{ ATP}
\end{aligned}
$$

The overall equation for the reaction of two acetyl CoA is

$$2 \text{ Acetyl CoA} \longrightarrow 4CO_2 + 20 \text{ ATP (two turns of the citric acid cycle)}$$

ATP from the Complete Oxidation of Glucose

⚛ **CORE CHEMISTRY SKILL**

Calculating the ATP Produced from Glucose

The total ATP production for the complete oxidation of glucose is calculated by combining the ATP produced from glycolysis plus the oxidation of pyruvate plus the citric acid cycle (see Figure 23.8). The ATP produced for these reactions is given in Table 23.1.

TABLE 23.1 ATP Produced by the Complete Oxidation of Glucose

Pathway	Reaction	Coenzymes	ATP Yield
Glycolysis	Oxidation of glyceraldehyde-3-phosphate	2 NADH	5 ATP
	Direct phosphorylation (2 triose phosphate)		2 ATP
	Summary: $C_6H_{12}O_6 \longrightarrow$ 2 pyruvate + $2H_2O$ Glucose		**7 ATP**
Oxidation and Decarboxylation	2 Pyruvate $\longrightarrow$ 2 acetyl CoA	2 NADH	5 ATP
Citric Acid Cycle (two turns)	Oxidation of 2 isocitrate	2 NADH	5 ATP
	Oxidation of 2 α-ketoglutarate	2 NADH	5 ATP
	2 Direct phosphate transfers (2 GTP)		2 ATP
	Oxidation of 2 succinate	2 FADH$_2$	3 ATP
	Oxidation of 2 malate	2 NADH	5 ATP
	Summary: 2 Acetyl CoA $\longrightarrow 4CO_2 + 2H_2O$		**20 ATP**
Total Yield	$C_6H_{12}O_6 + 6O_2 \longrightarrow 6CO_2 + 6H_2O$ Glucose		**32 ATP**

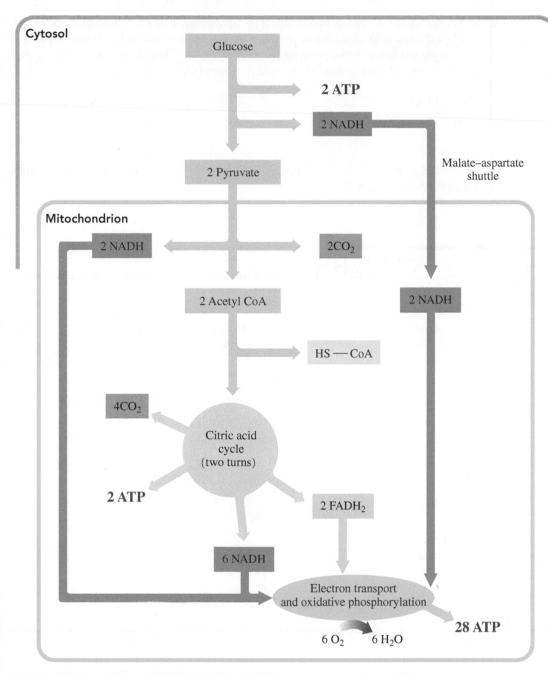

FIGURE 23.8 ▶ The complete oxidation of glucose from glycolysis, citric acid cycle, and electron transport yields a maximum of 32 ATP.

◎ Which metabolic pathway produces most of the ATP from the oxidation of glucose?

▶**SAMPLE PROBLEM 23.4 ATP Production**

As Natalie is walking on the treadmill during her fitness test, how many ATP are produced during each of the following oxidations?

a. two pyruvate to two acetyl CoA
b. one glucose to two acetyl CoA

SOLUTION

ANALYZE THE PROBLEM	Given	Need
	a. two pyruvate to two acetyl CoA	number of ATP
	b. one glucose to two acetyl CoA	number of ATP

a. The oxidation of two pyruvate to two acetyl CoA produces two NADH, which yields five ATP. We calculate this as:

2 NADH × 2.5 ATP/NADH = 5 ATP

b. Seven ATP are produced, two by direct phosphorylation and five from the two NADH, when glucose is oxidized to two pyruvate. Five ATP (from two NADH) are synthesized from the oxidation of two pyruvate to two acetyl CoA. Thus, a total of 12 ATP are produced when glucose is oxidized to yield two acetyl CoA.

STUDY CHECK 23.4

What are the sources of ATP for two turns of the citric acid cycle?

ANSWER

Six NADH provide 15 ATP, two $FADH_2$ provide three ATP, and two direct phosphate transfers provide two ATP.

Chemistry Link to **Health**
Efficiency of ATP Production

In a laboratory, a calorimeter is used to measure the heat energy from the combustion of glucose. In a calorimeter, 1 mole of glucose produces 690 kcal.

$$C_6H_{12}O_6 + 6O_2 \longrightarrow 6CO_2 + 6H_2O + 690\,\text{kcal}$$

We can compare the amount of energy produced from 1 mole of glucose in a calorimeter with the ATP energy produced in the mitochondria from glucose. We use the energy of the hydrolysis of ATP (7.3 kcal/mole of ATP). Because 1 mole of glucose generates energy for up to 32 moles of ATP, the total energy from the oxidation of 1 mole of glucose in the cells would be 230 kcal/mole.

$$\frac{32\ \text{moles ATP}}{1\ \text{mole glucose}} \times \frac{7.3\ \text{kcal}}{1\ \text{mole ATP}} = 230\,\text{kcal}/1\ \text{mole of glucose}$$

Compared to the energy produced by burning glucose in a calorimeter, our cells are about 33% efficient in converting the total available chemical energy in glucose to ATP.

$$\frac{230\ \text{kcal (cells)}}{690\ \text{kcal (calorimeter)}} \times 100\% = 33\%$$

The rest of the energy from glucose produced during the oxidation of glucose in our cells is lost as heat.

Calorimeter	Cells
Energy produced by 1 mole of glucose (690 kcal)	Stored as ATP (230 kcal)
	Lost as heat (460 kcal)

QUESTIONS AND PROBLEMS

23.3 ATP Energy from Glucose

LEARNING GOAL Account for the ATP produced by the complete oxidation of glucose.

23.43 How many turns of the citric acid cycle are required to oxidize one molecule of glucose?

23.44 Under aerobic conditions, what is the maximum number of ATP that can be produced from one glucose molecule?

23.45 What is the energy yield in ATP associated with each of the following?
   a. NADH $\longrightarrow$ NAD$^+$
   b. glucose $\longrightarrow$ 2 pyruvate
   c. 2 pyruvate $\longrightarrow$ 2 acetyl CoA + 2CO$_2$

23.46 What is the energy yield in ATP associated with each of the following?
   a. FADH$_2$ $\longrightarrow$ FAD
   b. glucose + 6O$_2$ $\longrightarrow$ 6CO$_2$ + 6H$_2$O
   c. acetyl CoA $\longrightarrow$ 2CO$_2$

Clinical Update
Improving Natalie's Overall Fitness

Natalie's exercise stress test results indicate that she has a $V_{O_2\,max}$ of 30 mL/kg min, which Angela, her exercise physiologist, classifies in the fair to poor range for her age. Natalie's blood oxygen measured 89%. The normal values for pulse oximeter readings are 95 to 100%, which means that Natalie's O_2 saturation is considered

Low-intensity exercises are used at the beginning of Natalie's exercise program.

low. Thus, Natalie does not have an adequate amount of O_2 in her blood, and may be hypoxic. This may be the reason she has noticed a shortness of breath and a dry cough. Her doctor diagnosed her with *interstitial lung disease*, which is scarring of the tissue of the lungs.

Angela teaches Natalie to inhale and exhale slower and deeper to fill the lungs with more air and thus more oxygen. Angela also develops a workout program with the goal of increasing Natalie's overall fitness level. They begin with low-intensity exercises that utilize smaller muscles instead of larger muscles, which require more O_2 and can deplete a significant amount of the O_2 in her blood. During the exercises, Angela continues to monitor Natalie's heart rate, blood O_2

level, and blood pressure to ensure that Natalie is exercising at a level that will enable her to become stronger without breaking down muscle due to a lack of oxygen.

As Natalie's $V_{O_2\,max}$ improves, Angela modifies her workouts to include larger muscle groups. Eventually Natalie will take a second exercise stress test to check her progress.

Clinical Applications

23.47 How would low oxygen levels affect the production of ATP?

23.48 If Natalie has low levels of NADH, how would her production of ATP be affected?

23.49 Natalie's low O_2 gives her only a 24% efficiency of ATP production from glucose. How many moles of ATP would she obtain from 25 g of glucose if glucose has a molar mass of 180.2 g/mole? (see Chemistry Link to Health "Efficiency of ATP Production")

23.50 Natalie's exercise program improves her O_2 blood level to give her a 30.% efficiency of ATP production from glucose. How many moles of ATP would she obtain from 25 g of glucose if glucose has a molar mass of 180.2 g/mole? (see Chemistry Link to Health "Efficiency of ATP Production")

CONCEPT MAP

METABOLISM AND ENERGY PRODUCTION

Acetyl CoA
enters the
Citric Acid Cycle
to yield
GTP | **NADH** | **FADH$_2$** | **CO$_2$**
that enter
Electron Transport
is converted to | provide energy for | provide
ATP Synthase | **H$^+$ and Electrons**
which produces | to
ATP | **O$_2$**
to produce
H$_2$O

CHAPTER REVIEW

23.1 The Citric Acid Cycle
LEARNING GOAL
Describe the oxidation of acetyl CoA in the citric acid cycle.

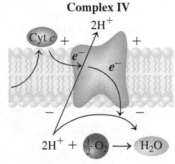

- In a sequence of reactions called the citric acid cycle, an acetyl group is combined with oxaloacetate to yield citrate.
- Citrate undergoes oxidation and decarboxylation to yield two CO_2, GTP, three NADH, and $FADH_2$ with the regeneration of oxaloacetate.
- The direct phosphate transfer of ADP by GTP yields ATP.

23.2 Electron Transport and ATP
LEARNING GOAL
Describe the transfer of hydrogen ions and electrons in electron transport and the process of oxidative phosphorylation in ATP synthesis.

- The reduced coenzymes NADH and $FADH_2$ from various metabolic pathways are oxidized to NAD^+ and FAD when their electrons are transferred through the electron transport system.

- The protein complexes in electron transport act as hydrogen ion pumps producing an H^+ gradient across the inner mitochondrial membrane.
- As the hydrogen ions return to the matrix by way of ATP synthase, energy is generated.
- This energy is used to drive the synthesis of ATP in a process known as oxidative phosphorylation.
- The ADP and ATP levels in the cells control the activity of electron transport.

23.3 ATP Energy from Glucose
LEARNING GOAL
Account for the ATP produced by the complete oxidation of glucose.

Calorimeter	Cells
Energy produced by 1 mole of glucose (690 kcal)	Stored as ATP (230 kcal)
	Lost as heat (460 kcal)

- The oxidation of NADH yields 2.5 ATP, and $FADH_2$ yields 1.5 ATP.
- The energy from the NADH produced in the cytosol is transferred into the matrix via a shuttle. The malate–aspartate shuttle is used in the heart and liver.
- Under aerobic conditions, the complete oxidation of glucose yields a maximum of 32 ATP from the oxidation of the reduced coenzymes NADH and $FADH_2$ by electron transport, oxidative phosphorylation, and from direct phosphate transfer.

SUMMARY OF KEY REACTIONS

The chapter sections to review are shown after the name of the reaction.

Citric Acid Cycle (23.1)

$$\text{Acetyl CoA} + 3NAD^+ + FAD + GDP + P_i + 2H_2O \longrightarrow$$
$$2CO_2 + 3NADH + 3H^+ + FADH_2 + GTP + HS{-}CoA$$

Electron Transport and Oxidative Phosphorylation (23.2)

$$NADH + H^+ \longrightarrow NAD^+ + 2.5\ ATP$$
$$FADH_2 \longrightarrow FAD + 1.5\ ATP$$

Phosphorylation of ADP (23.2)

$$ADP + P_i \longrightarrow ATP$$

Complete Oxidation of Glucose (23.3)

$$\underset{\text{Glucose}}{C_6H_{12}O_6} + 6O_2 + 32\ ADP + 32P_i \longrightarrow 6CO_2 + 6H_2O + 32\ ATP$$

KEY TERMS

ATP synthase An enzyme complex (V) that links the energy released by hydrogen ions returning to the matrix with the synthesis of ATP from ADP and P_i.

citric acid cycle A series of oxidation reactions in the mitochondria that converts acetyl CoA to CO_2 and yields NADH and $FADH_2$. It is also called the tricarboxylic acid cycle or the Krebs cycle.

coenzyme Q (CoQ) A mobile carrier that transfers electrons from NADH and FADH$_2$ to complex III.

cytochrome (cyt) An iron-containing protein that transfers electrons from CoQH$_2$ to oxygen.

electron transport A series of reactions in the mitochondria that transfers electrons from NADH and FADH$_2$ to electron carriers, and finally to O$_2$, which produces H$_2$O. Energy changes during these transfers provide energy for ATP synthesis.

hydrogen ion gradient A separation of charge across a membrane caused by the pumping of hydrogen ions from the matrix into the intermembrane space.

oxidative phosphorylation The synthesis of ATP using the energy of the hydrogen ions and electrons from the NADH and FADH$_2$ that enter electron transport to produce a hydrogen ion gradient.

⚛ CORE CHEMISTRY SKILLS

The chapter section containing each Core Chemistry Skill is shown in parentheses at the end of each heading.

Describing the Reactions in the Citric Acid Cycle (23.1)

• In the initial reaction of the citric acid cycle, an acetyl group combines with oxaloacetate to yield citrate.

• Citrate undergoes several reactions including oxidation, decarboxylation, and hydration to yield two CO$_2$, GTP, three NADH, one FADH$_2$, and to form another oxaloacetate.

Example: Identify the compound(s) in the citric acid cycle that undergo each of the following changes:

    a. loses a CO$_2$ molecule

    b. adds water

Answer: **a.** Isocitrate (6C) undergoes oxidation and decarboxylation to form α-ketoglutarate (5C), and α-ketoglutarate (5C) undergoes oxidation and decarboxylation to form succinyl CoA (4C).

    b. Fumarate, which has a double bond, adds an H$_2$O molecule to form malate.

Calculating the ATP Produced from Glucose (23.3)

• The reduced coenzymes NADH and FADH$_2$ from various metabolic pathways are oxidized to NAD$^+$ and FAD when their H$^+$ ions and electrons are transferred to the electron transport system.

• The energy released is used to synthesize ATP from ADP and P$_i$.

• The final acceptor, O$_2$, combines with H$^+$ ions and electrons to yield H$_2$O.

• The protein complexes I, III, and IV in electron transport move hydrogen ions into the intermembrane space, which produces the H$^+$ gradient.

• As the H$^+$ ions return to the matrix by way of ATP synthase, ATP energy is generated in a process known as oxidative phosphorylation.

• The oxidation of NADH yields 2.5 ATP, and the oxidation of FADH$_2$ yields 1.5 ATP.

• Under aerobic conditions, the complete oxidation of glucose yields a maximum of 32 ATP.

Example: Calculate the ATP produced from each of the following:

    a. one glucose to two pyruvate

    b. one NADH to one NAD$^+$

    c. complete oxidation of one glucose to 6CO$_2$ and 6H$_2$O

Answer: **a.** Glucose is converted to two pyruvate during glycolysis, which produces 2 ATP and 2 NADH for a total of 7 ATP.

    b. One NADH is converted to one NAD$^+$ in the electron transport system, which produces 2.5 ATP.

    c. Glucose is completely oxidized to 6CO$_2$ and 6H$_2$O in glycolysis, citric acid cycle, and electron transport, which produces a maximum of 32 ATP.

UNDERSTANDING THE CONCEPTS

The chapter sections to review are given in parentheses at the end of each question.

23.51 Identify each of the following as a substance that is part of the citric acid cycle, electron transport, or both: (23.1, 23.2)

    a. succinate   **b.** CoQH$_2$

    c. FAD   **d.** cyt *c* (Fe^{2+})

    e. citrate

23.52 Identify each of the following as a substance that is part of the citric acid cycle, electron transport, or both: (23.1, 23.2)

    a. succinyl CoA   **b.** acetyl CoA

    c. malate   **d.** NAD$^+$

    e. α-ketoglutarate

23.53 Complete the names of the missing compounds in the citric acid cycle: (23.1)

    a. citrate $\longrightarrow$ _____

    b. succinyl CoA $\longrightarrow$ _____

    c. malate $\longrightarrow$ _____

23.54 Complete the names of the missing compounds in the citric acid cycle: (23.1)

    a. oxaloacetate $\longrightarrow$ _____

    b. fumarate $\longrightarrow$ _____

    c. isocitrate $\longrightarrow$ _____

23.55 Identify the reactant and product for each of the following enzymes in the citric acid cycle: (23.1)

    a. aconitase

    b. succinate dehydrogenase

    c. fumarase

23.56 Identify the reactant and product for each of the following enzymes in the citric acid cycle: (23.1)
   a. isocitrate dehydrogenase
   b. succinyl CoA synthetase
   c. malate dehydrogenase

23.57 For each of the given enzymes (**a** to **c**), indicate which of the following are needed: NAD^+, H_2O, FAD, GDP. (23.1)
   a. aconitase
   b. succinate dehydrogenase
   c. isocitrate dehydrogenase

23.58 For each of the given enzymes (**a** to **c**), indicate which of the following are needed: NAD^+, H_2O, FAD, GDP. (23.1)
   a. fumarase
   b. succinyl CoA synthetase
   c. malate dehydrogenase

23.59 Identify the type(s) of reaction(s)—(1) oxidation, (2) decarboxylation, (3) hydrolysis, (4) hydration—catalyzed by each of the following enzymes (**a** to **c**): (23.1)
   a. aconitase
   b. succinate dehydrogenase
   c. isocitrate dehydrogenase

23.60 Identify the type(s) of reaction(s)—(1) oxidation, (2) decarboxylation, (3) hydrolysis, (4) hydration—catalyzed by each of the following enzymes (**a** to **c**): (23.1)
   a. fumarase
   b. α-ketoglutarate dehydrogenase
   c. malate dehydrogenase

23.61 How many H^+ are pumped across the inner mitochondrial membrane when one NADH undergoes oxidation via electron transport? (23.2)

23.62 How many H^+ are pumped across the inner mitochondrial membrane when one $FADH_2$ undergoes oxidation via electron transport? (23.2)

23.63 What is the maximum number of ATP produced by energy generated when electrons flow from NADH to oxygen (O_2)? (23.3)

23.64 What is the maximum number of ATP produced by energy generated when electrons flow from $FADH_2$ to oxygen (O_2)? (23.3)

ADDITIONAL QUESTIONS AND PROBLEMS

23.65 What is the main function of the citric acid cycle in energy production? (23.1)

23.66 Most metabolic pathways are not considered cycles. Why the citric acid cycle is considered a metabolic cycle? (23.1)

23.67 If there are no reactions in the citric acid cycle that use oxygen, O_2, why does the cycle operate only in aerobic conditions? (23.1)

23.68 What products of the citric acid cycle are needed for electron transport? (23.1)

23.69 Identify the compounds in the citric acid cycle that have the following: (23.1)
   a. six carbon atoms   **b.** five carbon atoms
   c. a keto group

23.70 Identify the compounds in the citric acid cycle that have the following: (23.1)
   a. four carbon atoms   **b.** a hydroxyl group
   c. a carbon–carbon double bond

23.71 In which reaction of the citric acid cycle does each of the following occur? (23.1)
   a. A five-carbon keto acid is decarboxylated.
   b. A carbon–carbon double bond is hydrated.
   c. NAD^+ is reduced.
   d. A secondary hydroxyl group is oxidized.

23.72 In which reaction of the citric acid cycle does each of the following occur? (23.1)
   a. FAD is reduced.
   b. A six-carbon keto acid is decarboxylated.
   c. A carbon–carbon double bond is formed.
   d. GDP undergoes direct phosphate transfer.

23.73 Indicate the coenzyme(s) for each of the following reactions: (23.1)
   a. isocitrate $\longrightarrow$ α-ketoglutarate
   b. α-ketoglutarate $\longrightarrow$ succinyl CoA

23.74 Indicate the coenzyme(s) for each of the following reactions: (23.1)
   a. succinate $\longrightarrow$ fumarate
   b. malate $\longrightarrow$ oxaloacetate

23.75 How does each of the following regulate the citric acid cycle? (23.1)
   a. high levels of NADH
   b. high levels of ATP

23.76 How does each of the following regulate the citric acid cycle? (23.1)
   a. high levels of ADP
   b. low levels of NADH

23.77 At which complexes in the electron transport system are hydrogen ions pumped into the intermembrane space? (23.2)

23.78 What is the effect of hydrogen ion accumulation in the intermembrane space? (23.2)

23.79 Which complex in electron transport is inhibited by each of the following? (23.2)
   a. Amytal and rotenone   **b.** antimycin A
   c. cyanide and carbon monoxide

23.80 a. When an inhibitor blocks electron transport, how are the coenzymes that precede the blocked site affected? (23.2)
   b. When an inhibitor blocks electron transport, how are the coenzymes that follow the blocked site affected?

23.81 In the chemiosmotic model, how is energy provided to synthesize ATP? (23.2)

23.82 Where does the synthesis of ATP take place in electron transport? (23.2)

23.83 Why do hydrogen ions tend to leave the intermembrane space and return to the matrix within a mitochondrion? (23.2)

23.84 Why do the enzyme complexes that pump hydrogen ions extend across the mitochondrial membrane from the matrix to the intermembrane space? (23.2)

23.85 Where is ATP synthase for oxidative phosphorylation located in the cell? (23.2)

23.86 How does the NADH generated in the cytosol during glycolysis get moved into the matrix? (23.3)

23.87 How many ATP are produced when glucose is oxidized to pyruvate compared to when glucose is oxidized to CO_2 and H_2O? (23.3)

23.88 Considering the efficiency of ATP synthesis, how many kilocalories of energy would be conserved from the complete oxidation of 4.0 moles of glucose? (23.3)

23.89 How is the energy from the hydrogen ion gradient utilized by ATP synthase? (23.2)

23.90 In electron transport, would the solution in the space between the outer and inner mitochondrial membrane be more or less acidic than the solution in the matrix? (23.2)

23.91 Why would a bear that is hibernating have more brown fat than one that is active? (23.2)

23.92 Why would an animal that lives in a warm climate have less brown fat than a similar animal that lives in a cold climate? (23.2)

CHALLENGE QUESTIONS

The following groups of questions are related to the topics in this chapter. However, they do not all follow the chapter order, and they require you to combine concepts and skills from several sections. These questions will help you increase your critical thinking skills and prepare for your next exam.

23.93 Using the value 7.3 kcal/mole for ATP, how many kilocalories can be produced from the ATP provided by the reaction of 1 mole of glucose in each of the following? (23.1, 23.3)
 a. glycolysis
 b. oxidation of pyruvate to acetyl CoA
 c. citric acid cycle
 d. complete oxidation to CO_2 and H_2O

23.94 In a calorimeter, the combustion of 1 mole of glucose produces 690 kcal. What percentage of ATP energy is produced from 1 mole of glucose by each of the reactions in problem 23.93 **a** to **d**? (23.1, 23.3)

23.95 What does it mean to say that the cell is 33% efficient in storing the energy from the complete combustion of glucose? (23.3)

23.96 If acetyl CoA has a molar mass of 809 g/mole, how many moles of ATP are produced when 1.0 μg of acetyl CoA completes the citric acid cycle? (23.3)

℞ Clinical Applications

23.97 A person's basal metabolic rate (BMR) gives the number of kilocalories utilized in one day to maintain weight. To lose weight, caloric intake needs to be lower or activity level can be increased. The resting BMR can be calculated in kilocalories by the following formula: (23.3)

Women: BMR kcal = 655 + (4.35 × weight lb) + (4.70 × height in.) − (4.70 × age in years)
 a. If a woman weighs 115 lb, is 5 ft 4 in. tall, and is 21 years old, what is her basal metabolic rate, rounded to the nearest 10 kilocalories?
 b. If the molar mass of ATP is 507 g/mole, how many kilograms of ATP is used in one day?

23.98 A person's basal metabolic rate (BMR) gives the number of kilocalories utilized in one day to maintain weight. To lose weight, caloric intake needs to be lower or activity level can be increased. The resting BMR can be calculated in kilocalories by the following formula: (23.3)

Men: BMR kcal = 66 + (6.23 × weight lb) + (12.7 × height in.) − (6.80 × age in years)
 a. If a man weighs 184 lb, is 6 ft 1 in. tall, and is 32 years old, what is his basal metabolic rate, rounded to the nearest 10 kilocalories?
 b. If the molar mass of ATP is 507 g/mole, how many kilograms of ATP is used in one day?

ANSWERS TO SELECTED QUESTIONS AND PROBLEMS

23.1 Krebs cycle and tricarboxylic acid cycle

23.3 $2CO_2$, 3 NADH + $3H^+$, $FADH_2$, GTP (ATP), and HS—CoA

23.5 a. Two reactions, reactions 3 and 4, involve oxidation and decarboxylation.
 b. Reaction 6 involves dehydration.
 c. Reactions 3, 4, and 8 involve reduction of NAD^+.

23.7 a. citrate and isocitrate
 b. A carbon atom is lost as CO_2 in decarboxylation.
 c. α-ketoglutarate
 d. reactions 3 and 8

23.9 a. citrate synthase
 b. succinate dehydrogenase and aconitase
 c. fumarase

23.11 a. NAD^+ **b.** FAD

23.13 Isocitrate dehydrogenase and α-ketoglutarate dehydrogenase are allosteric enzymes.

23.15 High levels of ADP increase the rate of the citric acid cycle.

23.17 malate dehydrogenase

23.19 oxidized

23.21 a. oxidation   **b.** reduction

23.23 NADH

23.25 $FADH_2$, CoQ, cytochrome c (Fe^{3+})

23.27 The mobile carrier CoQ transfers electrons from complex I to complex III.

23.29 NADH transfers electrons to complex I to give NAD^+.

23.31 a. $NADH + H^+ + CoQ \longrightarrow NAD^+ + CoQH_2$
b. $CoQH_2 + 2cyt\,c\,(Fe^{3+}) \longrightarrow$
$$CoQ + 2cyt\,c\,(Fe^{2+}) + 2H^+$$

23.33 In oxidative phosphorylation, the energy from the oxidation reactions in electron transport is used to synthesize ATP from ADP and P_i.

23.35 As hydrogen ions return to the lower energy environment in the matrix, they pass through ATP synthase where they release energy to drive the synthesis of ATP.

23.37 Glycolysis and the citric acid cycle produce the reduced coenzymes NADH and $FADH_2$, which enter electron transport and release hydrogen ions and electrons that are used to generate energy for the synthesis of ATP.

23.39 If CN^- binds to the heme of a cytochrome, electrons cannot reduce Fe^{3+} to Fe^{2+} and will not be transported, stopping electron transport.

23.41 Because dinitrophenol induces thermogenesis and inhibits ATP synthase, it raises body temperature to unsafe levels and can cause constant sweating.

23.43 Two. In glycolysis, one glucose molecule forms two pyruvate, which oxidize to give 2 acetyl CoA.

23.45 a. 2.5 ATP   **b.** 7 ATP   **c.** 5 ATP

23.47 Electron transport requires oxygen. A low level of oxygen will decrease the activity of electron transport and the formation of ATP.

23.49 3.2 moles of ATP

23.51 a. citric acid cycle   **b.** electron transport
c. both   **d.** electron transport
e. citric acid cycle

23.53 a. isocitrate   **b.** succinate
c. oxaloacetate

23.55 a. citrate, isocitrate   **b.** succinate, fumarate
c. fumarate, malate

23.57 a. Aconitase uses H_2O.
b. Succinate dehydrogenase uses FAD.
c. Isocitrate dehydrogenase uses NAD^+.

23.59 a. (4) hydration reaction
b. (1) oxidation reaction
c. (1) oxidation and (2) decarboxylation reaction

23.61 $10\,H^+$

23.63 2.5 ATP

23.65 The oxidation reactions of the citric acid cycle produce a source of reduced coenzymes for electron transport and ATP synthesis.

23.67 The oxidized coenzymes NAD^+ and FAD needed for the citric acid cycle are regenerated by electron transport, which requires oxygen.

23.69 a. citrate, isocitrate   **b.** α-ketoglutarate
c. α-ketoglutarate, succinyl CoA, oxaloacetate

23.71 a. In reaction 4, α-ketoglutarate, a five-carbon keto acid, is decarboxylated.
b. In reactions 2 and 7, double bonds in aconitate and fumarate are hydrated.
c. NAD^+ is reduced in reactions 3, 4, and 8.
d. In reactions 3 and 8, a secondary hydroxyl group in isocitrate and malate is oxidized.

23.73 a. NAD^+ **b.** NAD^+ and CoA

23.75 a. High levels of NADH inhibit isocitrate dehydrogenase and α-ketoglutarate dehydrogenase to slow the rate of the citric acid cycle.
b. High levels of ATP inhibit isocitrate dehydrogenase to slow the rate of the citric acid cycle.

23.77 complexes I, III, and IV

23.79 a. electron flow from complex I to CoQ
b. electron flow from complex III to cyt c
c. electron flow from cytochrome c to complex IV

23.81 Energy is released as hydrogen ions flow through ATP synthase back to the matrix and utilized for the synthesis of ATP.

23.83 Hydrogen ions flow through ATP synthase into the matrix where the H^+ concentration is lower.

23.85 ATP synthase is a protein complex, which spans the inner mitochondrial membrane.

23.87 The oxidation of glucose to pyruvate produces 7 ATP, whereas the oxidation of glucose to CO_2 and H_2O produces a maximum of 32 ATP.

23.89 As hydrogen ions from the hydrogen ion gradient move through the ATP synthase to return to the matrix, energy is released and used to synthesize ATP by ATP synthase.

23.91 A hibernating bear has more brown fat because it can be used during the winter for heat rather than ATP energy.

23.93 a. 51 kcal   **b.** 37 kcal
c. 150 kcal   **d.** 230 kcal

23.95 If the combustion of glucose produces 690 kcal, but only 230 kcal (from 32 ATP) in cells, the efficiency of glucose use in the cells is 230 kcal/690 kcal or 33%.

23.97 a. 1360 kcal   **b.** 94.5 kg

24

Metabolic Pathways for Lipids and Amino Acids

LUKE IS 48 YEARS OLD AND WORKS AS A PARAMEDIC.

Recently, blood work from his annual physical examination indicated a plasma cholesterol level of 256 mg/dL. Clinically, cholesterol levels are considered elevated if the total plasma cholesterol level exceeds 200 mg/dL. Luke's doctor ordered a liver profile that showed elevated liver enzymes: *Alanine transaminase* (ALT) 282 Units/L (normal ALT 5 to 35 Units/L) and *aspartate transaminase* (AST) 226 Units/L (normal AST 5 to 50 Units/L). Luke's doctor ordered a medication to lower Luke's plasma cholesterol.

During Luke's career as a paramedic, he was exposed several times to blood and was accidently stuck by a needle containing infected blood. Luke takes 8 to 10 ibuprofen tablets per month for pain and uses herbs, garlic, ginkgo, and antioxidants. Although herbs, antioxidants, and ibuprofen can cause liver inflammation, they would not usually cause the elevation of liver enzymes reported in Luke's blood tests. A hepatitis profile showed that Luke was positive for antibodies to both hepatitis B and C. His doctor diagnosed Luke with *chronic hepatitis C virus* (HCV) infection. Hepatitis C is an infection caused by a virus that attacks the liver and leads to inflammation. Most people infected with the hepatitis C virus have no symptoms. Hepatitis C is usually passed by contact with contaminated blood or by needles shared during illegal drug use. In *autoimmune hepatitis*, the immune system of a person's body destroys cells in the liver. As part of his treatment, Luke attended a class on living with hepatitis C given by Belinda, a public health nurse.

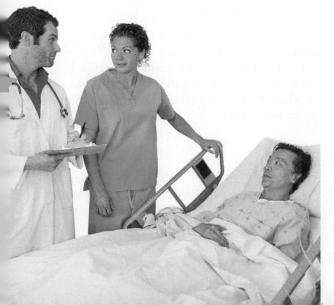

CAREER Public Health Nurse (PHN)

Hepatitis C virus is a common cause of liver disease and a major health problem worldwide. Patients diagnosed with HCV require lifelong monitoring and are usually cared for by specialist teams including a public health nurse. A public health nurse works in public health departments, correctional facilities, occupational health facilities, schools, and organizations that aim to improve health at the community level. They often focus on high-risk populations such as the elderly, the homeless, teen mothers, and those at risk for a communicable disease such as hepatitis.

Carbohydrate metabolism involves glucose as the primary fuel for the synthesis of ATP. However, lipids and proteins also play an important role in metabolism and energy production. In this chapter, we look at how the digestion of lipids produces fatty acids and glycerol and how the digestion of proteins yields amino acids. When our caloric intake exceeds the metabolic needs of our bodies, excess carbohydrates and fatty acids are converted to triacylglycerols and added to our fat cells of adipose tissue. Almost all of our stored energy is in the form of triacylglycerols in our fat cells, which can store unlimited quantities of fat. This fact has become quite apparent in the large number of people in the United States that are considered obese. We will see that the fatty acids in triacylglycerols produce more ATP when used for energy than a glucose molecule; however, they are not the preferred energy source of our bodies. This is why it is more difficult to lose weight (burn fat) than to store it.

The digestion and degradation of dietary proteins as well as body proteins provide amino acids, which are needed to synthesize nitrogen-containing compounds in our cells, such as new proteins and nucleic acids. Although amino acids are not considered a primary source of fuel, energy can be extracted from amino acids if glycogen and fat reserves have been depleted. When a person is fasting or starving, the breakdown of the body's own proteins eventually destroys essential body tissues, particularly muscles.

CHAPTER READINESS*

⚛ CORE CHEMISTRY SKILLS

- Identifying Fatty Acids (17.2)
- Drawing the Zwitterion for an Amino Acid (19.1)
- Identifying Important Coenzymes in Metabolism (22.3)
- Identifying the Compounds in Glycolysis (22.4)
- Identifying the Compounds and Enzymes in Glycogenesis and Glycogenolysis (22.6)
- Describing the Reactions in the Citric Acid Cycle (23.1)
- Calculating the ATP Produced from Glucose (23.3)

*These Core Chemistry Skills from previous chapters are listed here for your review as you proceed to the new material in this chapter.

LEARNING GOAL

Describe the sites and products obtained from the digestion of triacylglycerols.

24.1 Digestion of Triacylglycerols

Our adipose tissue is made of fat cells called *adipocytes*, which store triacylglycerols (see Figure 24.1). Let's compare the amount of energy stored in the fat cells to the energy from glucose, glycogen, and protein. A typical 70-kg (150-lb) person has about 140 000 kcal of energy stored as fat, 24 000 kcal as protein, 720 kcal as glycogen reserves, and 80 kcal as blood glucose. Therefore, the energy available from stored fats is about 85% of the total energy available in the body. Thus, body fat is our major source of stored energy.

Digestion of Dietary Fats

Just as oil and water do not mix, dietary fats do not readily mix with the aqueous environment of the small intestine where digestion begins. Natural emulsifiers, called bile salts containing hydrophobic and hydrophilic regions, are secreted from the gallbladder into the small intestine. These molecules are able to interact with both the hydrophobic fat

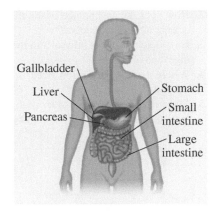

$$CH_2-O-\overset{\displaystyle O}{\overset{\|}{C}}-(CH_2)_{16}-CH_3$$

$$CH-O-\overset{\displaystyle O}{\overset{\|}{C}}-(CH_2)_{16}-CH_3$$

$$CH_2-O-\overset{\displaystyle O}{\overset{\|}{C}}-(CH_2)_{16}-CH_3$$

A triacylglycerol

FIGURE 24.1 ► The fat cells (adipocytes) that make up adipose tissue are capable of storing unlimited quantities of triacylglycerols.

◎ What are some sources of fats in our diet?

globules and the aqueous solution in the small intestine. In a process called *emulsification,* the bile salts break the fat globules into smaller droplets called *micelles* (pronounced *my-cells*). Emulsification also occurs in the creation of some sauces like a creamy salad dressing where oil and water are mixed with egg which provides a phospholipid emulsifier.

Next, *pancreatic lipases* released from the pancreas hydrolyze triacylglycerols to yield monoacylglycerols and fatty acids, which are absorbed into the intestinal lining, where they recombine to form triacylglycerols. The resulting nonpolar compounds are coated with phospholipids and proteins to form lipoproteins called *chylomicrons,* which makes them polar and soluble in the aqueous environment of the lymph and bloodstream (see Figure 24.2).

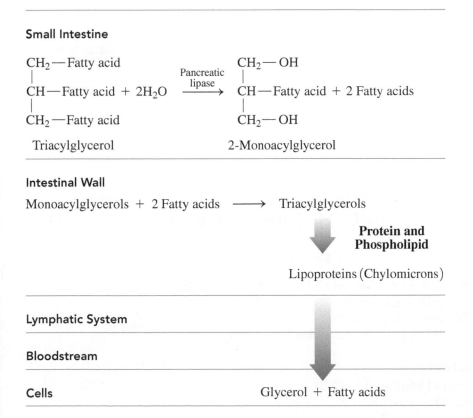

Small Intestine

$$\begin{array}{l}
CH_2-\text{Fatty acid} \\
| \\
CH-\text{Fatty acid} + 2H_2O \\
| \\
CH_2-\text{Fatty acid}
\end{array}
\xrightarrow[\text{lipase}]{\text{Pancreatic}}
\begin{array}{l}
CH_2-OH \\
| \\
CH-\text{Fatty acid} + 2 \text{ Fatty acids} \\
| \\
CH_2-OH
\end{array}$$

Triacylglycerol   2-Monoacylglycerol

Intestinal Wall

Monoacylglycerols + 2 Fatty acids ⟶ Triacylglycerols

⬇ **Protein and Phospholipid**

Lipoproteins (Chylomicrons)

Lymphatic System

Bloodstream

Cells   Glycerol + Fatty acids

FIGURE 24.2 ► The digestion of fats begins in the small intestine when bile salts emulsify fats that undergo hydrolysis to monoacylglycerols and fatty acids.

◎ What kinds of enzymes are secreted from the pancreas into the small intestine to hydrolyze triacylglycerols?

In the cells, lipases hydrolyze the triacylglycerols to yield glycerol and free fatty acids, which can be used for energy production. Fatty acids, which are the preferred fuel of the heart, are oxidized to acetyl CoA molecules for ATP synthesis. However, the brain and red blood cells cannot utilize fatty acids. Fatty acids cannot diffuse across the blood–brain barrier, and red blood cells have no mitochondria, which are where fatty acids are oxidized. Therefore, glucose and glycogen are the primary sources of energy for the brain and red blood cells.

Explore Your World
Digestion of Fats

Place some water and several drops of vegetable oil in a container with a top. Cap the container and shake. Observe. Add a few drops of liquid soap or detergent to the oil and water, cap the container again, and shake. Observe.

Questions

1. Why does the oil separate from the water?
2. How does the appearance of the oil change after soap is added?
3. How is soap like the bile salts in the digestion of fats?
4. Where does fat digestion occur in the body?
5. Many people with gallbladder problems take supplemental lipase. Why is this necessary?

Utilization of Fat Stores

When blood glucose is depleted and glycogen stores are low, the process of fat utilization is stimulated when the hormones glucagon or epinephrine are secreted into the bloodstream where they bind to receptors on the membrane of adipose tissue. A hormone-sensitive lipase within the fat cells catalyzes the hydrolysis of triacylglycerols to glycerol and free fatty acids, which then diffuse into the bloodstream and bind with plasma proteins (albumin) to be transported to the tissues, muscles, and fat cells. Most of the glycerol goes into the liver, where it is metabolized.

Metabolism of Glycerol

Enzymes in the liver convert glycerol to dihydroxyacetone phosphate in two steps. In the first step, glycerol is phosphorylated using ATP to yield glycerol-3-phosphate. In the second step, the secondary hydroxyl group is oxidized to yield dihydroxyacetone phosphate, which is an intermediate in several metabolic pathways including glycolysis and gluconeogenesis.

$$
\begin{array}{l}
CH_2-OH \\
| \\
CH-OH \quad + \quad \boxed{ATP} \quad \xrightarrow{\text{Glycerol kinase}} \quad
\begin{array}{l}
CH_2-OH \\
| \\
CH-OH \\
| \\
CH_2-O-\text{\textcircled{P}}
\end{array}
\quad + \quad \boxed{ADP} \\
CH_2-OH
\end{array}
$$

Glycerol   →   Glycerol-3-phosphate

$$
\begin{array}{l}
CH_2-OH \\
| \\
CH-OH \quad + \quad \boxed{NAD^+} \quad \xrightarrow{\text{Glycerol-3-phosphate dehydrogenase}} \quad
\begin{array}{l}
CH_2-OH \\
| \\
C=O \\
| \\
CH_2-O-\text{\textcircled{P}}
\end{array}
\quad + \quad \boxed{NADH + H^+} \\
CH_2-O-\text{\textcircled{P}}
\end{array}
$$

Glycerol-3-phosphate   →   Dihydroxyacetone phosphate

Glycolysis   **Gluconeogenesis**

The overall reaction for the metabolism of glycerol is written as follows:

Glycerol $+$ ATP $+$ NAD$^+$ $\longrightarrow$ dihydroxyacetone phosphate $+$ ADP $+$ NADH $+$ H$^+$

▶ **SAMPLE PROBLEM 24.1 Fats and Digestion**

Answer each of the following for the digestion of triacylglycerols:

a. Where does it take place?
b. What enzyme is involved?
c. What are the products of digestion?

SOLUTION

a. the small intestine
b. pancreatic lipase
c. monoacylglycerols and fatty acids

STUDY CHECK 24.1

How are the nonpolar triacylglycerols emulsified so that they can be digested?

ANSWER

The triacylglycerols entering the small intestine are emulsified by bile salts into smaller droplets of fat that can react with the lipases.

QUESTIONS AND PROBLEMS

24.1 Digestion of Triacylglycerols

LEARNING GOAL Describe the sites and products obtained from the digestion of triacylglycerols.

24.1 What is the role of bile salts in lipid digestion?

24.2 How are insoluble triacylglycerols transported to the tissues and fat cells?

24.3 When are fats released from fat stores?

24.4 What happens to the glycerol produced from the hydrolysis of triacylglycerols in adipose tissues?

24.5 How is glycerol converted to an intermediate of glycolysis?

24.6 How can glycerol be used to synthesize glucose?

℞ Clinical Applications

A person with Duchenne muscular dystrophy cannot convert glycerol to glycerol-3-phosphate.

24.7 What enzyme would be defective?

24.8 Why would a person with this enzyme deficiency have high blood glycerol levels?

24.2 Oxidation of Fatty Acids

A large amount of energy is obtained when fatty acids undergo oxidation in the mitochondria to yield acetyl CoA. In fat catabolism, fatty acids undergo **beta oxidation** (**β oxidation**), which removes two-carbon segments containing the alpha and beta carbon from the carboxyl end of the fatty acid.

LEARNING GOAL

Describe the metabolic pathway of β oxidation.

$$\underset{\beta}{CH_3 - (CH_2)_{14} - \overset{\beta \text{ oxidation} \atop occurs \text{ here}}{\downarrow} \atop} CH_2 - \underset{\alpha}{CH_2} - \overset{O}{\overset{\|}{C}} - OH$$

Stearic acid

Each cycle in β oxidation produces an acetyl CoA and a fatty acid that is shorter by two carbons. The cycle repeats until the original fatty acid is completely degraded to two-carbon units that form acetyl CoA that can enter the citric acid cycle in the same way as the acetyl CoA derived from glucose.

Fatty Acid Activation

The fatty acids, which are produced in the cytosol, must be transported through the inner mitochondrial membrane before they can undergo β oxidation in the matrix. In an *activation* process using ATP and catalyzed by *acyl CoA synthetase*, a fatty acid is combined with CoA to yield a high-energy fatty acyl CoA. The energy released by the hydrolysis of two high-energy bonds of ATP is used to drive the reaction, which gives AMP and two inorganic phosphates ($2P_i$). In our discussion of fatty acid activation, we will use the terms *acyl CoA* and *acetyl CoA*. The term *acyl* refers to a long-chain fatty acid that is bonded to coenzyme A, whereas *acetyl* refers to a two-carbon acetyl group that is bonded to coenzyme A.

$$CH_3 - (CH_2)_n - CH_2 - CH_2 - \overset{O}{\overset{\|}{C}} - OH + ATP + HS-CoA \xrightarrow{\text{Acyl CoA} \atop \text{synthetase}}$$

Fatty acid

$$CH_3 - (CH_2)_n - CH_2 - CH_2 - \overset{O}{\overset{\|}{C}} - S-CoA + AMP + 2P_i + H_2O$$

Fatty acyl CoA

Transport of Fatty Acyl CoA into the Mitochondria

The acyl CoA molecules formed in the cytosol cannot pass through the inner mitochondrial membrane into the matrix where β oxidation of fatty acids takes place. A transport system called the *carnitine shuttle* is used to carry fatty acids into the mitochondria. In the cytosol, *carnitine acyltransferase* catalyzes the transfer of a fatty acyl group to the hydroxyl group of carnitine to produce fatty acyl carnitine, which passes through the inner mitochondrial membrane into the matrix.

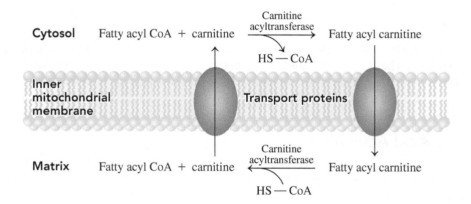

In the mitochondrial matrix, another *carnitine acyltransferase* catalyzes the reverse reaction that transfers the fatty acyl group to CoA to reform fatty acyl CoA. The carnitine is released and returns to the cytosol. Thus, the carnitine shuttle moves fatty acyl CoA from the cytosol into the matrix where the fatty acid can undergo β oxidation (see Figure 24.3).

FIGURE 24.3 ▶ In the carnitine shuttle system, fatty acids are activated and transported from the cytosol through the inner mitochondrial membrane into the matrix.

Q Why is carnitine needed to transport a fatty acid into the matrix?

Reactions of the β Oxidation Cycle

In the mitochondrial matrix, fatty acyl CoA molecules undergo β oxidation, which is a cycle of four reactions that convert the $-CH_2-$ of the β-carbon (carbon 3) in a long-chain fatty acyl group into a keto group. Once the β-keto group is formed, a two-carbon acetyl CoA is split from the original fatty acyl chain, which gives a shortened fatty acyl chain.

Reaction 1   Oxidation

In the first step of β oxidation, *acyl CoA dehydrogenase* catalyzes the transfer of hydrogen atoms from the α- and β-carbons of the activated fatty acid to form a trans carbon–carbon double bond and the reduced coenzyme $FADH_2$. Recall that oxidation can be the addition of oxygen *or* removal of hydrogen.

$$CH_3-(CH_2)_n-\underset{\beta}{CH_2}-\underset{\alpha}{CH_2}-\overset{\overset{\displaystyle O}{\|}}{C}-S-CoA \;+\; \boxed{FAD} \;\xrightarrow[\text{dehydrogenase}]{\text{Acyl CoA}}\; CH_3-(CH_2)_n-\underset{\underset{\displaystyle H}{|}}{\underset{\beta}{\overset{\overset{\displaystyle H}{|}}{C}}}=\underset{\alpha}{C}-\overset{\overset{\displaystyle O}{\|}}{C}-S-CoA \;+\; \boxed{FADH_2}$$

Fatty acyl CoA   *trans*-Enoyl CoA

Reaction 2 Hydration

In the second step, a hydration reaction catalyzed by *enoyl CoA hydratase* adds the components of water to the trans double bond, which forms a hydroxyl group ($-OH$) on the β-carbon.

$$CH_3-(CH_2)_n-\underset{\underset{\displaystyle H}{|}}{\underset{\beta}{\overset{\overset{\displaystyle H}{|}}{C}}}=\underset{\alpha}{C}-\overset{\overset{\displaystyle O}{\|}}{C}-S-CoA \;+\; H_2O \;\xrightarrow[\text{hydratase}]{\text{Enoyl CoA}}\; CH_3-(CH_2)_n-\underset{\underset{\displaystyle H}{|}}{\underset{\beta}{\overset{\overset{\displaystyle OH}{|}}{C}}}-\underset{\underset{\displaystyle H}{|}}{\overset{\overset{\displaystyle H}{|}}{\underset{\alpha}{C}}}-\overset{\overset{\displaystyle O}{\|}}{C}-S-CoA$$

trans-Enoyl CoA   3-Hydroxyacyl CoA

Reaction 3 Oxidation

In the third step, the secondary hydroxyl group on the β-carbon, which is carbon 3, is oxidized by *3-hydroxyacyl CoA dehydrogenase* to yield a ketone. The hydrogen atoms removed in the oxidation are transferred to NAD^+ to yield a β-keto or 3-keto group and the reduced coenzyme NADH.

$$CH_3-(CH_2)_n-\underset{\underset{\displaystyle H}{|}}{\underset{\beta}{\overset{\overset{\displaystyle OH}{|}}{C}}}-\underset{\underset{\displaystyle H}{|}}{\overset{\overset{\displaystyle H}{|}}{\underset{\alpha}{C}}}-\overset{\overset{\displaystyle O}{\|}}{C}-S-CoA \;+\; \boxed{NAD^+} \;\xrightarrow[\text{dehydrogenase}]{\text{3-Hydroxyacyl CoA}}\; CH_3-(CH_2)_n-\underset{\beta}{\overset{\overset{\displaystyle O}{\|}}{C}}-\underset{\underset{\displaystyle H}{|}}{\overset{\overset{\displaystyle H}{|}}{\underset{\alpha}{C}}}-\overset{\overset{\displaystyle O}{\|}}{C}-S-CoA \;+\; \boxed{NADH + H^+}$$

3-Hydroxyacyl CoA β-Ketoacyl CoA

Reaction 4 Cleavage (Thiolysis)

In the fourth step of β oxidation, the $C_\alpha-C_\beta$ bond is cleaved by *β-ketoacyl CoA thiolase* to yield a two-carbon acetyl CoA and a new fatty acyl CoA that is shortened by two carbon atoms. This new, shorter fatty acyl CoA repeats the four steps of the β oxidation cycle until the original fatty acid is completely degraded to two-carbon units of acetyl CoA.

$$CH_3-(CH_2)_n-\underset{\beta}{\overset{\overset{\displaystyle O}{\|}}{C}}-\underset{\underset{\displaystyle H}{|}}{\overset{\overset{\displaystyle H}{|}}{\underset{\alpha}{C}}}-\overset{\overset{\displaystyle O}{\|}}{C}-S-CoA \;+\; HS-CoA \;\xrightarrow[\text{thiolase}]{\beta\text{-Ketoacyl CoA}}$$

β-Ketoacyl CoA

$$CH_3-(CH_2)_{n-2}-\overset{\overset{\displaystyle O}{\|}}{C}-S-CoA \;+\; CH_3-\overset{\overset{\displaystyle O}{\|}}{C}-S-CoA$$

Fatty acyl CoA   Acetyl CoA
(2 C atoms shorter)

Fatty Acid Length Determines Cycle Repeats

The number of carbon atoms in a fatty acid determines the number of times the cycle repeats and the number of acetyl CoA units it produces. For example, the complete β oxidation of capric acid (C_{10}) produces five acetyl CoA groups, which is equal to one-half the number of carbon atoms in the chain. Because the final turn of the cycle produces two acetyl CoA units, the total number of times the cycle repeats is one less than the total number of acetyl groups it produces. Therefore, the C_{10} fatty acid goes through the cycle four times (see Figure 24.4).

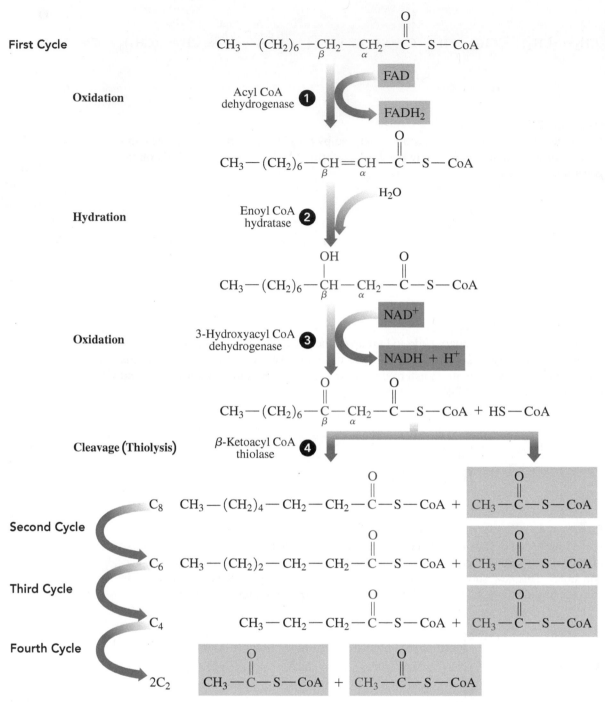

FIGURE 24.4 ▶ Capric acid (C_{10}) undergoes four oxidation cycles that repeat reactions 1 to 4 and yield five acetyl CoA molecules, four NADH, and four $FADH_2$.

Q How many NADH and $FADH_2$ molecules are produced in one turn of the fatty acid cycle of β oxidation?

For capric acid, the overall equation for the four cycles of β oxidation is

Caproyl (C_{10}) CoA + 4HS—CoA + $4NAD^+$ + 4FAD ⟶

$$5\text{acetyl CoA} + 4\text{NADH} + 4\text{H}^+ + 4\text{FADH}_2$$

Most fatty acids have an even numbers of carbon atoms. However, some odd-numbered chains of fatty acids are produced by other organisms and by bacteria. Essentially an odd-numbered fatty acid goes through the same four steps of β oxidation until the final cycle, in which the remaining fatty acyl CoA is cleaved, to yield a propionyl CoA (C_3 group) and an acetyl CoA.

Fatty Acid	Number of Carbon Atoms	Number of Acetyl CoA	Number of β Oxidation Cycles
Myristic acid	14	7	6
Palmitic acid	16	8	7
Stearic acid	18	9	8

Oxidation of Unsaturated Fatty Acids

We have shown the β oxidation sequence of reactions for saturated fatty acids with an even number of carbon atoms. However, the fats in our diets, particularly the oils, contain unsaturated fatty acids, which have one or more cis double bonds. The hydration reaction adds water to trans double bonds, not cis. When the double bond in an unsaturated fatty acid is ready for hydration, an isomerase forms a trans double bond between the α- and β-carbon atoms, which is the arrangement needed for the hydration reaction.

cis-Acyl CoA → *trans*-Acyl CoA → 3-Hydroxyacyl CoA

Because the isomerization provides the trans double bond for the hydration in reaction 2, it bypasses the first reaction. Therefore, the energy released by the β oxidation of an unsaturated fatty acid is slightly less because no $FADH_2$ is produced in that cycle. For unsaturated fatty acids, we will decrease the total $FADH_2$ yield by one for each double bond.

SAMPLE PROBLEM 24.2 β Oxidation

Match each of the following (**a** to **d**) with one of the reactions (**1** to **4**) in the β oxidation cycle:
(1) first oxidation   (2) hydration   (3) second oxidation   (4) cleavage (thiolysis)

a. Water is added to a trans double bond.
b. An acetyl CoA is removed.
c. FAD is reduced to $FADH_2$.
d. A 3-hydroxyacyl CoA is converted to 3-ketoacyl CoA.

SOLUTION

a. (2) hydration   **b.** (4) cleavage (thiolysis)   **c.** (1) first oxidation
d. (3) second oxidation

STUDY CHECK 24.2

Determine the number of β oxidation cycles and number of acetyl CoA molecules produced for cerotic acid (C_{26}), a fatty acid found in beeswax and carnauba wax.

ANSWER

Cerotic acid (C_{26}) requires 12 β oxidation cycles, and produces 13 acetyl CoA molecules.

QUESTIONS AND PROBLEMS

24.2 Oxidation of Fatty Acids

LEARNING GOAL Describe the metabolic pathway of β oxidation.

24.9 Where in the cell is a fatty acid activated?

24.10 What is the function of carnitine in the β oxidation of fatty acids?

24.11 What coenzymes are required for β oxidation?

24.12 When does an isomerization occur during the β oxidation of a fatty acid?

24.13 In each of the following acyl CoA molecules, identify the β-carbon:

a.

$$CH_3-CH_2-CH_2-CH_2-CH_2-CH_2-CH_2-\overset{\displaystyle O}{\overset{\displaystyle \|}{C}}-S-CoA$$

b.

[line-angle structure ending in C(=O)—S—CoA]

24.14 In each of the following acyl CoA molecules, identify the β-carbon:

a. $CH_3-(CH_2)_{14}-CH_2-CH_2-\overset{\displaystyle O}{\overset{\displaystyle \|}{C}}-S-CoA$

b.

[line-angle structure ending in C(=O)—S—CoA]

24.15 Draw the condensed or line-angle structural formula for the product(s) when each of the following undergoes the indicated reaction:

a.

[line-angle structure with C=C and C(=O)—S—CoA] $\xrightarrow{\text{Enoyl CoA hydratase}}$

b.

$$CH_3-(CH_2)_6-CH_2-CH_2-\overset{\displaystyle O}{\overset{\displaystyle \|}{C}}-S-CoA \xrightarrow{\text{Acyl CoA dehydrogenase}}$$

24.16 Draw the condensed or line-angle structural formula for the product(s) when each of the following undergoes the indicated reaction:

a.

[line-angle structure with two C=O and S—CoA] $\xrightarrow{\text{$\beta$-Ketoacyl CoA thiolase}}$

b.

$$CH_3-(CH_2)_8-\underset{\underset{\displaystyle H}{\displaystyle |}}{\overset{\overset{\displaystyle OH}{\displaystyle |}}{C}}-\underset{\underset{\displaystyle H}{\displaystyle |}}{\overset{\overset{\displaystyle H}{\displaystyle |}}{C}}-\overset{\displaystyle O}{\overset{\displaystyle \|}{C}}-S-CoA \xrightarrow{\text{3-Hydroxyacyl CoA dehydrogenase}}$$

24.17 Caprylic acid (octanoic acid) is a saturated C_8 fatty acid found in coconut and palm oil as well as cow, goat, and human milk.
   a. Draw the condensed structural formula for the activated form of caprylic acid.
   b. Indicate the α- and β-carbon atoms in caprylic acid.
   c. State the number of β oxidation cycles for the complete oxidation of caprylic acid.
   d. State the number of acetyl CoA units obtained from the complete oxidation of caprylic acid.

24.18 Lignoceric acid is a saturated C_{24} fatty acid found in small amounts in peanut oil.
   a. Draw the line-angle structural formula for the activated form of lignoceric acid.
   b. Indicate the α- and β-carbon atoms in lignoceric acid.
   c. State the number of β oxidation cycles for the complete oxidation of lignoceric acid.
   d. State the number of acetyl CoA units obtained from the complete oxidation of lignoceric acid.

LEARNING GOAL

Calculate the total ATP produced by the complete oxidation of a fatty acid.

⚛ CORE CHEMISTRY SKILL

Calculating the ATP from Fatty Acid Oxidation (β Oxidation)

24.3 ATP and Fatty Acid Oxidation

The total energy yield from the oxidation of a particular fatty acid depends on the number of β oxidation cycles needed for the long-chain fatty acid. After the initial input of two ATP, each β oxidation cycle produces one NADH, one $FADH_2$, and one acetyl CoA. Each NADH generates sufficient energy to synthesize 2.5 ATP, whereas each $FADH_2$ provides energy for the synthesis of 1.5 ATP. Thus, each β oxidation cycle produces a total of four ATP. However, the greatest amount of energy produced from a fatty acid is generated by the production of the acetyl CoA molecules that enter the citric acid cycle. For every acetyl CoA that enters the citric acid cycle, a total of 10 ATP are synthesized.

We have seen that capric acid, C_{10}, goes through four turns of the β oxidation cycle, which produces five acetyl CoA units, four NADH, and four $FADH_2$. The initial activation of capric acid requires the energy of two ATP. The total ATP produced is calculated as follows:

ATP Production from β Oxidation for Capric Acid (C_{10})		
Citric acid cycle: 5 acetyl CoA $\times \dfrac{10\ \text{ATP}}{\text{acetyl CoA}}$		= 50 ATP
β oxidation: 4 NADH $\times \dfrac{2.5\ \text{ATP}}{\text{NADH}}$		= 10 ATP
4 FADH$_2$ $\times \dfrac{1.5\ \text{ATP}}{\text{FADH}_2}$		= 6 ATP
Activation of capric acid:		= −2 ATP
Total		= 64 ATP

Chemistry Link to Health
Stored Fat and Obesity

The storage of fat is an important survival feature in the lives of many animals. In hibernating animals, large amounts of stored fat provide the energy for the entire hibernation period, which could be several months. In camels, large amounts of food are stored in the camel's hump, which is actually a huge fat deposit. When food resources are low, the camel can survive months without food or water by utilizing the fat reserves in the hump. Migratory birds preparing to fly long distances also store large amounts of fat. Whales are kept warm by a layer of body fat called "blubber," which can be as thick as 2 ft. Blubber also provides energy when whales must survive long periods of starvation. Penguins also have blubber, which protects them from the cold and provides energy when they are incubating their eggs.

Humans also have the capability to store large amounts of fat, although they do not hibernate or usually have to survive for long periods without food. When humans survived on sparse diets that were mostly vegetarian, about 20% of the dietary calories were from fat. Today, a typical diet includes more dairy products and foods with high fat levels, and as much as 60% of the calories are from fat. The U.S. Public Health Service now estimates that in the United States more than one-third of adults are obese. Obesity is defined as a body weight that is more than 20% over an ideal weight. Obesity is a major factor in health problems such as diabetes, heart disease, high blood pressure, stroke, and gallstones, as well as some cancers and forms of arthritis.

To maintain a constant weight, the energy intake (calories in food) must balance the energy expended (calories used by the body). Body weight and food intake are regulated by two "hunger hormones" called ghrelin and leptin. Ghrelin, an appetite-stimulating hormone of 28 amino acid residues, is secreted by an empty stomach and travels to the brain where it makes you feel hungry. After you eat a meal, the stomach is stretched, and ghrelin secretion stops. In people who are obese or have a high calorie intake, the ghrelin levels are low, whereas in people who are fasting, the ghrelin levels are high.

Leptin, a protein, is secreted mainly in the fat cells, also called *adipose*, and travels to the brain where it makes you feel full. The more adipose tissue present, the more leptin you produce. Obese patients have high levels of leptin, but they may be leptin-resistant, which means that they do not experience a sense of fullness that leptin signals to the brain in normal adults. Leptin acts on the liver and skeletal muscles, where it stimulates fatty acid oxidation in the mitochondria, which decreases fat stores.

One way we might control our appetites is by avoiding high-fat foods. When we eat foods high in fat, we tend to eat more. Eating a diet rich in whole grains or high in protein suppresses ghrelin more than a diet high in fat. Sleep deprivation also causes ghrelin levels to rise which can lead to overeating.

Marine mammals have thick layers of blubber that serve as insulation as well as energy storage.

A camel stores large amounts of fat in its hump.

Leptin, shown here as a ribbon model, is an appetite-repressing hormone that consists of 146 amino acid residues formed in the fat cells.

▶**SAMPLE PROBLEM 24.3 ATP Production from β Oxidation**

How many ATP will be produced from the β oxidation of palmitic acid, a C_{16} saturated fatty acid?

SOLUTION

ANALYZE THE PROBLEM	Given	Need
	β oxidation of palmitic acid (C_{16})	total ATP produced

Palmitic acid (C_{16}) requires seven β oxidation cycles, which produce seven NADH and seven $FADH_2$. The total number of acetyl CoA is eight. The activation of palmitic acid decreases the total produced by two ATP.

ATP Production from β Oxidation for Palmitic Acid (C_{16})

Citric acid cycle: $8 \text{ acetyl CoA} \times \dfrac{10 \text{ ATP}}{\text{acetyl CoA}}$ = 80 ATP

β oxidation: $7 \text{ NADH} \times \dfrac{2.5 \text{ ATP}}{\text{NADH}}$ = 17.5 ATP

$7 \text{ FADH}_2 \times \dfrac{1.5 \text{ ATP}}{\text{FADH}_2}$ = 10.5 ATP

Activation of palmitic acid: = −2 ATP

Total = 106 ATP

STUDY CHECK 24.3

Compare the total ATP from the reduced coenzymes and from acetyl CoA in the β oxidation of palmitic acid.

ANSWER

Eight acetyl CoA units yield 80 ATP whereas seven NADH and seven $FADH_2$ yield 28 ATP.

Explore Your World
Fat Storage and Blubber

Obtain four plastic freezer bags, masking tape, and some solid vegetable shortening (fat) used for cooking. Fill a bucket or container with enough water to cover both of your hands. Add ice until the water feels very cold.

Place 3 or 4 tablespoons of the shortening in one of the plastic bags. Place another plastic bag inside the first bag containing the fat. Tape the top edges of the two bags together, leaving the inside bag open. Using the remaining two plastic bags, place one inside the other, and tape the top edges together leaving the inside bag open. Now place one hand inside the bag with the vegetable shortening and distribute the fat around until a layer of about 2/3 in. (2 cm) of the fat in the inner bag covers your hand. Place your other hand inside

the other double bag and submerge both your hands in the ice water. Measure the time it takes for one hand to feel uncomfortably cold. Remove your hands before they get too cold.

Questions

1. How effective is the double bag with "blubber" in protecting your hand from the cold?
2. How would increasing the amount of vegetable shortening affect your results?
3. How does "blubber" help an animal survive starvation?
4. Why would animals in warm climates, such as camels and migratory birds, need to store fat?

QUESTIONS AND PROBLEMS

24.3 ATP and Fatty Acid Oxidation

LEARNING GOAL Calculate the total ATP produced by the complete oxidation of a fatty acid.

24.19 Why is the energy of fatty acid activation from ATP to AMP considered the same as the hydrolysis of 2 ATP $\longrightarrow$ 2 ADP?

24.20 What is the number of ATP molecules obtained from each acetyl CoA in the citric acid cycle?

℞ Clinical Applications

24.21 Behenic acid is a saturated fatty acid found in peanut and canola oils. Answer each of the following (**a** to **c**) for behenic acid:

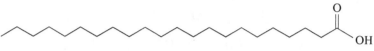

  a. How many cycles of β oxidation are needed?
  b. How many acetyl CoA units are produced?
  c. How many ATP can be generated from the β oxidation of behenic acid?

24.22 Stearic acid is a saturated fatty acid found in animal products. Answer each of the following (**a** to **c**) for stearic acid:

  a. How many cycles of β oxidation are needed?
  b. How many acetyl CoA units are produced?
  c. How many ATP can be generated from the β oxidation of stearic acid?

24.23 Oleic acid is a monounsaturated fatty acid common in animal and vegetable oils. Answer each of the following (**a** to **c**) for oleic acid:

  a. How many cycles of β oxidation are needed?
  b. How many acetyl CoA units are produced?
  c. How many ATP can be generated from the β oxidation of oleic acid?

24.24 Palmitoleic acid is a monounsaturated fatty acid common in animal and vegetable oils. Answer each of the following (**a** to **c**) for palmitoleic acid:

  a. How many cycles of β oxidation are needed?
  b. How many acetyl CoA units are produced?
  c. How many ATP can be generated from the β oxidation of palmitoleic acid?

24.4 Ketogenesis and Ketone Bodies

When carbohydrates are not available to meet energy needs, the body breaks down fatty acids, which undergo β oxidation to acetyl CoA. Normally, acetyl CoA would enter the citric acid cycle for further oxidation and energy production. However, when large quantities of fatty acids are degraded, too much acetyl CoA is produced and the citric acid cycle cannot oxidize it all. As a result, high levels of acetyl CoA accumulate in the liver. Then, acetyl CoA molecules combine in a pathway known as **ketogenesis** to form compounds called **ketone bodies** (see Figure 24.5). Ketone bodies are produced in the liver and transported to the cells in the heart, brain, and skeletal muscle.

LEARNING GOAL

Describe the pathway of ketogenesis.

⚛ CORE CHEMISTRY SKILL

Describing How Ketone Bodies are Formed

Reaction 1   Condensation

In ketogenesis, two molecules of acetyl CoA combine to form acetoacetyl CoA and HS—CoA. This condensation is in the reverse direction of the last step of β oxidation.

Reaction 2   Hydrolysis

The hydrolysis of acetoacetyl CoA forms acetoacetate, a ketone body, and HS—CoA. Acetoacetate can enter the citric acid cycle by reforming acetyl CoA for energy production or break down into other ketone bodies.

Reaction 3   Hydrogenation (Reduction)

Acetoacetate is reduced by 2H from NADH + H$^+$ to β-hydroxybutyrate, which is considered a ketone body even though it does not contain a keto group.

Reaction 4   Decarboxylation

Acetoacetate can also undergo decarboxylation to yield acetone, a ketone body, and CO_2.

FIGURE 24.5 ▶ In ketogenesis, molecules combine to produce ketone bodies: acetoacetate, β-hydroxybutyrate, and acetone.

Q What condition in the body leads to the formation of ketone bodies?

$$CH_3-\overset{\displaystyle O}{\overset{\|}{C}}-S-CoA \; + \; CH_3-\overset{\displaystyle O}{\overset{\|}{C}}-S-CoA$$

Acetyl CoA   Acetyl CoA

1

HS—CoA

$$CH_3-\overset{\displaystyle O}{\overset{\|}{C}}-CH_2-\overset{\displaystyle O}{\overset{\|}{C}}-S-CoA$$

Acetoacetyl CoA

2

HS—CoA

$$CH_3-\overset{\displaystyle O}{\overset{\|}{C}}-CH_2-\overset{\displaystyle O}{\overset{\|}{C}}-O^-$$

Acetoacetate

NADH + H$^+$

3

NAD$^+$

4 → CO_2

$$CH_3-\overset{\displaystyle OH}{\overset{|}{C}H}-CH_2-\overset{\displaystyle O}{\overset{\|}{C}}-O^- \qquad CH_3-\overset{\displaystyle O}{\overset{\|}{C}}-CH_3$$

β-Hydroxybutyrate   Acetone

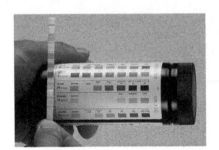

A ketone test strip indicates the level of ketone bodies in a urine sample.

Ketosis

The accumulation of ketone bodies may lead to a condition called **ketosis**, which occurs in severe diabetes, diets high in fat and low in carbohydrates, alcoholism, and starvation. Because two of the ketone bodies are carboxylic acids, they can lower the blood pH below 7.4. This condition is called **acidosis** and often accompanies ketosis. A drop in blood pH can interfere with the ability of the blood to carry oxygen and cause breathing difficulties.

▶**SAMPLE PROBLEM 24.4 Ketogenesis**

The process called ketogenesis takes place in the liver.

a. What are some conditions that promote ketogenesis?
b. What are the names of the three compounds called ketone bodies?
c. What ketone bodies are responsible for the acidosis that occurs in ketogenesis?

SOLUTION

a. When excess acetyl CoA cannot be processed by the citric acid cycle, acetyl CoA molecules enter the ketogenesis pathway and form ketone bodies.
b. The ketone bodies are acetoacetate, β-hydroxybutyrate, and acetone.
c. The ketone bodies acetoacetate and β-hydroxybutyrate, which are carboxylic acids, can decrease the pH of the blood (metabolic acidosis).

STUDY CHECK 24.4

Which ketone bodies contain each of the following functional groups?

a. ketone   **b.** alcohol

ANSWER

a. Acetone contains a ketone group.
b. β-Hydroxybutyrate contains an alcohol group.

Chemistry Link to Health
Diabetes and Ketone Bodies

Blood glucose is elevated within 30 min following a meal containing carbohydrates. The elevated level of glucose stimulates the secretion of the hormone *insulin* from the pancreas, which increases the flow of glucose into muscle and adipose tissue for the synthesis of glycogen. As blood glucose levels drop, the secretion of insulin decreases. When blood glucose is low, another hormone, *glucagon*, is secreted by the pancreas, which stimulates the breakdown of glycogen in the liver to yield glucose.

In *diabetes mellitus*, glucose cannot be utilized or stored as glycogen, because insulin is not secreted or does not function properly. In type 1, *insulin-dependent diabetes*, which often begins in childhood, the pancreas produces inadequate levels of insulin. This type of diabetes can result from damage to the pancreas by viral infections or from genetic mutations. In type 2, *insulin-resistant diabetes*, which usually occurs in adults, insulin is produced, but insulin receptors are not responsive. Thus, a person with type 2 diabetes will not respond to insulin therapy. *Gestational diabetes* can occur during pregnancy, but blood glucose levels usually return to normal after the baby is born.

Pregnant women with diabetes tend to gain weight and have large babies.

In all types of diabetes, insufficient amounts of glucose are available in the muscle, liver, and adipose tissue. As a result, liver cells synthesize glucose from noncarbohydrate sources via gluconeogenesis and use fatty acids for energy by breaking down fat, which elevates levels of acetyl CoA. Excess acetyl CoA undergoes ketogenesis, and ketone bodies accumulate in the blood. A person with uncontrolled diabetes can go into ketosis. Common symptoms of ketosis include an odor of acetone on the breath and lack of motor coordination due to low levels of glucose reaching the brain.

In uncontrolled diabetes, the concentration of blood glucose exceeds the ability of the kidney to reabsorb glucose, and glucose appears in the urine. High levels of glucose increase the osmotic pressure in the blood, which leads to an increase in urine output. Symptoms of diabetes include excessive thirst and frequent urination. Treatment for diabetes includes diet changes to limit carbohydrate intake and may require medication such as a daily injection of insulin or pills taken by mouth.

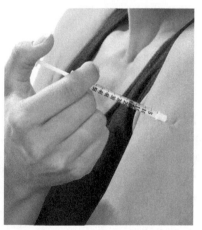

Type 1 diabetes can be treated with injections of insulin.

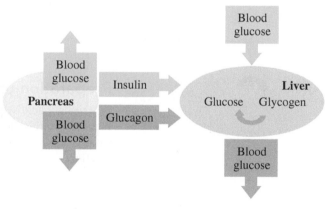

QUESTIONS AND PROBLEMS

24.4 Ketogenesis and Ketone Bodies

LEARNING GOAL Describe the pathway of ketogenesis.

24.25 What is ketogenesis?

24.26 If a person were fasting, why would they have high levels of acetyl CoA?

24.27 What type of reaction converts acetoacetate to 3-hydroxybutyrate?

24.28 How is acetone formed from acetoacetate?

℞ Clinical Applications

24.29 Diabetics often display signs of ketosis if insulin levels are not maintained. What is ketosis?

24.30 Why do diabetics produce high levels of ketone bodies?

Describe the biosynthesis of fatty acids from acetyl CoA.

24.5 Fatty Acid Synthesis

When the body has met all its energy needs and the glycogen stores are full, acetyl CoA from the breakdown of carbohydrates and fatty acids is used to synthesize new fatty acids in the cytosol. In the pathway called **lipogenesis**, two-carbon acetyl units are linked together to give a 16-carbon fatty acid, palmitic acid. Although the reactions appear much like the reverse of the reactions we discussed in fatty acid oxidation, the synthesis of fatty acids proceeds in a separate pathway with different enzymes. Fatty acid oxidation occurs in the mitochondria and uses FAD and NAD^+, whereas fatty acid synthesis occurs in the cytosol and uses the reduced coenzyme NADPH. The structure of NADPH is similar to NADH, except it has a phosphate group.

Synthesis of Acyl Carrier Protein (ACP)

In β oxidation, acetyl and acyl groups are activated using coenzyme A (HS—CoA). In fatty acid synthesis, an acyl carrier protein (HS—ACP) activates the acyl compounds. HS—ACP contains the thiol and pantothenic acid (vitamin B_5) groups found in acetyl CoA but now these groups are attached to a protein.

Aminoethanethiol   Pantothenic acid

Acyl carrier protein (ACP)
(HS—ACP)

Preparation of Activated Carriers

Before fatty acid synthesis can begin, the activated carriers must be synthesized. The synthesis of a three-carbon malonyl ACP requires the synthesis of malonyl CoA, when acetyl CoA combines with bicarbonate. The hydrolysis of ATP provides the energy for the reaction.

For fatty acid synthesis, the activated forms acetyl ACP and malonyl ACP are produced when the acyl group is combined with HS—ACP.

Synthesis of Fatty Acids (Palmitate)

The synthesis of a fatty acid in the cytosol requires a cycle of four reactions that adds two-carbon acetyl units to a growing carbon chain until it contains a total of 16 carbon atoms (palmitate).

Reaction 1 Condensation
In the first reaction, *3-ketoacyl ACP synthase* catalyzes the condensation of acetyl ACP and malonyl ACP to yield four-carbon acetoacetyl ACP and CO_2.

Reaction 2 Reduction
In the second reaction, *3-ketoacyl ACP reductase* reduces the 3-keto group using 2H from $NADPH + H^+$ to yield 3-hydroxyacyl ACP, an alcohol, and the oxidized coenzyme $NADP^+$. In the cytosol, NADPH is used to provide hydrogen for reduction reactions.

Reaction 3 Dehydration
In the third reaction, *3-hydroxyacyl ACP dehydrase* catalyzes the dehydration of the hydroxyl group to form a trans double bond in *trans*-2-enoyl ACP.

Reaction 4 Reduction
In the fourth reaction, *enoyl ACP reductase* uses hydrogen from $NADPH + H^+$ to reduce the double bond to a single bond, which forms butyryl ACP, a saturated four-carbon compound, which is two carbon atoms longer that the original acetyl ACP.

Cycle of Fatty Acid Synthesis Repeats

The cycle of fatty acid synthesis repeats with the four-carbon butyryl ACP condensing with another malonyl ACP to produce a six-carbon hexanoyl ACP. After seven cycles of fatty acid synthesis, the product, C_{16} palmitoyl ACP, is hydrolyzed to yield palmitate and HS—ACP (see Figure 24.6). The overall equation for the synthesis of palmitate from acetyl CoA is written as

$$8 \text{ Acetyl CoA} + 14\text{NADPH} + 7\text{ATP} \longrightarrow$$
$$\text{palmitate} + 14\text{NADP}^+ + 8\text{HS}-\text{CoA} + 7\text{ADP} + 7\text{P}_i + 6\text{H}_2\text{O}$$

Longer and Shorter Fatty Acids

Palmitate is the first fatty acid produced by fatty acid synthesis. However, shorter and longer fatty acids are also produced in cells. Shorter fatty acids are released earlier in the fatty acid synthesis process before there are 16 carbon atoms in the chain. Longer fatty acids are produced with special enzymes that add two-carbon acetyl units to the carboxyl end of the fatty acid chain.

Regulation of Fatty Acid Synthesis

Fatty acid synthesis takes place primarily in the adipose tissue, where triacylglycerols are formed and stored. The hormone *insulin* stimulates the formation of fatty acids. When blood glucose is high, insulin moves glucose into the cells. In the cell, insulin stimulates glycolysis and the oxidation of pyruvate, thereby producing acetyl CoA for fatty acid synthesis. By adding two carbons to the growing fatty acid chain by using three-carbon malonyl units, the transport of acyl groups into the matrix of the mitochondria is blocked, preventing their oxidation.

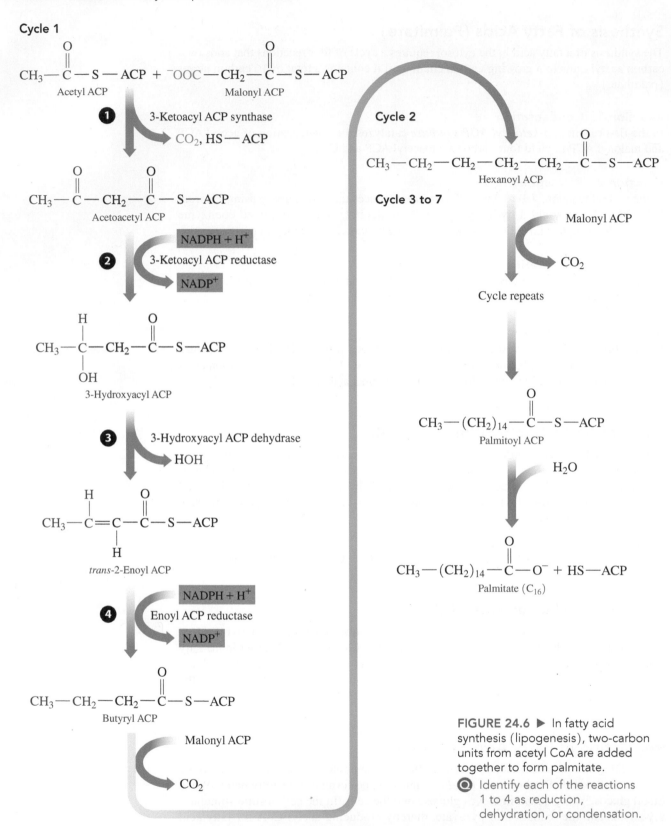

FIGURE 24.6 ▶ In fatty acid synthesis (lipogenesis), two-carbon units from acetyl CoA are added together to form palmitate.

🅠 Identify each of the reactions 1 to 4 as reduction, dehydration, or condensation.

Comparison of β Oxidation and Fatty Acid Synthesis

We have seen that many of the steps in the synthesis of palmitate are similar to those that occur in the β oxidation of palmitate. Synthesis combines two-carbon acetyl units to make long carbon chains, whereas β oxidation removes two-carbon acetyl units from long carbon chains. Synthesis of fatty acids involves reduction and dehydration, whereas β oxidation of fatty acids involves oxidation and hydration. We can distinguish between the two pathways by comparing some of their features in Table 24.1.

TABLE 24.1 A Comparison of β Oxidation and Fatty Acid Synthesis

	β Oxidation	Fatty Acid Synthesis (Lipogenesis)
Site	mitochondrial matrix	cytosol
Activated by	glucagon low blood glucose	insulin high blood glucose
Activator	coenzyme A (HS—CoA)	acyl carrier protein (HS—ACP)
Initial Substrate	fatty acid	acetyl CoA
Initial Coenzymes	FAD, NAD$^+$	NADPH + H$^+$
Types of Reactions	oxidation hydration cleavage	reduction dehydration condensation
Function	cleaves two-carbon acetyl group	adds two-carbon acetyl group
Final Product	acetyl CoA	palmitate (C_{16}) or other fatty acids
Final Coenzymes	FADH$_2$, NADH + H$^+$	NADP$^+$

SAMPLE PROBLEM 24.5 Fatty Acid Synthesis

Malonyl ACP is required for the elongation of fatty acid chains.

a. Complete the following equations for the formation of malonyl ACP from the starting material:

$$\text{Acetyl CoA} + \text{HCO}_3^- + \text{ATP} \longrightarrow$$

$$\text{Malonyl CoA} + \text{HS—ACP} \longrightarrow$$

b. What enzymes catalyze these reactions?

SOLUTION

a. Acetyl CoA combines with bicarbonate to form malonyl CoA, which reacts with ACP to form malonyl ACP.

$$\text{Acetyl CoA} + \text{HCO}_3^- + \text{ATP} \longrightarrow \text{malonyl CoA} + \text{ADP} + \text{P}_i + \text{H}^+$$

$$\text{Malonyl CoA} + \text{HS—ACP} \longrightarrow \text{malonyl ACP} + \text{HS—CoA}$$

b. The enzyme for the first reaction is acetyl CoA carboxylase. The enzyme for the second reaction is malonyl CoA transacylase.

STUDY CHECK 24.5

If malonyl ACP is a three-carbon acyl group, why are only two carbon atoms added each time malonyl ACP is combined with a fatty acid chain?

ANSWER

In each cycle of fatty acid synthesis, a two-carbon acetyl group from the three-carbon group in malonyl ACP adds to the growing fatty acid chain and one carbon forms CO_2.

QUESTIONS AND PROBLEMS

24.5 Fatty Acid Synthesis

LEARNING GOAL Describe the biosynthesis of fatty acids from acetyl CoA.

24.31 Where does fatty acid synthesis occur in the cell?

24.32 What compound is involved in the activation of acyl compounds in fatty acid synthesis?

24.33 What are the starting materials for fatty acid synthesis?

24.34 What is the function of malonyl ACP in fatty acid synthesis?

24.35 Identify the reaction (**a** to **c**) catalyzed by each of the following enzymes (**1** to **3**):
1. acetyl CoA carboxylase
2. acetyl CoA transacylase
3. malonyl CoA transacylase

a. converts malonyl CoA to malonyl ACP
b. combines acetyl CoA with bicarbonate to give malonyl CoA
c. converts acetyl CoA to acetyl ACP

24.36 Identify the reaction (**a** to **d**) catalyzed by each of the following enzymes (**1** to **4**):
1. 3-ketoacyl ACP synthase
2. 3-ketoacyl ACP reductase
3. 3-hydroxyacyl ACP dehydrase
4. enoyl ACP reductase

a. catalyzes the dehydration of an alcohol
b. converts a carbon–carbon double bond to a carbon–carbon single bond
c. combines a two-carbon acetyl group with a three-carbon acyl group accompanied by the loss of CO_2
d. reduces a keto group to a hydroxyl group

24.37 Determine the number of each of the following components involved in the synthesis of one molecule of capric acid, a C_{10} fatty acid:

a. HCO_3^-
b. ATP
c. acetyl CoA
d. malonyl ACP
e. NADPH
f. CO_2 removed

24.38 Determine the number of each of the following components involved in the synthesis of one molecule of myristic acid, a C_{14} fatty acid:

a. HCO_3^-
b. ATP
c. acetyl CoA
d. malonyl ACP
e. NADPH
f. CO_2 removed

Ⓡ Clinical Applications

24.39 Triclosan, which is used in antiseptic hand washes and lotions to inhibit the growth of bacteria, is an inhibitor of enoyl ACP reductase.

a. What reaction in fatty acid synthesis is catalyzed by enoyl ACP reductase?
b. If fatty acid synthesis is required for the formation of bacterial membranes, why is triclosan used to control the growth of bacteria?

24.40 Researchers have synthesized a compound from biotin called CABI that inhibits the catalytic activity of acetyl CoA carboxylase in the cytosol. Mice without acetyl CoA carboxylase activity were found to lose weight even though they ate more food.

CABI

Biotin

a. What reaction in fatty acid synthesis is catalyzed by acetyl CoA carboxylase?
b. How might CABI be useful in reducing obesity?

LEARNING GOAL

Describe the hydrolysis of dietary protein and the reactions of transamination and oxidative deamination in the degradation of amino acids.

24.6 Degradation of Proteins and Amino Acids

The major role of protein in the diet is to provide amino acids for the synthesis of new proteins for the body and nitrogen atoms for the synthesis of compounds such as nucleotides. We have seen that carbohydrates and lipids are major sources of energy, but when they are not available, amino acids are degraded to substrates that enter energy-producing pathways.

In stage 1, the digestion of proteins begins in the stomach, where hydrochloric acid (HCl) at pH 2 denatures proteins and activates enzymes such as *pepsin* that begin to hydrolyze peptide bonds. Polypeptides move out of the stomach into the small intestine, where *trypsin* and *chymotrypsin* complete the hydrolysis of the peptides to amino acids. The amino acids are absorbed through the intestinal walls into the bloodstream for transport to the cells (see Figure 24.7).

▶**SAMPLE PROBLEM 24.6 Digestion of Proteins**

What are the sites and end products for the digestion of proteins?

SOLUTION

The digestion of proteins begins in the stomach and is completed in the small intestine to yield amino acids.

STUDY CHECK 24.6

What is the function of HCl in the stomach?

ANSWER

HCl denatures proteins and activates enzymes such as pepsin.

Protein Turnover

Our bodies are constantly replacing old proteins with new ones. The process of breaking down proteins and synthesizing new proteins is called **protein turnover**. Many types of proteins, including enzymes, hormones, and hemoglobin, are synthesized in the cells and then degraded. For example, the hormone *insulin* has a half-life of 10 min, whereas the half-life of *lactate dehydrogenase* is about 2 days and hemoglobin is 120 days. Damaged and ineffective proteins are also degraded and replaced. Although most amino acids are used to build proteins, other compounds also require nitrogen for their synthesis, as seen in Table 24.2 (see Figure 24.8).

TABLE 24.2 Nitrogen-Containing Compounds

Type of Compound	Example
Nonessential amino acids	Alanine, aspartate, cysteine, glycine
Proteins	Muscle protein, enzymes
Neurotransmitters	Acetylcholine, dopamine, serotonin
Amino alcohols	Choline, ethanolamine
Heme	Hemoglobin, cytochrome *c*
Hormones	Thyroxine, epinephrine, insulin
Nucleotides (nucleic acids)	Purines, pyrimidines

Usually, we maintain a nitrogen balance in the cells so that the amount of protein we break down is equal to the amount that is reused. A diet that is high in protein, however, has a positive nitrogen balance because it supplies more nitrogen than we need. Because the body cannot store nitrogen, the excess is excreted as urea. Such high protein diets put extra demands on the liver and kidneys. A diet that does not provide sufficient protein has a negative nitrogen balance, which is a condition that occurs during starvation and fasting.

Energy from Amino Acids

Normally, only a small amount (about 10%) of our energy needs is supplied by amino acids. However, more energy is extracted from amino acids in conditions such as fasting or starvation, when carbohydrate and fat stores are exhausted. If amino acids remain the only source of energy for a long period of time, the breakdown of body proteins eventually leads to a destruction of essential body tissues. In *anorexia*, the loss of protein decreases muscle mass and may severely weaken the heart muscle and impair heart function.

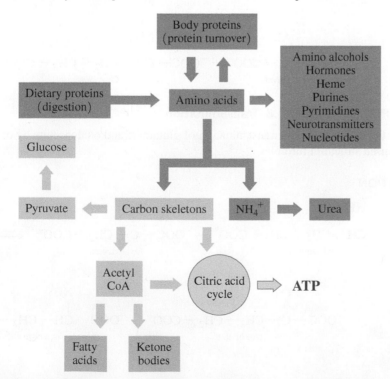

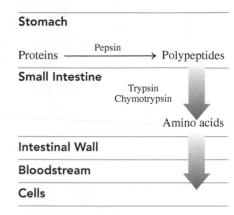

FIGURE 24.7 ▶ Proteins are hydrolyzed to polypeptides in the stomach and to amino acids in the small intestine.

What enzyme, secreted into the small intestine, hydrolyzes peptides?

FIGURE 24.8 ▶ Proteins are used in the synthesis of nitrogen-containing compounds or degraded to urea and carbon skeletons that enter other metabolic pathways.

What are some compounds that require nitrogen for their synthesis?

SAMPLE PROBLEM 24.7 Nitrogen Balance

With a positive nitrogen balance, why are excess amino acids excreted?

SOLUTION

Because the body cannot store nitrogen, amino acids that are not needed for the synthesis of proteins are excreted.

STUDY CHECK 24.7

Under what condition does the body have a negative nitrogen balance?

ANSWER

In conditions such as fasting or starvation, a diet insufficient in protein leads to a negative nitrogen balance.

Degradation of Amino Acids

When dietary protein exceeds the nitrogen needed for protein synthesis, the excess amino acids are degraded. The α-amino group is removed to yield an α-keto acid, which can be converted to an intermediate for other metabolic pathways. The carbon atoms from amino acids are used in the citric acid cycle as well as for the synthesis of fatty acids, ketone bodies, and glucose.

Transamination

The degradation of amino acids occurs primarily in the liver. In a **transamination** reaction, an α-amino group is transferred from an amino acid to an α-keto acid, usually α-ketoglutarate. A new amino acid and a new α-keto acid are produced.

We can write an equation to show the transfer of the amino group from alanine to α-ketoglutarate to yield glutamate, the new amino acid, and the α-keto acid pyruvate. The enzymes for the transfer of amino groups are known as *transaminases* or *aminotransferases*. Pyruvate can now enter the citric acid cycle for the production of energy.

$$CH_3-\overset{\overset{+}{N}H_3}{\underset{|}{C}H}-COO^- + {}^-OOC-\overset{O}{\overset{\|}{C}}-CH_2-CH_2-COO^- \underset{\longleftarrow}{\overset{\text{Alanine transaminase}}{\longrightarrow}}$$

Alanine $\qquad\qquad$ α-Ketoglutarate

$$CH_3-\overset{O}{\overset{\|}{C}}-COO^- + {}^-OOC-\overset{\overset{+}{N}H_3}{\underset{|}{C}H}-CH_2-CH_2-COO^-$$

Pyruvate $\qquad\qquad$ Glutamate

SAMPLE PROBLEM 24.8 Transamination

Write the equation for the transamination of glutamate and oxaloacetate by drawing the condensed structural formulas.

SOLUTION

$${}^-OOC-\overset{\overset{+}{N}H_3}{\underset{|}{C}H}-CH_2-CH_2-COO^- + {}^-OOC-\overset{O}{\overset{\|}{C}}-CH_2-COO^- \underset{\longleftarrow}{\overset{\text{Aspartate transaminase}}{\longrightarrow}}$$

Glutamate $\qquad\qquad$ Oxaloacetate

$${}^-OOC-\overset{O}{\overset{\|}{C}}-CH_2-CH_2-COO^- + {}^-OOC-\overset{\overset{+}{N}H_3}{\underset{|}{C}H}-CH_2-COO^-$$

α-Ketoglutarate $\qquad\qquad$ Aspartate

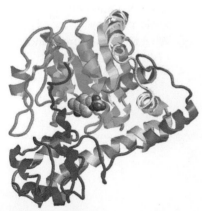

Aspartate transaminase (AST) catalyzes the reversible transfer of an amino group between glutamate and aspartate.

Oxidative Deamination

In a process called **oxidative deamination**, the amino group ($-NH_3^+$) in glutamate is removed as an ammonium ion, NH_4^+. The deamination reaction produces α-ketoglutarate, which can enter transamination with an amino acid. The reaction is catalyzed by *glutamate dehydrogenase*, which uses NAD^+ as a coenzyme.

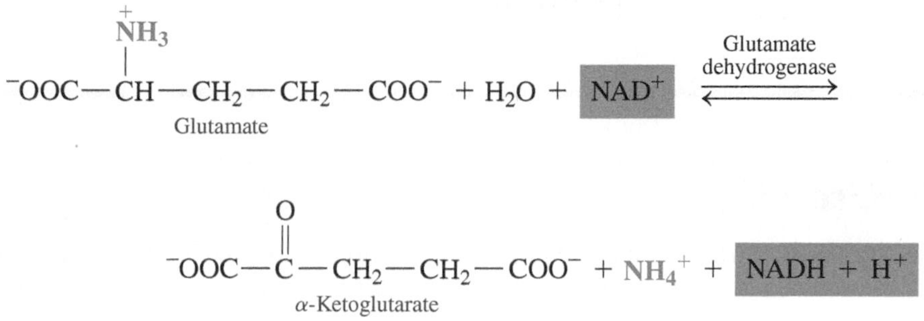

$$\underset{\text{Glutamate}}{^-OOC-\overset{\overset{+}{\underset{|}{NH_3}}}{CH}-CH_2-CH_2-COO^-} + H_2O + \boxed{NAD^+} \underset{\xleftarrow{\hspace{1cm}}}{\overset{\text{Glutamate}}{\overset{\text{dehydrogenase}}{\xrightarrow{\hspace{1cm}}}}}$$

$$\underset{\alpha\text{-Ketoglutarate}}{^-OOC-\overset{\overset{O}{\underset{||}{}}}{C}-CH_2-CH_2-COO^-} + NH_4^+ + \boxed{NADH + H^+}$$

Through transamination, the amino group from any amino acid can be used to form glutamate, which undergoes oxidative deamination, converting the amino group to an ammonium ion.

▶ **SAMPLE PROBLEM 24.9 Transamination and Oxidative Deamination**

Indicate whether each of the following represents a transamination or an oxidative deamination:

a. Glutamate is converted to α-ketoglutarate and NH_4^+.
b. Alanine and α-ketoglutarate react to form pyruvate and glutamate.

SOLUTION

a. Oxidative deamination occurs when the $-NH_3^+$ group in glutamate is removed as an ammonium ion, NH_4^+.
b. Transamination occurs when an amino group is transferred from an amino acid to an α-keto acid such as α-ketoglutarate.

STUDY CHECK 24.9

Is the reaction catalyzed by glutamate dehydrogenase, which requires NAD^+, an example of transamination or oxidative deamination?

ANSWER

oxidative deamination

▼

QUESTIONS AND PROBLEMS

24.6 Degradation of Proteins and Amino Acids

LEARNING GOAL Describe the hydrolysis of dietary protein and the reactions of transamination and oxidative deamination in the degradation of amino acids.

24.41 Where do dietary proteins undergo digestion in the body?

24.42 What is meant by protein turnover?

24.43 What are some nitrogen-containing compounds that need amino acids for their synthesis?

24.44 What is the fate of the amino acids obtained from a high protein diet?

24.45 What are the reactants and products in transamination reactions?

24.46 What types of enzymes catalyze transamination reactions?

24.47 Draw the condensed structural formula for the α-keto acid produced from each of the following in transamination:

a. $\overset{\overset{+}{N}H_3}{\underset{|}{H-CH-COO^-}}$ Glycine

b. $\overset{\overset{+}{N}H_3}{\underset{|}{HS-CH_2-CH-COO^-}}$ Cysteine

c. $\overset{CH_3 \quad \overset{+}{N}H_3}{\underset{| \quad\quad |}{CH_3-CH-CH-COO^-}}$ Valine

24.48 Draw the condensed structural formula for the α-keto acid produced from each of the following in transamination:

a. $\overset{\overset{+}{N}H_3}{\underset{|}{^-OOC-CH_2-CH-COO^-}}$ Aspartate

b. $\overset{CH_3 \quad \overset{+}{N}H_3}{\underset{| \quad\quad |}{CH_3-CH_2-CH-CH-COO^-}}$ Isoleucine

c. $\overset{\overset{+}{N}H_3}{\underset{|}{HO-CH_2-CH-COO^-}}$ Serine

24.49 Write the equation, using condensed structural formulas, for the oxidative deamination of glutamate.

24.50 How do all 20 amino acids produce ammonium ions in oxidative deamination?

LEARNING GOAL

Describe the formation of urea from an ammonium ion.

24.7 Urea Cycle

The ammonium ion, which is the end product of amino acid degradation, is toxic if it is allowed to accumulate. Thus, in the liver, the **urea cycle** converts ammonium ions to urea, which is transported to the kidneys to form urine.

$$2NH_4^+ + CO_2 \longrightarrow \overset{\overset{O}{\|}}{H_2N-C-NH_2} + 2H^+ + H_2O$$
$$\text{Urea}$$

In one day, a typical adult may excrete about 25 to 30 g of urea in the urine. This amount increases when a diet is high in protein. If urea is not properly excreted, it builds up quickly to a toxic level. To detect renal disease, the *blood urea nitrogen* (BUN) level is measured. If the BUN is high, protein intake must be reduced, and hemodialysis may be needed to remove toxic nitrogen waste from the blood.

Urea Cycle

The urea cycle in the liver cells consists of reactions that take place in both the mitochondria and cytosol (see Figure 24.9). In preparation for the urea cycle, ammonium ions react with carbon dioxide and water, using the energy from two ATP to yield carbamoyl phosphate.

$$NH_4^+ + CO_2 + \boxed{2 \text{ ATP}} + H_2O \xrightarrow{\underset{\text{synthetase}}{\overset{\text{Carbamoyl}}{\overset{\text{phosphate}}{}}}} \overset{\overset{O}{\|} \quad \overset{O}{\|}}{H_2N-C-O-\underset{\underset{O^-}{|}}{P}-O^-} + \boxed{2 \text{ ADP}} + P_i + 3H^+$$
$$\text{Carbamoyl phosphate}$$

Reaction 1   Transfer of the Carbamoyl Group

In the mitochondrial matrix, reaction 1 utilizes *ornithine transcarbamylase* to catalyze the transfer of the carbamoyl group from carbamoyl phosphate to ornithine (an amino acid not found in proteins) to yield citrulline, which is transported across the mitochondrial membrane by the citrulline transporter protein into the cytosol. The hydrolysis of the high-energy phosphate bond in carbamoyl phosphate provides the energy to drive the reaction.

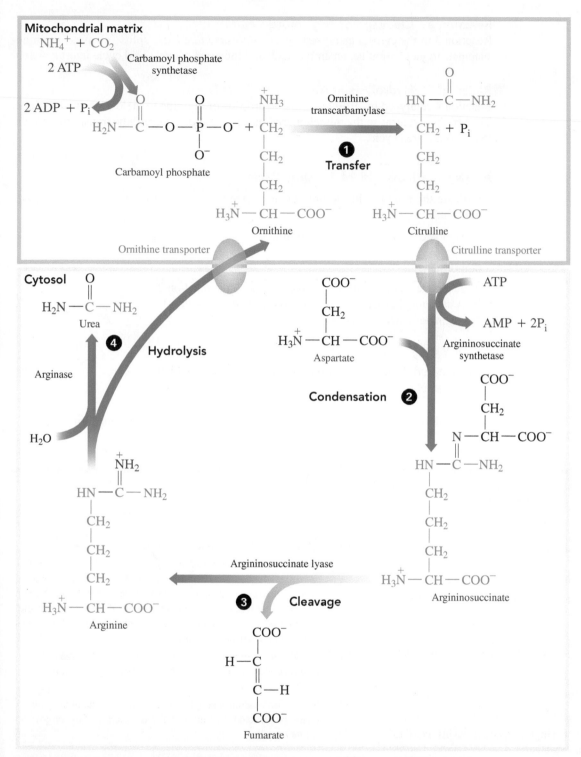

FIGURE 24.9 ▶ In the urea cycle, urea is formed from a carbon and nitrogen (blue) from carbamoyl phosphate (initially an ammonium ion from oxidative deamination) and a nitrogen atom from aspartate (magenta).

⊙ Where in the cell is urea formed?

Reaction 2 Condensation of Citrulline with Aspartate

In the cytosol, reaction 2, a condensation of citrulline with aspartate catalyzed by *argininosuccinate synthetase*, produces argininosuccinate. The energy for the reaction is supplied by the hydrolysis of two phosphate bonds in ATP to yield AMP and two inorganic phosphates. The nitrogen atom in aspartate becomes one of the nitrogen atoms in the urea molecule that is produced in the final reaction.

Reaction 3 Cleavage of Argininosuccinate

Reaction 3 in the cytosol catalyzed by *argininosuccinate lyase* splits (cleaves) argininosuccinate to yield arginine, an amino acid, and fumarate, a citric acid cycle intermediate.

Reaction 4 Hydrolysis of Arginine to Form Urea

Reaction 4 catalyzed by *arginase* is the hydrolysis of arginine to yield urea and ornithine. The ornithine returns to the mitochondrial matrix through the ornithine transporter protein to repeat the urea cycle.

▶ **SAMPLE PROBLEM 24.10** Urea Cycle

Indicate the reaction in the urea cycle where each of the following compounds is a reactant:

a. aspartate   **b.** ornithine   **c.** arginine

SOLUTION

a. Aspartate and citrulline undergo condensation in reaction 2.
b. A carbamoyl group is transferred to ornithine in reaction 1.
c. Arginine is cleaved in reaction 4.

STUDY CHECK 24.10

Name the products of each reaction in Sample Problem 24.10.

ANSWER

a. argininosuccinate   **b.** citrulline   **c.** urea and ornithine

---

QUESTIONS AND PROBLEMS

24.7 Urea Cycle

LEARNING GOAL Describe the formation of urea from an ammonium ion.

24.51 Draw the condensed structural formula for urea.

24.52 Draw the condensed structural formula for carbamoyl phosphate.

24.53 What is the source of carbon in urea?

24.54 How much ATP energy is required to drive one turn of the urea cycle?

℞ **Clinical Applications**

24.55 Why does the body convert NH_4^+ to urea?

24.56 Why would a person on a high-protein diet be instructed to drink large quantities of water?

Use the following information for problems 24.57 and 24.58:

Research indicates that *sudden infant death syndrome* may be the result of a deficiency of any one of the enzymes in the urea cycle. The *urea cycle disorders* (UCD) are a result of a genetic mutation that leads to a deficient enzyme. When the urea cycle is disrupted *hyperammonemia* (high ammonia levels) can cause irreversible changes in the brain.

24.57 In addition to ammonia, what intermediate of the urea cycle would be elevated if an infant has a deficiency of *argininosuccinate synthetase*?

24.58 In addition to ammonia, what intermediate of the urea cycle would be elevated if an infant has a deficiency of *argininosuccinate lyase*?

LEARNING GOAL

Describe where carbon atoms from amino acids enter the citric acid cycle or other pathways.

24.8 Fates of the Carbon Atoms from Amino Acids

The carbon skeletons from the transamination of amino acids are used as intermediates in the citric acid cycle or other metabolic pathways. We can classify the amino acids according to the number of carbon atoms in those intermediates (see Figure 24.10). The amino acids that provide three-carbon compounds are converted to pyruvate. The amino acids with four carbon atoms are converted to oxaloacetate, and the five-carbon amino acids provide α-ketoglutarate. Some amino acids are listed twice because they can enter different pathways to form citric acid cycle intermediates.

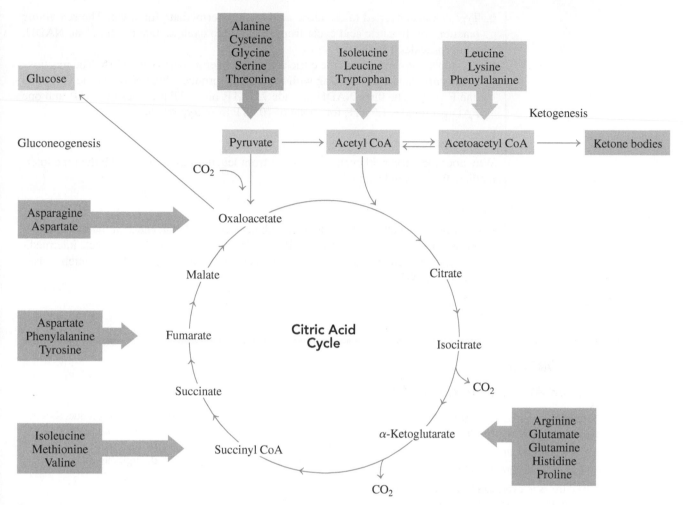

FIGURE 24.10 ▶ Carbon atoms from degraded amino acids are converted to the intermediates of the citric acid cycle or other pathways. Glucogenic amino acids (pink boxes) produce carbon skeletons that can form glucose, and ketogenic amino acids (green boxes) can produce ketone bodies.

Q Why is aspartate glucogenic, but leucine ketogenic?

A **glucogenic amino acid** generates pyruvate, α-ketoglutarate, succinyl CoA, fumarate, or oxaloacetate, which can be used to synthesize glucose by gluconeogenesis. A **ketogenic amino acid** produces acetoacetyl CoA or acetyl CoA, which can enter the ketogenesis pathway to form ketone bodies or the lipogenesis pathway to form fatty acids. Some amino acids can be both glucogenic and ketogenic.

▶ **SAMPLE PROBLEM 24.11 Degradation of Amino Acids**

Identify the citric acid cycle component and the number of ATP produced by each of the following amino acids:

a. proline   **b.** tyrosine   **c.** tryptophan

SOLUTION

	Given	Need
ANALYZE THE PROBLEM	proline, tyrosine, tryptophan	ATP produced via the citric acid cycle

a. Proline is converted to the citric acid cycle intermediate α-ketoglutarate. The reactions in the remaining part of the citric acid cycle from α-ketoglutarate to oxaloacetate produce two NADH, one GTP, and one $FADH_2$. The two NADH provide five ATP, one GTP provides one ATP, and one $FADH_2$ provides 1.5 ATP, for a total of 7.5 ATP from proline.

b. Tyrosine is converted to the citric acid cycle intermediate fumarate. The remaining reactions of the citric acid cycle from fumarate to oxaloacetate produce one NADH, which provides 2.5 ATP.

c. Tryptophan is converted to the citric acid cycle intermediate acetyl CoA. The reactions in the citric acid cycle starting with acetyl CoA produce three NADH, one GTP, and one $FADH_2$. The three NADH provide 7.5 ATP, one GTP provides one ATP, and one $FADH_2$ provides 1.5 ATP, for a total of 10 ATP from tryptophan.

STUDY CHECK 24.11

Why does the citric acid cycle component from leucine supply more ATP than the intermediate from phenylalanine?

ANSWER

Leucine forms the citric acid cycle intermediate acetyl CoA that enters at the beginning of the citric acid cycle to provide 10 ATP. Phenylalanine forms the citric acid cycle intermediate fumarate that enters later in the citric acid cycle to produce one NADH, which is used to provide 2.5 ATP.

QUESTIONS AND PROBLEMS

24.8 Fates of the Carbon Atoms from Amino Acids

LEARNING GOAL Describe where carbon atoms from amino acids enter the citric acid cycle or other pathways.

24.59 What is the function of a glucogenic amino acid?

24.60 What is the function of a ketogenic amino acid?

24.61 What component of the citric acid cycle can be produced from the carbon atoms of each of the following amino acids?
    a. alanine   **b.** asparagine
    c. valine   **d.** glutamine

24.62 What component of the citric acid cycle can be produced from the carbon atoms of each of the following amino acids?
    a. leucine   **b.** threonine
    c. cysteine   **d.** arginine

LEARNING GOAL

Illustrate how some nonessential amino acids are synthesized from intermediates in the citric acid cycle and other metabolic pathways.

TABLE 24.3 Essential and Nonessential Amino Acids in Adults

Essential	Nonessential
Histidine	Alanine
Isoleucine	Arginine
Leucine	Asparagine
Lysine	Aspartate
Methionine	Cysteine
Phenylalanine	Glutamate
Threonine	Glutamine
Tryptophan	Glycine
Valine	Proline
	Serine
	Tyrosine

24.9 Synthesis of Amino Acids

Plants and bacteria such as *E. coli* produce all of their amino acids using NH_4^+ and NO_3^-. However, humans can synthesize only 9 of the 20 amino acids found in their proteins. The nonessential amino acids are synthesized in the body, whereas the essential amino acids must be obtained from the diet (see Table 24.3). The amino acids arginine, cysteine, and tyrosine are essential in diets for infants and children due to their rapid growth requirements, but they are not essential amino acids for adults.

Some Pathways for Amino Acid Synthesis

A variety of pathways are involved in the synthesis of nonessential amino acids. When the body synthesizes nonessential amino acids, the α-keto acid carbon skeletons are obtained from the citric acid cycle or glycolysis and converted to amino acids by transamination (see Figure 24.11).

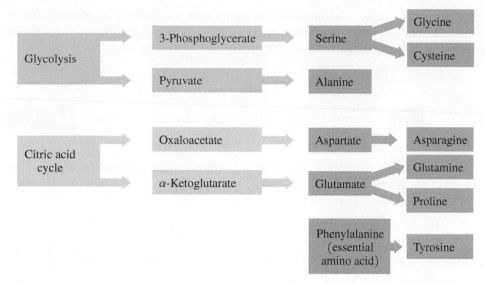

FIGURE 24.11 ▶ Nonessential amino acids are synthesized from intermediates of glycolysis and the citric acid cycle.

Q How is alanine formed from pyruvate?

Some of the amino acids are formed by reversing the transamination reaction that we saw in amino acid degradation. The transfer of an amino group from glutamate to pyruvate produces alanine, which is catalyzed by *alanine transaminase* (ALT).

$$\overset{\overset{+}{N}H_3}{\underset{\text{Glutamate}}{{}^-OOC-CH-CH_2-CH_2-COO^-}} + \underset{\text{Pyruvate}}{CH_3-\overset{O}{\overset{\|}{C}}-COO^-} \overset{\text{Alanine transaminase}}{\rightleftharpoons}$$

$$\underset{\text{Alanine}}{CH_3-\overset{\overset{+}{N}H_3}{CH}-COO^-} + \underset{\alpha\text{-Ketoglutarate}}{{}^-OOC-\overset{O}{\overset{\|}{C}}-CH_2-CH_2-COO^-}$$

Oxaloacetate, a keto acid from the citric acid cycle, undergoes transamination with glutamate to produce aspartate, an amino acid, and α-ketoglutarate. The transamination is catalyzed by *aspartate transaminase* (AST).

$$\underset{\text{Glutamate}}{{}^-OOC-\overset{\overset{+}{N}H_3}{CH}-CH_2-CH_2-COO^-} + \underset{\text{Oxaloacetate}}{{}^-OOC-CH_2-\overset{O}{\overset{\|}{C}}-COO^-} \overset{\text{Aspartate transaminase}}{\rightleftharpoons}$$

$$\underset{\text{Aspartate}}{{}^-OOC-CH_2-\overset{\overset{+}{N}H_3}{CH}-COO^-} + \underset{\alpha\text{-Ketoglutarate}}{{}^-OOC-\overset{O}{\overset{\|}{C}}-CH_2-CH_2-COO^-}$$

These two transaminases, ALT and AST, are abundant in the cells of the liver and heart, but they are present only in low levels in the bloodstream. When an injury or disease occurs, they are released from the damaged cells into the bloodstream. Elevated levels of serum ALT or AST provide a means to diagnose the extent of damage to the liver or the heart. *Alanine transaminase* is also known by the abbreviation SGPT (*serum glutamate pyruvate transaminase*) since it catalyzes the reversible transamination reaction between glutamate and pyruvate, and *aspartate transaminase* is also known by the abbreviation SGOT (*serum glutamate oxaloacetate transaminase*) since it catalyzes the reversible transamination reaction between glutamate and oxaloacetate.

⚛ CORE CHEMISTRY SKILL

Distinguishing Anabolic and Catabolic Pathways

The synthesis of the other nonessential amino acids may require several reactions in addition to transamination. For example, glutamine is synthesized when a second amino group is added to glutamate using the energy from the hydrolysis of ATP.

$$
\overset{+}{\underset{\text{Glutamate}}{\text{OOC}-\text{CH}-\text{CH}_2-\text{CH}_2-\text{COO}^-}} + \text{NH}_3 + \boxed{\text{ATP}} \xrightarrow{\text{Glutamine}\atop\text{synthetase}} \overset{+}{\underset{\text{Glutamine}}{\text{OOC}-\text{CH}-\text{CH}_2-\text{CH}_2-\overset{\text{O}}{\overset{\|}{\text{C}}}-\text{NH}_2}} + \boxed{\text{ADP} + \text{P}_i}
$$

Tyrosine, an aromatic amino acid with a hydroxyl group, is formed from phenylalanine, an essential amino acid, and oxygen.

$$
\underset{\text{Phenylalanine}}{\bigcirc-\text{CH}_2-\overset{+}{\overset{\text{NH}_3}{\text{CH}}}-\text{COO}^-} + \text{O}_2 + \boxed{\text{NADH} + \text{H}^+} \xrightarrow{\text{Phenylalanine}\atop\text{hydroxylase}} \underset{\text{Tyrosine}}{\text{HO}-\bigcirc-\text{CH}_2-\overset{+}{\overset{\text{NH}_3}{\text{CH}}}-\text{COO}^-} + \text{H}_2\text{O} + \boxed{\text{NAD}^+}
$$

Chemistry Link to Health

Phenylketonuria (PKU)

In the genetic disease *phenylketonuria* (PKU), a person cannot convert phenylalanine to tyrosine because the gene for an enzyme, *phenylalanine hydroxylase*, is defective. As a result, large amounts of phenylalanine accumulate. In this situation, a *transaminase* catalyzes the transfer of the —NH$_3^+$ from phenylalanine to pyruvate to form alanine and phenylpyruvate, which is then decarboxylated to phenylacetate. Large amounts of these compounds are excreted in the urine. Phenylacetate has a characteristic odor in the urine that was used to recognize PKU in infants.

In infants, high levels of phenylpyruvate and phenylacetate cause severe mental retardation. However, the defect can be identified at birth, and all newborns are now tested for PKU. By detecting PKU early, retardation is avoided by using an infant diet with proteins that are low in phenylalanine and high in tyrosine. It is also important to avoid the use of sweeteners and soft drinks containing aspartame, which contains phenylalanine as one of the two amino acids in its structure. In adulthood, some people with PKU can eat a nearly normal diet as long as they are checked for phenylpyruvate periodically.

$$
\underset{\text{Phenylalanine}}{\bigcirc-\text{CH}_2-\overset{+}{\overset{\text{NH}_3}{\text{CH}}}-\text{COO}^-} \xrightarrow{\text{Transaminase}} \underset{\text{Phenylpyruvate}}{\bigcirc-\text{CH}_2-\overset{\text{O}}{\overset{\|}{\text{C}}}-\text{COO}^-}
$$

$$
\Big\downarrow\kern-1.5em\times \;\;{\text{Phenylalanine}\atop\text{hydroxylase}} \qquad\qquad \Big\downarrow\;\text{CO}_2
$$

$$
\underset{\text{Tyrosine}}{\text{HO}-\bigcirc-\text{CH}_2-\overset{+}{\overset{\text{NH}_3}{\text{CH}}}-\text{COO}^-} \qquad\qquad \underset{\text{Phenylacetate}}{\bigcirc-\text{CH}_2-\text{COO}^-}
$$

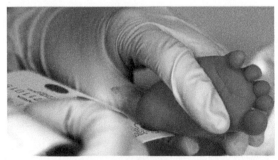

All newborns are tested for PKU.

Overview of Metabolism

Catabolic pathways degrade large molecules to small molecules that enter the citric acid cycle and electron transport to produce energy. Anabolic pathways use small molecules and energy to synthesize larger molecules in the cell. In the overall view of metabolism, there are several branch points from which compounds may be degraded for energy or used to synthesize larger molecules. For example, glucose can be degraded to pyruvate and then acetyl CoA for the citric acid cycle to produce energy. Glucose may also be converted to glycogen for storage. When glycogen stores are depleted, fatty acids from fats are degraded for energy. Amino acids normally used to synthesize nitrogen-containing compounds in the cells can also be used for energy after they are degraded to intermediates of the citric acid cycle. In the synthesis of nonessential amino acids, α-keto acids of the citric acid cycle enter into a variety of reactions that convert them to amino acids through transamination by glutamate (see Figure 24.12).

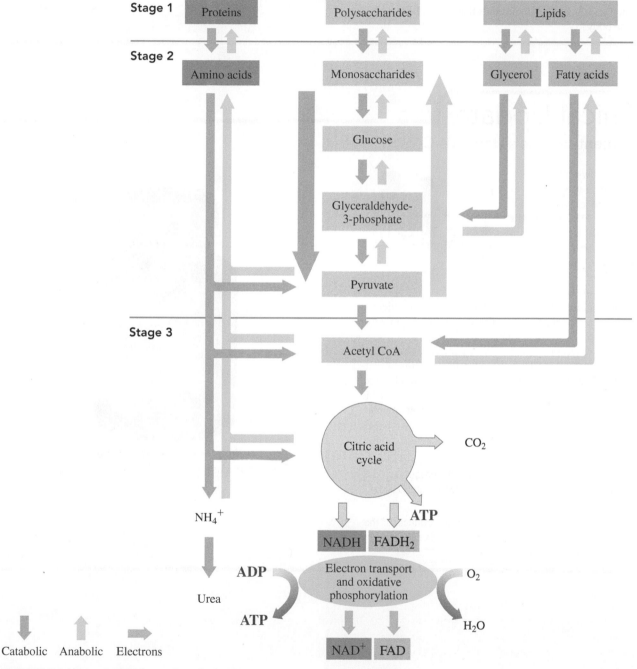

FIGURE 24.12 ▶ Catabolic and anabolic pathways in the cells provide the energy and necessary compounds for the cells.

◉ Under what conditions in the cell are amino acids degraded for energy?

QUESTIONS AND PROBLEMS

24.9 Synthesis of Amino Acids

LEARNING GOAL Illustrate how some nonessential amino acids are synthesized from intermediates in the citric acid cycle and other metabolic pathways.

24.63 What do we call the amino acids that humans can synthesize?

24.64 How do humans obtain the amino acids that cannot be synthesized in the body?

24.65 How is glutamate converted to glutamine?

24.66 What amino acid can be converted into the amino acid tyrosine?

24.67 What do the letters PKU mean?

24.68 How is PKU treated?

Clinical Update
Treatment of Luke's Hepatitis C

When Luke had a follow-up liver evaluation three months later, his liver enzymes were more elevated: ALT 356 Units/L and AST 418 Units/L. His doctor suggested that Luke begin interferon and ribavirin therapy for six months. Interferon and ribavirin work together as antiviral agents to inhibit the replication of the hepatitis C  virus and strengthen the immune system. The interferon is injected subcutaneously or intramuscularly three times a week for nine months. The ribavarin is taken orally as 400-mg tablets twice a day.

After eight weeks of treatment, Luke's liver enzymes had lowered to ALT 85 Units/L and AST 115 Units/L. After four months of therapy, his ALT and AST enzyme levels were within the normal range. Luke will continue to have a liver profile every three months for the next year, and then every six months. Monitoring of his liver enzymes will continue throughout his life.

℞ Clinical Applications

24.69 Draw the condensed structural formulas for the products of the reaction of alanine and α-ketoglutarate, which is catalyzed by *alanine transaminase* (ALT).

24.70 Draw the condensed structural formulas for the products of the reaction of aspartate and α-ketoglutarate, which is catalyzed by *aspartate transaminase* (AST).

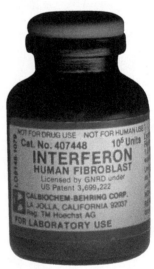

Interferon is one of the antiviral agents used to treat hepatitis C.

CONCEPT MAP

METABOLIC PATHWAYS FOR LIPIDS AND AMINO ACIDS

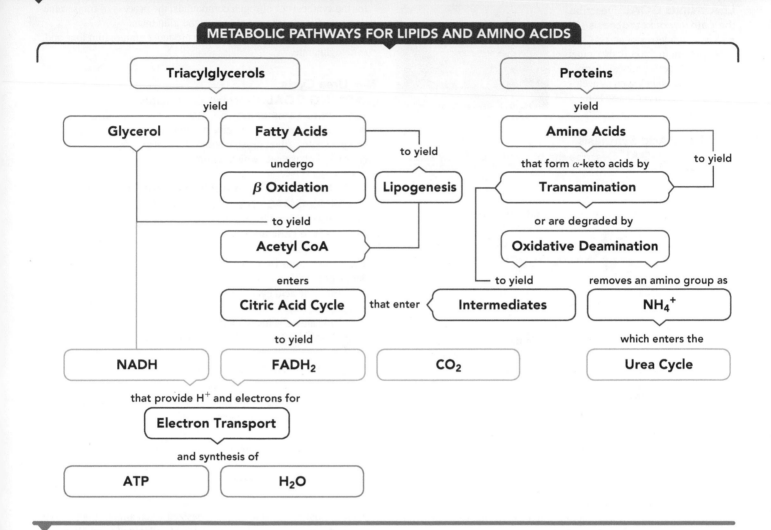

Triacylglycerols

yield

Glycerol   **Fatty Acids**

to yield

undergo

β Oxidation   **Lipogenesis**

to yield

Acetyl CoA

enters

Citric Acid Cycle   that enter   **Intermediates**

to yield

NADH   **FADH₂**   **CO₂**

that provide H⁺ and electrons for

Electron Transport

and synthesis of

ATP   **H₂O**

Proteins

yield

Amino Acids

to yield

that form α-keto acids by

Transamination

or are degraded by

Oxidative Deamination

to yield   removes an amino group as

NH₄⁺

which enters the

Urea Cycle

CHAPTER REVIEW

24.1 Digestion of Triacylglycerols
LEARNING GOAL
Describe the sites and products obtained from the digestion of triacylglycerols.

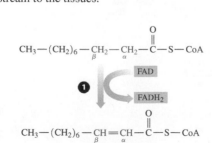

- Triacylglycerols are hydrolyzed in the small intestine to yield monoacylglycerols and fatty acids, which enter the intestinal wall and form new triacylglycerols.
- Triacylglycerols bind with proteins to form chylomicrons, which transport them through the lymphatic system and bloodstream to the tissues.

24.2 Oxidation of Fatty Acids
LEARNING GOAL Describe the metabolic pathway of β oxidation.

- When used as an energy source, fatty acids link

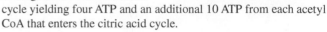

to coenzyme A to be transported into the mitochondria, where they undergo β oxidation.
- The acyl chain is oxidized to yield a shorter fatty acid, acetyl CoA, and the reduced coenzymes NADH and FADH₂.

24.3 ATP and Fatty Acid Oxidation
LEARNING GOAL Calculate the total ATP produced by the complete oxidation of a fatty acid.

- The activation of a fatty acid for β oxidation requires an input of two ATP.
- The energy obtained from a particular fatty acid depends on its length, with each oxidation cycle yielding four ATP and an additional 10 ATP from each acetyl CoA that enters the citric acid cycle.

24.4 Ketogenesis and Ketone Bodies
LEARNING GOAL Describe the pathway of ketogenesis.

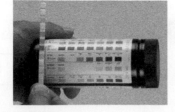

- When high levels of acetyl CoA are present in the cell, they enter the ketogenesis pathway, forming ketone bodies such as acetoacetate, which can cause ketosis and acidosis.

24.5 Fatty Acid Synthesis
LEARNING GOAL Describe the biosynthesis of fatty acids from acetyl CoA.

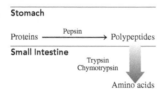

- When there is an excess of acetyl CoA in the cell, the two-carbon acetyl CoA units link together to synthesize palmitate, which is converted to triacylglycerols and stored in the adipose tissue.

24.6 Degradation of Proteins and Amino Acids
LEARNING GOAL Describe the hydrolysis of dietary protein and the reactions of transamination and oxidative deamination in the degradation of amino acids.

Stomach		
Proteins	—Pepsin→	Polypeptides

Small Intestine

Trypsin
Chymotrypsin

Amino acids

- The digestion of proteins, which begins in the stomach and continues in the small intestine, involves the hydrolysis of peptide bonds by proteases to yield amino acids that are absorbed through the intestinal wall and transported to the cells.

- When the amount of amino acids in the cells exceeds that needed for the synthesis of nitrogen compounds, the process of transamination converts them to α-keto acids and glutamate.
- Oxidative deamination of glutamate produces ammonium ions and α-ketoglutarate.

24.7 Urea Cycle
LEARNING GOAL Describe the formation of urea from an ammonium ion.

- Ammonium ions from oxidative deamination combine with carbon dioxide and ATP to form carbamoyl phosphate, which is converted to urea.

24.8 Fates of the Carbon Atoms from Amino Acids
LEARNING GOAL Describe where carbon atoms from amino acids enter the citric acid cycle or other pathways.

- The carbon atoms from the degradation of glucogenic amino acids enter the citric acid cycle or gluconeogenesis.
- Ketogenic amino acids produce acetyl CoA or acetoacetyl CoA for ketogenesis.

24.9 Synthesis of Amino Acids
LEARNING GOAL Illustrate how some nonessential amino acids are synthesized from intermediates in the citric acid cycle and other metabolic pathways.

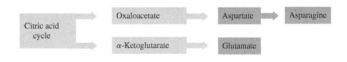

- Nonessential amino acids are synthesized when amino groups from glutamate are transferred to an α-keto acid obtained from glycolysis or the citric acid cycle.

SUMMARY OF KEY REACTIONS

The chapter sections to review are shown after the name of the reaction.

Digestion of Triacylglycerols (24.1)

$$\text{Triacylglycerols} + 2H_2O \xrightarrow{\text{Pancreatic lipase}} \text{monoacylglycerols} + 2 \text{ fatty acids}$$

Metabolism of Glycerol (24.1)

$$\text{Glycerol} + \text{ATP} + \text{NAD}^+ \longrightarrow \text{dihydroxyacetone phosphate} + \text{ADP} + \text{NADH} + H^+$$

Transamination (24.6)

$$\underset{\text{Alanine}}{CH_3-\underset{\overset{|}{\underset{}{NH_3^+}}}{CH}-COO^-} + \underset{\alpha\text{-Ketoglutarate}}{{}^-OOC-\underset{\overset{\|}{O}}{C}-CH_2-CH_2-COO^-} \underset{}{\overset{\text{Alanine}}{\underset{\text{transaminase}}{\rightleftarrows}}}$$

$$\underset{\text{Pyruvate}}{CH_3-\underset{\overset{\|}{O}}{C}-COO^-} + \underset{\text{Glutamate}}{{}^-OOC-\underset{\overset{|}{\underset{}{NH_3^+}}}{CH}-CH_2-CH_2-COO^-}$$

Oxidative Deamination (24.6)

$$\underset{\text{Glutamate}}{^-OOC - \overset{\overset{\displaystyle +}{\underset{|}{NH_3}}}{CH} - CH_2 - CH_2 - COO^-} + H_2O + \boxed{NAD^+} \underset{\xrightarrow{\hspace{1cm}}}{\overset{\text{Glutamate}}{\underset{\text{dehydrogenase}}{\rightleftharpoons}}}$$

$$\underset{\alpha\text{-Ketoglutarate}}{^-OOC - \overset{\overset{\displaystyle O}{\underset{\|}{}}}{C} - CH_2 - CH_2 - COO^-} + NH_4^+ + \boxed{NADH + H^+}$$

Urea Cycle (24.7)

$$2NH_4^+ + CO_2 \longrightarrow \underset{\text{Urea}}{H_2N - \overset{\overset{\displaystyle O}{\underset{\|}{}}}{C} - NH_2} + 2H^+ + H_2O$$

KEY TERMS

acidosis Low blood pH resulting from the formation of acidic ketone bodies.

beta oxidation (β oxidation) The degradation of fatty acids that removes two-carbon segments from a fatty acid chain at the oxidized β-carbon.

glucogenic amino acid An amino acid that provides carbon atoms for the synthesis of glucose.

ketogenesis The pathway that converts acetyl CoA to four-carbon acetoacetate and other ketone bodies.

ketogenic amino acid An amino acid that provides carbon atoms for the synthesis of fatty acids or ketone bodies.

ketone bodies The products of ketogenesis: acetoacetate, 3-hydroxybutyrate, and acetone.

ketosis A condition in which high levels of ketone bodies cannot be metabolized, leading to lower blood pH.

lipogenesis The synthesis of fatty acid in which two-carbon acetyl units link together to yield fatty acids, primarily palmitic acid.

oxidative deamination The loss of ammonium ion when glutamate is degraded to α-ketoglutarate.

protein turnover The amount of protein that we break down from our diet and utilize for synthesis of proteins and nitrogen-containing compounds.

transamination The transfer of an amino group from an amino acid to an α-keto acid.

urea cycle The process in which ammonium ions from the degradation of amino acids are converted to urea.

⚛ CORE CHEMISTRY SKILLS

The chapter section containing each Core Chemistry Skill is shown in parentheses at the end of each heading.

Calculating the ATP from Fatty Acid Oxidation (β Oxidation) (24.3)

• When needed as an energy source, fatty acids are linked to coenzyme A and transported into the mitochondria where they undergo β oxidation.

• The fatty acyl CoA is oxidized to yield a shorter fatty acyl CoA, acetyl CoA, and reduced coenzymes NADH and $FADH_2$.

• Although the energy from a particular fatty acid depends on its length, each oxidation cycle yields four ATP with another 10 ATP from each acetyl CoA that enters the citric acid cycle.

• When high levels of acetyl CoA are present in the cell, they enter the ketogenesis pathway, forming ketone bodies such as acetoacetate, which causes ketosis and acidosis.

Example: How many β oxidation cycles, acetyl CoA, and ATP are produced by the complete oxidation of caprylic acid, the C_8 saturated fatty acid?

Answer: An eight-carbon fatty acid will undergo three β oxidation cycles and produce four acetyl CoA. Each oxidation cycle produces four ATP (from one NADH and one $FADH_2$) for a total of 12 ATP. Each of the four acetyl CoA produces 10 ATP in the citric acid cycle or a total of 40 ATP. The 52 ATP minus two ATP for initial activation gives a total of 50 ATP from caprylic acid.

Describing How Ketone Bodies are Formed (24.4)

• Ketone bodies are formed when the body produces more acetyl CoA than it needs for energy.

• Excess acetyl CoA combines to form four-carbon and three-carbon ketone bodies.

• The ketone bodies are acetoacetate, β-hydroxybutyrate, and acetone.

Example: Acetone is a three-carbon ketone body. How is it formed from the two-carbon acetyl CoA?

Answer: Two acetyl CoA combine to form the four-carbon molecule, acetoacetate, which undergoes decarboxylation to form the three-carbon molecule acetone.

Distinguishing Anabolic and Catabolic Pathways (24.9)

- Pathways that degrade large molecules to small molecules to produce energy are catabolic.
- Those pathways that require energy for the biosynthesis of large molecules from small molecules are anabolic.

Example: Identify the following pathways as anabolic or catabolic:
- **a.** β oxidation of fatty acids
- **b.** synthesis of fatty acids
- **c.** degradation of amino acids
- **d.** synthesis of urea

Answer:
- **a.** catabolic
- **b.** anabolic
- **c.** catabolic
- **d.** anabolic

UNDERSTANDING THE CONCEPTS

The chapter sections to review are shown in parentheses at the end of each question.

24.71 Lauric acid, found in coconut oil, is a saturated C_{12} fatty acid. (24.2, 24.3)

Coconut oil contains lauric acid, a saturated C_{12} fatty acid.

- **a.** Draw the line-angle structural formula for the activated form of lauric acid.
- **b.** Indicate the α- and β-carbon atoms in the acyl molecule.
- **c.** How many cycles of β oxidation are needed?
- **d.** How many acetyl CoA units are produced?
- **e.** Calculate the total ATP yield from the complete β oxidation of lauric acid by completing the following:

Activation		−2 ATP
_____ NADH		_____ ATP
_____ FADH$_2$		_____ ATP
_____ Acetyl CoA		_____ ATP
Total		_____ ATP

24.72 Arachidic acid is a saturated C_{20} fatty acid found in peanut and fish oils. (24.2, 24.3)

Peanuts contain arachidic acid, a saturated C_{20} fatty acid.

- **a.** Draw the line-angle structural formula for the activated form of arachidic acid.
- **b.** Indicate the α- and β-carbon atoms in the acyl molecule.
- **c.** How many cycles of β oxidation are needed?
- **d.** How many acetyl CoA units are produced?
- **e.** Calculate the total ATP yield from the complete β oxidation of arachidic acid by completing the following:

Activation		−2 ATP
_____ NADH		_____ ATP
_____ FADH$_2$		_____ ATP
_____ Acetyl CoA		_____ ATP
Total		_____ ATP

ADDITIONAL QUESTIONS AND PROBLEMS

24.73 How are dietary triacylglycerols digested? (24.1)

24.74 What is a chylomicron? (24.1)

24.75 Why are the fats in the adipose tissues of the body considered the major form of stored energy? (24.1)

24.76 How are fatty acids obtained from stored fats? (24.1)

24.77 Why doesn't the brain utilize fatty acids for energy? (24.1)

24.78 Why don't red blood cells utilize fatty acids for energy? (24.1)

℞ Clinical Applications

24.79 A triacylglycerol is hydrolyzed in the fat cells of adipose tissues and the fatty acid is transported to the liver. (24.1, 24.2)
- **a.** What happens to the glycerol?
- **b.** Where in the liver cells is the fatty acid activated for β oxidation?
- **c.** What is the energy cost for activation of the fatty acid?
- **d.** What is the purpose of activating fatty acids?

24.80 Consider the β oxidation of a saturated fatty acid. (24.2, 24.3)
  a. What is the activated form of the fatty acid?
  b. Why is this oxidation called β oxidation?
  c. Which reactions in the fatty acid cycle require coenzymes?
  d. What is the yield in ATP for one cycle of β oxidation?

24.81 Identify each of the following as involved in β oxidation or in fatty acid synthesis: (24.2, 24.3, 24.5)
  a. NAD^+
  b. occurs in the mitochondrial matrix
  c. malonyl ACP
  d. cleavage of a two-carbon acetyl group
  e. acyl carrier protein
  f. carboxylase

24.82 Identify each of the following as involved in β oxidation or in fatty acid synthesis: (24.2, 24.3, 24.5)
  a. NADPH
  b. takes place in the cytosol
  c. FAD
  d. oxidation of a hydroxyl group
  e. coenzyme A
  f. hydration of a double bond

24.83 The metabolism of triacylglycerols and carbohydrates is influenced by the hormones insulin and glucagon. Indicate the results of each of the following as stimulating fatty acid oxidation or fatty acid synthesis: (24.2, 24.3, 24.5)
  a. high blood glucose
  b. secretion of glucagon

24.84 The metabolism of triacylglycerols and carbohydrates is influenced by the hormones insulin and glucagon. Indicate the results of each of the following as stimulating fatty acid oxidation or fatty acid synthesis: (24.2, 24.3, 24.5)
  a. low blood glucose
  b. secretion of insulin

24.85 Why is ammonium ion that is produced in the liver converted immediately to urea? (24.7)

24.86 What compound is regenerated to repeat the urea cycle? (24.7)

24.87 Indicate the reactant in the urea cycle that reacts with each of the following compounds: (24.7)
  a. aspartate   **b.** ornithine

24.88 Indicate the products in the urea cycle that are manufactured from the reaction that uses each of the following compounds: (24.7)
  a. arginine   **b.** argininosuccinate

24.89 What component of the citric acid cycle can be produced from the carbon atoms of each of the following amino acids? (24.8)
  a. serine   **b.** lysine
  c. methionine   **d.** glutamate

24.90 What component of the citric acid cycle can be produced from the carbon atoms of each of the following amino acids? (24.8)
  a. glycine   **b.** isoleucine
  c. histidine   **d.** phenylalanine

24.91 How much ATP can be produced by the degradation of serine? (24.8)

24.92 Calculate the total ATP produced in the complete oxidation of caproic acid, $C_6H_{12}O_2$, and compare it with the total ATP produced from the oxidation of glucose, $C_6H_{12}O_6$. (24.3)

CHALLENGE QUESTIONS

The following groups of questions are related to the topics in this chapter. However, they do not all follow the chapter order, and they require you to combine concepts and skills from several sections. These questions will help you increase your critical thinking skills and prepare for your next exam.

24.93 Identify each of the following reactions in the β oxidation of palmitic acid, a C_{16} fatty acid, as activation, transport into mitochondria, first oxidation, hydration, second oxidation, or cleavage (thiolysis): (24.2)
  a. Palmitoyl CoA and FAD form α,β-unsaturated palmitoyl CoA and $FADH_2$.
  b. 3-Ketopalmitoyl CoA forms myristoyl CoA and acetyl CoA.
  c. Palmitic acid, HS—CoA, and ATP form palmitoyl CoA.

24.94 Identify each of the following reactions in the β oxidation of palmitic acid, a C_{16} fatty acid, as activation, transport into mitochondria, first oxidation, hydration, second oxidation, or cleavage (thiolysis): (24.2)
  a. α,β-Unsaturated palmitoyl CoA and H_2O form 3-hydroxypalmitoyl CoA.
  b. 3-Hydroxypalmitoyl CoA and NAD^+ form 3-ketopalmitoyl CoA and $NADH + H^+$.
  c. Palmitoyl CoA condenses with carnitine to form palmitoyl carnitine.

24.95 Draw the condensed structural formula for and give the name of the amino acid formed when the following α-keto acids undergo transamination with glutamate: (24.9)

  a.
  $$CH_3-\underset{\underset{CH_3}{|}}{CH}-\underset{\underset{O}{\|}}{C}-\underset{\underset{O}{\|}}{C}-O^-$$

  b.
  $$CH_3-CH_2-\underset{\underset{CH_3}{|}}{CH}-\underset{\underset{O}{\|}}{C}-\underset{\underset{O}{\|}}{C}-O^-$$

24.96 Draw the condensed structural formula for and give the name of the amino acid formed when the following α-keto acids undergo transamination with glutamate: (24.9)

  a.
  $$^-O-\underset{\underset{O}{\|}}{C}-CH_2-\underset{\underset{O}{\|}}{C}-\underset{\underset{O}{\|}}{C}-O^-$$

  b.
  $$CH_3-\underset{\underset{CH_3}{|}}{CH}-CH_2-\underset{\underset{O}{\|}}{C}-\underset{\underset{O}{\|}}{C}-O^-$$

ANSWERS

Answers to Selected Questions and Problems

24.1 The bile salts emulsify fat so that it forms small fat globules for lipase hydrolysis.

24.3 Fats are released from fat stores when blood glucose and glycogen stores are depleted.

24.5 Glycerol is converted to glycerol-3-phosphate, and then to dihydroxyacetone phosphate, an intermediate of glycolysis.

24.7 The enzyme glycerol kinase would be defective.

24.9 In the cytosol at the outer mitochondrial membrane.

24.11 FAD, NAD^+, and HS—CoA

24.13 a.

$$CH_3-CH_2-CH_2-CH_2-CH_2-\underset{\beta}{CH_2}-CH_2-\overset{\overset{O}{\|}}{C}-S-CoA$$

b.

24.15 a.

b. $CH_3-(CH_2)_6-\overset{\overset{\displaystyle H}{|}}{C}=\overset{\overset{\displaystyle H\ \ O}{|\ \ \|}}{C}-\overset{}{C}-S-CoA$

24.17 a. and b. $CH_3-(CH_2)_4-\underset{\beta}{CH_2}-\underset{\alpha}{CH_2}-\overset{\overset{O}{\|}}{C}-S-CoA$

    c. three β oxidation cycles

    d. four acetyl CoA units

24.19 The hydrolysis of ATP to AMP involves the hydrolysis of ATP to ADP, and then ADP to AMP, which provides the same amount of energy as the hydrolysis of two ATP to two ADP.

24.21 a. 10 β oxidation cycles

    b. 11 acetyl CoA units

    c. 110 ATP from 11 acetyl CoA (citric acid cycle) + 25 ATP from 10 NADH + 15 ATP from 10 $FADH_2$ − 2 ATP (activation) = 148 ATP (total)

24.23 For the corresponding saturated acid stearic acid 18:0, we calculate:

    a. 8 cycles of β oxidation

    b. 9 acetyl CoA units

    c. 90 ATP from 9 acetyl CoA (citric acid cycle) + 20 ATP from 8 NADH + 10.5 ATP from 7 $FADH_2$ − 2 ATP (activation) = 118.5 ATP (total)

24.25 Ketogenesis is the synthesis of ketone bodies from excess acetyl CoA during fatty acid oxidation, which occurs when glucose is not available for energy, particularly in starvation, low-carbohydrate diets, fasting, alcoholism, and diabetes.

24.27 Acetoacetate undergoes reduction using NADH + H^+ to yield 3-hydroxybutyrate.

24.29 Ketosis is a condition characterized by acidosis (a drop in blood pH values), excessive urination, and strong thirst.

24.31 Fatty acid synthesis occurs in the cytosol of cells in liver and adipose tissue.

24.33 acetyl CoA, HCO_3^-, and ATP

24.35 a. (3) malonyl CoA transacylase

    b. (1) acetyl CoA carboxylase

    c. (2) acetyl CoA transacylase

24.37 a. 4 HCO_3^- **b.** 4 ATP

    c. 5 acetyl CoA   **d.** 4 malonyl ACP

    e. 8 NADPH   **f.** 4 CO_2 removed

24.39 a. Reaction 4, the reduction of the double bond to a single bond, is catalyzed by enoyl ACP reductase.

    b. If fatty acid synthesis is inhibited, the bacteria cannot form cell walls and will not thrive.

24.41 The digestion of proteins begins in the stomach and is completed in the small intestine.

24.43 Hormones, heme, purines and pyrimidines for nucleotides, proteins, nonessential amino acids, amino alcohols, and neurotransmitters require nitrogen obtained from amino acids.

24.45 The reactants are an amino acid and an α-keto acid, and the products are a new amino acid and a new α-keto acid.

24.47 a. $H-\overset{\overset{O}{\|}}{C}-COO^-$

    b. $HS-CH_2-\overset{\overset{O}{\|}}{C}-COO^-$

    c. $CH_3-\overset{\overset{\displaystyle CH_3}{|}}{CH}-\overset{\overset{O}{\|}}{C}-COO^-$

24.49

$$^-OOC-\underset{\underset{\text{Glutamate}}{}}{\overset{\overset{\displaystyle \overset{+}{NH_3}}{|}}{CH}}-CH_2-CH_2-COO^- + H_2O + NAD^+ \xrightarrow{\overset{\text{Glutamate}}{\text{dehydrogenase}}}$$

$$^-OOC-\overset{\overset{O}{\|}}{C}-CH_2-CH_2-COO^- + NH_4^+ + NADH + H^+$$

    α-Ketoglutarate

24.51

$$H_2N - \overset{\overset{\displaystyle O}{\|}}{C} - NH_2$$

24.53 CO_2 from the citric acid cycle

24.55 NH_4^+ is toxic if allowed to accumulate in the liver.

24.57 If there is a deficiency of argininosuccinate synthetase, citrulline will accumulate.

24.59 Glucogenic amino acids are used to synthesize glucose.

24.61 a. oxaloacetate   **b.** oxaloacetate
    c. succinyl CoA   **d.** α-ketoglutarate

24.63 nonessential amino acids

24.65 Glutamine synthetase catalyzes the addition of $-NH_3^+$ to glutamate using energy from the hydrolysis of ATP.

24.67 phenylketonuria

24.69

$$CH_3 - \overset{\overset{\displaystyle O}{\|}}{C} - COO^- \;+\; {}^-OOC - \overset{\overset{\displaystyle \overset{+}{N}H_3}{|}}{CH} - CH_2 - CH_2 - COO^-$$

Pyruvate   Glutamate

24.71 a. and b.

    c. Five cycles of β oxidation are needed.
    d. Six acetyl CoA units are produced.
    e.

Activation		-2 ATP
$5 \text{ NADH} \times \dfrac{2.5 \text{ ATP}}{\text{NADH}}$		12.5 ATP
$5 \text{ FADH}_2 \times \dfrac{1.5 \text{ ATP}}{\text{FADH}_2}$		7.5 ATP
$6 \text{ acetyl CoA} \times \dfrac{10 \text{ ATP}}{\text{acetyl CoA}}$		60 ATP
Total		78 ATP

24.73 Triacylglycerols are hydrolyzed to monoacylglycerols and fatty acids in the small intestine, which reform as triacylglycerols in the intestinal lining for transport as lipoproteins to the tissues.

24.75 Fats can be stored in unlimited amounts in adipose tissue compared to the limited storage of carbohydrates as glycogen.

24.77 The fatty acids cannot diffuse across the blood–brain barrier.

24.79 a. Glycerol is converted to glycerol-3-phosphate and then to dihydroxyacetone phosphate, which can enter glycolysis or gluconeogenesis.
    b. Activation of fatty acids occurs in the cytosol at the outer mitochondrial membrane.
    c. The energy cost is equal to two ATP.
    d. Only acyl CoA can move into the intermembrane space for transport by carnitine into the matrix.

24.81 a. β oxidation   **b.** β oxidation
    c. fatty acid synthesis   **d.** β oxidation
    e. fatty acid synthesis   **f.** fatty acid synthesis

24.83 a. fatty acid synthesis   **b.** fatty acid oxidation

24.85 Ammonium ion is toxic if allowed to accumulate in the liver.

24.87 a. citrulline   **b.** carbamoyl phosphate

24.89 a. oxaloacetate   **b.** acetyl CoA
    c. succinyl CoA   **d.** α-ketoglutarate

24.91 Serine is degraded to pyruvate, which is oxidized to acetyl CoA. The oxidation produces $NADH + H^+$, which provides 2.5 ATP. In one turn of the citric acid cycle, the acetyl CoA produces 10 ATP. Thus, serine can provide 12.5 ATP.

24.93 a. first oxidation   **b.** cleavage (thiolysis)
    c. activation

24.95 a.

$$CH_3 - \overset{\overset{\displaystyle CH_3}{|}}{CH} - \overset{\overset{\displaystyle \overset{+}{N}H_3}{|}}{CH} - \overset{\overset{\displaystyle O}{\|}}{C} - O^- \quad \text{Valine}$$

    b.

$$CH_3 - CH_2 - \overset{\overset{\displaystyle CH_3}{|}}{CH} - \overset{\overset{\displaystyle \overset{+}{N}H_3}{|}}{CH} - \overset{\overset{\displaystyle O}{\|}}{C} - O^- \quad \text{Isoleucine}$$

CI.47 Identify each of the following as a substance that is part of the citric acid cycle, electron transport, or both: (23.1, 23.2, 23.3)

    a. GTP   **b.** $CoQH_2$
    c. $FADH_2$ **d.** cyt c
    e. succinate dehydrogenase   **f.** complex I
    g. isocitrate   **h.** NAD^+

CI.48 Use the value of 7.3 kcal per mole of ATP to determine the total kilocalories stored as ATP from each of the following: (23.4, 24.2, 24.3, 24.8)

    a. the reactions of 1 mole of glucose in glycolysis
    b. the oxidation of 2 moles of pyruvate to 2 moles of acetyl CoA
    c. the complete oxidation of 1 mole of glucose to CO_2 and H_2O
    d. the β oxidation of 1 mole of lauric acid, a saturated C_{12} fatty acid
    e. the reaction of 1 mole of glutamate (from protein) in the citric acid cycle

CI.49 Acetyl CoA (HS—CoA) is the fuel for the citric acid cycle. It has the formula $C_{23}H_{38}N_7O_{17}P_3S$. (22.2, 23.1, 23.4)

    a. What are the components of acetyl CoA?
    b. What is the function of HS—CoA?
    c. Where does the acetyl group attach to HS—CoA?
    d. What is the molar mass (to three significant figures) of acetyl CoA?
    e. How many moles of ATP are produced when 1.0 mg of acetyl CoA completes one turn of the citric acid cycle?

CI.50 State if each of the following produces or consumes ATP: (22.5, 22.6, 23.1, 23.4, 24.2)

    a. citric acid cycle
    b. glucose forms two pyruvate
    c. pyruvate yields acetyl CoA
    d. glucose forms glucose-6-phosphate
    e. oxidation of α-ketoglutarate
    f. transport of NADH across the mitochondrial membrane
    g. activation of a fatty acid

CI.51 Butter is a fat that contains 80.% by mass triacylglycerols. Assume the triacylglycerol in butter is glyceryl tripalmitate. (17.4, 24.2, 24.3)

Butter is high in triacylglycerols.

    a. Write an equation for the hydrolysis of glyceryl tripalmitate.
    b. What is the molar mass of glyceryl tripalmitate, $C_{51}H_{98}O_6$?
    c. Calculate the ATP yield from the complete oxidation of 1 mole of palmitic acid, a saturated C_{16} fatty acid.
    d. How many kilocalories are released from the palmitate in 0.50 oz of butter?
    e. If running for exactly 1 h uses 750 kcal, how many ounces of butter would provide the energy (kcal) for a 45-min run?

CI.52 Match these ATP yields with the given reactions: 1 ATP, 1.5 ATP, 2 ATP, 2.5 ATP, 3 ATP, 5 ATP, 10 ATP, 15 ATP, 30 ATP (22.5, 22.6, 23.1, 23.4, 24.3)

    a. Glucose yields two pyruvate.
    b. Pyruvate yields acetyl CoA.
    c. Glucose yields two acetyl CoA.
    d. Acetyl CoA goes through one turn of the citric acid cycle.
    e. Succinyl CoA yield succinate.
    f. Glucose is completely oxidized to CO_2 and H_2O.
    g. $FADH_2$ is oxidized to FAD.

CI.53 Which of the following molecules will produce more ATP per mole when each is completely oxidized? (22.4, 22.5, 23.1, 23.4, 24.3)

    a. glucose or maltose
    b. myristic acid, $CH_3-(CH_2)_{10}-CH_2-CH_2-COOH$, or stearic acid, $CH_3-(CH_2)_{14}-CH_2-CH_2-COOH$
    c. glucose or two acetyl CoA

CI.54 Which of the following molecules will produce more ATP per mole when each is completely oxidized? (22.4, 22.5, 23.1, 23.4, 24.3)

    a. glucose or caprylic acid C_8
    b. citrate or succinate in one turn of the citric acid cycle
    c. glutamate or tyrosine in one turn of the citric acid cycle

ANSWERS

CI.47 a. citric acid cycle   **b.** electron transport
      c. both   **d.** electron transport
      e. citric acid cycle   **f.** electron transport
      g. citric acid cycle   **h.** both

CI.49 a. aminoethanethiol, pantothenic acid (vitamin B_5), and phosphorylated ADP
      b. Coenzyme A carries an acetyl group to the citric acid cycle for oxidation.
      c. The acetyl group links to the sulfur atom (—S—) in the aminoethanethiol part of CoA.
      d. 810. g/mole   **e.** 1.2×10^{-5} mole of ATP

CI.51 a.

$$CH_2-O-\overset{\overset{\displaystyle O}{\|}}{C}-(CH_2)_{14}-CH_3$$
$$CH-O-\overset{\overset{\displaystyle O}{\|}}{C}-(CH_2)_{14}-CH_3 + 3H_2O \longrightarrow$$
$$CH_2-O-\overset{\overset{\displaystyle O}{\|}}{C}-(CH_2)_{14}-CH_3$$

$$CH_2-OH$$
$$CH-OH + 3HO-\overset{\overset{\displaystyle O}{\|}}{C}-(CH_2)_{14}-CH_3$$
$$CH_2-OH$$

      b. 807 g/mole   **c.** 106 moles of ATP
      d. 33 kcal   **e.** 8.5 oz of butter

CI.53 a. maltose   **b.** stearic acid   **c.** glucose

Chapters 28-29 were taken from

Fundamentals of General, Organic, and Biological Chemistry,
Seventh Edition

by John McMurry, David S. Ballantine, Carl A. Hoeger, and
Virginia E. Peterson

CHAPTER 28

Chemical Messengers: Hormones, Neurotransmitters, and Drugs

CONTENTS

◄ Floods of chemical messengers help these athletes keep up the physical effort needed to complete the match.

At this point, you have seen a few of the hundreds of enzyme-catalyzed reactions that take place in cells. How are these individual reactions tied together? Clearly, the many thousands of reactions taking place in the billions of individual cells of our bodies do not occur randomly. There must be overall control mechanisms that coordinate these reactions, keeping us in chemical balance.

Two systems share major responsibility for regulating body chemistry—the *endocrine system* and the *nervous system*. The endocrine system depends on *hormones*, chemical messengers that circulate in the bloodstream. The nervous system relies primarily on a much faster means of communication—electrical impulses in nerve cells, triggered by its own chemical messengers, the *neurotransmitters*. Neurotransmitters carry signals from one nerve cell to another and also from nerve cells to their targets, the ultimate recipients of the messages.

Given the crucial role of hormones and neurotransmitters in the functioning of our bodies, it should not be surprising to find that many drugs act by mimicking, modifying, or opposing the action of chemical messengers.

28.1 Messenger Molecules

Coordination and control of your body's vital functions are accomplished by chemical messengers. Whether the messengers are hormones that arrive via the bloodstream or neurotransmitters released by nerve cells, such messengers ultimately connect with a *target*. The message is delivered by interaction between the chemical messenger and a **receptor** at the target. The receptor then acts like a light switch, causing some biochemical response to occur—the contraction of a muscle, for example, or the secretion of another biomolecule.

Noncovalent attractions draw messengers and receptors together, much as a substrate is drawn into the active site of an enzyme (Sections 18.8, 19.4). These attractions hold the messenger and receptor together long enough for the message to be delivered, but without any permanent chemical change to the messenger or the receptor. The results of this interaction are chemical changes within the target cell.

Receptor A molecule or portion of a molecule with which a hormone, neurotransmitter, or other biochemically active molecule interacts to initiate a response in a target cell.

▶▶▶ Figure 18.4 shows the various types of noncovalent forces that govern the shape of protein molecules. These same types of interactions mediate substrate–enzyme binding, as described in Section 19.4.

Hormone A chemical messenger secreted by cells of the endocrine system and transported through the bloodstream to target cells with appropriate receptors, where it elicits a response.

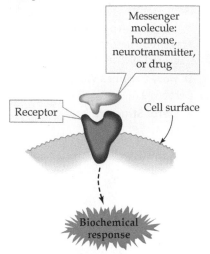

▲ **A general representation of the interaction between a messenger molecule and a cellular receptor.**

Neurotransmitter A chemical messenger that travels between a neuron and a neighboring neuron or other target cell to transmit a nerve impulse.

Endocrine system A system of specialized cells, tissues, and ductless glands that secretes hormones and shares with the nervous system the responsibility for maintaining constant internal body conditions and responding to changes in the environment.

Hormones are the chemical messengers of the endocrine system. These molecules are produced by endocrine glands and tissues in various parts of the body, often at distances far from their ultimate site of action. Because of this, hormones must travel through the bloodstream to their targets, and the responses they produce can require anywhere from seconds to hours to begin. The action or actions they elicit, however, may last a long time and can be wide-ranging. A single hormone will often affect many different tissues and organs—any cell with the appropriate receptors is a target. Insulin, for example, is a hormone secreted by the pancreas in response to elevated blood glucose levels. At target cells throughout the body, insulin accelerates uptake and utilization of glucose; in muscles it accelerates formation of glycogen, a glucose polymer that is metabolized when muscles need quick energy; and in fatty tissue it stimulates storage of triacylglycerols.

The chemical messengers of the nervous system are a set of molecules referred to as **neurotransmitters**. The electrical signals of the nervous system travel along nerve fibers, taking only a fraction of a second to reach their highly specific destinations. Most nerve cells, however, do not make direct contact with the cells they stimulate. A neurotransmitter must carry the message across the tiny gap separating the nerve cell from its target. Because neurotransmitters are released in very short bursts and are quickly broken down or reabsorbed by the nerve cell, their effects are short-lived. The nervous system is organized so that nearly all of its vital switching, integrative, and information-processing functions depend on neurotransmitters. Neurotransmitters are typically synthesized and released very close to their site of action.

In this chapter, we first discuss hormones and the endocrine system and include a detailed description of how one hormone—epinephrine (also known as adrenalin)—performs its functions. Next we discuss neurotransmitters, using the action of acetylcholine to illustrate how neurotransmitters act. It is essential to recognize that hormones and neurotransmitters play a fundamental role in maintaining your health by their influence on metabolic processes. (See Chemistry in Action: Homeostasis.) Finally, we briefly explore the discovery and design of drugs as chemical messengers.

PROBLEM 28.1

In humans, approximately 12% of all genes are regulatory genes necessary to maintain homeostasis within cells (see Chemistry in Action: Homeostasis). Health check-ups often include a blood panel; common compounds measured include blood glucose and triacylglycerols. Based on your knowledge of metabolism, why would these compounds be included in the blood test? What might that have to do with regulatory genes?

28.2 Hormones and the Endocrine System

The **endocrine system** includes all cells that secrete hormones into the bloodstream. Some of these cells are found in organs that also have non-endocrine functions (for example, the pancreas, which also produces digestive enzymes); others occur in glands devoted solely to hormonal control (for example, the thyroid gland). It is important to note, however, that hormones do *not* carry out chemical reactions. Hormones are simply messengers that alter the biochemistry of a cell by signaling the inhibition or activation of an existing enzyme, by initiating or altering the rate of synthesis of a specific protein, or in other ways.

The major endocrine glands are the thyroid gland, the adrenal glands, the ovaries and testes, and the pituitary gland (found in the brain). The hypothalamus, a section of the brain just above the pituitary gland, is in charge of the endocrine system. It communicates with other tissues in three ways:

- **Direct neural control** A nervous system message from the hypothalamus initiates release of hormones by the adrenal gland. For example,

$$\text{Hypothalamus} \xrightarrow{\text{Nerve message}} \text{Adrenal gland} \longrightarrow \text{Epinephrine}$$

Epinephrine is targeted to many cells; it increases heart rate, blood pressure, and glucose availability.

CHEMISTRY IN ACTION

Homeostasis

Homeostasis—the maintenance of a constant internal environment in the body—is as important to the study of living things as atomic structure is to the study of chemistry. The phrase "internal environment" is a general way to describe all the conditions within cells, organs, and body systems. Conditions such as body temperature, the availability of chemical compounds that supply energy, and the disposal of waste products must remain within specific limits for an organism to function properly. Throughout our bodies, sensors track the internal environment and send signals to restore proper balance if the environment changes. If oxygen is in short supply, for example, a signal is sent that makes us breathe harder. When we are cold, a signal is sent to constrict surface blood vessels and prevent further loss of heat.

At the chemical level, homeostasis regulates the concentrations of ions and many different organic compounds so that they stay near normal levels. The predictability of the concentrations of such substances is the basis for *clinical chemistry*—the chemical analysis of body tissues and fluids. In the clinical lab, various tests measure concentrations of significant ions and compounds in blood, urine, feces, spinal fluid, or other samples from a patient's body. Comparing the lab results with "norms" (average concentration ranges in a population of healthy individuals) shows which body systems are struggling, or possibly failing, to maintain homeostasis. To give just one example, urate (commonly known as uric acid) is an anion that helps to carry waste nitrogen from the body. A uric acid concentration higher than the normal range of about 2.5–7.7 mg/dL in blood can indicate the onset of gout or signal possible kidney malfunction.

A copy of a clinical lab report for a routine blood analysis is shown in the figure below. (Fortunately, this individual has no significant variations from normal.) The metal names in the report refer to the various cations, and the heading "Phosphorus" refers to the phosphate anion.

See Chemistry in Action Problems 28.86 and 28.87 at the end of the chapter.

TEST	RESULT	NORMAL RANGE	TEST	RESULT	NORMAL RANGE
Albumin	4.3 g/dL	3.5–5.3 g/dL	SGOT*	23 U/L	0–28 U/L
Alk. Phos.*	33 U/L	25–90 U/L	Total protein	5.9 g/dL	6.2–8.5 g/dL
BUN*	8 mg/dL	8–23 mg/dL	Triglycerides	75 mg/dL	36–165 mg/dL
Bilirubin T.*	0.1 mg/dL	0.2–1.6 mg/dL	Uric Acid	4.1 mg/dL	2.5–7.7 mg/dL
Calcium	8.6 mg/dL	8.5–10.5 mg/dL	GGT*	23 U/L	0–45 U/L
Cholesterol	227 mg/dL	120–250 mg/dL	Magnesium	1.7 mEq/L	1.3–2.5 mEq/L
Chol., HDL*	75 mg/dL	30–75 mg/dL	Phosphorus	2.6 mg/dL	2.5–4.8 mg/dL
Creatinine	0.6 mg/dL	0.7–1.5 mg/dL	SGPT*	13 U/L	0–26 U/L
Glucose	86 mg/dL	65–110 mg/dL	Sodium	137.7 mEq/L	135–155 mEq/L
Iron	101 mg/dL	35–140 mg/dL	Potassium	3.8 mEq/L	3.5–5.5 mEq/L
LDH*	48 U/L	50–166 U/L			

▲ A clinical lab report for routine blood analysis. The abbreviations marked with asterisks are for the following tests (alternative standard abbreviations are in parentheses): Alk. Phos., alkaline phosphatase (ALP); BUN, blood urea nitrogen; Bilirubin T., total bilirubin; Chol., HDL, cholesterol, high-density lipoproteins; LDH, lactate dehydrogenase; SGOT, serum glutamic oxaloacetic transaminase (AST); GGT, γ-glutamyl transferase; SGPT, serum glutamic pyruvic transaminase (ALT).

- **Direct release of hormones** Hormones move from the hypothalamus to the posterior pituitary gland, where they are stored until needed. For example,

$$\text{Hypothalamus} \longrightarrow \text{Antidiuretic hormone}$$

Antidiuretic hormone, which is stored in the posterior pituitary gland, targets the kidneys and causes retention of water and elevation of blood pressure.

- **Indirect control through release of regulatory hormones** In the most common control mechanism, *regulatory hormones* from the hypothalamus stimulate or inhibit the release of hormones by the anterior pituitary gland. Many of these pituitary hormones in turn stimulate release of still other hormones by their own target tissues. For example,

$$\text{Hypothalamus} \xrightarrow{\text{Releasing factor}} \text{Pituitary gland} \longrightarrow$$

$$\text{Thyrotropin (a regulatory hormone)} \longrightarrow$$

$$\text{Thyroid gland} \longrightarrow \text{Thyroid hormones}$$

Thyroid hormones are targeted to cells throughout the body; they affect oxygen availability, blood pressure, and other endocrine tissues.

Chemically, hormones are of three major types: (1) amino acid derivatives, small molecules containing amino groups; (2) polypeptides, which range from just a few amino acids to several hundred amino acids; and (3) steroids, which are lipids with the distinctive molecular structure based on four connected rings common to all sterols (see Section 23.6).

Melatonin, an amino acid derivative
(regulates day–night cycle)

Estradiol, a steroid
(an estrogen that acts in ovulation)

Vasopressin, a polypeptide
(controls urine volume)

Examples of the targets and actions of some hormones of each type are given in Table 28.1.

TABLE 28.1 Examples of Each Chemical Class of Hormones

Chemical Class	Hormone Examples	Source	Target	Major Action
Amino acid derivatives	Epinephrine and norepinephrine	Adrenal medulla	Most cells	Release glucose from storage; increase heart rate and blood pressure
	Thyroxine	Thyroid gland	Most cells	Influence energy use, oxygen consumption, growth, and development
Polypeptides (regulatory hormones)	Adrenocorticotropic hormone	Anterior pituitary	Adrenal cortex	Stimulate release of glucocorticoids (steroids), which control glucose metabolism
	Growth hormone	Anterior pituitary	Peripheral tissues	Stimulate growth of muscle and skeleton
	Follicle-stimulating hormone, luteinizing hormone	Anterior pituitary	Ovaries and testes	Stimulate release of steroid hormones
	Vasopressin	Posterior pituitary	Kidneys	Cause retention of water, elevation of blood volume and blood pressure
	Thyrotropin	Anterior pituitary	Thyroid gland	Stimulates release of thyroid hormones
Steroids	Cortisone and cortisol (glucocorticoids)	Adrenal cortex	Most cells	Counteract inflammation; control metabolism when glucose must be conserved
	Testosterone; estrogen, progesterone	Testes; ovaries	Most cells	Control development of secondary sexual characteristics, maturation of sperm and eggs

Upon arrival at its target cell, a hormone must deliver its signal to create a chemical response inside the cell. The signal enters the cell in ways determined by the chemical nature of the hormone (Figure 28.1). Because the cell is surrounded by a membrane composed of hydrophobic molecules, only nonpolar, hydrophobic molecules can move across it on their own. The steroid hormones are nonpolar, so they can enter the cell directly by diffusion; this is one of the ways a hormone delivers its message. Once within the cell's cytoplasm, a steroid hormone encounters a receptor molecule that carries it to its target, DNA in the nucleus of the cell. The result is some change in production of a protein governed by a particular gene.

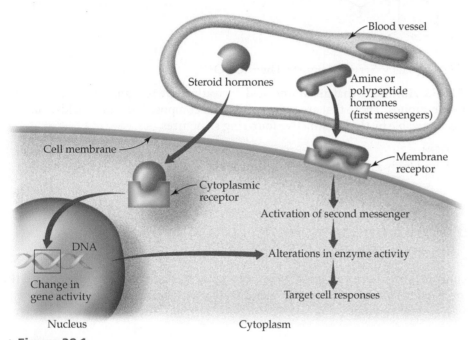

▲ **Figure 28.1**
Interaction of hormones and receptors at the cellular level.
Steroid hormones are hydrophobic and can cross the cell membrane to find receptors inside the cell. Amine and polypeptide hormones are hydrophilic and, because they cannot cross the cell membrane, act via second messengers.

In contrast, the polypeptide and amine hormones are water-soluble molecules and cannot cross the hydrophobic cell membranes. Rather than entering cells, they deliver their messages by bonding noncovalently with receptors on cell surfaces. The result is release of a **second messenger** within the cell. There are several different second messengers, and the specific sequence of events varies. In general, three membrane-bound proteins participate in release of the second messenger: (1) the receptor and (2) a *G protein* (a member of the guanine nucleotide-binding protein family) that transfer the message to (3) an enzyme. First, interaction of the hormone with its receptor causes a change in the receptor (much like the effect of an allosteric regulator on an enzyme; Section 19.7). This stimulates the G protein to activate an enzyme that participates in release of the second messenger. The action of epinephrine by way of a second messenger is described in Section 28.3. Further examples of amino acid, polypeptide, and steroid hormones are given in Sections 28.4 and 28.5.

Second messenger Chemical messenger released inside a cell when a hydrophilic hormone or neurotransmitter interacts with a receptor on the cell surface.

Worked Example 28.1 Classifying Hormones Based on Structure

Classify the following hormones as an amino acid derivative, a polypeptide, or a steroid.

(a)

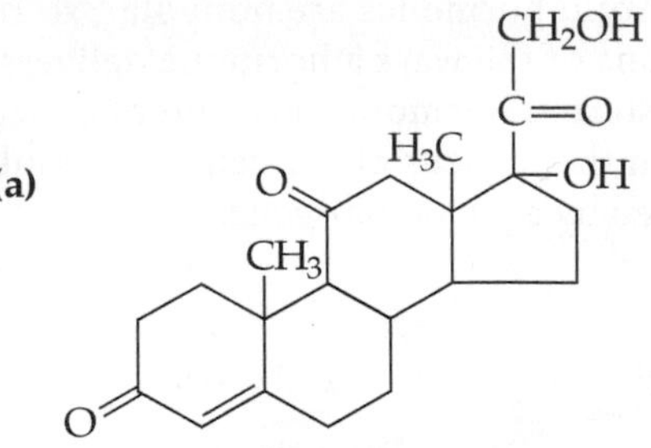

(b)

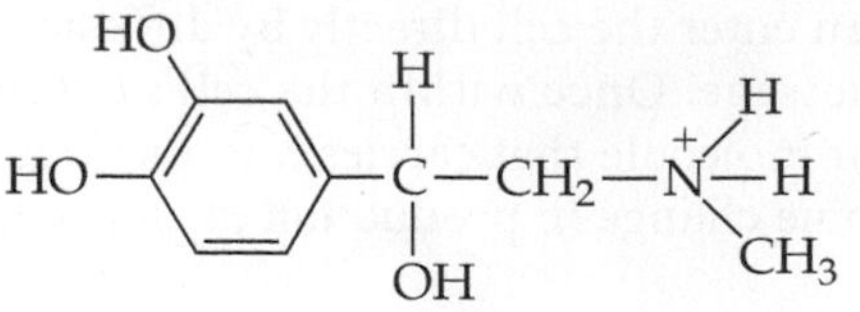

(c) ^+H_3N—His—Ser—Glu— ••• Thr—COO$^-$

ANALYSIS Hormones that are amino acid derivatives are recognized by the presence of amino groups. Those that are polypeptides are composed of amino acids. Steroids are recognizable by their distinctive four-ring structures.

SOLUTION
Compound (a) is a steroid, (b) is an amino acid derivative, and (c) is a polypeptide.

28.3 How Hormones Work: Epinephrine and Fight-or-Flight

Epinephrine (pronounced ep-pin-**eff**-rin), also known as *adrenaline*, is often called the *fight-or-flight hormone* because it is released from the adrenal glands when we need an instant response to danger.

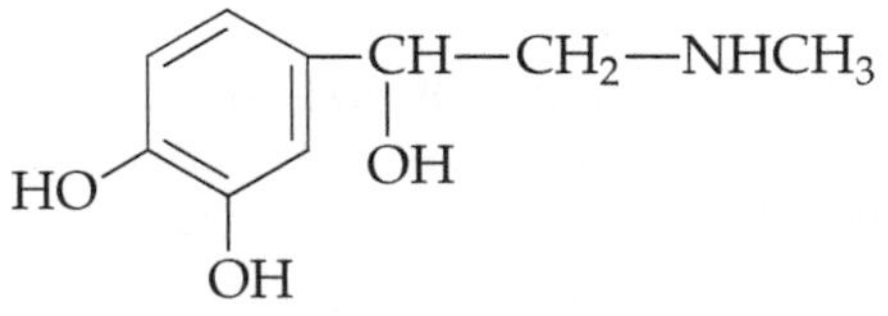

Epinephrine
(Adrenaline)

We have all felt the rush of epinephrine that accompanies a near-miss accident or a sudden loud noise. The main function of epinephrine in a "startle" reaction is a dramatic increase in the availability of glucose as a source of energy to deal with whatever stress is immediate. The time elapsed from initial stimulus to glucose release into the bloodstream is only a few seconds.

Epinephrine acts via *cyclic adenosine monophosphate* (*cyclic AMP, or cAMP*), an important second messenger. The sequence of events in this action, shown in Figure 28.2 and described below, illustrates one type of biochemical response to a change in an individual's external or internal environment.

- Epinephrine, a hormone carried in the bloodstream, binds to a receptor on the surface of a cell.
- The hormone–receptor complex activates a nearby G protein embedded in the interior surface of the cell membrane.
- GDP (guanosine disphosphate) associated with the G protein is exchanged for GTP (guanosine triphosphate) from the cytosol.

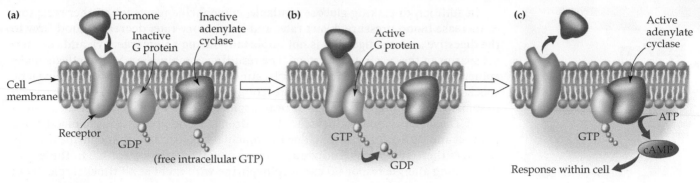

▲ **Figure 28.2**
Activation of cyclic AMP as a second messenger.
(a) The hormone receptor, inactive G protein, and inactive adenylate cyclase enzyme reside in the cell membrane. (b) On formation of the hormone–receptor complex, an allosteric change occurs in the G protein, resulting in the guanosine diphosphate (GDP) of the G protein being replaced by a free intracellular guanosine triphosphate (GTP). (c) The active G protein–GTP complex activates adenylate cyclase, causing production of cyclic AMP inside the cell, where it initiates the action called for by the hormone.

- The G protein–GTP complex activates *adenylate cyclase*, an enzyme that also is embedded in the interior surface of the cell membrane.
- Adenylate cyclase catalyzes production within the cell of the second messenger— *cyclic AMP*—from ATP, as shown in Figure 28.3.
- Cyclic AMP initiates reactions that activate glycogen phosphorylase, the enzyme responsible for release of glucose from storage. (Interaction of other hormones with their specific receptors results in initiation by cyclic AMP of other reactions.)
- When the emergency has passed, cyclic AMP is converted back to ATP.

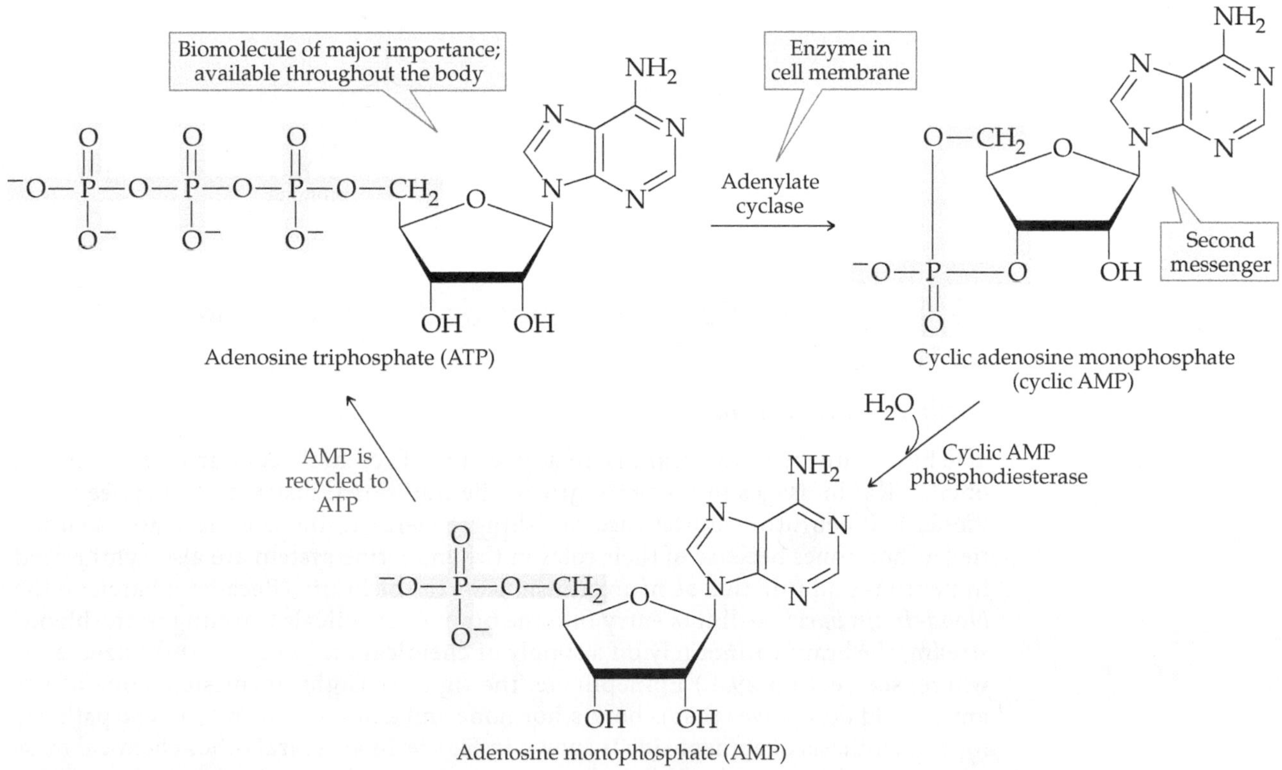

▲ **Figure 28.3**
Production of cyclic AMP as a second messenger.
The reactions shown take place within the target cell after epinephrine or some other chemical messenger interacts with a receptor on the cell surface. (The major role of ATP in providing energy for biochemical reactions was discussed in Section 20.5.)

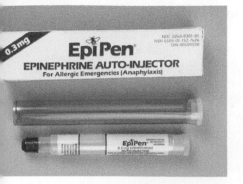

▲ An epinephrine autoinjection pen. Such devices are carried by individuals at risk of an anaphylactic reaction to an allergen.

In addition to making glucose available, epinephrine reacts with other receptors to increase blood pressure, heart rate, and respiratory rate; decrease blood flow to the digestive system (digestion is not important during an emergency); and counteract spasms in the respiratory system. The resulting combined and rapid effects make epinephrine the most crucial drug for treatment of *anaphylactic shock*. Anaphylactic shock is the result of a severe allergic reaction, perhaps to a bee sting, a drug, or even to something seemingly as benign as peanuts; it is an extremely serious medical emergency. The major symptoms include a severe drop in blood pressure due to blood vessel dilation and difficulty breathing due to bronchial constriction. Epinephrine directly counters these symptoms. Individuals who know they are susceptible to these life-threatening allergic responses carry epinephrine with them at all times (typically in the form of an autoinjector known as an "EpiPen®").

PROBLEM 28.2

A phosphorus-containing anion is removed from ATP in its conversion to cyclic AMP, as shown in Figure 28.3. The anion is often abbreviated as PP_i. Which of the following anions is represented by PP_i?

(a) $P_3O_{10}^{5-}$ (b) $P_2O_7^{4-}$ (c) PO_4^{3-} (d) $H_2PO_4^-$

🔑 KEY CONCEPT PROBLEM 28.3

Caffeine and theobromine (from chocolate) act as stimulants. They work by altering the cAMP signal. Refer to Figure 28.3 and decide how these molecules might interact with an enzyme in the cAMP pathway to enhance the effect of cAMP.

Caffeine   Theobromine

28.4 Amino Acid Derivatives and Polypeptides as Hormones

Amino Acid Derivatives

The biochemistry of the brain is an active area of research. As our understanding of chemical messages in the brain grows, the traditional distinctions between hormones and neurotransmitters are vanishing. Several amino acid derivatives classified as hormones because of their roles in the endocrine system are also synthesized in neurons and function as neurotransmitters in the brain. (Because a barrier—the *blood–brain barrier*—limits entry into the brain of chemicals traveling in the bloodstream, the brain cannot rely on a supply of chemical messengers synthesized elsewhere; see Section 29.4.) Epinephrine, the fight-or-flight hormone, is one of the amino acid derivatives that is both a hormone and a neurotransmitter. The pathway for the synthesis of epinephrine is shown in Figure 28.4; several other chemical messengers are also formed in this pathway.

Thyroxine, another amino acid derivative, is also a hormone. It is one of two iodine-containing hormones produced by the thyroid gland, and our need for dietary iodine is due to these hormones. Unlike other hormones derived from amino acids,

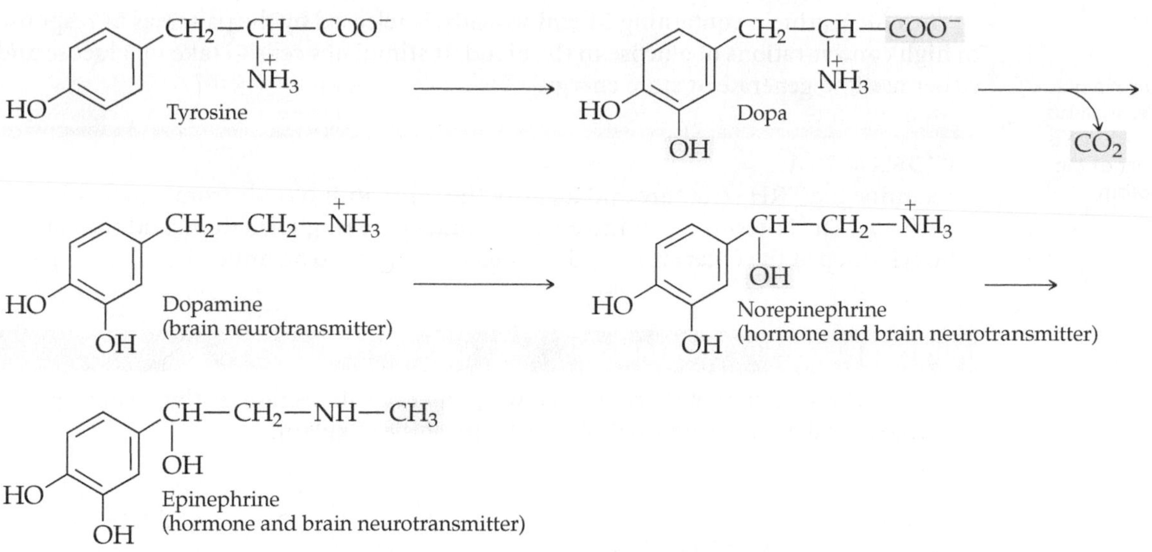

▲ **Figure 28.4**
Synthesis of chemical messengers from tyrosine.
The changes in each step are highlighted in gold for additions and in green for losses.

thyroxine is a nonpolar compound that can cross cell membranes and enter cells, where it activates the synthesis of various enzymes. When dietary iodine is insufficient, the thyroid gland compensates by enlarging in order to produce more thyroxine. Thus, a greatly enlarged thyroid gland (a *goiter*) is a symptom of iodine deficiency. In developed countries, where iodine is added to table salt, goiter is uncommon. In some regions of the world, however, iodine deficiency is a common and serious problem that results not only in goiter but also in severe mental retardation in infants (*cretinism*).

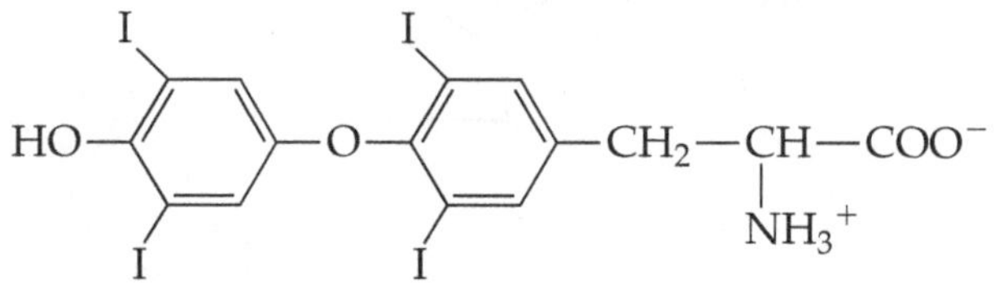

Thyroxine

Polypeptides

Polypeptides are the largest class of hormones. They range widely in molecular size and complexity, as illustrated by two hormones that control the thyroid gland, *thyrotropin-releasing hormone (TRH)* and *thyroid-stimulating hormone (TSH)*. TRH, a modified tripeptide, is a regulatory hormone released by the hypothalamus. At the pituitary gland, TRH activates release of TSH, a protein that has 208 amino acid residues in two chains. TSH in turn triggers release of amino acid derivative hormones from the thyroid gland.

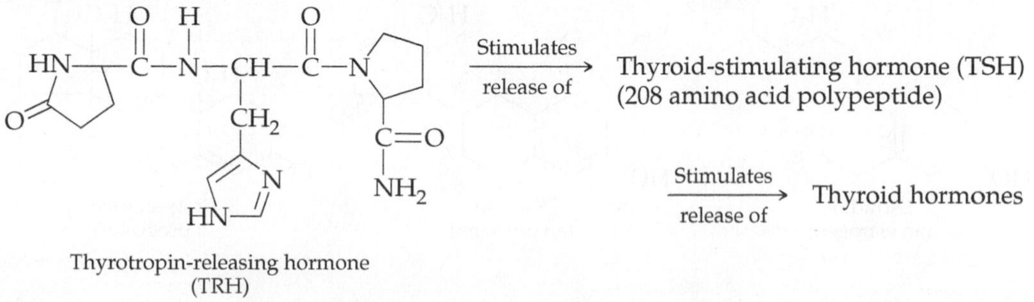

$$\xrightarrow[\text{release of}]{\text{Stimulates}}$$ Thyroid-stimulating hormone (TSH)
(208 amino acid polypeptide)

$$\xrightarrow[\text{release of}]{\text{Stimulates}}$$ Thyroid hormones

Thyrotropin-releasing hormone
(TRH)

Insulin, a protein containing 51 amino acids, is released by the pancreas in response to high concentrations of glucose in the blood. It stimulates cells to take up glucose and either use it to generate or store energy.

▶▶▶ Because of its importance in glucose metabolism and diabetes mellitus, the function of insulin as a hormone is described in Chapter 22 as part of the discussion of glucose metabolism.

PROBLEM 28.4

Examine the TRH structure and identify the three amino acids from which it is derived. (The N-terminal amino acid has undergone ring formation, and the carboxyl group at the C-terminal end has been converted to an amide.)

🔑 **KEY CONCEPT PROBLEM 28.5**

Look at the structure of thyroxine shown earlier in this section. Is thyroxine, an amino acid derivative, hydrophobic or hydrophilic? Explain.

28.5 Steroid Hormones

Sterols have in common a central structure composed of the four connected rings you saw in Chapter 23 (see p. 738). Recall that because they are soluble in hydrophobic solvents and not in water, sterols are classified as lipids. Sterol hormones, referred to as steroids, are divided according to function into three types: mineralcorticoids, glucocorticoids (these were discussed in Chapter 23), and the sex hormones, responsible for male and female hormonal and physical characteristics.

The two most important male sex hormones, or androgens, are testosterone and androsterone. These steroids are responsible for the development of male secondary sex characteristics during puberty and for promoting tissue and muscle growth.

Male sex hormones (androgens)

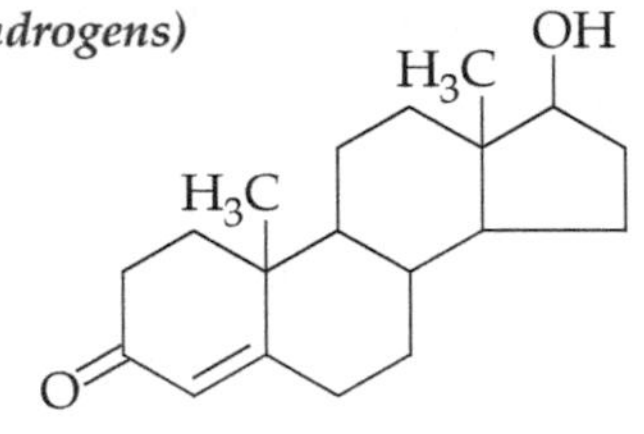

Testosterone 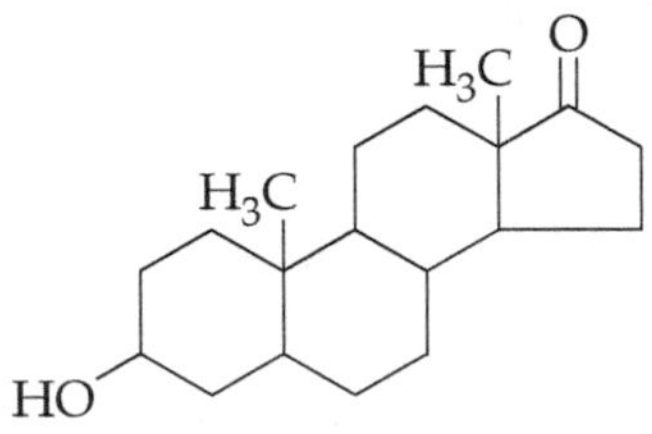   Androsterone

Estrone and *estradiol*, the female steroid hormones known as *estrogens*, are synthesized from testosterone, primarily in the ovaries but also to a small extent in the adrenal cortex. Estrogens govern development of female secondary sex characteristics and participate in regulation of the menstrual cycle. The *progestins*, principally *progesterone*, are released by the ovaries during the second half of the menstrual cycle and prepare the uterus for implantation of a fertilized ovum should conception occur.

Female sex hormones

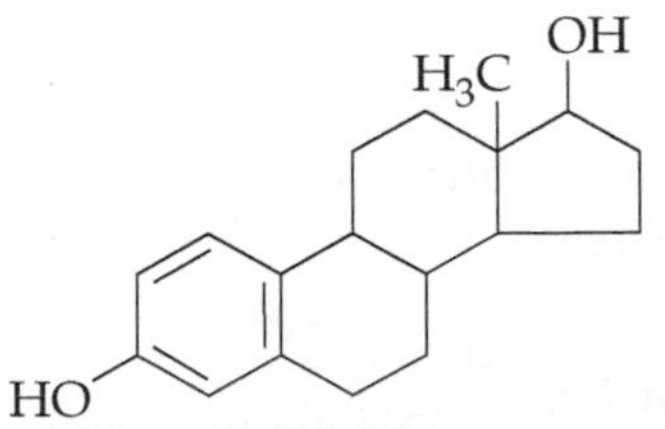

Estradiol
(an estrogen)

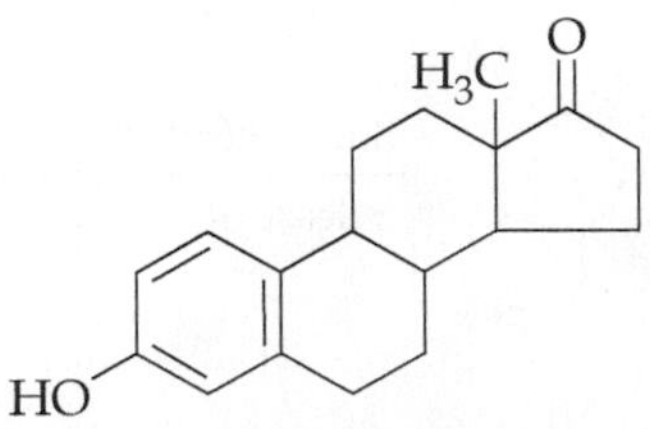

Estrone
(an estrogen)

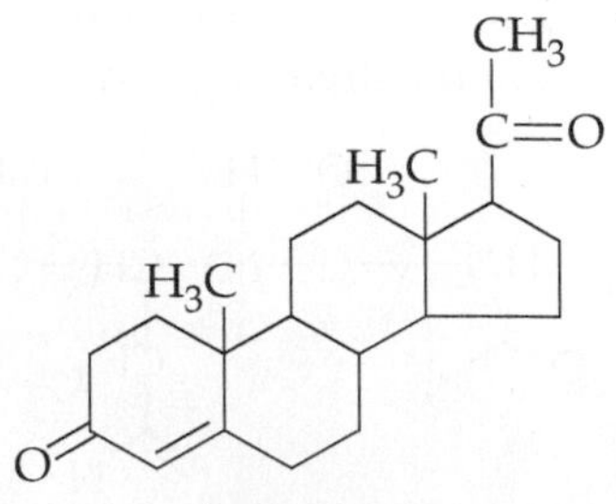

Progesterone
(a progestin)

In addition to the several hundred known steroids isolated from plants and animals, others have been synthesized in the laboratory in the search for new drugs. Most birth control pills are a mixture of the synthetic estrogen *ethynyl estradiol* and the synthetic progestin *norethindrone*. These steroids function by tricking the body into a false pregnant state, making it temporarily infertile. The compound known as *RU-486*, or *mifepristone*, is effective as a "morning after" pill. It prevents pregnancy by binding strongly to the progesterone receptor, thereby blocking implantation in the uterus of a fertilized egg cell. The morning after pill is available in the United States, but must be dispensed by a physician.

Ethynyl estradiol
(a synthetic estrogen)

Norethindrone
(a synthetic progestin)

RU-486
(Mifepristone)

Anabolic steroids, which have the ability to increase muscle mass and consequently strength, are drugs that resemble androgenic (male) hormones, such as testosterone. These steroids have been used by bodybuilders for decades to change their body shape to a more muscular, bulky form; some professional and semiprofessional athletes (both men and women) have used them in the hope of gaining weight, strength, power, speed, endurance, and aggressiveness. Unfortunately, many serious side effects can arise from this abuse of anabolic steroids. Stunted bone growth in adolescents; cancer of the liver, prostate, and kidney; high blood pressure; aggressive behavior; liver damage; irregular heartbeat; and nosebleeds (arising out of blood coagulation disorders) are but a few of the short- and long-term side effects of these agents. Today, most organized amateur and professional sports have banned the use of these and other "performance-enhancing" drugs.

Despite bans, the use of "roids" is widespread in sports. For example, so many baseball players have apparently used anabolic steroids that several congressional hearings have been held on this topic in recent years. Several trainers and players from baseball and other sports have testified, and as a result some individual records are now in question. One of the first athletes outside of baseball to be investigated was Marion Jones, a high-profile track star. She pled guilty in 2007 to using steroids while training for and during her Olympic medal events. She has been stripped of her medals, as have her relay teammates. The list of anabolic steroid users is long and includes cyclists, shot putters, and sprinters. Bulgaria's weightlifters did not participate in the 2008 Summer Olympic Games because routine testing revealed the presence of a banned steroid in every team member.

Did you know that it is legal to treat race horses with anabolic steroids in nearly every state? However, this use has been curtailed in some states, as it has been in humans, spurred by the events of the 2008 Kentucky Derby, when the horse Eight Belles collapsed at the finish line and had to be destroyed. The consensus of racing officials and horse owners is that because Eight Belles was given anabolic steroids, her muscle growth far outpaced bone growth. The combined stress of disproportionately high muscle mass and running the race caused both front ankles to break at the finish line.

To enforce the ban on anabolic steroids, athletes are subjected to random drug screening, but some athletes attempt to get around the screenings by using *designer steroids*—steroids that cannot be detected with current screening methods because identification depends on knowing the compound's structure. However, analysis of a synthetic steroid to determine its structure is easily done. For example, in October 2003, chemists announced that they had identified a new performance-enhancing (and previously undetectable) synthetic steroid. The illegal use of this new compound, tetrahydrogestrinone (THG), was discovered when an anonymous coach sent a spent syringe to U.S. antidoping officials because he was concerned that athletes might be using a mysterious performance-enhancing drug. THG is similar in chemical structure to two other previously banned synthetic anabolic steroids, trenbolone (used by cattle ranchers to increase the size of cattle) and gestrinone (used to treat endometriosis in women). A test for THG was quickly developed and is now used routinely. Despite the apparent victory over THG, chemists know that it is just a matter of time before the next designer steroid becomes available; new tests and procedures for detection are constantly being developed.

Designer Anabolic Steroids

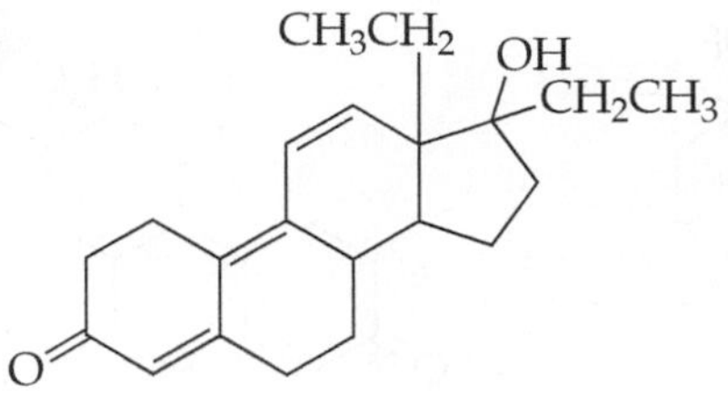

Tetrahydrogestrinone
(THG)

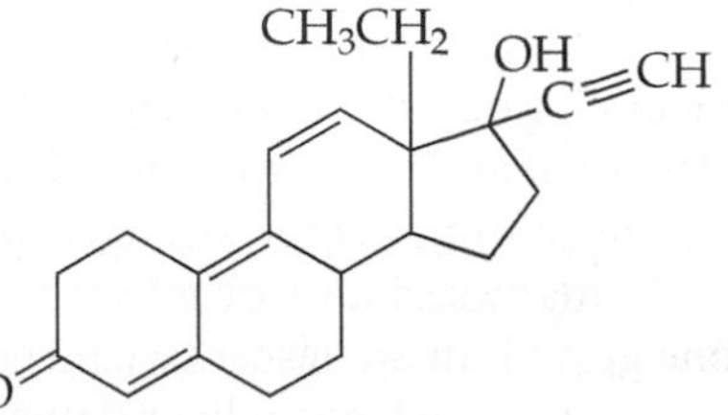

Gestrinone

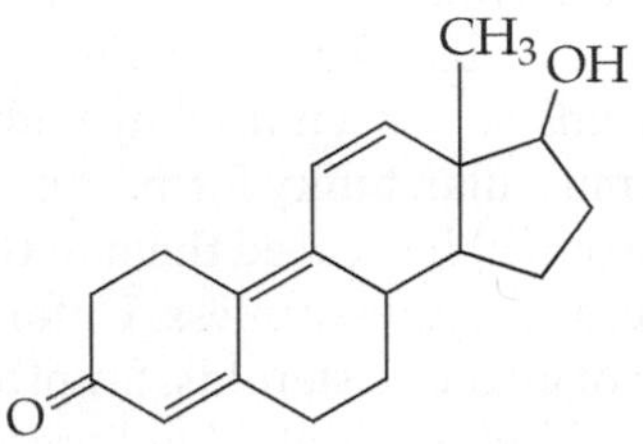

Trenbolone

PROBLEM 28.6

Nandrolone is an anabolic, or tissue-building, steroid sometimes taken by athletes seeking to build muscle mass (it is banned by the International Olympic Committee as well as other athletic organizations). Among its effects is a high level of androgenic activity. Which of the androgens shown on p. 852 does it most closely resemble? How does it differ from that androgen?

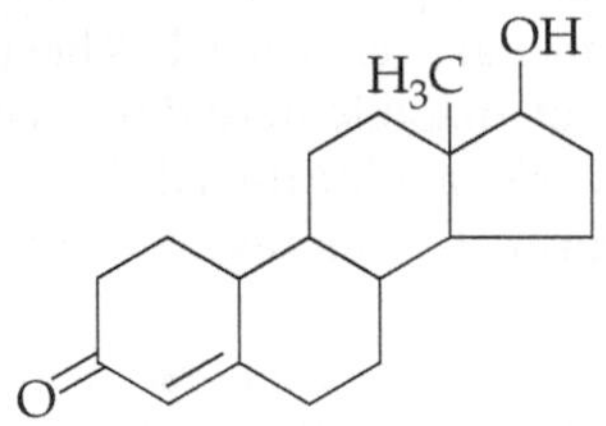

Nandrolone,
an anabolic steroid

PROBLEM 28.7

The phytohormone brassinolide, a member of the brassinoisteroid group of plant hormones, was first isolated in 1979. It is involved with pollen tube formation as well as senescence (cellular death). To what general class of hormones does this phytohormone belong? What do you expect its core structure to resemble? (See Chemistry in Action: Plant Hormones.)

CHEMISTRY IN ACTION

Plant Hormones

Would you believe that plants have hormones? Actually, plants do have hormones, and they are just as important to the health and development of plants as human hormones are to us. But since plants are not animals, there are some differences in how hormones work in them. Plants do not have endocrine systems, nor do they have fluids like blood that continuously circulate so that chemicals can be picked up where they are created and distributed to wherever they are needed.

Unlike animal hormones, which must be transported to their targets, plant hormones (known as *phytohormones*) are synthesized in the cells they affect. They may also reach nearby cells by diffusion or travel upward with water from the roots or downward with sugars made by photosynthesis in the leaves. A very simple alkene, ethylene gas, $CH_2{=}CH_2$, functions as a hormone in plants. At one time, citrus growers ripened oranges that they picked green in rooms heated with kerosene stoves. Mysteriously, when the stoves were replaced with other means of heating, the oranges no longer ripened. It turned out that the ripening was hastened by the ethylene released by burning kerosene, not by the warmth. Plants produce ethylene when it is time for fruit to ripen. Today, bananas, tomatoes, and other fruits are picked hard and unripe to make them easier to ship; they are thereafter ripened by exposure to ethylene. You can try this at home. Enclose some less-than-perfectly ripe pears or peaches in a brown paper bag along with, for example, a very ripe banana. Be careful, though: "One rotten apple can spoil the barrel." With too much exposure to ethylene, ripening can be overdone. The artificial ripening produced commercially by ethylene exposure is, however, by and large a superficial process; true ripening is much more complex. The majority of ethylene production occurs in the final stages of the ripening process.

▲ **These sunflowers move to face the sun as the earth rotates. This behavior is a hormonal response.**

Just by watching our houseplants, we know that plants turn toward the sun, a phenomenon known as *phototropism*. Charles Darwin was one of the first to wonder why this happens. He observed that covering the growing tips of the plants prevented phototropism. The explanation lies in the formation in the tip of an *auxin*, a hormone that travels downward and stimulates elongation of the stem. When light distribution is uneven, auxin concentrates on the shady side of the stem, causing it to grow faster so that the stem bends toward the sun. Auxin is produced in seed embryos, young leaves, and growing tips of plants. Interestingly, plants synthesize auxin from tryptophan, the starting compound in the synthesis of several mammalian chemical messengers. As is the case with ethylene, the effects of auxin can also be overdone. An excessive concentration of auxin kills plants by overaccelerating their growth. The most familiar synthetic auxin, 2,4-D, is an herbicide that is widely used to kill broad-leaved weeds in this manner.

See Chemistry in Action Problems 28.88 and 28.89 at the end of the chapter.

28.6 Neurotransmitters

Neurotransmitters are the chemical messengers of the nervous system. They are released by nerve cells (*neurons*) and transmit signals to neighboring target cells, such as other nerve cells, muscle cells, or endocrine cells. Structurally, nerve cells that rely on neurotransmitters typically have a bulb-like body connected to a long, thin stem called an *axon* (Figure 28.5). Short, tentacle-like appendages, the *dendrites*, protrude from the bulbous end of the neuron, and numerous filaments protrude from the axon at the opposite end. The filaments lie close to the target cell, separated only by a narrow gap—the **synapse**.

A nerve impulse is transmitted along a nerve cell by variations in electrical potential caused by the exchange of positive and negative ions across the cell membrane. Chemical transmission of the impulse between a nerve cell and its target occurs when neurotransmitter molecules are released from a *presynaptic neuron*, cross the synapse, and bind to receptors on the target cell. When the target is another nerve cell it is called a *postsynaptic neuron*, where the neurotransmitter is received by receptors on the postsynaptic neuron's dendrites as shown in Figure 28.5. Once neurotransmitter–receptor

Synapse The place where the tip of a neuron and its target cell lie adjacent to each other.

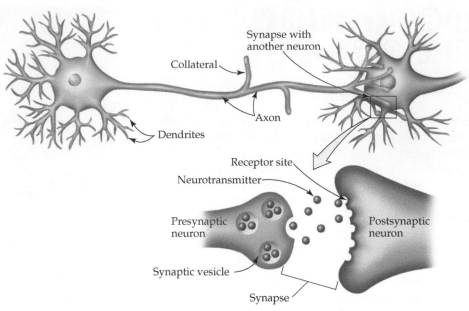

▲ **Figure 28.5**

A nerve cell and transmission of a nerve signal by neurotransmitters.
Transmission occurs between neurons when a neurotransmitter is released by the presynaptic neuron, crosses the synapse, and fits into a receptor on the postsynaptic neuron or other target cell.

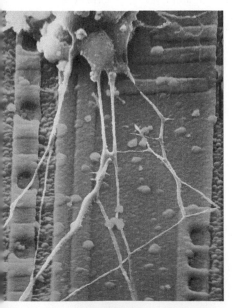

▲ **Two ways to send messages. This photograph shows a human neuron growing on the surface of a silicon computer chip.**

binding has occurred, the message has been delivered. The postsynaptic neuron then transmits the nerve impulse down its own axon until a neurotransmitter delivers the message to the next neuron or other target cell.

Neurotransmitter molecules are synthesized in the presynaptic neurons and stored there in small pockets, known as *vesicles,* from which they are released as needed. After a neurotransmitter has done its job, it must be *rapidly* removed from the synaptic cleft so that the postsynaptic neuron is ready to receive another impulse. This occurs in one of two ways. Either a chemical change catalyzed by an enzyme available in the synaptic cleft inactivates the neurotransmitter or, alternatively, the neurotransmitter is returned to the presynaptic neuron and placed in storage until it is needed again.

Most neurotransmitters are amines and are synthesized from amino acids. The synthesis of dopamine, norepinephrine, and epinephrine from tyrosine was shown in Figure 28.4. The synthesis of serotonin and melatonin from tryptophan is shown in Figure 28.6. Some neurotransmitters act directly by causing changes in adjacent cells as soon as they connect with their receptors. Others rely on second messengers, often cyclic AMP, the same second messenger utilized by hormones. Individual neurotransmitters have been associated with emotions, drug addiction, pain relief, and other brain functions, as we shall see in the following sections.

PROBLEM 28.8

Which of the following transformations of amines in Figure 28.6 is (1) an acetylation, (2) a methylation, (3) a decarboxylation?

(a) 5-Hydroxytryptophan to serotonin

(b) Serotonin to *N*-acetylserotonin

(c) *N*-Acetylserotonin to melatonin

Tryptophan

5-Hydroxytryptophan

CO_2

Serotonin
(brain neurotransmitter)

N-Acetylserotonin

Melatonin (hormone)

▲ **Figure 28.6**
Synthesis of chemical messengers from tryptophan.
The changes in each step are highlighted in gold for additions and in green for losses.

28.7 How Neurotransmitters Work: Acetylcholine, Its Agonists and Antagonists

Acetylcholine in Action

Acetylcholine is a neurotransmitter responsible for the control of skeletal muscles. It is also widely distributed in the brain, where it may play a role in the sleep–wake cycle, learning, memory, and mood. Nerves that rely on acetylcholine as their neurotransmitter are classified as *cholinergic* nerves.

Acetylcholine is synthesized in presynaptic neurons and stored in their vesicles. The rapid sequence of events in the action of acetylcholine in communicating between nerve cells, illustrated in Figure 28.7, is as follows:

Acetylcholine

- A nerve impulse arrives at the presynaptic neuron.
- The vesicles move to the cell membrane, fuse with it, and release their acetylcholine molecules (several thousand molecules from each vesicle).
- Acetylcholine crosses the synapse and binds to receptors on the postsynaptic neuron, causing a change in membrane permeability to ions.
- The resulting change in the permeability to ions of the postsynaptic neuron initiates the nerve impulse in that neuron.
- With the message delivered, acetylcholinesterase present in the synaptic cleft catalyzes the decomposition of acetylcholine:

$$CH_3-\overset{O}{\overset{||}{C}}-O-CH_2-CH_2-\overset{+}{N}(CH_3)_3 \quad \xrightarrow[H_2O]{Acetylcholinesterase} \quad CH_3COO^- \ + \ HO-CH_2-CH_2-\overset{+}{N}(CH_3)_3$$

Acetylcholine (ACh)   Acetate   Choline

- Choline is absorbed back into the presynaptic neuron, where new acetylcholine is synthesized.

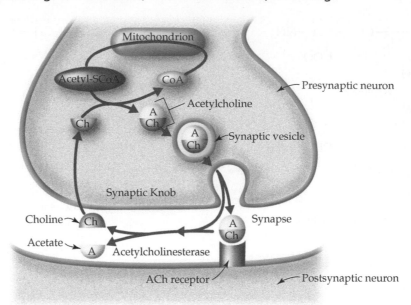

▶ Figure 28.7
Acetylcholine release and re-uptake.
Acetylcholine is stored in vesicles in the presynaptic neuron. After it is released into the synapse and connects with its receptor, it is broken down by hydrolysis into acetate and choline in a reaction catalyzed by acetylcholinesterase. The choline is taken back into the synaptic knob and reused to synthesize acetylcholine, which is then stored in the vesicles until needed.

PROBLEM 28.9

Propranolol (trade name, Inderal®) is an antagonist for certain epinephrine receptors and is a member of the class of drugs known as beta blockers (because they block what are known as beta receptors). Circle the functional groups in propranolol and name them. Compare the structure of propranolol with the structure of epinephrine and describe the differences.

$$O-CH_2CHCH_2NHCHCH_3$$

Propranolol
(Inderal®)

Epinephrine
(adrenaline)

Drugs and Acetylcholine

Drug Any substance that alters body function when it is introduced from an external source.

Many drugs act at acetylcholine synapses, where the tip of a neuron that releases acetylcholine and its target cell lie adjacent to each other. A **drug** is any molecule that alters normal functions when it enters the body from an external source. The action is at the molecular level, and it can be either therapeutic or poisonous. To have an effect, many drugs must connect with a receptor just as a substrate must bind to an enzyme or as a hormone or neurotransmitter must bind to a receptor. In fact, many drugs are designed to mimic a given hormone or neurotransmitter and in so doing elicit either an enhanced or attenuated effect.

Agonist A substance that interacts with a receptor to cause or prolong the receptor's normal biochemical response.

Antagonist A substance that blocks or inhibits the normal biochemical response of a receptor.

Pharmacologists classify some drugs as **agonists**—substances that act to produce or prolong the normal biochemical response of a receptor. Other drugs are classified as **antagonists**—substances that block or inhibit the normal response of a receptor. Many agonists and antagonists compete with normal signaling molecules for interaction with the receptor, just as inhibitor molecules compete with substrate for the active site in an enzyme. To illustrate the ways in which drugs can affect our biochemical activity, we next describe the action of a group of drugs. These drugs are all members of the same drug family in the sense that their biochemical activity occurs at acetylcholine synapses in the central nervous system. The locations of their actions can be seen in Figure 28.7.

- ***Botulinus toxin (an antagonist) blocks acetylcholine release and causes botulism.*** The toxin, which is produced by bacterial growth in improperly canned food, binds irreversibly to the presynaptic neuron, where acetylcholine would be released. It prevents this release, frequently causing death due to muscle paralysis. Commercially, this toxin (marketed as Botox®) has found use in cosmetic surgery, where carefully controlled doses of it are used to temporarily tighten up wrinkled skin without the need for invasive surgical procedures. Recent experiments have shown that Botox® does not stay at the injection site but migrates along neurons to the brain, far from the original injection.

- ***Black widow spider venom (an agonist) releases excess acetylcholine.*** In the opposite reaction from that of botulism toxin, the synapse is flooded with acetylcholine, resulting in muscle cramps and spasms.

- ***Organophosphorus insecticides (antagonists) inhibit acetylcholinesterase.*** All of the organophosphorus insecticides (a few examples are shown below) prevent acetylcholinesterase from breaking down acetylcholine within the synapse. As a result, the nerves are overstimulated, causing a variety of symptoms including muscle contraction and weakness, lack of coordination, and at high doses, convulsions. Recently, the death of thousands of honeybees was attributed to clothianidin dust released from the protective coating on corn seeds during planting. Many organophosphorus compounds are also used as nerve gasses, which is why agriculturists receive special safety training before using these insecticides on crops.

Parathion   Diazinon   Malathion

- ***Nicotine binds to acetylcholine receptors.*** *Nicotine* at low doses is a stimulant (an agonist) because it activates acetylcholine receptors. The sense of alertness and well-being produced by inhaling tobacco smoke is a result of this effect. At high doses, nicotine is an antagonist. It irreversibly blocks the acetylcholine receptors and can cause their degeneration. Nicotine has no therapeutic use in humans other than in overcoming addiction to smoking. Nicotine transdermal patches, which release a small, controlled dose of nicotine through the skin, and chewing gum containing nicotine are used to help smokers overcome nicotine addiction. Nicotine (along with its sulfate salt) is one of the most toxic botanical insecticides known and has been used since the 1600s as a contact poison.

- ***Atropine (an antagonist) competes with acetylcholine at receptors.*** Atropine, found naturally in the nightshade plant, is an alkaloid that is a poison at high doses. At controlled doses, its therapeutic uses include acceleration of abnormally slow heart rate, paralysis of eye muscles during surgery, and relaxation of intestinal muscles in gastrointestinal disorders. Most importantly, it is a specific antidote for acetylcholinesterase poisons such as organophosphorus insecticides. By blocking activation of the receptors, it counteracts the excess acetylcholine created by acetylcholinesterase inhibitors.

▶▶▶ Alkaloids are naturally occurring, nitrogen-containing compounds isolated from plants; usually basic, bitter, and poisonous (see Section 15.6).

- ***Tubocurarine (an antagonist) competes with acetylcholine at receptors.*** Purified from curare, a mixture of chemicals extracted from a plant found in South America, the alkaloid tubocurarine is used to paralyze patients in conjunction with anesthesia drugs prior to surgery. In the last 30 years, researchers have developed safer, more easily purified synthetic derivatives that have the same mode of action. These molecules have nearly replaced use of tubocurarine in medical procedures.

PROBLEM 28.10

The LD_{50} values (lethal dose in mg/kg, for rats; see Chemistry in Action: How Toxic Is Toxic? p. 499) for the three organophosphorus insecticides listed in this section are parathion, 3–13 mg/kg; diazinon, 250–285 mg/kg; and malathion, 1000–1375 mg/kg. (a) Which would you choose for use in your garden and why? (b) Which is most dangerous for mammals to ingest? Why?

🔑 **KEY CONCEPT PROBLEM 28.11**

Some drugs are classified as agonists whereas others are classified as antagonists.

(a) Sumatripan, sold as Imitrex®, is effective in treating migraine headaches. It acts as an agonist at the serotonin receptor. Explain the effect Imitrex® has on the serotonin receptor.

(b) Ondansetron, sold as Zofran®, acts on a subclass of serotonin receptors to inhibit nausea and vomiting; it is frequently prescribed to patients in chemotherapy. It acts as an antagonist at these receptors. Explain the effect Zofran® has on these receptors.

28.8 Histamine and Antihistamines

Histamine is the neurotransmitter responsible for the symptoms of the allergic reaction so familiar to hay fever sufferers or those who are allergic to animals. It is also the chemical that causes an itchy bump when an insect bites you. In the body, histamine is produced by decarboxylation of the amino acid histidine:

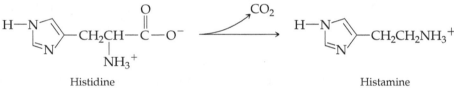

Histidine   Histamine

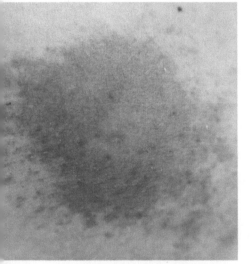

▲ The swelling and inflammation surrounding this insect bite are due to a histamine response.

The *antihistamines* are a family of drugs that counteract the effect of histamine because they are histamine-receptor antagonists. They competitively block the attachment of histamine to its receptors. Members of this family all have in common a disubstituted ethylamine side chain, usually with two *N*-methyl groups. As illustrated by the examples below, the R′ and R″ groups at the other end of the molecule tend to be bulky and aromatic.

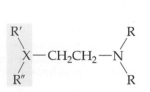

General antihistamine structure

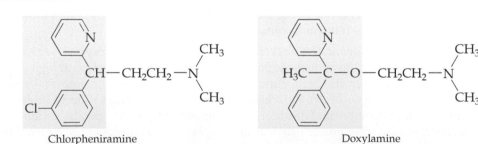

Chlorpheniramine (an antihistamine)   Doxylamine (an antihistamine)

Histamine also activates secretion of acid in the stomach. Development of an antagonist for this function of histamine was accomplished by what is today commonly known as *rational drug design*. After synthesis of about 200 different compounds with systematic variations on the histamine structure, the goal of attaining a histamine antagonist was achieved. The result was *cimetidine*, widely publicized as a treatment for heartburn under its trade name of Tagamet®. Today many other histamine antagonists exist, including ranitidine, sold under its trade name of Zantac®.

$$CH_3$$

$$H-N \overset{CH_3}{\underset{N}{\diagup}} -CH_2-S-CH_2CH_2NH-\underset{\underset{N-C\equiv N}{\|}}{C}-NHCH_3$$

Cimetidine
(Tagamet®)

$$CH_3CH_2 \diagdown_O \diagup -CH_2-S-CH_2CH_2NH-\underset{\underset{HC-NO_2}{\|}}{C}-CH_3$$

Ranitidine
(Zantac®)

28.9 Serotonin, Norepinephrine, and Dopamine

The Monoamines and Therapeutic Drugs

Serotonin, norepinephrine, and dopamine could be called the "big three" of neurotransmitters. Regular news reports appear as discoveries about them accumulate. Collectively, serotonin, norepinephrine, and dopamine are known as *monoamines*. (Their biochemical syntheses are shown in Figures 28.4 and 28.6.) All are active in the brain and all have been identified in various ways with mood, the experiences of fear and pleasure, mental illness, and drug addiction. Needless to say, chemistry plays a central role in mental illness—that has become an inescapable conclusion.

One well-established relationship is the connection between major depression and a deficiency of serotonin, norepinephrine, and dopamine. The evidence comes from the different modes of action of three families of drugs used to treat depression. Amitriptyline, phenelzine, and fluoxetine are representative of these three types of drugs. Each in its own way increases the concentration of the neurotransmitters at synapses.

$$CHCH_2CH_2N(CH_3)_2$$

Amitriptyline, a tricyclic antidepressant
(Elavil®)

$$-CH_2CH_2NHNH_2$$

Phenelzine, an MAO inhibitor
(Nardil®)

$$F_3C- \bigcirc -CHCH_2CH_2NHCH_3$$

Fluoxetine, an SSRI
(Prozac®)

- Amitriptyline is representative of the *tricyclic antidepressants*, which were the first generation of these drugs. The tricyclics prevent the re-uptake of serotonin and norepinephrine from within the synapse. Serotonin is important in mood-control pathways and functions more slowly than other neurotransmitters; slowing its re-uptake often improves mood in depressed patients.
- Phenelzine is a *monoamine oxidase (MAO) inhibitor*, one of a group of medications that inhibit the enzyme that breaks down monoamine neurotransmitters. This inhibition of *monoamine oxidase* allows the concentrations of monoamines at synapses to increase.
- Fluoxetine represents the newest class of antidepressants, the *selective serotonin re-uptake inhibitors (SSRI)*. They are more selective than the tricyclics because they inhibit only the re-uptake of serotonin. Fluoxetine (Prozac®) has rapidly become the most widely prescribed drug for all but the most severe forms of depression. Most antidepressants cause unpleasant side effects; fluoxetine does not, a major benefit.

It is important to note that the relief of the symptoms of depression by these drugs is not evidence that either the chemical basis of depression is fully understood or that increasing neurotransmitter concentration is the only action of these drugs. The brain still holds many secrets. As one of the pharmacologists who developed fluoxetine put it, "If the human brain were simple enough for us to understand, we would be too simple to understand it."

The complex and not yet fully understood relationships between neurotransmitter activity and behavior are illustrated by the use of fluoxetine for conditions other than depression. It is used to treat obsessive compulsive disorder, bulimia, obesity, panic disorder, body dysmorphic disorder, teen depression, and premenstrual dysphoric disorder (formerly known as PMS). New uses for this class of drugs are constantly being explored.

Dopamine and Drug Addiction

Dopamine plays a role in the brain in processes that control movement, emotional responses, and the experiences of pleasure and pain. It interacts with five different kinds of receptors in different parts of the brain. An oversupply of dopamine is associated with schizophrenia, and an undersupply results in the loss of fine motor control in Parkinson's disease (see Chemistry in Action: The Blood–Brain Barrier, p. 878). Dopamine also plays an important role in the brain's reward system. An ample supply of brain dopamine produces the pleasantly satisfied feeling that results from a rewarding experience—a "natural high." Herein lies the role of dopamine in drug addiction: the more the dopamine receptors are stimulated, the greater the high.

Experiments show that cocaine blocks re-uptake of dopamine from the synapse, and amphetamines accelerate release of dopamine. Studies have linked increased brain levels of dopamine to alcohol and nicotine addiction as well. The higher-than-normal stimulation of dopamine receptors by drugs results in tolerance. In the drive to maintain constant conditions (see Chemistry in Action: Homeostasis, p. 845), the number of dopamine receptors decreases and the sensitivity of those that remain decreases. Consequently, brain cells require more and more of a drug for the same result, a condition that contributes to addiction.

Marijuana also creates an increase in dopamine levels in the same brain areas where dopamine levels increase after administration of heroin or cocaine. The most-active ingredient in marijuana is tetrahydrocannabinol (THC). The use of marijuana medically for chronic pain relief has become a controversial topic in recent years, as questions about its benefits and drawbacks are debated.

Tetrahydrocannabinol (THC)

🔑 KEY CONCEPT PROBLEM 28.12

Identify the functional groups present in THC. Is the molecule likely to be hydrophilic or hydrophobic? Would you expect THC to build up in fatty tissues in the body, or would it be readily eliminated in the urine?

Worked Example 28.2 Predicting Biological Activity Based on Structure

The relationship between the structure of a molecule and its biochemical function is an essential area of study in biochemistry and the design of drugs. Terfenadine (Seldane®) was one of the first of the new generation of "nondrowsy" antihistamines (it was removed from the market due to potential heart toxicity). Based solely on what you have learned so far, suggest which of its structural features make it an antihistamine.

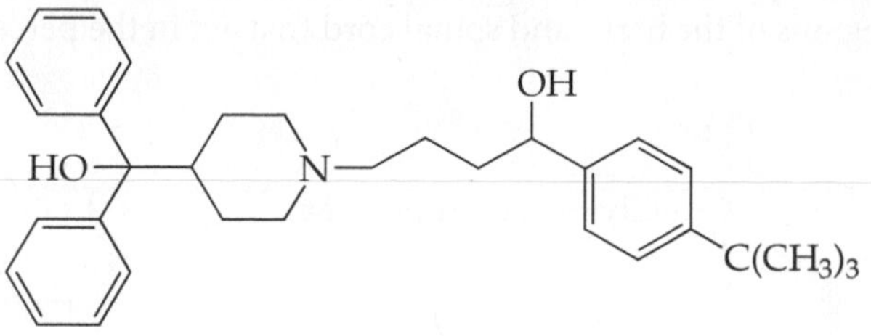

Terfenadine

ANALYSIS From Section 28.8, we see that members of the antihistamine family have in common the general structure shown here: an X group (usually a CH) to which two aromatic groups (noted as *aryl* in the drawing) are attached. The X is also attached to a disubstituted nitrogen by a carbon chain:

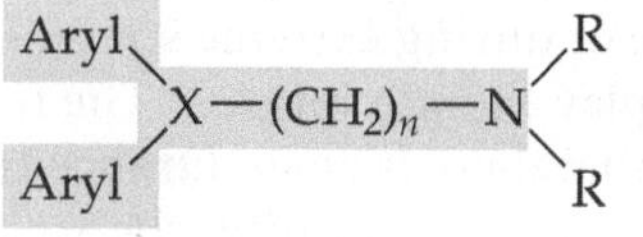

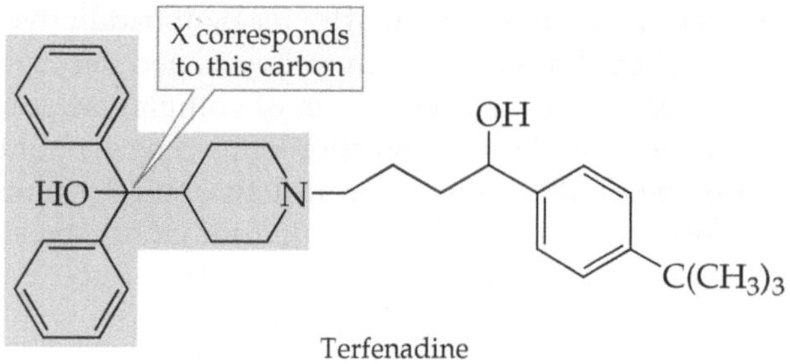

Terfenadine

SOLUTION
Since terfenadine contains the same basic structure as a general antihistamine, its biological function should be similar.

KEY CONCEPT PROBLEM 28.13

Predict which of the following compounds is an antihistamine and which is an antidepressant.

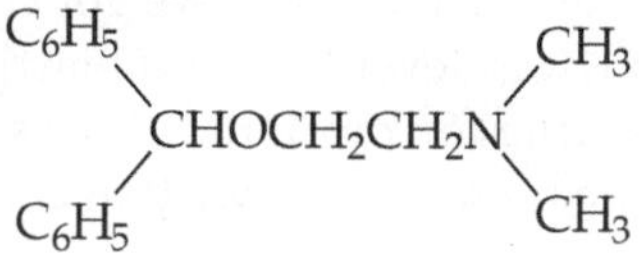

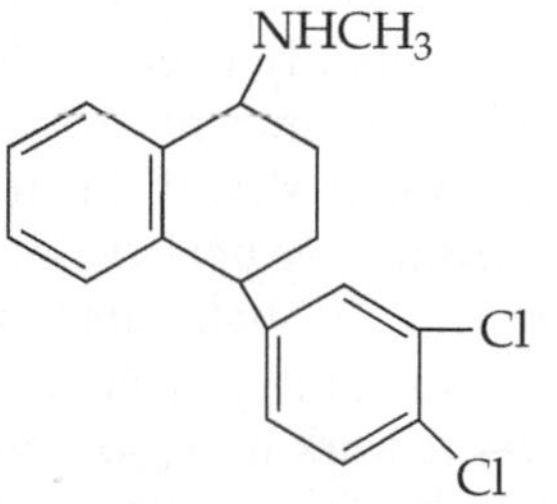

28.10 Neuropeptides and Pain Relief

Studies of morphine and other opium derivatives in the 1970s revealed that these addictive but effective pain-killing substances act via their own specific brain receptors. This raised some interesting questions: why are there brain receptors for chemicals from a plant? Could it be that there are animal neurotransmitters that act at the same receptors?

The two pentapeptides *Met-enkephalin* and *Leu-enkephalin* (Met and Leu stand for the carboxy terminal amino acids, Section 18.3) were discovered in the effort to answer these questions.

Met-enkephalin: Tyr-Gly-Gly-Phe-Met
Leu-enkephalin: Tyr-Gly-Gly-Phe-Leu

▲ Endorphin Rush hot sauce.

Both exert morphine-like suppression of pain when injected into the brains of experimental animals. The structural similarity between Met-enkephalin and morphine, highlighted below, supports the concept that both interact with the same receptors, which are located in regions of the brain and spinal cord that act in the perception of pain.

Met-enkephalin

Morphine

Subsequently, about a dozen natural pain-killing polypeptides that act via the opiate receptors have been found. They are classified as *endorphins*. A 31-amino acid polypeptide that ends with the same five-amino acid sequence as Met-enkephalin is a more potent pain suppressor than morphine. Disappointingly, though, none of these compounds is the long-sought-after ideal, nonaddictive painkiller—all are addictive.

Although there is much to be learned, enkephalins have been implicated in the "runner's high," the regulation of complex behavior states such as anger and sexual excitement, and the suppression of pain by acupuncture or during extreme stress—for example, in the competitive athlete who continues to play though injured. The term *endorphin* has entered the popular idiom to the extent that there is an endurance trial known as the Endorphin Fix Adventure Race, endorphin label running shoes, and even an Endorphin Rush® hot sauce.

28.11 Drug Discovery and Drug Design

In a tropical rain forest, a botanist trudges after a native healer, taking notes about the plants the healer chooses. In a pristine laboratory, scientists monitor an army of robots and computer screens. In yet another laboratory, researchers stare at computer-drawn pictures of candidate molecules connecting with receptors. Any of these activities can start a new drug on its path to medical success.

Plants were our first source for drugs. By trial and error, our human ancestors learned which plants dulled pain, caused "visions," and cured diseases. This was the beginning of drug discovery. From generation to generation, the knowledge was added to and passed along. Eventually, chemists learned how to identify the structures of the active molecules and sometimes to improve upon them. This is how we got codeine for pain (from opium poppies), quinine for malaria (from fever tree), vinblastine for Hodgkin's disease (from rosy periwinkle), scopolamine for motion sickness (from jimson weed), and others. Estimates are that 25% of the prescriptions written each year in North America are for plant-derived drugs.

Today *ethnobotanists* work in remote regions of the world to learn what indigenous people have discovered about the healing powers of plants. The botanists are pursuing drug discovery in a race against time, both because forests and jungles are disappearing with the pressures of population expansion and because the aging healers who learned their skills years ago as apprentices to their elders are not finding new apprentices to teach.

Probably the first *synthetic* chemicals used in medicine were diethyl ether and chloroform as anesthetics:

$$CH_3CH_2OCH_2CH_3 \qquad CHCL_3$$

Diethyl ether   Chloroform

The technique of modifying a known structure to improve its biochemical activity was developed after cocaine was first used as a local anesthetic in 1884. The actual structure of cocaine was not known, but its hydrolysis products could be identified and showed that cocaine might be an ester of benzoic acid. Experiments with other benzoic acid esters in the early 1900s yielded benzocaine and procaine (Novocaine®), both still in use:

Cocaine $\xrightarrow{\text{Hydrolysis}}$ Benzoic acid + CH_3OH + HO—

Benzocaine: H_2N— —$C(=O)$—O—CH_2—CH_3

Procaine hydrochloride (Novocaine®): $Cl^- H_3\overset{+}{N}$— —$C(=O)$—O—CH_2—CH_2—$N(CH_2CH_3)(CH_2CH_3)$

Also in the late 1800s, phenacetin was introduced as an analgesic. The use of acetanilide preceded it; however, acetanilide was soon withdrawn because of its toxicity. Derived as it was from the results of animal experiments with aniline, phenacetin was one of the first drugs designed with some knowledge of biochemistry. It remained on the market for many years until it was eventually withdrawn as a result of the accumulation of evidence for its toxicity and possible carcinogenicity. Acetaminophen, introduced in 1893, is widely used today under such familiar trade names as Tylenol®. We now know that it is produced in the body during metabolism of acetanilide and phenacetin. Other analgesics, such as ibuprofen (Motrin®) and naproxen (Aleve®), also share this general structure.

Aniline (NH_2)

Acetanilide ($NHCCH_3$, O)

Phenacetin ($NHCCH_3$, O; OCH_2CH_3)

Acetaminophen (Tylenol®) ($NHCCH_3$, O; OH)

Ibuprofen (Motrin®): CH_3—CH—COOH; CH_2; CH; CH_3 CH_3

Naproxen (Aleve®): CH_3—CH—COOH; OCH_3

Interestingly, the mode of action of these well-known pain relievers is still unclear. It is believed that they inhibit the formation of the prostaglandins (Section 23.9). Meanwhile, expanding knowledge of the structure of biochemically active molecules, combined with advancing technology, have opened the door to a new era. Drug *discovery* is merging with drug *design*.

One new technology, *combinatorial chemistry*, arrived on the scene in 1991 and since 2005 has become a routine and powerful tool in drug discovery and design. It involves mass production at the molecular level. Suppose it is believed that some unknown combination of a defined set of molecular building blocks will yield an effective drug. The techniques of combinatorial chemistry allow the building blocks to react in every possible combination,

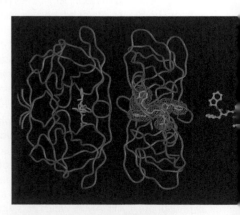

▲ Computer modeling of HIV-1 proteinase has led to the discovery of new drugs for the treatment of AIDS.

not one reaction at a time but hundreds at a time. Reactions are carried out on a microgram scale in tiny tubes or with molecules held down on solid supports. By combining reactants, dividing up the products, adding other reactants, and continuing this process, millions of related compounds can be synthesized. Robots help with the mixing of chemicals. Computers track the combinations and screen the products for some type of activity. Since, on average, only 5 in 5000 compounds prepared in the lab ever make it to human testing and only one of these five will ever be approved for general clinical use, hope runs high that this combinatorial approach will lead to a significant decrease in the average of 12 years and $802 million (in 2005 dollars) needed for the initial discovery and ultimate development of a new drug.

In another rapidly developing technology, supercomputers and molecular graphics now allow an approach that goes right to the heart of drug action—the drug–receptor connection. The ability to find the structure of proteins, once a tedious and lengthy activity, is advancing every day. Suppose that the complete tertiary structure of an enzyme has been found, the active site identified, and a search for an inhibitor for this enzyme is underway. The computer can consult a database of quantitative information about drug–receptor interactions and other important properties such as hydrophobic versus hydrophilic solubilities. Once potential inhibitors are identified, pictures of such molecules entering the active site can be created on the computer screen. The pictures can be rotated and the fit examined from many angles. In this way, it is increasingly possible to design a molecule with just the right chemical and physical properties needed to connect with a biomolecule and produce a desired result. For those students who would like to see the results of computer modeling first hand, a free web-browser plug-in called Chime (from Elsevier MDL) exists. After installation on your personal computer, Chime allows you to view thousands of drugs that have been modeled. A quick search of the Internet using the combination search terms *chime + drugs* gave 1,880,000 hits in 2011. Indeed, many of the molecules discussed in this chapter are easily found on the web as models that are viewable using Chime.

SUMMARY: REVISITING THE CHAPTER GOALS

1. What are hormones, and how do they function? *Hormones* are the chemical messengers of the *endocrine system*. Under control of the hypothalamus they are released from various locations, many in response to intermediate, regulatory hormones. Hormones travel in the bloodstream to target cells, where they connect with receptors that initiate chemical changes within cells (*see Problems 1, 21–24, 87, and 88*).

2. What is the chemical nature of hormones? Hormones are *polypeptides, steroids,* or *amino acid derivatives.* Many are polypeptides, which range widely in size and include small molecules such as vasopressin and oxytocin, larger ones like insulin, and all of the regulatory hormones. Steroids have a distinctive four-ring structure and are classified as lipids because they are hydrophobic. All of the sex hormones are steroids. Hormones that are amino acid derivatives are synthesized from amino acids (Figures 28.4 and 28.6). Epinephrine and norepinephrine act as hormones throughout the body and also act as neurotransmitters in the brain (*see Problems 4–8, 14, 16, 25–33, 44–51, 54, 55, 88, 89, 97, 98, 101, and 102*).

3. How does the hormone epinephrine deliver its message, and what is its mode of action? Epinephrine, the fight-or-flight hormone, acts via a cell-surface receptor and a G protein that connects with an enzyme, both of which are embedded in the cell membrane. The enzyme adenylate cyclase transfers the message to a *second messenger*, a cyclic adenosine monophosphate (cyclic AMP), which acts within the target cell (*see Problems 9, 15, 34–43, and 100*).

4. What are neurotransmitters, and how do they function? *Neurotransmitters* are synthesized in presynaptic neurons and stored there in vesicles from which they are released when needed. They travel across a *synaptic cleft* to *receptors* on adjacent target cells. Some act directly via their receptors; others utilize cyclic AMP or other second messengers. After their message is delivered, neurotransmitters must be broken down rapidly or taken back into the presynaptic neuron so that the receptor is free to receive further messages (*see Problems 2, 3, 10, 17, 18, 52, 53, 56–59, and 92–96*).

5. How does acetylcholine deliver its message, and how do drugs alter its function? Acetylcholine is released from the vesicles of a presynaptic neuron and connects with receptors that initiate continuation of a nerve impulse in the postsynaptic neuron. It is then broken down in the synaptic cleft by acetylcholinesterase to form choline, which is returned to the presynaptic neuron, where it is converted back to acetylcholine. *Agonists*, such as nicotine at low doses, activate acetylcholine receptors and are stimulants. *Antagonists*, such as tubocurarine or atropine, which block activation of the receptors, are toxic in high doses, but at low doses are useful as muscle relaxants (*see Problems 60–65, 90, and 91*).

6. Which neurotransmitters and what kinds of drugs play roles in allergies, mental depression, drug addiction, and pain? *Histamine,* an amino acid derivative, causes allergic symptoms. *Antihistamines* are antagonists with a general structure that resembles histamines, but with bulky groups at one end. Monoamines (serotonin, norepinephrine, and dopamine) are brain neurotransmitters; a deficiency of any of these molecules is associated with mental depression. *Drugs* that increase their activity include *tricyclic antidepressants* (for example, amitriptyline), *monoamine* *oxidase (MAO) inhibitors* (for example, phenelzine), and *selective serotonin re-uptake inhibitors (SSRI)* (for example, fluoxetine). An increase of dopamine activity in the brain is associated with the effects of most addictive substances. A group of neuropeptides acts at opiate receptors to counteract pain; all may be addictive *(see Problems 11–13, 19, 66–81, and 99).*

7. What are some of the methods used in drug discovery and design? *Ethnobotanists* work to identify the medicinal products of plants known to native peoples. *Chemical synthesis* is used to improve on the medicinal properties of known compounds by creating similar structures. *Combinatorial chemistry* produces many related molecules for drug screening. *Computer design* is used to select the precise molecular structure to fit a given receptor *(see Problems 82–84).*

KEY WORDS

Agonist, *p. 858*

Antagonist, *p. 858*

Drug, *p. 858*

Endocrine system, *p. 844*

Hormone, *p. 844*

Neurotransmitter, *p. 844*

Receptor, *p. 843*

Second messenger, *p. 847*

Synapse, *p. 855*

UNDERSTANDING KEY CONCEPTS

28.14   In many species of animals, at the onset of pregnancy, luteinizing hormone is released; it promotes the synthesis of progesterone—a major hormone in maintaining the pregnancy.

    (a) Where is LH produced, and to what class of hormones does it belong?

    (b) Where is progesterone produced, and to what class of hormones does it belong?

    (c) Do progesterone-producing cells have LH receptors on their surface, or does LH enter the cell to carry out its function?

    (d) Does progesterone bind to a cell-surface receptor, or does it enter the cell to carry out its function? Explain.

28.15   The "rush" of epinephrine in response to danger causes the release of glucose in muscle cells so that those muscles can carry out either "fight or flight." Very small amounts of the hormone produced in the adrenal gland cause a powerful response. To get such a response, the original signal (epinephrine) must be amplified many times. At what step in the sequence of events (Section 28.3) would you predict that the signal is amplified? Explain. How might that amplification take place?

28.16   Diabetes occurs when there is a malfunction in the uptake of glucose from the bloodstream into the cells. Your friend's youngest brother was just diagnosed with type I diabetes, and she has asked you the following questions. How would you answer them?

    (a) What hormone is involved, and what class is it?

    (b) Where is the hormone released?

    (c) How is this hormone transported to the cells that need it to allow glucose to enter?

    (d) Would you expect the hormone to enter the cell to carry out its function? Explain.

28.17   Give two mechanisms by which neurotransmitters exert their effects.

28.18   When an impulse arrives at the synapse, the synaptic vesicles open and release neurotransmitters into the cleft within a thousandth of a second. Within another ten-thousandth of a second, these molecules have diffused across the cleft and bound to receptor sites in the effector cell. In what two ways is transmission across a synapse terminated so that the neuron's signal is concluded?

28.19   What is the significance of dopamine in the addictive effects of cocaine, amphetamines, and alcohol?

ADDITIONAL PROBLEMS

CHEMICAL MESSENGERS

28.20   What do the terms *chemical messenger, target tissue,* and *hormone receptor* mean?

28.21   What is a hormone? What is the function of a hormone? How is the presence of a hormone detected by its target?

28.22   What is the main difference between a hormone and a vitamin?

28.23   What is the main difference between a hormone and a neurotransmitter?

28.24   Is a hormone changed as a result of binding to a receptor? Is the receptor changed as a result of binding the hormone? What are the binding forces between hormone and receptor?

28.25   How is hormone binding to its receptor more like an allosteric regulator binding to an enzyme than a substrate binding to an enzyme?

HORMONES AND THE ENDOCRINE SYSTEM

28.26   What is the purpose of the body's endocrine system?

28.27   Name as many endocrine glands as you can.

28.28   List the three major classes of hormones.

28.29   Give two examples of each of the three major classes of hormones.

28.30   What is the structural difference between an enzyme and a hormone?

28.31   What is the relationship between enzyme specificity and tissue specificity for a hormone?

28.32   Describe in general terms how a peptide hormone works.

28.33   Describe in general terms how a steroid hormone works.

HOW HORMONES WORK: EPINEPHRINE

28.34 In what gland is epinephrine produced and released?

28.35 Under what circumstances is epinephrine released?

28.36 How does epinephrine reach its target tissues?

28.37 What is the main function of epinephrine at its target tissues?

28.38 In order of their involvement, name the three membrane-bound proteins involved in transmitting the epinephrine message across the cell membrane.

28.39 What is the "second messenger" inside the cell that results from the epinephrine message? Is the ratio of epinephrine molecules to second messenger less than $1:1$, $1:1$, or greater than $1:1$? Explain.

28.40 What role does the second messenger play in a cell stimulated by epinephrine?

28.41 What enzyme catalyzes hydrolysis of the second messenger to terminate the message? What is the product called?

28.42 Epinephrine is used clinically in the treatment of what life-threatening allergic response?

28.43 People susceptible to anaphylactic shock due to insect stings or certain food allergies must be prepared to treat themselves in case of exposure. How are they prepared and what must they do?

HORMONES

28.44 Give an example of a polypeptide hormone. How many amino acids are in the hormone? Where is the hormone released? Where does the hormone function? What is the result of the hormone message?

28.45 Give an example of a steroid hormone. What is the structure of the hormone? Where is the hormone released? Where does the hormone function? What is the result of the hormone message?

28.46 What do the three major classes of steroid hormones have in common?

28.47 What molecule are the steroid hormones derived from? How does that make the physical properties of steroid hormones different from the other hormones?

28.48 Name the two primary male sex hormones.

28.49 Name the three principal female sex hormones.

28.50 Until relatively recently, the use of androgens by athletes was a common, legal practice. What are the advantages of using androgens during athletic training and competition?

28.51 The use of androgens during athletic training and competition has been banned in national and international sports. What are the disadvantages of using androgens during athletic training and competition?

28.52 List two hormones that also function as neurotransmitters.

28.53 Explain why epinephrine can act as both a neurotransmitter and a hormone without "crossover" between the two functions.

28.54 Identify the class to which each of these hormones belongs:

(a) $HO\text{—}\underset{HO}{\bigcirc}\text{—}CH_2CH_2NH_2$

(b) Insulin

(c)

28.55 Identify the class to which each of these hormones belongs:

(a) Glucagon

(b)

Thyroxine

(c)

Estradiol

NEUROTRANSMITTERS

28.56 What is a synapse, and what role does it play in nerve transmission?

28.57 What is an axon, and what role does it play in nerve transmission?

28.58 List three cell types that might receive a message transmitted by a neurotransmitter.

28.59 What kinds of cellular or organ actions would you expect to be influenced by neurotransmitters?

28.60 Describe in general terms how a nerve impulse is passed from one neuron to another.

28.61 What are the two methods for removing the neurotransmitter once its job is done?

28.62 List the three steps in chemical transmission of the impulse between a nerve cell and its target.

28.63 Write an equation for the reaction that is catalyzed by acetylcholinesterase.

28.64 Why are enkephalins sometimes called *neurohormones*?

28.65 Outline the six steps in cholinergic nerve transmission.

CHEMICAL MESSENGERS AND DRUGS

28.66 Describe the difference between drugs that are agonists and those that are antagonists.

28.67 Give an example of a drug that acts as an agonist for acetylcholine receptors and one that acts as an antagonist for these receptors.

28.68 Give examples of two histamine antagonists that have very different tissue specificities and functions.

28.69 Give an example of a drug from each family in Problem 28.68.

28.70 Name three families of drugs used to treat depression.

28.71 Name the "big three" monoamine neurotransmitters.

28.72 What is the impact and mode of action of cocaine on dopamine levels in the brain?

28.73 What is the impact and mode of action of amphetamines on dopamine levels in the brain?

28.74 How is the tetrahydrocannabinol of marijuana similar in action to heroin and cocaine?

28.75 Why do we have brain receptors that respond to morphine and other opium derivatives from plants?

28.76 In schizophrenia, the neurons affected by dopamine are overstimulated. This condition is treated with drugs like chlorpromazine (Thorazine®), which bind to the affected receptors and inhibit the dopamine signal. Does chlorpromazine act as an agonist or antagonist?

28.77 Methamphetamine "highs" often are accompanied by behavioral changes that resemble schizophrenia. Does methamphetamine act as an agonist or antagonist?

28.78 What are endorphins? Where in the body are they found?

28.79 "Runner's high," sexual excitement, and other complex behaviors are believed to involve which neuropeptides?

28.80 Enkephalins and endorphins are referred to as "nature's opiates." Explain this saying.

28.81 Why might it be an advantage for an animal to produce its own pain suppressing molecules?

28.82 What does an ethnobotanist do?

28.83 Combinatorial chemistry has added hundreds of drugs to the pharmaceutical market in recent years. What is the basis of the combinatorial approach to drug design? What advantages might the combinatorial approach have for the pharmaceutical industry?

28.84 In what ways are studies of the exact size and shape of biomolecules (such as enzymes, receptors, signal transducers, and so on) leading to the development of new drugs to treat disease?

28.85 How are computers used in the development of new drugs to treat disease?

CHEMISTRY IN ACTION

28.86 One of the responsibilities of the endocrine system is maintenance of homeostasis in the body. Briefly explain what is meant by the term *homeostasis*. [*Homeostasis, p. 845*]

28.87 What is the goal of the measurements of clinical chemistry? [*Homeostasis, p. 845*]

28.88 In animals, hormones are produced by the endocrine glands and tissues in various parts of the body. Why is it

necessary for plants to synthesize the hormones in the cells where they are needed rather than in specialized cells? [*Plant Hormones, p. 855*]

28.89 How does 2,4-D, a weed killer, take advantage of the function of a plant hormone? [*Plant Hormones, p. 855*]

GENERAL QUESTIONS AND PROBLEMS

28.90 Suppose you are hiking in the Alaskan wilderness when your path crosses that of a bear. What hormone is responsible for your immediate response?

28.91 How do curare-treated arrows work?

28.92 What characteristics in their mechanism of action does thyroxine share with the steroid hormones?

28.93 List and describe the functions of the three types of proteins involved in transmission of a hormone signal.

28.94 The cyclic AMP (second messenger) of signal transmission is very reactive and breaks down rapidly after synthesis. Why is this important to the signal-transmission process?

28.95 We say that there is signal amplification in the transmission process. Explain how signal amplification occurs and what it means for transmission of the signal to the sites of cellular activity.

28.96 The phosphodiesterase that catalyzes hydrolysis of cyclic AMP is inhibited by caffeine. What overall effect would caffeine have on a signal that is mediated by cAMP?

28.97 Compare the structures of the sex hormones testosterone and progesterone. What portions of the structures are the same? Where do they differ?

28.98 When you compare the structures of ethynyl estradiol to norethindrone, where do they differ? Where is ethynyl estradiol similar to estradiol? Where is norethindrone similar to progesterone?

28.99 Anandamides have been isolated from brain tissues and appear to be the natural ligand for the receptor that also binds tetrahydrocannabinol. Anandamides have also been discovered in chocolate and cocoa powder. How might the craving for chocolate be explained?

An anandamide structure

28.100 Identify the structural changes that occur in the first two steps in the conversion of tyrosine to epinephrine (Figure 28.4). To what main classes and subclasses of enzymes do the enzymes that catalyze these reactions belong?

28.101 Look at the structures of the two male sex hormones shown on p. 852. Identify the type of functional group change that interconverts testosterone and androsterone. To which class of chemical reactions does this change belong?

28.102 Look at the structures of the three female sex hormones shown on p. 852. Identify the type of functional group change that interconverts estradiol and estrone. To which class of chemical reactions does this change belong?

CHAPTER 29

Body Fluids

CONTENTS

◄ Blood and other body fluids help maintain the delicate balance between life and death often faced during medical emergencies.

CHAPTER GOALS

1. **How are body fluids classified?**
   THE GOAL: Be able to describe the major categories of body fluids, their general composition, and the exchange of solutes between them. (◀◀◀ A, B.)

2. **What are the roles of blood in maintaining homeostasis?**
   THE GOAL: Be able to explain the composition and functions of blood. (◀◀◀ B, C.)

3. **How do blood components participate in the body's defense mechanisms?**
   THE GOAL: Be able to identify and describe the roles of blood components

   that participate in inflammation, the immune response, and blood clotting.

4. **How do red blood cells participate in the transport of blood gases?**
   THE GOAL: Be able to explain the relationships among O_2 and CO_2 transport, and acid–base balance. (◀◀◀ D.)

5. **How is the composition of urine controlled?**
   THE GOAL: Be able to describe the transfer of water and solutes during urine formation and give an overview of the composition of urine. (◀◀◀ B, C.)

CONCEPTS TO REVIEW
◀◀◀

A. Solutions
(Sections 9.1, 9.2, 9.10)

B. Osmosis and Osmotic Pressure
(Section 9.12)

C. Dialysis
(Section 9.13)

D. pH
(Sections 10.7, 10.8)

We have chosen to put this chapter as the last one in your text because just about every aspect of chemistry you have studied so far applies to the subject of this chapter—body fluids. Electrolytes, nutrients and waste products, metabolic intermediates, and chemical messengers flow through your body in blood and in lymph fluid and exit as waste in the urine and feces. The chemical compositions of blood and urine mirror chemical reactions throughout the body. Fortunately, samples of these fluids are easily collected and studied. Many advances in understanding biological chemistry have been based on information obtained from analysis of blood and urine. As a result, studies of blood and urine chemistry provide information essential for the diagnosis and treatment of disease.

29.1 Body Water and Its Solutes

All body fluids have water as the solvent; in fact, the water content of the human body averages about 60% (by weight). Physiologists describe body water as occupying two different "compartments"—the *intracellular* and the *extracellular* compartments. We have looked primarily at the chemical reactions occurring in the **intracellular fluid** (the fluid inside cells), which includes about two-thirds of all body water (Figure 29.1). We now turn our attention to the remaining one-third of body water, the **extracellular fluid**, which includes mainly **blood plasma** (the fluid portion of blood) and **interstitial fluid** (the fluid that fills the spaces between cells).

To be soluble in water, a substance must be an ion, a gas, a small polar molecule, or a large molecule having many polar, hydrophilic (water-loving) or ionic groups on its surface. All four types of solutes are present in body fluids. The majority are inorganic ions and ionized biomolecules (mainly proteins), as shown in the comparison of blood plasma, interstitial fluid, and intracellular fluid in Figure 29.2. Although these fluids have different compositions, their **osmolarities** are the same; that is, they have the same number of moles of dissolved solute particles (ions or molecules) per liter. The osmolarity is kept in balance by the passage of water across cell membranes by osmosis, which occurs in response to osmolarity differences.

Inorganic ions, known collectively as *electrolytes* (Section 9.9), are major contributors to the osmolarity of body fluids and they move about as necessary to maintain charge balance. Water-soluble proteins make up a large proportion of the solutes in blood plasma and intracellular fluid; 100 mL of blood contains about 7 g of protein.

Intracellular fluid Fluid inside cells.

Extracellular fluid Fluid outside cells.

Blood plasma Liquid portion of the blood: an extracellular fluid.

Interstitial fluid Fluid surrounding cells: an extracellular fluid.

Osmolarity Amount of dissolved solute per volume of solution.

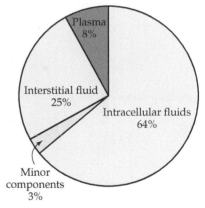

▲ **Figure 29.1**
Distribution of body water.
About two-thirds of body water is intracellular—within cells. The extracellular fluids include blood plasma, fluids surrounding cells (interstitial), and such minor components as lymph, cerebrospinal fluid, and the fluid that lubricates joints (synovial fluid).

▶▶▶ In osmosis, water moves across a semipermeable membrane from the more dilute solution to the more concentrated solution (see Section 9.12).

871

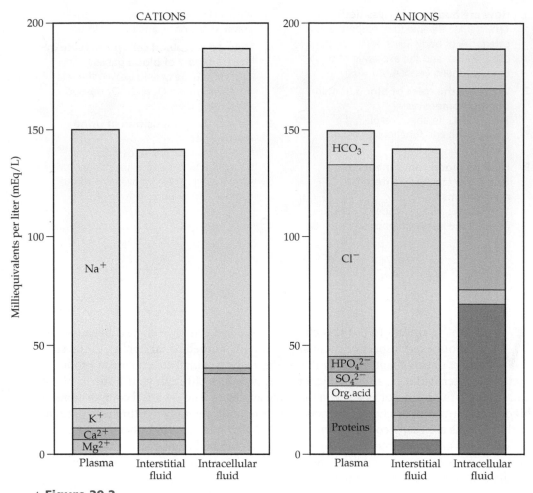

▲ **Figure 29.2**

The distribution of cations and anions in body fluids.
Outside cells, Na^+ is the major cation and Cl^- is the major anion. Inside cells, K^+ is the major cation and HPO_4^{2-} is the major anion. Note that at physiological pH, proteins are negatively charged.

Blood proteins are used to transport lipids and other molecules, and they play essential roles in blood clotting (Section 29.5) and the immune response (Section 29.4). The blood gases (oxygen and carbon dioxide), along with glucose, amino acids, and the nitrogen-containing by-products of protein catabolism, are the major small molecules in body fluids.

Blood travels through peripheral tissue in a network of tiny, hair-like capillaries that connect the arterial and venous parts of the circulatory system (Figure 29.3). Capillaries are where nutrients and end products of metabolism are exchanged between blood and interstitial fluid. Capillary walls consist of a single layer of loosely spaced cells. Water and many small solutes move freely across the capillary walls in response to differences in fluid pressure and concentration (see Figure 29.3).

Solutes that can cross membranes freely (passive diffusion) move from regions of high solute concentration to regions of low solute concentration. On the arterial ends of capillaries, blood pressure is higher than interstitial fluid pressure and solutes and water are pushed into interstitial fluid. On the venous ends of the capillaries, blood pressure is lower, and water and solutes from the surrounding tissues are able to reenter the blood plasma. The combined result of water and solute exchange at capillaries is that blood plasma and interstitial fluid are similar in composition (except for protein content; see Figure 29.2).

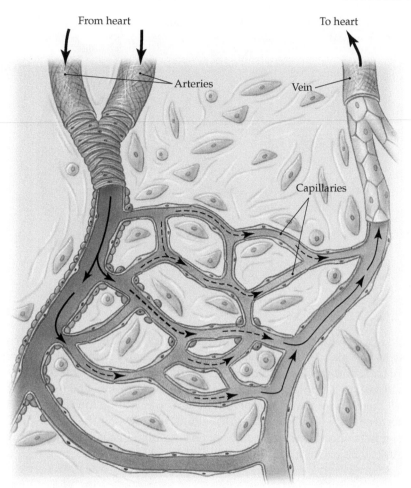

From heart

To heart

Arteries

Vein

Capillaries

◄ Figure 29.3
The capillary network.
Solute exchange between blood and interstitial fluid occurs across capillary walls.

In addition to blood capillaries, peripheral tissue is networked with lymph capillaries (Figure 29.4). The lymphatic system collects excess interstitial fluid, debris from cellular breakdown, and proteins and lipid droplets too large to pass through capillary walls. Interstitial fluid and the substances that accompany it into the lymphatic system are referred to as *lymph*, and the walls of lymph capillaries are constructed so that lymph cannot return to the surrounding tissue. Ultimately, lymph enters the bloodstream at the thoracic duct.

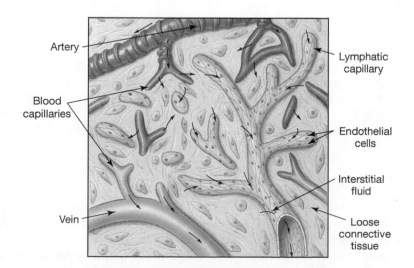

Artery

Blood capillaries

Vein

Lymphatic capillary

Endothelial cells

Interstitial fluid

Loose connective tissue

◄ Figure 29.4
Blood and lymph capillaries.
The arrows show the flow of fluids in and out of the various components of peripheral tissue.

▶ **Figure 29.5**

Exchange among body fluids.
Water exchanges freely in most tissues, with the result that the osmolarities of blood plasma, interstitial fluid, and intracellular fluid are the same. Large proteins cross neither capillary walls nor cell membranes, leaving the interstitial fluid protein concentration low. Concentration differences between interstitial fluid and intracellular fluid are maintained by active transport of Na^+ and K^+.

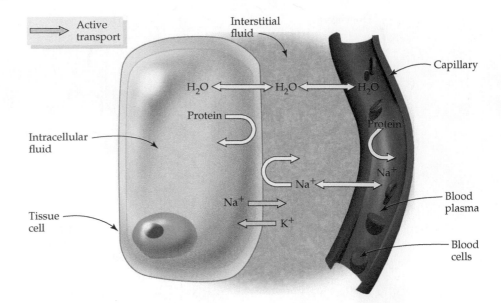

Exchange of solutes between the interstitial fluid and the intracellular fluid occurs by crossing cell membranes. Here, major differences in concentration are maintained by active transport (transport requiring energy) *against* concentration gradients (from regions of *low* concentration to regions of *high* concentration) and by the impermeability of cell membranes to certain solutes, notably the sodium ion (Figure 29.5). Sodium ion concentration is high in extracellular fluids and low in intracellular fluids, whereas potassium ion concentrations are just the reverse: high inside cells and low outside cells (see Figure 29.2).

🔑 KEY CONCEPT PROBLEM 29.1

The drug cisplatin is used to treat various forms of cancer in humans. As with many other drugs, the difficult part in designing the cisplatin molecule was to have a structure that ensures transport into the cell. The equilibrium reaction that takes place in the body when cisplatin is administered is

$$\begin{bmatrix} Cl & NH_3 \\ & Pt \\ Cl & NH_3 \end{bmatrix}(aq) + H_2O(l) \rightleftharpoons \begin{bmatrix} Cl & NH_3 \\ & Pt \\ H_2O & NH_3 \end{bmatrix}^{+}(aq) + Cl^-(aq)$$

Cisplatin   Monoaquacisplatin

(This is an example of *ligand exchange*.) Which form of cisplatin would you expect to exist inside the cell (where chloride concentrations are small)? Which form of cisplatin would you expect to exist outside the cell (where chloride concentrations are high)? Which form—cisplatin or monoaquacisplatin—enters the cell most readily? Why?

29.2 Fluid Balance

As you might imagine, preserving fluid balance—a constant amount of fluid in the body—is crucial in maintaining physiological homeostasis. One way we accomplish this is by ensuring that our daily intake of water is roughly enough to equal our daily output of water. Consider the following average intake/output water data for an adult human under normal environmental conditions, shown in Table 29.1.

Table 29.1 Adult Human Daily Average Water Intake/Output

Water Intake	(mL/day)	Water Output (mL/day)	
Drinking water	1200	Urine	1400
Water from food	1000	Skin	400
Water from metabolic oxidation of food	300	Lungs	400
		Sweat	100
		Feces	200
Total	2500		2500

What are the physiological effects if this delicate balance is not maintained? This question is especially important to endurance athletes such as marathon runners and cyclists. During the course of a typical endurance event, especially when performed in the heat, much fluid loss occurs with minimal fluid intake to counter it. This typically results in a loss of body mass during the event and makes it easy to monitor performance versus fluid loss. This has been studied and the results can be summarized as shown in Table 29.2.

Table 29.2 Effects of Body Mass Loss During Athletic Endurance Events

% Loss of Body Mass	Symptoms and Performance
0%	Normal heat regulation and performance
1%	Thirst is stimulated, heat regulation during exercise is altered, performance begins to decline
2–3%	Further decrease in heat regulation, increased thirst, worsening performance
4%	Exercise performance cut by 20–30%
5%	Headache, irritability, "spaced-out" feeling, fatigue
6%	Weakness, severe loss of thermoregulation
7%	Collapse is likely unless exercise is stopped

Exercise physiologists consider 4% body mass loss and above to be the "danger zone." In fact, the sports drink Gatorade® was developed in 1965 for just this reason. Doctors at the University of Florida developed the original formula to solve a serious problem for the school's football team: dehydration. This formula was so successful that by 1868 Gatorade® had become the official sports drink of the National Football League and today commands a major share of the sports-drink market, with gross sales of over 800 million dollars per year. One can see why research into hydration strategies has led to the plethora of "sports drinks" that are now available in your local supermarket. (See Chemistry in Action: Electrolytes, Fluid Replacement, and Sports Drinks, on p. 276.)

Physiologically, the intake of water and electrolytes is regulated, but not closely. However, the output of these substances is *very* closely controlled. Both the intake and output of water are controlled by hormones. Receptors in the hypothalamus monitor the concentration of solutes in blood plasma, and as little as a 2% change in osmolarity can cause an adjustment in hormone secretion. For example, when a rise in blood osmolarity indicates an increased concentration of solutes and therefore a shortage of water, secretion of *antidiuretic hormone* (ADH; also known as *vasopressin*) increases. One key role of the kidneys is to keep water and electrolytes in balance by increasing or decreasing the amounts eliminated. In the kidney, antidiuretic hormone causes a decrease in the water content of the urine. At the same time, osmoreceptors in the hypothalamus and baroreceptors in the heart and blood vessels activate the thirst mechanism, triggering increased water intake.

Antidiuretic hormone (ADH) is so tightly regulated that both oversecretion and undersecretion of this hormone can lead to serious disease states. Excess secretion can lead to what physicians refer to as the *syndrome of inappropriate antidiuretic hormone secretion (SIADH)*. Two of the many causes of SIADH are regional low blood volume arising from decreased blood return to the heart (caused by, for example, asthma, pneumonia, pulmonary obstruction, or heart failure) and misinterpretation by the hypothalamus of osmolarity (due, for example, to central-nervous-system disorders, barbiturates, or morphine). When ADH secretion is too high, the kidney excretes too little water, the water content of body compartments increases, and serum concentrations of electrolytes drop to dangerously low levels.

The reverse problem, inadequate secretion of antidiuretic hormone, is often a result of injury to the hypothalamus, and causes *diabetes insipidus*. In this condition (unrelated to diabetes mellitus), up to 15 L of dilute urine is excreted each day. Administration of synthetic hormone can control the problem.

29.3 Blood

Blood flows through the body in the circulatory system, which in the absence of trauma or disease, is essentially a closed system. About 55% of blood is plasma, which contains the proteins and other solutes shown in Figure 29.6; the remaining 45% is a mixture of red blood cells (**erythrocytes**), platelets, and white blood cells (**leukocytes**).

The plasma and cells together make up **whole blood**, which is what is usually collected for clinical laboratory analysis. The whole blood sample is collected directly into evacuated tubes that contain an anticoagulant to prevent clotting (which would normally occur within 20-26 minutes at room temperature). Typical anticoagulants include heparin (which interferes with the action of enzymes needed for clotting) and citrate or oxalate ion (either of which form precipitates with calcium ion, which is also needed for blood clotting, thereby removing it from solution). Plasma is separated from blood cells by spinning the sample in a centrifuge, which causes the blood cells to clump together at the bottom of the tube, leaving the plasma at the top.

Many laboratory analyses are performed on **blood serum**, the fluid remaining after blood has completely clotted. Blood serum composition is not the same as that of blood plasma—as we'll see in Section 29.5, blood clots are not simply clumps of cells, but also include networks of protein that originated from the plasma. When a serum sample is desired, whole blood is collected in the presence of an agent that hastens clotting. Thrombin, a natural component of the clotting system, is often used for this purpose. Centrifugation separates the clot and cells to leave behind the serum.

Major Components of Blood:

- **Whole blood**

    Blood plasma—fluid part of blood containing water-soluble solutes
    Blood cells—red blood cells (carry gases)
        —white blood cells (part of immune system)
        —platelets (help to initiate blood clotting)
- **Blood serum**—fluid portion of plasma left after blood has clotted

The functions of the major protein and cellular components of blood are summarized in Table 29.3. These functions fall into three categories.

Major Functions of Blood:

- **Transport** The circulatory system is the body's equivalent of an interstate highway network, transporting materials from where they enter the system to where they are used or disposed of. Oxygen and carbon dioxide are carried to and from by red blood cells. Nutrients are carried from the intestine to the sites of their catabolism. Waste products of metabolism are carried to the kidneys. Hormones from endocrine glands are delivered to their target tissues.
- **Regulation** Blood redistributes body heat as it flows along, thereby participating in the regulation of body temperature. It also picks up or delivers water and

Erythrocytes Red blood cells; transporters of blood gases.

Leukocytes White blood cells.

Whole blood Blood plasma plus blood cells.

Blood serum Fluid portion of blood remaining after clotting has occurred.

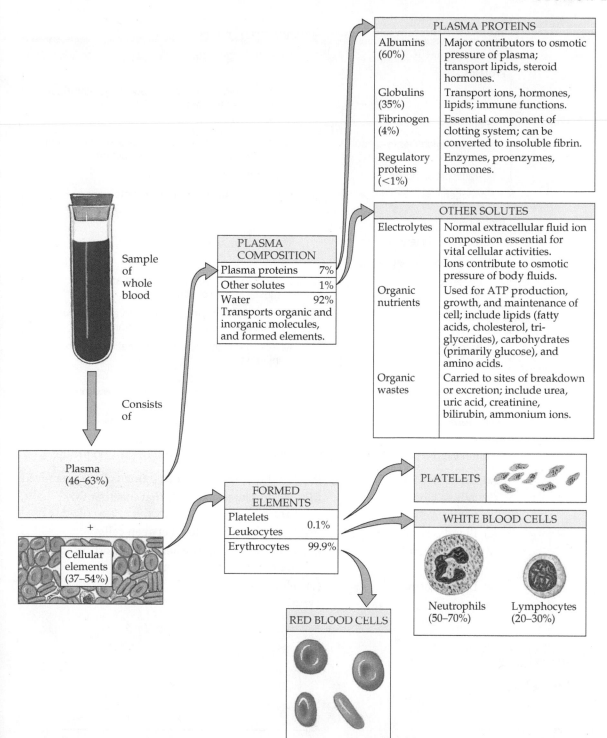

PLASMA PROTEINS	
Albumins (60%)	Major contributors to osmotic pressure of plasma; transport lipids, steroid hormones.
Globulins (35%)	Transport ions, hormones, lipids; immune functions.
Fibrinogen (4%)	Essential component of clotting system; can be converted to insoluble fibrin.
Regulatory proteins (<1%)	Enzymes, proenzymes, hormones.

OTHER SOLUTES	
Electrolytes	Normal extracellular fluid ion composition essential for vital cellular activities. Ions contribute to osmotic pressure of body fluids.
Organic nutrients	Used for ATP production, growth, and maintenance of cell; include lipids (fatty acids, cholesterol, tri-glycerides), carbohydrates (primarily glucose), and amino acids.
Organic wastes	Carried to sites of breakdown or excretion; include urea, uric acid, creatinine, bilirubin, ammonium ions.

Sample of whole blood

PLASMA COMPOSITION	
Plasma proteins	7%
Other solutes	1%
Water	92%

Transports organic and inorganic molecules, and formed elements.

Consists of

Plasma (46–63%)

+

Cellular elements (37–54%)

FORMED ELEMENTS	
Platelets Leukocytes	0.1%
Erythrocytes	99.9%

PLATELETS

WHITE BLOOD CELLS

Neutrophils (50–70%)   Lymphocytes (20–30%)

RED BLOOD CELLS

▲ **Figure 29.6**
The composition of whole blood.

electrolytes as they are needed. In addition, blood buffers are essential to the maintenance of acid–base balance.

- **Defense** Blood carries the molecules and cells needed for two major defense mechanisms: (1) the immune response, which destroys foreign invaders; and (2) blood clotting, which prevents loss of blood and begins the healing of wounds.

We will take a closer look at the defense functions of blood—the immune response and blood clotting and then finish our discussion by examining the transport of blood gases (Section 29.6). (Lipid transport was discussed in Chapter 24.)

Table 29.3 Protein and Cellular Components of Blood

Blood Component	Function
Proteins	
Albumins	Transport lipids, hormones, drugs; major contributor to plasma osmolarity
Globulins	
Immunoglobulins (γ-globulins, antibodies)	Identify antigens (microorganisms and other foreign invaders) and initiate their destruction
Transport globulins	Transport lipids and metal ions
Fibrinogen	Forms fibrin, the basis of blood clots
Blood cells	
Red blood cells (erythrocytes)	Transport O_2, CO_2, H^+
White blood cells (leukocytes)	
Lymphocytes	Defend against specific pathogens and foreign substances (T cells and B cells)
Phagocytes	Carry out phagocytosis—engulf foreign invaders (neutrophils, eosinophils, and monocytes)
Basophils	Release histamine during inflammatory response of injured tissue
Platelets	Help to initiate blood clotting

PROBLEM 29.2

Match each term in the **(a)–(e)** group with its definition from the **(i)–(v)** group:

(a) Interstitial fluid   (i) Fluid that remains when blood cells are removed

(b) Whole blood   (ii) Fluid, solutes, and cells that together flow through veins and arteries

(c) Blood serum   (iii) Fluid that fills spaces between cells

(d) Intracellular fluid   (iv) Fluid that remains when blood clotting agents are removed from plasma

(e) Blood plasma   (v) Fluid within cells

CHEMISTRY IN ACTION

The Blood–Brain Barrier

Nowhere in human beings is the maintenance of a constant internal environment more important than in the brain. If the brain were exposed to the fluctuations in concentrations of hormones, amino acids, neurotransmitters, and potassium that occur elsewhere in the body, inappropriate nervous activity would result. Therefore, the brain must be rigorously isolated from variations in blood composition.

How can the brain receive nutrients from the blood in capillaries and yet be protected? The answer lies in the unique structure of the *endothelial cells* that form the walls of brain capillaries. Unlike the cells in most other capillaries, those in

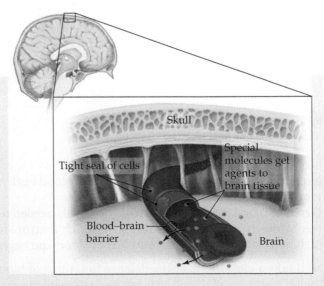

▲ The blood–brain barrier.

brain capillaries form a series of continuous tight junctions so that nothing can pass between them. To reach the brain, therefore, a substance must cross this blood–brain barrier (BBB) by crossing the endothelial cell membranes. The BBB serves as internal protection for the brain just as the skull serves as the brain's external protection.

The brain, of course, cannot be completely isolated or it will die from lack of nourishment. Glucose, the main source of energy for brain cells, and certain amino acids the brain cannot manufacture are recognized and brought across the cell membranes by transport mechanisms specific to each nutrient. Similar specific transporters move surplus substances out of the brain.

An asymmetric (one-way) transport system exists for glycine, a small amino acid that is a potent neurotransmitter. Glycine inhibits rather than activates transmission of nerve signals, and its concentration must be held at a lower level in the brain than in the blood. To accomplish this, there is a glycine transport system in the cell membrane closest to the brain, but no matching transport system on the other side. Thus, glycine can be transported out of the brain but not into it.

The brain is also protected by the "metabolic" blood–brain barrier. In this case, a compound that gets into an endothelial cell is converted within the cell to a metabolite that is unable to enter the brain. A striking demonstration of the metabolic brain barrier is provided by *dopamine*, a neurotransmitter, and L-*dopa*, a metabolic precursor of dopamine.

L-Dopa can both enter and leave the brain because it is recognized by an amino acid transporter. However, the brain is protected from an entering excess of L-dopa by its conversion to dopamine within the endothelial cells. Like glycine, dopamine, which is also produced from L-dopa within the brain, can leave the brain but cannot enter it. The dopamine deficiency that occurs in Parkinson's disease is therefore treated by administration of L-dopa.

Since crossing the endothelial cell membrane is the route into the brain, substances soluble in the membrane lipids readily breach the blood–brain barrier. Among such substances are nicotine, caffeine, codeine, diazepam (Valium®, an antidepressant), and heroin. Heroin differs from morphine in having two nonpolar acetyl groups where the morphine has polar hydroxyl groups (Section 15.6). The resulting difference in lipid solubil-

ity allows heroin to enter the brain much more efficiently than morphine. Once heroin is inside the brain, enzymes remove the acetyl groups to give morphine, in essence trapping it in the brain, a general strategy many medicinal chemists try to capitalize upon. Finding ways to breach the blood–brain barrier is of major concern to medicinal chemists. For example, brain tumors are currently treated with either radiation or surgery, as the chemical agents used to typically treat cancer cannot cross the BBB. Researchers at the St. Louis University School of Medicine have been studying compounds that can sneak past the barrier, a discovery that could help doctors better treat a range of invasive brain malignancies. "The bottom line is, if you can get drugs into the brain, you can cure brain cancer," states Dr. William Banks, a member of the St. Louis research team. The St. Louis team has also been examining compounds that can be used to treat Alzheimer's disease; the key here also being how to get them to cross the BBB. Researchers at UCLA have begun to examine *chimeric therapeutics*, materials that are half drug (which do not cross the BBB) and half "molecular Trojan horse" (genetically engineered proteins that do cross the BBB). As our understanding of this crucial barrier unfolds, we can expect many advances in the treatment of diseases of the brain that thus far have been treatable by only the most invasive of techniques.

See Chemistry in Action Problems 29.63 through 29.66 at the end of the chapter.

29.4 Plasma Proteins, White Blood Cells, and Immunity

An **antigen** is any molecule or portion of a molecule recognized by the body as a foreign invader. An antigen might be a molecule never seen before by the body or a molecular segment recognized as an invader (for example, a protein on the surface of a bacterium or virus). Antigens can also be small molecules, known as *haptens*, that are only recognized as antigens after they have bonded to carrier proteins. Haptens include some antibiotics, environmental pollutants, and allergens from plants and animals.

The recognition of an antigen can initiate three different responses. The first, the **inflammatory response**, is a non-specific, localized response to a given antigen.

Antigen A substance foreign to the body that triggers the immune response.

Inflammatory response A nonspecific defense mechanism triggered by antigens or tissue damage.

▶ **Figure 29.7**
The immune response.
The attack on antigens
occurs by cell-mediated
and antibody-mediated
immune responses.

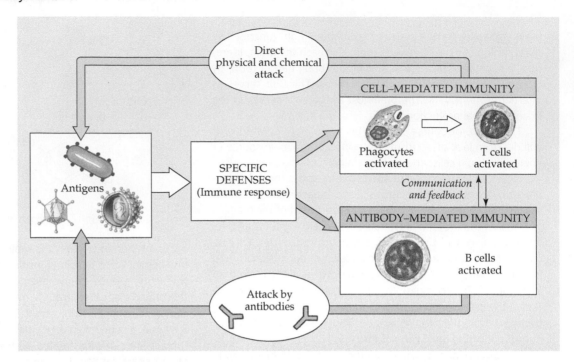

▶ **Figure 29.7**
The immune response.
The attack on antigens occurs by cell-mediated and antibody-mediated immune responses.

Immune response Defense mechanism of the immune system dependent on the recognition of specific antigens, including viruses, bacteria, toxic substances, and infected cells; either cell-mediated or antibody-mediated.

Antibody (immunoglobulin) Glycoprotein molecule that identifies antigens.

The two remaining types of **immune response** (cell-mediated response and antibody-mediated response) do depend on recognition of *specific* invaders (such as viruses, bacteria, toxic substances, or infected cells; Figure 29.7). At the molecular level, the invading antigen is detected by an interaction very much like that between an enzyme and its substrate. Noncovalent attraction allows a spatial fit between the antigen and a defender that is specific to that antigen. The *cell-mediated immune response* depends on white blood cells known as *T cells*. The *antibody-mediated immune response* depends on **antibodies** (or **immunoglobulins**) produced by the white blood cells known as *B cells*.

Both inflammation and the immune responses require normal numbers of white blood cells to be effective (5 to 10 million white blood cells per milliliter). If the white blood cell count falls below 1000 per milliliter of blood, any infection can be life-threatening. The devastating results of white blood cell destruction in AIDS is an example of this condition (see Chemistry in Action: Viruses and AIDS on p. 794).

Inflammatory Response

Inflammation Result of the inflammatory response; includes swelling, redness, warmth, and pain.

Cell damage due to infection or injury initiates **inflammation**, a nonspecific defense mechanism that produces swelling, redness, warmth, and pain. For example, the swollen, painful, red bump that develops around a splinter in your finger is an inflammation (generally known as a *wheal-and-flare reaction*). Chemical messengers released at the injured site direct the inflammatory response. One such messenger is histamine, which is synthesized from the amino acid histidine and is stored in cells throughout the body. Histamine release is also triggered by an allergic response.

$$\text{Histidine} \xrightarrow[\text{decarboxylase}]{\text{Histidine}} \text{Histamine} + CO_2$$

Histidine

Histamine

Histamine sets off dilation of capillaries and increases the permeability of capillary walls. The resulting increased blood flow into the damaged area reddens and warms the skin, and swelling occurs as plasma carrying blood-clotting factors and defensive proteins enters the intercellular space. At the same time, white blood cells cross capillary walls to attack invaders.

Bacteria or other antigens at the inflammation site are destroyed by white blood cells known as *phagocytes*, which engulf invading cells and destroy them by enzyme-catalyzed hydrolysis reactions. Phagocytes also emit chemical messengers that help to direct the inflammatory response. An inflammation caused by a wound will heal completely only after all infectious agents have been removed, with dead cells and other debris absorbed into the lymph system.

Cell-Mediated Immune Response

The cell-mediated immune response is under the control of several kinds of *T lymphocytes*, or *T cells*. The cell-mediated immune response principally guards against abnormal cells and bacteria or viruses entering the normal cells; it also guards against the invasion of some cancer cells and causes the rejection of transplanted organs.

A complex series of events begins when a T cell recognizes an antigenic cell. The result of these events is production of *cytotoxic*, or *killer*, T cells that can destroy the invader (for example, by releasing a toxic protein that kills the antigenic invaded perforating cell membranes) and *helper* T cells, which enhance the body's defenses against the invader. Thousands of *memory* T cells are also produced; they remain on guard and will immediately generate the appropriate killer T cells if the same pathogen reappears.

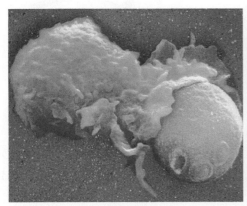 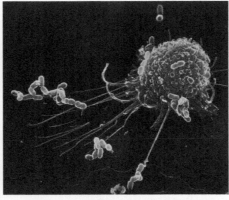

◀ White blood cells. (left) A lymphocyte phagocytizing a yeast cell. (right) A lymphocyte reaches out to snare several *E. coli* bacteria.

Antibody-Mediated Immune Response

The white blood cells known as *B lymphocytes* or *B cells*, with the assistance of T cells, are responsible for the antibody-mediated immune response. Unlike T cells, which identify only antigenic cells, B cells identify antigens adrift in body fluids. A B cell is activated when it first binds to an antigen and then encounters a helper T cell that recognizes the same antigen. This activation can take place anywhere in the body, but it often occurs in lymph nodes, tonsils, or the spleen, which have large concentrations of lymphocytes.

Once activated, B cells divide to form plasma cells that secrete antibodies specific to the antigen. The antibodies are *immunoglobulins*. The body contains up to 10,000 different immunoglobulins at any given time, and we have the capacity to make more than 100 million others. The immunoglobulins are glycoproteins composed of two "heavy" polypeptide chains and two "light" polypeptide chains joined by disulfide bonds, as shown in Figure 29.8. The variable regions are sequences of amino acids that will bind a specific antigen. Once synthesized, antibodies spread out to find their antigens.

▸ **Figure 29.8**
Structure of an immunoglobulin, which is an antibody.
(a) The regions of an immunoglobulin. The disulfide bridges that hold the chains together are shown in orange.
(b) Molecular model of an immunoglobulin; the heavy chains are gray and blue and both light chains are red.

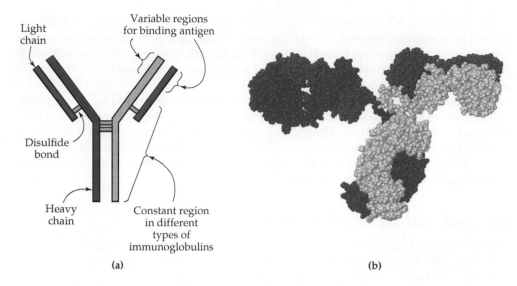

(a)   (b)

Formation of an antigen–antibody complex (Figure 29.9) inactivates the antigen by one of several methods. The complex may, for example, attract phagocytes, or it may block the mechanism by which the invader connects with a target cell.

▸ **Figure 29.9**
Antigen–antibody complexes.
(a) Antigens bind to antigenic-determinant sites on the surface of, for example, a bacterium. (b) Because each antibody has two binding sites, the interaction of many antigens and antibodies creates a large immune complex.

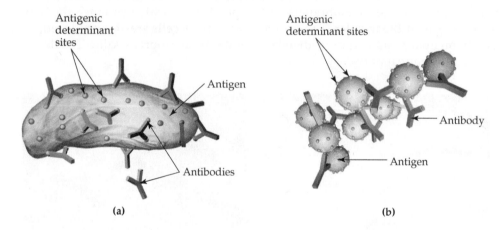

(a)   (b)

Activated B-cell division also yields memory cells that remain on guard and quickly produce more plasma cells if the same antigen reappears. The long-lived B and T memory cells are responsible for long-term immunity to diseases after the first illness or after a vaccination.

Several classes of immunoglobulins have been identified. *Immunoglobulin G antibodies* (known as *gamma globulins*), for example, protect against viruses and bacteria. Allergies and asthma are caused by an oversupply of *immunoglobulin E*. Numerous disorders result from the mistaken identification of normal body constituents as foreign and the overproduction of antibodies to combat them. These **autoimmune diseases** include attack on connective tissue at joints in rheumatoid arthritis, attack on pancreatic islet cells in some forms of diabetes mellitus, and a generalized attack on nucleic acids and blood components in systemic lupus erythematosus.

Autoimmune disease Disorder in which the immune system identifies normal body components as antigens and produces antibodies to them.

Fibrin Insoluble protein that forms the fiber framework of a blood clot.

Vitamin K
(Phylloquinone)

29.5 Blood Clotting

A blood clot consists of blood cells trapped in a mesh of the insoluble fibrous protein known as **fibrin**. Clot formation is a multiple-step process requiring participation of 12 clotting factors; calcium ion is one of the clotting factors. Others, most of which are glycoproteins, are synthesized in the liver by pathways that require vitamin K as a coenzyme. Therefore, a deficiency of vitamin K, the presence of a competitive inhibitor of vitamin K, or a deficiency of a clotting factor can cause excessive bleeding, sometimes from even minor tissue damage. Hemophilia is a disorder caused by an inherited genetic defect that results in the absence of one or more of the clotting factors. Hemophilia occurs in 1 in 10,000 individuals, with 80–90% of people with hemophilia being male.

The body's mechanism for halting blood loss from even the tiniest capillary is referred to as **hemostasis**. The first events in hemostasis are (1) constriction of surrounding blood vessels and (2) formation of a plug composed of the blood cells known as *platelets* at the site of tissue damage.

Hemostasis The stopping of bleeding.

Next, a **blood clot** is formed in a process that is triggered by two pathways: (1) The *intrinsic pathway* begins when blood makes contact with the negatively charged surface of the fibrous protein collagen, which is exposed at the site of tissue damage. Clotting is activated in exactly the same manner when blood is placed in a glass tube, because glass is also negatively charged. (2) The *extrinsic pathway* begins when damaged tissue releases an integral membrane glycoprotein known as *tissue factor*.

Blood clot A network of fibrin fibers and trapped blood cells that forms at the site of blood loss.

The result of either pathway is a cascade of reactions that is initiated when an inactive clotting factor (a zymogen, Section 19.9) is converted to its active form by cleavage of specific polypeptide sequences on its surface. Commonly, the newly activated enzyme then catalyzes the activation of the next factor in the cascade. The two pathways merge and, in the final step of the common pathway, the enzyme *thrombin* catalyzes cleavage of small polypeptides from the soluble plasma protein fibrinogen. Negatively charged groups in these polypeptides make fibrinogen soluble and keep the molecules apart. Once these polypeptides are removed, the resulting insoluble fibrin molecules immediately associate with each other by noncovalent interactions. Then they are bound into fibers by formation of amide cross-links between lysine and glutamine side chains in a reaction catalyzed by another of the clotting factors:

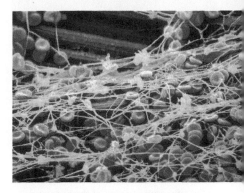

▲ Colorized electron micrograph of a blood clot. Red blood cells can be seen enmeshed in the network of fibrin threads.

$$Gln-CH_2CH_2-\overset{\overset{\displaystyle O}{\|}}{C}-NH_2 \ + \ H_3\overset{+}{N}CH_2CH_2CH_2CH_2-Lys \ \longrightarrow$$

Protein chain

$$Gln-CH_2CH_2-\overset{\overset{\displaystyle O}{\|}}{C}-NHCH_2CH_2CH_2CH_2-Lys \ + \ NH_4^+$$

Cross-link between protein chains

Once the clot has done its job of preventing blood loss and binding together damaged surfaces as they heal, the clot is broken down by hydrolysis of its peptide bonds.

29.6 Red Blood Cells and Blood Gases

Red blood cells, or erythrocytes, have one major purpose: to transport blood gases. Erythrocytes in mammals have no nuclei or ribosomes and cannot replicate themselves. In addition, they have no mitochondria or glycogen and must obtain glucose from the surrounding plasma. Their enormous number—about 250 million in a single drop of blood—and their large surface area provide for rapid exchange of gases throughout the body. Because they are small and flexible, erythrocytes can squeeze through the tiniest capillaries one at a time.

Of the protein in an erythrocyte, 95% is hemoglobin, the transporter of oxygen and carbon dioxide. Hemoglobin (Hb) is composed of four polypeptide chains with the quaternary structure shown earlier in Figure 18.8. Each protein chain has a central heme molecule in a crevice in its nonpolar interior, and each of the four hemes can combine with one O_2 molecule.

Oxygen Transport

The iron(II) ion, Fe^{2+}, sits in the center of each heme molecule and is the site to which O_2 binds through one of oxygen's unshared electron pairs. In contrast to the

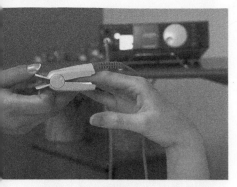

▲ **Figure 29.10**

A pulse oximetry sensor for continuous monitoring of blood oxygen. One side of the sensor contains two light-emitting diodes (LEDs), one that emits in the visible red range (better absorbed by dark-red deoxygenated blood) and one that emits in the infrared range (better absorbed by oxygenated blood, which is bright red). On the opposite side of the sensor, a photodetector measures the light that passes through and sends the signal to an instrument that computes the percent oxygen saturation of the blood and also records the pulse. Normal oxygen saturation is 95–100%. Below 85%, tissues are at risk, and below 70% is typically life-threatening.

cytochromes of the respiratory chain, where iron cycles between Fe^{2+} and Fe^{3+}, heme iron must remain in the reduced Fe^{2+} state to maintain its oxygen-carrying ability. Hemoglobin (Hb) carrying four oxygens (oxyhemoglobin) is bright red. Hemoglobin that has lost one or more oxygens (deoxyhemoglobin) is dark red-purple, which accounts for the darker color of venous blood. Dried blood is brown, because exposure to atmospheric oxygen has oxidized the iron (think of rust). The color of arterial blood carrying oxygen is used in a clinically valuable method for monitoring oxygenation (known as *pulse oximetry*, Figure 29.10).

At normal physiological conditions, the percentage of heme molecules that carry oxygen, known as the *percent saturation*, is dependent on the partial pressure of oxygen in surrounding tissues (Figure 29.11). The shape of the curve indicates that binding of oxygen to heme is allosteric in nature (see Section 19.7). Each O_2 that binds causes changes in the hemoglobin quaternary structure that enhance binding of the next O_2, and releasing each oxygen enhances release of the next. As a result, oxygen is more readily released to tissue where the partial pressure of oxygen is low. The average oxygen partial pressure in peripheral tissue is 40 mmHg, a pressure at which Hb remains 75% saturated by oxygen, leaving a large amount of O_2 in reserve for emergencies. Note, however, the rapid drop in the curve between 40 mmHg and 20 mmHg, which is the oxygen pressure in tissue where metabolism is occurring rapidly.

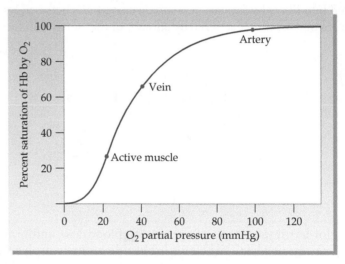

▲ **Figure 29.11**

Oxygen saturation of hemoglobin at normal physiological conditions. Oxygen pressure is about 100 mmHg in arteries and 20 mmHg in active muscles. Note the large release of oxygen as the partial pressure drops from 40 mmHg to 20 mmHg.

Carbon Dioxide Transport, Acidosis, and Alkalosis

Oxygen and carbon dioxide are the "blood gases" transported by erythrocytes. By way of the bicarbonate ion/carbon dioxide buffer, the intimate relationships among H^+ and HCO_3^- concentrations and O_2 and CO_2 partial pressures are essential to maintaining electrolyte and acid–base balance:

$$\underbrace{CO_2(aq) + H_2O(l)}_{\text{Controlled by the lungs}} \rightleftharpoons H_2CO_3(aq) \rightleftharpoons \underbrace{HCO_3^-(aq) + H^{+(aq)}}_{\text{Controlled by the kidneys}}$$

In a clinical setting, "monitoring blood gases" usually refers to measuring the pH of blood as well as the gas concentrations. Carbon dioxide from metabolism in peripheral cells diffuses into interstitial fluid and then into capillaries, where it is transported in the blood three ways: (1) as dissolved $CO_2(aq)$, (2) bonded to Hb, or (3) as HCO_3^- in solution. About 7% of the CO_2 produced dissolves in blood plasma. The rest enters erythrocytes, where some of it binds to the protein portion of hemoglobin by reaction with the nonionized amino acid $-NH_2$ groups present:

$$Hb-NH_2 + CO_2 \rightleftharpoons Hb-NHCOO^- + H^+$$

Most of the CO_2 is rapidly converted to bicarbonate ion within erythrocytes, which contain a large concentration of carbonic anhydrase. The resulting water-soluble HCO_3^- ion can leave the erythrocyte and travel in the blood to the lungs, where it will be converted back to CO_2 for exhalation. To maintain electrolyte balance, a Cl^- ion enters the erythrocyte for every HCO_3^- ion that leaves, and the process is reversed when the blood reaches the lungs:

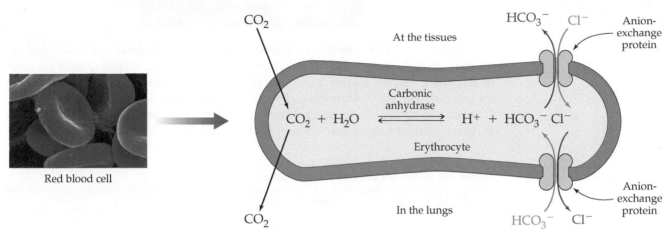

A cell-membrane protein controls this ion exchange, which is passive, as the ions move from higher to lower concentrations.

Without some compensating change, the result of hemoglobin reacting with CO_2 and the action of carbonic anhydrase would be an unacceptably large increase in acidity. To cope with this, hemoglobin responds by reversibly binding hydrogen ions:

$$Hb \cdot 4\,O_2 + 2\,H^+ \rightleftharpoons Hb \cdot 2\,H^+ + 4\,O_2$$

The release of oxygen is enhanced by allosteric effects when the hydrogen ion concentration increases, and oxygen is held more firmly when the hydrogen ion concentration decreases.

The changes in the oxygen saturation curve with CO_2 and H^+ concentrations and with temperature are shown in Figure 29.12. The curve shifts to the right, indicating

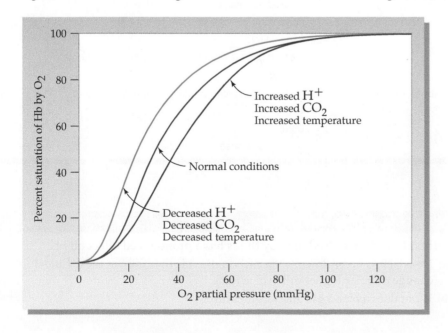

◄ **Figure 29.12**
Changes in oxygen affinity of hemoglobin with changing conditions.
The normal curve of Figure 29.11 is shown in red here.

decreased affinity of Hb for O_2, when the H^+ and CO_2 concentrations increase and when the temperature increases. These are exactly the conditions in muscles that are working hard and need more oxygen. The curve shifts to the left, indicating increased affinity of Hb for oxygen, under the opposite conditions of decreased H^+ and CO_2 concentrations and lower temperature.

Homeostasis requires a blood pH between 7.35 and 7.45. A pH outside this range results in either **acidosis** or **alkalosis**.

Acidosis The abnormal condition associated with a blood plasma pH below 7.35; may be respiratory or metabolic.

Alkalosis The abnormal condition associated with a blood plasma pH above 7.45; may be respiratory or metabolic.

Acidosis	Normal	Alkalosis
Blood pH Below 7.35	Blood pH 7.35–7.45	Blood pH Above 7.45

The wide variety of conditions that cause acidosis or alkalosis can be divided between respiratory malfunctions and metabolic malfunctions. Examples of each are given in Table 29.4. *Respiratory* disruption of acid–base balance can result when carbon dioxide generation by metabolism and carbon dioxide removal at the lungs are out of balance. *Metabolic* disruption of acid–base balance can result from abnormally high acid generation or failure of buffer systems and kidney function to regulate bicarbonate concentration.

Table 29.4 Causes of Acidosis and Alkalosis

Type of Imbalance	Causes
Respiratory acidosis	CO_2 buildup due to: Decreased respiratory activity (hypoventilation) Cardiac insufficiency (for example, congestive failure, cardiac arrest) Deterioration of pulmonary function (for example, asthma, emphysema, pulmonary obstruction, pneumonia)
Respiratory alkalosis	Loss of CO_2 due to: Excessive respiratory activity (hyperventilation, due, for example, to high fever, nervous condition)
Metabolic acidosis	Increased production of metabolic acids due to: Fasting or starvation Untreated diabetes Excessive exercise Decreased acid excretion in urine due to: Poisoning Renal failure Decreased plasma bicarbonate concentration due to: Diarrhea
Metabolic alkalosis	Elevated plasma bicarbonate concentration due to: Vomiting Diuretics Antacid overdose

KEY CONCEPT PROBLEM 29.3

Carbon dioxide dissolved in body fluids has a pronounced effect on pH.

(a) Does pH go up or down when carbon dioxide dissolves in these fluids? Does this change indicate higher or lower acidity?

(b) What does a blood gas analysis measure?

PROBLEM 29.4

Classify the following conditions as a cause of respiratory or metabolic acidosis or alkalosis (consult Table 29.4).

(a) Emphysema

(b) Kidney failure

(c) Overdose of an antacid

PROBLEM 29.5

Classify the following conditions as a cause of respiratory or metabolic acidosis or alkalosis (consult Table 29.4).

(a) Severe panic attack

(b) Congestive heart failure

(c) Running a marathon

PROBLEM 29.6

In Chemistry in Action: The Blood–Brain Barrier, the fact that heroin was better able to cross the blood–brain barrier than morphine was discussed. Looking at the structures of these two molecules (refer to Section 15.6), circle the areas where they differ and why this explains the difference between the potencies of heroin and morphine as analgesics.

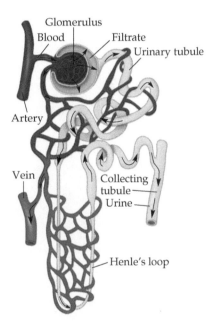

▲ **Figure 29.13**
Structure of a nephron.
Water moves out of the urinary tubule and the collecting tubule. The concentration of solutes in urine is established as they move both in and out along the tubules.

29.7 The Kidney and Urine Formation

The kidneys bear the major responsibility for maintaining a constant internal environment in the body. By managing the elimination of appropriate amounts of water, electrolytes, hydrogen ions, and nitrogen-containing wastes, the kidneys respond to changes in health, diet, and physical activity.

About 25% of the blood pumped from the heart goes directly to the kidneys, where the functional units are the *nephrons* (Figure 29.13). Each kidney contains over a million of them. Blood enters a nephron at a *glomerulus* (at the top in Figure 29.13), a tangle of capillaries surrounded by a fluid-filled space. **Filtration**, the first of three essential kidney functions, occurs here. The pressure of blood pumped into the glomerulus directly from the heart is high enough to push plasma and all its solutes except large proteins across the capillary membrane into the surrounding fluid, the **glomerular filtrate**. The filtrate flows from the capsule into the tubule that makes up the rest of the nephron, and the blood enters the network of capillaries intertwined with the tubule.

About 125 mL of filtrate per minute enters the kidneys, and they produce 180 L of filtrate per day. This filtrate contains not only waste products but also many solutes the body cannot afford to lose, such as glucose and electrolytes. Since we excrete only about 1.4 L of urine each day you can see that another important function of the kidneys is **reabsorption**—the recapture of water and essential solutes by moving them out of the tubule.

Reabsorption alone, however, is not sufficient to provide the kind of control over urine composition that is needed. More of certain solutes must be excreted than are present in the filtrate. This situation is dealt with by **secretion**—the transfer of solutes *into* the kidney tubule.

Reabsorption and secretion require the transfer of solutes and water among the filtrate, the interstitial fluid surrounding the tubule, and blood in the capillaries. Some of the substances reabsorbed or secreted are listed in Table 29.5. Solutes cross the tubule and capillary membranes by passive diffusion in response to concentration or ionic charge differences, or by active transport. Water moves in response to differences in the osmolarity of the fluids on the two sides of the membranes. Solute and water movement is also controlled by hormone-directed variations in the permeability of the tubule membrane.

Filtration (kidney) Filtration of blood plasma through a glomerulus and into a kidney nephron.

Glomerular filtrate Fluid that enters the nephron from the glomerulus; filtered blood plasma.

Reabsorption (kidney) Movement of solutes out of filtrate in a kidney tubule.

Secretion (kidney) Movement of solutes into filtrate in a kidney tubule.

Table 29.5 Reabsorption and Secretion in Kidney Tubules
Reabsorbed
Ions
Na^+, Cl^-, K^+, Ca^{2+}, Mg^{2+}, PO_4^{3-}, SO_4^{2-}, HCO_3^-
Metabolites
Glucose
Amino acids
Proteins
Vitamins
Secreted
Ions
K^+, H^+, Ca^{2+}
Wastes
Creatinine
Urea
Ammonia
Various organic acids and bases (including uric acid)
Miscellaneous
Neurotransmitters
Histamine
Drugs (penicillin, atropine, morphine, numerous others)

29.8 Urine Composition and Function

Urine contains the products of glomerular filtration, minus the substances reabsorbed in the tubules, plus the substances secreted in the tubules. The actual concentrations of these substances in urine at any time are determined by the amount of water being excreted, which can vary significantly with water intake, exercise, temperature, and state of health. (For identical quantities of solutes, concentration *decreases* when the quantity of solvent water *increases*, and concentration *increases* when the quantity of water *decreases*.)

About 50 g of solids in solution are excreted every day—about 20 g of electrolytes and 30 g of nitrogen-containing wastes (urea and ammonia from amino acid catabolism, creatinine from breakdown of creatine phosphate in muscles, and uric acid from purine catabolism). Normal urine composition is usually reported as the quantity of each solute excreted per day, and laboratory urinalysis often requires collection of all urine excreted during a 24-hour period.

The following paragraphs briefly describe a few of the mechanisms that control the composition of urine.

Acid–Base Balance

Respiration, buffers, and excretion of hydrogen ions in urine combine to maintain acid–base balance. Metabolism normally produces an excess of hydrogen ions; a portion of these must be excreted each day to prevent acidosis. Very little free hydrogen ion exists in blood plasma, and therefore very little enters the glomerular filtrate. Instead, the H^+ to be eliminated is produced by the reaction of CO_2 with water in the cells lining the tubules of the nephrons:

$$CO_2 + H_2O \xrightarrow{\text{Carbonic anhydrase}} H^+ + HCO_3^-$$

To bloodstream
To filtrate

CHEMISTRY IN ACTION

Automated Clinical Laboratory Analysis

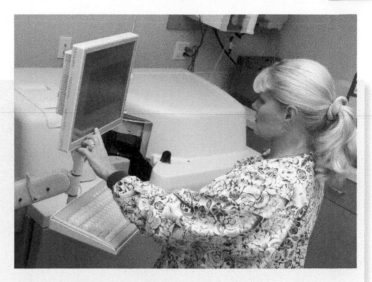

What happens when a physician orders chemical tests of blood, urine, or spinal fluid? The sample goes to a clinical chemistry laboratory, often in a hospital, where most tests are done by automated clinical chemistry analyzers. There are basically two types of chemical analysis, one for the quantity of a chemical (a natural biochemical, a drug, or a toxic substance) and the other for the quantity of an enzyme with a specific metabolic activity.

The quantity of a given chemical in the blood is determined either directly or indirectly. Many chemical components are measured directly by mixing a reagent with the sample—the *analyte*—and noting the quantity of a colored product formed by using a photometer, an instrument that measures the absorption of light of a wavelength specific to the product. For each test specified, a portion of the sample is mixed with the appropriate reagent and the photometer is adjusted to the exact wavelength necessary.

When it is not possible to utilize this direct technique, other indirect methods that produce a detectable product have been devised. Many analytes are substrates for enzyme catalyzed reactions, and analysis of the substrate concentration is therefore often made possible by treating the analyte with appropriate enzymes. Glucose is determined in this manner by utilizing a pair of enzyme-catalyzed reactions: the glucose is converted to glucose 6-phosphate using its hexokinase-catalyzed reaction with ATP; the glucose 6-phosphate is then oxidized by $NADP^+$; and the quantity of NADPH produced is measured photometrically.

The second type of analysis, determination of the quantity of a specific enzyme or the ratio of two or more enzymes, is invaluable in detecting organ damage that allows enzymes to leak into body fluids. For example, elevation of both ALT (alanine aminotransferase) and AST (aspartate aminotransferase) with an AST/ALT ratio greater than 1.0 is characteristic of liver disease. If, however, the AST is greatly elevated and the AST/ALT ratio is higher than 1.5, a myocardial infarction (heart attack) may likely have occurred. When the substance being analyzed is an enzyme, its presence is detected, monitored, and quantified with an assay that employs a substrate of the enzyme in question; levels of the enzyme are measured by monitoring the substrate's appearance or disappearance. ALT, for example, is determined by photometrically monitoring the disappearance

of NADH in the following pair of coupled reactions (where LD = lactate dehydrogenase):

$$\text{L-Alanine} + \alpha\text{-Ketoglutarate} \xrightarrow{\text{ALT}} \text{Pyruvate} + \text{L-Glutamate}$$

$$\text{Pyruvate} + \text{NADH/H}^+ \xrightarrow{\text{LD}} \text{Lactate} + \text{NAD}^+$$

As ALT causes pyruvate to form, LD causes the pyruvate to react with NADH to form lactate and NAD^+. By knowing how fast this reaction will occur with a given amount of LD, and by knowing how fast a given amount of ALT carries out the first reaction, the amount of ALT can be directly quantified in the sample being examined.

Automated analyzers rely on premixed reagents and automatic division of a fluid sample into small portions for each test. A low-volume analyzer that provides rapid results for a few tests accepts a bar-coded serum or plasma sample cartridge followed by bar-coded reagent cartridges. The instrument software reads the bar codes and directs an automatic pipette (which removes small samples of precisely measured volumes) to transfer the appropriate volume of sample to each test cartridge. The instrument then moves the test cartridge along as the sample and reagents are mixed, the reaction takes place for a measured amount of time, and the photometer reading is taken and converted to the test result.

A high-volume analyzer with more complex software randomly accesses 40 or more tests and runs over 400 tests per hour at a cost of less than 10 cents per test. The end result is a printed report on each sample listing the types of tests, the sample values, and a normal range for each test.

See Chemistry in Action Problems 29.67 through 29.69 at the end of the chapter.

The HCO_3^- ions return to the bloodstream, and the H^+ ions enter the filtrate. Thus, the more hydrogen ions there are to be excreted, the more bicarbonate ions are returned to the bloodstream.

The urine must carry away the necessary quantity of H^+ without becoming excessively acidic. To accomplish this, the H^+ is tied up by reaction with HPO_4^{2-} absorbed at the glomerulus, or by reaction with NH_3 produced in the tubule cells by deamination of glutamate:

$$H^+ + HPO_4^{2-} \longrightarrow H_2PO_4^-$$

$$H^+ + NH_3 \longrightarrow NH_4^+$$

When acidosis occurs, the kidney responds by synthesizing more ammonia, thereby increasing the quantity of H^+ eliminated.

A further outcome of H^+ production in tubule cells is the net reabsorption of the HCO_3^- that entered the filtrate at the glomerulus. The body cannot afford to lose its primary buffering ion, HCO_3^-. If HCO_3^- were to be lost, the body would have to produce more; the result would be production of additional acid from carbon dioxide by reaction with water. Instead, H^+ secreted into the filtrate combines with HCO_3^- in the filtrate to produce CO_2 and water:

$$\underset{\text{In the filtrate}}{H^+ \; + \; HCO_3^-} \longrightarrow \underset{\text{To bloodstream}}{CO_2 \; + \; H_2O}$$

Upon returning to the bloodstream, the CO_2 is reconverted to HCO_3^-.

In summary, acid–base reactions in the kidneys have the following results:

- Secreted H^+ is eliminated in the urine as NH_4^+ or $H_2PO_4^-$.
- Secreted H^+ combines with filtered HCO_3^-, producing CO_2 that returns to the bloodstream and again is converted to HCO_3^-.

Fluid and Na$^+$ Balance

The amount of water reabsorbed is dependent on the osmolarity of the fluid passing through the kidneys, the antidiuretic hormone–controlled permeability of the collecting duct membrane, and the amount of Na^+ actively reabsorbed. Increased sodium reabsorption means higher interstitial osmolarity, greater water reabsorption, and decreased urine volume. In the opposite condition of decreased sodium reabsorption, less water is reabsorbed and urine volume increases. "Loop diuretic" drugs such as furosemide (trademarked as Lasix®), which is used in treating hypertension and congestive heart failure, act by inhibiting the active transport of Na^+ out of the region of the urinary tubule called Henle's loop. Caffeine acts as a diuretic in a similar way.

The reabsorption of Na^+ is normally under the control of the steroid hormone aldosterone. The arrival of chemical messengers signaling a decrease in total blood plasma volume accelerates the secretion of aldosterone. The result is increased Na^+ reabsorption in the kidney tubules accompanied by increased water reabsorption.

SUMMARY: REVISITING THE CHAPTER GOALS

1. How are body fluids classified? Body fluids are either intracellular or extracellular. *Extracellular fluid* includes *blood plasma* (the fluid part of blood) and *interstitial fluid*. *Blood serum* is the fluid remaining after blood has clotted. Solutes in body fluids include blood gases, electrolytes, metabolites, and proteins. Solutes are carried throughout the body in blood and lymph. Exchange of solutes between blood and interstitial fluid occurs at the network of blood and lymph capillaries in peripheral tissues. Exchange of solutes between interstitial fluid and intracellular fluid occurs by passage across cell membranes (*see Problems 7, 14–16, 19–20, 24, 27–28, 55–59*).

2. What are the roles of blood in maintaining homeostasis? The principal functions of blood are (1) transport of solutes and blood gases, (2) regulation, such as regulation of heat and acid–base balance, and (3) defense, which includes the *immune*

response and *blood clotting*. In addition to plasma and proteins, blood is composed of red blood cells (*erythrocytes*), which transport blood gases; white blood cells (*leukocytes*), for defense functions; and *platelets*, which participate in blood clotting (Table 29.3) (*see Problems 8, 16–18, 26*).

3. How do blood components participate in the body's defense mechanisms? The presence of an *antigen* (a substance foreign to the body) initiates (1) the inflammatory response, (2) the cell-mediated immune response, and (3) the antibody-mediated immune response. The *inflammatory response* is initiated by histamine and accompanied by the destruction of invaders by *phagocytes*. The *cell-mediated response* is effected by *T cells* that can, for example, release a toxic protein that kills invaders. The *antibody-mediated response* is effected by *B cells*, which generate *antibodies (immunoglobulins)*, proteins that complex with antigens and destroy them. Blood clotting occurs in a cascade of reactions in which a series of zymogens are activated, ultimately resulting in the formation of a clot composed of *fibrin* and platelets (*see Problems 8, 10–13, 23, 25, 29, 30–40*).

4. How do red blood cells participate in the transport of blood gases? Oxygen is transported bonded to Fe^{2+} ions in hemoglobin. The percent saturation of hemoglobin with oxygen (Figure 29.12) is governed by the partial pressure of oxygen in surrounding tissues and allosteric variations in hemoglobin structure. Carbon dioxide is transported in blood as a solute, bonded to hemoglobin, or in solution as bicarbonate ion. In peripheral tissues, carbon dioxide diffuses into red blood cells, where it is converted to bicarbonate ion. Acid–base balance is controlled as hydrogen ions generated by bicarbonate formation are bound by hemoglobin. At the lungs, oxygen enters the cells, and bicarbonate and hydrogen ions leave. A blood pH outside the normal range of 7.35–7.45 can be caused by respiratory or metabolic imbalance, resulting in the potentially serious conditions of *acidosis* or *alkalosis* (*see Problems 9, 23, 25–29, 41–52, 60–62*).

5. How is the composition of urine controlled? The first essential kidney function is *filtration*, in which plasma and most of its solute cross capillary membranes and enter the *glomerular filtrate*. Water and essential solutes are then reabsorbed, whereas additional solutes for elimination are secreted into the filtrate. Urine is thus composed of the products of filtration, minus the substances reabsorbed, plus the secreted substances. It is composed of water, nitrogen-containing wastes, and electrolytes (including $H_2PO_4^-$ and NH_4^+) that are excreted to help maintain acid–base balance. The balance between water and Na^+ excreted or absorbed is governed by the osmolarity of fluid in the kidney, the hormone aldosterone, and various chemical messengers (*see Problems 13, 22, 53–54, 60*).

KEY WORDS

Acidosis, *p. 886*

Alkalosis, *p. 886*

Antibody (immunoglobulin), *p. 880*

Antigen, *p. 879*

Autoimmune disease, *p. 882*

Blood clot, *p. 883*

Blood plasma, *p. 871*

Blood serum, *p. 876*

Erythrocytes, *p. 876*

Extracellular fluid, *p. 871*

Fibrin, *p. 882*

Filtration (kidney), *p. 887*

Glomerular filtrate, *p. 887*

Hemostasis, *p. 883*

Immune response, *p. 880*

Inflammation, *p. 880*

Inflammatory response, *p. 879*

Interstitial fluid, *p. 871*

Intracellular fluid, *p. 871*

Leukocytes, *p. 876*

Osmolarity, *p. 871*

Reabsorption (kidney), *p. 887*

Secretion (kidney), *p. 887*

Whole blood, *p. 876*

UNDERSTANDING KEY CONCEPTS

29.7   Body fluids occupy two different compartments, either inside the cells or outside the cells.

    (a) What are body fluids found inside the cell called?

    (b) What are body fluids found outside the cell called?

    (c) What are the two major subclasses of fluids found outside the cells?

    (d) What major electrolytes are found inside the cells?

    (e) What major electrolytes are found outside the cells?

29.8   In the diagram shown here, fill in the blanks with the names of the principal components of whole blood:

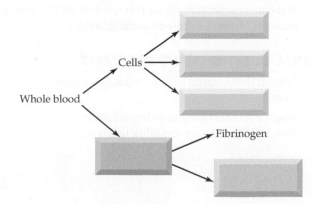

29.9   Fill in the blanks to identify some of the major functions of blood:

    (a) Blood carries _____ from lungs to tissues.

    (b) Blood carries _____ from the tissues to lungs.

    (c) Blood transports _____ from the digestive system to the tissues.

    (d) Blood carries _____ from the tissues to the site of excretion.

    (e) Blood transports _____ from the endocrine glands to their site of binding.

    (f) Blood transports defensive agents such as _____ to destroy foreign material and to prevent blood loss.

29.10   List four symptoms of inflammation.

29.11   Explain how the chemical messenger histamine is biosynthesized and how it elicits each symptom of inflammation.

29.12   Differentiate between cell-mediated immune response and antibody-mediated immune response.

29.13   How does the composition of urine help to maintain a healthy physiological acid–base balance?

ADDITIONAL PROBLEMS

BODY FLUIDS

29.14 What are the three principal body fluids and the approximate percentage of total body water accounted for by each?

29.15 What characteristics are needed for a substance to be soluble in body fluids?

29.16 Give an example of a substance found in tissues that is not soluble in blood. How are components that are not normally soluble in blood transported?

29.17 What effects do the differences in pressure between arterial capillaries, interstitial fluids, and venous capillaries have on solutes crossing cell membranes?

29.18 How does blood pressure compare with the interstitial fluid pressure in arterial capillaries? With the interstitial fluid pressure in venous capillaries?

29.19 What is the purpose of the lymphatic system?

29.20 Where in the body does the lymph enter the bloodstream?

29.21 What is vasopressin?

29.22 What happens when excess secretion of antidiuretic hormone occurs? State two causes of this.

29.23 What is the difference between blood plasma and blood serum?

29.24 At what percent of body-mass loss is collapse very likely to occur?

29.25 What are the three main types of blood cells?

29.26 What is the major function of each of the three types of blood cells?

29.27 What solutes in body fluids are referred to as electrolytes?

29.28 What are the major electrolytes inside cells and outside cells?

29.29 What is an antigen, and what are the three types of responses the body makes upon exposure to an antigen?

29.30 Antihistamines are often prescribed to counteract the effects of allergies. Explain how these drugs work. (Hint: See also Section 9.9.)

29.31 How are specific immune responses similar to the enzyme–substrate interaction?

29.32 What class of plasma proteins is involved in the antibody-mediated immune response?

29.33 What kinds of cells are associated with the antibody-directed immune response, and how do they work?

29.34 State the three major functions of T cells.

29.35 T cells are often discussed in conjunction with the disease AIDS, in which a virus destroys these cells. How do T cells work to combat disease?

29.36 What are memory cells, and what is their role in the immune response?

29.37 What is a blood clot? What is it composed of?

29.38 What vitamin and what mineral are specifically associated with the clotting process?

29.39 Describe the intrinsic pathway in blood clotting.

29.40 Why, do you suppose, are many of the enzymes involved in blood clotting secreted by the body as zymogens?

29.41 How many O_2 molecules can be bound by each hemoglobin tetramer?

29.42 What must be the charge of the iron in hemoglobin for it to perform its function?

29.43 What color is deoxyhemoglobin? Why?

29.44 How does the degree of saturation of hemoglobin vary with the partial pressure of O_2 in the tissues?

29.45 Oxygen has an allosteric interaction with hemoglobin. What are the results of this interaction as oxygen is bonded and as it is released?

29.46 What are the three ways of transporting CO_2 in the body?

29.47 Use Figure 29.11 to estimate the partial pressure of O_2 at which hemoglobin is 50% saturated with oxygen under normal conditions. Dry air at sea level is about 21% oxygen. What would be the percentage saturation of your hemoglobin under these conditions?

29.48 When an actively metabolizing tissue produces CO_2, the H^+ concentration of blood increases. Explain how this happens using a chemical equation.

29.49 Do the following conditions cause hemoglobin to release more O_2 to the tissues or to absorb more O_2?

(a) Raising the temperature

(b) Increased production of CO_2

(c) Increasing the H^+ concentration

29.50 What are the two types of acidosis? How do they differ?

29.51 Ketoacidosis is a condition that can arise in an individual with diabetes due to excessive production of ketone bodies. Is this condition classified as metabolic acidosis or respiratory acidosis? Explain.

29.52 What are the two types of alkalosis? How do they differ?

29.53 Kidneys are often referred to as filters that purify the blood. What other two essential functions do the kidneys perform to help maintain homeostasis?

29.54 Write the reactions by which HPO_4^{2-} and HCO_3^- absorb excess H^+ from the urine before elimination.

GENERAL QUESTIONS AND PROBLEMS

29.55 What is the chemical basis for ethanol's solubility in blood?

29.56 Nursing mothers are able to impart some immunity to their infants. Why do you think this is so?

29.57 Many people find they retain water after eating salty food, evidenced by swollen fingers and ankles. Explain this phenomenon in terms of how the kidneys operate.

29.58 How does active transport differ from osmosis?

29.59 When is active transport necessary to move substances through cell membranes?

29.60 Discuss the importance of the CO_2/HCO_3^- equilibrium in blood and in urine.

29.61 We have discussed homeostasis throughout this text. But what is *hemostasis*? Is it related to homeostasis?

29.62 When people panic, cry, or have a high fever, they often begin to hyperventilate. Hyperventilation is abnormally fast or deep respiration, which results in the loss of carbon dioxide from the blood. Explain how hyperventilation changes the blood chemistry. Why can breathing into a paper bag alleviate hyperventilation?

CHEMISTRY IN ACTION

29.63 How do endothelial cells in brain capillaries differ from those in other capillary systems? [*The Blood–Brain Barrier, p. 879*]

29.64 What is meant by an asymmetric transport system? Give one specific example of such a system. [*The Blood–Brain Barrier, p. 879*]

29.65 What type of substance is likely to breach the blood–brain barrier? Would ethanol be likely to cross this barrier? Why or why not? [*The Blood–Brain Barrier, p. 879*]

29.66 What is the metabolic blood–brain barrier? [*The Blood–Brain Barrier, p. 879*]

29.67 How are photometers used in automated analysis? [*Automated Clinical Laboratory Analysis, p. 889*]

29.68 Why is automated analysis useful to test for enzyme levels in body fluids? [*Automated Clinical Laboratory Analysis, p. 889*]

29.69 In analyzing body fluids for medical diagnoses, what are some advantages of using automated analyzers rather than technicians? [*Automated Clinical Laboratory Analysis, p. 889*]

Scientific Notation

What Is Scientific Notation?

The numbers that you encounter in chemistry are often either very large or very small. For example, there are about 33,000,000,000,000,000,000,000 H_2O molecules in 1.0 mL of water, and the distance between the H and O atoms in an H_2O molecule is 0.000 000 000 095 7 m. These quantities are more conveniently written in *scientific notation* as 3.3×10^{22} molecules and 9.57×10^{-11} m, respectively. In scientific notation (also known as *exponential notation*), a quantity is represented as a number between 1 and 10 multiplied by a power of 10. In this kind of expression, the small raised number to the right of the 10 is the exponent.

Number	Exponential Form	Exponent
1,000,000	1×10^6	6
100,000	1×10^5	5
10,000	1×10^4	4
1,000	1×10^3	3
100	1×10^2	2
10	1×10^1	1
1		
0.1	1×10^{-1}	−1
0.01	1×10^{-2}	−2
0.001	1×10^{-3}	−3
0.000 1	1×10^{-4}	−4
0.000 01	1×10^{-5}	−5
0.000 001	1×10^{-6}	−6
0.000 000 1	1×10^{-7}	−7

Numbers greater than 1 have *positive* exponents, which tell how many times a number must be *multiplied* by 10 to obtain the correct value. For example, the expression 5.2×10^3 means that 5.2 must be multiplied by 10 three times:

$$5.2 \times 10^3 = 5.2 \times 10 \times 10 \times 10 = 5.2 \times 1000 = 5200$$

Note that doing this means moving the decimal point three places to the right:

$$5200.$$
$$\underset{123}{}$$

The value of a positive exponent indicates *how many places to the right the decimal point must be moved* to give the correct number in ordinary decimal notation.

Numbers less than 1 have *negative exponents,* which tell how many times a number must be *divided* by 10 (or multiplied by one-tenth) to obtain the correct value. Thus, the expression 3.7×10^{-2} means that 3.7 must be divided by 10 two times:

$$3.7 \times 10^{-2} = \frac{3.7}{10 \times 10} = \frac{3.7}{100} = 0.037$$

Note that doing this means moving the decimal point two places to the left:

$$0.037$$
$$\underset{21}{}$$

The value of a negative exponent indicates *how may places to the left the decimal point must be moved* to give the correct number in ordinary decimal notation.

Representing Numbers in Scientific Notation

How do you convert a number from ordinary notation to scientific notation? If the number is greater than or equal to 10, shift the decimal point to the *left* by n places until you obtain a number between 1 and 10. Then, multiply the result by 10^n. For example, the number 8137.6 is written in scientific notation as 8.1376×10^3:

Number of places decimal point was shifted to the left

$$8137.6 = 8.1376 \times 10^3$$

Shift decimal point to the left by 3 places to get a number between 1 and 10

When you shift the decimal point to the left by three places, you are in effect dividing the number by $10 \times 10 \times 10 = 1000 = 10^3$. Therefore, you must multiply the result by 10^3 so that the value of the number is unchanged.

To convert a number less than 1 to scientific notation, shift the decimal point to the *right* by n places until you obtain a number between 1 and 10. Then, multiply the result by 10^{-n}. For example, the number 0.012 is written in scientific notation as 1.2×10^{-2}:

Number of places decimal point was shifted to the right

$$0.012 = 1.2 \times 10^{-2}$$

Shift decimal point to the right by 2 places to get a number between 1 and 10

When you shift the decimal point to the right by two places, you are in effect multiplying the number by $10 \times 10 = 100 = 10^2$. Therefore, you must multiply the result by 10^{-2} so that the value of the number is unchanged. ($10^2 \times 10^{-2} = 10^0 = 1$.)

The following table gives some additional examples. To convert from scientific notation to ordinary notation, simply reverse the preceding process. Thus, to write the number 5.84×10^4 in ordinary notation, drop the factor of 10^4 and move the decimal point 4 places to the *right* ($5.84 \times 10^4 = 58,400$). To write the number 3.5×10^{-1} in ordinary notation, drop the factor of 10^{-1} and move the decimal point 1 place to the *left* ($3.5 \times 10^{-1} = 0.35$). Note that you don't need scientific notation for numbers between 1 and 10 because $10^0 = 1$.

Number	Scientific Notation
58,400	5.84×10^4
0.35	3.5×10^{-1}
7.296	$7.296 \times 10^0 = 7.296 \times 1$

Mathematical Operations with Scientific Notation

Addition and Subtraction in Scientific Notation

To add or subtract two numbers expressed in scientific notation, both numbers must have the same exponent. Thus, to add 7.16×10^3 and 1.32×10^2, first write the latter number as 0.132×10^3 and then add:

$$
\begin{array}{r}
7.16 \ \times 10^3 \\
+0.132 \times 10^3 \\
\hline
7.29 \ \times 10^3
\end{array}
$$

The answer has three significant figures. (Significant figures are discussed in Section 2.4.) Alternatively, you can write the first number as 71.6×10^2 and then add:

$$
\begin{array}{r}
7.16 \times 10^2 \\
+\ 1.32 \times 10^2 \\
\hline
72.9\ \ \times 10^2 = 7.29 \times 10^3
\end{array}
$$

Subtraction of these two numbers is carried out in the same manner.

$$
\begin{array}{rcr}
7.16\ \ \times 10^3 & & 7.16 \times 10^2 \\
-0.132 \times 10^3 & \text{or} & -1.32 \times 10^2 \\
\hline
7.03\ \ \times 10^3 & & 70.3 \times 10^2 = 7.03 \times 10^3
\end{array}
$$

Multiplication in Scientific Notation

To multiply two numbers expressed in scientific notation, multiply the factors in front of the powers of 10 and then add the exponents. For example,

$$(2.5 \times 10^4)(4.7 \times 10^7) = (2.5)(4.7) \times 10^{4+7} = 10 \times 10^{11} = 1.2 \times 10^{12}$$

$$(3.46 \times 10^5)(2.2 \times 10^{-2}) = (3.46)(2.2) \times 10^{5+(-2)} = 7.6 \times 10^3$$

Both answers have two significant figures.

Division in Scientific Notation

To divide two numbers expressed in scientific notation, divide the factors in front of the powers of 10 and then subtract the exponent in the denominator from the exponent in the numerator. For example,

$$\frac{3 \times 10^6}{7.2 \times 10^2} = \frac{3}{7.2} \times 10^{6-2} = 0.4 \times 10^4 = 4 \times 10^3 \ (1 \text{ significant figure})$$

$$\frac{7.50 \times 10^{-5}}{2.5 \times 10^{-7}} = \frac{7.50}{2.5} \times 10^{-5-(-7)} = 3.0 \times 10^2 \ (2 \text{ significant figures})$$

Scientific Notation and Electronic Calculators

With a scientific calculator you can carry out calculations in scientific notation. You should consult the instruction manual for your particular calculator to learn how to enter and manipulate numbers expressed in an exponential format. On most calculators, you enter the number $A \times 10^n$ by (i) entering the number A, (ii) pressing a key labeled EXP or EE, and (iii) entering the exponent n. If the exponent is negative, you press a key labeled $+/-$ before entering the value of n. (Note that you do not enter the number 10.) The calculator displays the number $A \times 10^n$ with the number A on the left followed by some space and then the exponent n. For example,

$$4.625 \times 10^2 \quad \text{is displayed as} \quad 4.625\ 02$$

To add, subtract, multiply, or divide exponential numbers, use the same sequence of keystrokes as you would in working with ordinary numbers. When you add or subtract on a calculator, the numbers need not have the same exponent; the calculator automatically takes account of the different exponents. Remember, though, that the calculator often gives more digits in the answer than the allowed number of significant figures. It's sometimes helpful to outline the calculation on paper, as in the preceding examples, to keep track of the number of significant figures.

PROBLEM A.1

Perform the following calculations, expressing the results in scientific notation with the correct number of significant figures. (You don't need a calculator for these.)

(a) $(1.50 \times 10^4) + (5.04 \times 10^3)$

(b) $(2.5 \times 10^{-2}) - (5.0 \times 10^{-3})$

(c) $(6.3 \times 10^{15}) \times (10.1 \times 10^{3})$

(d) $(2.5 \times 10^{-3}) \times (3.2 \times 10^{-4})$

(e) $(8.4 \times 10^{4}) \div (3.0 \times 10^{6})$

(f) $(5.530 \times 10^{-2}) \div (2.5 \times 10^{-5})$

ANSWERS

(a) 2.00×10^{4} (b) 2.0×10^{-2} (c) 6.4×10^{19}

(d) 8.0×10^{-7} (e) 2.8×10^{-2} (f) 2.2×10^{3}

PROBLEM A.2

Perform the following calculations, expressing the results in scientific notation with the correct number of significant figures. (Use a calculator for these.)

(a) $(9.72 \times 10^{-1}) + (3.4823 \times 10^{2})$

(b) $(3.772 \times 10^{3}) - (2.891 \times 10^{4})$

(c) $(1.956 \times 10^{3}) \div (6.02 \times 10^{23})$

(d) $3.2811 \times (9.45 \times 10^{21})$

(e) $(1.0015 \times 10^{3}) \div (5.202 \times 10^{-9})$

(f) $(6.56 \times 10^{-6}) \times (9.238 \times 10^{-4})$

ANSWERS

(a) 3.4920×10^{2} (b) -2.514×10^{4} (c) 3.25×10^{-21}

(d) 3.10×10^{22} (e) 1.925×10^{11} (f) 6.06×10^{-9}

Conversion Factors

Length SI Unit: Meter (m)

1 meter = 0.001 kilometer (km)

= 100 centimeters (cm)

= 1.0936 yards (yd)

1 centimeter = 10 millimeters (mm)

= 0.3937 inch (in.)

1 nanometer = 1×10^{-9} meter

1 Angstrom (Å) = 1×10^{-10} meter

1 inch = 2.54 centimeters

1 mile = 1.6094 kilometers

Volume SI Unit: Cubic meter (m^3)

1 cubic meter = 1000 liters (L)

1 liter = 1000 cubic centimeters (cm^3)

= 1000 milliliters (mL)

= 1.056710 quarts (qt)

1 cubic inch = 16.4 cubic centimeters

Temperature SI Unit: Kelvin (K)

0 K = $-273.15 \,^{\circ}C$

= $-459.67 \,^{\circ}F$

$^{\circ}F = (9/5)^{\circ}C + 32^{\circ}; ^{\circ}F = (1.8 \times \,^{\circ}C) + 32^{\circ}$

$^{\circ}C = (5/9)(^{\circ}F - 32^{\circ}); ^{\circ}C = \dfrac{(^{\circ}F - 32^{\circ})}{1.8}$

$K = \,^{\circ}C + 273.15^{\circ}$

Mass SI Unit: Kilogram (kg)

1 kilogram = 1000 grams (g)

= 2.205 pounds (lb)

1 gram = 1000 milligrams (mg)

= 0.03527 ounce (oz)

1 pound = 453.6 grams

1 atomic mass unit = 1.66054×10^{-24} gram

Pressure SI Unit: Pascal (Pa)

1 pascal = 9.869×10^{-6} atmosphere

1 atmosphere = 101,325 pascals

= 760 mmHg (Torr)

= 14.70 lb/in^2

Energy SI Unit: Joule (J)

1 joule = 0.23901 calorie (cal)

1 calorie = 4.184 joules

1 Calorie (nutritional unit) = 1000 calories

= 1 kcal

Glossary

1,4 Link A glycosidic link between the hemiacetal hydroxyl group at C1 of one sugar and the hydroxyl group at C4 of another sugar.

Acetal A compound that has two ether-like —OR groups bonded to the same carbon atom.

Acetyl coenzyme A (acetyl-CoA) Acetyl-substituted coenzyme A—the common intermediate that carries acetyl groups into the citric acid cycle.

Acetyl group A $CH_3C{=}O$ group.

Achiral The opposite of chiral; having no right- or left-handedness and no nonsuper-imposable mirror images.

Acid A substance that provides H^+ ions in water.

Acid dissociation constant (K_a) The equilibrium constant for the dissociation of an acid (HA), equal to $[H^+][A^-]/[HA]$

Acidosis The abnormal condition associated with a blood plasma pH below 7.35; may be respiratory or metabolic.

Acid-base indicator A dye that changes color depending on the pH of a solution.

Activation (of an enzyme) Any process that initiates or increases the action of an enzyme.

Activation energy (E_{act}) The amount of energy necessary for reactants to surmount the energy barrier to reaction; affects reaction rate.

Active site A pocket in an enzyme with the specific shape and chemical makeup necessary to bind a substrate.

Active transport Movement of substances across a cell membrane with the assistance of energy (for example, from ATP).

Actual Yield The amount of product actually formed in a reaction.

Acyl group An $RC{=}O$ group.

Addition reaction A general reaction type in which a substance X—Y adds to the multiple bond of an unsaturated reactant to yield a saturated product that has only single bonds.

Addition reaction, aldehydes and ketones Addition of an alcohol or other compound to the carbon-oxygen double bond to give a carbon-oxygen single bond.

Adenosine triphosphate (ATP) The principal energy-carrying molecule; removal of a phosphoryl group to give ADP releases free energy.

Aerobic In the presence of oxygen.

Agonist A substance that interacts with a receptor to cause or prolong the receptor's normal biochemical response.

Alcohol A compound that has an —OH group bonded to a saturated, alkane-like carbon atom, R—OH.

Alcoholic fermentation The anaerobic breakdown of glucose to ethanol plus carbon dioxide by the action of yeast enzymes.

Aldehyde A compound that has a carbonyl group bonded to one carbon and one hydrogen, RCHO.

Aldose A monosaccharide that contains an aldehyde carbonyl group.

Alkali metal An element in group 1A of the periodic table.

Alkaline earth metal An element in group 2A of the periodic table.

Alkaloid A naturally occurring nitrogen-containing compound isolated from a plant; usually basic, bitter, and poisonous.

Alkalosis The abnormal condition associated with a blood plasma pH above 7.45; may be respiratory or metabolic.

Alkane A hydrocarbon that has only single bonds.

Alkene A hydrocarbon that contains a carbon-carbon double bond.

Alkoxide ion The anion resulting from deprotonation of an alcohol, RO^-.

Alkoxy group An —OR group.

Alkyl group The part of an alkane that remains when a hydrogen atom is removed.

Alkyl halide A compound that has an alkyl group bonded to a halogen atom, R—X.

Alkyne A hydrocarbon that contains a carbon-carbon triple bond.

Allosteric control An interaction in which the binding of a regulator at one site on a protein affects the protein's ability to bind another molecule at a different site.

Allosteric enzyme An enzyme whose activity is controlled by the binding of an activator or inhibitor at a location other than the active site.

Alpha (α) particle A helium nucleus (He^{2+}), emitted as α-radiation.

Alpha- (α-) amino acid An amino acid in which the amino group is bonded to the carbon atom next to the —COOH group.

Alpha- (α-) helix Secondary protein structure in which a protein chain forms a right-handed coil stabilized by hydrogen bonds between peptide groups along its backbone.

Amide A compound that has a carbonyl group bonded to a carbon atom and a nitrogen atom group, $RCONR_2{}'$, where the R' groups may be alkyl groups or hydrogen atoms.

Amine A compound that has one or more organic groups bonded to nitrogen; primary, RNH_2; secondary, R_2NH; or tertiary, R_3N.

Amino acid A molecule that contains both an amino group and a carboxylic acid functional group.

Amino acid pool The entire collection of free amino acids in the body.

Amino group The —NH_2 functional group.

Amino-terminal (N-terminal) amino acid The amino acid with the free —NH^{3+} group at the end of a protein.

Ammonium ion A positive ion formed by addition of hydrogen to ammonia or an amine (may be primary, secondary, or tertiary).

Ammonium salt An ionic compound composed of an ammonium cation and an anion; an amine salt.

Amorphous solid A solid whose particles do not have an orderly arrangement.

Amphoteric Describing a substance that can react as either an acid or a base.

Anabolism Metabolic reactions that build larger biological molecules from smaller pieces.

Anaerobic In the absence of oxygen.

Anion A negatively charged ion.

Anomeric carbon atom The hemiacetal C atom in a cyclic sugar; the C atom bonded to an —OH group and an O in the ring.

Anomers Cyclic sugars that differ only in positions of substituents at the hemiacetal carbon (the anomeric carbon); the α form has the —OH on the opposite side from the —CH_2OH; the β form has the —OH on the same side as the —CH_2OH.

Antagonist A substance that blocks or inhibits the normal biochemical response of a receptor.

Antibody (immunoglobulin) Glycoprotein molecule that identifies antigens.

Anticodon A sequence of three ribonucleotides on tRNA that recognizes the complementary sequence (the codon) on mRNA.

Antigen A substance foreign to the body that triggers the immune response.

Antioxidant A substance that prevents oxidation by reacting with an oxidizing agent.

Aromatic The class of compounds containing benzene-like rings.

Artificial transmutation The change of one atom into another brought about by a nuclear bombardment reaction.

Atom The smallest and simplest particle of an element.

Atomic mass unit (amu) A convenient unit for describing the mass of an atom; 1 amu = 1/12 the mass of a carbon-12 atom.

Atomic number (Z) The number of protons in an atom.

Atomic theory A set of assumptions proposed by English scientist John Dalton to explain the chemical behavior of matter.

Atomic weight The weighted average mass of an element's atoms.

ATP synthase The enzyme complex in the inner mitochondrial membrane at which hydrogen ions cross the membrane and ATP is synthesized from ADP.

Autoimmune disease Disorder in which the immune system identifies normal body components as antigens and produces antibodies to them.

Avogadro's law Equal volumes of gases at the same temperature and pressure contain equal numbers of molecules (V/n = constant, or $V_1/n_1 = V_2/n_2$).

Avogadro's number (N_A) The number of units in 1 mole of anything; 6.02×10^{23}.

Balanced equation Describing a chemical equation in which the numbers and kinds of atoms are the same on both sides of the reaction arrow.

Base A substance that provides OH^- ions in water.

Base pairing The pairing of bases connected by hydrogen bonding (G-C and A-T), as in the DNA double helix.

Beta- (β-) Oxidation pathway A repetitive series of biochemical reactions that degrades fatty acids to acetyl-SCoA by removing carbon atoms two at a time.

Beta (β) particle An electron (e⁻), emitted as β radiation.

Beta- (β-) Sheet Secondary protein structure in which adjacent protein chains either in the same molecule or in different molecules are held in place by hydrogen bonds along the backbones.

Bile Fluid secreted by the liver and released into the small intestine from the gallbladder during digestion; contains bile acids, bicarbonate ion, and other electrolytes.

Bile acids Steroid acids derived from cholesterol that are secreted in bile.

Binary compound A compound formed by combination of two different elements.

Blood clot A network of fibrin fibers and trapped blood cells that forms at the site of blood loss.

Blood plasma Liquid portion of the blood: an extracellular fluid.

Blood serum Fluid portion of blood remaining after clotting has occurred.

Boiling point (bp) The temperature at which liquid and gas are in equilibrium.

Bond angle The angle formed by three adjacent atoms in a molecule.

Bond dissociation energy The amount of energy that must be supplied to break a bond and separate the atoms in an isolated gaseous molecule.

Bond length The optimum distance between nuclei in a covalent bond.

Boyle's law The pressure of a gas at constant temperature is inversely proportional to its volume ($PV =$ constant, or $P_1V_1 = P_2V_2$).

Branched-chain alkane An alkane that has a branching connection of carbons.

Brønsted-Lowry acid A substance that can donate a hydrogen ion, H⁺, to another molecule or ion.

Brønsted-Lowry base A substance that can accept H⁺ from an acid.

Buffer A combination of substances that act together to prevent a drastic change in pH; usually a weak acid and its conjugate base.

Carbohydrate A member of a large class of naturally occurring polyhydroxy ketones and aldehydes.

Carbonyl compound Any compound that contains a carbonyl group $C=O$.

Carbonyl group A functional group that has a carbon atom joined to an oxygen atom by a double bond, $C=O$.

Carbonyl-group substitution reaction A reaction in which a new group replaces (substitutes for) a group attached to a carbonyl-group carbon in an acyl group.

Carboxyl group The —COOH functional group.

Carboxyl-terminal (C-terminal) amino acid The amino acid with the free —COO⁻ group at the end of a protein.

Carboxylate anion The anion that results from ionization of a carboxylic acid, RCOO⁻.

Carboxylic acid A compound that has a carbonyl group bonded to a carbon atom and an —OH group, RCOOH.

Carboxylic acid salt An ionic compound containing a carboxylic anion and a cation.

Catabolism Metabolic reaction pathways that break down food molecules and release biochemical energy.

Catalyst A substance that speeds up the rate of a chemical reaction but is itself unchanged.

Cation A positively charged ion.

Centromeres The central regions of chromosomes.

Chain reaction A reaction that, once started, is self-sustaining.

Change of state The conversion of a substance from one state to another—for example, from a liquid to a gas.

Charles's law The volume of a gas at constant pressure is directly proportional to its Kelvin temperature ($V/T =$ constant, or $V_1/T_1 = V_2/T_2$).

Chemical change A change in the chemical makeup of a substance.

Chemical compound A pure substance that can be broken down into simpler substances by chemical reactions.

Chemical equation An expression in which symbols and formulas are used to represent a chemical reaction.

Chemical equilibrium A state in which the rates of forward and reverse reactions are the same.

Chemical formula A notation for a chemical compound using element symbols and subscripts to show how many atoms of each element are present.

Chemical reaction A process in which the identity and composition of one or more substances are changed.

Chemistry The study of the nature, properties, and transformations of matter.

Chiral carbon atom (chirality center) A carbon atom bonded to four different groups.

Chiral Having right- or left-handedness; able to have two different mirror-image forms.

Chromosome A complex of proteins and DNA; visible during cell division.

Cis-trans isomers Alkenes that have the same connections between atoms but differ in their three-dimensional structures because of the way that groups are attached to different sides of the double bond. The cis isomer has hydrogen atoms on the same side of the double bond; the trans isomer has them on opposite sides.

Citric acid cycle The series of biochemical reactions that breaks down acetyl groups to produce energy carried by reduced coenzymes and carbon dioxide.

Clones Identical copies of organisms, cells, or DNA segments from a single ancestor.

Codon A sequence of three ribonucleotides in the messenger RNA chain that codes for a specific amino acid; also the three nucleotide sequence (a stop codon) that stops translation.

Coefficient A number placed in front of a formula to balance a chemical equation.

Coenzyme An organic molecule that acts as an enzyme cofactor.

Cofactor A nonprotein part of an enzyme that is essential to the enzyme's catalytic activity; a metal ion or a coenzyme.

Colligative property A property of a solution that depends only on the number of dissolved particles, not on their chemical identity.

Colloid A homogeneous mixture that contains particles that range in diameter from 2 to 500 nm.

Combined gas law The product of the pressure and volume of a gas is proportional to its temperature ($PV/T =$ constant, or $P_1V_1/T_1 = P_2V_2/T_2$).

Combustion A chemical reaction that produces a flame, usually because of burning with oxygen.

Competititve (enzyme) inhibition Enzyme regulation in which an inhibitor competes with a substrate for binding to the enzyme active site.

Concentration A measure of the amount of a given substance in a mixture.

Concentration gradient A difference in concentration within the same system.

Condensed structure A shorthand way of drawing structures in which C—C and C—H bonds are understood rather than shown.

Conformation The specific three-dimensional arrangement of atoms in a molecule at a given instant.

Conformers Molecular structures having identical connections between atoms.

Conjugate acid The substance formed by addition of H⁺ to a base.

Conjugate acid-base pair Two substances whose formulas differ by only a hydrogen ion, H⁺.

Conjugate base The substance formed by loss of H⁺ from an acid.

Conjugated protein A protein that incorporates one or more non-amino acid units in its structure.

Constitutional isomers Compounds with the same molecular formula but different connections among their atoms.

Conversion factor An expression of the relationship between two units.

Coordinate covalent bond The covalent bond that forms when both electrons are donated by the same atom.

Cosmic rays A mixture of high-energy particles—primarily of protons and various atomic nuclei—that shower the earth from outer space.

Covalent bond A bond formed by sharing electrons between atoms.

Critical mass The minimum amount of radioactive material needed to sustain a nuclear chain reaction.

Crystalline solid A solid whose atoms, molecules, or ions are rigidly held in an ordered arrangement.

Cycloalkane An alkane that contains a ring of carbon atoms.

Cycloalkene A cyclic hydrocarbon that contains a double bond.

Cytoplasm The region between the cell membrane and the nuclear membrane in a eukaryotic cell.

Cytosol The fluid part of the cytoplasm surrounding the organelles within a cell.

***d*-Block element** A transition metal element that results from the filling of d orbitals.

ᴅ-Sugar Monosaccharide with the —OH group on the chiral carbon atom farthest from the carbonyl group pointing to the right in a Fischer projection.

Dalton's law The total pressure exerted by a mixture of gases is equal to the sum of the partial pressures exerted by each individual gas.

Decay series A sequential series of nuclear disintegrations leading from a heavy radioisotope to a nonradioactive product.

Degree of unsaturation The number of carbon-carbon double bonds in a molecule.

Dehydration The loss of water from an alcohol to yield an alkene.

Denaturation The loss of secondary, tertiary or quaternary protein structure due to disruption of noncovalent interactions and/or disulfide bonds that leaves peptide bond and primary structure intact.

Density The physical property that relates the mass of an object to its volume; mass per unit volume.

Deoxyribonucleotide A nucleotide containing 2-deoxy-D-ribose.

Diabetes mellitus A chronic condition due to either insufficient insulin or failure of insulin to activate crossing of cell membranes by glucose.

Diastereomers Stereoisomers that are not mirror images of each other.

Digestion A general term for the breakdown of food into small molecules.

Dilution factor The ratio of the initial and final solution volumes (V_1/V_2).

Dipole-dipole force The attractive force between positive and negative ends of polar molecules.

Disaccharide A carbohydrate composed of two monosaccharides.

Dissociation The splitting apart of an acid in water to give H^+ and an anion.

Disulfide A compound that contains a sulfur-sulfur bond, RS-SR.

Disulfide bond (in protein) An S-S bond formed between two cysteine side chains; can join two peptide chains together or cause a loop in a peptide chain.

DNA (deoxyribonucleic acid) The nucleic acid that stores genetic information; a polymer of deoxyribonucleotides.

Double bond A covalent bond formed by sharing two electron pairs.

Double helix Two strands coiled around each other in a screwlike fashion; in most organisms the two polynucleotides of DNA form a double helix.

Drug Any substance that alters body function when it is introduced from an external source.

Eicosanoid A lipid derived from a 20-carbon unsaturated carboxylic acid.

Electrolyte A substance that produces ions and therefore conducts electricity when dissolved in water.

Electron A negatively charged subatomic particle.

Electron affinity The energy released on adding an electron to a single atom in the gaseous state.

Electron capture A process in which the nucleus captures an inner-shell electron from the surrounding electron cloud, thereby converting a proton into a neutron.

Electron configuration The specific arrangement of electrons in an atom's shells and subshells.

Electron shell A grouping of electrons in an atom according to energy.

Electron subshell A grouping of electrons in a shell according to the shape of the region of space they occupy.

Electron-dot symbol An atomic symbol with dots placed around it to indicate the number of valence electrons.

Electron-transport chain The series of biochemical reactions that passes electrons from reduced coenzymes to oxygen and is coupled to ATP formation.

Electronegativity The ability of an atom to attract electrons in a covalent bond.

Element A fundamental substance that can't be broken down chemically into any simpler substance.

Elimination reaction A general reaction type in which a saturated reactant yields an unsaturated product by losing groups from two adjacent carbon atoms.

Enantiomers, optical isomers The two mirror-image forms of a chiral molecule.

Endergonic A nonspontaneous reaction or process that absorbs free energy and has a positive ΔG.

Endocrine system A system of specialized cells, tissues, and ductless glands that excretes hormones and shares with the nervous system the responsibility for maintaining constant internal body conditions and responding to changes in the environment.

Endothermic A process or reaction that absorbs heat and has a positive ΔH.

Energy The capacity to do work or supply heat.

Enthalpy A measure of the amount of energy associated with substances involved in a reaction.

Enthalpy change (ΔH) An alternative name for heat of reaction.

Entropy (S) The amount of disorder in a system.

Entropy change (ΔS) A measure of the increase in disorder ($\Delta S = +$) or decrease in disorder ($\Delta S = -$) as a chemical reaction or physical change occurs.

Enzyme A protein or other molecule that acts as a catalyst for a biological reaction.

Equilibrium constant (K) Value of the equilibrium constant expression for a given reaction.

Equivalent For ions, the amount equal to 1 mol of charge.

Equivalent of acid Amount of an acid that contains 1 mole of H^+ ions.

Equivalent of base Amount of base that contains 1 mole of OH^- ions.

Erythrocytes Red blood cells; transporters of blood gases.

Essential amino acid An amino acid that cannot be synthesized by the body and thus must be obtained in the diet.

Ester A compound that has a carbonyl group bonded to a carbon atom and an —OR′ group, RCOOR′.

Esterification The reaction between an alcohol and a carboxylic acid to yield an ester plus water.

Ether A compound that has an oxygen atom bonded to two organic groups, R—O—R.

Ethyl group The —CH$_2$CH$_3$ alkyl group.

Exergonic A spontaneous reaction or process that releases free energy and has a negative ΔG.

Exon A nucleotide sequence in DNA that is part of a gene and codes for part of a protein.

Exothermic A process or reaction that releases heat and has a negative ΔH.

Extracellular fluid Fluid outside cells.

f-Block element An inner transition metal element that results from the filling of f orbitals.

Facilitated diffusion Passive transport across a cell membrane with the assistance of a protein that changes shape.

Factor-label method A problem-solving procedure in which equations are set up so that unwanted units cancel and only the desired units remain.

Fat A mixture of triacylglycerols that is solid because it contains a high proportion of saturated fatty acids.

Fatty acid A long-chain carboxylic acid; those in animal fats and vegetable oils often have 12–22 carbon atoms.

Feedback control Regulation of an enzyme's activity by the product of a reaction later in a pathway.

Fermentation The production of energy under anaerobic conditions.

Fibrin Insoluble protein that forms the fiber framework of a blood clot.

Fibrous protein A tough, insoluble protein whose protein chains form fibers or sheets.

Filtration (kidney) Filtration of blood plasma through a glomerulus and into a kidney nephron.

Fischer projection Structure that represents chiral carbon atoms as the intersections of two lines, with the horizontal lines representing bonds pointing out of the page and the vertical lines representing bonds pointing behind the page. For sugars, the aldehyde or ketone is at the top.

Formula unit The formula that identifies the smallest neutral unit of a compound.

Formula weight The sum of the atomic weights of the atoms in one formula unit of any compound.

Free radical An atom or molecule with an unpaired electron.

Free-energy change (ΔG) The criterion for spontaneous change (negative ΔG; $\Delta G = \Delta H - T\Delta S$).

Functional group An atom or group of atoms within a molecule that has a characteristic structure and chemical behavior.

Functional group isomer Isomers having the same chemical formula but belonging to different chemical families due to differences in bonding; ethyl alcohol and dimethyl ether are examples of functional group isomers.

Gamma (γ) radiation Radioactivity consisting of high-energy light waves.

Gas A substance that has neither a definite volume nor a definite shape.

Gas constant (R) The constant R in the ideal gas law, $PV = nRT$.

Gas laws A series of laws that predict the influence of pressure (P), volume (V), and temperature (T) on any gas or mixture of gases.

Gay-Lussac's law For a fixed amount of gas at a constant voume, pressure is directly proportional to the Kelvin temperature $(P/T = \text{constant, or } P_1/T_1 = P_2/T_2)$.

Gene Segment of DNA that directs the synthesis of a single polypeptide.

Genetic (enzyme) control Regulation of enzyme activity by control of the synthesis of enzymes.

Genetic code The sequence of nucleotides, coded in triplets (codons) in mRNA, that determines the sequence of amino acids in protein synthesis.

Genome All of the genetic material in the chromosomes of an organism; its size is given as the number of base pairs.

Genomics The study of whole sets of genes and their functions.

Globular protein A water-soluble protein whose chain is folded in a compact shape with hydrophilic groups on the outside.

Glomerular filtrate Fluid that enters the nephron from the glomerulus; filtered blood plasma.

Gluconeogenesis The biochemical pathway for the synthesis of glucose from non-carbohydrates, such as lactate, amino acids, or glycerol.

Glycerophospholipid (phosphoglyceride) A lipid in which glycerol is linked by ester bonds to two fatty acids and one phosphate, which is in turn linked by another ester bond to an amino alcohol (or other alcohol).

Glycogenesis The biochemical pathway for synthesis of glycogen.

Glycogenolysis The biochemical pathway for breakdown of glycogen to free glucose.

Glycol A dialcohol, or diol having the two —OH groups on adjacent carbons.

Glycolipid A lipid with a fatty acid bonded to the $C2—NH_2$ and a sugar bonded to the $C1—OH$ group of sphingosine.

Glycolysis The biochemical pathway that breaks down a molecule of glucose into two molecules of pyruvate plus energy.

Glycoprotein A protein that contains a short carbohydrate chain.

Glycoside A cyclic acetal formed by reaction of a monosaccharide with an alcohol, accompanied by loss of H_2O.

Glycosidic bond Bond between the anomeric carbon atom of a monosaccharide and an —OR group.

Gram-equivalent For ions, the molar mass of the ion divided by the ionic charge.

Group One of the 18 vertical columns of elements in the periodic table.

Guanosine diphosphate (GDP) An energy-carrying molecule that can gain or lose a phosphoryl group to transfer energy.

Guanosine triphosphate (GTP) An energy-carrying molecule similar to ATP; removal of a phosphoryl group to give GDP releases free energy.

Half-life ($t_{1/2}$) The amount of time required for one-half of a radioactive sample to decay.

Halogen An element in group 7A of the periodic table.

Halogenation (alkene) The addition of Cl_2 or Br_2 to a multiple bond to give a 1,2-dihalide product.

Halogenation (aromatic) The substitution of a halogen group (—X) for a hydrogen on an aromatic ring.

Heat The kinetic energy transferred from a hotter object to a colder object when the two are in contact.

Heat of fusion The quantity of heat required to completely melt a substance once it has reached its melting point.

Heat of reaction (ΔH) The amount of heat absorbed or released in a reaction.

Heat of vaporization The quantity of heat needed to completely vaporize a liquid once it has reached its boiling point.

Hemiacetal A compound with both an alcohol-like —OH group and an ether-like —OR group bonded to the same carbon atom.

Hemostasis The stopping of bleeding.

Henderson-Hasselbalch equation The logarithmic form of the K_a equation for a weak acid, used in applications involving buffer solutions.

Henry's law The solubility of a gas in a liquid is directly proportional to its partial pressure over the liquid at constant temperature.

Heterocycle A ring that contains nitrogen or some other atom in addition to carbon.

Heterogeneous mixture A nonuniform mixture that has regions of different composition.

Heterogeneous nuclear RNA The initially synthesized mRNA strand containing both introns and exons.

Homogeneous mixture A uniform mixture that has the same composition throughout.

Hormone A chemical messenger secreted by cells of the endocrine system and transported through the bloodstream to target cells with appropriate receptors where it elicits a response.

Hydration The addition of water to a multiple bond to give an alcohol product.

Hydrocarbon An organic compound that contains only carbon and hydrogen.

Hydrogen bond The attraction between a hydrogen atom bonded to an electronegative O, N, or F atom and another nearby electronegative O, N, or F atom.

Hydrogenation The addition of H_2 to a multiple bond to give a saturated product.

Hydrohalogenation The addition of HCl or HBr to a multiple bond to give an alkyl halide product.

Hydrolysis A reaction in which a bond or bonds are broken and the H— and —OH of water add to the atoms of the broken bond or bonds.

Hydronium ion The H_3O^+ ion, formed when an acid reacts with water.

Hydrophilic Water-loving; a hydrophilic substance dissolves in water.

Hydrophobic Water-fearing; a hydrophobic substance does not dissolve in water.

Hygroscopic Having the ability to pull water molecules from the surrounding atmosphere.

Hyperglycemia Higher-than-normal blood glucose concentration.

Hypertonic Having an osmolarity greater than the surrounding blood plasma or cells.

Hypoglycemia Lower-than-normal blood glucose concentration.

Hypotonic Having an osmolarity less than the surrounding blood plasma or cells.

Ideal gas A gas that obeys all the assumptions of the kinetic-molecular theory.

Ideal gas law A general expression relating pressure, volume, temperature, and amount for an ideal gas: $PV = nRT$.

Immune response Defense mechanism of the immune system dependent on the recognition of specific antigens, including viruses, bacteria, toxic substances, and infected cells; either cell-mediated or antibody-mediated.

Induced-fit model A model of enzyme action in which the enzyme has a flexible active site that changes shape to best fit the substrate and catalyze the reaction.

Inflammation Result of the inflammatory response; includes swelling, redness, warmth, and pain.

Inflammatory response A nonspecific defense mechanism triggered by antigens or tissue damage.

Inhibition (of an enzyme) Any process that slows or stops the action of an enzyme.

Inner transition metal element An element in one of the 14 groups shown separately at the bottom of the periodic table.

Intermolecular force A force that acts between molecules and holds molecules close to one another in liquids and solids.

Interstitial fluid Fluid surrounding cells: an extracellular fluid.

Intracellular fluid Fluid inside cells.

Intron A portion of DNA between coding regions of a gene (exons); is transcribed and then removed from final messenger RNA.

Ion An electrically charged atom or group of atoms.

Ion-product constant for water (K_w) The product of the H_3O^+ and OH^- molar concentrations in water or any aqueous solution ($K_w = [H_3O^+][OH^-] = 1.00 \times 10^{-14}$).

Ionic bond The electrical attractions between ions of opposite charge in a crystal.

Ionic compound A compound that contains ionic bonds.

Ionic equation An equation in which ions are explicitly shown.

Ionic solid A crystalline solid held together by ionic bonds.

Ionization energy The energy required to remove one electron from a single atom in the gaseous state.

Ionizing radiation A general name for high-energy radiation of all kinds.

Irreversible (enzyme) inhibition Enzyme deactivation in which an inhibitor forms covalent bonds to the active site, permanently blocking it.

Isoelectric point (pI) The pH at which a sample of an amino acid has equal number of + and − charges.

Isomers Compounds with the same molecular formula but different structures.

Isopropyl group The branched-chain alkyl group —$CH(CH_3)_2$.

Isotonic Having the same osmolarity.

Isotopes Atoms with identical atomic numbers but different mass numbers.

Ketoacidosis Lowered blood pH due to accumulation of ketone bodies.

Ketogenesis The synthesis of ketone bodies from acetyl-SCoA.

Ketone A compound that has a carbonyl group bonded to two carbons in organic groups that can be the same or different, $R_2C=O$, RCOR'.

Ketone bodies Compounds produced in the liver that can be used as fuel by muscle and brain tissue; 3-hydroxybutyrate, ace-toacetate, and acetone.

Ketose A monosaccharide that contains a ketone carbonyl group.

Kinetic energy The energy of an object in motion.

Kinetic-molecular theory (KMT) of gases A group of assumptions that explain the behavior of gases.

L-Sugar Monosaccharide with the —OH group on the chiral carbon atom farthest from the carbonyl group pointing to the left in a Fischer projection.

Law of conservation of energy Energy can be neither created nor destroyed in any physical or chemical change.

Law of conservation of mass Matter can be neither created nor destroyed in any physical or chemical change.

Le Châtelier's principle When a stress is applied to a system in equilibrium, the equilibrium shifts to relieve the stress.

Lewis base A compound containing an unshared pair of electrons.

Lewis structure A molecular representation that shows both the connections among atoms and the locations of lone-pair valence electrons.

Limiting reagent The reactant that runs out first in a chemical reaction.

Line structure A shorthand way of drawing structures in which atoms aren't shown; instead, a carbon atom is understood to be at every intersection of lines, and hydrogens are filled in mentally.

Lipid A naturally occurring molecule from a plant or animal that is soluble in nonpolar organic solvents.

Lipid bilayer The basic structural unit of cell membranes; composed of two parallel sheets of membrane lipid molecules arranged tail to tail.

Lipogenesis The biochemical pathway for synthesis of fatty acids from acetyl-CoA.

Lipoprotein A lipid-protein complex that transports lipids.

Liposome A spherical structure in which a lipid bilayer surrounds a water droplet.

Liquid A substance that has a definite volume but that changes shape to fit its container.

London dispersion force The short-lived attractive force due to the constant motion of electrons within molecules.

Lone pair A pair of electrons that is not used for bonding.

Main group element An element in one of the two groups on the left or the six groups on the right of the periodic table.

Markovnikov's rule In the addition of HX to an alkene, the H becomes attached to the carbon that already has the most H's, and the X becomes attached to the carbon that has fewer H's.

Mass A measure of the amount of matter in an object.

Mass/mass percent concentration [(m/m)%] Concentration expressed as the number of grams of solute per 100 grams of solution.

Mass number (A) The total number of protons and neutrons in an atom.

Mass/volume percent concentration [(m/v)%] Concentration expressed as the number of grams of solute per 100 mL of solution.

Matter The physical material that makes up the universe; anything that has mass and occupies space.

Melting point (mp) The temperature at which solid and liquid are in equilibrium.

Messenger RNA (mRNA) The RNA that carries the code transcribed from DNA and directs protein synthesis.

Metal A malleable element with a lustrous appearance that is a good conductor of heat and electricity.

Metalloid An element whose properties are intermediate between those of a metal and a nonmetal.

Methyl group The $-CH_3$ alkyl group.

Methylene Another name for a $-CH_2$ unit.

Micelle A spherical cluster formed by the aggregation of soap or detergent molecules so that their hydrophobic ends are in the center and their hydrophilic ends are on the surface.

Miscible Mutually soluble in all proportions.

Mitochondrial matrix The space surrounded by the inner membrane of a mitochondrion.

Mitochondrion (plural, mitochondria) An egg-shaped organelle where small molecules

are broken down to provide the energy for an organism.

Mixture A blend of two or more substances, each of which retains its chemical identity.

Mobilization (of triacylglycerols) Hydrolysis of triacylglycerols in adipose tissue and release of fatty acids into the bloodstream.

Molar mass The mass in grams of one mole of a substance, numerically equal to the molecular weight.

Molarity (M) Concentration expressed as the number of moles of solute per liter of solution.

Mole The amount of a substance corresponding to 6.02×10^{23} units.

Molecular compound A compound that consists of molecules rather than ions.

Molecular formula A formula that shows the numbers and kinds of atoms in one molecule of a compound.

Molecular weight The sum of the atomic weights of the atoms in a molecule.

Molecule A group of atoms held together by covalent bonds.

Monomer A small molecule that is used to prepare a polymer.

Monosaccharide (simple sugar) A carbohydrate with 3–7 carbon atoms.

Mutagen A substance that causes mutations.

Mutarotation Change in rotation of plane-polarized light resulting from the equilibrium between cyclic anomers and the open-chain form of a sugar.

Mutation An error in base sequence that is carried along in DNA replication.

Native protein A protein with the shape (secondary, tertiary, and quaternary structure) in which it exists naturally in living organisms.

Net ionic equation An equation that does not include spectator ions.

Neurotransmitter A chemical messenger that travels between a neuron and a neighboring neuron or other target cell to transmit a nerve impulse.

Neutralization reaction The reaction of an acid with a base.

Neutron An electrically neutral subatomic particle.

Nitration The substitution of a nitro group ($-NO_2$) for a hydrogen on an aromatic ring.

Noble gas An element in group 8A of the periodic table.

Noncovalent forces Forces of attraction other than covalent bonds that can act between molecules or within molecules.

Nonelectrolyte A substance that does not produce ions when dissolved in water.

Nonessential amino acid One of 11 amino acids that are synthesized in the body and are therefore not necessary in the diet.

Nonmetal An element that is a poor conductor of heat and electricity.

Normal boiling point The boiling point at a pressure of exactly 1 atmosphere.

Normality (N) A measure of acid (or base) concentration expressed as the number of acid (or base) equivalents per liter of solution.

Nuclear decay The spontaneous emission of a particle from an unstable nucleus.

Nuclear fission The fragmenting of heavy nuclei.

Nuclear fusion The joining together of light nuclei.

Nuclear reaction A reaction that changes an atomic nucleus, usually causing the change of one element into another.

Nucleic acid A polymer of nucleotides.

Nucleon A general term for both protons and neutrons.

Nucleoside A 5-carbon sugar bonded to a cyclic amine base; like a nucleotide but missing the phosphate group.

Nucleotide A 5-carbon sugar bonded to a cyclic amine base and one phosphate group (a nucleoside monophosphate); monomer for nucleic acids.

Nucleus The dense, central core of an atom that contains protons and neutrons.

Nuclide The nucleus of a specific isotope of an element.

Octet rule Main-group elements tend to undergo reactions that leave them with 8 valence electrons.

Oil A mixture of triacylglycerols that is liquid because it contains a high proportion of unsaturated fatty acids.

Orbital A region of space within an atom where an electron in a given subshell can be found.

Organic chemistry The study of carbon compounds.

Osmolarity (osmol) The sum of the molarities of all dissolved particles in a solution.

Osmosis The passage of solvent through a semipermeable membrane separating two solutions of different concentration.

Osmotic pressure The amount of external pressure applied to the more concentrated solution to halt the passage of solvent molecules across a semipermeable membrane.

Oxidation The loss of one or more electrons by an atom.

Oxidation number A number that indicates whether an atom is neutral, electron-rich, or electron-poor.

Oxidation-Reduction, or Redox, reaction A reaction in which electrons are transferred from one atom to another.

Oxidative deamination Conversion of an amino acid $-NH_2$ group to an α-keto group, with removal of NH_4^+.

Oxidative phosphorylation The synthesis of ATP from ADP using energy released in the electron-transport chain.

Oxidizing agent A reactant that causes an oxidation by taking electrons from or increasing the oxidation number of another reactant.

p-Block element A main group element that results from the filling of p orbitals.

p function The negative common logarithm of some variable, $pX = -(\log X)$.

Partial pressure The pressure exerted by a gas in a mixture.

Parts per billion (ppb) Number of parts of solute (in mass or volume) per one billion parts of solution.

Parts per million (ppm) Number of parts of solute (in mass or volume) per one million parts of solution.

Passive transport Movement of a substance across a cell membrane without the use of energy, from a region of higher concentration to a region of lower concentration.

Pentose phosphate pathway The biochemical pathway that produces ribose (a pentose), NADPH, and other sugar phosphates from glucose; an alternative to glycolysis.

Peptide bond An amide bond that links two amino acids together.

Percent yield The percent of the theoretical yield actually obtained from a chemical reaction.

Period One of the seven horizontal rows of elements in the periodic table.

Periodic table A table of the elements in order of increasing atomic number and grouped according to their chemical similarities.

pH A measure of the acid strength of a solution; the negative common logarithm of the H_3O^+ concentration.

Phenol A compound that has an —OH group bonded directly to an aromatic, benzene-like ring, Ar—OH.

Phenyl The C_6H_5— group.

Phosphate ester A compound formed by reaction of an alcohol with phosphoric acid; may be a monoester, $ROPO_3H_2$; a diester, $(RO)_2PO_3H$; or a triester, $(RO)_3PO$; also may be a di- or triphosphate.

Phospholipid A lipid that has an ester link between phosphoric acid and an alcohol (glycerol or sphingosine).

Phosphoryl group The —PO_3^{2-} group in organic phosphates.

Phosphorylation Transfer of a phosphoryl group, —PO_3^{2-}, between organic molecules.

Physical change A change that does not affect the chemical makeup of a substance or object.

Physical quantity A physical property that can be measured.

Polar covalent bond A bond in which the electrons are attracted more strongly by one atom than by the other.

Polyatomic ion An ion that is composed of more than one atom.

Polymer A large molecule formed by the repetitive bonding together of many smaller molecules.

Polymorphism A variation in DNA sequence within a population.

Polysaccharide (complex carbohydrate) A carbohydrate that is a polymer of monosaccharides.

Polyunsaturated fatty acid A long-chain fatty acid that has two or more carbon-carbon double bonds.

Positron A "positive electron," which has the same mass as an electron but a positive charge.

Potential energy Energy that is stored because of position, composition, or shape.

Precipitate An insoluble solid that forms in solution during a chemical reaction.

Pressure The force per unit area pushing against a surface.

Primary carbon atom A carbon atom with one other carbon attached to it.

Primary protein structure The sequence in which amino acids are linked by peptide bonds in a protein.

Product A substance that is formed in a chemical reaction and is written on the right side of the reaction arrow in a chemical equation.

Property A characteristic useful for identifying a substance or object.

propyl group The straight-chain alkyl group —$CH_2CH_2CH_3$.

Protein A large biological molecule made of many amino acids linked together through amide (peptide) bonds.

Proton A positively charged subatomic particle.

Pure substance A substance that has uniform chemical composition throughout.

Quaternary ammonium ion A positive ion with four organic groups bonded to the nitrogen atom.

Quaternary ammonium salt An ionic compound composed of a quaternary ammonium ion and an anion.

Quaternary carbon atom A carbon atom with four other carbons attached to it.

Quaternary protein structure The way in which two or more protein chains aggregate to form large, ordered structures.

Radioactivity The spontaneous emission of radiation from a nucleus.

Radioisotope A radioactive isotope.

Radionuclide The nucleus of a radioactive isotope.

Reabsorption (kidney) Movement of solutes out of filtrate in a kidney tubule.

Reactant A substance that undergoes change in a chemical reaction and is written on the left side of the reaction arrow in a chemical equation.

Reaction mechanism A description of the individual steps by which old bonds are broken and new bonds are formed in a reaction.

Reaction rate A measure of how rapidly a reaction occurs.

Rearrangement reaction A general reaction type in which a molecule undergoes bond reorganization to yield an isomer.

Receptor A molecule or portion of a molecule with which a hormone, neurotransmitter, or other biochemically active molecule interacts to initiate a response in a target cell.

Recombinant DNA DNA that contains segments from two different species.

Reducing agent A reactant that causes a reduction by giving up electrons or increasing the oxidation number of another reactant.

Reducing sugar A carbohydrate that reacts in basic solution with a mild oxidizing agent.

Reduction The gain of one or more electrons by an atom.

Reductive deamination Conversion of an α-keto acid to an amino acid by reaction with NH_4^+.

Regular tetrahedron A geometric figure with four identical triangular faces.

Replication The process by which copies of DNA are made when a cell divides.

Residue (amino acid) An amino acid unit in a polypeptide.

Resonance The phenomenon where the true structure of a molecule is an average among two or more conventional structures.

Reversible reaction A reaction that can go in either the forward direction or the reverse direction, from products to reactants or reactants to products.

Ribonucleotide A nucleotide containing D-ribose.

Ribosomal RNA (rRNA) The RNA that is complexed with proteins in ribosomes.

Ribosome The structure in the cell where protein synthesis occurs; composed of protein and rRNA.

Ribozyme RNA that acts as an enzyme.

RNA (ribonucleic acids) The nucleic acids (messenger, transfer, and ribosomal) responsible for putting the genetic information to use in protein synthesis; polymers of ribonucleotides.

Rounding off A procedure used for deleting nonsignificant figures.

s-Block element A main group element that results from the filling of an s orbital.

Salt An ionic compound formed from reaction of an acid with a base.

Saponification The reaction of an ester with aqueous hydroxide ion to yield an alcohol and the metal salt of a carboxylic acid.

Saturated A molecule whose carbon atoms bond to the maximum number of hydrogen atoms.

Saturated fatty acid A long-chain carboxylic acid containing only carbon-carbon single bonds.

Saturated solution A solution that contains the maximum amount of dissolved solute at equilibrium.

Scientific Method Systematic process of observation, hypothesis, and experimentation to expand and refine a body of knowledge.

Scientific notation A number expressed as the product of a number between 1 and 10, times the number 10 raised to a power.

Second messenger Chemical messenger released inside a cell when a hydrophilic hormone or neurotransmitter interacts with a receptor on the cell surface.

Secondary carbon atom A carbon atom with two other carbons attached to it.

Secondary protein structure Regular and repeating structural patterns (for example, α-helix, β-sheet) created by hydrogen bonding between backbone atoms in neighboring segments of protein chains.

Secretion (kidney) Movement of solutes into filtrate in a kidney tubule.

SI units Units of measurement defined by the International System of Units.

Side chain (amino acid) The group bonded to the carbon next to the carboxyl group in an amino acid; different in different amino acids.

Significant figures The number of meaningful digits used to express a value.

Simple diffusion Passive transport by the random motion of diffusion through the cell membrane.

Simple protein A protein composed of only amino acid residues.

Single bond A covalent bond formed by sharing one electron pair.

Single-nucleotide polymorphism Common single-base-pair variation in DNA.

Soap The mixture of salts of fatty acids formed on saponification of animal fat.

Solid A substance that has a definite shape and volume.

Solubility The maximum amount of a substance that will dissolve in a given amount of solvent at a specified temperature.

Solute A substance dissolved in a liquid.

Solution A homogeneous mixture that contains particles the size of a typical ion or small molecule.

Solvation The clustering of solvent molecules around a dissolved solute molecule or ion.

Solvent The liquid in which another substance is dissolved.

Specific gravity The density of a substance divided by the density of water at the same temperature.

Specific heat The amount of heat that will raise the temperature of 1 g of a substance by 1 °C.

Specificity (enzyme) The limitation of the activity of an enzyme to a specific substrate, specific reaction, or specific type of reaction.

Spectator ion An ion that appears unchanged on both sides of a reaction arrow.

Sphingolipid A lipid derived from the amino alcohol sphingosine.

Spontaneous process A process or reaction that, once started, proceeds on its own without any external influence.

Standard molar volume The volume of one mole of a gas at standard temperature and pressure (22.4 L).

Standard temperature and pressure (STP) Standard conditions for a gas, defined as 0 °C (273 K) and 1 atm (760 mmHg) pressure.

State of matter The physical state of a substance as a solid, a liquid, or a gas.

Stereoisomers Isomers that have the same molecular and structural formulas, but different spatial arrangements of their atoms.

Sterol A lipid whose structure is based on the following tetracyclic (four-ring) carbon skeleton.

Straight-chain alkane An alkane that has all its carbons connected in a row.

Strong acid An acid that gives up H^+ easily and is essentially 100% dissociated in water.

Strong base A base that has a high affinity for H^+ and holds it tightly.

Strong electrolyte A substance that ionizes completely when dissolved in water.

Structural formula A molecular representation that shows the connections among atoms by using lines to represent covalent bonds.

Subatomic particles Three kinds of fundamental particles from which atoms are made: protons, neutrons, and electrons.

Substituent An atom or group of atoms attached to a parent compound.

Substitution reaction A general reaction type in which an atom or group of atoms in a molecule is replaced by another atom or group of atoms.

Substrate A reactant in an enzyme catalyzed reaction.

Sulfonation The substitution of a sulfonic acid group ($—SO_3H$) for a hydrogen on an aromatic ring.

Supersaturated solution A solution that contains more than the maximum amount of dissolved solute; a nonequilibrium situation.

Synapse The place where the tip of a neuron and its target cell lie adjacent to each other.

Telomeres The ends of chromosomes; in humans, contain long series of repeating groups of nucleotides.

Temperature The measure of how hot or cold an object is.

Tertiary carbon atom A carbon atom with three other carbons attached to it.

Tertiary protein structure The way in which an entire protein chain is coiled and folded into its specific three-dimensional shape.

Theoretical yield The amount of product formed assuming complete reaction of the limiting reagent.

Thiol A compound that contains an $—SH$ group, $R—SH$.

Titration A procedure for determining the total acid or base concentration of a solution.

Transamination The interchange of the amino group of an amino acid and the keto group of an α-keto acid.

Transcription The process by which the information in DNA is read and used to synthesize RNA.

Transfer RNA (tRNA) The RNA that transports amino acids into position for protein synthesis.

Transition metal element An element in one of the 10 smaller groups near the middle of the periodic table.

Translation The process by which RNA directs protein synthesis.

Transmutation The change of one element into another.

Triacylglycerol (triglyceride) A triester of glycerol with three fatty acids.

Triple bond A covalent bond formed by sharing three electron pairs.

Turnover number The maximum number of substrate molecules acted upon by one molecule of enzyme per unit time.

Uncompetitive (enzyme) inhibition Enzyme regulation in which an inhibitor binds to an enzyme elsewhere than at the active site, thereby changing the shape of the enzyme's active site and reducing its efficiency.

Unit A defined quantity used as a standard of measurement.

Unsaturated A molecule that contains a carbon–carbon multiple bond, to which more hydrogen atoms can be added.

Unsaturated fatty acid A long-chain carboxylic acid containing one or more carbon–carbon double bonds.

Urea cycle The cyclic biochemical pathway that produces urea for excretion.

Valence electron An electron in the outermost, or valence, shell of an atom.

Valence shell The outermost electron shell of an atom.

Valence-shell electron-pair repulsion (VSEPR) model A method for predicting molecular shape by noting how many electron charge clouds surround atoms and assuming that the clouds orient as far away from one another as possible.

Vapor The gas molecules in equilibrium with a liquid.

Vapor pressure The partial pressure of gas molecules in equilibrium with a liquid.

Vitamin An organic molecule, essential in trace amounts that must be obtained in the diet because it is not synthesized in the body.

Volume/volume percent concentration [(v/v)%] Concentration expressed as the number of milliliters of solute dissolved in 100 mL of solution.

Wax A mixture of esters of long-chain carboxylic acids with long-chain alcohols.

Weak acid An acid that gives up H^+ with difficulty and is less than 100% dissociated in water.

Weak base A base that has only a slight affinity for H^+ and holds it weakly.

Weak electrolyte A substance that is only partly ionized in water.

Weight A measure of the gravitational force that the earth or other large body exerts on an object.

Whole blood Blood plasma plus blood cells.

X rays Electromagnetic radiation with an energy somewhat less than that of γ rays.

Zwitterion A neutral dipolar ion that has one + charge and one − charge.

Zymogen A compound that becomes an active enzyme after undergoing a chemical change.

Short answers are given for in-chapter problems, *Understanding Key Concepts* problems, and even-numbered end-of-chapter problems. Explanations and full answers for all problems are provided in the accompanying *Study Guide and Solutions Manual*.

Chapter 1

1.1 physical: (a), (d); chemical: (b), (c) **1.2** solid **1.3** mixture (heterogeneous): (a), (d); pure (element): (b), (c) **1.4** physical: (a), (c); chemical: (b), (d) **1.5** chemical change **1.6** (a) 2 (b) 1 (c) 6 (d) 5 (e) 4 (f) 3 **1.7** (a) 1 nitrogen atom, 3 hydrogen atoms (b) 1 sodium atom, 1 hydrogen atom, 1 carbon atom, 3 oxygen atoms (c) 8 carbon atoms, 18 hydrogen atoms (d) 6 carbon atoms, 8 hydrogen atoms, 6 oxygen atoms **1.8** Metalloids are at the boundary between metals and nonmetals. **1.9** metal; physical properties—solubility of compounds, tendency of elemental form to vaporize; chemical; reacts to form soluble compounds **1.10** (a) 0.01 m (b) 0.1 g (c) 1000 m (d) 0.000 001 s (e) 0.000 000 001 g **1.11** (a) 3 (b) 4 (c) 5 (d) exact **1.12** 32.3 °C; three significant figures **1.13** (a) 5.8×10^{-2} g (b) 4.6792×10^{4} m (c) 6.072×10^{-3} cm (d) 3.453×10^{2} kg **1.14** (a) 48,850 mg (b) 0.000 008 3 m (c) 0.0400 m **1.15** (a) 6.3000×10^{5} (b) 1.30×10^{3} (c) 7.942×10^{11} **1.16** (a) 2.30 g (b) 188.38 mL (c) 0.009 L (d) 1.000 kg **1.17** (a) 50.9 mL (b) 0.078 g (c) 11.9 m (d) 51 mg (e) 103 **1.18** (a) 454 g (b) 2.5 L (c) 105 qt **1.19** 795 mL **1.20** 7.36 m/s **1.21** (a) 10.6 mg/kg (b) 36 mg/kg **1.22** 331.0 K **1.23** 39 °C; 102 °F **1.24** 7,700 cal **1.25** 0.21 cal/g · °C **1.26** float; density = 0.637 g/cm³ **1.27** 8.392 mL **1.28** more dense **1.29** gases: helium (He), neon (Ne), argon (Ar), krypton (Kr), xenon (Xe), radon (Rn) coinage metals: copper (Cu), silver (Ag), gold (Au) **1.30** red: vanadium, metal; green: boron, metalloid; blue: bromine, nonmetal **1.31** Americium, a metal **1.32** (a) 0.978 (b) three (c) less dense **1.33** The smaller cylinder is more precise because the gradations are smaller. **1.34** 3 1/8 in.; 8.0 cm **1.35** start: 0.11 mL stop: 0.25 mL volume: 0.14 mL **1.36** higher in chloroform **1.38** physical: (a), (d); chemical (b), (c) **1.40** A gas has no definite shape or volume; a liquid has no definite shape but has a definite volume; a solid has a definite volume and a definite shape. **1.42** gas **1.44** mixture: (a), (b), (d), (f); pure: (c), (e) **1.46** (a) reactant: hydrogen peroxide; products: water, oxygen (b) compounds: hydrogen peroxide, water; element: oxygen **1.48** Metals: lustrous, malleable, conductors of heat and electricity; nonmetals: gases or brittle solids, nonconductors; metalloids: properties intermediate between metals and nonmetals. **1.50** (a) Gd (b) Ge (c) Tc (d) As (e) Cd **1.52** (a) Br (b) Mn (c) C (d) K **1.54** Carbon, hydrogen, nitrogen, oxygen; ten atoms **1.56** $C_{13}H_{18}O_2$ **1.58** A physical quantity consists of a number and a unit. **1.60** (a) cubic centimeter (b) decimeter (c) millimeter (d) nanoliter (e) milligram (f) cubic meter **1.62** 10^9 pg, 3.5×10^4 pg **1.64** (a) 9.457×10^3 (b) 7×10^{-5} (c) 2.000×10^{10} (d) 1.2345×10^{-2} (e) 6.5238×10^2 **1.66** (a) 6 (b) 3 (c) 3 (d) 4 (e) 1 to 5 (f) 2 or 3 **1.68** (a) 7,926 mi, 7,900 mi, 7,926.38 mi (b) 7.926381×10^3 mi **1.70** (a) 12.1 g (b) 96.19 cm (c) 263 mL (d) 20.9 mg **1.72** (a) 0.3614 cg (b) 0.0120 ML (c) 0.0144 mm (d) 60.3 ng (e) 1.745 dL (f) 1.5×10^3 cm **1.74** (a) 97.8 kg (b) 0.133 mL (c) 0.46 ng **1.76** (a) 62.1 mi/hr (b) 91.1 ft/s **1.78** (a) 6×10^{-4} cm (b) 2×10^3 cells/cm; 4×10^3 cells/in. **1.80** 10 g **1.82** 6×10^{10} cells **1.84** 537 cal = 0.537 kcal **1.86** 0.092 cal/g · °C **1.88** Hg: 76 °C; Fe: 40.7 °C **1.90** 0.179 g/cm³ **1.92** 11.4 g/cm³ **1.94** 159 mL **1.96** 9 carbons, 8 hydrogens, 4 oxygens; 21 atoms; solid **1.98** −2 °C; 271 K **1.100** (a) BMI = 29 (b) BMI = 23.7 (c) BMI = 24.4; individual (a) **1.102** nonmetal, solid, nonconducting, not malleable **1.104** 3.12 in; 7.92 cm Discrepancies are due to rounding errors and changes in significant figures. **1.106** (a) 3.5×10^5 cal (1.46×10^6 J); (b) 9.86 °C **1.108** 3.9×10^{-2} g/dL iron, 8.3×10^{-3} g/dL calcium, 2.24×10^{-1} g/dL cholesterol **1.110** 7.8×10^6 mL/day **1.112** 0.13 g **1.114** 4.4 g; 0.0097 lb **1.116** 2200 mL **1.118** 2.2 tablespoons **1.120** iron **1.122** float

Chapter 2

2.1 1.39×10^{-8} g **2.2** 6.02×10^{23} atoms in all cases **2.3** When the mass in grams is numerically equal to the mass in amu, there are 6.02×10^{23} atoms. **2.4** 1.1×10^{-15} (or 1.1×10^{-13} %) **2.5** (a) Re (b) Sr (c) Te **2.6** 27 protons, 27 electrons, 33 neutrons **2.7** The answers agree. **2.8** $^{79}_{35}$Br, $^{81}_{35}$Br **2.9** $^{35}_{17}$Cl $^{37}_{17}$Cl **2.10** group 3A, period 3 **2.11** silver, calcium **2.12** nitrogen (2), phosphorus (3), arsenic (4), antimony (5), bismuth (6) **2.13** Metals: titanium, scandium; nonmetals: selenium, argon, astatine; metalloids: tellurium **2.14** (a) nonmetal, main group, noble gas (b) metal, main group (c) nonmetal, main group (d) metal, transition element **2.15** thirteen He-4 nuclei; four additional neutrons **2.16** (a) Na-23, Group 1A, third period, metal; (b) O-18, Group 6A, sixth period, nonmetal **2.17** 12, magnesium **2.18** sulfur; main group (6A); nonmetal; last electron found in a $3p$ orbital. **2.19** (a) $1s^2 2s^2 2p^2$ (b) $1s^2 2s^2 2p^6 3s^2 3p^3$ (c) $1s^2 2s^2 2p^6 3s^2 3p^5$ (d) $1s^2 2s^2 2p^6 3s^2 3p^6 4s^1$ **2.20** $4p^3$, all are unpaired **2.21** gallium **2.22** (a) $1s^2 2s^2 2p^5$; [He] $2s^2 2p^5$ (b) $1s^2 2s^2 2p^6 3s^2 3p^1$; [Ne] $3s^2 3p^1$ (c) $1s^2 2s^2 2p^6 3s^2 3p^6 4s^2 3d^{10} 4p^3$; [Ar] $4s^2 3d^{10} 4p^3$ **2.23** group 2A **2.24** group 7A, $1s^2 2s^2 2p^6 3s^2 3p^5$ **2.25** group 6A, $ns^2 np^4$ **2.26** ·X· **2.27** :R̈n: ·Pb· :Ẍe: ·Ra· **2.28** red = 700 − 780 nm; blue = 400 − 480 nm; blue = higher energy **2.29**

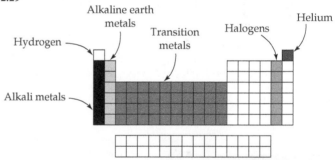

2.30 red: gas (fluorine); blue: atomic number 79 (gold); green: (calcium); beryllium, magnesium, strontium, barium, and radium are similar. **2.31**

Two p electrons in 3rd shell

$ns^2 np^5$

Completely filled valence shell

2.32 selenium **2.33** $1s^2 2s^2 2p^6 3s^2 3p^6 4s^2 3d^{10} 4p^3$ **2.34** Matter is composed of atoms. Atoms of different elements differ. Compounds consist of different atoms combined in specific proportions. Atoms do not change in chemical reactions. **2.36** (a) 3.4702×10^{-22} g (b) 2.1801×10^{-22} g (c) 6.6465×10^{-24} g **2.38** 14.01 g **2.40** 6.022×10^{23} atoms **2.42** protons (+ charge, 1 amu); neutrons (no charge, 1 amu); electrons (− charge, 0.0005 amu). **2.44** 18, 20, 22 **2.46** (a) and (c) **2.48** (a) $^{14}_{6}$C (b) $^{39}_{19}$K (c) $^{20}_{10}$Ne **2.50** $^{12}_{6}$C—six neutrons $^{13}_{6}$C—seven neutrons $^{14}_{6}$C—eight neutrons **2.52** 63.55 amu **2.54** Eight electrons are needed to fill the $3s$ and $3p$ subshells. **2.56** Am, metal **2.58** (a, b) transition metals (c) $3d$ **2.60** (a) Rb: (i), (v), (vii) (b) W: (i), (iv) (c) Ge: (iii), (v) (d) Kr: (ii), (v), (vi) **2.62** selenium **2.64** sodium, potassium, rubidium, cesium, francium **2.66** 2 **2.68** 2, 8, 18 **2.70** 3, 4, 5 **2.72** 10, neon

2.74 (a) two paired, two unpaired **(b)** four paired, one unpaired **(c)** two unpaired **2.76** 2, 1, 2, 1, 3, 3 **2.78** 2 **2.80** beryllium, $2s$; arsenic, $4p$ **2.82 (a)** 8 **(b)** 4 **(c)** 2 **(d)** 1 **(e)** 3 **(f)** 7 **2.84** A scanning tunneling microscope has much higher resolution. **2.86** H, He **2.88 (a)** ultraviolet **(b)** gamma waves **(c)** X rays **2.90** He, Ne, Ar, Kr, Xe, Rn **2.92** Tellurium atoms have more neutrons than iodine atoms. **2.94** 1 (2 e), 2 (8 e), 3 (18 e), 4 (32 e), 5 (18 e), 6 (4 e) **2.96** 79.90 amu **2.98** Sr, metal, group 2A, period 5, 38 protons **2.100** 2, 8, 18, 18, 4; metal **2.102 (a)** The $4s$ subshell fills before $3d$ **(b)** The $2s$ subshell fills before $2p$. **(c)** Silicon has 14 electrons: $1s^2\,2s^2\,2p^6\,3s^2\,3p^2$ **(d)** The $3s$ electrons have opposite spins. **2.104** Electrons will fill or half-fill a d subshell instead of filling an s subshell of a higher shell. **2.106** $7p$

Chapter 3

3.1 Mg^{2+} is a cation **3.2** S^{-2} is an anion **3.3** O^{2-} is an anion **3.4** less than Kr, but higher than most other elements **3.5 (a)** B **(b)** Ca **(c)** Sc **3.6 (a)** H **(b)** S **(c)** Cr **3.7** Common ionic substances: high-melting crystalline solids, good conductors of electricity when molten or in solution. Ionic liquids: low-melting, low volatility, high viscosity, low to moderate conductivity. **3.8** Potassium $(1s^2\,2s^2\,2p^6\,3s^2\,3p^6\,4s^1)$ can gain the argon configuration by losing 1 electron. **3.9** Aluminum must lose 3 electrons to form Al^{3+} **3.10** X: + ·Ẏ· ⟶ X²⁺ + :Ÿ:²⁻ **3.11** cation **3.12 (a)** $Se + 2e^- \rightarrow Se^{2-}$ **(b)** $Ba \rightarrow Ba^{2+} + 2e^-$ **(c)** $Br + e^- \rightarrow Br^-$ **3.13** 3.4 gal **3.14 (a)** copper(II) ion **(b)** fluoride ion **(c)** magnesium ion **(d)** sulfide ion **3.15 (a)** Ag^+ **(b)** Fe^{2+} **(c)** Cu^+ **(d)** Te^{2-} **3.16** Na^+, sodium ion; K^+, potassium ion; Ca^{2+}, calcium ion; Cl^-, chloride ion **3.17 (a)** nitrate ion **(b)** cyanide ion **(c)** hydroxide ion **(d)** hydrogen phosphate ion **3.18** Group 1 A: Na^+, K^+; Group 2A: Ca^{2+}, Mg^{2+}; transition metals: Fe^{2+}; halogens: Cl^- **3.19 (a)** AgI **(b)** Ag_2O **(c)** Ag_3PO_4 **3.20 (a)** Na_2SO_4 **(b)** $FeSO_4$ **(c)** $Cr_2(SO_4)_3$ **3.21** $(NH_4)_2CO_3$ **3.22** $Al_2(SO_4)_3$, $Al(CH_3CO_2)_3$ **3.23** blue: K_2S; red: $BaBr_2$; green: Al_2O_3 **3.24** Ca_3N_2 **3.25** silver(I) sulfide **3.26 (a)** tin(IV) oxide **(b)** calcium cyanide **(c)** sodium carbonate **(d)** copper(I) sulfate **(e)** barium hydroxide **(f)** iron(II) nitrate **3.27 (a)** Li_3PO_4 **(b)** $CuCO_3$ **(c)** $Al_2(SO_3)_3$ **(d)** CuF **(e)** $Fe_2(SO_4)_3$ **(f)** NH_4Cl **3.28** Cr_2O_3 chromium (III) oxide **3.29** Acids: (a), (d); bases (b), (c) **3.30 (a)** HCl **(b)** H_2SO_4
3.31

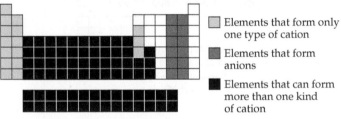

☐ Elements that form only one type of cation

▨ Elements that form anions

■ Elements that can form more than one kind of cation

All of the other elements form neither anions nor cations readily.
3.32

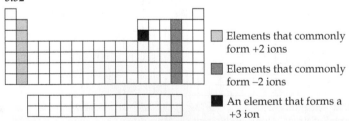

☐ Elements that commonly form +2 ions

▨ Elements that commonly form −2 ions

■ An element that forms a +3 ion

3.33 (a) O^{2-} **(b)** Na^+ **(c)** Ca^{2+} **(d)** Fe^{2+} **3.34 (a)** sodium atom (larger) **(b)** Na^+ ion (smaller) **3.35 (a)** chlorine atom (smaller) **(b)** Cl^- anion (larger) **3.36** iron (II) chloride or ferrous chloride, $FeCl_2$; iron (III) chloride or ferric chloride, $FeCl_3$; iron (II) oxide or ferrous oxide, FeO; iron (III) oxide or ferric oxide, Fe_2O_3; lead (II) chloride, $PbCl_2$; lead (IV) chloride, $PbCl_4$; lead (II) oxide, PbO; lead (IV) oxide, PbO_2 **3.37 (a)** ZnS **(b)** $PbBr_2$ **(c)** CrF_3 **(d)** Al_2O_3 **3.38 (a)** $Ca \rightarrow Ca^{2+} + 2e^-$ **(b)** $Au \rightarrow Au^+ + e^-$ **(c)** $F + e^- \rightarrow F^-$ **(d)** $Cr \rightarrow Cr^{3+} + 3e^-$ **3.40** true: (d); false: (a), (b), (c) **3.42** Main group atoms undergo reactions that leave them with a noble gas electron configuration. **3.44** Se^{2-} **3.46 (a)** Sr **(b)** Br **3.48 (a)** $1s^2\,2s^2\,2p^6\,3s^2\,3p^6\,4s^2\,3d^{10}\,4p^6$ **(b)** $1s^2\,2s^2\,2p^6\,3s^2\,3p^6\,4s^2\,3d^{10}\,4p^6$

(c) $1s^2\,2s^2\,2p^6\,3s^2\,3p^6$ **(d)** $1s^2\,2s^2\,2p^6\,3s^2\,3p^6\,4s^2\,3d^{10}\,4p^6\,5s^2\,4d^{10}\,5p^6$ **(e)** $1s^2\,2s^2\,2p^6$ **3.50 (a)** O **(b)** Li **(c)** Zn **(d)** N **3.52** none **3.54** Cr^{2+}: $1s^2\,2s^2\,2p^6\,3s^2\,3p^6\,3d^4$; Cr^{3+}: $1s^2\,2s^2\,2p^6\,3s^2\,3p^6\,3d^3$ **3.56** greater **3.58 (a)** sulfide ion **(b)** tin(II) ion **(c)** strontium ion **(d)** magnesium ion **(e)** gold(I) ion **3.60 (a)** Se^{2-} **(b)** O^{2-} **(c)** Ag^+ **3.62 (a)** OH^- **(b)** HSO_4^- **(c)** $CH_3CO_2^-$ **(d)** MnO_4^- **(e)** OCl^- **(f)** NO_3^- **(g)** CO_3^{2-} **(h)** $Cr_2O_7^{2-}$ **3.64 (a)** $Al_2(SO_4)_3$ **(b)** Ag_2SO_4 **(c)** $ZnSO_4$ **(d)** $BaSO_4$ **3.66 (a)** $NaHCO_3$ **(b)** KNO_3 **(c)** $CaCO_3$ **(d)** NH_4NO_3

3.68

	S^{2-}	Cl^-	PO_4^{3-}	CO_3^{2-}
copper(II)	CuS	$CuCl_2$	$Cu_3(PO_4)_2$	$CuCO_3$
Ca^{2+}	CaS	$CaCl_2$	$Ca_3(PO_4)_2$	$CaCO_3$
NH_4^+	$(NH_4)_2S$	NH_4Cl	$(NH_4)_3PO_4$	$(NH_4)_2CO_3$
ferric ion	Fe_2S_3	$FeCl_3$	$FePO_4$	$Fe_2(CO_3)_3$

3.70 copper(II) sulfide, copper(II) chloride, copper(II) phosphate, copper(II) carbonate; calcium sulfide, calcium chloride, calcium phosphate, calcium carbonate; ammonium sulfide, ammonium chloride, ammonium phosphate, ammonium carbonate; iron(III) sulfide, iron(III) chloride, iron(III) phosphate, iron(III) carbonate **3.72 (a)** magnesium carbonate **(b)** calcium acetate **(c)** silver(I) cyanide **(d)** sodium dichromate **3.74** $Ca_3(PO_4)_2$ **3.76** An acid gives H^+ ions in water; a base gives OH^- ions. **3.78 (a)** $H_2CO_3 \rightarrow 2H^+ + CO_3^{2-}$ **(b)** $HCN \rightarrow H^+ + CN^-$ **(c)** $Mg(OH)_2 \rightarrow Mg^{2+} + 2OH^-$ **(d)** $KOH \rightarrow K^+ + OH^-$ **3.80** The bulky cations prevent close packing of particles and prevent crystallization. **3.82** 2300 mg; 4 tsp **3.84** Sodium protects against fluid loss and is necessary for muscle contraction and transmission of nerve impulses. **3.86** $10\,Ca^{2+}$, $6\,PO_4^{3-}$, $2\,OH^-$ **3.88** H^- has the helium configuration, $1s^2$ **3.90 (a)** CrO_3 **(b)** VCl_5 **(c)** MnO_2 **(d)** MoS_2 **3.92 (a)** -1 **(b)** 3 gluconate ions per iron(III) **3.94 (a)** $Co(CN)_2$ **(b)** UO_3 **(c)** $SnSO_4$ **(d)** MnO_2 **(e)** K_3PO_4 **(f)** Ca_3P_2 **(g)** $LiHSO_4$ **(h)** $Al(OH)_3$ **3.96 (a)** metal **(b)** nonmetal **(c)** X_2Y_3 **(d)** X: group 3A; Y: group 6A

Chapter 4

4.1 :Ï:Ï: ; xenon **4.2 (a)** P 3, H 1 **(b)** Se 2, H 1 **(c)** H 1, Cl 1 **(d)** Si 4, F 1 **4.3** $P\ddot{b}Cl_2$ = ionic; $PbCl_4$ = covalent **4.4 (a)** CH_2Cl_2 **(b)** BH_3 **(c)** NI_3 **(d)** $SiCl_4$

4.5

H   :O:
| ‖
H—C—C—Ö—H
|
H

4.6

[structure of caffeine with CH₃ groups, N, C atoms, and O]

4.7 $AlCl_3$ is a covalent compound, and Al_2O_3 is ionic

4.8

H
|
H—C—N̈—H
| |
H H

4.9 (a)

H
|
H—C—Ö—H
|
H

(b)

H
|
:N≡C—C—H
|
H

(c)

:Ċl:
|
:N—Ċl:
|
:Ċl:

4.10
(a)

:O:
‖
:Ċl—C—Ċl:

(b)

:Ö—Ċl:⁻

(c)

H—Ö—Ö—H

(d)

:Ċl—S̈—Ċl:

4.11

:O:
‖
:Ö—N—Ö—H

4.12 (a) $C_6H_{10}O_2$ **(b)**

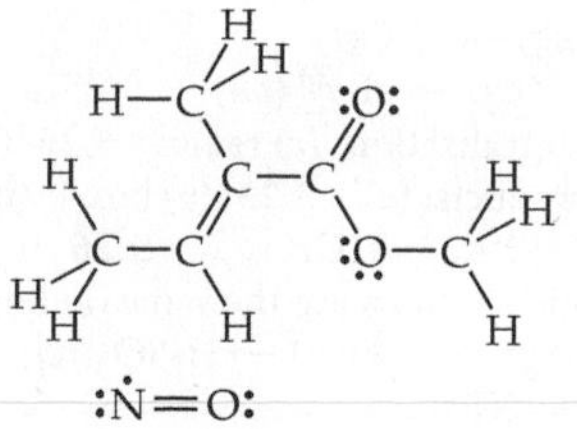

[structure]

4.13 :C≡O: :N̈=O:

CO is reactive because it can form coordinate covalent bonds; NO is reactive because it has an unpaired electron.

4.14

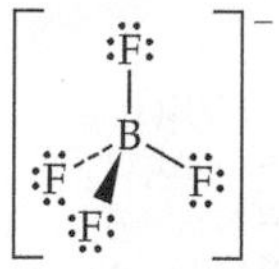

$$\left[\begin{array}{c} :\ddot{F}: \\ | \\ :\ddot{F}-B-\ddot{F}: \\ | \\ :\ddot{F}: \end{array} \right]^-$$ tetrahedral

4.15 chloroform, $CHCl_3$—tetrahedral; dichloroethylene—planar
4.16 a = tetrahedral; b = trigonal planar   **4.17** Both are bent.

4.18

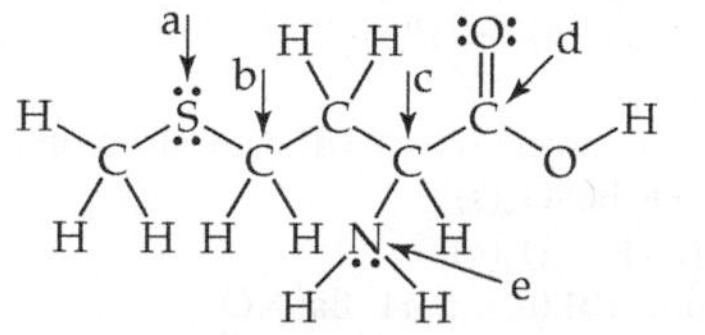

[structure]

(a) bent
(b) tetrahedral
(c) tetrahedral
(d) trigonal planar
(e) pyramidal

4.19 H = P < S < N < O
4.20 (a) polar covalent **(b)** ionic **(c)** covalent **(d)** polar covalent

$$\overset{\delta^+}{I}-\overset{\delta^-}{Cl} \qquad \overset{\delta^+}{P}-\overset{\delta^-}{Br}$$

4.21

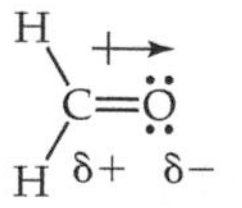

[structure]

4.22 The carbons are tetrahedral; the oxygen is bent, the molecule is polar.

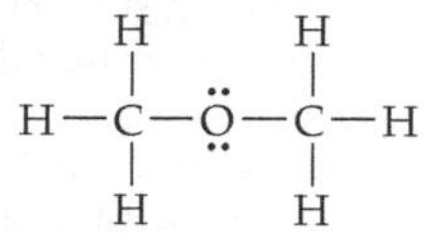

[structure]

4.23

[structure]

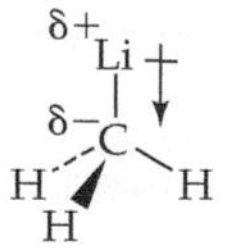

4.24 (a) disulfur dichloride **(b)** iodine monochloride **(c)** iodine trichloride
4.25 (a) SeF_4 **(b)** P_2O_5 **(c)** BrF_3
4.26

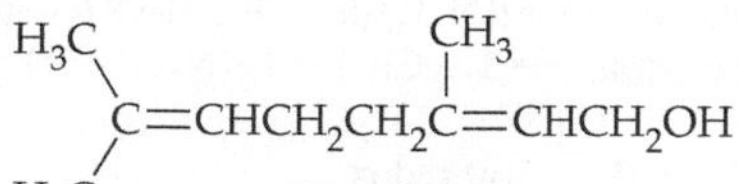

H_3C CH_3
    C=CHCH$_2$CH$_2$C=CHCH$_2$OH
H_3C Geraniol

4.27 (a) tetrahedral **(b)** pyramidal **(c)** trigonal planar
4.28 (c) is square planar   **4.29 (a)** $C_8H_9NO_2$
(b)

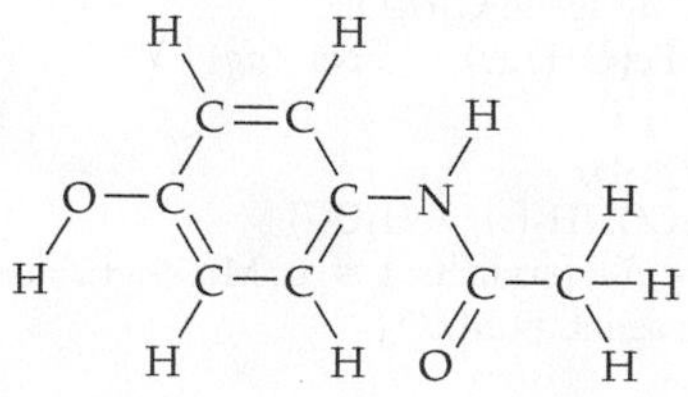

[structure]

(c) All carbons are trigonal planar except the —CH$_3$ carbon. Nitrogen is pyramidal.
4.30

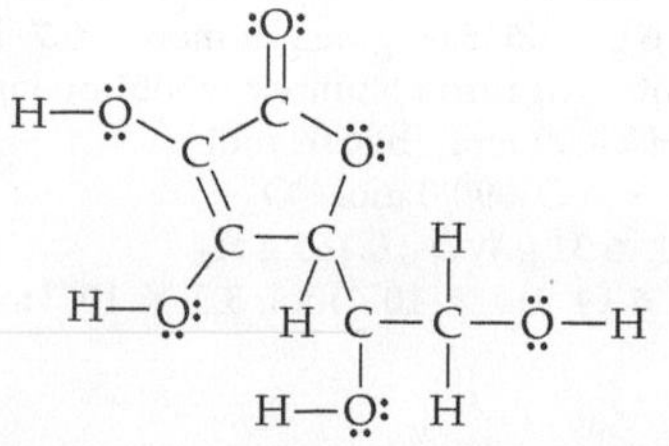

[structure]

4.31 $C_{13}H_{10}N_2O_4$

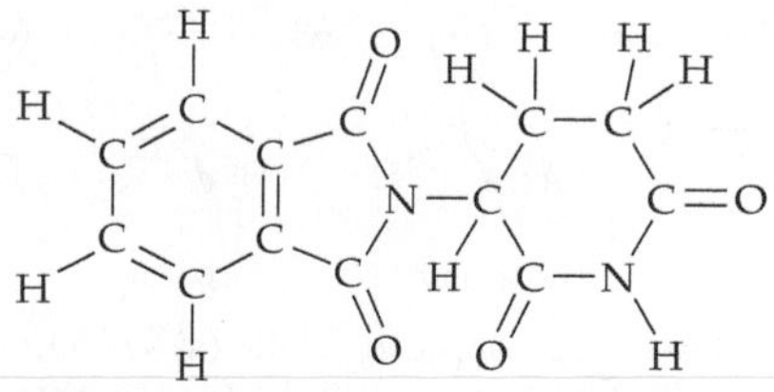

[structure]

4.32

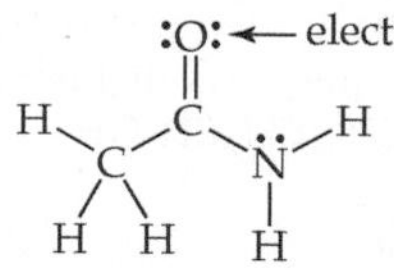

[structure] :O: ← electron-rich

4.34 In a coordinate covalent bond, both electrons in the bond come from the same atom.   **4.36** covalent bonds: **(a) (b)**; ionic bonds: **(c) (d) (e)**   **4.38** two covalent bonds   **4.40 (b), (c)**   **4.42** $SnCl_4$ **4.44** the N—O bond   **4.46 (a)** A molecular formula shows the numbers and kinds of atoms; a structural formula shows how the atoms are bonded to one another. **(b)** A structural formula shows the bonds between atoms; a condensed structure shows atoms but not bonds. **(c)** A lone pair of valence electrons is not shared in a bond; a shared pair of electrons is shared between two atoms.   **4.48 (a)** 10; triple bond **(b)** 18; double bond between N,O **(c)** 24; double bond between C,O **(d)** 20   **4.50** too many hydrogens
4.52 (a)   **(b)**   **(c)**

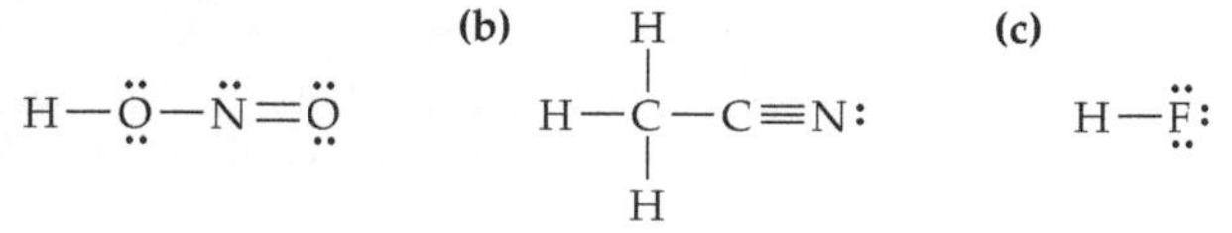

[structures]

H—Ö—N̈=Ö   H—C—C≡N: H—F̈:

4.54 (a) $CH_3CH_2CH_3$ **(b)** $H_2C = CHCH_3$ **(c)** CH_3CH_2Cl
4.56 CH_3COOH
4.58
(a)   **(b)**   **(c)**

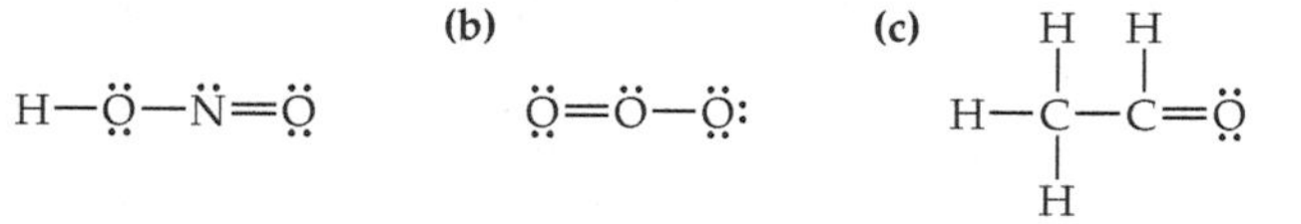

H—Ö—N̈=Ö   Ö=Ö—Ö: [structure]

4.60

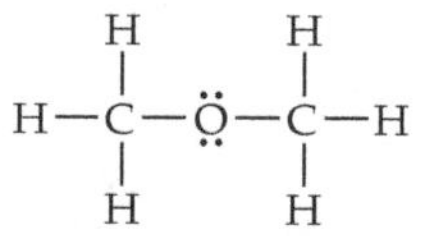

[structure] Dimethyl ether

4.62 [structure] Tetrachloroethylene contains a double bond

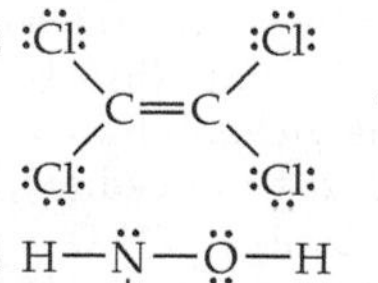

4.64 H—N̈—Ö—H

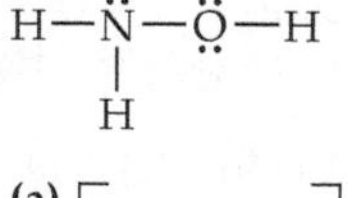

4.66 (a) [structure] **(b)** [structure] **(c)** [structure]

(d) [structure] **(e)** [structure]

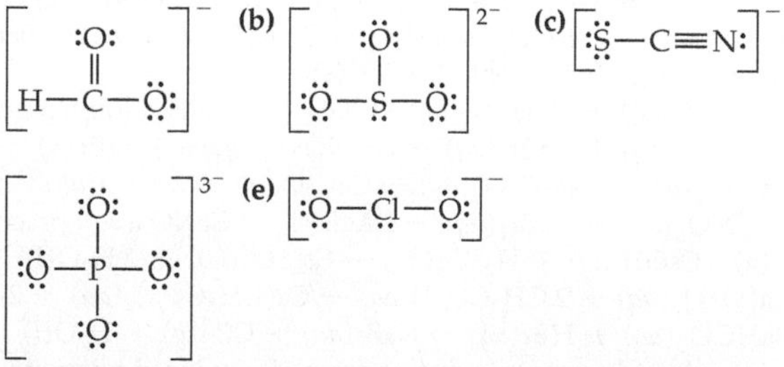

4.68 tetrahedral; pyramidal; bent   **4.70 (a), (b)** tetrahedral **(c), (d)** trigonal planar **(e)** pyramidal   **4.72** All are trigonal planar, except for the —CH$_3$ carbon, which is tetrahedral.   **4.74** It should have low electronegativity, like other alkali metals.   **4.76** Cl > C > Cu > Ca > Cs
4.78 (a) $\overset{\delta^-}{O}-\overset{\delta^+}{Cl}$ **(b) (c) (d)** nonpolar **(e)** $\overset{\delta^+}{C}-\overset{\delta^-}{O}$
4.80 PH_3 < HCl < H_2O < CF_4

4.82 **(a)** 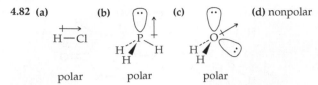 **(b)** **(c)** **(d)** nonpolar

polar   polar   polar

4.84 S—H bonds are nonpolar.   **4.86** **(a)** selenium dioxide **(b)** xenon tetroxide **(c)** dinitrogen pentasulfide **(d)** triphosphorus tetraselenide **4.88** **(a)** $SiCl_4$ **(b)** NaH **(c)** SbF_5 **(d)** OsO_4 **4.90** It relaxes arterial walls. **4.92** Carbohydrates, DNA, and proteins are all polymers that occur in nature.   **4.94** $CH_3(CH_3)C\!=\!CHCH_2CH_2CH(CH_3)CH_2CH_2OH$

4.96 **(a)**

(b) The C=O carbons are trigonal planar; the other carbons are tetrahedral. **(c)** The C=O bonds are polar.   **4.98** **(a)** C forms 4 bonds **(b)** N forms 3 bonds **(c)** S forms 2 bonds **(d)** could be correct   **4.100** **(b)** tetrahedral **(c)** contains a coordinate covalent bond **(d)** has 19 p and 18 e⁻

4.102 **(a)** calcium chloride **(b)** tellurium dichloride **(c)** boron trifluoride **(d)** magnesium sulfate **(e)** potassium oxide **(f)** iron(III) fluoride **(g)** phosphorus trifluoride

4.104   **4.106**

4.108 **(a)**   **(b)**

Chapter 5

5.1 **(a)** Solid cobalt(II) chloride plus gaseous hydrogen fluoride yields solid cobalt(II) fluoride plus gaseous hydrogen chloride. **(b)** Aqueous lead(II) nitrate plus aqueous potassium iodide yields solid lead(II) iodide plus aqueous potassium nitrate.   **5.2** balanced:**(a)**, **(c)** **5.3** $3 O_2 \rightarrow 2 O_3$ **5.4** **(a)** $Ca(OH)_2 + 2 HCl \rightarrow CaCl_2 + 2 H_2O$ **(b)** $4 Al + 3 O_2 \rightarrow 2 Al_2O_3$ **(c)** $2 CH_3CH_3 + 7 O_2 \rightarrow 4 CO_2 + 6 H_2O$ **(d)** $2 AgNO_3 + MgCl_2 \rightarrow 2 AgCl + Mg(NO_3)_2$ **5.5** $2 A + B_2 \rightarrow A_2B_2$ **5.6** **(a)** precipitation **(b)** redox **(c)** acid–base neutralization   **5.7** $6 CO_2 + 6 H_2O \rightarrow C_6H_{12}O_6 + 6 O_2$; redox reaction **5.8** Soluble: **(b)**, **(d)**; insoluble: **(a)**, **(c)**, **(e)** **5.9** **(a)** $NiCl_2(aq) + (NH_4)_2S(aq) \rightarrow NiS(s) + 2 NH_4Cl(aq)$; precipitation **(b)** $2 AgNO_3(aq) + CaBr_2(aq) \rightarrow Ca(NO_3)_2(aq) + 2 AgBr(s)$ **5.10** $CaCl_2(aq) + Na_2C_2O_4(aq) \rightarrow CaC_2O_4(s) + 2 NaCl(aq)$ **(b)** $2 AgNO_3(aq) + CaBr_2(aq) \rightarrow 2 AgBr(s) + CaNO_3(aq)$; precipitation **5.11** **(a)** $2 CsOH(aq) + H_2SO_4(aq) \rightarrow Cs_2SO_4(aq) + 2 H_2O(l)$ **(b)** $Ca(OH)_2(aq) + 2 CH_3CO_2H(aq) \rightarrow Ca(CH_3CO_2)_2(aq) + 2 H_2O(l)$ **(c)** $NaHCO_3(aq) + HBr(aq) \rightarrow NaBr(aq) + CO_2(g) + H_2O(l)$ **5.12** **(a)** oxidized reactant (reducing agent): Fe; reduced reactant (oxidizing agent): Cu^{2+} **(b)** oxidized reactant (reducing agent): Mg; reduced reactant (oxidizing agent): Cl_2; **(c)** oxidized reactant (reducing agent): Al; reduced reactant (oxidizing agent): Cr_2O_3;   **5.13** $2 K(s) + Br_2(l) \rightarrow 2 KBr(s)$; oxidizing agent: Br_2; reducing agent: K   **5.14** Li is oxidized and I_2 is reduced. **5.15** **(a)** V(III) **(b)** Sn(IV) **(c)** Cr(VI) **(d)** Cu(II) **(e)** Ni(II)   **5.16** **(a)** not redox **(b)** Na oxidized from 0 to +1; H reduced from +1 to 0 **(c)** C oxidized from 0 to +4; O reduced from 0 to −2 **(d)** not redox **(e)** S oxidized from +4 to +6; Mn reduced from +7 to +2 **5.17** **(b)** oxidizing agent: H_2; reducing agent: Na **(c)** oxidizing agent: O_2; reducing agent: C **(e)** oxidizing agent: MnO_4^-; reducing agent: SO_2 **5.18** **(a)** $Zn(s) + Pb^{2+}(aq) \rightarrow Zn^{2+}(aq) + Pb(s)$

(b) $OH^-(aq) + H^+(aq) \rightarrow H_2O(l)$ **(c)** $2 Fe^{3+}(aq) + Sn^{2+}(aq) \rightarrow 2 Fe^{2+}(aq) + Sn^{4+}(aq)$ **5.19** **(a)** redox **(b)** neutralization **(c)** redox   **5.20** **(d)**   **5.21** **(c)** **5.22** reactants: **(d)**; products: **(c)**   **5.23** **(a)** box 1 **(b)** box 2 **(c)** box 3 **5.24** $2 Ag^+ + CO_3^{2-}; 2 Ag^+ + CrO_4^{2-}$ **5.26** In a balanced equation, the numbers and kinds of atoms are the same on both sides of the reaction arrow.   **5.28** **(a)** $SO_2(g) + H_2O(g) \rightarrow H_2SO_3(aq)$ **(b)** $2 K(s) + Br_2(l) \rightarrow 2 KBr(s)$ **(c)** $C_3H_8(g) + 5 O_2(g) \rightarrow 3 CO_2(g) + 4 H_2O(l)$ **5.30** **(a)** $2 C_2H_6(g) + 7 O_2(g) \rightarrow 4 CO_2(g) + 6 H_2O(g)$ **(b)** balanced **(c)** $2 Mg(s) + O_2(g) \rightarrow 2 MgO(s)$ **(d)** $2 K(s) + 2 H_2O(l) \rightarrow 2 KOH(aq) + H_2(g)$ **5.32** **(a)** $Hg(NO_3)_2(aq) + 2 LiI(aq) \rightarrow 2 LiNO_3(aq) + HgI_2(s)$ **(b)** $I_2(s) + 5 Cl_2(g) \rightarrow 2 ICl_5(s)$ **(c)** $4 Al + 3 O_2(g) \rightarrow 3 Al_2O_3(s)$ **(d)** $CuSO_4(aq) + 2 AgNO_3(aq) \rightarrow Ag_2SO_4(s) + Cu(NO_3)_2(aq)$ **(e)** $2 Mn(NO_3)_3(aq) + 3 Na_2S(aq) \rightarrow Mn_2S_3(s) + 6 NaNO_3(aq)$ **5.34** **(a)** $2 C_4H_{10}(g) + 13 O_2(g) \rightarrow 8 CO_2(g) + 10 H_2O(l)$ **(b)** $C_2H_6O(g) + 3 O_2(g) \rightarrow 2 CO_2(g) + 3 H_2O(l)$ **(c)** $2 C_8H_{18}(g) + 25 O_2(g) \rightarrow 16 CO_2(g) + 18 H_2O(l)$ **5.36** $4 HF + SiO_2 \rightarrow SiF_4 + 2 H_2O$ **5.38** **(a)** redox **(b)** neutralization **(c)** precipitation **(d)** neutralization **5.40** **(a)** $Ba^{2+}(aq) + SO_4^{2-}(aq) \rightarrow BaSO_4(s)$ **(b)** $Zn(s) + 2 H^+(aq) \rightarrow Zn^{2+}(aq) + H_2(g)$ **5.42** precipitation: **(a)** **(d)** **(e)**; redox: **(b)** **(c)**   **5.44** $Ba(NO_3)_2$ **5.46** **(a)** $2 NaBr(aq) + Hg_2(NO_3)_2(aq) \rightarrow Hg_2Br_2(s) + 2 NaNO_3(aq)$ **(d)** $(NH_4)_2CO_3(aq) + CaCl_2(aq) \rightarrow CaCO_3(s) + 2 NH_4Cl(aq)$ **(e)** $2 KOH(aq) + MnBr_2(aq) \rightarrow Mn(OH)_2(s) + 2 KBr(aq)$ **(f)** $3 Na_2S(aq) + 2 Al(NO_3)_3(aq) \rightarrow Al_2S_3(s) + 6 NaNO_3(aq)$ **5.48** **(a)** $2 Au^{3+}(aq) + 3 Sn(s) \rightarrow 3 Sn^{2+}(aq) + 2 Au(s)$ **(b)** $2 I^-(aq) + Br_2(l) \rightarrow 2 Br^-(aq) + I_2(s)$ **(c)** $2 Ag^+(aq) + Fe(s) \rightarrow Fe^{2+}(aq) + 2 Ag(s)$ **5.50** **(a)** $Sr(OH)_2(aq) + FeSO_4(aq) \rightarrow SrSO_4(s) + Fe(OH)_2(s)$ **(b)** $S^{2-}(aq) + Zn^{2+}(aq) \rightarrow ZnS(s)$ **5.52** Most easily oxidized: metals on left side; most easily reduced: groups 6A and 7A   **5.54** oxidation number increases: **(b)**,**(c)**; oxidation number decreases **(a)**, **(d)**   **5.56** **(a)** Co: +3 **(b)** Fe: +2 **(c)** U: +6 **(d)** Cu: +2 **(e)** Ti: +4 **(f)** Sn: +2   **5.58** **(a)** oxidized: S; reduced: O **(b)** oxidized: Na; reduced: Cl **(c)** oxidized: Zn; reduced: Cu **(d)** oxidized: Cl; reduced: F **5.60** **(a)** $N_2O_4(l) + 2 N_2H_4(l) \rightarrow 3 N_2(g) + 4 H_2O(g)$ **(b)** $CaH_2(s) + 2 H_2O(l) \rightarrow Ca(OH)_2(aq) + 2 H_2(g)$ **(c)** $2 Al(s) + 6 H_2O(l) \rightarrow 2 Al(OH)_3(s) + 3 H_2(g)$ **5.62** oxidizing agents: N_2O_4, H_2O; reducing agents: N_2H_4, CaH_2, Al **5.64** redox equation: $2 C_5H_4N_4 + 3 O_2 \rightarrow 2 C_5H_4N_4O_3$ **5.66** Zn is the reducing agent, and Mn^{2+} is the oxidizing agent **5.68** $Li_2O(s) + H_2O(g) \rightarrow 2 LiOH(s)$; not a redox reaction **5.70** **(a)** $Al(OH)_3(aq) + 3 HNO_3(aq) \rightarrow Al(NO_3)_3(aq) + 3 H_2O(l)$ neutralization **(b)** $3 AgNO_3(aq) + FeCl_3(aq) \rightarrow 3 AgCl(s) + Fe(NO_3)_3(aq)$ precipitation **(c)** $(NH_4)_2Cr_2O_7(s) \rightarrow Cr_2O_3(s) + 4 H_2O(g) + N_2(g)$ redox **(d)** $Mn_2(CO_3)_3(s) \rightarrow Mn_2O_3(s) + 3 CO_2(g)$ redox **5.72** **(a)** $2 SO_2(g) + O_2(g) \rightarrow 2 SO_3(g)$ **(b)** $SO_3(g) + H_2O(g) \rightarrow H_2SO_4(l)$ **(c)** SO_2: +4; SO_3, H_2SO_4: +6 **5.74** **(a)** +6 **(b)** −2 in ethanol; +4 in CO_2 **(c)** oxidizing agent: $Cr_2O_7^{2-}$; reducing agent: C_2H_5OH **5.76** $Fe^{3+}(aq) + 3 NaOH(aq) \rightarrow Fe(OH)_3(s) + 3 Na^+(aq)$ $Fe^{3+}(aq) + 3 OH^-(aq) \rightarrow Fe(OH)_3(s)$ **5.78** $2 Bi^{3+}(aq) + 3 S^{2-}(aq) \rightarrow Bi_2S_3(s)$ **5.80** $CO_2(g) + 2 NH_3(g) \rightarrow NH_2CONH_2(s) + H_2O(l)$ **5.82** **(a)** reactants: I = −1, Mn = −4; products: I = 0, Mn = +2 **(b)** reducing agent = NaI; oxidizing agent = MnO_2

Chapter 6

6.1 **(a)** 206.0 amu **(b)** 232.0 amu   **6.2** 1.71×10^{21} molecules   **6.3** 0.15 g **6.4** 111.0 amu   **6.5** 0.217 mol; 4.6 g   **6.6** 5.00 g weighs more   **6.7** If all of these were true, the estimate of Avogadro's Number would be larger. **6.8** **(a)** $Ni + 2 HCl \rightarrow NiCl_2 + H_2$; 4.90 mol **(b)** 6.00 mol **6.9** $6 CO_2 + 6 H_2O \rightarrow C_6H_{12}O_6 + 6 O_2$; 90.0 mol CO_2 **6.10** **(a)** 39.6 mol **(b)** 13.8 g   **6.11** 6.31 g WO_3; 0.165 g H_2 **6.12** 44.7 g; 57.0%   **6.13** 47.3 g   **6.14** 1.4×10^{-4} mol; 3.2×10^{-4} mol

6.15 A_2 **6.16** $C_5H_{11}NO_2S$; MW = 149.1 amu
6.17 **(a)** $A_2 + 3 B \rightarrow 2 AB_3$ **(b)** 2 mol AB_3; 0.67 mol AB_3
6.18 10 AB ($2B_2$ left over)   **6.19** Blue is the limiting reagent, yield: 73%
6.20 22 g, 31 g   **6.22** molecular weight = sum of the weights of individual atoms in a molecule; formula weight = sum of weights of individual atoms in a formula unit; molar mass = mass in grams of 6.022×10^{23} molecules or formula units of any substance   **6.24** 5.25 mol ions   **6.26** 10.6 g uranium   **6.28** **(a)** 1 mol **(b)** 1 mol **(c)** 2 mol   **6.30** 6.44×10^{-4} mol
6.32 284.5 g   **6.34** **(a)** 0.0132 mol **(b)** 0.0536 mol **(c)** 0.0608 mol
(d) 0.0129 mol   **6.36** 0.27 g; 9.0×10^{20} molecules aspirin
6.38 1.4×10^{-3} mol; 0.18 g   **6.40** **(a)** $C_4H_8O_2(l) + 2 H_2(g) \rightarrow$ $2 C_2H_6O(l)$ **(b)** 3.0 mol **(c)** 138 g **(d)** 12.5 g **(e)** 0.55 g
6.42 **(a)** $N_2(g) + 3 H_2(g) \rightarrow 2 NH_3(g)$ **(b)** 0.471 mol **(c)** 16.1 g
6.44 **(a)** $Fe_2O_3(s) + 3 CO(g) \rightarrow 2 Fe(s) + 3 CO_2(g)$ **(b)** 1.59 g **(c)** 141 g
6.46 158 kg   **6.48** 6×10^9 mol H_2SO_4; 6×10^8 kg H_2SO_4
6.50 17 mol SO_2 **6.52** **(a)** CO is limiting **(b)** 11.4 g **(c)** 83.8%
6.54 **(a)** $CH_4(g) + 2 Cl_2(g) \rightarrow CH_2Cl_2(l) + 2 HCl(g)$ **(b)** 444 g
(c) 202 g   **6.56** **(a)** HNO_3 **(b)** 53.6 g (0.436 mol)   **6.58** measuring the area of the oil, density of oil, molar mass of oil, mass of oil
6.60 $FeSO_4$; 151.9 g/mol; 91.8 mg Fe   **6.62** 6×10^{13} molecules
6.64 **(a)** $C_{12}H_{22}O_{11}(s) \rightarrow 12 C(s) + 11 H_2O(l)$ **(b)** 25.3 g C
(c) 8.94 g H_2O **6.66** **(a)** 6.40 g **(b)** 104 g
6.68 **(a)** $4 NH_3(g) + 5 O_2(g) \rightarrow 4 NO(g) + 6 H_2O(g)$ **(b)** 30.0 g NO
6.70 **(a)** $BaCl_2(aq) + Na_2SO_4(aq) \rightarrow BaSO_4(s) + 2 NaCl(aq)$ **(b)** 45.0 g
6.72 **(a)** 45 g **(b)** 78%
6.74 **(a)** $P_4(s) + 10 Cl_2(g) \rightarrow 4 PCl_5(s)$ **(b)** 102 g PCl_5
6.76 $6 NH_4ClO_4(s) + 10 Al(s) \rightarrow 4 Al_2O_3(s) + 2 AlCl_3(s) + 12 H_2O(g) + 3 N_2(g)$ **(b)** 310 mol gases

Chapter 7

7.1 **(a)** ΔH = +652 kcal/mol (2720 kJ/mol) **(b)** endothermic
7.2 **(a)** endothermic **(b)** 200 kcal; 836 kJ **(c)** 74.2 kcal; 310 kJ
7.3 91 kcal; 380 kJ   **7.4** 303 kcal/mol; 6.4 kcal/g   **7.5** **(a)** increase
(b) decrease **(c)** decrease   **7.6** **(a)** 31.3 kcal/mol; 131 kJ/mol; not spontaneous **(b)** spontaneous at higher temperatures   **7.7** **(a)** +0.06 kcal/mol (+0.25 kJ/mol); nonspontaneous **(b)** 0.00 kcal/mol; equilibrium
(c) −0.05 kcal/mol (−0.21 kJ/mol); spontaneous   **7.8** **(a)** positive
(b) spontaneous at all temperatures
7.9

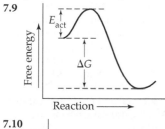

7.10

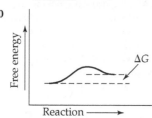

7.11 **(a)** see blue curve, Fig. 7.4 **(b)** increase the temperature, add a catalyst, increase the concentration of reagents   **7.12** 1260 g
7.13 **(a)** $K = \dfrac{[NO_2]^2}{[N_2O_4]}$ **(b)** $K = \dfrac{[H_2O]^2}{[H_2S]^2[O_2]}$ **(c)** $K = \dfrac{[Br_2][F_2]^5}{[BrF_5]^2}$
7.14 **(a)** products strongly favored **(b)** reactants strongly favored
(c) products somewhat favored
7.15 K = 29.0
7.16 **(a)** $K = \dfrac{[AB]^2}{[A_2][B_2]}$; $K = \dfrac{[AB]^2}{[A_2][B]^2}$ **(b)** K = 0.11; K = 0.89
7.17 reaction favored by high pressure and low temperature
7.18 **(a)** favors reactants **(b)** favors product **(c)** favors product
7.19 $Cu_2O(s) + C(s) \rightarrow 2 Cu(s) + CO(g)$; ΔG = −3.8 kJ (−1.0 kcal)

7.20 ΔH is positive; ΔS is positive; ΔG is negative
7.21 ΔH is negative; ΔS is negative; ΔG is negative
7.22 **(a)** $2 A_2 + B_2 \rightarrow 2 A_2B$
(b) ΔH is negative; ΔS is negative; ΔG is negative
7.23 **(a)** blue curve represents faster reaction **(b)** red curve is spontaneous

7.24
(a)   **(b)**

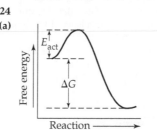   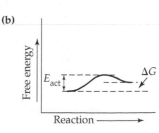

7.25 **(a)** positive **(b)** nonspontaneous at low temperature; spontaneous at high temperature   **7.26** lower enthalpy for reactants
7.28 **(a)** $Br_2(l) + 7.4$ kcal/mol $\rightarrow Br_2(g)$ **(b)** 43 kcal **(c)** 15.9 kJ
7.30 **(a)** $2 C_2H_2(g) + 5 O_2(g) \rightarrow 4 CO_2(g) + 2 H_2O(g)$
(b) −579 kcal/mol (−2420 kJ/mol) **(c)** 11.2 kcal/g (47 kJ/g); one of the highest energy values   **7.32** **(a)** $C_6H_{12}O_6 + 6 O_2 \rightarrow 6 CO_2 + 6 H_2O$
(b) -1.0×10^3 kcal/mol (-4.2×10^3 kJ/mol) **(c)** +57 kcal (+240 kJ)
7.34 increased disorder: **(a)**; decreased disorder: **(b)**, **(c)**
7.36 release or absorption of heat, and increase or decrease in entropy
7.38 ΔH is usually larger than $T\Delta S$
7.40 **(a)** endothermic **(b)** increases **(c)** $T\Delta S$ is larger than ΔH
7.42 **(a)** $H_2(g) + Br_2(l) \rightarrow 2 HBr(g)$ **(b)** increases **(c)** yes, because ΔH is negative and ΔS is positive **(d)** ΔG = −25.6 kcal/mol (−107 kJ/mol)
7.44 the amount of energy needed for reactants to surmount the barrier to reaction
7.46
(a)   **(b)**

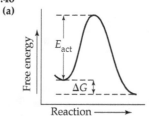   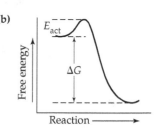

7.48 A catalyst lowers the activation energy.   **7.50** **(a)** yes **(b)** reaction rate is slow   **7.52** At equilibrium, the rates of forward and reverse reactions are equal. Amounts of reactants and products need not be equal.
7.54 **(a)** $K = \dfrac{[CO_2]^2}{[CO]^2[O_2]}$ **(b)** $K = \dfrac{[H_2][MgCl_2]}{[HCl]^2}$
(c) $K = \dfrac{[H_3O^+][F^-]}{[HF]}$ **(d)** $K = \dfrac{[SO_2]}{[O_2]}$
7.56 $K = 7.19 \times 10^{-3}$; reactants are favored   **7.58** **(a)** 0.0869 mol/L
(b) 0.0232 mol/L   **7.60** more reactant   **7.62** **(a)** endothermic
(b) reactants are favored **(c)** (1) favors ozone; (2) favors ozone; (3) favors O_2; (4) no effect; (5) favors ozone   **7.64** **(a)** decrease **(b)** no effect **(c)** increase
7.66 increase   **7.68** **(a)** increase **(b)** decrease **(c)** no effect **(d)** decrease
7.70 fat   **7.72** thyroid, hypothalamus
7.74 **(a)** ADP + phosphoenolpyruvate $\rightarrow$ pyruvate + ATP
(b) −31.4 kJ/mol   **7.76** **(a)** $C_2H_5OH(l) + 3 O_2(g) \rightarrow 2 CO_2(g) + 3 H_2O(g)$
(b) negative **(c)** 35.5 kcal **(d)** 5.63 g **(e)** 5.60 kcal/mL (23.4 kJ/mL)
7.78 **(a)** $Fe_3O_4(s) + 4 H_2(g) \rightarrow 3 Fe(s) + 4 H_2O(g)$
ΔH = +36 kcal/mol **(b)** 12 kcal (50 kJ) **(c)** 3.6 g H_2 **(d)** reactants
7.80 **(a)**   **(b)** −20 kcal/mol (−84 kJ/mol)

7.82 **(a)** $4 NH_3(g) + 5 O_2(g) \rightarrow 4 NO(g) + 6 H_2O(g)$ + heat
(b) $K = \dfrac{[NO]^4[H_2O]^6}{[NH_3]^2[O_2]^5}$ **(c)** (1) favors reactants (2) favors reactants
(3) favors reactants (4) favors products
7.84 **(a)** exergonic **(b)** ΔG = −10 kcal/mol (−42 kJ/mol)
7.86 −1.91 kcal (−7.99 kJ/mol); exothermic

Chapter 8

8.1 (a) disfavored by ΔH; favored by ΔS (b) +0.02 kcal/mol (+0.09 kJ/mol) (c) $\Delta H = -9.72$ kcal/mol (−40.6 kJ/mol); $\Delta S = -2.61$ cal/(mol·K) [−109 J/(mol·K)] **8.2** (a) decrease (b) increase **8.3** (a), (c) **8.4** (a) London forces (b) hydrogen bonds, dipole–dipole forces, London forces (c) dipole–dipole forces, London forces **8.5** 220 mmHg; 4.25 psi; 2.93×10^4 Pa **8.6** Atmospheric CO_2 levels would remain constant. **8.7** 1000 mmHg **8.8** 450 L **8.9** 1.3 L, 18 L **8.10** 2.16 psi/1.45 psi **8.11** 637 °C; −91 °C **8.12** 33 psi **8.13** 352 L **8.14** balloon (a) **8.15** 4.46×10^3 mol; 7.14×10^4 g CH_4; 1.96×10^5 g CO_2 **8.16** 5.0 atm **8.17** 1,100 mol; 4,400 g

8.18 (a)   (b)

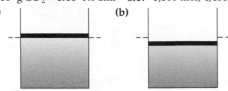

8.19 9.3 atm He; 0.19 atm O_2 **8.20** 75.4% N_2, 13.2% O_2, 5.3% CO_2, 6.2% H_2O **8.21** 35.0 mmHg **8.22** $P_{He} = 500$ mmHg; $P_{Xe} = 250$ mmHg **8.23** 1.93 kcal, 14.3 kcal **8.24** 102 kJ **8.25** gas

8.26

(a)   (b)   (c)

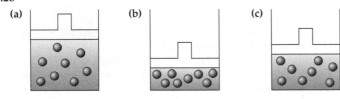

(a) volume increases by 50% (b) volume decreases by 50% (c) volume unchanged **8.27** (b); (c) **8.28** (c)

8.29

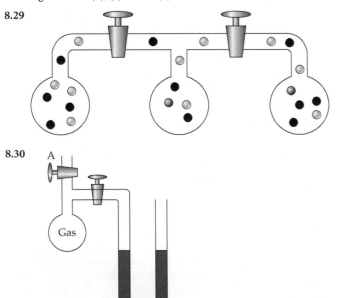

8.30

8.31 (a) 10 °C (b) 75 °C (c) 1 kcal/mol (d) 7.5 kcal/mol
8.32 (a)   (b)   (c)

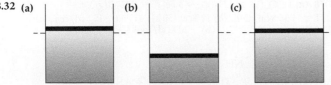

8.33 red = 360 mmHg; yellow = 120 mmHg; total pressure = 720 mmHg **8.34** (a) all molecules (b) molecules with polar covalent bonds (c) molecules with —OH or —NH bonds **8.36** Ethanol forms hydrogen bonds. **8.38** One atmosphere is equal to exactly 760 mmHg. **8.40** (1) A gas

consists of tiny particles moving at random with no forces between them. (2) The amount of space occupied by the gas particles is small. (3) The average kinetic energy of the gas particles is proportional to the Kelvin temperature. (4) Collisions between particles are elastic. **8.42** (a) 760 mmHg (b) 1310 mmHg (c) 5.7×10^3 mmHg (d) 711 mmHg (e) 0.314 mmHg **8.44** 930 mmHg; 1.22 atm **8.46** V varies inversely with P when n and T are constant. **8.48** 101 mL **8.50** 1.75 L **8.52** V varies directly with T when n and P are constant. **8.54** 364 K = 91 °C **8.56** 220 mL **8.58** P varies directly with T when n and V are constant. **8.60** 1.2 atm **8.62** 493 K = 220 °C **8.64** 68.4 mL **8.66** (a) P increases by factor of 4 (b) P decreases by factor of 4 **8.68** Because gas particles are so far apart and have no interactions, their chemical identity is unimportant. **8.70** 2.7×10^{22} molecules/L; 1.4 g **8.72** 11.8 g **8.74** 15 kg **8.76** $PV = nRT$ **8.78** Cl_2 has fewer molecules but weighs more. **8.80** 370 atm; 5400 psi **8.82** 2.2×10^4 mm Hg **8.84** 22.3 L **8.86** the pressure contribution of one component in a mixture of gases **8.88** 93 mmHg **8.90** the partial pressure of the vapor above the liquid **8.92** Increased pressure raises a liquid's boiling point; decreased pressure lowers it. **8.94** (a) 29.2 kcal (b) 173 kcal **8.96** Atoms in a crystalline solid have a regular, orderly arrangement. **8.98** 4.82 kcal **8.100** increase in atmospheric $[CO_2]$; increase in global temperatures **8.102** Systolic pressure is the maximum pressure just after contraction; diastolic pressure is the minimum pressure at the end of the heart cycle. **8.104** A supercritical fluid is intermediate in properties between liquid and gas. **8.106** As temperature increases, molecular collisions become more violent. **8.108** 0.13 mol; 4.0 L **8.110** 590 g/day **8.112** 0.92 g/L; less dense than air at STP **8.114** (a) 0.714 g/L (b) 1.96 g/L (c) 1.43 g/L

8.116 (a)   (b)

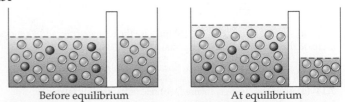

(c) Ethylene glycol forms hydrogen bonds. **8.118** (a) 492 °R (b) $R = 0.0455$ (L·atm)/(mol·°R)

Chapter 9

9.1 (a) heterogeneous mixture (b) homogeneous solution (c) homogeneous colloid (d) homogeneous solution **9.2** (c), (d) **9.3** $Na_2SO_4 \cdot 10H_2O$ **9.4** 322 g **9.5** unsaturated; cooling makes the solution supersaturated **9.6** 5.6 g/100 mL **9.7** 6.8×10^{-5} g/100 mL **9.8** 56 mm Hg; ~90% saturated **9.9** 231 g **9.10** Place 38 mL acetic acid in flask and dilute to 500.0 mL. **9.11** 0.0086% (m/v) **9.12** (a) 20 g (b) 60 mL H_2O **9.13** 1.6 ppm **9.14** Pb: 0.015 ppm, 0.0015 mg; Cu: 1.3 ppm, 0.13 mg **9.15** 0.927 M **9.16** (a) 0.061 mol (b) 0.67 mol **9.17** 0.48 g **9.18** (a) 0.0078 mol (b) 0.39 g **9.19** 39.1 mL **9.20** 750 L **9.21** (a) 39.1 g; 39.1 mg (b) 79.9 g; 79.9 mg (c) 12.2 g; 12.2 mg (d) 48.0 g; 48.0 mg (e) 9.0 g; 9.0 mg (f) 31.7 g; 31.7 mg **9.22** 9.0 mg **9.23** $Na^+ = 0.046$ m/v %; $K^+ = 0.039$ m/v % **9.24** (a) 2.0 mol ions; (b) 2.0 °C **9.25** weak electrolyte **9.26** (a) red curve is pure solvent; green curve is solution (b) solvent bp = 62 °C; solution bp = 69 °C (c) 2 M **9.27** −1.9 °C **9.28** 3 ions/mol **9.29** (a) 0.70 osmol (b) 0.30 osmol **9.30** (a) 0.090 M Na^+; 0.020 M K^+; 0.110 M Cl^-; 0.11 M glucose (b) 0.33 osmol

9.31

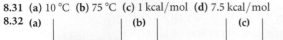

Before equilibrium   At equilibrium

9.32 HCl completely dissociates into ions; acetic acid dissociates only slightly. **9.33** Upper curve: HF; lower curve: HBr **9.34** (a) **9.35** (d) **9.36** homogeneous: mixing is uniform; heterogeneous: mixing is nonuniform **9.38** polarity **9.40** (b), (d) **9.42** 15.3 g/100 mL **9.44** Concentrated solutions can be saturated or not; saturated solutions can be concentrated or not. **9.46** Molarity is the number of moles of solute per liter of solution.

9.48 Dissolve 45.0 mL of ethyl alcohol in water and dilute to 750.0 mL
9.50 Dissolve 1.5 g NaCl in water to a final volume of 250 mL.
9.52 (a) 7.7% (m/v) (b) 3.9% (m/v) **9.54** (a) 0.054 mol (b) 0.25 mol
9.56 230 mL, 1600 mL **9.58** 10 ppm **9.60** (a) 0.425 M (b) 1.53 M
(c) 1.03 M **9.62** 5.3 mL **9.64** 38 g **9.66** 500 mL **9.68** 0.53 L
9.70 600 mL **9.72** a substance that conducts electricity when dissolved in
water **9.74** Ca^{2+} concentration is 0.0015 M **9.76** 40 mEq **9.78** 0.28 L
9.80 $Ba(OH)_2$ **9.82** 26.9 mol **9.84** The inside of the cell has higher
osmolarity than water, so water passes in and increases pressure. **9.86** (a) 0.20 M
Na_2SO_4 (b) 3% (m/v) NaOH **9.88** 2.4 osmol **9.90** The body manufactures more hemoglobin. **9.92** Sports drinks contain electrolytes,
carbohydrates, and vitamins. **9.94** (a) 680 mmHg (b) 1.9 g/100²mL
9.96 (a) 0.0067% (m/v) (b) 67 ppm (c) 0.000 40 M **9.98** (a) 9.4 mL
(b) 0.75 L **9.100** NaCl: 0.147 M; KCl: 0.0040 M; $CaCl_2$: 0.0030 M
9.102 0.00020% (m/v) **9.104** 4.0 mL
9.106 (a) $CoCl_2(s) + 6 H_2O(l) \rightarrow CoCl_2 \cdot 6H_2O(s)$
(b) 1.13 g **9.110** (a) 1.36 mol particles (b) 2.53 °C

Chapter 10

10.1 (a), (b) **10.2** (a), (c) **10.3** (a) H_2S (b) $HPO_4{}^{2-}$ (c) $HCO_3{}^-$ (d) NH_3
10.4 acids: HF, H_2S; bases: HS^-, F^-; conjugate acid–base pairs: H_2S and HS^-, HF
and F^- **10.5** (a) $NH_4{}^+$ (b) H_2SO_4 (c) H_2CO_3 **10.6** (a) F^- (b) OH^-
10.7 $HPO_4{}^{2-} + OH^- \rightleftharpoons PO_4{}^{3-} + H_2O$; favored in forward direction
10.8 $HCl(aq) + CO_3{}^{2-}(aq) \rightleftharpoons HCO_3{}^-(aq) + Cl^-(aq)$ conjugate acid–
base pairs: $HCO_3{}^-$ and $CO_3{}^{2-}$, HCl and Cl^- **10.9** The $-NH_3{}^+$ hydrogens are
most acidic **10.10** benzoate **10.11** (a) basic, $[OH^-] = 3.2 \times 10^{-3}$ M
(b) acidic, $[OH^-] = 2.5 \times 10^{-12}$ M **10.12** (a) 11.51 (b) 2.40
10.13 (a) $[H_3O^+] = 1 \times 10^{-13}$ M; $[OH^-] = 0.1$ M (b) $[H_3O^+] = 1 \times 10^{-3}$ M; $[OH^-] = 1 \times 10^{-11}$ M (c) $[H_3O^+] = 1 \times 10^{-8}$ M; $[OH^-] = 1 \times 10^{-6}$ M (b) is most acidic; (a) is most basic **10.14** 0.010 M HNO_2;
weaker acid **10.15** (a) acidic; $[H_3O^+] = 3 \times 10^{-7}$ M; $[OH^-] = 3 \times 10^{-8}$ M (b) most basic; $[H_3O^+] = 1 \times 10^{-8}$ M; $[OH^-] = 1 \times 10^{-6}$ M
(c) acidic; $[H_3O^+] = 2 \times 10^{-4}$ M; $[OH^-] = 5 \times 10^{-11}$ M
(d) most acidic; $[H_3O^+] = 3 \times 10^{-4}$ M; $[OH^-] = 3 \times 10^{-11}$ M
10.6 (a) 8.28 (b) 5.05 **10.17** 2.60 **10.18** 3.38 **10.19** 9.45
10.20 bicarbonate/carbonic acid = 10/1 **10.21** 9.13 **10.22** (a) 0.079 Eq
(b) 0.338 Eq (c) 0.14 Eq **10.23** (a) 0.26 N (b) 1.13 N (c) 0.47 N
10.24 $Al(OH)_3 + 3 HCl \rightarrow AlCl_3 + 3 H_2O$; $Mg(OH)_2 + 2 HCl \rightarrow MgCl_2 +$
$2 H_2O$ **10.25** (a) $2 HCO_3{}^-(aq) + H_2SO_4(aq) \rightarrow 2 H_2O(l) + 2 CO_2(g) +$
$SO_4{}^{2-}$ (b) $CO_3{}^{2-}(aq) + 2 HNO_3(aq) \rightarrow H_2O(l) + CO_2(g) + 2 NO_3{}^-(aq)$
10.26 $H_2SO_4(aq) + 2 NH_3(aq) \rightarrow (NH_4)_2SO_4(aq)$ **10.27** $CH_3CH_2NH_2 +$
$HCl \rightarrow CH_3CH_2NH_3{}^+Cl^-$ **10.28** 0.730 M **10.29** 133 mL
10.30 (a) 2.41×10^{-3} M; 4.83×10^{-3} Eq (b) 0.225 M
10.31 2.23×10^{-4} M; pH = 3.65 **10.32** (a) neutral (b) basic (c) basic
(d) acidic **10.33** (a) box 2 (b) box 3 (c) box 1 **10.34** The $O-H$ hydrogen in each is most acidic; acetic acid **10.35** (a) box 1 (b) box 2 (c) box 1
10.36 (a) box 3 (b) box 1 **10.37** 0.67 M **10.38** HBr dissociates into ions
10.40 KOH dissociates into ions **10.42** A monoprotic acid can donate
one proton; a diprotic acid can donate two. **10.44** (a), (e) **10.46** (a) acid
(b) base (c) neither (d) acid (e) neither (f) acid **10.48** (a) CH_2ClCO_2H
(b) $C_5H_5NH^+$ (c) $HSeO_4{}^-$ (d) $(CH_3)_3NH^+$ **10.50** (a) $HCO_3{}^- + HCl \rightarrow$
$H_2O + CO_2 + Cl^-$; $HCO_3{}^- + NaOH \rightarrow H_2O + Na^+ + CO_3{}^{2-}$
(b) $H_2PO_4{}^- + HCl \rightarrow H_3PO_4 + Cl^-$; $H_2PO_4{}^- + NaOH \rightarrow$
$H_2O + Na^+ + HPO_4{}^{2-}$ **10.52** (a) $HCl + NaHCO_3 \rightarrow H_2O + CO_2 +$
$NaCl$ (b) $H_2SO_4 + 2 NaHCO_3 \rightarrow 2 H_2O + 2 CO_2 + Na_2SO_4$
10.54 $K_a = \dfrac{[H_3O^+][A^-]}{[HA]}$ **10.56** $K_w = [H_3O^+][OH^-] = 1.0 \times 10^{-14}$
10.58 CH_3CO_2H is a weak acid and is only partially dissociated.
10.60
$$K_a = \frac{[H_2PO_4{}^{2-}][H_3O^+]}{[H_3PO_4]} \quad K_a = \frac{[HPO_4{}^-][H_3O^+]}{[H_2PO_4{}^{2-}]} \quad K_a = \frac{[PO_4{}^3][H_3O^+]}{[HPO_4{}^-]}$$
10.62 basic; 1×10^{-8} **10.64** $[H_3O^+] = 1 \times 10^{-4}$ M − 1.6×10^{-7};
three orders of magnitude **10.66** pH = 1.7; pH = 12.3 **10.68** (a) 7.60
(b) 3.30 (c) 11.64 (d) 2.40 **10.70** (a) 1×10^{-4} M; 1×10^{-10} M;
(b) 1×10^{-11} M; 1×10^{-3} M (c) 1 M; 1×10^{-14} M (d) 4.2×10^{-2} M;
2.4×10^{-13} M (e) 1.1×10^{-8} M; 9.1×10^{-7} M **10.72** A buffer contains a
weak acid and its anion. The acid neutralizes any added base, and the anion neutralizes any added acid.

10.74 (a) $pH = pK_a + \log\dfrac{[CH_3CO_2{}^-]}{[CH_3CO_2H]} = 4.74 + \log\dfrac{[0.100]}{[0.100]} = 4.74$
(b) $CH_3CO_2{}^- \cdot Na^+ + H_3O^+ \rightarrow CH_3CO_2H + Na^+$; $CH_3CO_2H + OH^- \rightarrow$
$CH_3CO_2{}^- + H_2O$ **10.76** 9.19 **10.78** 9.07 **10.80** An equivalent is the
formula weight in grams divided by the number of H_3O^+ or OH^- ions produced. **10.82** 63.0 g; 32.7 g; 56.1 g; 29.3 g **10.84** 25 mL; 50 mL
10.86 (a) 0.50 Eq (b) 0.084 Eq (c) 0.25 Eq **10.88** 0.13 M; 0.26 N
10.90 0.23 M **10.92** 0.075 M **10.94** (a) pH = 2 to 3 (b) $NaHCO_3 +$
$HCl \rightarrow CO_2 + H_2O + NaCl +$ (c) 20 mg **10.96** Intravenous bicarbonate neutralizes the hydrogen ions in the blood and restores pH.
10.98 3×10^{-6} M **10.100** (a) 0.613 mol (b) 2.45 M (c) pH = 0.39
10.102 Citric acid reacts with sodium bicarbonate to release CO_2.
10.104 Both have the same amount of acid; HCl has higher $[H_3O^+]$ and
lower pH. **10.106** 0.70 N; 0.35 M **10.108** (a) $NH_4{}^+$, acid; OH^-,
base; NH_3, conjugate base; H_2O, conjugate acid (b) 5.56 g
10.110 (a) $Na_2O(aq) + H_2O(l) \rightarrow 2 NaOH(aq)$ (b) 13.0 (c) 5.00 L

Chapter 11

11.1 $^{218}_{84}Po$ **11.2** $^{226}_{88}Ra$ **11.3** $^{89}_{38}Sr \rightarrow {}^{0}_{-1}e + {}^{89}_{39}Y$
11.4 (a) $^{3}_{1}H \rightarrow {}^{0}_{-1}e + {}^{3}_{2}He$ (b) $^{210}_{82}Pb \rightarrow {}^{0}_{-1}e + {}^{210}_{83}Bi$ (c) $^{20}_{9}F \rightarrow {}^{0}_{-1}e + {}^{20}_{10}Ne$
11.5 (a) $^{38}_{20}Ca \rightarrow {}^{0}_{1}e + {}^{38}_{19}K$ (b) $^{118}_{54}Xe \rightarrow {}^{0}_{1}e + {}^{118}_{53}I$ (c) $^{79}_{37}Rb \rightarrow {}^{0}_{1}e + {}^{79}_{36}Kr$
11.6 (a) $^{62}_{30}Zn + {}^{0}_{-1}e \rightarrow {}^{62}_{29}Cu$ (b) $^{110}_{50}Sn + {}^{0}_{-1}e \rightarrow {}^{110}_{49}In$ (c) $^{86}_{36}Kr + {}^{0}_{-1}e \rightarrow {}^{81}_{35}Br$
11.7 $^{120}_{49}In \rightarrow {}^{0}_{-1}e + {}^{120}_{50}Sn$ **11.8** 12% **11.9** 5.0 L **11.10** 3 days
11.11 13m **11.12** 2% **11.13** 175 μCi **11.14** 2×10^4 rem; 4×10^5 rem
11.15 $^{237}_{93}Np$ **11.16** $^{241}_{95}Am + {}^{4}_{2}He \rightarrow 2 {}^{1}_{0}n + {}^{243}_{97}Bk$ **11.17** $^{40}_{18}Ar + {}^{1}_{1}H \rightarrow$
$^{1}_{0}n + {}^{40}_{19}K$ **11.18** 60 hours (10 half lives) **11.19** $^{235}_{92}U + {}^{1}_{0}n \rightarrow 2 {}^{1}_{0}n +$
$^{137}_{52}Te + {}^{97}_{40}Zr$ **11.20** $^{3}_{2}He$ **11.21** 2 half-lives **11.22** $^{28}_{12}Mg \rightarrow {}^{0}_{-1}e + {}^{23}_{13}Al$
11.23

○ Aluminum—28
○ Magnesium—28

11.24 $^{14}_{6}C$ **11.25** The shorter arrow represent β emission; longer arrows
represent α emission. **11.26** $^{241}_{94}Pu \rightarrow {}^{241}_{95}Am \rightarrow {}^{237}_{93}Np \rightarrow {}^{233}_{91}Pa \rightarrow {}^{233}_{92}U$
11.27 $^{148}_{69}Tm \rightarrow {}^{0}_{1}e \rightarrow {}^{148}_{68}Er$ or $^{148}_{69}Tm + {}^{0}_{-1}e \rightarrow {}^{148}_{68}Er$ **11.28** 3.5 years
11.29 The curve doesn't represent nuclear decay. **11.30** It emits radiation
by decay of an unstable nucleus. **11.32** A nuclear reaction changes the identity of the atoms, is unaffected by temperature or catalysts, and often releases
a large amount of energy. A chemical reaction does not change the identity
of the atoms, is affected by temperature and catalysts, and involves relatively small energy changes. **11.34** by breaking bonds in DNA **11.36** A
neutron decays to a proton and an electron. **11.38** The number of nucleons and the number of charges is the same on both sides. **11.40** α emission: Z decreases by 2 and A decreases by 4; β emission: Z increases by
1 and A is unchanged **11.42** In fission, a nucleus fragments to smaller
pieces. **11.44** (a) $^{35}_{17}Cl$ (b) $^{24}_{11}Na$ (c) $^{90}_{39}Y$ **11.46** (a) $^{109}_{47}Ag$ (b) $^{10}_{5}B$
11.48 (a) $^{4}_{0}n$ (b) $^{146}_{57}La$ **11.50** $^{198}_{80}Hg + {}^{1}_{0}n \rightarrow {}^{198}_{79}Au + {}^{1}_{1}H$; a proton
11.52 $^{228}_{90}Th$ **11.54** Half of a sample decays in that time. **11.56** (a) 2.3
half-lives (b) 0.0063 g **11.58** 1 ng; 2×10^{-3} ng **11.60** The inside walls
of a Geiger counter tube are negatively charged, and a wire in the center is
positively charged. Radiation ionizes argon gas inside the tube, which creates a
conducting path for current between the wall and the wire. **11.62** In a scintillation counter, a phosphor emits a flash of light when struck by radiation,
and the flashes are counted. **11.64** more than 25 rems **11.66** 1.9 mL
11.68 (a) 4.7 rem (b) 1.9 rem **11.70** in vivo procedures, therapeutic procedures, boron neutron capture **11.72** Irradiation kills harmful microorganisms by destroying their DNA. **11.74** They yield more data, including
three-dimensional images. **11.76** no filter −α radiation; plastic −β radiation; foil −γ radiation **11.78** Nuclear decay is an intrinsic property of a
nucleus and is not affected by external conditions. **11.80** 112 cpm
11.82 (a) β emission (b) Mo-98 **11.84** (a) $^{238}_{94}Pu \rightarrow {}^{4}_{2}He + {}^{234}_{92}U$
(b) for radiation shielding **11.86** Their cells divide rapidly. **11.88** advan-
tages: few harmful byproducts, fuel is inexpensive; disadvantage: needs a
high temperature **11.90** (a) $^{253}_{99}Es + {}^{4}_{2}He \rightarrow {}^{256}_{101}Md + {}^{1}_{0}n$ (b) $^{250}_{98}Cf +$
$^{11}_{5}B \rightarrow {}^{257}_{103}Lr + 4 {}^{1}_{0}n$ **11.92** $^{10}_{5}B + {}^{1}_{0}n \rightarrow {}^{7}_{3}Li + {}^{4}_{2}He$
11.94 $^{238}_{92}U + 3 {}^{4}_{2}He \rightarrow {}^{246}_{98}Cf + 4 {}^{1}_{0}n$

Chapter 12

12.1 (a) alcohol, carboxylic acid (b) double bond, ester (c) aromatic ring, amine, carboxylic acid

12.2 (a) CH_3CH_2CHO (b) CH_3COCH_3 (c) $CH_3CH_2CO_2H$ **12.3** (a) $CH_3CH_2CH_2CH_2CH_2CH_2CH_3$
(b) $CH_3CH_2CH_2CH_2CH_2CH_2CH_2CH_2CH_3$

12.4

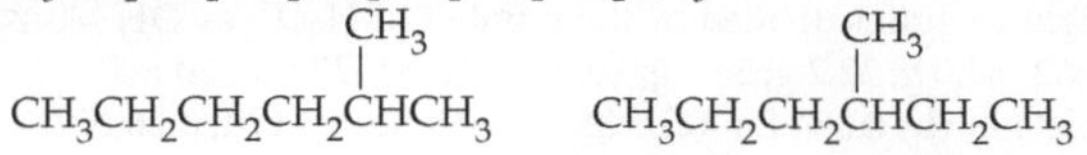

$CH_3CH_2CH_2CH_2\overset{\overset{\displaystyle CH_3}{|}}{C}HCH_3$ $CH_3CH_2CH_2\overset{\overset{\displaystyle CH_3}{|}}{C}HCH_2CH_3$

12.5 (a)

$CH_3CH_2CH_2CH_2CH_3$
Pentane

(b) $CH_3\overset{\overset{\displaystyle CH_3}{|}}{C}HCH_2CH_3$
2-Methylbutane

(c) $CH_3\overset{\overset{\displaystyle CH_3}{|}}{\underset{\underset{\displaystyle CH_3}{|}}{C}}CH_3$
2,2-Dimethylpropane

12.6 (a)   (b)   (c)

12.7 (a) $CH_3CH_2\overset{\overset{\displaystyle H_3C}{|}}{\underset{\underset{\underset{\underset{\displaystyle CH_3}{|}}{\displaystyle CH_2CHCH_3}}{|}}{C}}\!-\!\overset{\overset{\displaystyle Cl}{|}}{C}HCH_2CH_3$

(b) $CH_3\overset{\overset{\displaystyle H_3C\;\;CH_3}{\diagup}}{C}\!-\!CH\!-\!\overset{\overset{\displaystyle H_3C\;\;CH_3}{\diagup}}{\underset{\underset{\displaystyle CH_2CH_3}{|}}{C}}CH_3$

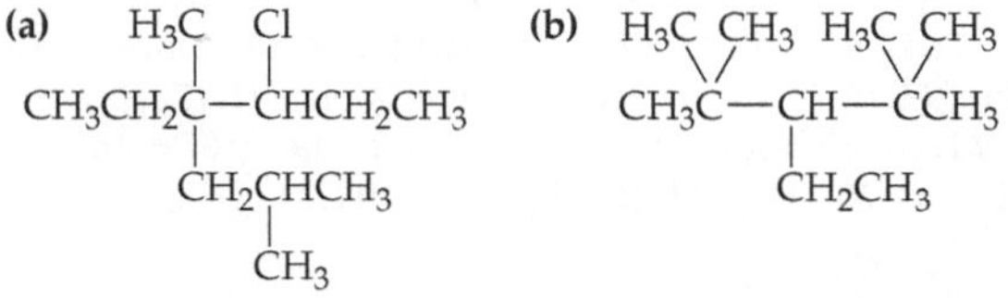

12.8 (a) CH_3CH_2O (b) CH_3COCH_3 (c) $CH_3CH_2CO_2H$

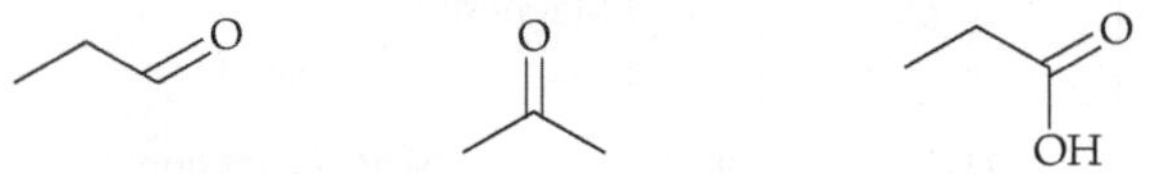

12.9 Structures (a) and (c) are identical, and are isomers of (b).

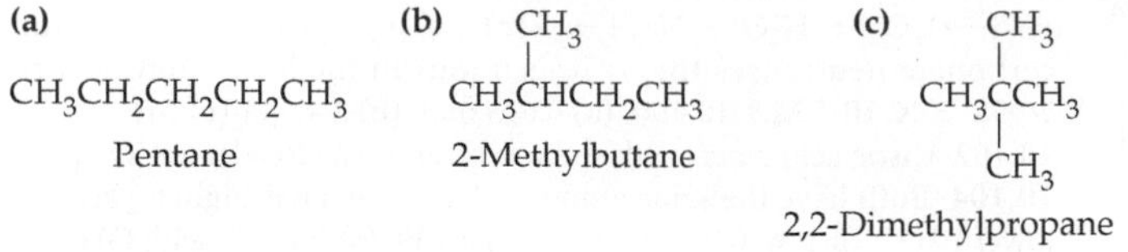

12.10

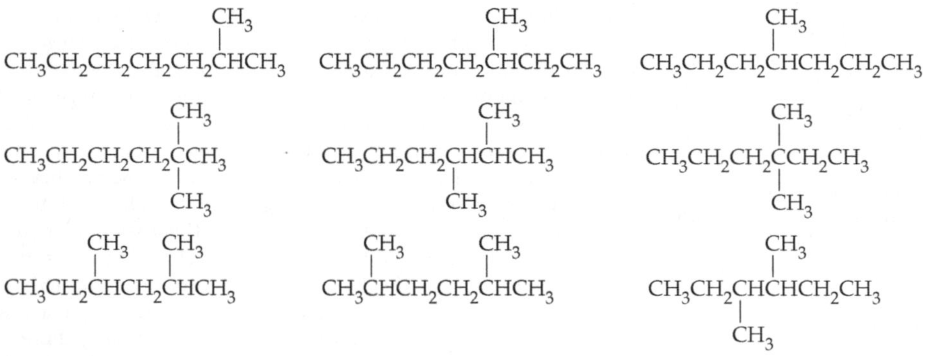

$CH_3CH_2CH_2CH_2CH_2\overset{\overset{\displaystyle CH_3}{|}}{C}HCH_3$ $CH_3CH_2CH_2CH_2\overset{\overset{\displaystyle CH_3}{|}}{C}HCH_2CH_3$ $CH_3CH_2CH_2\overset{\overset{\displaystyle CH_3}{|}}{C}HCH_2CH_2CH_3$

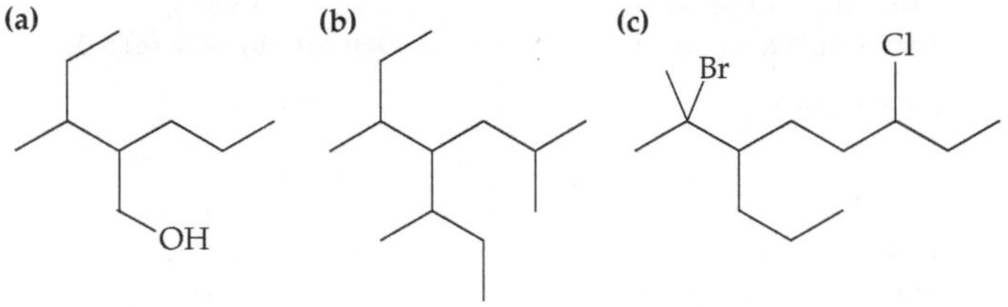

$CH_3CH_2CH_2CH_2\overset{\overset{\displaystyle CH_3}{|}}{\underset{\underset{\displaystyle CH_3}{|}}{C}}CH_3$ $CH_3CH_2CH_2\overset{\overset{\displaystyle CH_3}{|}}{C}H\overset{\overset{\displaystyle CH_3}{|}}{C}HCH_3$ $CH_3CH_2CH_2\overset{\overset{\displaystyle CH_3}{|}}{\underset{\underset{\displaystyle CH_3}{|}}{C}}CH_2CH_3$

$CH_3CH_2\overset{\overset{\displaystyle CH_3}{|}}{C}HCH_2\overset{\overset{\displaystyle CH_3}{|}}{C}HCH_3$ $CH_3\overset{\overset{\displaystyle CH_3}{|}}{C}HCH_2CH_2\overset{\overset{\displaystyle CH_3}{|}}{C}HCH_3$ $CH_3CH_2\overset{\overset{\displaystyle CH_3}{|}}{C}H\overset{\overset{\displaystyle }{}}{C}HCH_2CH_3$ with CH_3

12.11

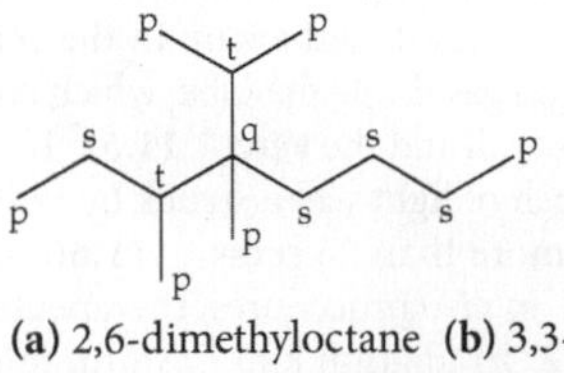

12.12 (a) 2,6-dimethyloctane (b) 3,3-diethylheptane

12.13

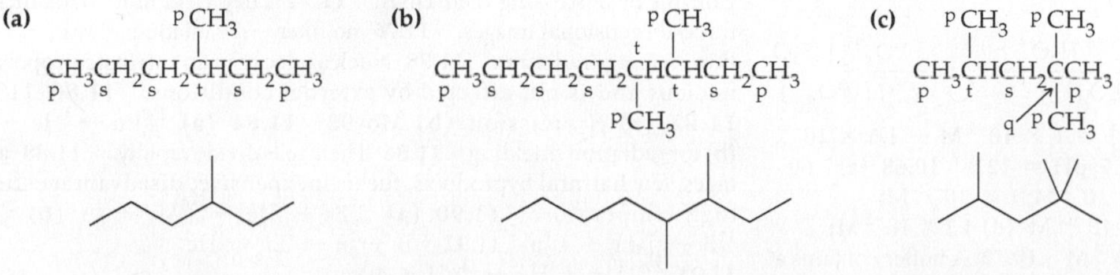

(a) $CH_3CH_2CH_2\overset{\overset{\displaystyle P\,CH_3}{|}}{C}HCH_2CH_3$

(b) $CH_3CH_2CH_2CH_2\overset{\overset{\displaystyle P\,CH_3}{|}}{\underset{\underset{\displaystyle P\,CH_3}{|}}{C}}HCHCH_2CH_3$

(c) $CH_3\overset{\overset{\displaystyle P\,CH_3}{|}}{C}HCH_2\overset{\overset{\displaystyle P\,CH_3}{|}}{\underset{\underset{\displaystyle P\,CH_3}{|}}{C}}CH_3$

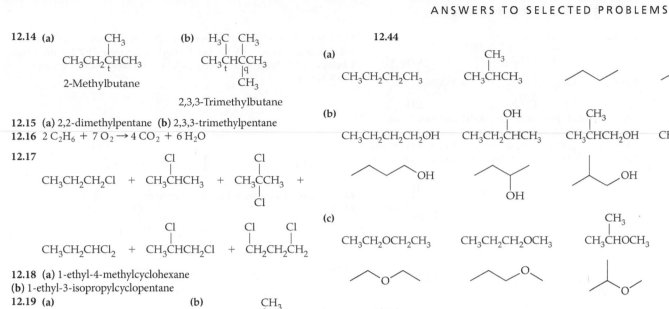

12.14 (a)

CH₃
|
CH₃CH₂CHCH₃
t
2-Methylbutane

(b)

H₃C CH₃
|
CH₃CHCCH₃
t |q
CH₃
2,3,3-Trimethylbutane

12.15 (a) 2,2-dimethylpentane **(b)** 2,3,3-trimethylpentane
12.16 $2\,C_2H_6 + 7\,O_2 \rightarrow 4\,CO_2 + 6\,H_2O$

12.17

Cl   Cl
| |
CH₃CH₂CH₂Cl + CH₃CHCH₃ + CH₃CCH₃ +
                        |
                        Cl

Cl   Cl   Cl
| | |
CH₃CH₂CHCl₂ + CH₃CHCH₂Cl + CH₂CH₂CH₂

12.18 (a) 1-ethyl-4-methylcyclohexane
(b) 1-ethyl-3-isopropylcyclopentane
12.19 (a)

CH₂CH₃
CH₂CH₃

(b)

CH₃
H₃C   CH₃

12.20 (a) plastics **(b)** more resistant to heat and cold   **12.21** propylcyclohexane   **12.22 (a)** 12 hydrogens **(b)** 10 hydrogens **(c)** 8 hydrogens
12.23 (a)

CH₃
|
CH₃CCH₂CH₃
|
CH₃

(b)

CH₃
|
CH₃CHCHCH₃
|
OH

12.24 (a)

(cyclopentanone) O

(b)

CH₃
NH₂

12.25 (a) double bond, ketone, ether **(b)** double bond, amine, carboxylic acid
12.26 (a) 2,3-dimethylpentane **(b)** 2,5-dimethylhexane   **12.27 (a)** 1,1-dimethylcyclopentane **(b)** isopropylcyclobutane   **12.28** The methyl groups are on the same side of the ring in one structure, and on opposite sides in the other.   **12.30** groups of atoms that have a characteristic reactivity; chemistry of compounds is determined by their functional groups   **12.32** A polar covalent bond is a covalent bond in which electrons are shared unequally.
12.34 (a) (i) amine; (ii) amide; (iii) ester; (iv) aldehyde **(b)** (v) ketone; (vi) aromatic ring; (vii) alcohol; (viii) carboxylic acid
12.36 (a)

O
‖
CH₃CH₂CH₂CH₂CH
Aldehyde

(b)

O
‖
CH₃CH₂CH₂C—OCH₂CH₃
Ester

(c)

O
‖
HS—CH₂CH₂C—NH₂
Amide, thiol

12.38 They must have the same molecular formula but different structures.
12.40 A primary carbon is bonded to one other carbon; a secondary carbon is bonded to two other carbons; a tertiary carbon is bonded to three other carbons; and a quaternary carbon is bonded to four other carbons.
12.42 (a) 2,3-dimethylbutane **(b)** cyclopentane

12.44

(a)

CH₃CH₂CH₂CH₃

CH₃
|
CH₃CHCH₃

(pentane skeleton)

(2-methylbutane skeleton)

(b)

CH₃CH₂CH₂CH₂OH

CH₃
|
CH₃CH₂CHCH₃

OH

CH₃
|
CH₃CHCH₂OH

CH₃
|
CH₃CHCH₂OH

(butanol structures with OH)

(c)

CH₃CH₂OCH₂CH₃

CH₃CH₂CH₂OCH₃

CH₃
|
CH₃CHOCH₃

(ether skeleton structures)

12.46

(a)

CH₃CH₂CH₂CH₂OH

OH
|
CH₃CH₂CHCH₃

CH₃
|
CH₃CHCH₂OH

OH
|
CH₃CCH₃
|
CH₃

(b)

CH₃CH₂CH₂NH₂

NH₂
|
CH₃CHCH₃

H
|
CH₃CH₂NCH₃

CH₃
|
CH₃NCH₃

(c)

O
‖
CH₃CH₂CH₂CCH₃

O
‖
CH₃CH₂CCH₂CH₃

O
‖
CH₃CHCCH₃
|
CH₃

12.48 identical: **(a)**; isomers: **(b), (d), (e)**; unrelated: **(c)**   **12.50** All have a carbon with five bonds.   **12.52 (a)** 4-ethyl-3-methyloctane **(b)** 5-isopropyl-3-methyloctane **(c)** 2,2,6-trimethylheptane **(d)** 4-isopropyl-4-methyloctane **(e)** 2,2,4,4-tetramethylpentane **(f)** 4,4-diethyl-2-methylhexane **(g)** 2,2-dimethyldecane
12.54

(a)

H₃C   C(CH₃)₃
| |
CH₃CH₂C—CHCHCH₂CH₃
| |
CH₃   CH₃

(b)

CH₃   CH₃
| |
CH₃CHCH₂CHCH₃

(c)

H₃C   CH₂CH₃
| |
CH₃CH₂CHCCH₂CH₂CH₂CH₃
|
CH₂CH₃

(d)

CH₃CHCH₃ CH₃
| |
CH₃CHCCH₂CH₂CHCHCH₂CH₃
| |
H₃C CH₃   CH₃

(e)

CH₃CH   CH₂CHCH₃
| |
H₃C   CH₃

CH₃

(f)

CH₃
CH₃
H₃C

12.56 (a) 1-ethyl-3-methylcyclobutane **(b)** 1,1,3,3-tetramethylcyclopentane **(c)** 1-ethyl-3-propylcyclohexane **(d)** 4-butyl-1,1,2,2-tetramethylcyclopentane
12.58 (a) 2,2-dimethylpentane **(b)** 2,4-dimethylpentane **(c)** isobutylcyclobutane   **12.60** heptane, 2-methylhexane, 3-methylhexane, 2,2-dimethylpentane, 2,3-dimethylpentane, 2,4-dimethylpentane, 3,3-dimethylpentane, 3-ethylpentane, 2,2,3-trimethylbutane

12.62 $C_3H_8 + 5 O_2 \rightarrow 3 CO_2 + 4 H_2O$

12.64

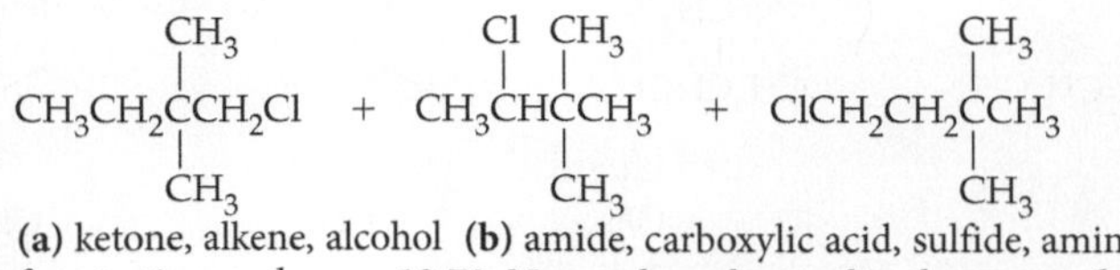

12.66 (a) ketone, alkene, alcohol **(b)** amide, carboxylic acid, sulfide, amine
12.68 four tertiary carbons **12.70** Non-polar solvents dissolve non-polar substances. **12.72** pentane; greater London forces **12.74** A chemical feedstock is a simple organic chemical used as the starting material in many organic reactions.

12.76

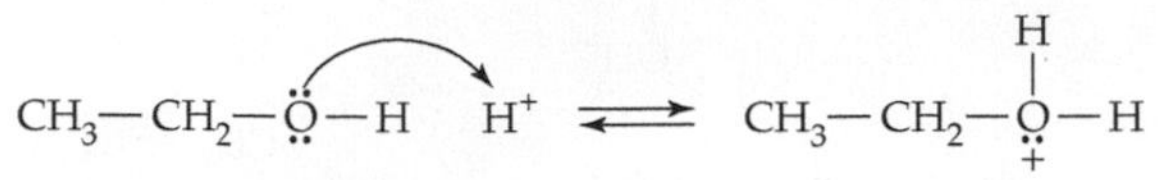

Chapter 13

13.1 (a) 2-methyl-3-heptene **(b)** 2-methyl-1,5-hexadiene **(c)** 3-methyl-3-hexene
(d) 3-ethyl-6-methyl-4-octyne
13.2

(a)

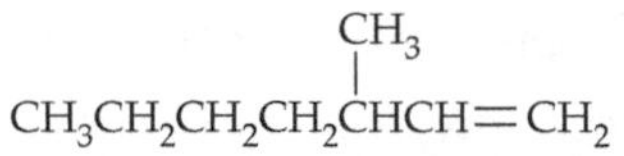

(b)

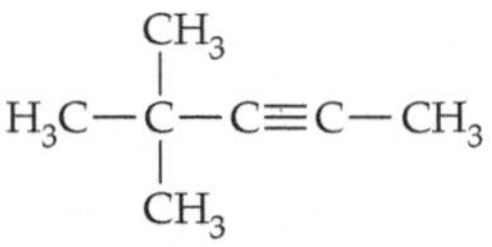

(c)

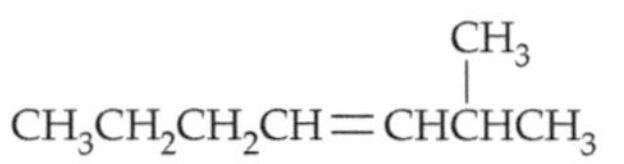

(d)

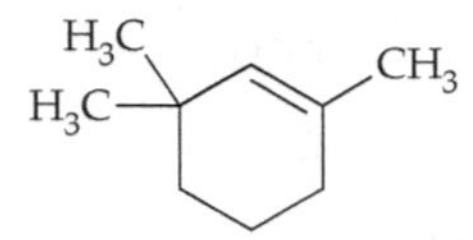

13.3 (a) 2,3-dimethyl-1-pentene **(b)** 2,3-dimethyl-2-hexene **13.4 (a), (c)**
13.5

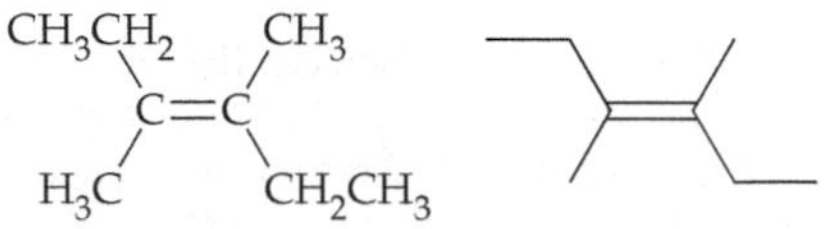

13.6 (a) *cis*-4-methyl-2-hexene **(b)** *trans*-5,6-dimethyl-3-heptene
13.7 (a) substitution **(b)** addition **(c)** elimination **13.8 (a)** rearrangement
(b) 28 hydrogens **(c)** aldehyde, carbon–carbon double bond (alkene)
13.9

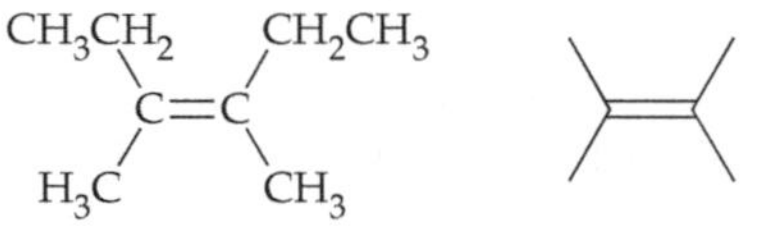

(a)

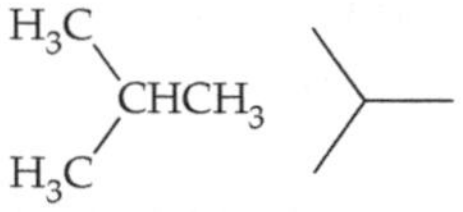

(b) $CH_3CH_2CH_2CH_3$

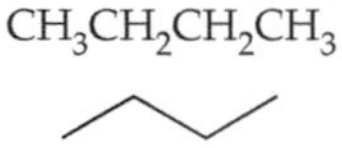

(c) $CH_3CH_2CH_2CH_2CH_2CH_2CH_3$

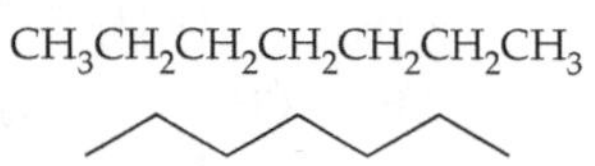

(d)

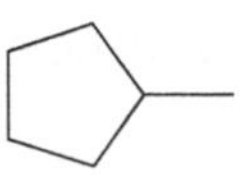

13.10 (a) 1,2-dibromo-2-methylpropane **(b)** 1,2-dichloropentane
(c) 4,5-dichloro-2,4-dimethylheptane **(d)** 1,2-dibromocyclopentane
13.11

major   minor

13.12 (a) 1-chloro-1-methylcyclopentane **(b)** 2-bromobutane **(c)** 2-chloro-2,
4-dimethylpentane **13.13 (a)** 3-ethyl-2-pentene **(b)** 2,3-dimethyl-
1-butene or 2,3-dimethyl-2-butene **13.14** 2-bromo-2,4-dimethylhexane
13.15 (a)(b)

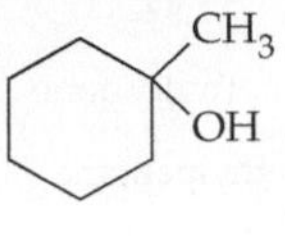

(c)

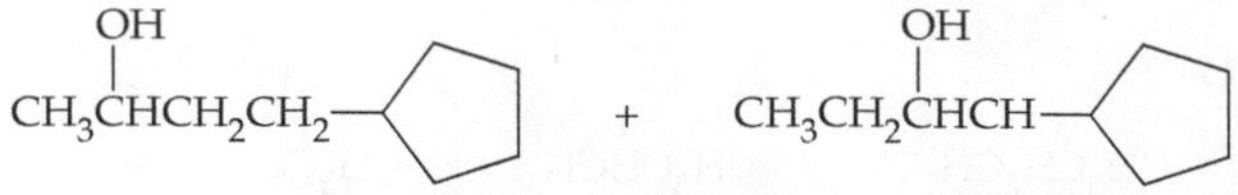

13.16 2-ethyl-1-butene or 3-methyl-2-pentene
13.17

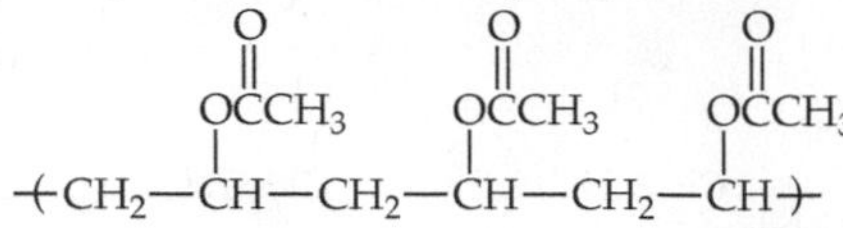

13.18 (a)

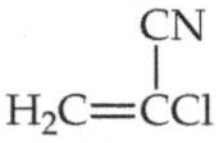

(b)

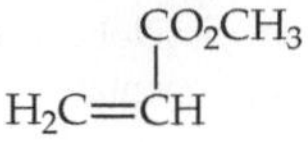

13.19 (a) *m*-ethylphenol **(b)** *m*-chlorotoluene **(c)** 1-ethyl-3-isopropylbenzene
13.20

(a)

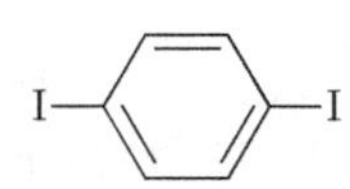

(b)

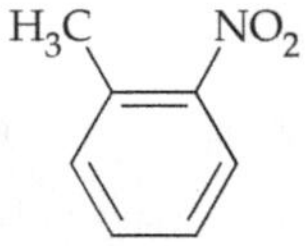

(c)

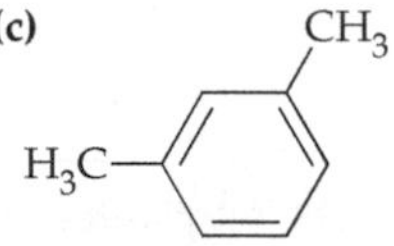

(d)

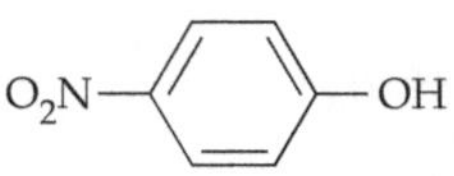

13.21 (a) *o*-isopropylphenol **(b)** *p*-bromoaniline
13.22

(a)

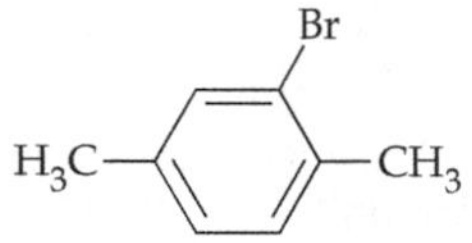

(b)

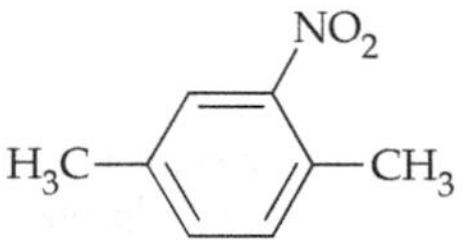

(c)

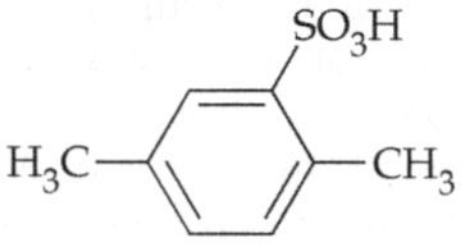

13.23 *o*-, *m*-, and *p*-bromophenol
13.24 (a) 2,5-Dimethyl-2-heptene

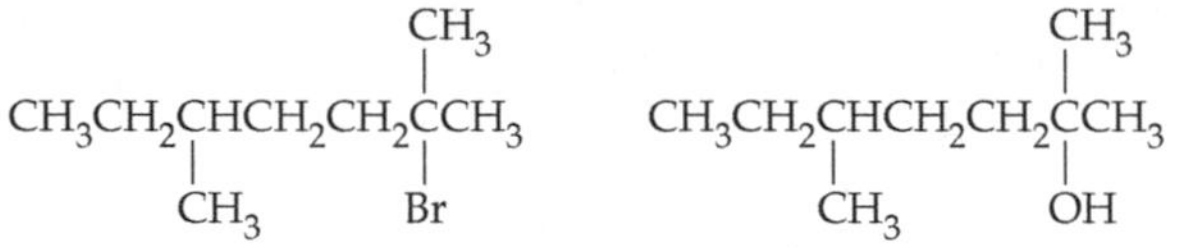

(b) 3,3-Dimethylcyclopentene

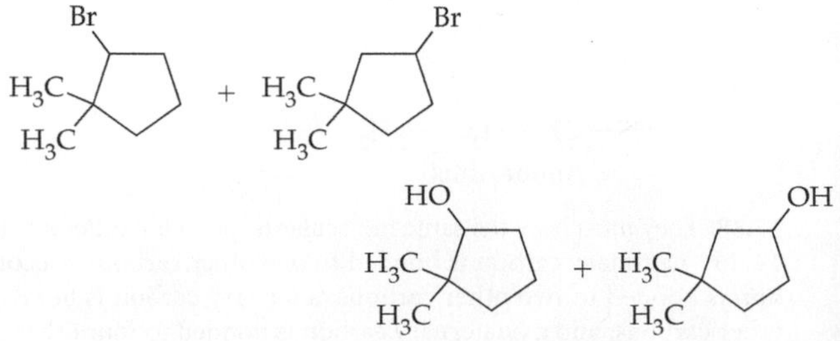

13.25 (a) 4,4-dimethyl-1-hexyne (b) 2,7-dimethyl-4-octyne

13.26 (a) *m*-isopropylphenol (b) *o*-bromobenzoic acid

13.27 (a)

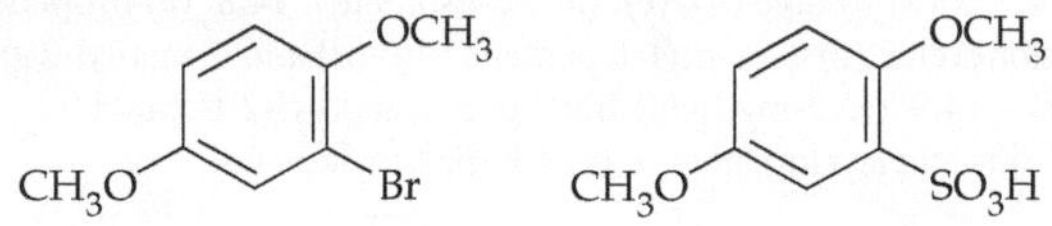

(b)

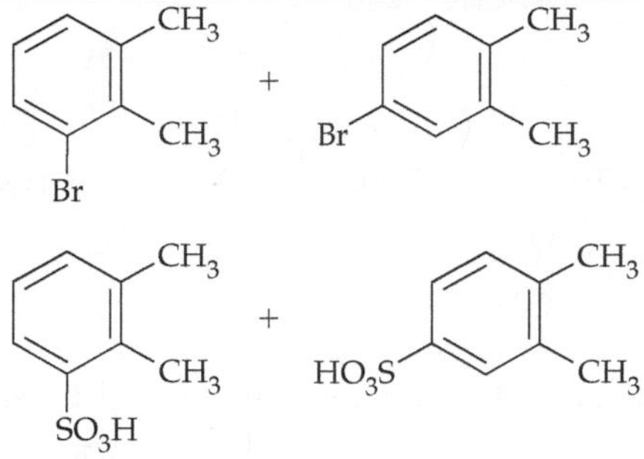

13.28

(a)

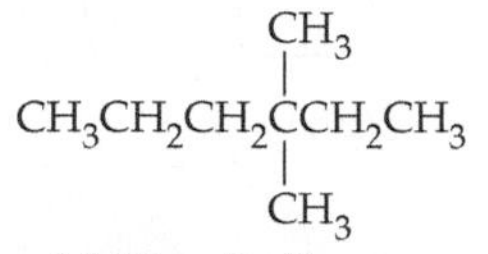

$$CH_3CH_2CH_2CCH_2CH_3$$ with CH_3 substituents

3,3-Dimethylhexane

(b)

$$CH_3CHCH_2CH_2CH_2CH_2CHCH_3$$ with CH_3 substituents

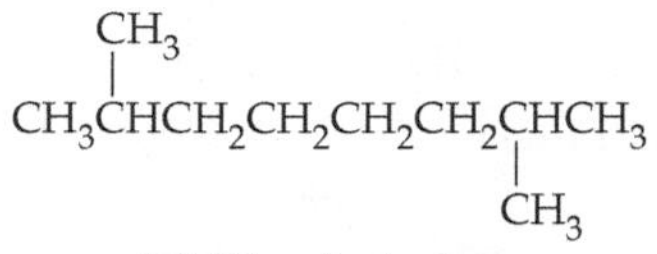

2,7-Dimethyloctane

13.29

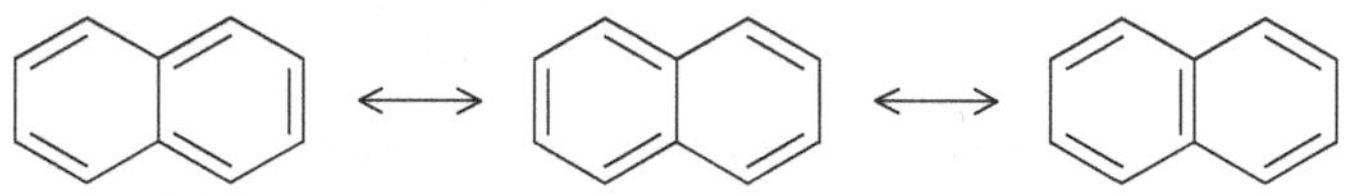

13.30 They have C—C multiple bonds and can add hydrogen.

13.32 alkene: –*ene*; alkyne: –*yne*; aromatic: –*benzene*

13.34

(a)

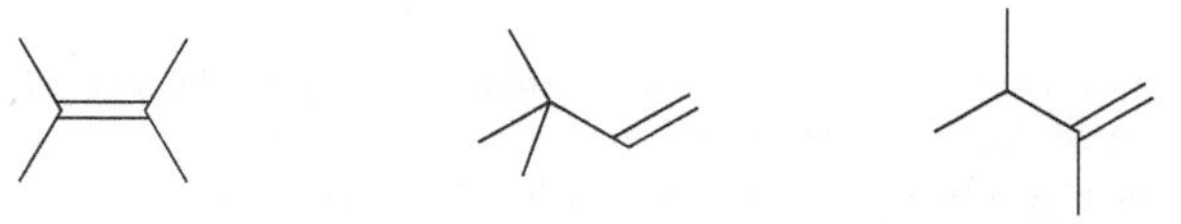

(b)

$$CH_3CH_2CH_2C\equiv CH \qquad CH_3CH_2C\equiv CCH_3 \qquad CH_3CHC\equiv CH$$ (with CH_3)

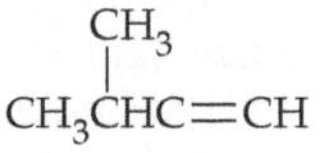

(c)

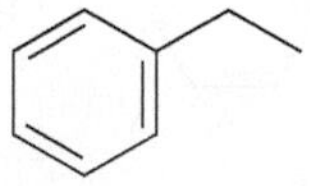

(d)

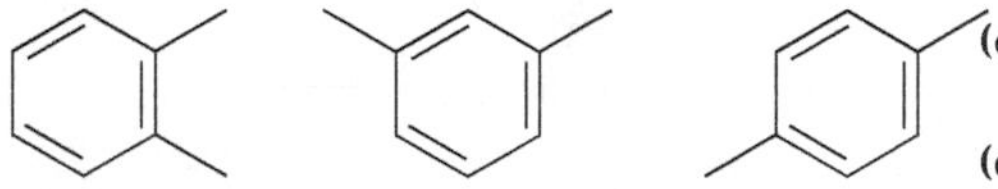

13.36 (a) 2-pentene (b) 2,5-dimethyl-3-hexyne (c) 3,4-diethyl-3-hexene (d) 2,4-dimethyl-2,4-hexadiene (e) 3,6-dimethylcyclohexene (f) 4-ethyl-1,2-dimethylcyclopentene

13.38

(a)

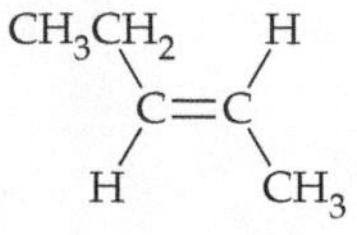

(b)

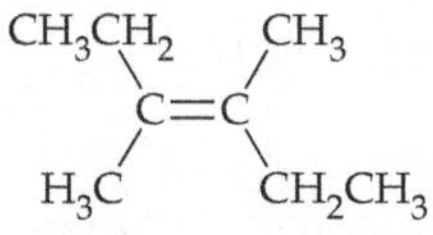

(c)

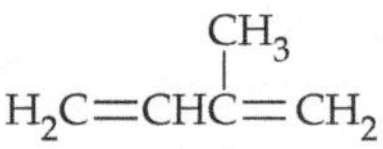

$$H_2C=CHC=CH_2$$ (with CH_3)

(d)

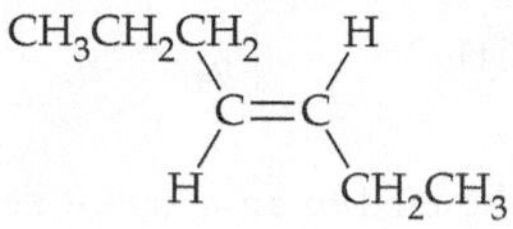

(e)

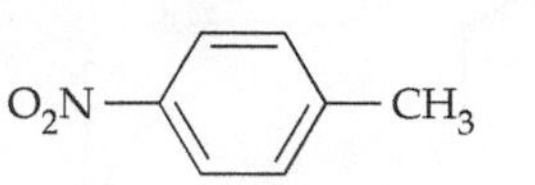

$$O_2N-\text{(ring)}-CH_3$$

(f)

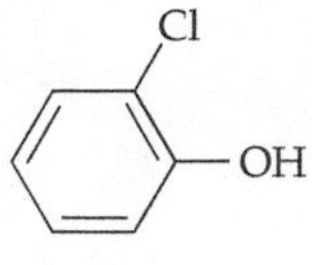

(g)

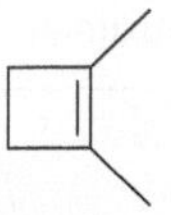

(h)

$$CH_3CH_2CH_2CHCH=CHCCH_2CH_3$$ (with CH_3, CH_2CH_3, CH_2CH_3)

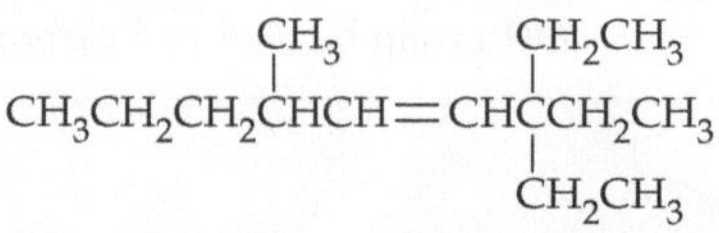

13.40 1-hexyne, 2-hexyne, 3-hexyne, 3-methyl-1-pentyne, 4-methyl-1-pentyne, 4-methyl-2-pentyne, 3,3-dimethyl-1-butyne   **13.42** 1-pentene, *cis*-2-pentene, *trans*-2-pentene, 2-methyl-1-butene, 3-methyl-1-butene, 2-methyl-2-butene   **13.44** Each double bond carbon must be bonded to two different groups.   **13.46** 2-pentene

13.48

(a)

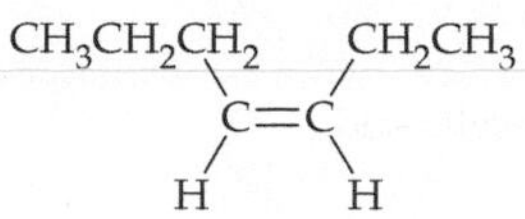

(b)

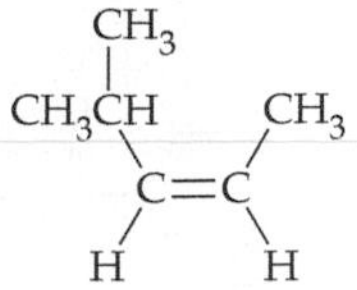

(c)

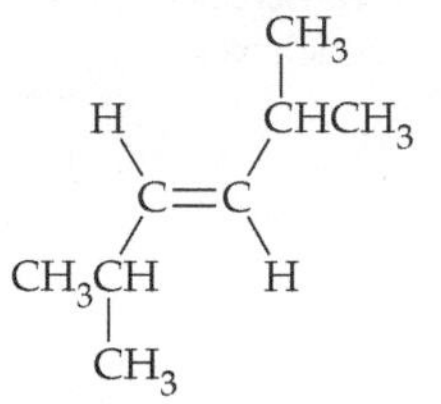

13.50 (a) identical (b) identical   **13.52** substitution: two reactants exchange parts to give two products; addition: two reactants add to give one product   **13.54** rearrangement   **13.56** (a) substitution (b) rearrangement

13.58 (a)

$$CH_3CH_2CH_2CH_3$$

(b)

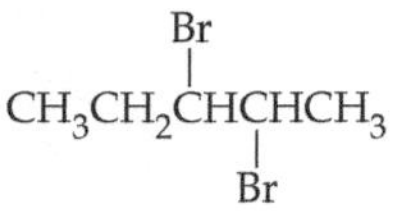

$$CH_3CH_2CHCHCH_3$$ (with two Br)

(c)

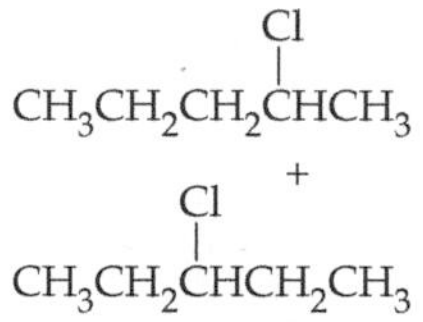

$$CH_3CH_2CH_2CHCH_3 \text{ (with Cl)}$$
+
$$CH_3CH_2CHCH_2CH_3 \text{ (with Cl)}$$

(d)

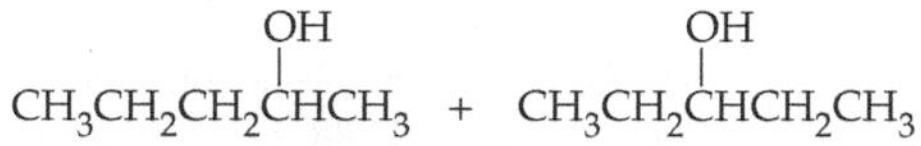

$$CH_3CH_2CH_2CHCH_3 \text{ (with OH)} \;+\; CH_3CH_2CHCH_2CH_3 \text{ (with OH)}$$

13.60

(a) 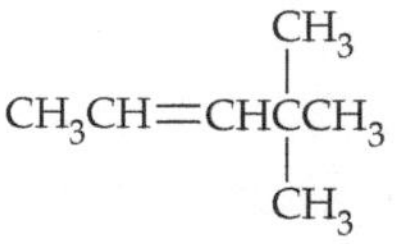 $CH_3CH=CHCCH_3$ (with two CH_3) $+ Cl_2$ (b) $CH_3CH=CH_2 + H_2$

(c) $CH_3CH=CHCH_3$ or $H_2C=CHCH_2CH_3 + HBr$

(d)

$+ H_2O$

(e)

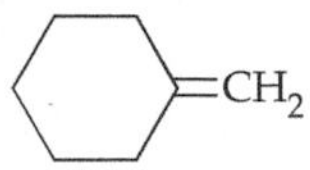

$=CH_2 + Cl_2$

13.62 $CH_3CH_2CH_2CH=CHBr \;+\; CH_3CH_2CH_2C=CH_2$ (with Br)

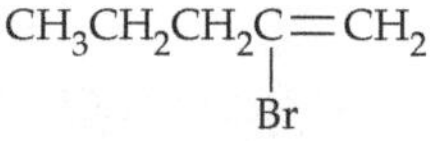

13.64 $H_2C=CCl_2$

13.66 (a)

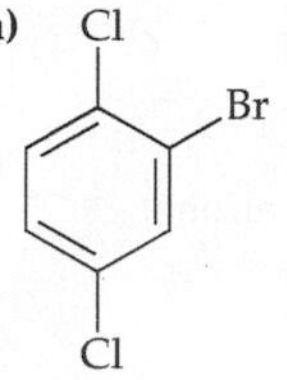

(b)

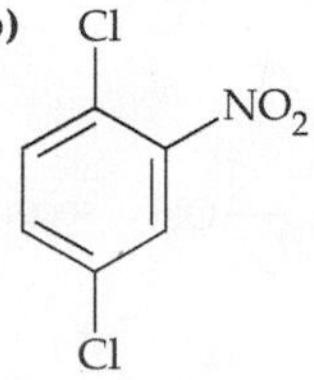

(c)

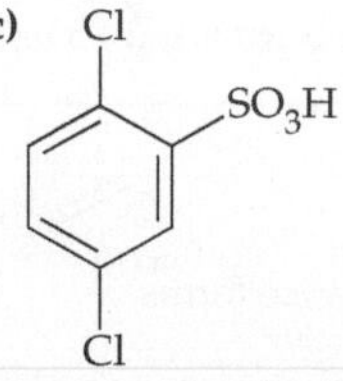

(d)

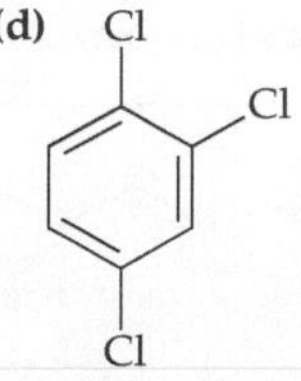

13.68

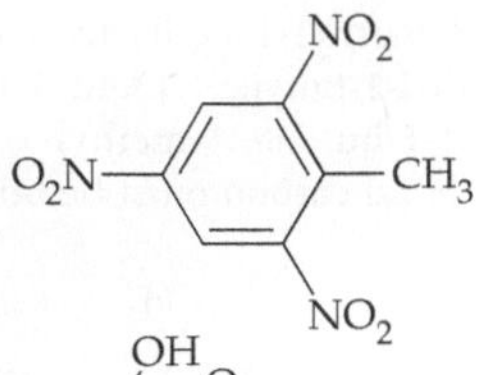

TNT

13.70

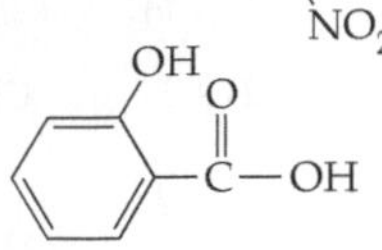

Salicylic acid

13.72 (a) 5-methyl-2-hexene (b) 4-methyl-2-heptyne (c) 2,3-dimethyl-1-butene (d) 1,2,4-trinitrobenzene (e) 3,4-dimethylcyclohexene (f) 3-methyl-1,3-pentadiene **13.74** Br_2 reacts only with cyclohexene.

13.76

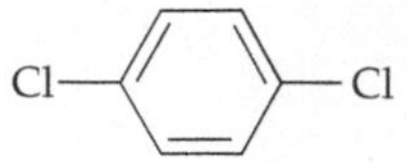

13.78

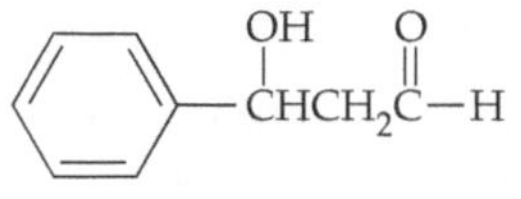

13.80

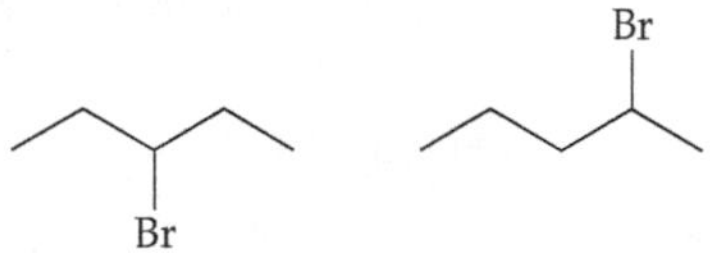

Both ends of the double bond have the same number of hydrogens, and both products can form.

13.82

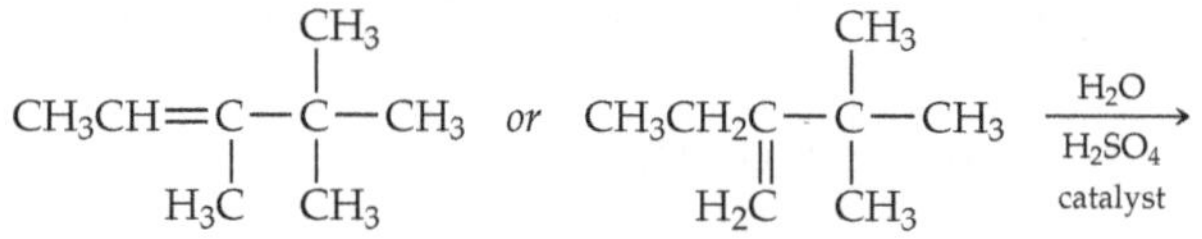

13.84 Rod cells are responsible for vision in dim light; cone cells are responsible for color vision. **13.86** ultraviolet range **13.88** a compound that has two or more benzene-like rings that share a common bond **13.90** $(CH_3)_3C^+$ **13.92** *See below for answer.*

Chapter 14

14.1 (a) alcohol (b) alcohol (c) phenol (d) alcohol (e) ether (f) ether
14.2 The ether oxygen can form hydrogen bonds with water.
14.3 (a)

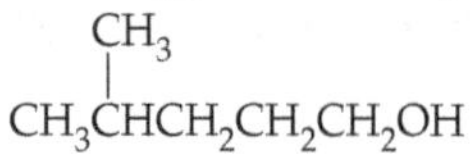

primary alcohol

(b)

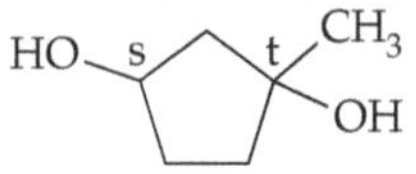

secondary, tertiary alcohol

(c)

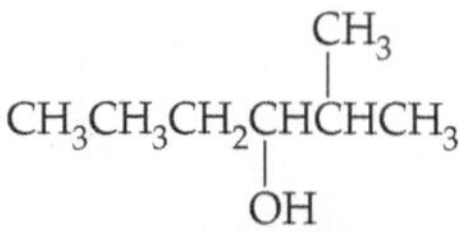

secondary alcohol

(d)

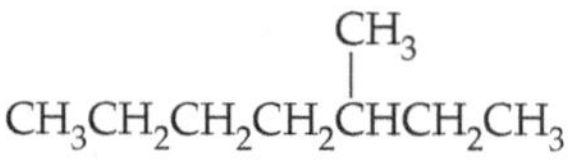

secondary alcohol

(e)

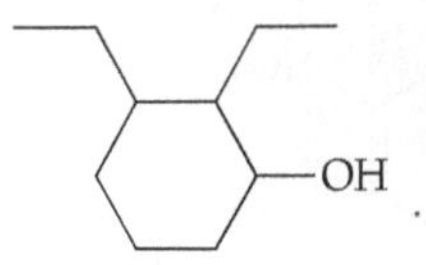

secondary alcohol

14.4 (a) 2-methyl-2-propanol (*tert*-butyl alcohol), tertiary (b) 3-methyl-2-pentanol,

secondary (c) 5-chloro-2-ethyl-1-hexanol, primary (d) 1,2-cyclopentanediol, secondary **14.5** See 14.3 and 14.4 **14.6** highest (d), (b), (a), (c) lowest **14.7** most soluble (b), (c), (a) least soluble **14.8** (a) propene (b) cyclohexene (c) 4-methyl-1-pentene (minor) and 4-methyl-2-pentene (major) **14.9** (a) 2-methyl-2-butanol or 3-methyl-2-butanol (b) 1,2-dimethylcyclopentanol (c) 1,2-diphenylethanol
14.10

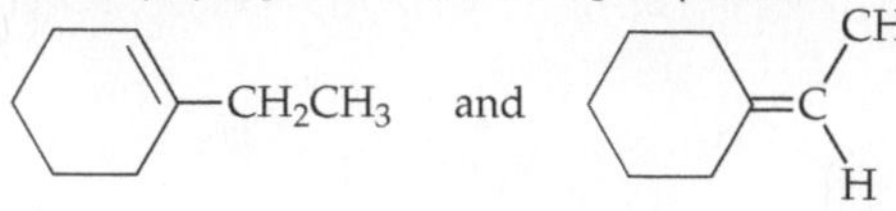

14.11 (a)

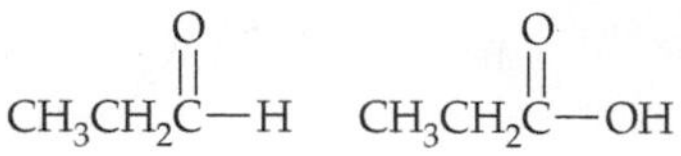

(b)

(c)

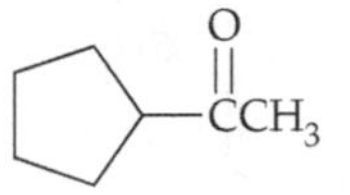

14.12 (a) 2-propanol (b) cycloheptanol (c) 3-methyl-1-butanol
14.13 (a)

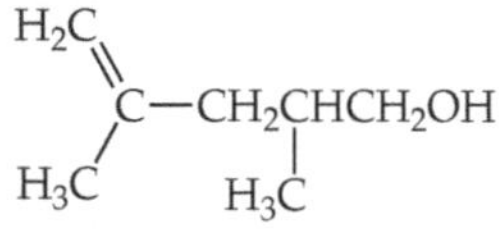

(b)

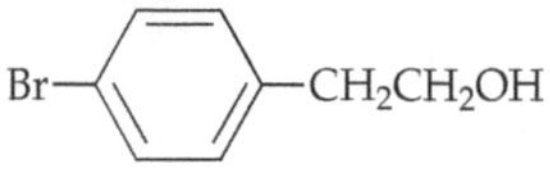

14.14 (a)

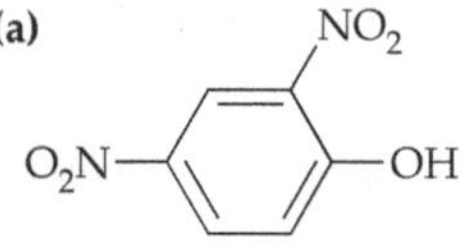

(b)

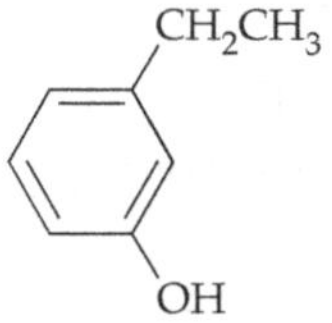

14.15 (a) 2,4-dibromophenol (b) 3-iodo-2-methylphenol
14.16

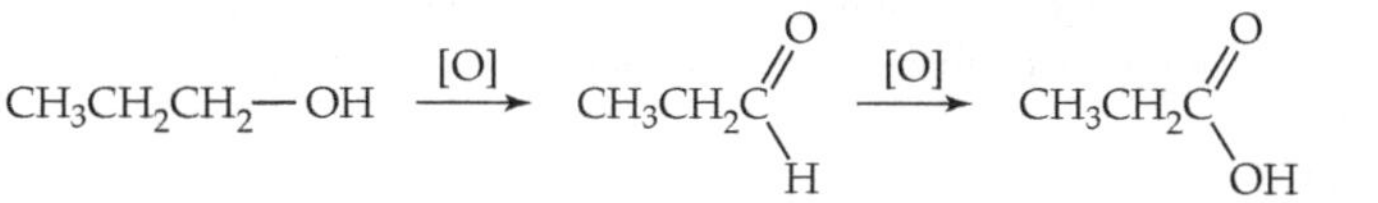

14.17 (a) 1,2-dimethoxypropane (b) *p*-methoxynitrobenzene (c) *tert*-butyl methyl ether **14.18** They inhibit free-radical chain reactions in unsaturated fats. **14.19** (a) $CH_3CH_2CH_2S-SCH_2CH_2CH_3$ (b) $(CH_3)_2CHCH_2CH_2S-SCH_2CH_2CH(CH_3)_2$
14.20 (a) 1-chloro-1-ethylcyclopentane (b) 3-bromo-5-methylheptane
14.21 (a) 5-methyl-3-hexanol (b) *m*-methoxytoluene (c) 3-methylcyclohexanol
14.22

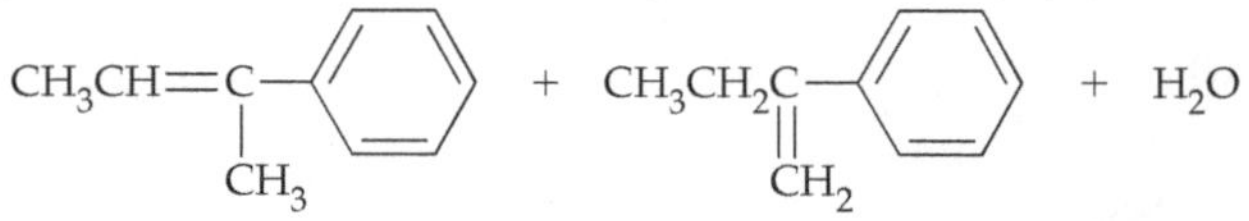

14.23 $(CH_3)_2CHCH_2CH_2CHO$, $(CH_3)_2CHCH_2CH_2CO_2H$
14.24

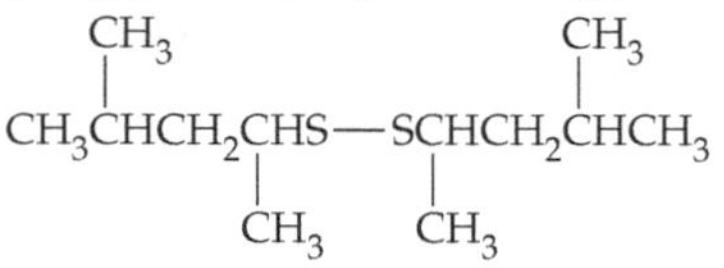

14.25
(a)

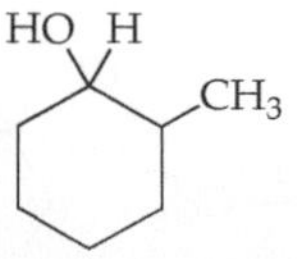

(b)

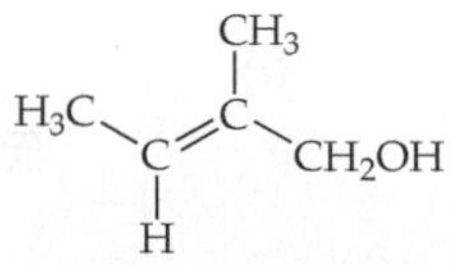

(c)

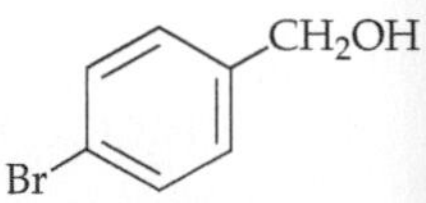

14.26 Alcohols have an —OH group bonded to an alkane-like carbon atom; ethers have an oxygen atom bonded to two carbon atoms; and phenols have an —OH group bonded to a carbon of an aromatic ring.

13.92

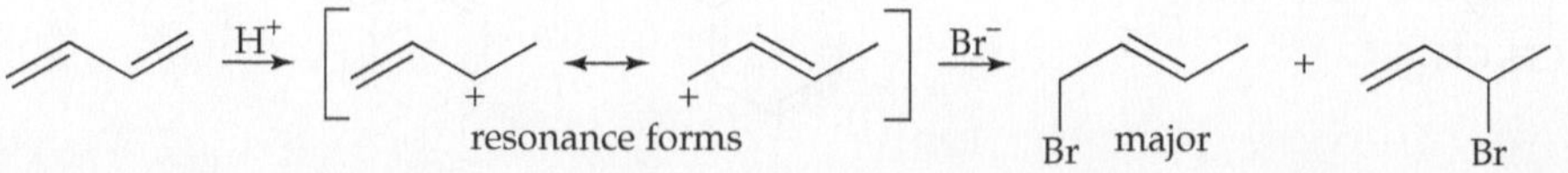

Addition of H^+ produces a carbocation that can be represented as two resonance forms. Br^- adds to produce the observed alkene.

14.28 Alcohols form hydrogen bonds. **14.30** ketone, carbon–carbon double bond, alcohol **14.32** (a) 2-methyl-2-propanol (*tert*-butyl alcohol) (b) 2-methyl-1-propanol (c) 1,2,4-butanetriol (d) 2-methyl-2-phenyl-1-propanol (e) 3-methylcyclohexanol (f) 3-ethyl-3-methyl-2-hexanol

14.34 (a)

$$CH_3CH_2CH_2CHCH_2CCH_3$$ with CH_3, CH_3 groups and OH

(b) cyclohexane ring with OH, OCH_3, OCH_3

(c) $CH_3CH_2CCH_2CH_2CH_2CH_2OH$ with CH_2CH_3 and CH_3 groups

(d) $CH_3CH_2CHCHCHCH_3$ with CH_3CH_2, OH, CH_2CH_3 groups

(e) cyclooctane ring with H_3C, CH_3, HO, C_6H_5

(f) $CH_3CHCH_2CH_2CCH_2CH_2OH$ with OH, CH_2CH_3, CH_2CH_3 groups

14.36 (a) tertiary (b) primary (c) primary, secondary (d) primary (e) secondary (f) secondary
14.38 lowest (a) < (c) < (b) highest
14.40 a ketone **14.42** a carboxylic acid
14.44 Phenols dissolve in aqueous NaOH; alcohols don't.
14.46
(a) cyclopentane ring with OH, CH_2CH_3, CH_2CH_3

(b) HO structure and OH structure

(c) $CH_3CH_2CH_2CH_2CCH_3$ with OH, C_6H_5 and $CH_3CH_2CH_2CHCHCH_3$ with OH, C_6H_5

(d) benzofuran-type bicyclic ring with OH, O

(e) $HOCH_2CH_2CH_2CH_2CH_2OH$

(f) cyclohexane with OH, CCH_3, CH_3 and cyclohexane with $CHCH_2OH$, CH_3

14.48
(a) structures: benzene ring—$CH_2C(=O)H$ and benzene ring—$CH_2C(=O)OH$

(b) $CH_3CH_2CCH_3$ with $=O$

(c) $CH_3CH_2CCCH_3$ with two $=O$

(d) NR (e) NR (f) benzene ring—CCH_2CH_3 with $=O$

14.50 odor
14.52

$$HOCCHCH_2S—SCH_2CHCOH$$ with O (top), NH_2, NH_2 (bottom), O

14.54 Alcohols can form hydrogen bonds; thiols and alkyl chlorides can't.
14.56

structures labeled: 1-hexanol (OH at end), 2-hexanol (OH), 3-hexanol (OH)

dipropyl ether, methyl pentyl ether, butyl ethyl ether

14.58 Alcohols become less soluble as their nonpolar part becomes larger.
14.60 An antiseptic kills microorganisms on living tissue; a disinfectant is used on nonliving matter. **14.62** (a) *p*-dibromobenzene (b) 1,2-dibromo-1-butene (c) *m*-propylanisole (d) 1,1-dibromocyclopentane (e) 2,4-dimethyl-2,4-pentanediol (f) 4-methyl-2,4,5-heptanetriol (g) 4-bromo-6,6-dimethyl-2-heptyne (h) 1-chloro-2-iodocyclobutane
14.64 3,7-Dimethyl-2,6-octadiene-1-ol

$$CH_3C=CHCH_2CH_2C=CHC—H$$ with CH_3, CH_3, O

14.66 $C_2H_6O + 3 O_2 \rightarrow 2 CO_2 + 3 H_2O$ **14.68** slurred speech: 300–400 mg/dL lethal concentration: 600 mg/dL **14.70** A person breathes into a tube containing potassium dichromate (yellow-orange). If there is alcohol in the breath, it is oxidized by dichromate, which is reduced to Cr(III) (blue green). **14.72** Vitamin E **14.74** the concentration of anesthetic that results in anesthesia in 50% of patients

14.76 (a)

$$CH_3CH_2CH_2C—CH_3 \;(\text{with } CH_3, :OH, H^+) \rightleftharpoons CH_3CH_2CH_2C—CH_3 \;(\text{with } CH_3, OH_2^+) \rightleftharpoons CH_3CH_2CH—C—CH_3 \;(\text{with } CH_3, +, H)$$

with $H_2O:$

$$H_3O^+ + CH_3CH_2CH=C \;(\text{with } CH_2CH_3, CH_2CH_3)$$

(b)

$$CH_3CH_2C—CH_2CH_3 \;(\text{with } CH_2CH_3, :OH, H^+) \rightleftharpoons CH_3CH_2C—CH_2CH_3 \;(\text{with } CH_2CH_3, OH_2^+) \rightleftharpoons CH_3CH—C—CH_2CH_3 \;(\text{with } CH_2CH_3, +, H)$$

with $H_2O:$

$$H_3O^+ + CH_3CH=C \;(\text{with } CH_2CH_3, CH_2CH_3)$$

Chapter 15

15.1 (a) primary (b) secondary (c) primary (d) secondary (e) tertiary
15.2 (a) tripropylamine (b) N-ethyl-N-methylcyclopentylamine
(c) N-isopropylaniline
15.3 (a) $CH_3CH_2CH_2CH_2CH_2CH_2CH_2CH_2NH_2$

(b)  $CH_3CH_2CH_2CH_2CH_2 \overset{\overset{\displaystyle CH_3}{|}}{N}H$

(c) 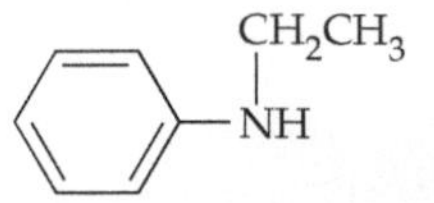 (d) 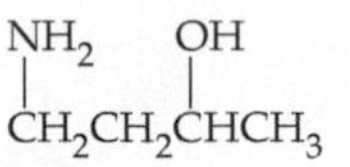 $\overset{\overset{\displaystyle NH_2 \quad OH}{|\quad\quad|}}{CH_2CH_2CHCH_3}$

15.4 pharmaceuticals. Manufacturers don't make their MSDS available to avoid patient confusion.
15.5 The ion has one less electron than the neutral atoms.

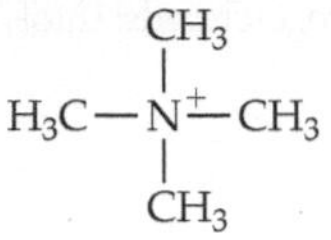

15.6 $CH_3CH_2CH_2CH_2NHCH_2CH_3$ N-ethylbutylamine **15.7** Compound (a) is lowest boiling; (b) is highest boiling (strongest hydrogen bonds).
15.8

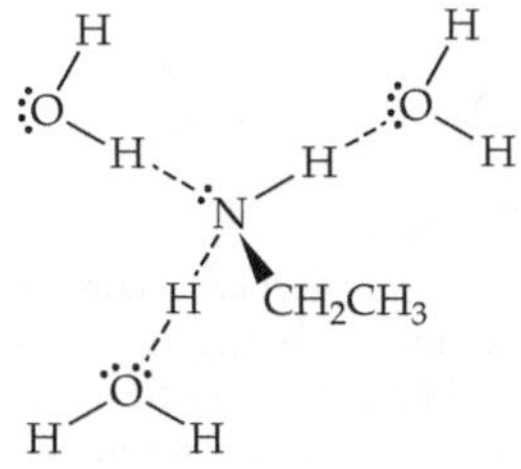

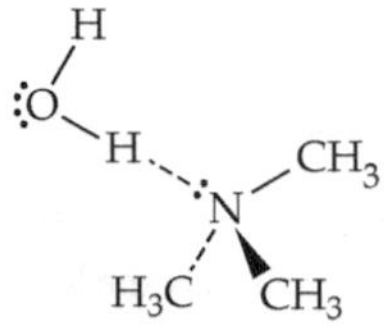

15.9 (a) methylamine, ethylamine, dimethylamine, trimethylamine
(b) pyridine (c) aniline **15.10** (a) pyrimidine: $C_4H_4N_2$ (b) purine: $C_5H_4N_4$ **15.11** (a) and (d)
15.12

(a)

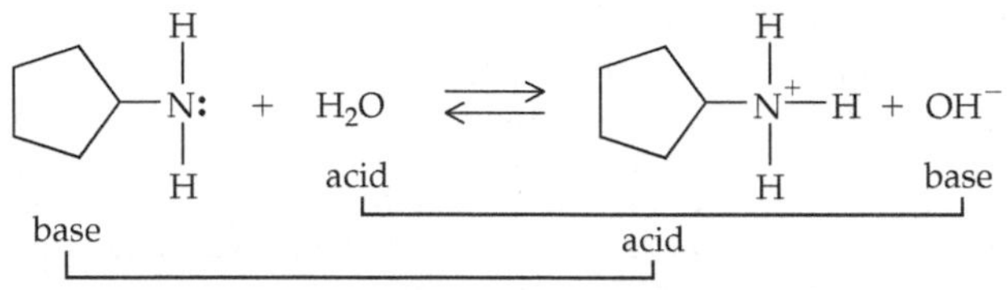

(b)

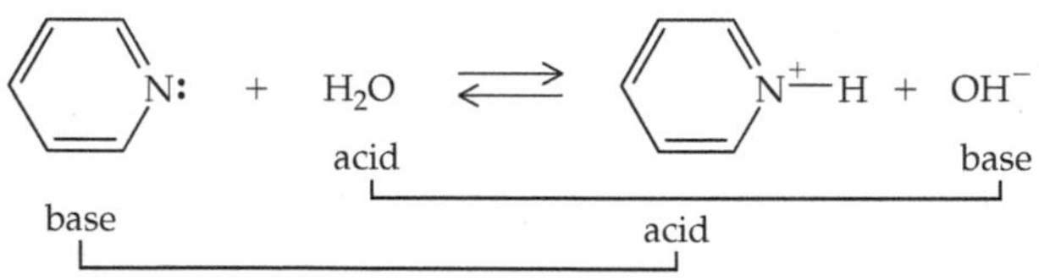

15.13

(a) 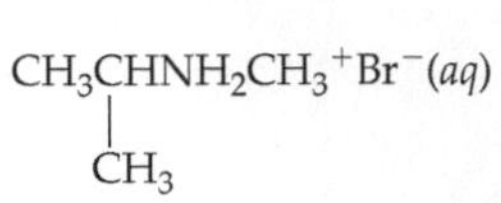 $\overset{\overset{\displaystyle \quad}{}}{CH_3CHNH_2CH_3{}^+Br^-(aq)} \atop \overset{|}{CH_3}$ (b)

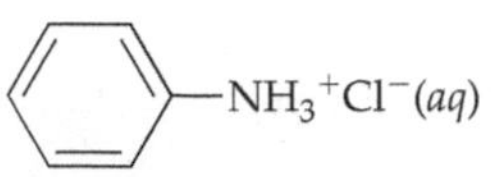

(c) 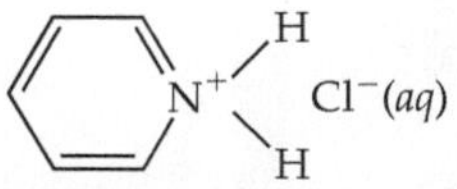 $Cl^-(aq)$ (d) $(CH_3)_3CNH_2 + H_2O\,(l) + Na^+(aq)$

15.14 (a) N-methylisopropylammonium bromide (b) anilinium chloride
(c) piperidinium chloride **15.15** (a) ethylamine (b) triethylamine

15.16
(a) 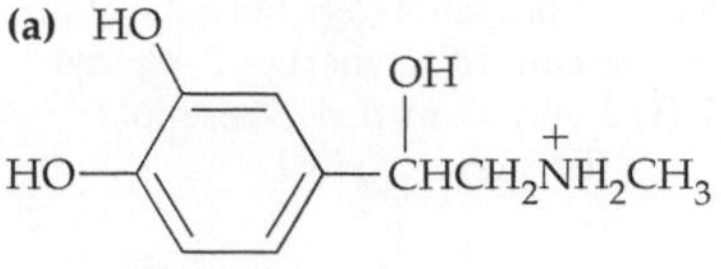 (b)

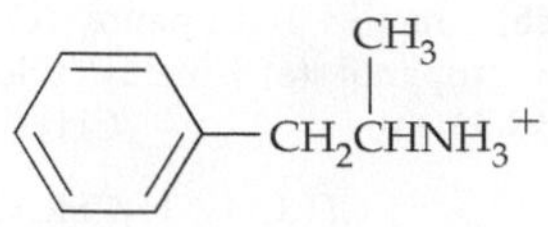

15.17–15.18

(a) 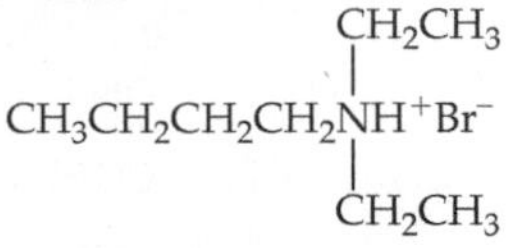 $CH_3CH_2CH_2CH_2\overset{\overset{\displaystyle CH_2CH_3}{|}}{\underset{\underset{\displaystyle CH_2CH_3}{|}}{N}}H^+Br^-$ (b) $(CH_3CH_2CH_2CH_2)_4N^+OH^-$

Butyldiethylammonium bromide
or N,N–Diethylbutylammonium bromide
salt of a tertiary amine

Tetrabutylammonium hydroxide
salt of a quaternary amine

(c) $CH_3CH_2CH_2NH_3{}^+I^-$ (d) $\overset{\overset{\displaystyle CH_3}{|}}{\underset{\underset{\displaystyle CH_3}{|}}{CH_3CHNH_2}}{}^+Cl^-$

Propylammonium iodide
salt of a primary amine

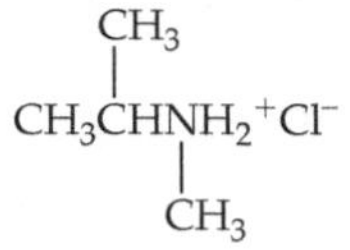

Isopropylmethylammonium chlorid
salt of a secondary amine

15.19 $CH_3CH_2CH_2CH_2NH_3^+Cl^-(aq) + NaOH(aq) \rightarrow$
$CH_3CH_2CH_2CH_2NH_2 + H_2O(l) + NaCl(aq)$
15.20 Benadryl has the general structure. In Benadryl, R $= -CH_3$, and
R$' =$ R$'' = C_6H_5-$.
15.21

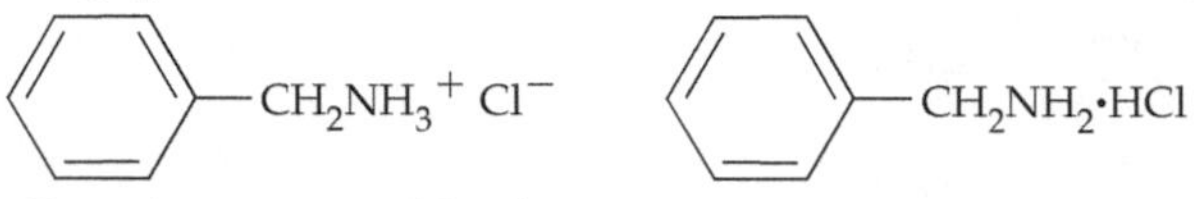

Benzylammonium chloride

15.22 carboxylic acid/carboxylate; amine/ammonium group; phosphate/diphosphate
15.23

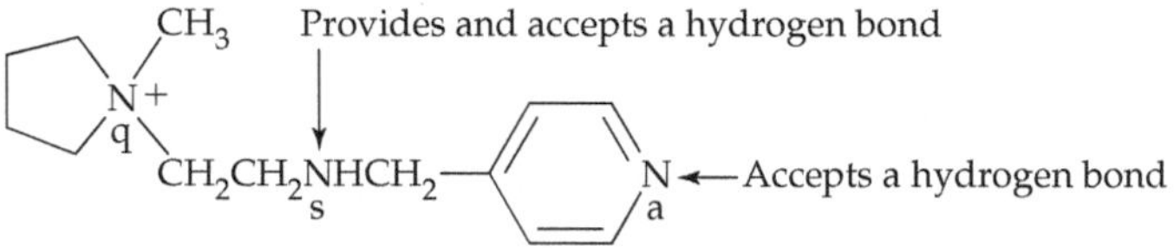

15.24 (a) Both amine groups can participate in hydrogen bonding.
(b) Lysine is water-soluble because it can form hydrogen bonds with water.
15.25 (a)

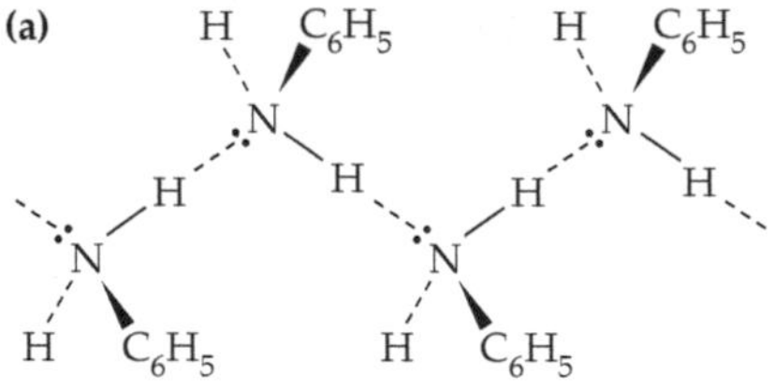

(b)

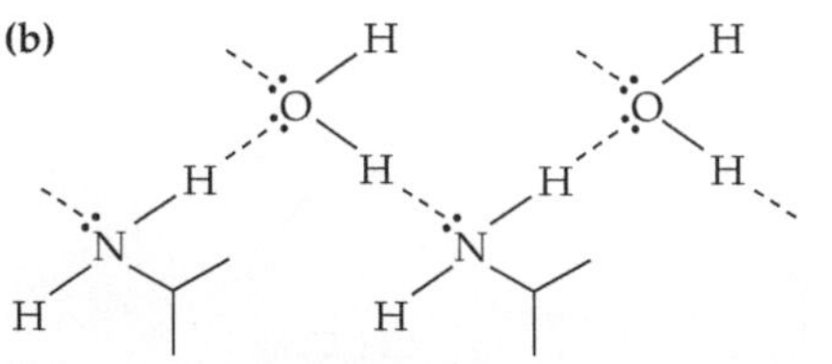

(c)

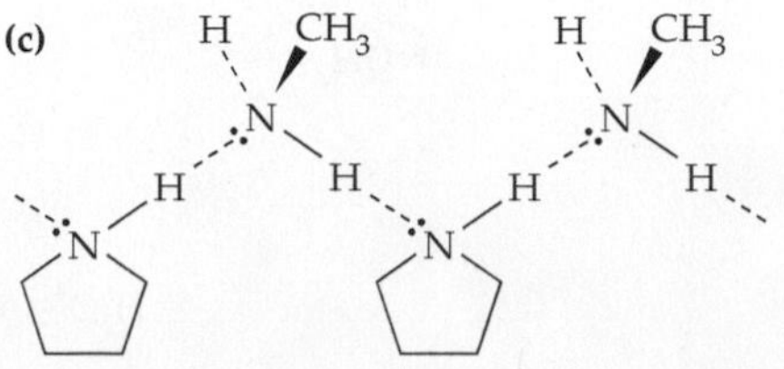

15.26

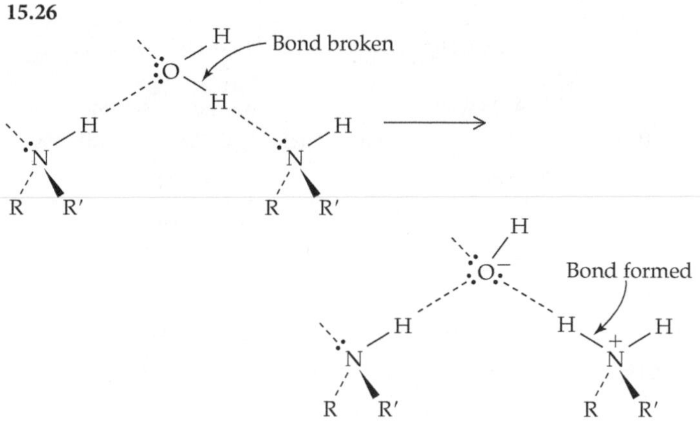

Bond broken / Bond formed

15.27 strongest base:$(CH_3)_2NH$ weakest base:$C_6H_5NH_2$

15.28 (a)

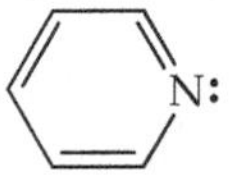

$N: + H_2O$ **(b)** $(CH_3)_2CH\overset{+}{N}H_3 + OH^-$

(c) $(CH_3CH_2)_3\overset{+}{N}H \ Br^-$ **(d)** 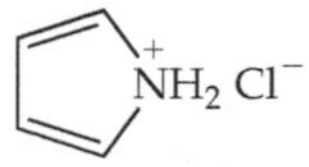 $\overset{+}{N}H_2 \ Cl^-$

15.30 (a) 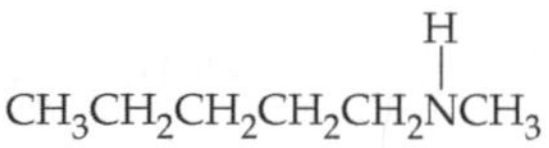 $CH_3CH_2CH_2CH_2CH_2\overset{H}{\underset{|}{N}}CH_3$ **(b)** 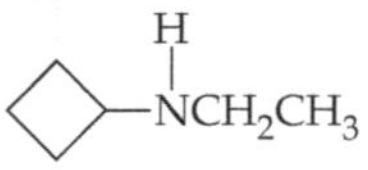 $-\overset{H}{\underset{|}{N}}CH_2CH_3$

(c) 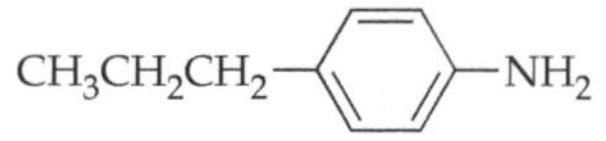 $CH_3CH_2CH_2-$$-NH_2$

15.32 (a) N-ethylcyclopentylamine (secondary) **(b)** cycloheptylamine
(primary) **15.34** diethylamine
15.36
(a) N-methyl-2-butylammonium nitrate (salt of a secondary amine).

(b)

$NH^+ \ Cl$

(salt of a heterocyclic amine)

(c) $CH_3\overset{CH_3}{\underset{|}{CH}}CH_3$
$CH_3CH_2CH_2CH_2CH_2CH_2\overset{+}{N}H^+Cl^-$
$\underset{|}{CH_2CH_2CH_2CH_3}$

(salt of a tertiary amine)

15.38

Cocaine

15.40

Quinine hydrochloride

15.42 (a)

$-NH_2 + HCl \longrightarrow$ $-\overset{+}{N}H_3 \ Cl^-$

(b)

$CH_3CH_2CH_2\overset{H}{\underset{}{N}}CH_3 + H_2O \rightleftharpoons CH_3CH_2CH_2\overset{H}{\underset{H}{\overset{+}{N}}}CH_3 + OH^-$

(c)

$+ NaOH \longrightarrow$

$+ H_2O$
$+ NaBr$

15.44 Choline doesn't react with HCl because its nitrogen isn't basic.
15.46 Its large hydrocarbon region is water-insoluble.
15.48

$H_2N-$$-\overset{O}{\overset{\|}{C}}-OH$

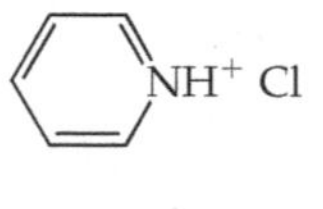

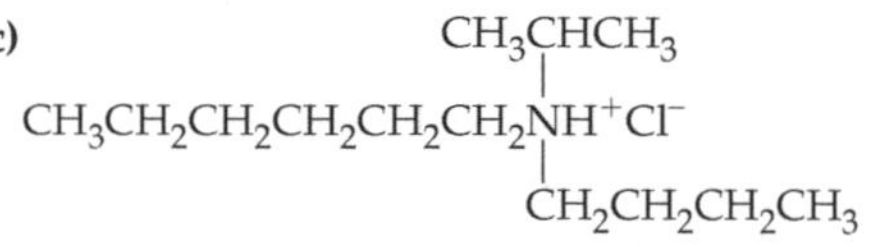

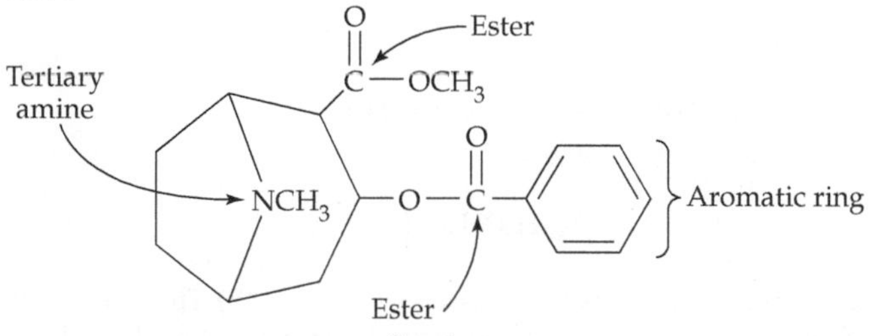

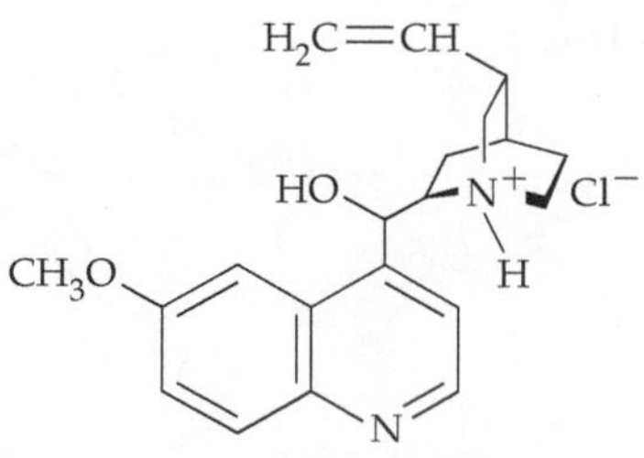

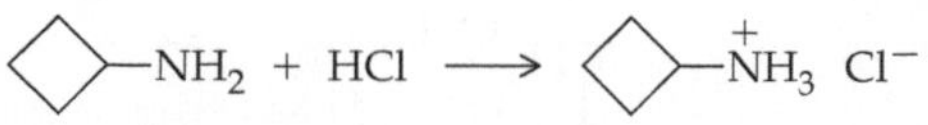

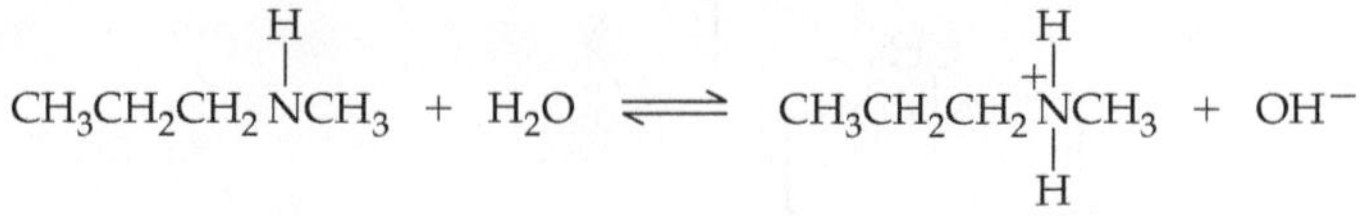

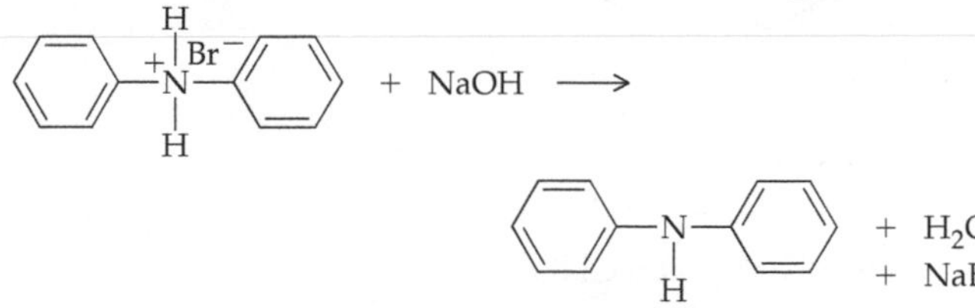

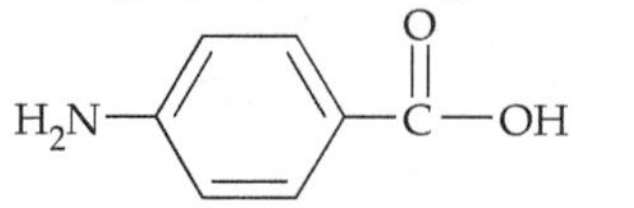

PABA

15.50 Amide

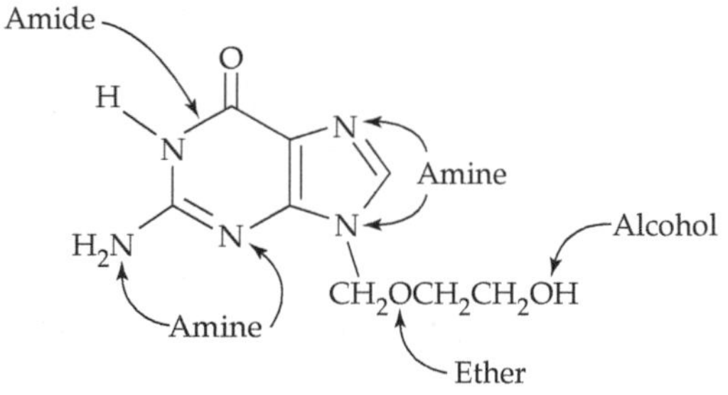

Acyclovir—related to purine

15.52 Amines: foul-smelling, somewhat basic, lower boiling(weaker hydrogen bonds) Alcohols: pleasant-smelling, not basic, higher boiling (stronger hydrogen bonds) **15.54 (a)** 6-methyl-2-heptene **(b)** p-isopropylphenol **(c)** dibutylamine **15.56** Molecules of hexylamine can form hydrogen bonds to each other, but molecules of triethylamine can't. **15.58** Baeocystin is related to indole. **15.60** Pyridine forms H-bonds with water; benzene doesn't form H-bonds. **15.62** OSHA requires MSDS for occupational use of hazardous chemicals. You might need a MSDS for NaCl if your job involved working with large amounts of NaCl on a daily basis.
15.64

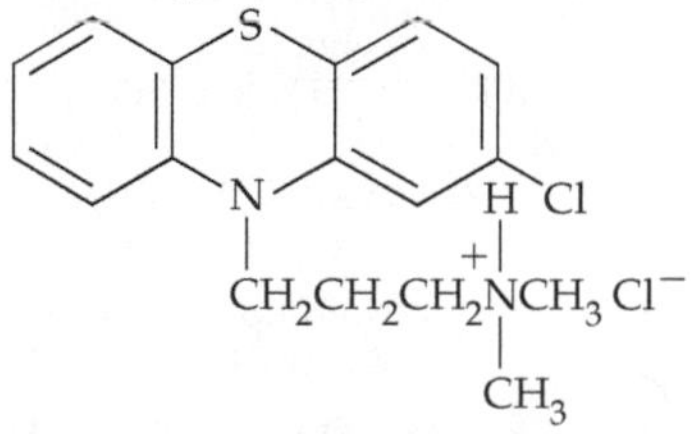

15.65 (a) A forensic toxicologist deals with criminal cases involving drug abuse and poisoning. **(b)** the structure of the toxin, its mode of action, a mechanism to reverse its effects

Chapter 16

16.1 (a)

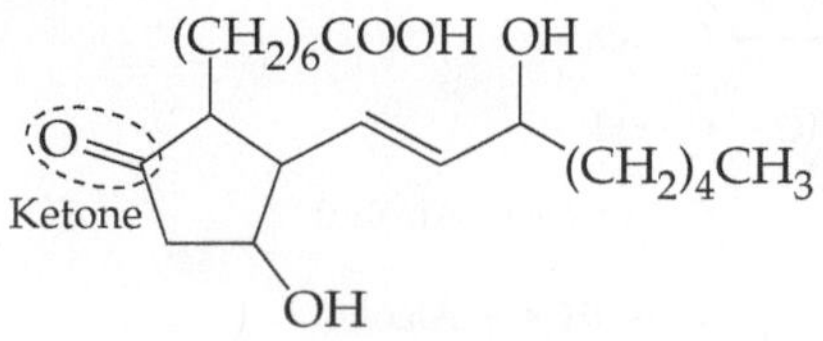

Prostaglandin E_1

(b)

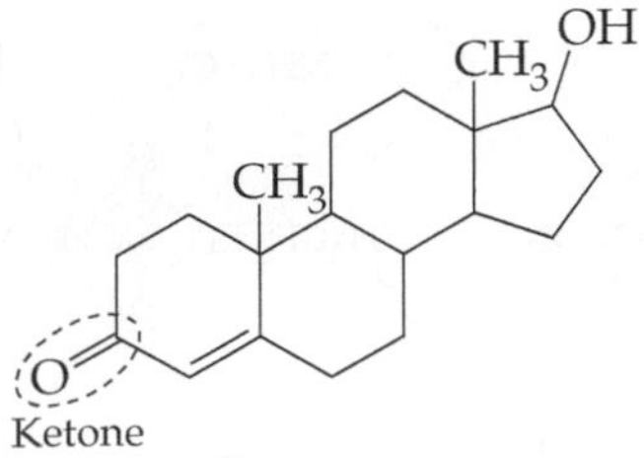

Ketone

Testosterone

(c) CH₃O

Aldehyde

HO —CHO

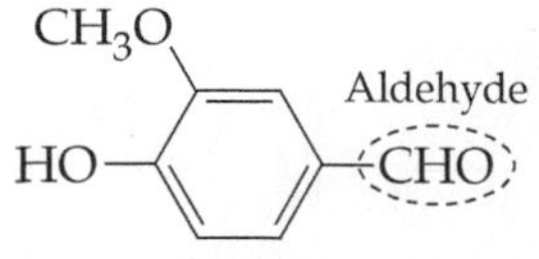

Vanillin

(d) C₄H₉COCH₃   **(e)** C₄H₉CHO

Ketone   Aldehyde

16.2 (d)

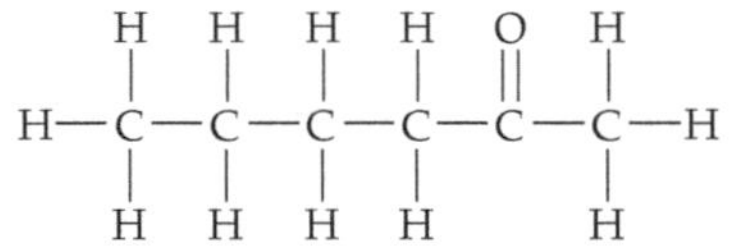

(e)

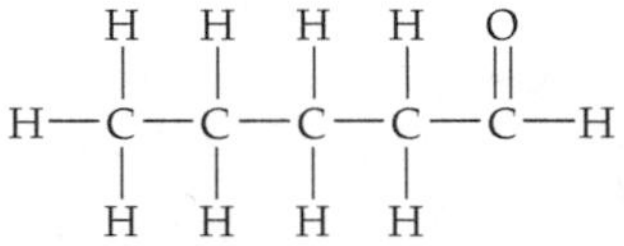

16.3 (a)

CH₃CH₂CH₂CH₂CH₂CH₂CH₂CH   **(b)**

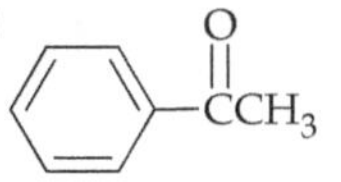

(c)

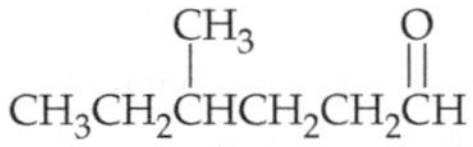

CH₃CH₂CHCH₂CH₂CH   **(d)** H₃C O

CH₃C—CCH₃

CH₃

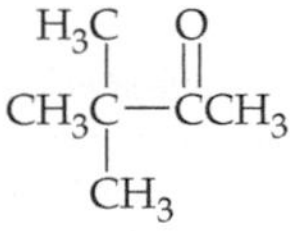

16.4 (a) pentanal **(b)** 3-pentanone **(c)** 4-methylhexanal **(d)** 4-heptanone

16.5

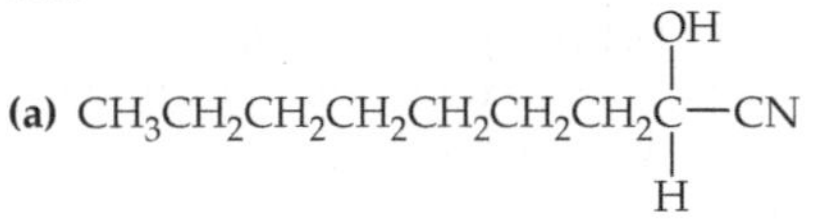

(a) CH₃CH₂CH₂CH₂CH₂CH₂CH₂C—CN   **(b)**

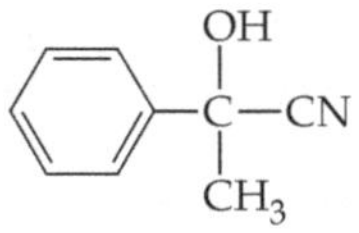

16.6 (a) CH₃ O

CH₃CHCH₂CCH₂CH₃

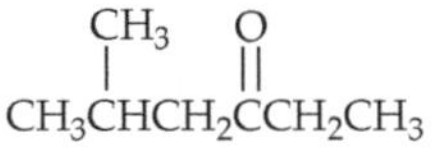

C₇H₁₄O

5-Methyl-3-hexanone
A ketone

(b) CH₃ O

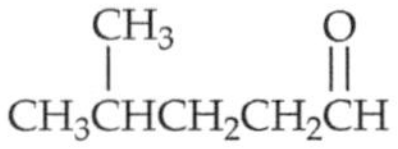

CH₃CHCH₂CH₂CH

C₆H₁₂O

4-Methylpentanal
An aldehyde

16.7 (a) polar, flammable, liquid, b.p. < 150°C **(b)** polar, flammable, liquid, b.p. < 150°C **(c)** nonpolar, flammable, liquid, b.p. < 150°C **16.8** Alcohols form hydrogen bonds, which raise their boiling points. Aldehydes and ketones have higher boiling points than alkanes because they are polar.

16.9 (a)

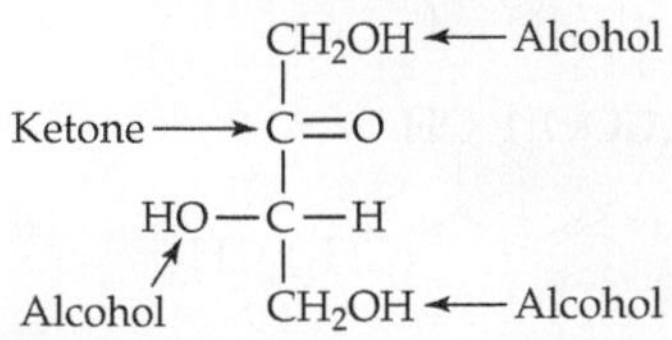

(b)

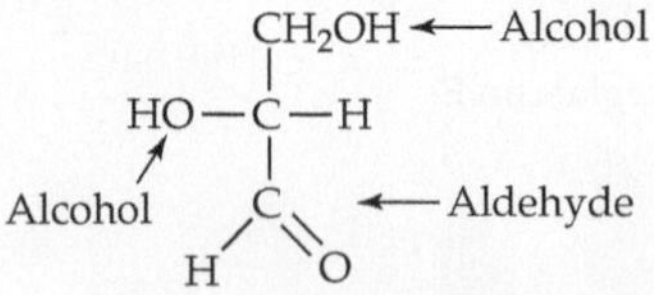

(c)

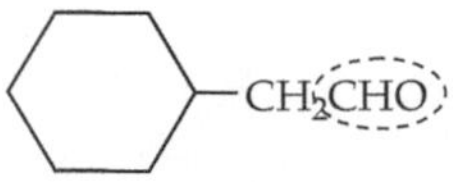

Aldehyde

(d)

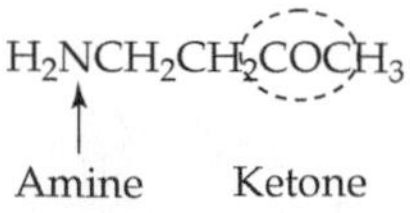

H₂NCH₂CH₂COCH₃

Amine   Ketone

16.10 (a)

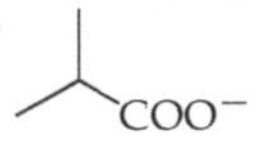

(b) NR **(c)** COO⁻

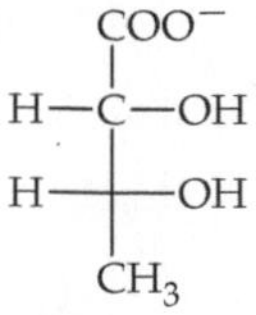

H—C—OH

H—C—OH

CH₃ **(d)** NR

16.11

(a) CH₃ OH

CH₃CH—CHCH₃ **(b)**

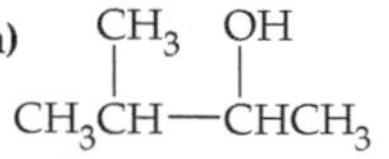

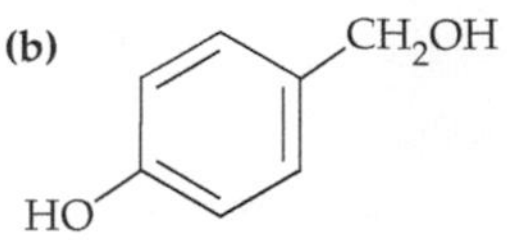

(c)

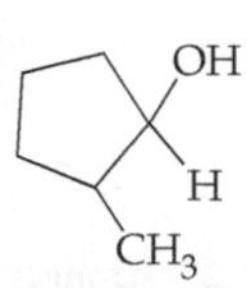

16.12

(a)

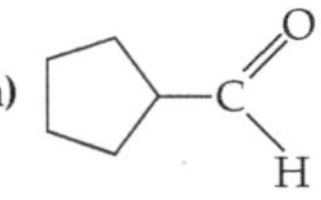

(b)

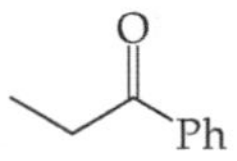

(c)

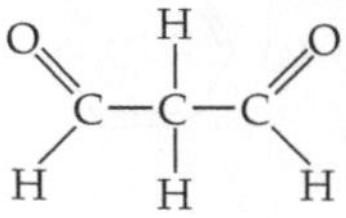

16.13 Compounds (a), (d)

16.14 (a)

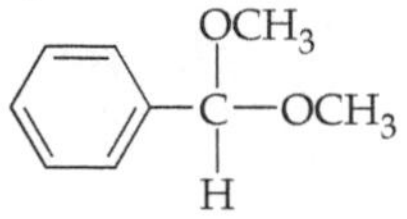

(b)

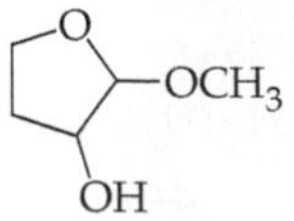

16.15 (a)

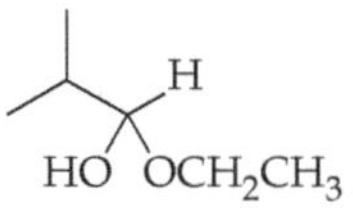

(b)

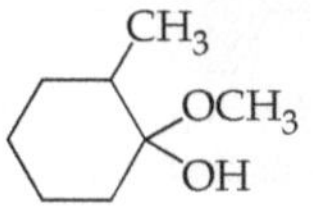

16.16 (a)

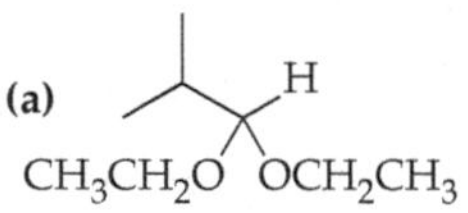

(b)

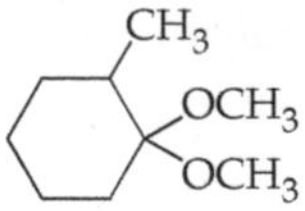

16.17 (a) neither **(b)** neither **(c)** acetal **(d)** hemiacetal   **16.18** two caps

16.19 (a)

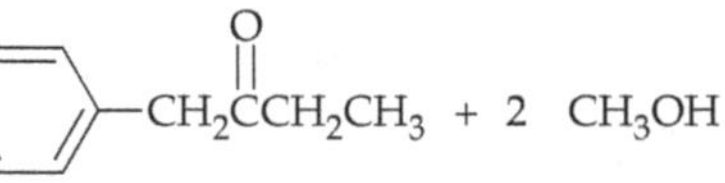

+ 2 CH₃OH

(b)

CH₃CH₂OH + 2 CH₃CH₂CH₂OH

(c) O

HCH + 2 CH₃CH₂CH₂OH

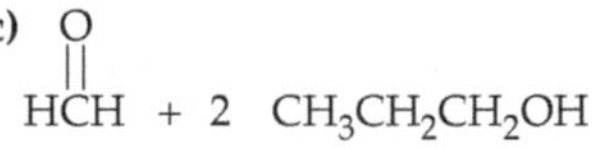

16.20. (a) Hydride adds to the carbonyl carbon. **(b)** The arrow to the right represents reduction, and the arrow to the left represents oxidation. **16.21** Aldehydes can be oxidized to carboxylic acids. Tollens' reagent differentiates an aldehyde from a ketone.

16.22

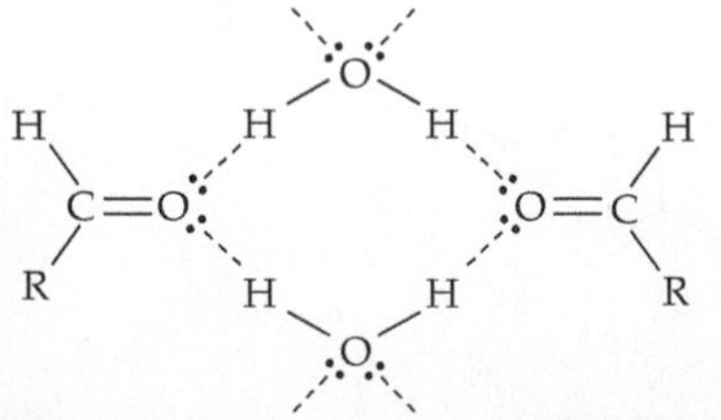

16.23 (a) Under acidic conditions, an alcohol adds to the carbonyl group of an aldehyde to form a hemiacetal, which is unstable and further reacts to form an acetal.

(b)

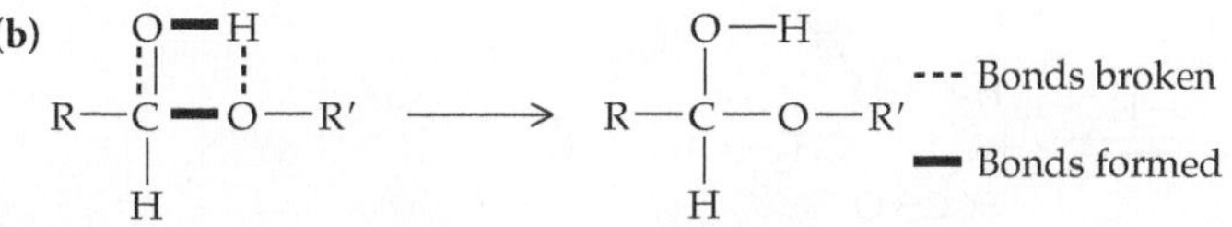

--- Bonds broken
— Bonds formed

16.24 In solution, glucose exists as a cyclic hemiacetal because this structure is more stable. **16.25** In addition to the two oxygens, an acetal carbon of a ketone is bonded to two carbons. The acetal carbon of an aldehyde is bonded to a carbon and a hydrogen.

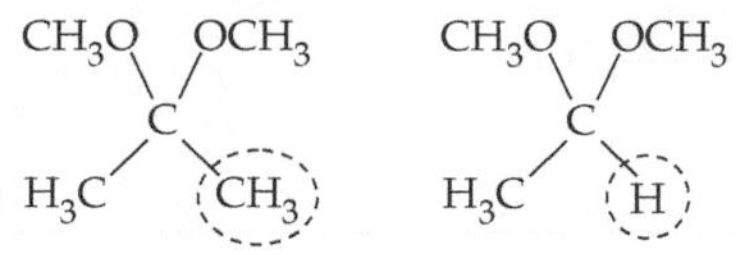

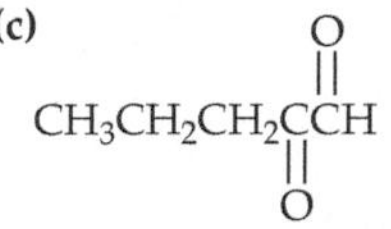

Ketone   Aldehyde

16.26 (a)

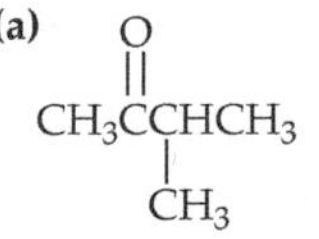

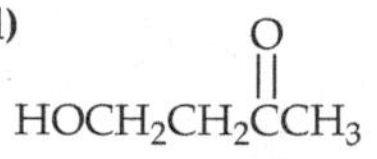

16.28 Structure (c) has an aldehyde group, and structures (a), (b), and (f) have ketone groups.

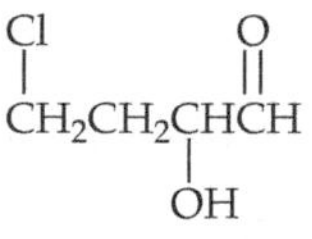

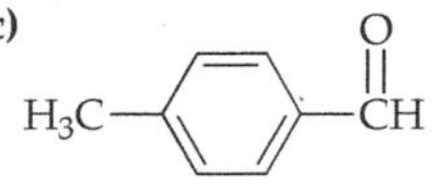

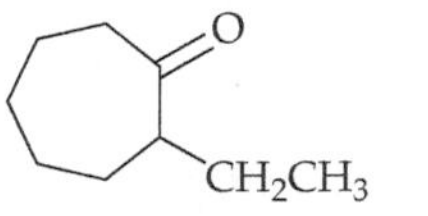

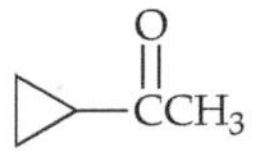

16.30 (a)

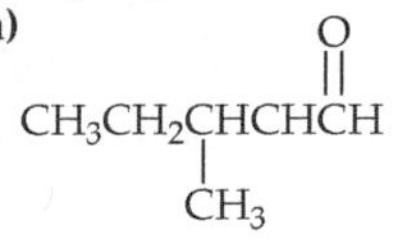

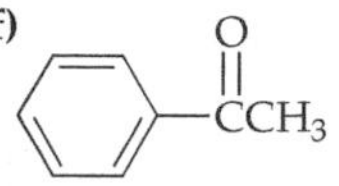

16.32 (a) 2,2-dimethylbutanal **(b)** 2-hydroxy-2-methylpentanal
(c) 3-methylbutanal **(d)** 4-methyl-3-hexanone
(e) 3-hydroxy-2-methylcyclohexanone
16.34 For (a), a ketone can't occur at the end of a carbon chain. For **(b)**, the methyl group receives the lowest possible number. For **(c)**, numbering must start at the end of the carbon chain closer to the carbonyl group.
16.36 A hemiacetal is produced.
16.38 (a) NR; cyclopentanol

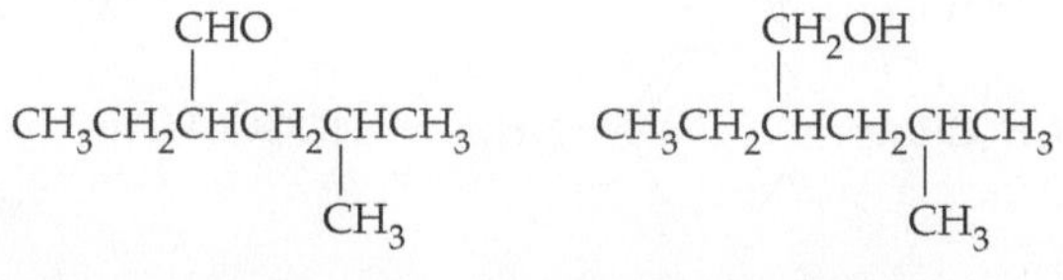

(b)

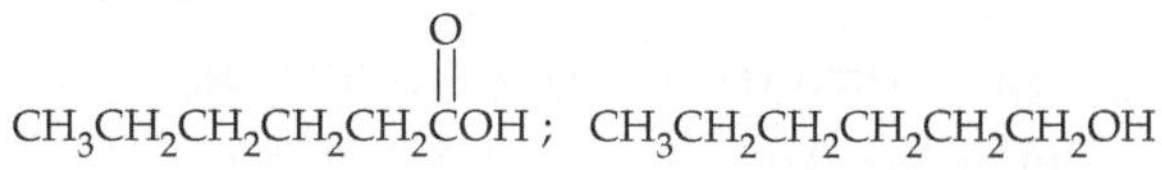

(c)

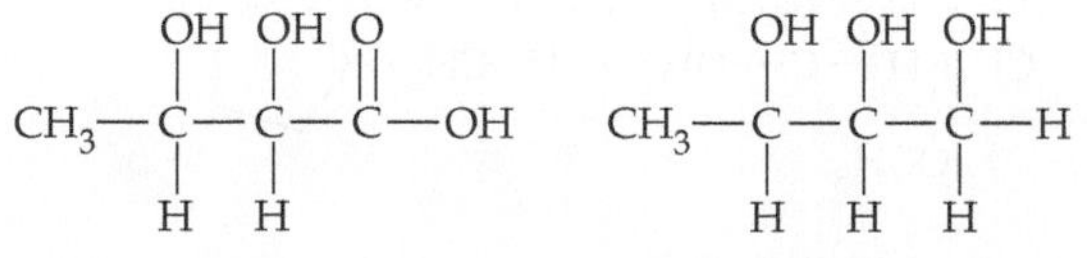

16.40 (a)

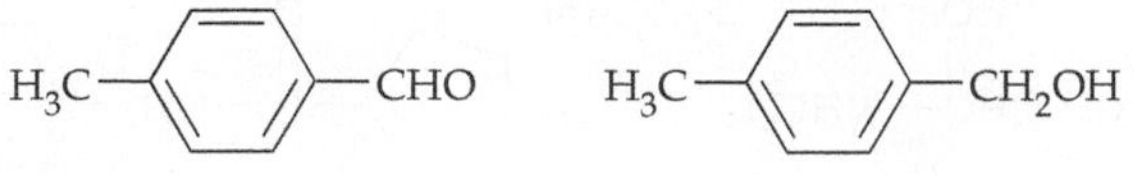

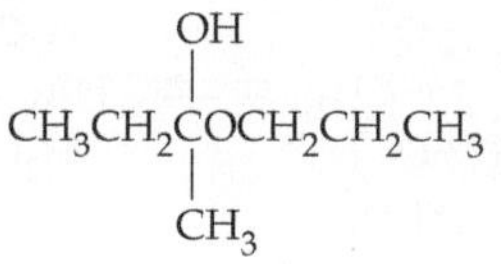

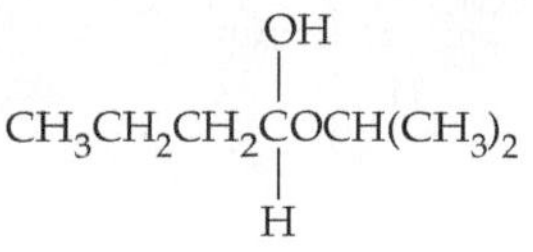

16.42

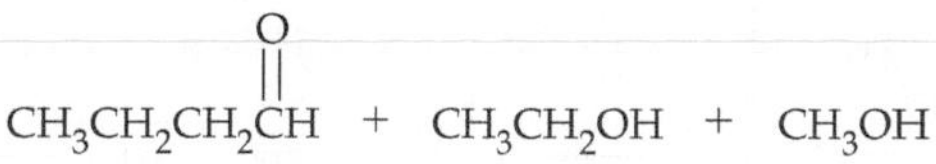

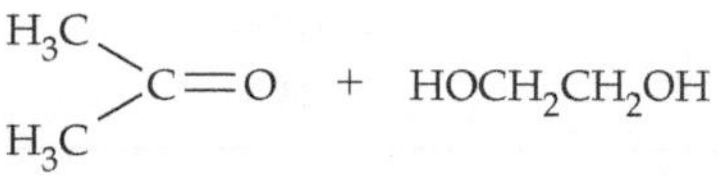

16.44 CH$_3$CHCH$_2$CH$_2$CH$_2$CH 5-Hydroxyhexanal
16.46 HOCH$_2$CH$_2$CH$_2$OH and CH$_2$O (formaldehyde).
16.48

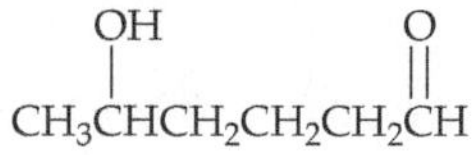

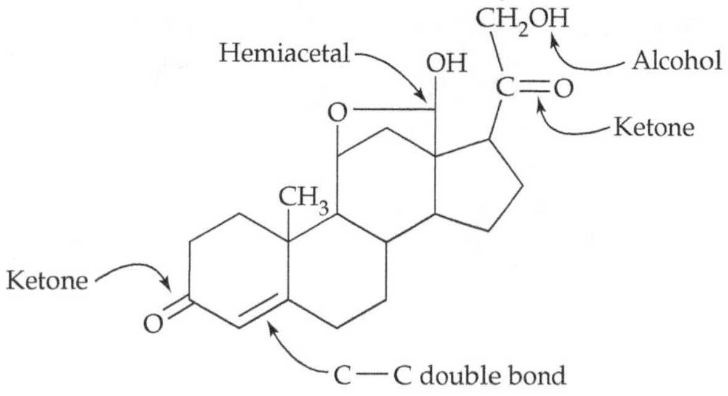

Aldosterone

16.50 p-methoxybenzaldehyde **16.52** Aldehydes are easily oxidized.
16.54 (a) 2-methyl-3-pentanone **(b)** 1,5-hexadiene **(c)** m-bromotoluene
(d) 4,5,5- trimethyl-3-hexanone
16.56

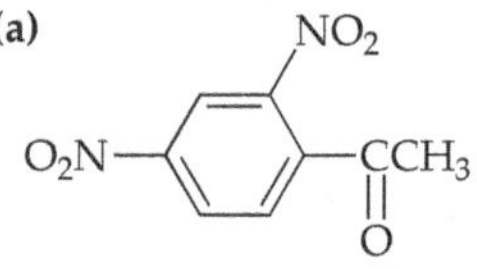

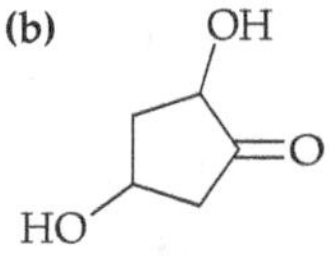

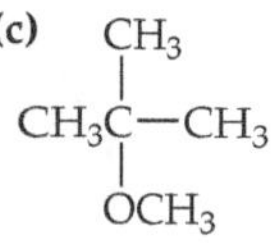

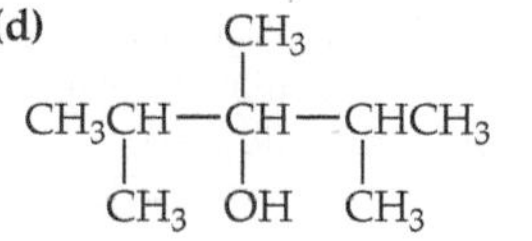

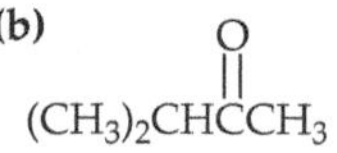

16.58

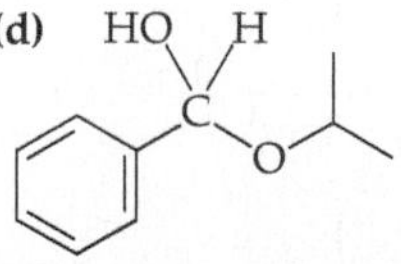

16.60 Tollens' reagent reacts with hexanal but not with 3-hexanone.
16.62 2-Heptanone is less soluble in water because it has a longer hydrocarbon chain. **16.64** The cyanohydrin that decomposes to form HCN is nontoxic and is stable inside the millipede's body. **16.66 (a)** Advantages: inexpensive, no need to sacrifice animals, **(b)** Disadvantage: results of tests on cultured cells may not be reliable for more complex organisms.
16.68 30 mg

16.70

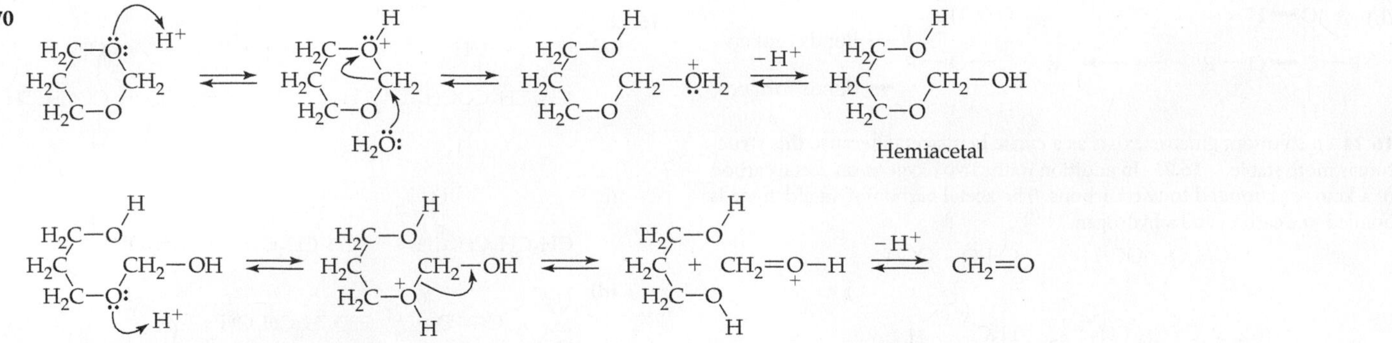

Hemiacetal

Chapter 17

17.1 carboxylic acid: **(c)** amides: **(a)** **(f)** **(h)** ester: **(d)** none: **(b)** **(e)** **(g)**

17.2 (a)

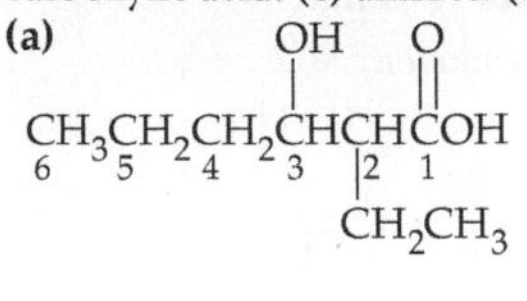

$$\underset{6}{CH_3}\underset{5}{CH_2}\underset{4}{CH_2}\underset{3}{CH}\underset{2}{\overset{OH}{CH}}\underset{1}{\overset{O}{C}OH}$$
$$\overset{|}{CH_2CH_3}$$

(b)

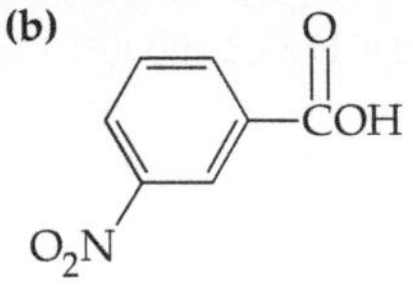

17.3

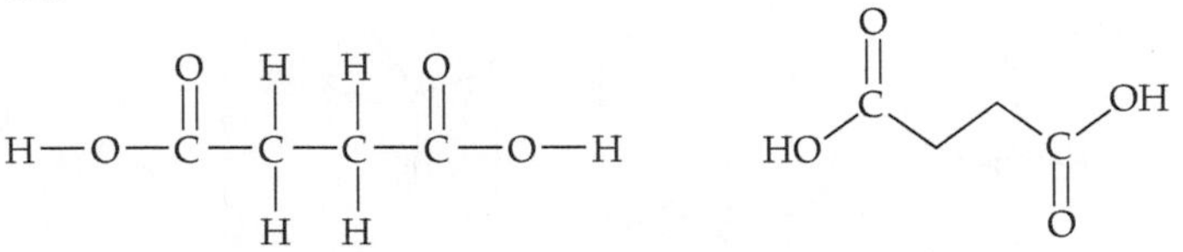

17.4

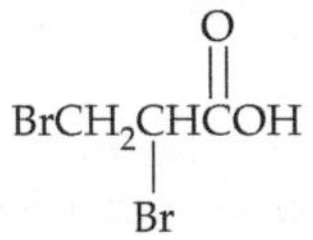

BrCH$_2$CHCOH   2,3-Dibromopropanoic acid
      |
      Br

17.5 (a)

(b)
HCOCH$_3$

(c)
CH$_2$=CHCOCH$_2$CH$_3$

17.6 CH$_3$COOH is highest boiling (most H-bonding). CH$_3$CH$_2$CH$_3$ is lowest boiling (nonpolar).   **17.7 (a)** C$_3$H$_7$COOH is more soluble (smaller —R group). **(b)** (CH$_3$)$_2$CHCOOH is more soluble (carboxylic acid).

17.8
(a)

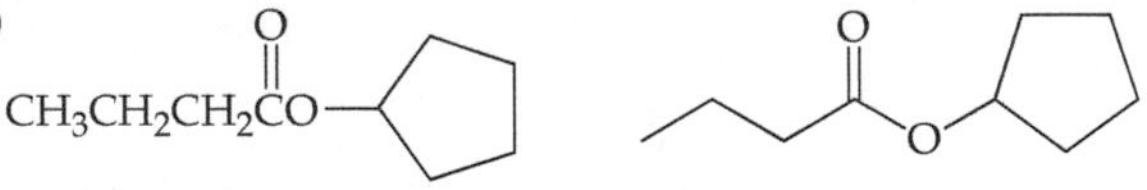

(b)

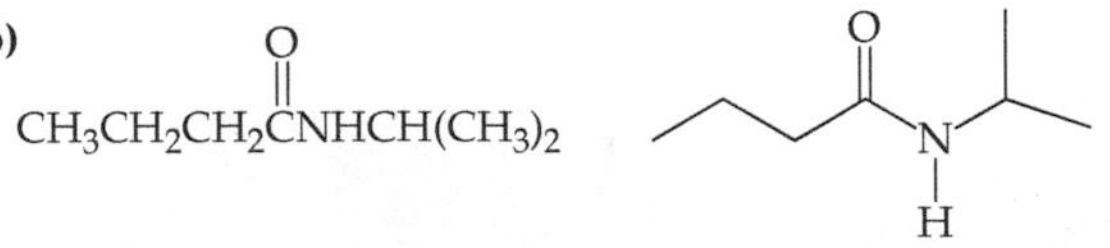

(c)

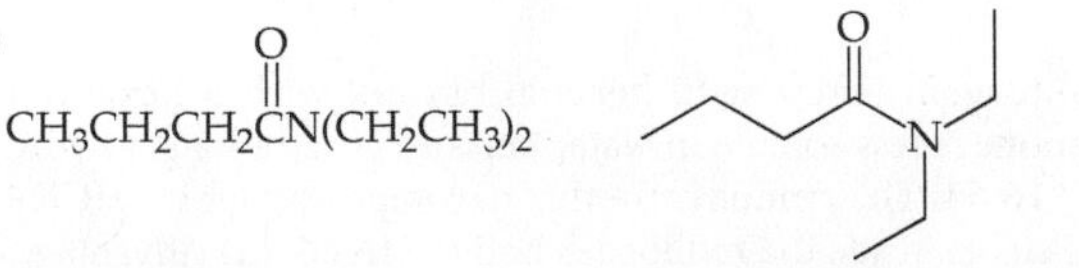

(d) cyclopentyl butyrate N-isopropylbutyramide N,N-diethylbutyramide
17.9 (a) tert-butyl 2-bromobutanoate **(b)** N,N-dimethyl-o-nitrobenzamide
17.10 (a)

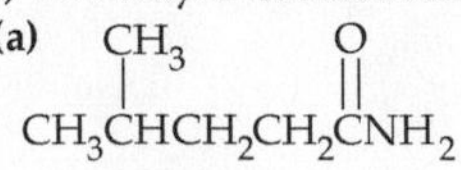

(b)

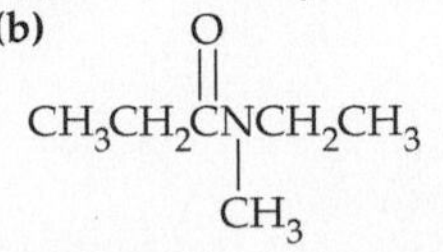

17.11

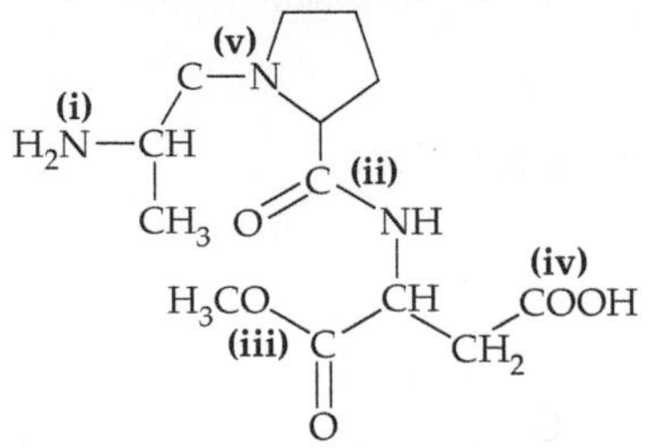

17.12 (a) (ii) **(b)** (i) **(c)** (iii) **(d)** (i) **(e)** (i) **(f)** (iii)

17.13

(a)
C$_6$H$_5$CNH$_2$
amide (C$_7$H$_7$NO)

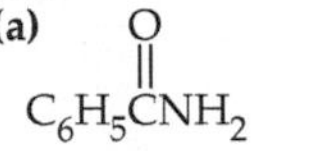

(b) 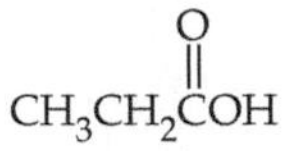
CH$_3$CH$_2$COH
carboxylic acid (C$_3$H$_6$O$_2$)

(c)
CH$_3$COCH$_2$CH$_3$
ester (C$_4$H$_8$O$_2$)

17.14 (a)

CH$_3$CHC—O$^-$Na$^+$ + H$_2$O

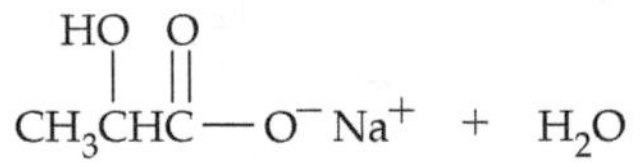

(b)

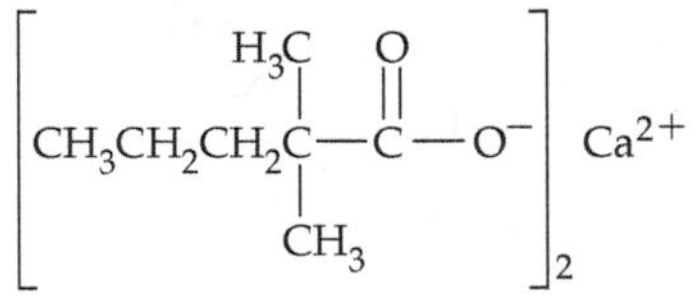

17.15 (a)

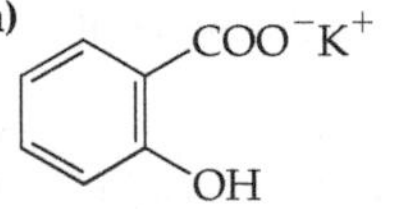

(b) Na$^+$ $^-$OOCCOO$^-$ Na$^+$

17.16 CH$_3$COO$^-$ $^-$OOCCH$_2$CH$_2$CH$_2$COO$^-$ **17.17** hydroxyacetic acid (glycolic acid); 2-hydroxypropionic acid (lactic acid); o-hydroxybenzoic acid (salicylic acid)   **17.18** HCOOCH$_2$CH(CH$_3$)$_2$

17.19 (a)

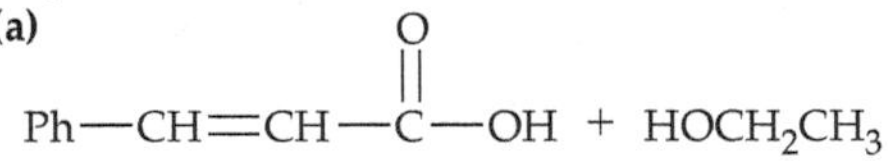

Ph—CH=CH—C—OH + HOCH$_2$CH$_3$

(b)

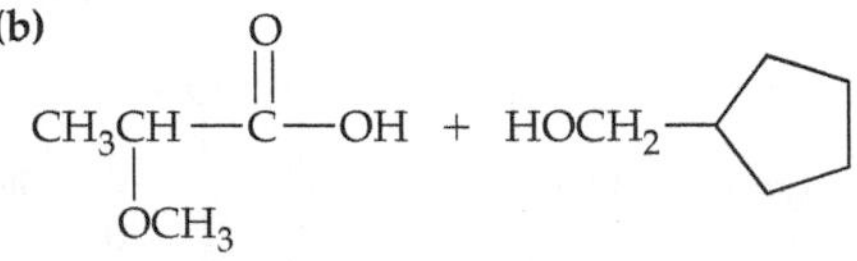

17.20
(a)

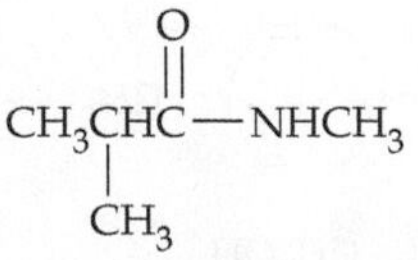

(b)

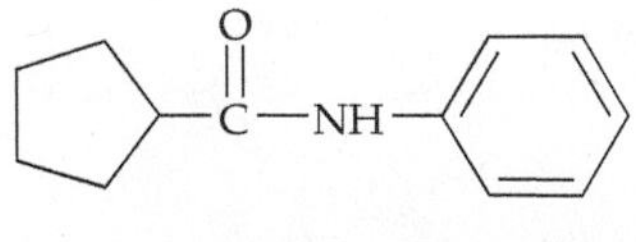

17.21

CH$_3$CH$_2$O—⟨benzene⟩—NH$_2$ + HOOCCH$_3$

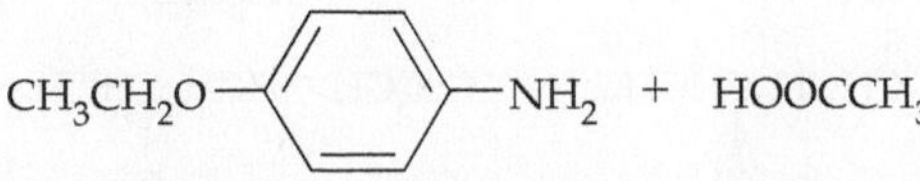

17.22

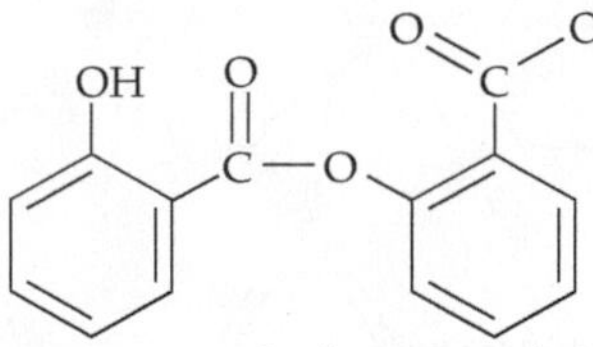

17.23 Aspirin is acidic (—COOH), lidocaine is basic (amine), benzocaine is weakly basic (aromatic amine), acetaminophen is weakly acidic (phenol).

17.24 Moisture in the air hydrolyzes the ester bond.

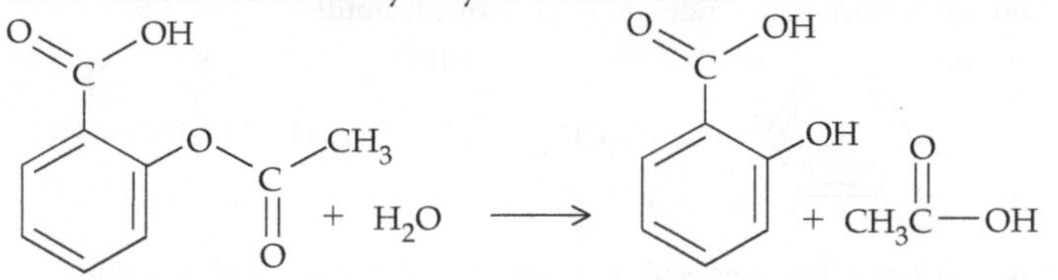

17.25 (a) p-nitrobenzoic acid + 2-propanol (b) phenol + 2-cyclopentene-carboxylic acid (c) 2-aminopropionic acid + ethanol

17.26 (a) 2-butenoic acid + methylamine
(b) p-nitrobenzoic acid + dimethylamine

17.27

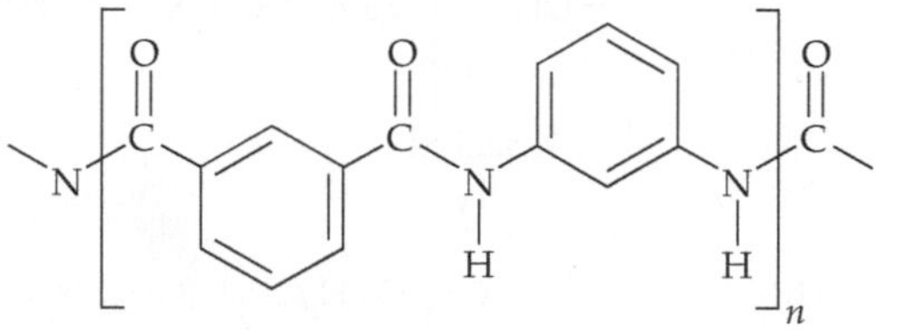

Nomex

17.28 (a)

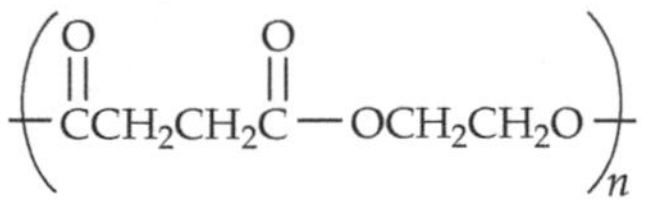

(b)

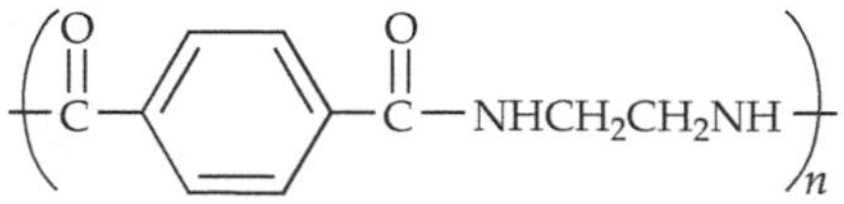

17.29

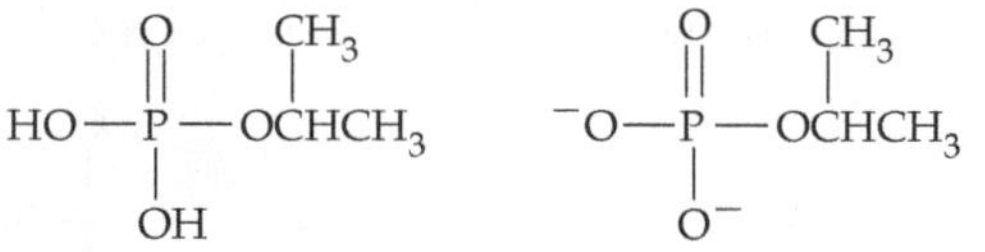

17.30 (a) amide + $H_2O \longrightarrow CH_3COOH + NH_3$
(b) phosphate monoester + $H_2O \longrightarrow CH_3CH_2OH + HOPO_3^{2-}$
(c) carboxylic acid ester + $H_2O \longrightarrow CH_3CH_2COOH + HOCH_3$

17.31

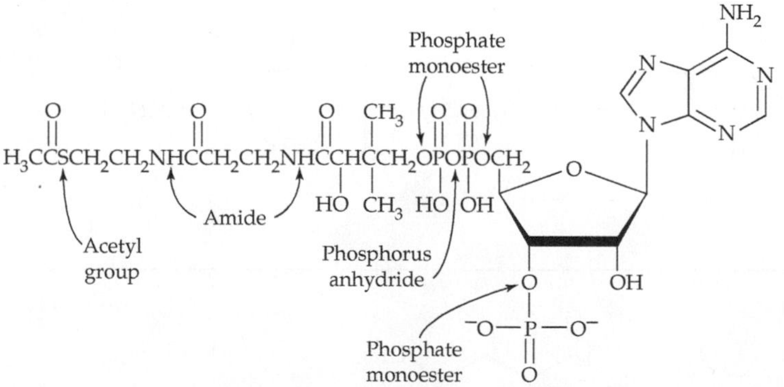

17.32 (a) At pH = 7.4, pyruvate and lactate are anions.
(b)

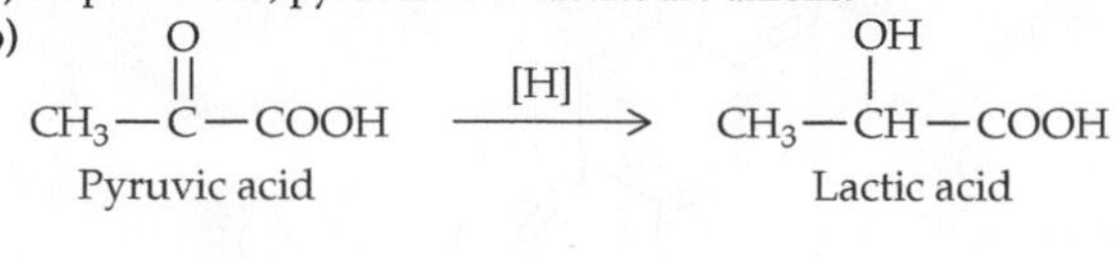

Pyruvic acid   Lactic acid

(c) Pyruvate and lactate have similar solubilities in water.

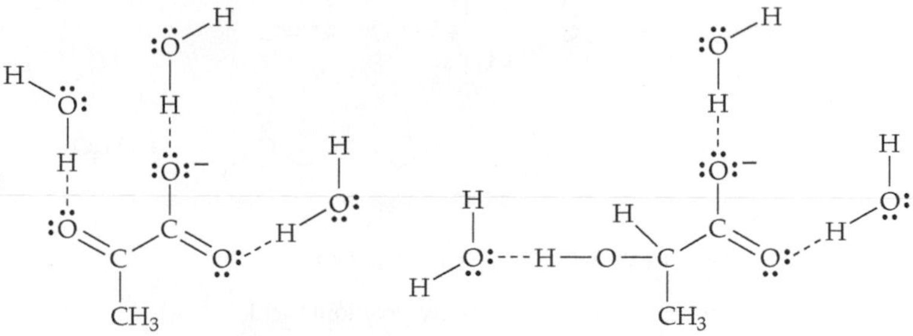

17.33 (a) H_2O + acid or base
(b)

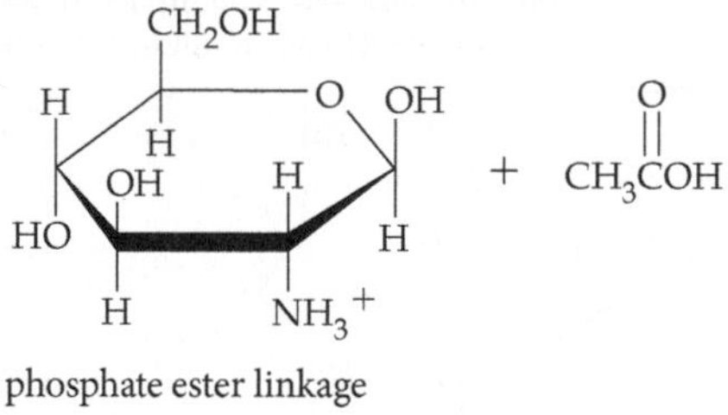

$+ CH_3COH$

17.34 (a) a phosphate ester linkage
(b)

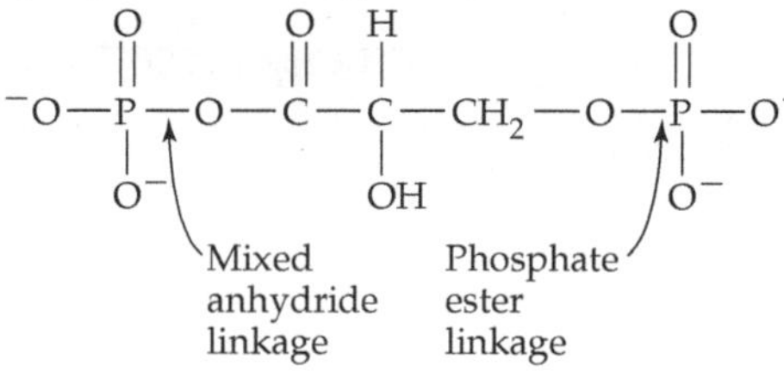

Mixed anhydride linkage   Phosphate ester linkage

17.35

$^-OOCCOO^-$ $^-OOCCH_2COO^-$ $^-OOCCH_2CH_2COO^-$ $^-OOCCH_2CH_2CH_2COO^-$
oxalate   malonate   succinate   glutarate

$^-OOCCH_2CH_2CH_2CH_2COO^-$ $^-OOCCH_2CH_2CH_2CH_2CH_2COO^-$
adipate   pimelate

17.36 (a)

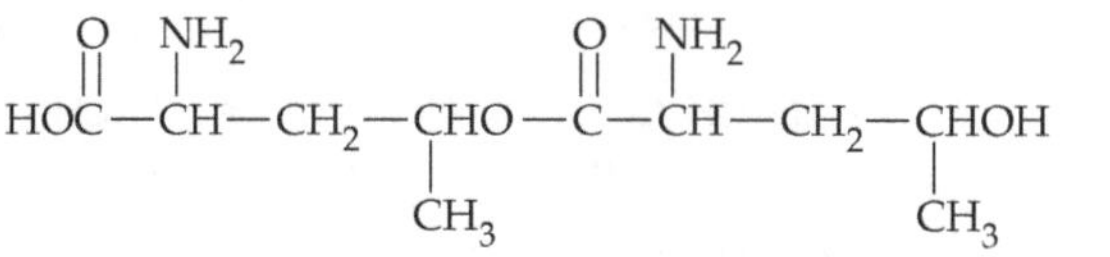

(b)

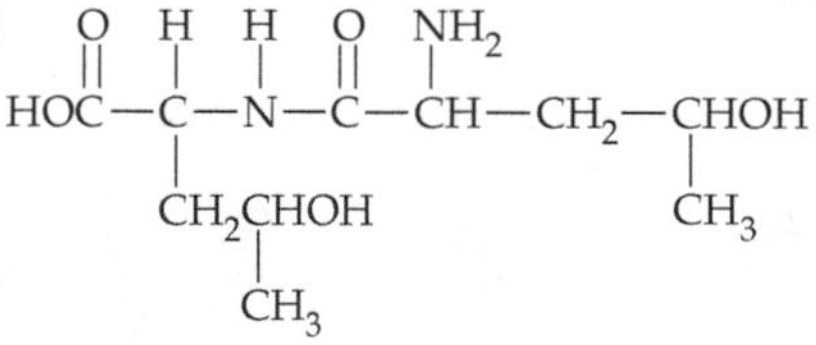

(c)

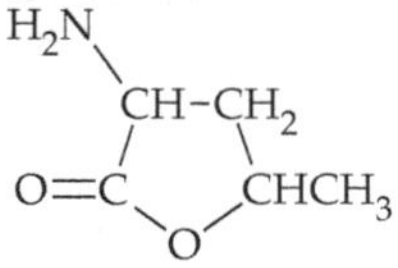

17.37
(a) (i)

(ii)

(iii)

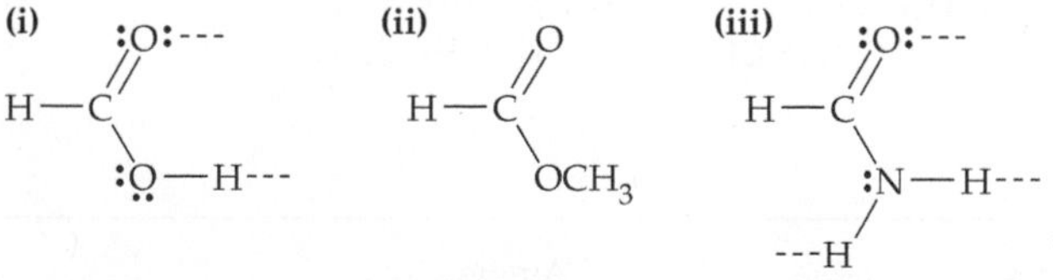

Formic acid   Methyl formate   Formamide

(b) Methyl acetate is lowest boiling (no hydrogen bonds); acetamide is highest boiling

17.38

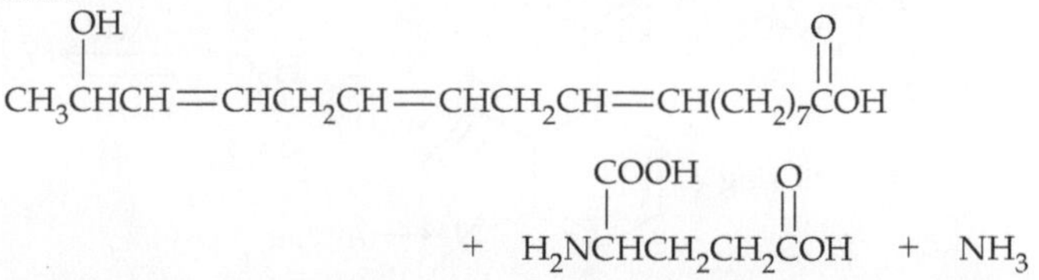

$+ H_2NCHCH_2CH_2COH + NH_3$

17.39 (a) N-ethyl acetamide (b) diethylglutarate (c) methyl 2-chlorocyclopentanecarboxylate (d) N-ethyl-N-methylformamide.

17.40

[structure: pentanoic acid] + H_2O ⇌

[structure: pentanoate anion] + H_3O^+

17.42

$CH_3CH_2CH_2COOH$

$CH_3\overset{\displaystyle CH_3}{\underset{}{CH}}COOH$

Butanoic acid   2-Methylpropionic acid

17.44 **(a)** 3-hydroxy-4-methylpentanoic acid **(b)** nonanedioic acid (azelaic acid) **(c)** 4-chlorocyclohexanecarboxylic acid **(d)** p-aminobenzoic acid

17.46 **(a)** potassium 3-ethylpentanoate **(b)** ammonium benzoate **(c)** calcium propanoate

17.48 **(a)**

$CH_3CH_2\overset{CH_3}{\underset{}{CH}}CH\overset{O}{\underset{CH_3}{CH}}CH_2\overset{O}{\underset{}{C}}OH$

(b)

[benzene ring]—CH_2—$\overset{O}{\underset{}{C}}OH$

(c)

[structure: O_2N and O_2N substituted benzene with COH]

(d)

$CH_3CH_2CH_2\overset{O}{\underset{}{C}}O^-\ {}^+NH(CH_2CH_3)_3$

17.50

$HO\overset{O}{\underset{}{C}}CH_2\overset{OH}{\underset{}{CH}}\overset{O}{\underset{}{C}}OH$

17.52

$NH_4^+\ {}^-O\overset{O}{\underset{}{C}}CH=CH\overset{O}{\underset{}{C}}O^-\ NH_4^+$

17.54 **(a)** $CH_3CH_2CH_2CH_2CONH_2$ $CH_3CH_2CONHCH_2CH_3$
          Pentanamide   N-Ethylpropanamide

$HCON(CH_2CH_3)_2$
N,N-Diethylformamide

(b) $CH_3CH_2CH_2CH_2COOCH_3$ $CH_3CH_2COOCH_2CH_2CH_3$
      Methyl pentanoate   Propyl propanoate

$HCOOCH_2CH_2CH_2CH_2CH_3$
Pentyl formate

17.56 **(a)** 3-methylbutyl acetate **(b)** methyl 4-methylpentanoate
(c)

$CH_3\overset{O}{\underset{}{C}}O$—[cyclohexane]

(d)

[salicylate phenyl ester structure with OH]

17.58 **(a)** $CH_3COOH + HOCH_2CH_2CH(CH_3)_2$
(b) $(CH_3)_2CHCH_2CH_2COOH + HOCH_3$

(c)

COOH + HO—[cyclohexane]

(d)

[salicylic acid structure with OH, COOH] + HO—[phenyl]

17.60 **(a)** 2-ethylbutanamide **(b)** N-phenylbenzamide
(c)

[benzene ring]—$\overset{O}{\underset{}{C}}N\overset{}{\underset{CH_3}{}}CH_2CH_3$

(d)

$CH_3CH_2CH_2\overset{Br}{\underset{}{CH}}\overset{O}{\underset{Br}{CH}}CNH_2$

17.62 **(a)** 2-ethylbutanoic acid + ammonia **(b)** benzoic acid + aniline **(c)** benzoic acid + N-methylethylamine **(d)** 2,3-dibromohexanoic acid + ammonia

17.64

H_2N—[benzene ring]—$\overset{O}{\underset{}{C}}$—OH + $HOCH_2CH_2N(CH_2CH_3)_2$

↓ Acid catalyst

H_2N—[benzene ring]—$\overset{O}{\underset{}{C}}$—$OCH_2CH_2N(CH_2CH_3)_2$

Amine   Aromatic ring   Ester   Amine
          Procaine

17.66 $HOCH_2CH_2CH_2COOH$
17.68 *See below for answer.*
17.70

[polymer chain structure]

17.68

Amide   Amine

CH_3CH_2—N—$\overset{O}{\underset{}{C}}$—[ring system]—N—$CH_3$

CH_3CH_2

LSD

Aromatic ring {[fused ring system with N—H]}—Amine

* = C—C double bond

+ H_2O ⇌ (Acid catalyst)

$HO\overset{O}{\underset{}{C}}$—[ring system]—N—$CH_3$

CH_3CH_2—NH +

CH_3CH_2

[fused ring system with N—H]

17.72 Dihydroxyacetone and hydrogen phosphate anion.
17.74

$$HO-\overset{\overset{\displaystyle O}{\|}}{\underset{\underset{\displaystyle OH}{|}}{P}}-O-\overset{\overset{\displaystyle O}{\|}}{C}-CH_3$$

17.76 A cyclic phosphate diester is formed when a phosphate group forms an ester with two hydroxyl groups in the same molecule. **17.78** N, N-Dimethylformamide is lowest boiling because it doesn't form hydrogen bonds. Propanamide is highest boiling because it forms the most hydrogen bonds. **17.80** Both propanamide and methyl acetate are water-soluble because they can form hydrogen bonds with water. Propanamide is higher boiling because molecules of propanamide can form hydrogen bonds with each other.
17.82

$$\begin{array}{l} CH_2O-\overset{\overset{\displaystyle O}{\|}}{C}(CH_2)_{16}CH_3 \\ \\ CHO-\overset{\overset{\displaystyle O}{\|}}{C}(CH_2)_{16}CH_3 \qquad \text{Glyceryl tristearate} \\ \\ CH_2O-\overset{\overset{\displaystyle O}{\|}}{C}(CH_2)_{16}CH_3 \end{array}$$

17.84 Trichloroacetic acid: used for chemical peeling of the skin. Lactic acid: used for wrinkle removal and moisturizing. **17.86** strong acids and bases.

Chapter 18

18.1 Aromatic ring: phenylalanine, tyrosine, tryptophan Contain sulfur: cysteine, methionine
Alcohols: serine, threonine, tyrosine (phenol) Alkyl side chain: alanine, valine, leucine, isoleucine

18.2
$$\begin{array}{c} COOH \\ | \\ H\cdots C \\ \diagup \ \ \diagdown \\ H_3C \quad\ NH_2 \end{array}$$

18.3
$$\begin{array}{cc} COOH & COOH \\ | & | \\ H\cdots C & H\cdots C \\ \diagup\ \ \diagdown & \diagup\ \ \diagdown \\ HOCH_2\ \ NH_2 & (CH_3)_2CH\ \ NH_2 \\ \text{Serine} & \text{Valine} \end{array}$$
The serine side chain has a polar hydroxyl group; the valine side chain has a nonpolar isopropyl group.

18.4 α-amino acids: (a), (d)
18.5 (b) Asn, Ser (c) Thr, Tyr

Asn $HC-CH_2C-\overset{H}{\underset{..}{N}}-H\cdots\cdots:\overset{..}{O}-CH_2-CH$ Ser

Tyr $HC-CH_2-$ ⟨ring⟩ $-\overset{..}{O}-H\cdots\cdots:\overset{..}{O}-CH-CH$ Thr

18.6

Amino group → $H_2N-\overset{\overset{\displaystyle O}{\|}}{\underset{\underset{\displaystyle CH}{|}}{C}}-OH$ ← Carboxylic acid group

$H_3C\diagdown\quad\diagup CH_3$ } "R" group
Valine

18.7

$$\begin{array}{cc} H_3\overset{+}{N}-\overset{|}{\underset{|}{CH}}-\overset{\overset{\displaystyle O}{\|}}{C}-OH & H_2N-\overset{|}{\underset{|}{CH}}-\overset{\overset{\displaystyle O}{\|}}{C}-O^- \\ CH_2 \quad\text{at low pH} & CH_2 \quad\text{at high pH} \\ | & | \\ CH_2-C-OH & CH_2-C-O^- \\ \| & \| \\ O & O \end{array}$$

18.8 In the zwitterionic form of an amino acid, the $-NH_3^+$ group is an acid, and the $-COO^-$ group is a base. **18.9** chiral: (a), (b), (d)
18.10 Handed: wrench, corkscrew, jar lid Not handed: thumbtack, pencil, straw **18.11** 2-Aminobutane has a carbon with 4 different groups bonded to it. **18.12** chiral: (b), (c)

18.13
$$\begin{array}{cc} COOH & COOH \\ | & | \\ H_2N-\overset{*}{C}-H & H_2N-\overset{*}{C}-H \\ | & | \\ H-\overset{*}{C}-OH & H_3C-\overset{*}{C}-H \\ | & | \\ CH_3 & CH_2CH_3 \\ \text{Threonine} & \text{Isoleucine} \end{array}$$

18.14
$$\begin{array}{cc} H\ \ H & H\ \ H \\ | \ \ | & | \ \ | \\ H-C-C-H & H-C-\overset{*}{C}-Br \\ | \ \ | & | \ \ | \\ Br\ \ Cl & H\ \ Cl \end{array}$$

18.15
$$H_2N-CH-\overset{\overset{\displaystyle O}{\|}}{C}-NH-CH-\overset{\overset{\displaystyle O}{\|}}{C}-OH$$
$$\underset{\text{Serine}}{CH_2OH} \qquad \underset{\text{Valine}}{CH(CH_3)_2}$$

$$H_2N-CH-\overset{\overset{\displaystyle O}{\|}}{C}-NH-CH-\overset{\overset{\displaystyle O}{\|}}{C}-OH$$
$$\underset{\text{Valine}}{CH(CH_3)_2} \qquad \underset{\text{Serine}}{CH_2OH}$$

18.16 (a) Gly—Ser—Tyr Tyr—Ser—Gly Ser—Tyr—Gly
Gly—Tyr—Ser Tyr—Gly—Ser Ser—Gly—Tyr
(b)

$$H_3\overset{+}{N}-CH_2-\overset{\overset{\displaystyle O}{\|}}{C}-NH-CH-\overset{\overset{\displaystyle O}{\|}}{C}-NH-CH-\overset{\overset{\displaystyle O}{\|}}{C}-O^-$$
$$\qquad\qquad CH_2OH \qquad\qquad CH_2$$

Gly–Ser–Tyr (with phenol ring, OH)

$$H_3\overset{+}{N}-CH_2-\overset{\overset{\displaystyle O}{\|}}{C}-NH-CH-\overset{\overset{\displaystyle O}{\|}}{C}-NH-CH-\overset{\overset{\displaystyle O}{\|}}{C}-O^-$$
$$\qquad\qquad CH_2 \qquad\qquad CH_2OH$$

Gly–Tyr–Ser (with phenol ring, OH)

18.17 Ile—Arg—Val Arg—Ile—Val Val—Arg—Ile
Ile—Val—Arg Arg—Val—Ile Val—Ile—Arg
18.18 (a) Leu-Asp (nonpolar, polar) (b) Tyr-Ser-Lys (all polar)

18.19

Tyr–Ser–Lys

18.20 Asp-Tyr + Phe + Glu-Asn-Cys-Pro-Lys-Gly
18.21 (a) hydrogen bond (b) hydrophobic interaction (c) salt bridge
(d) hydrophobic interaction **18.22** (a) Tyr, Asp, Ser (b) Ala, Ile, Val, Leu
18.23 eleven backbone atoms **18.24** (a) hydrogen bonding (b) Hydrogen bonding takes place between an amide hydrogen and an amide carbonyl oxygen on an adjacent chain. **18.25** Secondary structure: stabilized by hydrogen bonds between amide nitrogens and carbonyl oxygens of polypeptide backbone. Tertiary structure: stabilized by hydrogen bonds between amino acid side-chain groups. **18.26** In a-keratin, pairs of a-helixes twist together into small fibrils that are twisted into larger bundles. In tropocollagen, three coiled chains wrap around each other to form a triple helix.
18.27 (a) tertiary; (b) secondary; (c) quaternary **18.28** At low pH, the groups at the end of the polypeptide chain exist as $-NH_3^+$ and $-COOH$. At high pH, they exist as $-NH_2$ and $-COO^-$. In addition, side chain functional groups may be ionized as follows: (a) no change (b) Arg positively charged at low pH; neutral at high pH: (c) Tyr neutral at low pH, negatively charged at high pH: (d) Glu, Asp neutral at low pH, negatively charged at high pH: (e) no change: (f) Cys neutral at low pH, negatively charged at high pH. **18.29** (a) 1, 4 (b) 2, 4 (c) 2
18.30 *See below for answer.*
18.31 *Fibrous Proteins*: structural proteins, water-insoluble, contain many Gly and Pro residues, contain large regions of α-helix or β-sheet, few side-chain interactions. Examples: Collagen, α-Keratin, Fibroin. *Globular Proteins*: enzymes and hormones, usually water-soluble, contain most amino acids, contain smaller regions of α-helix and β-sheet, complex tertiary structure. Examples: Ribonuclease, hemoglobin, insulin.
18.32 (a) Leu, Phe, Ala or any other amino acid with a nonpolar side chain. (b), (c) Asp, Lys, Thr or any other amino acid with a polar side chain.

18.33

The upper chiral carbon is responsible for the **D, L** configuration.

18.34 (a)

(b)

(c)

18.36 (a)

Cysteine (Cys)

(b)

Tyrosine (Tyr)

18.38 neutral: (a), (c); positive charge: (b)
18.40 (a), (c) low pH; (b) high pH
18.42 A chiral object is handed. Examples : glove, car.
18.44 (a), (b)
18.46 (a)

Achiral

(b)

Chiral

(c)

Chiral

18.48

18.50 A simple protein is composed only of amino acids. A conjugated protein consists of a protein associated with one or more nonprotein molecules.
18.52

Type of protein	Function	Example
Enzymes:	Catalyze biochemical reactions	Ribonuclease
Hormones:	Regulate body functions	Insulin
Storage proteins:	Store essential substances	Myoglobin
Transport proteins:	Transport substances through body fluids	Serum albumin
Structural proteins:	Provide shape and support	Collagen
Protective proteins:	Defend the body against foreign matter	Immunoglobulins
Contractile proteins:	Do mechanical work	Myosin and actin

18.30

Asp–Gly–Phe–Leu–Glu–Ala

18.54 (a) *Primary structure:* the sequence of connection of amino acids in a protein. (b) *Secondary structure:* the orientation of segments of the protein chain into a regular pattern, such as an α-helix or a β-sheet, by hydrogen bonding between backbone atoms. (c) *Tertiary structure:* the coiling and folding of the entire protein chain into a three-dimensional shape as a result of interactions between amino acid side chains. (d) *Quaternary structure:* the aggregation of several protein chains to form a larger structure.
18.56 Disulfide bonds stabilize tertiary structure. **18.58** In *hydrophobic interactions,* hydrocarbon side chains cluster in the center of proteins and make proteins spherical. Examples: Phe, Ile. *Salt bridges* bring together distant parts of a polypeptide chain. Examples: Lys, Asp. **18.60** When a protein is denatured, its nonprimary structure is disrupted, and it can no longer catalyze reactions. **18.62** Val—Met—Leu, Met—Val—Leu, Leu—Met—Val, Val—Leu—Met, Met—Leu—Val, Leu—Val—Met. **18.64** *Outside:* Asp, His (They can form H-bonds.) *Inside:* Val, Ala (They have hydrophobic interactions.)
18.66 N-terminal   C-terminal

18.68 (a) $H_3\overset{+}{N}CH_2COOH$ (b) $H_3\overset{+}{N}CH_2COOCH_3$ **18.70** N-terminal: Val—Gly—Ser—Ala—Asp C-terminal **18.72** A peptide rich in Asp and Lys is more soluble, because its side chains are more polar and can form hydrogen bonds with water. **18.74** People need a daily source of protein in the diet because the human body doesn't store the protein or the amino acids needed for its continuous synthesis of proteins. The body does store fats and carbohydrates. **18.76** Food from animal sources is more likely to contain complete protein than food from plant sources because the proteins in animals contain all of the common amino acids. **18.78** At pH = 6.6, collagen (pI = 6.6) has as many positive charges as negative charges and does not migrate. Bovine insulin (pI = 5.4) is negatively charged and migrates to the positively charged electrode. Human hemoglobin (pI = 7.1) is positively charged and migrates to the negative electrode. **18.80** People were unable to find fresh fruit and vegetables to eat. Fresh produce contains vitamin C, which is necessary for the synthesis of collagen. Without vitamin C, collagen is defective, and scurvy results. **18.82** A change in protein secondary structure from α-helix to β-pleated sheet alters the shape of the prion and causes groups that were close together in the normal prion to be farther apart in the altered prion. This change disrupts hydrogen bonds and salt bridges that were present in the normal protein and results in the formation of new tertiary interactions. **18.84** Protein digestion = hydrolysis of peptide bonds to form amino acids. Protein denaturation = disruption of secondary, tertiary, or quaternary structure without disrupting peptide bonds. **18.86** (a) *See below for answer.*

(b) Proline rings introduce kinks and bends and prevent hydrogen bonds from forming.
18.88

Oxytocin

18.90 Arg, Asp, Asn, Glu, Gln, His, Lys, Ser, Thr, Tyr

18.92 On the outside of a globular protein: Glu, Ser. On the outside of a fibrous protein: Ala, Val. On the outside of neither: Leu, Phe. **18.94** Asp is similar in size and function to Glu. **18.96** Canned pineapple has been heated to inactivate enzymes. **18.98** Enzymes would hydrolyze insulin. **18.100** A combination of grains, legumes, and nuts in each meal provides all of the essential amino acids.

Chapter 19

19.1 ribonuclease **19.2** The enzyme might catalyze reactions within the eye; saline is sterile and isotonic. **19.3** iron, copper, manganese, molybdenum, vanadium, cobalt, nickel, chromium **19.4** (a) NAD^+, coenzyme A, FAD; (b) The remaining cofactors are minerals. **19.5** (a) catalyzes the removal of two —H from an alcohol, (b) catalyzes the transfer of an amino group from aspartate to a second substrate, (c) catalyzes the synthesis of tyrosine–tRNA from tyrosine and its tRNA, coupled with ATP hydrolysis. (d) catalyzes the isomerization of a phosphohexose. **19.6** (a) urease (b) cellulase **19.7** transferase. It catalyzes the transfer of a phosphoryl group to a hexose. **19.8** Water adds to fumarate (substrate) to give L-malate (product). **19.9** Reaction (a) **19.10** Acidic, basic and polar side chains take part in catalytic activity. All types of side chains hold the enzyme in the active site. **19.11** Substrate molecules are bound to all of the active sites, (a) no effect; (b) increases the rate. **19.12** higher at 35°C in both cases **19.13** The rate is much greater at pH = 2. **19.14** Two strategies keep the enzyme active: (1) Use of chaperonins, enzymes that return a protein to its active form; (2) The protein itself is rigid and resists heat denaturation. **19.15** CPK, AST, and LDH_1 leak from damaged heart vessels. **19.16** (a) E1 (b) no **19.17** molecule (b), because it resembles the substrate **19.18** a product that resembles the substrate **19.19** irreversible inhibition **19.20** (a) competitive inhibition (b) covalent modification or feedback control (c) covalent modification (d) genetic control **19.21** Vitamin A-long hydrocarbon chain. Vitamin C-polar hydroxyl groups.

18.86 (a)

Arg———Pro———Pro———Gly———Phe———Ser———Pro———Phe———Arg

19.22 Retinal - aldehyde. Retinoic acid - carboxylic acid. **19.23** enzyme cofactors; antioxidants; aid in absorption of calcium and phosphate ions; aid in synthesis of visual pigments and blood clotting factors. **19.24** Vitamins C and E, β-carotene; These vitamins scavenge damaging free radicals. **19.25** copper, selenium; Both have a biological function and are toxic only in excess.
19.26

19.27 (a) oxidoreductase (b) dehydrogenase (c) L-lactate (d) pyruvate (e) L-lactate dehydrogenase **19.28** No. An enzyme usually catalyzes the reaction of only one isomer. D-Lactate might be a competitive inhibitor. **19.29** NAD^+ is an oxidizing agent and includes the vitamin niacin. **19.30** (a) Rate increases when [substrate] is low, but max. rate is soon reached; max. rate is always lower than max. rate of uninhibited reaction. (b) Rate increases. **19.31** (a) Addition or removal of a covalently bonded group changes the activity of an enzyme (b) Hormones control the synthesis of enzymes. (c) Binding of the regulator at a site away from the catalytic site changes the shape of the enzyme. (d) Feedback inhibition occurs when the product of a series of reactions serves as an inhibitor for an earlier reaction. **19.32** (a) feedback inhibition (b) irreversible inhibition (c) genetic control (d) noncompetitive inhibition **19.33** From left to right: aspartate (acidic), serine, glutamine, arginine (basic), histidine (basic). **19.34** (a) removal of two —H from a substrate to form a double bond; (b) replacement of a carboxyl group by —H; (c) hydrolysis of ester groups in lipids **19.36** (a) amylase (b) peroxidase (c) DNAse **19.38** An enzyme is a large three-dimensional molecule with a catalytic site into which a substrate can fit. Enzymes are specific in their action because only one or a few molecules have the appropriate shape and functional groups to fit into the catalytic site. **19.40** (a) hydrolase (b) lyase (c) oxidoreductase **19.42** (a) loss of H_2O from a substrate to give a double bond; (b) transfer of a methyl group between substrates; (c) reduction of a substrate **19.44** hydrolase **19.46** (a) riboflavin (B_2) (b) pantothenic acid (B_5) (c) niacin (B_3) **19.48** Lock-and-key: An enzyme is rigid(lock) and only one specific substrate(key) can fit in the active site. Induced fit: An enzyme can change its shape to accommodate the substrate and to catalyze the reaction. **19.50** No. Protein folding can bring the residues close to each other.

19.52 In the stomach, an enzyme must be active at an acidic pH. In the intestine, an enzyme needs to be active at a higher pH and need not be active at pH = 1.5. **19.54** At a high substrate concentration relative to enzyme concentration, the rate of reaction triples if the concentration of enzyme is tripled. **19.56** (a) (b) lowers rate; (c) denatures the enzyme and stops reaction **19.58** *Uncompetitive inhibition:* Inhibitor binds reversibly and noncovalently away from the active site and changes the shape of the site to make it difficult for the enzyme to catalyze reactions. *Competitive inhibition:* Inhibitor binds reversibly and noncovalently at the active site and keeps the substrate from entering. *Irreversible inhibition:* Inhibitor irreversibly forms a covalent bond at the active site and destroys the catalytic ability of the enzyme. **19.60** diagram B **19.62** (1) displacing an essential metal from an active site; (2) bonding to a cysteine residue (irreversible) **19.64** Papain catalyzes the hydrolysis of peptide bonds and partially digests the proteins in meat. **19.66** One site is for catalysis, and one site is for regulation. **19.68** The end product of a reaction series is an inhibitor for an earlier step. **19.70** A zymogen is an enzyme synthesized in a form different from its active form because it might otherwise harm the organism. **19.72** Vitamins are small essential organic molecules that must be obtained from food. **19.74** Vitamin C is excreted, but Vitamin A is stored in fatty tissue. **19.76** Bone is composed of both calcium and phosphorus. **19.78** Reactions can be run at higher temperatures, increasing the rate. **19.80** earliest: CPK; after several days: LDH **19.82** A mild inhibitor allows closer control of blood pressure. A modification to pit viper protein might be to introduce an —SH residue near proline. **19.84** Vitamin A: 0%; Vitamin C 0%; Calcium: 4%; Iron: 6% This food is not a good source of vitamins and minerals. **19.86** They are the most important for maintaining good health. **19.88** *See below for answer.*
19.90 11 L apple juice **19.92** Because competitive inhibition is reversible, addition of a large amount of the normal substrate will reverse the binding of the inhibitor, and the rate of reaction of the normal substrate will return to its usual value. The effects of uncompetitive inhibition can't be reversed by addition of excess substrate. **19.94** Serine to valine would destroy catalytic activity, since the serine —OH group is essential for catalysis. Aspartate to glutamate might or might not affect catalytic activity since both amino acids have the same functional groups.

Chapter 20

20.1 exergonic: (a), (c); endergonic: (b); releases the most energy: (a) **20.2** Both pathways produce the same amount of energy. **20.3** (a) exergonic: oxidation of glucose; endergonic: photosynthesis (b) sunlight
20.4 (a)
Carbohydrates $\xrightarrow{\text{digestion}}$ Glucose, sugars $\xrightarrow{\text{glycolysis}}$ Pyruvate → Acetyl-CoA $\xrightarrow[\text{cycle}]{\text{citric acid}}$ Reduced coenzymes $\xrightarrow[\text{transport}]{\text{electron}}$ ATP
    (b) pyruvate, acetyl-CoA, citric acid cycle intermediates.

19.88

20.5

$$H_3C-\overset{\overset{\displaystyle O}{\|}}{C}-O-\overset{\overset{\displaystyle O}{\|}}{\underset{\underset{\displaystyle O^-}{|}}{P}}-O^- \; + \; H_2O \longrightarrow$$

$$H_3C-\overset{\overset{\displaystyle O}{\|}}{C}-O^- \; + \; {}^-O-\overset{\overset{\displaystyle O}{\|}}{\underset{\underset{\displaystyle OH}{|}}{P}}-O^- \; + \; H^+$$

20.6 Energy is produced only when it is needed.

20.7

$$HOCH_2\overset{\overset{\displaystyle OH}{|}}{C}HCH_2OH \xrightarrow[\text{ATP} \quad \text{ADP}]{} HOCH_2\overset{\overset{\displaystyle OH}{|}}{C}HCH_2O-\overset{\overset{\displaystyle O}{\|}}{\underset{\underset{\displaystyle O^-}{|}}{P}}-O^-$$

20.8 If a process is exergonic, its exact reverse is endergonic and can't occur unless it is coupled with an exergonic reaction in a different pathway.
20.9 66 min. **20.10** favorable ($\Delta G = -3.0$ kcal/mol; -12.3 kJ/mol).
20.11 (b), (c), (d) FAD has five heterocyclic rings (three in the ADP part, and two in the site of reaction on the left).
20.12 (a)

(b) oxidoreductases
20.13 Citric acid, isocitric acid. **20.14** steps 3, 4, 6, 8. **20.15** Succinic dehydrogenase catalyzes the removal of two hydrogens from succinate to yield fumarate, and FAD is the coenzyme associated with dehydrogenations.
20.16 citrate (tertiary); isocitrate (secondary); malate (secondary)
20.17 isocitrate **20.18** Steps 1–4 correspond to the first stage, and steps 5–8 correspond to the second stage. **20.19** Mitochondrial matrix
20.20 *Similarities*: both involve the reaction of glucose, oxygen, carbon dioxide, and water; both take place in organelles (chloroplasts, mitochondria); both involve large, metal-ion-containing molecules (chlorophyll, heme); both involve electron transfer; both involve similar coenzymes. *Differences*: photosynthesis captures energy, whereas electron transport releases energy; photosynthesis requires light, whereas oxidative phosphorylation doesn't. **20.21** O_2. Movement of H^+ from a region of high $[H^+]$ to a region of low $[H^+]$ releases energy that is used in ATP synthesis.
20.22 (a) Succinyl phosphate $+ H_2O \longrightarrow$
$$\text{Succinate} + \text{HOPO}_3^{2-} + H^+$$
(b) $ADP + HOPO_3^{2-} + H^+ \longrightarrow ATP + H_2O$
$$\Delta G = +7.3 \text{ kcal/mol } (+30.5 \text{ kJ/mol})$$
20.23 (a) Stage 1 (digestion) (b) Stage 4 (ATP synthesis) (c) Stage 2 (glycolysis) (d) Stage 3 (citric acid cycle). **20.24** Endergonic; coupled reactions **20.25** NAD^+ accepts hydride ions; hydrogen ions are released to the mitochondrial matrix, and ultimately combine with reduced O_2 to form H_2O. **20.26** (a) Step A (NAD^+) (b) Step B (c) product of A (d) oxidoreductase **20.27** Step 1: lyase Step 2: isomerase Step 3: oxidoreductase Step 4: oxidoreductase, lyase Step 5: ligase Step 6: oxidoreductase Step 7: lyase Step 8: oxidoreductase **20.28** Metals are better oxidizing and reducing agents. Also, they can accept and donate electrons in one-electron increments. **20.30** An endergonic reaction requires energy, and an exergonic reaction releases energy. **20.32** Enzymes affect only the rate of a reaction, not the size or sign of ΔG. **20.34** exergonic: (a), (b) ; endergonic: (c). Reaction (b) proceeds farthest toward products. **20.36** prokaryote: (b), (e); eukaryote: (a), (b), (c), (d) **20.38** Organelles are subcellular structures that perform specialized tasks within the cell. **20.40** Cristae, the folds of the inner mitochondrial membrane, provide extra surface area for electron transport and ATP production to take place. **20.42** Metabolism refers to all reactions that take place inside cells. Digestion is the process of breaking food into small organic molecules prior to cellular absorption. **20.44** acetyl-CoA **20.46** An ATP molecule transfers a phosphoryl group to another molecule in exergonic reactions. **20.48** $\Delta G = -4.5$ kcal/mol (-18.8 kJ/mol). **20.50** not favorable (positive ΔG) **20.52** (a) NAD^+ is reduced, (b) NAD^+ is an oxidizing agent, (c) NAD^+ participates in the oxidation of a secondary alcohol to a ketone, (d) $NADH/H^+$
(e)

$$H-\overset{|}{\underset{|}{C}}-OH \xrightarrow[\quad]{NAD^+ \quad NADH/H^+} \overset{|}{C}=O$$

20.54 mitochondria **20.56** Both carbons are oxidized to CO_2.
20.58 3 NADH, one $FADH_2$. **20.60** Step 3 (isocitrate $\rightarrow \alpha$-ketoglutarate), Step 4 (α-ketoglutarate $\rightarrow$ succinyl $-$ SCoA) and Step 8 (malate $\rightarrow$ oxaloacetate) store energy as NADH. **20.62** One complete citric acid cycle produces four reduced coenzymes, which enter the electron transfer chain and ultimately generate ATP. **20.64** H_2O, ATP, oxidized coenzymes **20.66** (a) FAD = flavin adenine dinucleotide; (b) CoQ = coenzyme Q; (c) $NADH/H^+$ = reduced nicotinamide adenine dinucleotide, plus hydrogen ion; (d) Cyt c = Cytochrome c **20.68** NADH, coenzyme Q, cytochrome c **20.70** The citric acid cycle would stop. **20.72** In oxidative phosphorylation, reduced coenzymes are oxidized, and ADP is phosphorylated. **20.74** H^+ ions pass through a channel that is part of the ATP synthase enzyme, where they release energy that drives oxidative phosphorylation. **20.76** Oxygen consumption increases because the proton gradient from ATP production dissipates. **20.78** A seal has more brown fat because it needs to keep warm. **20.80** Bacteria use H_2S because no light is available for the usual light-dependent reaction of H_2O that provides O_2 and electrons. **20.82** (no answer) **20.84** Daily activities such as walking use energy, and thus the body requires a larger caloric intake than that needed to maintain basal metabolism. **20.86** The light reaction produces O_2, NADPH, and ATP. The dark reaction produces carbohydrates from water and CO_2. **20.88** Refrigeration slows the breakdown of carbohydrates by decreasing the rate of respiration.
20.90

$$CoAS-\overset{\overset{\displaystyle O}{\|}}{C}-CH_3 \; + \; \overset{\overset{\displaystyle COO^-}{|}}{\underset{\underset{\displaystyle COO^-}{|}}{\underset{\displaystyle CH_2}{|}}}C=O \xrightarrow{\text{condensation}}$$

$$CoAS-\overset{\overset{\displaystyle O}{\|}}{C}-CH_2-\overset{\overset{\displaystyle COO^-}{|}}{\underset{\underset{\displaystyle COO^-}{|}}{\underset{\displaystyle CH_2}{|}}}OH$$

20.92 oxidoreductases **20.94** FAD; oxidoreductases **20.96** Energy from combustion is released to the surroundings as heat and is wasted. Energy from metabolic oxidation is released in several steps and is stored in each step so that is available for use in other metabolic processes. **20.98** The enzymes superoxide dismutase and catalase and vitamins E, C, and A can inactivate these species. **20.100** adipose tissue, skin cells, skeletal muscle, heart muscle. **20.102** mitochondrial matrix **20.104** *least oxidized*: succinate; fumarate; malate; oxaloacetate; *most oxidized*

Chapter 21

21.1 (a) aldopentose (b) ketotriose (c) aldotetrose
21.2

$$HOCH_2-\overset{\overset{\displaystyle OH}{|}}{C}H-\overset{\overset{\displaystyle OH}{|}}{C}H-\overset{\overset{\displaystyle OH}{|}}{C}H-\overset{\overset{\displaystyle O}{\|}}{C}H$$

An aldopentose

$$HOCH_2-\overset{\overset{\displaystyle OH}{|}}{C}H-\overset{\overset{\displaystyle OH}{|}}{C}H-\overset{\overset{\displaystyle OH}{|}}{C}H-\overset{\overset{\displaystyle O}{\|}}{C}-CH_2OH$$

A ketohexose

21.3 32 stereoisomers **21.4** (d) **21.5** The bottom carbon is not chiral. The orientations of the hydroxyl groups bonded to the chiral carbons must be shown in order to indicate which stereoisomer is pictured.

21.6 (a)

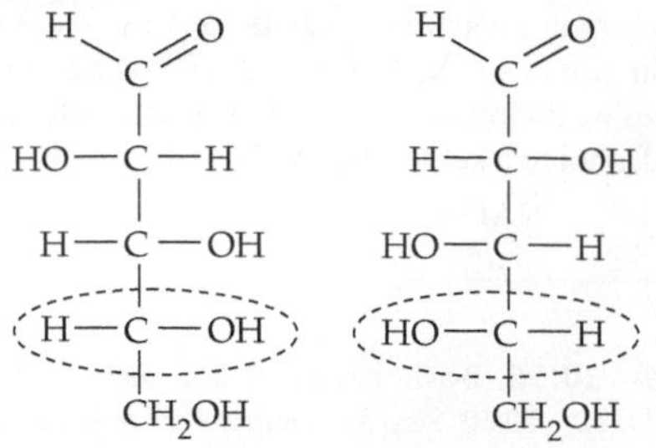

A D-aldopentose   An L-aldopentose

(b)

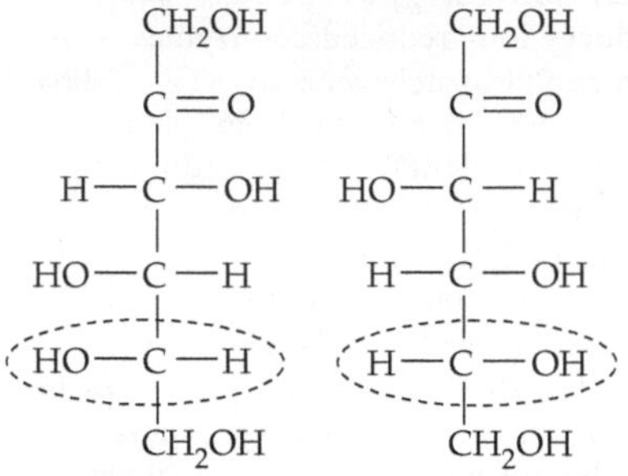

An L-ketohexose   A D-ketohexose

21.7 An enzymatic path would produce only the desired enantiomer. This would provide the desired product without need for separation of enantiomers and would eliminate the need to test both enantiomers.

21.8

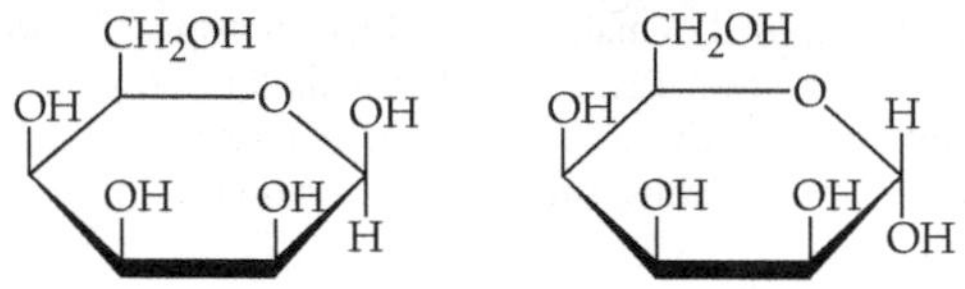

β-anomer   α-anomer

21.9

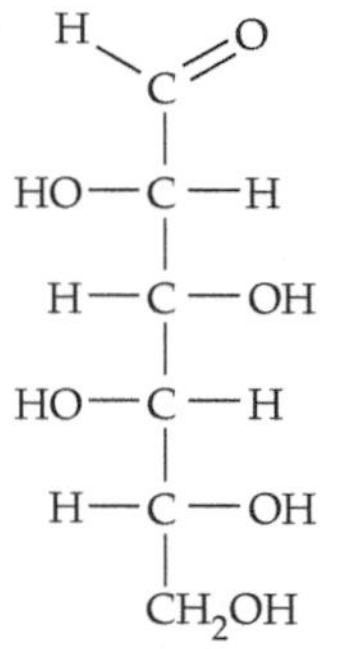

D-Idose

21.10 (a) Rings **1** and **4** (5 carbons) are amino sugars, **(b)** Ring **3** (4 carbons) is an unmodified sugar, **(c)** Ring **2** (6 carbons) is a nonsugar.

21.11

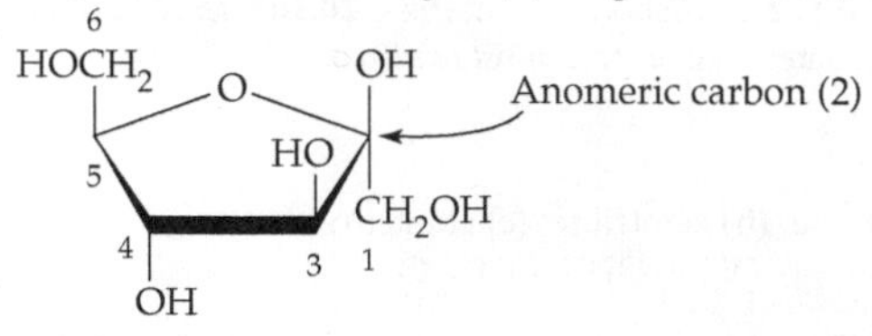

Anomeric carbon (2)

β-anomer

21.12
(a)   (b)

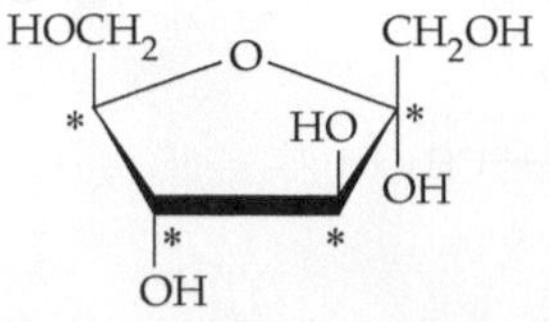

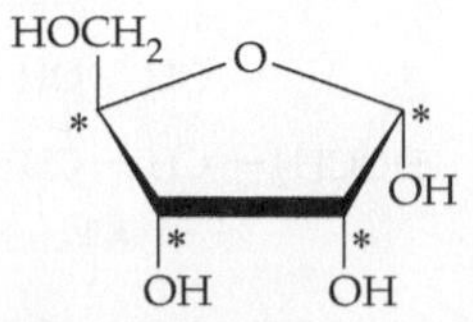

(c)

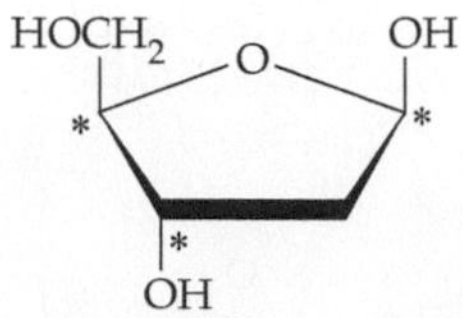

21.13 (a) an α anomer (b) carbon 6 (c) Groups that are below the plane of the ring in D-galactose are above the plane of the ring in L-fucose. Groups that are above the plane of the ring in D-galactose are below the plane of the ring in L-fucose. (d) yes **21.14** N-acetyl-D-glucosamine, D-galactose, and L-fucose are found in all blood types.

21.15

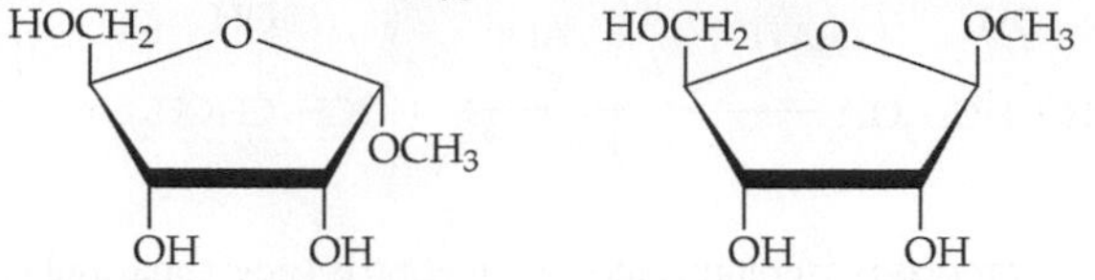

Methyl α-D-riboside   Methyl β-D-riboside

21.16 a β-1,4 glycosidic link **21.17** β-D-Glucose + β-D-Glucose **21.18 (a)** maltose; fermenting grain **(b)** sucrose; sugar beets **(c)** lactose; milk **21.19** Glucose and fructose are simple carbohydrates; starch is a complex carbohydrate. Soluble and insoluble fiber are complex carbohydrates that are not digestible by humans. **21.20** glutamine, asparagine **21.21** an α-1,4 glycosidic link **21.22** No. There are too few hemiacetal units to give a detectable result. **21.23** The spherical particles of glycogen are compact and easily available as a source of glucose. The chains of cellulose serve as structural components of plants. **21.24** irreversible inhibition; permanently inactivates an enzyme's active site; inhibits the synthesis of bacterial cell walls; modified sugar polymers, peptidoglycans

21.25   Starch $\xrightarrow{\text{Amylase}}$ Maltose $\xrightarrow{\text{Maltase}}$ Glucose
polysaccharide   disaccharide   monosaccharide

21.26 (a) diastereomers, anomers **(b)** enantiomers **(c)** diastereomers
21.27 (a) (b)

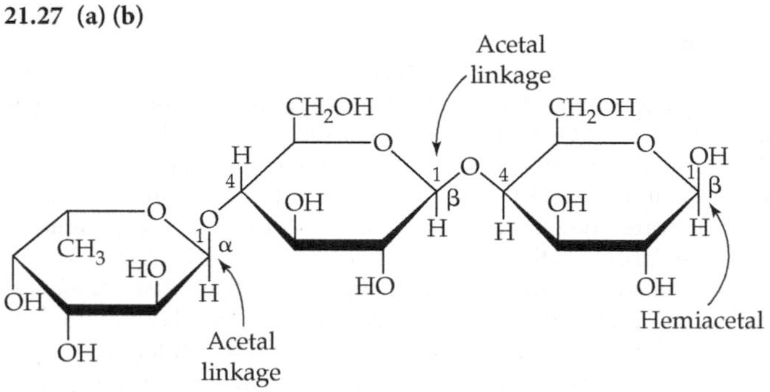

Acetal linkage

Acetal linkage

Hemiacetal

A   B   C
α-anomer   β-anomer   β-anomer

(c) α-1,4 linkage between C4 of B and C1 of A **(d)** β-1,4 linkage between C4 of C and C1 of B **21.28 (a) (b)** No monosaccharides are identical, and none are enantiomers. **(c) (d)**

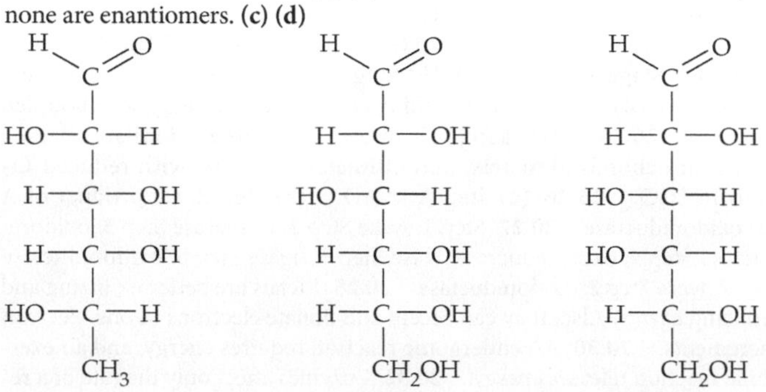

L-Fucose   D-Glucose   D-Galactose

21.29 Monosaccharide C is oxidized. Identification of the carboxylic acid also identifies the terminal monosaccharide.

21.30 No

21.31

Polysaccharide	Linkage	Branching?
Cellulose	β-1,4	no
Amylose	α-1,4	no
Amylopectin	α-1,4	yes: α-1,6 branches occur ~ every 25 units
Glycogen	α-1,4	yes: even more α-1,6 branches than in amylopectin

21.32 Glucose is in equilibrium with its open-chain aldehyde form, which reacts with an oxidizing agent.

21.34 -ose   **21.36** (a) aldotetrose (b) ketopentose (c) aldopentose (d) ketohexose   **21.38** right part = 4 chiral carbons; left part = 5 chiral carbons; total = nine chiral carbons

21.40

A four-carbon deoxy sugar

21.42 glucose—energy source; galactose—brain tissue, fructose—energy source; ribose—nucleic acids, coenzymes   **21.44** They are mirror images (enantiomers).   **21.46** The reduction product of D-erythrose is achiral. **21.48** A polarimeter measures the degree of rotation of plane-polarized light by a solution of an optically active compound. **21.50** Equimolar solutions of enantiomers rotate light to the same degree but in opposite directions.   **21.52** A reducing sugar contains an aldehyde or ketone group.   **21.54** An anomer is one of a pair of hemiacetal stereoisomers formed when an open-chain sugar cyclizes. Anomers differ in the orientation of the hydroxyl group at the anomeric carbon.   **21.56** the α form

21.58

β-D-Altrose

α-D-Altrose

21.60

21.62

22.64 A glycoside is an acetal that is formed when the hemiacetal —OH group of a carbohydrate reacts with an alcohol.

21.66

Hemiacetal carbon

The hemiacetal carbon in this problem is in equilibrium with an open-chain aldehyde that is a reducing sugar.

21.68 Sucrose has no hemiacetal group.   **21.70** Amylose and amylopectin are both components of starch and both consist of long polymers of α-D-glucose linked by α-1,4 glycosidic bonds. Amylopectin is much larger and has α-1,6 branches every 25 units or so along the chain.   **21.72** Gentiobiose contains both an acetal grouping and a hemiacetal grouping. Gentiobiose is a reducing sugar. A β-1,6 linkage connects the two monosaccharides. **21.74** Trehalose is a nonreducing sugar because it contains no hemiacetal linkages. The two D-glucose monosaccharides are connected by an α-1,1 acetal link.   **21.76** Starch is the storage form of glucose in plants; glycogen serves the same purpose in animals.   **21.78** Enzyme-catalyzed reactions usually produce only one enantiomer.   **21.80** People with type O blood can receive blood only from other donors that have type O blood. People with type AB blood can give blood only to other people with type AB blood. **21.82** pectin and vegetable gum: found in fruits, barley, oats and beans. **21.84** glucose; cellulose in a matrix of pectin, lignin, and cellulose **21.86** Penicillin inhibits the enzyme that synthesizes bacterial cell walls. Mammals don't have this synthetic pathway.   **21.88** No. they are not mirror images.

21.90

Raffinose

21.92

1,3,4-Trihydroxy-2-butanone

1,3,4-Trihydroxy-2-butanone has one chiral carbon and exists as a pair of enentiomers.

21.94 Enzymes produced by the bacteria in yogurt predigest most of the lactose, making it possible for lactose-intolerant people to eat yogurt without symptoms.

21.96

$$CH_2OH$$
$$H \;—\; OH$$
$$HO \;—\; H$$
Dulcitol - - - - - - - - - Plane of symmetry
$$HO \;—\; H$$
$$H \;—\; OH$$
$$CH_2OH$$

Dulcitol is optically inactive because it has a plane of symmetry and thus doesn't have an enantiomer. **21.98** 170 kcal (710 kJ) **21.100** fructose: fruit; lactose: milk; amylose: wheat starch **21.102** Cellulose is rigid and is insoluble in water; glycogen coils up, is flexible, and dissolves in water.

Chapter 22

22.1 (a) glycogenesis (b) glycogenolysis (c) gluconeogenesis **22.2** glycogenesis, pentose phosphate pathway, glycolysis **22.3** (a) steps 6 and 7 (b) steps 9 and 10 **22.4** Isomerizations: steps 2, 5, 8
22.5

$$\begin{array}{c} H \quad \diagdown C \diagup O \\ H—C—OH \\ HO—C—H \\ H—C—OH \\ H—C—OH \\ CH_2OPO_3{}^{2-} \end{array} \quad \rightleftharpoons \quad \begin{array}{c} CH_2OH \\ C{=}O \\ HO—C—H \\ H—C—OH \\ H—C—OH \\ CH_2OPO_3{}^{2-} \end{array}$$

22.6 (a) pyruvate (b) Step 6: glyceraldehyde 3-phosphate is oxidized; NAD^+ is the oxidizing agent **22.7** Table sugar (sucrose) promotes the growth of bacteria that cause tooth decay; honey (glucose + fructose) does not.
22.8

Fructose 6-phosphate enters glycolysis at Step 3.

22.9 Glucose and galactose differ in configuration at C4. **22.10** (a) The energy is lost as heat. (b) The reverse of fermentation is very endothermic; loss of CO_2 drives the reaction to completion in the forward direction. **22.11** in preparation of bread, yogurt, cheese, beer, and wine **22.12** Insulin decreases; blood glucose decreases, the level of glucagon increases. Glucagon causes the breakdown of liver glycogen and the release of glucose. As glycogen is used up, the level of free fatty acids and ketone bodies increases. **22.13** fasting blood sugar check, glucose tolerance test
22.14

$$CH_2OH$$
$$H—C—OH$$
$$HO—C—H$$
$$H—C—OH$$
$$H—C—OH$$
$$CH_2OH$$
Sorbitol

Sorbitol can not form a cyclic acetal because it does not have a carbonyl group.

22.15 (a) The increase in $[H^+]$ drives the equilibrium shown in Section 22.9 to the right, causing the production of CO_2. (b) Le Châtelier's Principle. **22.16** Creatine phosphate, stored in muscles, is an immediate source of ATP. ATP from glucose and glycogen metabolism is a slower process. **22.17** phosphorylation, oxidation **22.18** hydrolases **22.19** (a) when the supply of glucose is adequate and the body needs energy. (b) when the body needs free glucose. (c) when ribose 5-phosphate or NADPH are needed. (d) when glucose supply is adequate, and the body doesn't need to use glucose for energy production. **22.20** Phosphorylations of glucose and fructose 6-phosphate produce important intermediates that repay the initial energy investment. Fructose 1,6-bisphosphate is cleaved into two three-carbon compounds, which are converted to pyruvate. **22.21** (a) when the body needs energy, in mitochondria; (b) under anaerobic conditions, in yeast; (c) under anaerobic conditions, in muscle, red blood cells; (d) when the body needs free glucose, in the liver **22.22** Step 1: transferase Step 2: isomerase Step 3: transferase Step 4: lyase Step 5: isomerase Step 6: oxidoreductase, transferase Step 7: transferase Step 8: isomerase Step 9: lyase Step 10: transferase. transferases (because many reactions involve phosphate transfers). Ligases are associated with reactions that synthesize molecules, not with reactions that break down molecules. **22.23** (g), (c), (b), (e), (f), (a), (d) **22.24** Sources of compounds for gluconeogenesis: pyruvate, lactate, citric acid cycle intermediates, many amino acids. Gluconeogenesis takes place when glucose levels are low. **22.25** Germinating seeds need to synthesize carbohydrates from fats; humans obtain carbohydrates from food. **22.26** (a) No (b) Molecular oxygen appears in the last step of the electron transport chain, where it combines with water, H^+ and electrons (from electron transport) to form H_2O. **22.28** glucose + galactose; in the lining of the small intestine
22.30

Type of Food Molecules	Products of Digestion
Proteins	Amino acids
Triacylglycerols	Glycerol and fatty acids
Sucrose	Glucose and fructose
Lactose	Glucose and galactose
Starch, maltose	Glucose

22.32 acetyl-CoA; lactate; ethanol + CO_2 **22.34** glycogenesis: synthesis of glycogen from glucose; glycogenolysis: breakdown of glycogen to form glucose **22.36** ribose 5-phosphate, glycolysis intermediates **22.34** (a) all organs; (b) liver; (c), (d) muscle, liver **22.40** None of steps of glycolysis require oxygen. **22.42** (a) steps 1, 3, 6, 7, 10; (b) step 6; (c) step 9 **22.44** (a) Substrate-level phosphorylation: 2 mol ATP; oxidative phosphorylation (ideal): 6 ATP (b) Oxidative phosphorylation: 3 mol ATP (c) Substrate-level phosphorylation: 1 mol ATP; oxidative phosphorylation: 11 mol ATP. Substrate-level phosphorylation is formation of ATP as a by-product of a reaction; oxidative phosphorylation is formation of ATP as a byproduct of electron transport.
22.46

$$\begin{array}{c} OH \quad O \\ CH_3CH—C—O^- \end{array} \xrightarrow[\text{Lactate dehydrogenase}]{NAD^+ \quad NADH/H^+} \begin{array}{c} O \quad O \\ CH_3C—C—O^- \end{array}$$
Lactate — Pyruvate

22.48 4 mol acetyl-CoA **22.50** *Hypoglycemia*: low blood sugar; weakness, sweating, rapid heartbeat, confusion, coma, death *Hyperglycemia*: high blood sugar; increased urine flow, low blood pressure, coma, death **22.52** ketone bodies **22.54** In Type 2 diabetes, insulin is in good supply, but cell membrane receptors fail to recognize insulin. **22.56** Excess glucose is converted to sorbitol, which can't be transported out of cells. This buildup changes osmolarity and causes cataracts and blindness. **22.58** muscle cells **22.60** Glycogenolysis uses less energy because it is a hydrolysis reaction. **22.62** pyruvate, lactate **22.64** Several steps in the reverse of glycolysis are energetically unfavorable. **22.66** Steps 1, 3, 10 of glycolysis; all involve phosphate transfers **22.68** when muscle glucose is depleted and oxygen is in short supply **22.70** glycoproteins, bacteria, dextran, polysaccharide storage granules **22.72** In an environment rich in sucrose, bacteria secrete an enzyme that transfers glucose units from digested sucrose to the dextran polymer. The residual fructose is metabolized to lactate, which lowers pH. The resulting acidic environment in the mouth dissolves minerals in teeth, leading to cavities.   **22.74** beer, wine, cheese, yogurt, sour cream, and buttermilk   **22.76** 140 g/dL vs 90 g/dL   **22.78** The curve lies between the curve for a diabetic person and a nondiabetic person   **22.80** *First used → Last used* ATP, creatine phosphate, glucose, glycogen, fatty acids from triacylglycerols   **22.82** phosphoryl group transfers   **22.84** Glucose obtained from the hydrolysis of glycogen is phosphorylated by reaction with inorganic phosphate ion and enters the glycolysis pathway as glucose 6–phosphate. Thus, one fewer ATP is needed (at Step 1), and one more ATP is produced.   **22.86** In the absence of oxygen, pyruvate from catabolism of glucose in wine was fermented by yeast enzymes to ethanol and CO_2, which increased the pressure in the bottle and popped the cork.   **22.88** (a) consumes energy (b) yields energy **22.90** (1) Lactate can only be converted to glucose in the liver; (2) Lactate lowers the pH in muscle cells and must be removed.   **22.92** (a) when glucose is abundant and the body needs energy; (b) when glucose is in short supply, as in starvation or fasting

Chapter 23

23.1 (a) eicosanoid (b) glycerophospholipid (c) wax
23.2

$$CH_3(CH_2)_{18}\overset{O}{\underset{\|}{C}}-OCH_2(CH_2)_{30}CH_3$$

23.3

23.4 cookies (lower in both total fat and saturated fat)   **23.5** (a) butter (b) soybean oil (c) soybean oil   **23.6** *See below for answer.*
23.7 When two different fatty acids are bonded to C1 and C3 of glycerol, C2 is chiral.   **23.8** London forces; weak; hydrogen bonds between water molecules are stronger than London forces.
23.9 The resulting acyl groups are from stearic acid.

23.10 Both soaps and detergents consist of ionic heads and hydrophobic tails, and both clean by forming micelles around greasy dirt. Unlike detergents, soaps can form soap scum when used in hard water.

23.11

$\xrightarrow{\text{NaOH, H}_2\text{O}}$

$2\ CH_3(CH_2)_{16}COO^-\ Na^+$

$CH_3(CH_2)_7CH{=}CH(CH_2)_7COO^-\ Na^+$

23.12 Lecithins emulsify fats in the same way as soaps dissolve grease: The fats are coated by the nonpolar part of a lecithin, and the polar part of lecithins allows fats to be suspended in aqueous solution.   **23.13** (a) glycerol, phosphate ion, choline, $RCOO^-Na^+$, $R'COO^-Na^+$, (b) sphingosine, phosphate ion, choline, sodium palmitate

23.14

23.15

23.16 (a), (c), (e), (f)   **23.17** in butter: cholesterol; in margarine: trans fatty acids   **23.18** They must be hydrophobic, contain many amino acids

23.6

with nonpolar side chains, and must be folded so that the hydrophilic regions face outward. **23.19** yes **23.20** Glucose 6-phosphate has a charged phosphate group and can't pass through the hydrophobic lipid bilayer. **23.21** The surfaces are in different environments and serve different functions. **23.22** carboxylic acid (most acidic), alcohol, C—C double bonds, ethers. The molecule has both polar and nonpolar regions. Form hydrogen bonds: —COOH, —OH. **23.23** A has the highest melting point. B and C are probably liquids at room temperature. **23.24** 12.2% palmitic acid, 87.5% stearic acid; more like C

23.25

A glycerophospholipid

23.26 Because the membrane is fluid, it can flow together after an injury. **23.27** C_{16} saturated fatty acids. The polar head lies in lung tissue, and the hydrocarbon tails protrude into the alveoli. **23.28** A lipid is a naturally-occurring molecule that dissolves in nonpolar solvents. **23.30** $CH_3(CH_2)_{16}COOH$: straight chain **23.32** *Saturated fatty acids* are long-chain carboxylic acids that contain no carbon–carbon double bonds. *Monounsaturated fatty acids* contain one carbon–carbon double bond. *Polyunsaturated fatty acids* contain two or more carbon–carbon double bonds. **23.34** An essential fatty acid can't be synthesized by the human body and must be part of the diet. **23.36** (a) The double bonds in an unsaturated fatty acid (linolenic acid) make it harder for them to be arranged in a crystal. **23.38** Fats: saturated and unsaturated fatty acids, solids; Oils: mostly unsaturated fatty acids, liquids.

23.40

23.42 a protective coating

23.44

Cetyl palmitate

23.46

23.48 hydrogenation **23.50** saponification **23.52** The product is shown in Problem 23.9 **23.54** Glycerophospholipids have polar heads (point outward) and nonpolar tails that cluster to form the membrane. Triacylglycerols don't have polar heads. **23.56** A sphingomyelin and a cerebroside are similar in that both have a sphingosine backbone. The difference between the two occurs at C1 of sphingosine. A sphingomyelin has a phosphate group bonded to an amino alcohol at C1; a cerebroside has a glycosidic link to a monosaccharide at C1. **23.58** Glycerophospholipids have an ionic phosphate group that is solvated by water. **23.60** In a soap micelle, the polar hydrophilic heads are on the exterior, and the hydrophobic tails cluster in the center. In a membrane bilayer, hydrophilic heads are on both the exterior and interior surfaces of the membrane, and the region between the two surfaces is occupied by hydrophobic tails. **23.62** glycolipids, cholesterol, proteins **23.64** *See below for answer.*

23.66

A glycerophospholipid

23.68 Active transport requires energy because it is a process in which substances are transported across a membrane in a direction opposite to their tendency to diffuse. **23.70** (a) simple diffusion (b) facilitated diffusion (c) active transport **23.72** Cholesterol is a component of cell membranes and is the starting material for the synthesis of all other steroids. **23.74** *Male sex hormones:* androsterone, testosterone *Female sex hormones:* estrone, estradiol, progesterone **23.76** They are synthesized near their site of action. **23.78** linolenic acid **23.80** Leukotrienes are responsible for triggering asthmatic attacks, inflammation and allergic reactions. **23.82** By transferring its acetyl group, aspirin inhibits the enzyme that is responsible for the first step in the conversion of arachidonic acid to prostaglandins. **23.84** meat, fish, poultry, dairy products, nuts, seeds, processed foods **23.86** Both soaps

23.64

A cerebroside

and detergents consist of ionic heads and hydrophobic tails, and both clean by forming micelles around greasy dirt. The polar heads make the cluster soluble.   **23.88** Margarine contains more mono- and polyunsaturated fats but is also more likely to contain trans fats.   **23.90** (b) (c) (e) (f)

23.92

$$CH_2-O-\overset{\overset{\displaystyle O}{\|}}{C}-(CH_2)_{12}CH_3$$

$$CH-O-\overset{\overset{\displaystyle O}{\|}}{C}-(CH_2)_7CH=CHCH_2CH=CHCH_2CH_3$$

$$CH_2-O-\overset{\overset{\displaystyle O}{\|}}{C}-(CH_2)_{12}CH_3$$

or

$$CH_2-O-\overset{\overset{\displaystyle O}{\|}}{C}-(CH_2)_{12}CH_3$$

$$CH-O-\overset{\overset{\displaystyle O}{\|}}{C}-(CH_2)_{12}CH_3$$

$$CH_2-O-\overset{\overset{\displaystyle O}{\|}}{C}-(CH_2)_7CH=CHCH_2CH=CHCH_2CH_3$$

23.94 (a) beef fat (b) plant oil (c) lard   **23.96** It is saponifiable.   **23.98** sphingomyelins, cerebrosides, gangliosides   **23.100** multiple sclerosis   **23.102** (a) (d)   **23.104** 11.5 g

Chapter 24

24.1 Cholate has 4 polar groups on its hydrophilic side that allow it to interact with an aqueous environment; its hydrophobic side interacts with TAGs. Cholate and cholesterol can't change roles.   **24.2** Arterial plaque is made up of cholesterol and other lipid-containing materials. HDL removes cholesterol, whereas LDL delivers cholesterol to tissues.   **24.3** Dihydroxyacetone phosphate is isomerized to glyceraldehyde 3-phosphate, which enters glycolysis.   **24.4** Storage of excess fat is linked to increased risk of developing type II diabetes, stroke, heart attacks, and colon cancer.   **24.5** (a), (b) *Step 1*; a C=C double bond is introduced; FAD is the oxidizing agent. *Step 3*; an alcohol is oxidized to a ketone; NAD$^+$ is the oxidizing agent. (c) *Step 2*; water is added to a carbon-carbon double bond. (d) *Step 4*; HSCoA displaces acetyl-CoA, producing a chain-shortened acyl-SCoA fatty acid   **24.6** (a) 8 acetyl-CoA, 7 β oxidations (b) 12 acetyl-CoA, 11 β oxidations   **24.7** step 6, step 7, step 8   **24.8** It is the largest reservoir of blood in the body; it is the site of numerous metabolic processes; it is the site of storage of many biomolecules   **24.9** (d)   **24.10** (a) Acetyl-CoA provides the acetyl groups used in synthesis of ketone bodies, (b) 3 (c) The body uses ketone bodies as an energy source during starvation.   **24.11** 7 additional acetyl-CoA; 8 additional CO$_2$ **24.12** Oxygen is needed to reoxidize reduced coenzymes, formed in β oxidation, that enter the electron transport chain.   **24.13** (a) chylomicrons; because they have the greatest ratio of lipid to protein (b) chylomicrons (c) HDL (d) LDL (e) HDL (f) VLDL; used for storage or energy production (g) LDL   **24.14** high blood glucose → high insulin/low glucagon → fatty acid and triacylglycerol synthesis: low blood glucose → low insulin/high glucagon → triacylglycerol hydrolysis; fatty acid oxidation   **24.15** Formation of a fatty acyl-CoA is coupled with conversion of ATP to AMP and pyrophosphate. This energy expenditure is recaptured in β oxidation.   **24.16** Less acetyl-CoA can be catabolized in the citric acid cycle, and acetyl-CoA is diverted to ketogenesis.   **24.17** Catabolism of fat provides more energy per gram than does catabolism of glycogen, and thus fats are a more efficient way to store energy.   **24.18** Ketone bodies can be metabolized to form acetyl-CoA, which provides energy.   **24.19** No. Although both these processes add or remove two carbon units, one is not the reverse of the other. The two processes involve different enzymes, coenzymes and

activation steps.   **24.20** They slow the rate of movement of food through the stomach.   **24.22** Bile emulsifies lipid droplets.   **24.24** products are mono- and diacylglycerols, stearic acid, oleic acid, linoleic acid, glycerol   **24.26** Acylglycerols, fatty acids, and protein are combined to form *chylomicrons*, which are lipoproteins used to transport lipids from the diet into the bloodstream.   **24.28** by serum albumins   **24.30** Steps 6–10 of the glycolysis pathway.   **24.32** 9 molecules ATP; 21 molecules ATP   **24.34** An adipocyte is a cell, almost entirely filled with fat globules, in which triacylglycerols are stored and mobilized.   **24.36** heart, liver, muscle cells   **24.38** A fatty acid is converted to its fatty acyl-CoA in order to activate it for catabolism.   **24.40** The carbon β to the thioester group (two carbons away from the thioester group) is oxidized in the process.   **24.42** FAD, NAD$^+$ **24.44** 17 ATP   **24.46** *Least* glucose, sucrose, capric acid, myristic acid *Most*   **24.48**

(a)
$$CH_3CH_2CH_2CH=CHC\overset{\overset{\displaystyle O}{\|}}{}SCoA$$

(b)
$$CH_3CH_2CH_2CH\overset{\overset{\displaystyle OH}{|}}{}CH_2C\overset{\overset{\displaystyle O}{\|}}{}SCoA$$

(c)
$$CH_3CH_2CH_2C\overset{\overset{\displaystyle O}{\|}}{}CH_2C\overset{\overset{\displaystyle O}{\|}}{}SCoA$$

(d)
$$CH_3CH_2CH_2C\overset{\overset{\displaystyle O}{\|}}{}SCoA \ + \ CH_3C\overset{\overset{\displaystyle O}{\|}}{}SCoA$$

24.50 (a) 7 acetyl-CoA, 6 cycles (b) 4 acetyl-CoA, 3 cycles   **24.52** lipogenesis   **24.54** acetyl-CoA   **24.56** 8 rounds   **24.58** Fatty acid synthesis takes place in the cytosol; fatty acid degradation takes place in mitochondria.   **24.60** Total cholesterol: 200 mg/dL or lower. LDL: 130 mg/dL or lower. HDL: 40 mg/dL or higher.   **24.62** LDL carries cholesterol from the liver to tissues; HDL carries cholesterol from tissues to the liver, where it is converted to bile and excreted.   **24.64** type II diabetes, colon cancer, heart attacks, stroke   **24.66** calorie-dense food, lack of exercise   **24.68** The liver synthesizes many important biomolecules, it catabolizes glucose, fatty acids and amino acids, it stores many substances, and it inactivates toxic substances.   **24.70** The excess acetyl-CoA from catabolism of carbohydrates is stored as fat. The body can't resynthesize carbohydrate from acetyl-CoA.   **24.72** The alcohol intermediate is chiral.   **24.74** Ketosis is a condition in which ketone bodies accumulate in the blood faster than they can be metabolized. Since two of the ketone bodies are carboxylic acids, they lower the pH of the blood, producing the condition known as ketoacidosis. Symptoms of ketoacidosis include dehydration, labored breathing, and depression; prolonged ketoacidosis may lead to coma and death.   **24.76** Ketones have little effect on pH, but the two other ketone bodies are acidic, and they lower the pH of urine.   **24.78** The energy yield from fats is almost twice the energy yield from carbohydrates. A carbohydrate has fewer carbons than a fat of similar molar mass, and 1/3 of the carbons of a carbohydrate are lost as CO$_2$.   **24.80** The body synthesizes cholesterol when no cholesterol is present in the diet. The body needs cholesterol for membrane function and for synthesis of steroid hormones.   **24.82** H$_2$C=CHC(CH$_3$)=CH$_2$. Since cholesterol has 27 carbons, at least 6 2-methyl-1,3-butadiene molecules are needed.

Chapter 25

25.1

2'-Deoxythymidine

25.2 D-Ribose ($C_5H_{10}O_5$) has one more oxygen atom than 2-deoxy-D-ribose ($C_5H_{10}O_4$), and thus can form more hydrogen bonds.

25.3

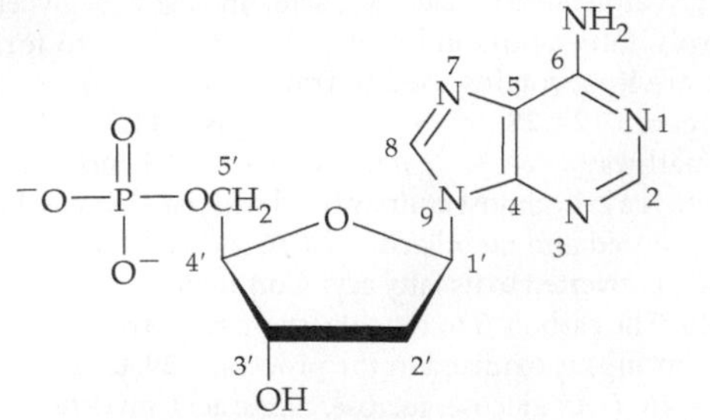

2'-Deoxyadenosine 5'-monophosphate

25.4

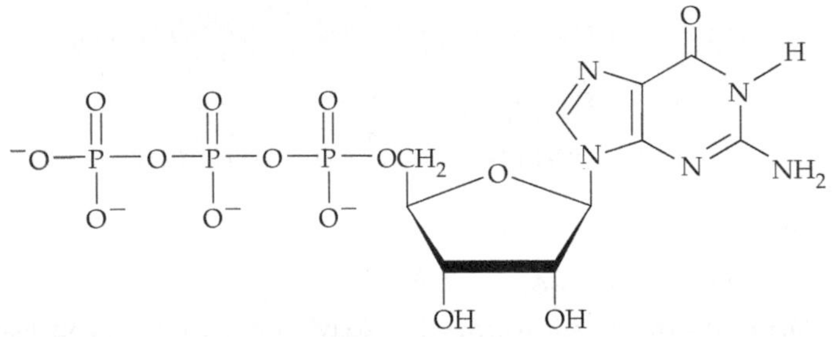

Guanosine 5'-triphosphate (GTP)

25.5 dUMP–2'-Deoxyuridine 5'-monophosphate; UMP–Uridine 5'-monophosphate; CDP–Cytidine 5'-diphosphate; AMP–Adenosine 5'-monophosphate; ATP–Adenosine 5'-triphosphate **25.6** guanine–adenine–uracil–cytosine–adenine. The pentanucleotide comes from RNA because uracil is present.

25.7

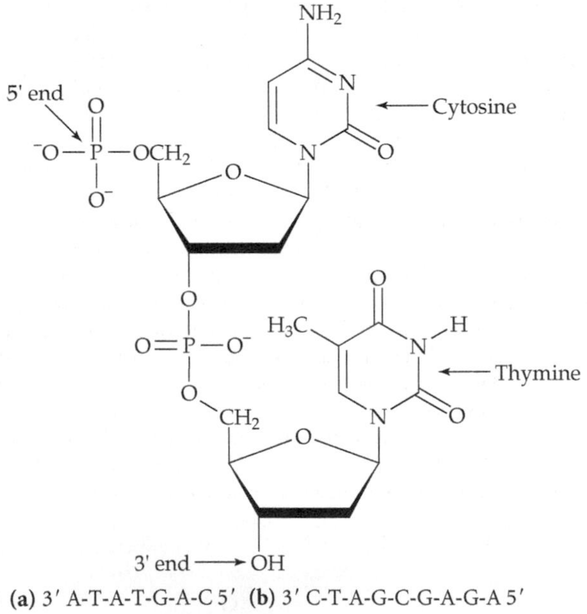

25.8 (a) 3' A-T-A-T-G-A-C 5' **(b)** 3' C-T-A-G-C-G-A-G-A 5'

25.9

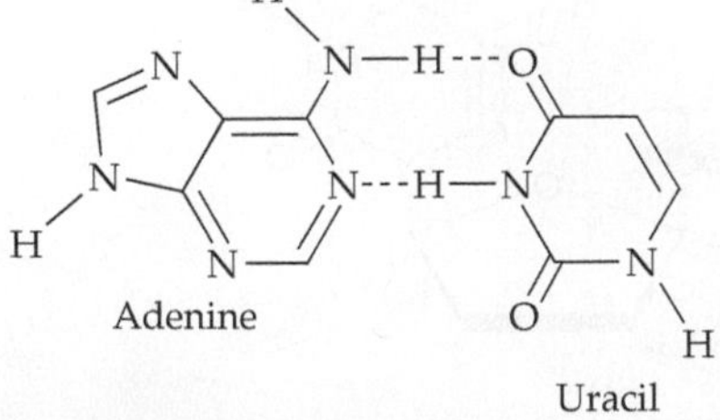

25.10 negatively charged (because of the phosphate groups) **25.11 (a)** A longer strand has more hydrogen bonds, **(b)** A chain with a higher percent of G/C pairs has a higher melting point, because it has more hydrogen bonds.

25.12 Okazaki fragments are segments of DNA synthesized by using the lagging strand as a template. The fragments are later joined by a DNA ligase enzyme. **25.13** In spliceosomes, introns from hnRNA are removed to yield mRNA; in ribosomes, proteins are synthesized, using mRNA as a template. Each process uses a different RNA enzyme. **25.14 (a)** 3' G-U-A-C-G-A-G-A-U-G-U-C 5' **(b)** 5' A-U-A-A-U-C-G-C-U-G-G-C 3' **25.15 (a)** GUU GUC GUA GUG **(b)** UUU UUC **(c)** AAU AAC **(d)** GGU GGC GGA GGG **(e)** AUG **25.16** The sequence guanine-adenine-guanine codes for glutamate. **25.17 (a)** Ile **(b)** Ala **(c)** Arg **(d)** Lys **25.18** Six mRNA triplets can code for Leu: UUA, UUG, CUU, CUC, CUA, CUG if no codons are duplicated. Among the possible combinations:

  5'UUAUUGCUU 3'   5' UUAUUGCUC 3'   5' UUAUUGCUA 3'
  5'UUAUUGCUG 3'   5' UUACUUCUC 3'   5' UUACUUCUA 3'

25.19 Viruses consist of a strand of nucleic acid wrapped in a protein coat; viruses can't replicate or manufacture protein independent of a host cell.

25.20–25.21

mRNA
sequence: 5'   CUC——AUU——CCA——UGC——GAC——GUA 3'
Amino-acid
sequence: L e u——I l e——P r o——C y s——A s p——V a l
tRNA
anticodons: 3' GAG   UAA   GGU   ACG   CUG   CAU 5'

25.22 The influenza virus mutates rapidly.

25.23

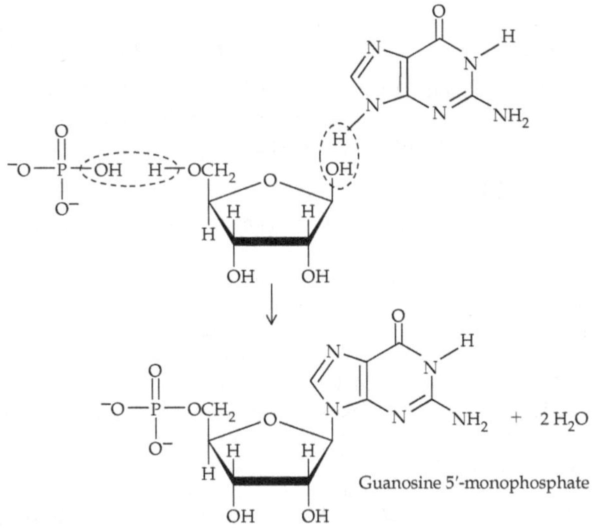

Guanosine 5'-monophosphate

25.24

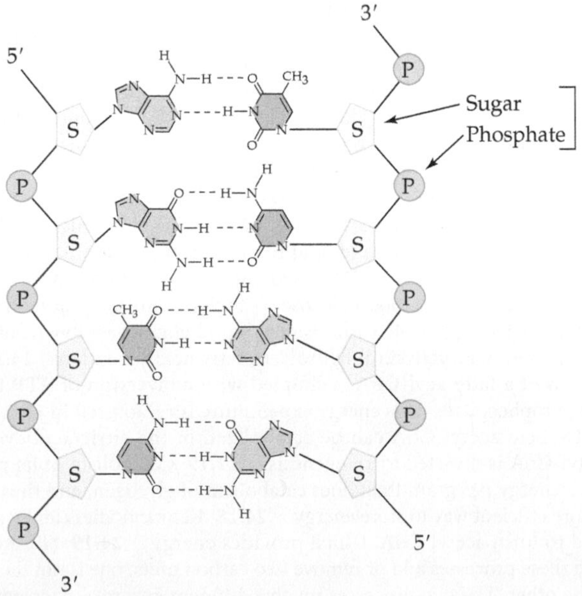

Sequence of the left chain: 5' A-G-T-C 3'
Sequence of the right chain: 5' G-A-C-T 3'

25.25

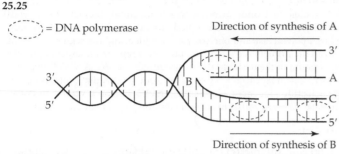

25.26 The sugar-phosphate backbone is found on the outside of the DNA double helix. Histones are positively charged; they contain groups such as Lys, Arg and His.

25.27

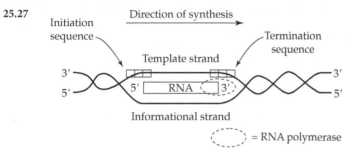

25.28 More than one codon can code for each amino acid. Only one possibility is shown.

(a) 5′ | C | A | A | C | A | C | C | C | C | G | G | G | 3′ mRNA

(b) 3′ | G | T | T | G | T | G | G | G | G | C | C | C | 5′ DNA template strand

(c) 5′ | C | A | A | C | A | C | C | C | C | G | G | G | 3′ DNA informational strand

(d) 64 possible sequences

25.30 2-deoxyribose (DNA); ribose (RNA). 2-Deoxyribose is missing an —OH group at C2.   **25.32** The purine bases (two fused heterocyclic rings) are adenine and guanine. The pyrimidine bases (one heterocyclic ring) are cytosine, thymine (in DNA) and uracil (in RNA).   **25.34** DNA is largest; tRNA is smallest.   **25.36** *Similarities:* All are polymerizations; all use a nucleic acid as a template; all use hydrogen bonding to bring the subunits into position. *Differences:* In replication, DNA makes a copy of itself. In transcription, DNA is used as a template for the synthesis of mRNA. In translation, mRNA is used as a template for the synthesis of proteins. Replication and transcription take place in the nucleus of cells, and translation takes place in ribosomes.   **25.38** DNA, protein   **25.40** 46 chromosomes (23 pairs)   **25.42** They always occur in pairs: they always H-bond with each other.   **25.44** 22% G, 22% C, 28% A, 28% T. (%G = %C; %A = %T: %T + %A + %C + %G = 100%)   **25.46** 5′ to 3′
25.48

25.50

25.52 Introns may be parts of other genes, they may regulate genes, they may stabilize the genome. Exons carry the code for a gene.   **25.54** to increase the speed of replication of DNA   **25.56** A codon is a sequence of three nucleotides on mRNA that codes for a specific amino acid in protein synthesis.   **25.58** A tRNA molecule is cloverleaf-shaped. The tRNA anticodon triplet is on one "leaf," and an amino acid bonds covalently to the 3′ end.   **25.60** Ser, Arg, and Leu each have six codons; Ala, Gly, Pro, Val, and Thr each have four. Met and Trp each have only one codon. These numbers are somewhat correlated with the relative abundance of these amino acids in proteins.   **25.62 (a)** proline **(b)** alanine **(c)** leucine
25.64 Codons are written (5′ → 3′), and anticodons are written (3′ → 5′)

(a)	Val	Codons:	GUU	GUC	GUA	GUG	
		Anticodons:	CAA	CAG	CAU	CAC	
(b)	Arg	Codons:	CGU	CGG	CGA	CGC	
		Anticodons:	GCA	GCC	GCU	GCG	
(c)	Ser	Codons:	UCU	UCC	UCA	UCG	AGU AGC
		Anticodons:	AGA	AGG	AGU	AGC	UCA UCG

25.66 (5′ → 3′) UACCCU   **25.68** Val–Ser–Thr–Leu
25.70 Informational strand (5′ → 3′): TAT–GGT–GGT–TTT–ATG–TAA
Template strand (3′ → 5′):   ATA–CCA–CCA–AAA–TAC–ATT
Other sequences are possible   **25.72** Ribozyme activity is common among the simplest and most primitive life forms, such as viroids, leading scientists to speculate that ribozyme catalysis might have preceded enzyme catalysis.
25.74 To be effective, a drug must be powerful enough to act on viruses within cells without damaging the cells and their genetic material.
25.76 Influenza A viruses are described by a code that describes the hemagglutinins (H) and the neuraminidases (N) in the virus. The H1N1 virus was responsible for the 1918 influenza pandemic, and the H5N1 virus is present in avian flu. Since these viruses can undergo antigenic shift in host animals, there is concern when infected birds and animals harbor influenza viruses.   **25.78** 249 bases   **25.80** Met is removed after synthesis is complete.

Chapter 26

26.1 "the fat red rat ate the bad rat"   **26.2** As a result of the SNP, the base sequence codes for Trp, instead of Cys. This change would probably affect the functioning of the protein.   **26.3** The sample might not be random; the donors might not be anonymous; issues of informed consent might arise   **26.4** 3′ –T–C–T–A–G–//–A– 5′   **26.5** 3′ –C–T–T–A–A–//–G– 5′
26.6 (a) sticky **(b) (c)** not sticky   **26.7** Taq polymerase can withstand high temperatures and doesn't need to be replaced for each PCR cycle.

26.8 4 people   **26.9** (a) comparative genomics (b) genetic engineering (c) pharmacogenetics (d) bioinformatics   **26.10** (1) A genetic map, which shows the location of markers one million nucleotides apart, is created. (2) Next comes a physical map, which refines the distance between markers to 100,000 base pairs. (3) The chromosome is cleaved into large segments of overlapping clones. (4) The clones are fragmented into 500 base pieces, which are sequenced.   **26.11** The variations are only a small part of the genome; the rest is identical among humans. A diverse group of individuals contributed DNA to the project.   **26.12** *telomeres* (protect the chromosome from damage, involved with aging), *centromeres* (involved with cell division), *promoter sequences* (determine which genes will be replicated), *introns* (function unknown)   **26.13** Similarities: both are variations in base sequences. Differences: A mutation is an error that is transferred during replication and affects only a few people; a polymorphism is a variation in sequence that is common within a population.   **26.14** Recombinant DNA contains two or more DNA segments that do not occur together in nature. The DNA that codes for a specific human protein can be incorporated into a bacterial plasmid using recombinant DNA technology. The plasmid is then reinserted into a bacterial cell, where its protein-synthesizing machinery makes the desired protein.   **26.15** Major benefits of genomics: creation of disease-resistant and nutrient-rich crops, gene therapy, genetic screening. Major negative outcomes: misuse of an individual's genetic information, prediction of a genetic disease for which there is no cure.   **26.16** Celera broke the genome into many unidentified fragments. The fragments were multiplied and cut into 500 base pieces, which were sequenced. A supercomputer was used to determine the order of the bases. This approach allowed for faster sequencing of the human genome.   **26.18** 50%   **26.20** (a) Approx. 200 genes are shared between bacteria and humans, (b) A single gene may produce several proteins.   **26.22** The clones used in DNA mapping are identical copies of DNA segments from a single individual. In mapping, it is essential to have a sample large enough for experimental manipulation.   **26.24** The youngest cells have long telomeres, and the oldest cells have short telomeres.   **26.26** It is the constriction that determines the shape of a chromosome during cell division.   **26.28** A silent mutation is a single base change that specifies the same amino acid.   **26.30** random and spontaneous events, exposure to a mutagen   **26.32** A SNP can result in the change in identity of an amino acid inserted into a protein a particular location in a polypeptide chain. The effect of a SNP depends on the function of the protein and the nature of the SNP.   **26.34** A physician could predict the age at which inherited diseases might become active, their severity, and the response to various types of treatment.   **26.36** a change in the type of amino acid side chain   **26.38** (a) Both codons code for Ala (b) Substitution of lle for Thr is more serious because the amino acids have very different side chains.   **26.40** Proteins can be produced in large quantities.   **26.42** Sticky ends are unpaired bases at the end of a DNA fragment. Recombinant DNA is formed when the sticky ends of the DNA of interest and of the DNA of the plasmid have complementary base pairs and can be joined by a DNA ligase.   **26.44** (a) sticky (b) not sticky   **26.46** Pharmacogenomics is the study of the genetic basis of responses to drug treatment. Pharmacogenomics helps doctors prescribe the most effective medicine for a patient, based on the patient's genetic makeup.   **26.48** corn, soybeans   **26.50** a DNA chip   **26.52** A monogenic disease is caused by the variation in just one gene.   **26.54** ATACTGA   **26.56** A restriction endonuclease is an enzyme that recognizes a specific DNA sequence and cleaves the DNA between two particular nucleotides in that sequence.   **26.58** If the DNA from an individual or a single ethnic group had been used, it would have been impossible to map traits due to genetic variability.   **26.60** (1)A solution of DNA that is to be copied is heated so that the DNA separates into two strands. (2) Two oligonucleotide primers, which are complementary to the ends of the segment of DNA to be copied, are attached to the DNA strands. (3) DNA polymerase and nucleotides are added, and the segment of DNA between the primers is copied. The process is repeated many times until a large amount of the desired DNA is produced.   **26.62** A VNTR (variable number tandem repeat) is a region of noncoding DNA that contains repeating nucleotide sequences. Comparing the VNTRs on several genes of an individual allows scientists to create a DNA fingerprint of that, person.

Chapter 27

27.1 (a) false (b) true (c) true (d) false (e) false   **27.2** oxidoreductase; lyase

27.3

$$\underset{\text{4-Hydroxy-}\alpha\text{-ketopentanoate}}{CH_3\overset{OH}{\underset{|}{C}}HCH_2\overset{O}{\underset{\|}{C}}COO^-}$$

27.4

$$\underset{\text{4-Hydroxy-}\alpha\text{-ketopentanoate}}{CH_3\overset{OH}{\underset{|}{C}}HCH_2\overset{O}{\underset{\|}{C}}COO^-}$$

27.5 by the loss of two hydrogens to either NAD^+ or $NADP^+$
27.6 valine, leucine, isoleucine

$$\underset{\text{Valine}}{CH_3\overset{H_3C}{\underset{|}{C}}H\overset{NH_3^+}{\underset{|}{C}}HCOO^-} + \underset{\alpha\text{-Ketoglutarate}}{{}^-OOCCH_2CH_2\overset{O}{\underset{\|}{C}}COO^-}$$

$$\downarrow$$

$$\underset{\alpha\text{-Keto-3-methylbutanoate}}{CH_3\overset{H_3C}{\underset{|}{C}}H\overset{O}{\underset{\|}{C}}COO^-} + \underset{\text{Glutamate}}{{}^-OOCCH_2CH_2\overset{NH_3^+}{\underset{|}{C}}HCOO^-}$$

27.7 (a) (b) (c)

(d) (e)

27.8 *See below for answer.*   **27.9** (a) 5 (b) 1 (c) 3
27.10 They are essential only under certain conditions.

27.8

(1) oxidative deamination; (2) hydrolysis; (3) oxidation

27.11 3-Phosphoglycerate → 3-Phosphohydroxypyruvate (oxidation)
3-Phosphohydroxypyruvate → 3-Phosphoserine (transamination)
3-Phosphoserine → Serine (hydrolysis)

27.12

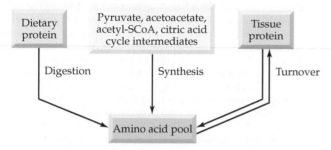

27.13 (1) Catabolism of an amino acid begins with a transamination reaction that removes the amino nitrogen. (2) The resulting α-keto acid, which contains the carbon atoms, is converted to a common metabolic intermediate. (3) The amino group of glutamate (from the amino acid) is removed by oxidative deamination. (4) The amino nitrogen is transformed to urea in the urea cycle and is excreted. **27.14** glutamate dehydrogenase; alanine aminotransferase. Alanine is the product. **27.15** The carbon atoms from ketogenic amino acids can be converted to ketone bodies or to acetyl-SCoA. The carbon atoms from glucogenic amino acids can be converted to compounds that can enter gluconeogenesis and can form glucose, which can enter glycolysis and also yield acetyl-CoA. **27.16** All amino acids are necessary for protein synthesis. The body can synthesize only some of them; the others must be provided by food and are thus essential in the diet. **27.17** to quickly remove ammonia from the body; buildup of urea and shortage of ornithine **27.18** throughout the body **27.20** pyruvate, 3-phosphoglycerate **27.22** In transamination, a keto group of an α-keto acid and an amino group of an amino acid change places.

27.24

(a)

$$^-O-\overset{\overset{\displaystyle O}{\|}}{C}-CH_2CH_2-\overset{\overset{\displaystyle O}{\|}}{C}-COO^-$$

(b)

$$CH_3-\overset{\overset{\displaystyle O}{\|}}{C}-COO^-$$

27.26 An —NH_3^+ group of an amino acid is replaced by a carbonyl group, and ammonium ion is eliminated. Oxidative deamination is an oxidation, rather than a transfer.

27.28

(a)

$$\overset{\overset{\displaystyle CH_3}{|}}{CH_3CHCH_2}-\overset{\overset{\displaystyle O}{\|}}{C}-COO^-$$

(b)

$$-CH_2-\overset{\overset{\displaystyle O}{\|}}{C}-COO^-$$

27.30 A ketogenic amino acid is catabolized to acetoacetyl-CoA or acetyl-CoA. Examples: leucine, isoleucine, lysine **27.32** Ammonia is toxic. **27.34** One nitrogen comes from carbamoyl phosphate, which is synthesized from ammonium ion by oxidative deamination. The other nitrogen comes from aspartate **27.36** Nonessential amino acids are synthesized in humans in 1–3 steps. Essential amino acids are synthesized in microorganisms in 7–10 steps. **27.38** legumes, meat **27.40** phenylketonuria; mental retardation; restriction of phenylalanine in the diet **27.42 (b) (c) (d)** **27.44** isoleucine + pyruvate → α-keto-3-methylpentanoate + alanine **27.46** yes. Some amino acids yield two kinds of products—those that can enter the citric acid cycle and those that are intermediates of fatty acid metabolism. **27.48** Tissue is dynamic because its components are constantly being broken down and reformed **27.50 (b) → (e) → (d) → (f) → (a) → (c).** **27.52** (1) The amino group is removed; (2) Nitrogen is either used in synthesis of new nitrogen—containing compounds or excreted as urea; (3) The remaining carbon atoms are converted into compounds that can enter the citric acid cycle. **27.54** An excess of one amino acid might overwhelm a transport system that other amino acids use, resulting in a deficiency of those amino acids. **27.56** Oxidized allopurinol inhibits the enzyme that converts xanthine to uric acid. The more soluble intermediates are excreted. The nitrogen at position 7 of hypoxanthine is at position 8 in allopurinol, where it blocks oxidation of xanthine. **27.58** tryptophan; emotional and behavioral problems

Chapter 28

28.1 Both compounds reflect homeostasis. The glucose level is regulated by an endocrine hormone. **28.2 (b)** **28.3** The molecules resemble the heterocyclic part of cAMP, and they might act as inhibitors to the enzyme that inactivates cAMP. **28.4** Glu-His-Pro **28.5** The hydrophobic part of the structure is larger than the polar, hydrophilic part. **28.6** Testosterone has a —CH_3 group between the first two rings; nandrolone doesn't. Otherwise, their structures are identical. **28.7** Brassinolide has a core structure that resembles a steroid framework. **28.8 (a)** 3 **(b)** 1 **(c)** 2 **28.9** Similarities: both structures have aromatic rings, secondary amine groups, alcohol groups. Differences: propranolol has an ether group and a naphthalene ring system; epinephrine has two phenol hydroxyl groups; the compounds have different side-chain carbon skeletons. **28.10 (a)** Malathion: it's the least toxic, **(b)** Parathion is most toxic (smallest LD_{50}). **28.11 (a)** prolongs the effect of serotonin **(b)** blocks the response at the receptor **28.12** phenol hydroxyl group, ether, carbon–carbon double bond, aromatic ring. THC is hydrophobic and is likely to accumulate in fatty tissue. **28.13 (a)** antihistamine **(b)** antidepressant **28.14 (a)** polypeptide hormone (produced in the anterior pituitary gland) **(b)** steroid hormone (produced in ovaries) **(c)** Progesterone-producing cells have LH receptors, **(d)** Progesterone is lipid-soluble and can enter cells. **28.15** Adenylate cyclase can produce a great many molecules of cAMP, which phosphorylate kinase enzymes. These enzymes can cause the breakdown of glycogen to yield glucose. **28.16 (a)** insulin (polypeptide hormone) **(b)** pancreas **(c)** in the bloodstream **(d)** Insulin doesn't enter cells directly because it can't pass through cell membranes. Instead, it binds with a cell surface receptor. **28.17** binding to receptors; activating second messengers **28.18** Enzymatic inactivation; reuptake by presynaptic neuron. **28.19** These substances increase dopamine levels in the brain. The brain responds by decreasing the number and sensitivity of dopamine receptors. Thus more of the substance is needed to elevate dopamine levels, leading to addiction. **28.20** A *chemical messenger* is a molecule that travels from one part of the body to another location, where it delivers a signal or acts to control metabolism. The *target tissue* is the cell or group of cells whose activity is regulated by the messenger. A *hormone receptor* is the molecule with which the chemical messenger interacts if it is a hormone. **28.22** A vitamin is usually an enzyme cofactor, whereas a hormone regulates enzyme activity. **28.24** Neither a hormone nor its receptor is changed as a result of binding to each other. The binding forces between hormone and receptor are noncovalent. **28.26** The endocrine system manufactures and secretes hormones. **28.28** polypeptide hormones, steroid hormones, amino acid derivatives **28.30** Enzymes are proteins; hormones may be polypeptides, proteins, steroids or amino acid derivatives. **28.32** Polypeptide hormones travel through the bloodstream and bind to cell receptors, which are on the outside of a cell. The receptors cause production within cells of "second messengers" that activate enzymes. **28.34** the adrenal medulla **28.36** through the bloodstream **28.38** In order of involvement; the hormone receptor, G protein, and adenylate cyclase. **28.40** It initiates reactions that release glucose from storage. Termination occurs when phosphodiesterase converts cAMP to AMP. **28.42** anaphylaxis **28.44** Insulin contains 51 amino acids, is released from the pancreas, and acts at cells, causing them to take up glucose. **28.46** Mineralocorticoids (aldosterone), glucocorticoids (cortisone), and sex hormones (testosterone, estrone) all have the four-fused-ring skeleton. **28.48** androsterone, testosterone **28.50** Androgens increase muscle mass and strength. **28.52** epinephrine, norepinephrine, dopamine **28.54 (a)** amino acid derivative **(b)** polypeptide hormone **(c)** steroid hormone **28.56** A synapse is the gap between two nerve cells that neurotransmitters cross to transmit their message. **28.58** nerve cell, muscle cell, endocrine cell **28.60** A nerve impulse arrives at the presynaptic end of a neuron. The nerve impulse stimulates the movement of a vesicle, containing neurotransmitter molecules, to the cell membrane. The vesicle fuses with the cell membrane and releases the neurotransmitter, which crosses the synaptic cleft to a receptor site on the postsynaptic end of a second neuron. After reception, the cell transmits an electrical signal down its axon and passes on the impulse. Enzymes then deactivate the neurotransmitter so that the neuron can receive the next impulse. Alternatively, the neurotransmitter may be returned to the presynaptic neuron. **28.62** (1) Neurotransmitter molecules are released from a presynaptic neuron. (2) Neurotransmitter molecules bind to receptors on the target cell. (3) The neurotransmitter is deactivated. **28.64** They are secreted in the central nervous system and have receptors in brain tissue. **28.66** Agonists prolong the response of a receptor. Antagonists block the response of a receptor. **28.68** Antihistamines such as doxylamine counteract allergic responses caused by histamine by blocking histamine receptors in mucous membranes. Antihistamines such as cimetidine block receptors for histamine that stimulate production of stomach acid. **28.70** *Tricyclic antidepressant:* Elavil™ *MAO inhibitor:* Nardil™ *SSRI:* Prozac™ **28.72** Cocaine increases dopamine levels by blocking reuptake. **28.74** Tetrahydrocannabinol (THC) increases dopamine levels in the same brain areas where dopamine levels increase after administration of heroin and cocaine. **28.76** antagonist **28.78** Endorphins are polypeptides with morphine-like activity. They are produced by the pituitary gland and have receptors in the brain. **28.80** They interact with the same receptors as opioids. **28.82** An ethnobotanist discovers what indigenous people have learned about the healing power of plants. **28.84** Scientists who know about the exact size and shape of enzymes and receptors can design drugs that interact with the active sites of these biomolecules. **28.86** Homeostasis is the maintenance of a constant internal environment. **28.88** Plants don't have endocrine systems or a circulatory fluid like blood. **28.90** epinephrine **28.92** Both have large nonpolar regions and can cross cell membranes to activate the synthesis of enzymes. **28.94** (1) Once the message has been delivered, cyclic AMP is no longer needed. (2) The precursor to cyclic AMP must be ready for the next signal. **28.96** The response to a hormonal signal is prolonged. **28.98** Ethynyl estradiol and norethindrone differ only in the ring on the far left: the ring is a phenol in ethynyl estradiol and is an enone in norethindrone. Ethynyl estradiol and estradiol differ only in the five-membered ring: a —C≡CH group is present in ethynyl estradiol and absent in estradiol. Norethindrone is similar to progesterone in all but two respects: progesterone has a methyl group between the first two rings, and has an acetyl group in the five-membered ring, instead of the two groups of norethindrone. **28.100** substitution of —OH for —H (oxidoreductase); loss of CO_2 (lyase) **28.102** oxidation of —OH to a ketone

Chapter 29

29.1 In the cell: the charged form. Outside the cell: the uncharged form. The uncharged form enters the cell more readily. **29.2** (a) iii (b) ii (c) iv (d) v (e) i **29.3** (a) pH goes down; more acidic (b) $[O_2]$, $[CO_2]$, $[pH]$ **29.4** (a) respiratory acidosis (b) metabolic acidosis (c) metabolic alkalosis **29.5** (a) respiratory alkalosis (b) respiratory acidosis (c) metabolic acidosis **29.6** Heroin has two acetyl groups in the same location as the two hydroxyl groups of morphine. These nonpolar acetyl groups make heroin soluble in the membrane lipids of endothelial cells and more able to pass into these cells. **29.7** (a) intracellular fluid (b) extracellular fluid (c) blood plasma, interstitial fluid (d) K^+, Mg^{2+}, HPO_4^{2-} (e) Na^+, Cl^-

29.8

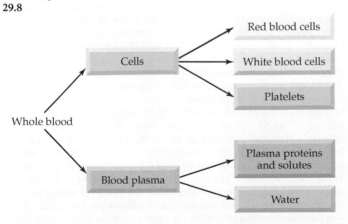

29.9 (a) O_2 (b) CO_2 (c) nutrients (d) waste products (e) hormones (f) white blood cells, platelets **29.10** swelling, redness, warmth, pain **29.11** Histamine is synthesized by the enzymatic decarboxylation of histidine. Histamine dilates capillaries, increasing blood flow that reddens and warms the skin. Blood-clotting factors and defensive proteins cause pain and swelling. **29.12** *Cell-mediated immune response:* under control of T cells; arises when abnormal cells, bacteria or viruses enter cells; invaders killed by T cells. *Antibody-mediated immune response:* under control of B cells, assisted by T cells; occurs when antigens enter cells; B cells divide to produce plasma cells, which form antibodies; an antibody-antigen complex inactivates the antigen. **29.13** Excess hydrogen ions are excreted by reaction with NH_3 or HPO_4^{2-}. H^+ ions also combine with bicarbonate, producing CO_2 that returns to the bloodstream. **29.14** intracellular fluid (64%), interstitial fluid (25%), plasma (8%) **29.16** Substances not soluble in blood, such as lipids, are transported by blood proteins. **29.18** Blood pressure in arterial capillaries is higher than interstitial fluid pressure, and blood pressure in venous capillaries is lower than interstitial fluid pressure. **29.20** the thoracic duct **29.22** An excess of antidiuretic hormone causes a decrease in the water content of the urine. This excess may be caused by pulmonary or central nervous system disorders. **29.24** 7% **29.26** *Red blood cells* transport blood gases. *White blood cells* protect the body from foreign substances. *Platelets* assist in blood clotting. **29.28** *Inside cells:* K^+, Mg^{2+}, HPO_4^{2-}; *Outside cells:* Na^+, Cl^- **29.30** Antihistamines block attachment of the neurotransmitter histamine to its receptors. **29.32** immunoglobulins **29.34** Killer T cells destroy the invader; helper T cells enhance defenses; memory T cells can produce new killer T cells if needed. **29.36** Memory cells "remember" an antigen and are capable of producing antibodies to it for a long time. **29.38** Vitamin K, Ca^{2+} **29.40** They are released as zymogens in order to avoid undesirable clotting in noninjured tissues. **29.42** +2 **29.44** If pO_2 is below 10 mm Hg, hemoglobin is unsaturated. If pO_2 is greater than 100 mm Hg, hemoglobin is completely saturated. Between these pressures, hemoglobin is partially saturated. **29.46** a dissolved gas, bound to hemoglobin, bicarbonate ion

29.48 $$CO_2 + H_2O \underset{}{\overset{\text{Carbonic anhydrase}}{\rightleftharpoons}} HCO_3^- + H^+$$

29.50 *Respiratory acidosis* occurs when there is buildup of CO_2 in the blood; *Metabolic acidosis* is due to increased production of metabolic acids. **29.52** *Respiratory alkalosis* occurs when there is a loss of CO_2; *Metabolic alkalosis* occurs when there is elevated plasma bicarbonate concentration.

29.54 $$H^+ + HCO_3^- \rightleftharpoons CO_2 + H_2O$$

$$H^+ + HPO_4^{2-} \rightleftharpoons H_2PO_4^-$$

29.56 A nursing mother's antibodies can be passed to her baby in breast milk. **29.58** Active transport is the movement of solutes from regions of low concentration to regions of high concentration, a process that requires energy. Osmosis is the movement of water through a semipermeable membrane from a dilute solution to a more concentrated solution, a process that requires no energy. **29.60** In the blood, CO_2 from metabolism reacts to form $HCO_3^- + H^+$. The H^+ is bound to hemoglobin, which releases O_2, and is carried to the lungs. There, the H^+ is released and O_2 is bound to hemoglobin. In the urine, CO_2 reacts to form HCO_3^- and H^+. The HCO_3^- returns to the bloodstream, and the H^+ is neutralized by reaction with HPO_4^{2-} or NH_3. Whenever excess HCO_3^- accumulates in blood or urine, it can react with H^+ to form $H_2O + CO_2$. **29.62** When blood CO_2 level drops, the following reaction occurs to restore CO_2 supply:

$$H^+ + HCO_3^- \longrightarrow H_2CO_3 \longrightarrow CO_2 + H_2O$$

This reaction uses up H^+ ions and leads to alkalosis. Breathing into a paper bag recaptures the expired CO_2 and restores the blood CO_2 level. **29.64** Substances can either be transported into a cell or be transported out of a cell, but not both. **29.66** The metabolic blood–brain barrier is a pathway in which a substance is converted in an epithelial cell to a metabolite that can't enter the brain. **29.68** Automated analysis can reproducibly detect changes in enzyme levels that might indicate organ damage.

Taken from *Fundamentals of General, Organic, and Biological Chemistry*, Seventh Edition by John McMurry, David S. Ballantine, Carl A. Hoeger, and Virginia E. Peterson

Credits

Text and Art Credits

Chapter 8: 219, Adapted from NASA, Goddard Institute for Space Studies, Surface Temperature Analysis (GIS Temp), http://data.giss.nasa.gov/gistemp.

Chapter 15: 465, Content was copied from MSDS of *Fisher Chemical* brand product, with permission.

Chapter 16: 489, Adapted from *Introduction to Ecological Biochemistry*, 2/e by J.B. Harborne. Academic Press, Inc., 1982.

Photo Credits

Chapter 1: 2, imagebroker.net/SuperStock; **5,** Richard Megna/Fundamental Photographs; **8,** PhilSigin/iStockphoto; **12(a) top,** Norov Dmitriy/iStockphoto; **12(b) top,** Ben Mills; **12(c) top,** Shutterstock; **12(a) middle,** Andraž Cerar/Shutterstock; **12(b) middle,** Leeuwtje/iStockphoto; **12(c) middle,** Ben Mills; **12(a) bottom,** Russell Lappa/Photo Researchers, Inc.; **12(b) bottom,** Texas Instruments Inc.; **14(a),** Richard Megna/Fundamental Photographs; **14(b),** Richard Megna/Fundamental Photographs; **14(c),** Richard Megna/Fundamental Photographs; **15,** eROMAZe/iStockphoto; **16,** Centers for Disease Control; **17,** Richard Megna/Fundamental Photographs; **19,** Pearson Education/McCracken Photographers; **21,** artkamalov/Shutterstock; **22,** Pearson Education/Eric Schrader; **24,** Pearson Education/Eric Schrader; **25,** tdbp/Alamy; **28,** Pearson Education/Michal Heron; **30,** Richard Megna/Fundamental Photographs; **31,** Stockbyte/Photolibrary; **33,** Claire VD/Shutterstock; **35,** Ivica Drusany/iStockphoto; **36,** BD Adams; **38,** Pearson Education/Eric Schrader.

Chapter 2: 44, Katie Dickinson/Shutterstock; **46,** AP Photo/Donna Carson; **48,** IBM Research, Almaden Research Center; **52,** Richard Megna/Fundamental Photographs; **54,** Richard Megna/Fundamental Photographs; **56,** NASA, ESA and H.E. Bond (STScI); **57,** Michael Neary Photography/iStockphoto; **66,** James Benet/iStockphoto.

Chapter 3: 72, Juan Jose Rodriguez Velandia/Shutterstock; **74,** Pearson Education/Eric Schrader; **76(a),** Richard Megna/Fundamental Photographs; **76(b),** Richard Megna/Fundamental Photographs; **77 top,** NASA; **77 bottom,** Richard Megna/Fundamental Photographs; **78 both,** Dimitris S. Argyropoulos; **83,** Daniella Zalcman/Shutterstock; **93,** Steve Gschmeissner/SPL/Photo Researchers, Inc.

Chapter 4: 98, David R. Frazier Photolibrary, Inc./Alamy; **100,** Martin Barraud/Alamy; **113,** Upsidedowndog/iStockphoto; **118,** Claudia Veja/Alamy; **125,** Yakobchuk Vasyl/Shutterstock.

Chapter 5: 132, Harald Sund/Brand X Pictures/Getty Images; **137,** David R. Frazier/Photo Researchers, Inc.; **138,** Richard Megna/Fundamental Photographs; **140,** Dr. P. Marazzi/Photo Researchers, Inc.; **143 left,** Richard Megna/Fundamental Photographs; **143 right,** Richard Megna/Fundamental Photographs; **147 top,** Luca DiCecco/Alamy; **147 bottom,** sciencephotos/Alamy.

Chapter 6: 158, AFP/Getty Images/Newscom; **160,** Richard Megna/Fundamental Photographs; **164 left,** Library of Congress; **164 right,** Science Photo Library/Photo Researchers, Inc.; **172,** Jane Norton/Shutterstock.

Chapter 7: 178, Ron Lewis/Icon SMI/Newscom; **181,** Richard Megna/Fundamental Photographs; **185,** discpicture/Shutterstock; **186,** GeoStock/Getty Images; **187 left,** Aaron Amat/Shutterstock; **187 right,** Samuel Perry/Shutterstock; **194,** AC/General Motors/Peter Arnold Images/Photolibrary; **195,** Reuters/Vladimir Davydov; **196,** Photolibrary/Indexopen; **204,** Myles Dumas/iStockphoto.

Chapter 8: 212, Tony Waltham/AGE Fotostock; **221,** NASA; **227,** Stephen Sweet/iStockphoto; **228,** Laura Stone/Shutterstock; **238,** Richard Megna/Fundamental Photographs; **239 top,** Alexei Zaycev/iStockphoto; **239 middle,** Harry Taylor/Dorling Kindersley; **239 bottom,** AGE Fotostock; **240 left,** Jens Mayer/Shutterstock; **240 right,** Jonny Kristoffersson/iStockphoto.

Chapter 9: 252, Phil Schermeister/NGS Images; **256,** Pearson Education/Tom Bochsler; **259,** Richard Megna/Fundamental Photographs; **263,** AP Photo/Gurinder Osan; **265(a),** Richard Megna/Fundamental Photographs; **265(b),** Richard Megna/Fundamental Photographs; **265(c),** Richard Megna/Fundamental Photographs; **273(a),** Richard Megna/Fundamental Photographs; **273(b),** Richard Megna/Fundamental Photographs; **276,** Jason Getz/Atlanta Journal-Constitution/MCT/Newscom; **281(a),** Sam Singer; **281(b),** Sam Singer; **281(c),** Sam Singer; **284 left,** Martin Dohrn/SPL/Photo Researchers, Inc.; **284 right,** Lev Dolgachov/Shutterstock.

Chapter 10: 290, Liga Lauzuma/iStockphoto; **292,** Pearson Education/Eric Schrader; **299,** Gastrolab/Photo Researchers, Inc.; **308(a),** Richard Megna/Fundamental Photographs; **308(b),** Pearson Education/Tom Bochsler; **308 left,** Pearson Education/Tom Bochsler; **312,** Robert Caplin/Newscom; **316,** Pearson Education/Eric Schrader; **318(a),** Richard Megna/Fundamental Photographs; **318(b),** Richard Megna/Fundamental Photographs; **320 top,** RMAX/iStockphoto; **320 bottom,** National Atmospheric Deposition Program.

Chapter 11: 328, P. Berndt/Custom Medical Stock Photo/Newscom; **338 top,** Simon Fraser/RVI/SPL/Photo Researchers, Inc.; **338 bottom,** Media Minds/Alamy; **343,** Stanford Dosimetry, LLC; **344,** Mark Kostich/iStockphoto; **345,** Tony Freeman/PhotoEdit; **347,** Stephen Uber/iStockphoto; **348,** Custom Medical Stock Photo.

Chapter 12: 356, Kevin Burke/Corbis; **359,** Xinhua News Agency/Newscom; **385,** Chloe Johnson/Alamy.

Chapter 13: 394, Larry Hales/iStockphoto; **409(a),** Richard Megna/Fundamental Photographs; **409(b),** Richard Megna/Fundamental Photographs; **417(a),** Pearson Education/Eric Schrader; **417(b),** Pearson Education/Michal Heron; **419,** kryczka/iStockphoto; **420,** Denis Tabler/Shutterstock.

Chapter 14: 432, davidf/iStockphoto; **446,** Pearson Education/Eric Schrader; **448,** norcon/iStockphoto; **449,** Pearson Education/Eric Schrader; **451,** Rod Planck/Photo Researchers, Inc.; **452,** Coleman515/iStockphoto; **453,** Prisma Archivo/Alamy.

Chapter 15: 460, Tim Messick/iStockphoto; **474,** Pearson Science/Eric Schader; **477 top,** Pearson Science/Eric Schader; **477 bottom,** Allan Rosenberg/Getty Images–Photodisc; **478,** aaM Photography, Ltd./iStockphoto.

Chapter 16: 484, Elke Dennis/Shutterstock; **489,** Paul Marek; **493,** Baloncici/iStockphoto; **495(a),** Richard Megna/Fundamental Photographs; **495(b),** Richard Megna/Fundamental Photographs; **499,** Dušan Zidar/iStockphoto.

Chapter 17: 514, Warren Photographic Ltd.; **520,** RedHelga/iStockphoto; **528,** Pearson Education/Eric Schrader; **529,** Andrei Rybachuk/Shutterstock; **532,** Drug Enforcement Administration; **538,** Pearson Education/Tom Bochsler; **539,** Pearson Education/Eric Schrader.

Chapter 18: 548, Fresh Food Images/Photolibrary; **558 top,** sunnyfrog/iStockphoto; **558 bottom,** sturmwarnung/iStockphoto; **562,** Centers for Disease Control; **564,** swalls/iStockphoto; **565,** USDA; **571 top,** Natalia Clarke/Shutterstock; **571 bottom,** Larry Ye/Shutterstock; **573(a),** Pearson Education/Kim M Gernert; **573(b),** Pearson Education/Kim M Gernert;

Credits

Taken from *General, Organic, and Biological Chemistry: Structures of Life*, Fifth Edition
by Karen C. Timberlake

Photo Credits

Chapter 1

p. 1 — *bottom, left:* anyaivanova / Shutterstock
p. 1 — *top, right:* whiteboxmedia limited / Alamy
p. 2 — *center, left:* Andreas Reh / iStock / Getty Images
p. 2 — *bottom, right:* Pearson Education
p. 3 — *bottom, center:* Stephen Coburn / 123RF
p. 3 — *top, right:* Eric Schrader / Pearson Education
p. 4 — J.R. Eyerman / Time & Life Pictures / Getty Images
p. 5 — *top, right:* Photos.com / Getty Images
p. 5 — *bottom, left:* Mark III Photonics / Shutterstock
p. 5 — *bottom, center:* webphotographeer / E+ / Getty Images
p. 6 — Eugene Bochkarev / Getty Images
p. 7 — Chris Schmidt / Getty Images
p. 8 — Steve Nagy / Design Pics Inc / Alamy
p. 11 — f9photos / Fotolia
p. 12 — spxChrome / E+ / Getty Images
p. 13 — Kevin Peschke / Alamy
p. 15 — Jason Stitt / Shutterstock
p. 16 — Heather Davies / Science Photo Library / Alamy
p. 19 — anyaivanova / Shutterstock
p. 20 — *top, left:* Pearson Education
p. 20 — *top, right:* Chris Schmidt / Getty Images
p. 20 — *bottom, right:* Jason Stitt / Shutterstock
p. 22 — *bottom, center:* Pressmaster / Shutterstock
p. 22 — *center:* ostill / Shutterstock

Chapter 2

p. 25 — AVAVA / Shutterstock
p. 26 — Rod Ferris / Shutterstock
p. 27 — *bottom, right:* Pearson Education
p. 27 — *top, center:* Scott Leigh / Getty Images
p. 28 — *center, left:* Richard Megna / Fundamental Photographs
p. 28 — *bottom, right:* Pearson Education
p. 28 — *top, left:* National Institute of Standards and Technology
p. 28 — *bottom, left:* Pearson Education
p. 29 — Cheryl Casey / Shutterstock
p. 31 — Nick M. Do / iStock / Getty Images
p. 33 — Radu Razvan / Shutterstock
p. 34 — emin kuliyev / Shutterstock
p. 37 — *bottom, left:* CHASSENET / BSIP SA / Alamy
p. 37 — *top, right:* legolex / Fotolia
p. 37 — *center, left:* Monkey Business Images / Shutterstock.com
p. 38 — Pearson Education
p. 39 — Pearson Education
p. 41 — *top, right:* Eric Schrader / Pearson Education
p. 41 — *center, right:* Syner-Comm / Alamy
p. 41 — *bottom, right:* Pearson Education
p. 42 — *top, left:* CMSP / Custom Medical Stock Photo
p. 42 — *center, left:* Pearson Education
p. 43 — *top, right:* Julie Woodhouse f / Alamy
p. 43 — *bottom, right:* Congressional Quarterly / Newscom
p. 43 — *center, right:* ExQuisine / Fotolia
p. 47 — WavebreakMediaMicro / Fotolia
p. 48 — *top, left:* Carlos Alvarez / Getty Images
p. 48 — *center, right:* Jakub Jirsák / Fotolia
p. 49 — Pearson Education
p. 50 — *bottom, left:* Pearson Education
p. 50 — *bottom, right:* Pearson Education

p. 51 — *top, left:* Professor Pietro M. Motta / Science Source
p. 51 — *center:* Professor Pietro M. Motta / Science Source
p. 51 — *top, right:* VOISIN / PHANIE / Science Source
p. 52 — *center, left:* Jpc-Prod / Fotolia
p. 52 — *bottom, center:* Dallas Events Inc / Shutterstock
p. 53 — *bottom, center:* AVAVA / Shutterstock
p. 53 — *bottom, right:* Editorial Image, LLC / Alamy
p. 54 — *center:* Pearson Education
p. 54 — *bottom, right:* emin kuliyev / Shutterstock
p. 55 — *center:* Eric Schrader / Pearson Education
p. 55 — *top, right:* Jakub Jirsák / Fotolia
p. 55 — *center, right:* Pearson Education
p. 57 — romans14 / Fotolia
p. 59 — Cristian Ciureanu / Alamy

Chapter 3

p. 63 — Network Photographer / Alamy
p. 64 — Norman Chan / Fotolia
p. 65 — *top, right:* Bomshtein / Shutterstock
p. 65 — *bottom, right:* Eric Schrader / Pearson Education
p. 65 — *center:* Pearson Education / Pearson Science
p. 65 — *center, left:* Pearson Science / Pearson Education
p. 66 — *bottom, left:* Richard Megna / Fundamental Photographs
p. 66 — *center, left:* David Murray and Jules Selmes / Dorling Kindersley
p. 66 — *bottom, right:* Eric Schrader / Pearson Education
p. 66 — *top, center:* Lagui / Shutterstock
p. 66 — *top, right:* Pearson Education / Pearson Science
p. 66 — *top, center:* Pearson Education / Pearson Science
p. 66 — *top, left:* rsooll / Fotolia
p. 67 — Charles Stirling (Diving) / Alamy
p. 68 — *center, left:* Justinb / Fotolia
p. 68 — *center, right:* Lisa Kyle Young / E+ / Getty Images
p. 68 — *top, left:* Siede Preis / Photodisc / Getty Images
p. 69 — *top, center:* Elena Elisseeva / Shutterstock
p. 69 — *center, right:* Rafa Irusta / www.shutterstock
p. 69 — *top, left:* Ray Roberts / Alamy
p. 69 — *bottom, right:* Westend61 GmbH / Alamy
p. 70 — Digital Vision / Alamy
p. 74 — JenniferPhotographyImaging / E+ / Getty Images
p. 75 — Science Photo Library / Alamy
p. 77 — NASA
p. 78 — Pearson Education / Pearson Science
p. 80 — Stockbyte / Getty Images
p. 81 — *bottom, right:* Alan Holden / Alamy
p. 81 — *center, right:* Celso Pupo / Fotolia
p. 83 — *center:* John A. Rizzo / Photodisc / Getty Images
p. 83 — *top:* Mark Downey / Getty Images
p. 84 — wsphotos / Getty Images
p. 85 — *bottom, right:* Nikkytok / Fotolia
p. 85 — *center, right:* Pearson Education / Pearson Science
p. 85 — *center, left:* Pearson Education / Pearson Science
p. 86 — *top, left:* John Scrivener / E+ / Getty Images
p. 86 — *center, left:* Pearson Education / Pearson Science
p. 87 — nikkytok / Fotolia

p. 88 — *center, left:* John A. Rizzo / Photodisc / Getty Images
p. 88 — *top, right:* Mark Downey / Getty Images
p. 91 — Network Photographer / Alamy
p. 92 — *bottom, center:* Richard Megna / Fundamental Photographs
p. 92 — *bottom, right:* Justinb / Fotolia
p. 93 — *top, right:* Celso Pupo / Fotolia
p. 93 — *center:* JenniferPhotographyImaging / E+ / Getty Images
p. 93 — *center:* Pearson Education / Pearson Science
p. 95 — *center:* Franz Pfluegl / Getty Images
p. 95 — *bottom, left:* Pearson Education / Pearson Science
p. 95 — *bottom, center:* Spencer Jones / Photodisc / Getty Images
p. 95 — *bottom, right:* teleginatania / Fotolia
p. 96 — Fuat Kose / E+ / Getty Images
p. 97 — Khoroshunova Olga / Shutterstock
p. 100 — *center, right:* Eric Schrader / Pearson Education
p. 100 — *top, left:* Impala / Fotolia
p. 100 — *center, left:* Shalom Ormsby / Photodisc / Getty Images
p. 101 — *top, left:* Aleksandr Volkov / Fotolia
p. 101 — Fuse / Getty Images

Chapter 4

p. 103 — Martin Harvey / Alamy
p. 105 — *top, right:* Pearson Science / Pearson Education
p. 105 — *center, right:* Pearson Science / Pearson Education
p. 105 — *center, right:* Pearson Science / Pearson Education
p. 105 — *bottom, right:* Pearson Science / Pearson Education
p. 105 — *bottom, right:* Pearson Science / Pearson Education
p. 106 — marcel / Fotolia
p. 108 — *top, left:* Pearson Science / Pearson Education
p. 108 — *center, left:* Pearson Science / Pearson Education
p. 108 — *bottom, left:* Pearson Science / Pearson Education
p. 109 — Pearson Science / Pearson Education
p. 110 — *top, left:* Pearson Science / Pearson Education
p. 110 — *center, left:* Polushkin Ivan / Shutterstock
p. 113 — *center, right:* IBM Research Division
p. 113 — *top, right:* Russ Lappa / Pearson Education
p. 114 — Pearson Science / Pearson Education
p. 116 — Eric Schrader / Fundamental Photographs
p. 118 — *center, right:* Atiketta Sangasaeng / Shutterstock
p. 118 — *center, left:* gabyjalbert / Getty Images
p. 119 — Pearson Science / Pearson Education
p. 120 — *center, right:* Nancy Ross / iStock / Getty Images
p. 120 — *bottom, left:* Tarasov / Shutterstock
p. 121 — ANATOL ADUTSKEVICH / Getty Images
p. 124 — Cindy Minear / Shutterstock
p. 125 — Thorsten Rust / Shutterstock
p. 128 — olly / Fotolia
p. 143 — Nigel Cattlin / Alamy
p. 144 — Pearson Science / Pearson Education
p. 148 — craftvision / E+ / Getty Images

Chapter 5

p. 153 — Monkey Business Images / Shutterstock
p. 156 — *center, left:* 4x6 / Getty Images
p. 156 — *bottom, left:* Josh Sher / Science Source
p. 158 — Stephen Uber / E+ / Getty Images

Chapter 17

p. 608	michaeljung / Fotolia
p. 613	*center, right:* Bjorn Heller / Getty Images
p. 613	*center, left:* Charles Brutlag / Getty Images
p. 615	Jupiterimages / Getty Images
p. 617	*center, right:* blickwinkel / Jagel / Alamy
p. 617	*top, right:* Tischenko Irina / Shutterstock
p. 618	*top, left:* John Pitcher / Getty Images
p. 618	*bottom, left:* kuleczka / Shutterstock
p. 619	Pearson Education / Pearson Science
p. 621	Pearson Education / Pearson Science
p. 622	Shelby Allison / Shutterstock
p. 625	L.G. Patterson / AP Images
p. 628	Audrey Snider-Bell / Shutterstock
p. 631	Santibhavank P / Shutterstock
p. 633	*top, right:* National Heart, Lung, and Blood Institut
p. 633	*bottom:* National Heart, Lung, and Blood Institute
p. 634	Martin / Custom Medical Stock Photo
p. 636	CoverSpot / Alamy
p. 640	*top, left:* michaeljung / Fotolia
p. 640	*bottom, right:* Matt Rourke / AP Images
p. 640	*bottom, left:* Robert Clare / Alamy
p. 641	Pearson Education / Pearson Science
p. 642	Pearson Education / Pearson Science
p. 644	*top, right:* Pearson Education / Pearson Science
p. 644	*bottom, left:* rangerx / Getty Images
p. 644	*bottom, right:* sampsyseeds / Getty Images
p. 645	*center, left:* Elena Schweitzer / Getty Images
p. 645	*top, right:* Lauree Feldman / Photolibrary / Getty Images
p. 646	Pearson Education / Pearson Science

Chapter 18

p. 649	Bart Coenders / E+ / Getty Images
p. 653	*left:* blickwinkel / Alamy
p. 653	*bottom, center:* Harvey Male / Imagestate Media Partners Limited - Impact Photos / Alamy
p. 658	Pearson Education / Pearson Science
p. 659	*bottom, right:* Brasil2 / Getty Images
p. 659	*bottom, right:* David Orcea / Shutterstock
p. 659	*top, right:* Pearson Education
p. 661	Pearson Education
p. 662	*center, left:* MikhailSh / Shutterstock
p. 662	*top, center:* Pearson Education
p. 663	De Meester Johan / Arterra Picture Library / Alamy
p. 666	Rosen / Custom Medical Stock Photo / Newscom
p. 667	Eric Schrader
p. 669	*center, right:* Eric Schrader
p. 669	*top, right:* Iain Cooper / Alamy
p. 675	Pearson Education
p. 678	David Hoffman Photo Library / Alamy
p. 679	*top, right:* Iain Cooper / Alamy
p. 679	*bottom, center:* Pearson Education
p. 681	*bottom, right:* DenisNata / Shutterstock
p. 681	*bottom, right:* Eric Schrader
p. 681	*bottom, left:* Pearson Education
p. 682	Eric Schrade / Pearson Education
p. 683	Tereshchenko Dmitry / Shutterstock
p. 686	*center, right:* Analia Valeria Urani / Shutterstock
p. 686	*top, left:* David Zaitz / Alamy
p. 686	*top, right:* Pearson Education
p. 686	*bottom, left:* worldswildlifewonders / Shutterstock
p. 687	Dustin Dennis / Shutterstock

Chapter 19

p. 688	Tyler Olson / Shutterstock
p. 689	DHuss / Getty Images
p. 693	Pearson Education
p. 700	OxytocinLg / APP Pharmaceuticals
p. 703	Brasil2 / E+ / Getty image

p. 705	Laurence Mouton / PhotoAlto sas / Alamy
p. 708	janol / Getty Images
p. 710	Janice Haney Carr / Center for Disease Control
p. 712	Pearson Education
p. 714	*bottom, left:* Susan Landau and William Jagust, UC Berkeley
p. 714	*top, left:* Tyler Olson / Shutterstock
p. 715	DHuss / Getty Images
p. 717	Pearson Education
p. 718	*top, left:* Miep Van Damm / Pearson Education
p. 718	*bottom, right:* Pearson Education

Chapter 20

p. 722	Diedra Laird / The Charlotte Observer / MCT / Newscom
p. 730	Natalia Pushchina / Shutterstock
p. 740	Pearson Education
p. 743	*center, right:* Mivr / Fotolia
p. 743	*bottom, right:* Oleg Zaslavsky / Shutterstock
p. 743	*center, left:* Pearson Education
p. 744	Diedra Laird / The Charlotte Observer / MCT / Newscom
p. 745	The Photo Works / Alamy
p. 748	*top, left:* Andy Crawford / Dorling Kindersley
p. 748	*bottom, left:* arska n / Fotolia
p. 748	*top, right:* Jane norton / E+ / Getty Images
p. 748	*bottom, right:* Pearson Education
p. 751	GlaxoSmithKline

Chapter 21

p. 753	Malcom Park / RGB Ventures / SuperStock / Alamy
p. 778	John R. Kreul / khunaspix / 123RF
p. 782	Tek Image / Science Source
p. 785	Alfred Pasieka / Science Source
p. 786	Malcom Park / RGB Ventures / SuperStock / Alamy
p. 787	Mark Thomas / Alamy
p. 789	*top, right:* John R. Kreul / khunaspix / 123RF
p. 789	*center, right:* Tek Image / Science Source
p. 795	Martin M. Rotker / Science Source

Chapter 22

p. 797	KatarzynaBialasiewicz / Getty Images
p. 799	viafilms / Getty Images
p. 802	*bottom:* Koji Aoki / Getty Images
p. 802	*bottom, left:* phasinphoto / Fotolia
p. 804	Benis Arapovic / 123RF
p. 817	Andy Clark AC / TZ / Reuters
p. 818	*top, left:* Oleksii Sergieiev / Fotolia
p. 818	*center, left:* Pearson Education
p. 822	Biophoto Associates / Science Source
p. 824	Alexey Fursov / Shutterstock
p. 829	KatarzynaBialasiewicz / Getty Images
p. 830	*center, right:* Oleksii Sergieiev / Fotolia
p. 830	*bottom, right:* Alexey Fursov / Shutterstock
p. 830	*top, left:* viafilms / Getty Images
p. 832	Karen Timberlake

Chapter 23

p. 836	*bottom, left:* Javier Larrea / AGE Fotostock
p. 836	*top, right:* juanrvelasco / Fotolia
p. 838	viafilms / Getty Images
p. 839	Africa Studio / Fotolia
p. 842	yurakp / Fotolia
p. 847	Allik Camazine / Alamy
p. 849	Jill Lang / Shutterstock
p. 855	Lumi Images / Dario Secen / Getty Images

Chapter 24

p. 861	Tyler Olson / Fotolia
p. 863	Science Photo Library - STEVE GSCHMEISSNER. / Getty Images
p. 871	*center, left:* David Pruter / Getty Images
p. 871	*bottom, left:* Javier GonzA!lez / Getty Images
p. 874	Pearson Education

p. 875	*bottom, left:* Dewayne Flowers / Shutterstock
p. 875	*center:* Dmitry Lobanov / Shutterstock
p. 890	US Navy
p. 892	*center, right:* SIU BIOMED COMM Custom Medical Stock Photo / Newscom
p. 892	*center, left:* Tyler Olson / Fotolia
p. 893	Javier GonzA!lez / Getty Images
p. 894	Pearson Education
p. 896	*center, left:* Floortje / Getty Images
p. 896	*center, right:* Pearson Education
p. 900	Pearson Education

Text Credits

Chapter 1

p. 4	John Horgan, 1993. Profile: Linus C. Pauling, Stubbornly Ahead of His Time, *Scientific American*, March 1993, 36–37

Chapter 11

p. 432	Based on 2004 MedicineNet, Inc.

Chapter 17

p. 629	© Pearson Education, Inc.

Chapter 20

p. 724	Lactase image by L. Frost of 1JYN (D.H. Juers, T.D. Heightman, A. Vasella, J.D. McCarter, L. Mackenzie, S.G. Withers, B.W. Matthews (2001) *Biochemistry* 40: 14781-14794) created in Rasmol 2.7.5.2 (R. Sayle, E.J. White (1995) Trends in Biochemical Sciences (TIBS), 20(9):374.)
p. 726	Alanine transaminase Image by L. Frost of 3IHJ (M. Wisniewska, M.I. Siponen, C.H. Arrowsmith, H. Berglund, C. Bountra, R. Collins, A.M. Edwards, S. Flodin, A. Flores, S. Graslund, M. Hammarstrom, A. Johansson, I. Johansson, T. Karlberg, T. Kotenyova, A. Kotzsch, M. Moche, T.K. Nielsen, P. Nordlund, T. Nyman, C. Persson, A.K. Roos, P. Schutz, L. Svensson, A.G. Thorsell, L. Tresaugues, S. Van Den Berg, J. Weigelt, M. Welin, H. Schuler. Human alanine aminotransferase 2 in complex with PLP) created in Rasmol 2.7.5.2 (R. Sayle, E.J. White (1995) Trends in Biochemical Sciences (TIBS), 20(9):374.)
p. 732	Trypsin Image by L. Frost of 2PTN (J. Walter, W. Steigemann, T.P. Singh, H. Bartunik, W. Bode, R. Huber (1982) Acta Crystallogr. Sect.B 38: 1462-1472.) created in Rasmol 2.7.5.2 (R. Sayle, E.J. White (1995) Trends in Biochemical Sciences (TIBS), 20(9):374.)
p. 734	Alpha-chymotrypsin image by L. Frost of 3CHA (R.S. Blevins, A. Tulinsky (1985) J. Biol. Chem. 260: 4262–4275) created in Rasmol 2.7.5.2 (R. Sayle, E.J. White (1995) Trends in Biochemical Sciences (TIBS), 20(9):374.)

Chapter 21

p. 765	© Pearson Education, Inc.
p. 787	Estrogen receptor image by L. Frost of 2ERD (A.K. Shiau, D. Barstad, P.M. Loria, L. Chemg, P.J. Kushner, D.A. Agard, G.L. Greene (1998) Cell (Cambridge, MA) 95:927–937) created in Rasmol 2.7.5.2 (R. Sayle, E.J. White (1995) Trends in Biochemical Sciences (TIBS), 20(9):374.)

Index taken from

Fundamentals of General, Organic, and Biological Chemistry,
Seventh Edition

by John McMurry, David S. Ballantine, Carl A. Hoeger, and
Virginia E. Peterson

Index

Note: Page numbers in **boldface** type indicate definitions of terms.

Index taken from

General, Organic, and Biological Chemistry: Structures of Life,
Fifth Edition

by Karen C. Timberlake

Glossary/Index

A

Abbreviated configuration, 129
Absolute zero, 70
Acceptor stem, 767
Accutane, 122
Acetaldehyde, 518
  from alcohol oxidation, 503, 505
  oxidization of, 509, 887
  produced in liver, 505
Acetal The product of the addition of two alcohols to an aldehyde or ketone, 527–530, 540
Acetaminophen (Tylenol), 475, 476, 650, 675
Acetate ion, 197
Acetic acid, 326, 330, 582
Acetoacetate, 873
  from amino acid degradation, 887
  ketosis and, 873–874
Acetoacetyl CoA, 887
Acetone, 521
Acetyl ACP, 878
Acetylcholine, 666
Acetylcholinesterase inhibitors, 666, 737
Acetyl CoA The compound that forms when a two-carbon acetyl unit bonds to coenzyme A, 798–799, 807
  accumulation in liver, ketone bodies and, 873
  from amino acid degradation, 887
  beta oxidation and, 865–869
  citric acid cycle and, 843
  cleavage of, 867
  ketogenesis and, 873
  ketogenic amino acid and, 887
  lipogenesis and, 876
  from pyruvate, 814, 828
Acetylene, 460
Acetylene torch, 263
Acetylsalicylic acid. *See* Aspirin
Achiral Molecules with mirror images that are superimposable, 531–533
Achiral compound, 532
Acid A substance that dissolves in water and produces hydrogen ions (H^+), according to the Arrhenius theory. All acids are hydrogen ion donors, according to the Brønsted–Lowry theory, 399–442, 711–713
  bases and (neutralization), 423
  Brønsted–Lowry, 403
  carboxylic. *See* Carboxylic acid
  characteristics of, 402, 412
  conjugate acid–base pair, 404–405
  diprotic, 408–409
  and hydroxides, 423
  naming, 401
  reaction with carbonates or bicarbonates, 423
  reactions of, 423–425
  stomach, 422
  strength of, 406–411
  strong, 406–408, 412
  weak, 406–408, 412
Acid–base titration, 425–427
Acid dissociation constant K_a The product of the concentrations of the ions from the dissociation of a weak acid divided by the concentration of the weak acid, 411–413
Acidic amino acid An amino acid that has an R group with a carboxylate group ($-COO^-$), 689, 690–692
  acidic, 690
  basic, 690
  classification of, 690–692
  polar and nonpolar, 690
  structure, 690
Acidic solution, 414, 415
  pH of, 416
  stomach acid, 422
Acidosis A condition in which the blood has a lower pH than normal, 431, 874
Acid reflux disease, 432
Acid hydrolysis The splitting of an ester molecule in the presence of a strong acid to produce a carboxylic acid and an alcohol, 596
  of amides, 676

Aconitase, 839
ACP (acyl carrier protein), 876, 878
Acquired immune deficiency syndrome (AIDS), 783–785
Actin, 803
Actinides, 106
Activation energy The energy that must be provided by a collision to break apart the bonds of the reacting molecules, 372–373
Activators, 770
Active learning, 7
  study plan for learning, 6–9
Active site A pocket in a part of the tertiary enzyme structure that binds substrate and catalyzes a reaction, 724
Active transport, 639
Activity The rate at which an enzyme catalyzes the reaction that converts a substrate to a product, 729–731
Actual yield The actual amount of product produced by a reaction, 269
Acyl carrier protein (ACP), 876, 878
Acyl CoA synthetase, 866
Addition
  negative numbers, 11
  positive numbers, 11
  significant figures, 34
Addition reaction A reaction in which atoms or groups of atoms bond to a carbon–carbon double bond. Addition reactions include the addition of hydrogen (hydrogenation) and water (hydration), 468–473
  hydration, 469–470
  hydrogenation, 468
Adenine (A), 754–755
Adenosine monophosphate (AMP), 757, 801
Adenosine triphosphate. *See* ATP
Adipocytes, 862
ADP Adenosine diphosphate, formed by the hydrolysis of ATP; consists of adenine, a ribose sugar, and two phosphate groups, 801, 843
Adrenal corticosteroid, 637
Adrenal gland, 637
Adrenaline (epinephrine), 536, 650
Aerobic An oxygen-containing environment in the cells, 816–817
Aerosol medications, 288
Agitation, 713
α (alpha) helix A secondary level of protein structure, in which hydrogen bonds connect the N—H of one peptide bond with the C=O of a peptide bond farther down the chain to form a coiled or corkscrew structure, 703
AIDS (acquired immune deficiency syndrome), 783–785
α-keratin, 708
Alanine, 691
  from conversion of tryptophan, 887
  converting to pyruvate, 887
Albinism, 778
Albumin, 38
Alchemists, 5
Alcohol An organic compound that contains the hydroxyl functional group (—OH) attached to a carbon atom, 489–495
  abuse of, 505
  ball-and-stick model, 489
  blood alcohol concentration (BAC), 505
  boiling points, 498, 499
  breathalyzer test, 505
  classifying, 489
  dehydrating to form alkene, 501–502
  disinfectant, 712
  fermentation, 818
  household products, 491
  hydroxyl groups in, 489–490
  important, 492–493
  naming, 490, 509
  oxidation, 502–504
  oxidation in body, 505
  oxidation to acetaldehyde, 503, 505
  reactions of, 501–506
  solubility in water, 498, 499
  sugar, 562, 567
Alcoholic beverages, 334

Functional Groups of Importance in Biochemical Molecules

Functional Group	Structure	Type of Biomolecule
Amino group	$-NH_3^+$, $-NH_2$	Alkaloids and neurotransmitters; amino acids and proteins (Sections 15.1, 15.3, 15.6, 18.3, 18.7, 28.6)
Hydroxyl group	$-OH$	Monosaccharides (carbohydrates) and glycerol: a component of triacylglycerols (lipids) (Sections 17.4, 21.4, 23.2)
Carbonyl group	$-\overset{\overset{\displaystyle O}{\|}}{C}-$	Monosaccharides (carbohydrates); in acetyl group (CH_3CO) used to transfer carbon atoms during catabolism (Sections 16.1, 17.4, 20.4, 20.8, 21.4)
Carboxyl group	$-\overset{\overset{\displaystyle O}{\|}}{C}-OH$, $-\overset{\overset{\displaystyle O}{\|}}{C}-O^-$	Amino acids, proteins, and fatty acids (lipids) (Sections 17.1, 18.3, 18.7, 23.2)
Amide group	$-\overset{\overset{\displaystyle O}{\|}}{C}-\overset{\overset{\displaystyle}{\|}}{N}-$	Links amino acids in proteins; formed by reaction of amino group and carboxyl group (Sections 17.1, 17.4, 18.7)
Carboxylic acid ester	$-\overset{\overset{\displaystyle O}{\|}}{C}-O-R$	Triacylglycerols (and other lipids); formed by reaction of carboxyl group and hydroxyl group (Sections 17.1, 17.4, 23.2)
Phosphates: mono-, di-, tri-	$-\overset{\overset{\displaystyle}{\|}}{C}-O-\overset{\overset{\displaystyle O}{\|}}{\underset{\underset{\displaystyle O^-}{\|}}{P}}-O^-$ $-\overset{\overset{\displaystyle}{\|}}{C}-O-\overset{\overset{\displaystyle O}{\|}}{\underset{\underset{\displaystyle O^-}{\|}}{P}}-O-\overset{\overset{\displaystyle O}{\|}}{\underset{\underset{\displaystyle O^-}{\|}}{P}}-O^-$ $-\overset{\overset{\displaystyle}{\|}}{C}-O-\overset{\overset{\displaystyle O}{\|}}{\underset{\underset{\displaystyle O^-}{\|}}{P}}-O-\overset{\overset{\displaystyle O}{\|}}{\underset{\underset{\displaystyle O^-}{\|}}{P}}-O-\overset{\overset{\displaystyle O}{\|}}{\underset{\underset{\displaystyle O^-}{\|}}{P}}-O^-$	ATP and many metabolism intermediates (Sections 17.8, 20.5, and throughout metabolism sections)
Hemiacetal group	$-\overset{\overset{\displaystyle}{\|}}{\underset{\underset{\displaystyle OR}{\|}}{C}}-OH$	Cyclic forms of monosaccharides; formed by a reaction of carbonyl group with hydroxyl group (Sections 16.7, 21.4)
Acetal group	$-\overset{\overset{\displaystyle}{\|}}{\underset{\underset{\displaystyle OR}{\|}}{C}}-OR$	Connects monosaccharides in disaccharides and larger carbohydrates; formed by reaction of carbonyl group with hydroxyl group (Sections 16.7, 21.7, 21.9)
Thiols	$-SH$	Found in amino acids cysteine, methionine; structural components of proteins (Sections 14.9, 18.3, 18.8, 18.10)
Sulfides	$-S-$	
Disulfides	$-S-S-$	

Elements Essential for Human Life[†]

Element	Symbol	Function
Carbon	C	These four elements are present throughout all living organisms
Hydrogen	H	
Oxygen	O	
Nitrogen	N	
Arsenic	As	May affect cell growth and heart function
Boron	B	Aids in the use of Ca, P, and Mg
Calcium[†]	Ca	Necessary for growth of teeth and bones
Chlorine[†]	Cl	Necessary for maintaining salt balance in body fluids
Chromium	Cr	Aids in carbohydrate metabolism
Cobalt	Co	Component of vitamin B_{12}
Copper	Cu	Necessary to maintain blood chemistry
Fluorine	F	Aids in the development of teeth and bones
Iodine	I	Necessary for thyroid function
Iron	Fe	Necessary for oxygen-carrying ability of blood
Magnesium[†]	Mg	Necessary for bones, teeth, and muscle and nerve action
Manganese	Mn	Necessary for carbohydrate metabolism and bone formation
Molybdenum	Mo	Component of enzymes necessary for metabolism
Nickel	Ni	Aids in the use of Fe and Cu
Phosphorus[†]	P	Necessary for growth of bones and teeth; present in DNA/RNA
Potassium[†]	K	Component of body fluids; necessary for nerve action
Selenium	Se	Aids vitamin E action and fat metabolism
Silicon	Si	Helps form connective tissue and bone
Sodium[†]	Na	Component of body fluids; necessary for nerve and muscle action
Sulfur[†]	S	Component of proteins; necessary for blood clotting
Zinc	Zn	Necessary for growth, healing, and overall health

[†]C, H, O, and N are present in all foods. Other elements listed vary in their distribution in different foods. Those marked with a dagger are *macronutrients,* essential in the diet at more than 100 mg/day; the rest, other than C, H, O, and N, are *micronutrients,* essential at 15 mg or less per day.

Tables and Figures Useful for Reference

Description	Table or Figure	Description	Table or Figure
Electron configurations of the first twenty elements	Table 2.3	Glucose metabolism	Figure 22.2
		Glycolysis	Figure 22.3
Common ions	Tables 3.2, 3.3	Families of lipids	Figure 23.1
Molecular geometry	Table 4.2	Cell membrane	Figure 23.7
No. of bonds, main group elements	Figure 4.3	Triacylglycerol digestion	Figure 24.1
Gas laws	Table 8.3	Triacylglycerol metabolism	Figure 24.6
Units for solution concentration	Table 9.5	β-Oxidation of fatty acids	Figure 24.7
Relative strengths of acids and bases	Table 10.1	Pathway of nutrients through anabolism and catabolism	Figure 24.8
Acid dissociation constants	Tables 10.2, 17.2		
pH Scale	Figure 10.2	Genetic code	Table 25.4
Families of organic molecules	Table 12.1	Protein synthesis	Figure 25.8
Common alkyl groups	Figure 12.3	Protein digestion	Figure 27.1
Amino acids	Table 18.3	Protein and amino acid metabolism	Figure 27.2
Catabolism overview	Figure 20.5	Urea cycle	Figure 27.4
Citric acid cycle	Figure 20.9	Cations and anions in body fluids	Figure 29.2
Carbohydrate digestion	Figure 22.1	Composition of whole blood	Figure 29.6